CGP

Mathematics
for A-Level

This gigantic CGP book is jam-packed with thousands of practice questions covering the new AS and A-Level Maths courses.

There are also plenty of worked examples along the way — very handy for reminding you about the key methods you'll need for each topic!

The Textbook

Contents

Published by CGP

Editors:
Chris Corrall, Sammy El-Bahrawy, Will Garrison, Paul Jordin, Simon Little, Alison Palin and Caley Simpson.

Contributors:
Andy Ballard, Jean Blencowe, Katharine Brown, Jane Chow, Michael Coe, Claire Creasor, Margaret Darlington, Alastair Duncombe, Anna Gainey, Allan Graham, Stephen Green, Dave Harding, Phil Harvey, Claire Jackson, Barbara Mascetti, Alan Mason, Mark Moody, James Nicholson, Charlotte O'Brien, Andy Pierson, Rosemary Rogers, Gary Rowlands, Manpreet Sambhi, Mike Smith, Janet West

ISBN: 978 1 78294 723 3

With thanks to Mona Allen, Elizabeth Best, Janet Dickinson, Ann Francis, Paul Garrett, Allan Graham and Glenn Rogers for the proofreading.
With thanks to Ana Pungartnik for the copyright research.

Printed by Elanders Ltd, Newcastle upon Tyne.
Clipart from Corel®

About This Book

In this book you'll find...

Explanations
Clear explanations for every topic, including all the formulas and methods required.

Examples
Plenty of step-by-step worked examples.

Exercises
Lots of practice for every topic, with solutions at the back of the book.

2. Definite Integration

Evaluating definite integrals

Definite integrals have **limits** (little numbers) next to the integral sign — they tell you the **range of x-values** to integrate between. To find a definite integral, integrate the function as normal, but **don't** add a **constant of integration**. Work out the **value** of the definite integral by **putting in the limits**:

If you know that the integral of f(x) is $\int f(x)\, dx = g(x) + C$ then:

$$\text{lower limit} \underset{}{\overset{\text{upper limit}}{\int_a^b}} f(x)\, dx = \left[g(x) \right]_a^b = g(b) - g(a)$$

Subtract the value of g at the **lower** limit from the value of g at the **upper** limit.

Example   Evaluate $\int_1^3 (x^2 + 2)\, dx$.

1. Find the integral in the normal way but use the notation above:
$$\int_1^3 (x^2 + 2)\, dx = \left[\frac{x^3}{3} + 2x \right]_1^3$$

2. Put in the limits: $\left[\frac{x^3}{3} + 2x \right]_1^3 = \left(\frac{3^3}{3} + 6 \right) - \left(\frac{1^3}{3} + 2 \right) = 15 - \frac{7}{3} = \frac{38}{3}$

Example   Find the possible values for A that satisfy $\int_1^4 \left(\frac{3}{7}x^2 + \frac{2A}{\sqrt{x}} \right) dx = 5A^2$. (PROBLEM SOLVING)

1. First, evaluate the integral. Treat the A as a constant for now.
$$\int_1^4 \left(\frac{3}{7}x^2 + 2Ax^{-\frac{1}{2}} \right) dx = \left[\frac{1}{7}x^3 + 4Ax^{\frac{1}{2}} \right]_1^4 = \left(\frac{64}{7} + 8A \right) - \left(\frac{1}{7} + 4A \right) = \frac{63}{7} + 4A = 9 + 4A$$

2. You know that this is equal to $5A^2$ from the question, so form a quadratic in A and solve it:
$$9 + 4A = 5A^2 \Rightarrow 5A^2 - 4A - 9 = 0 \Rightarrow (5A - 9)(A + 1) = 0$$

3. So the solutions are: $A = \frac{9}{5}$ or -1

Exercise 2.1

Q1 Find the value of the following, giving exact answers:

a) $\int_2^0 (4x^3 + 2x)\, dx$ b) $\int_0^1 (x^3 + x)\, dx$ c) $\int_{-5}^{-2} (x + 1)^2\, dx$ d) $\int_1^4 (6x^{-4} + x^{-2})\, dx$

e) $\int_{-1}^2 \left(x^2 + \frac{1}{x^2} \right) dx$ f) $\int_1^4 (3x^{-4} + \sqrt{x})\, dx$ g) $\int_0^1 ((2x + 3)(x + 2))\, dx$ h) $\int_1^4 \left(\frac{x^2 + 2}{\sqrt{x}} \right) dx$

i) $\int_4^9 \left(\frac{1}{x} + \sqrt{x} \right)^2 dx$ j) $\int_4^{16} \left(\frac{\sqrt{x} - 1}{x^3} \right) dx$ k) $\int_1^4 x^{\frac{1}{2}}(5x - x^{\frac{1}{2}})\, dx$ l) $\int_{-1}^2 (1 + x^3)(1 + \sqrt{x})\, dx$

Q2 Integrate the function $4x - 5x^3 + 7$ between the limits $x = -1$ and $x = 3$.

Q3 Find the integral of f(x) between $x = 0$ and $x = 1$, if $f(x) = 3 - 4\sqrt{x} + \frac{1}{2}x^2$.

Review Exercise — Chapter 8

Q1 Differentiate the following functions from first principles:
a) $y = x + 1$ b) $y = 4x^2$ c) $y = \frac{3}{x}$

Q2 Differentiate these functions with respect to x:
a) $y = x^2 + 2$ b) $y = x^4 + \sqrt{x}$ c) $y = \frac{7}{x^2} - \frac{3}{\sqrt{x}} + 12x^3$

Q3 Find the gradients of these graphs at $x = 2$:

a)

$y = 2x^2 + 10$

b)
$y = 4x^2 - x + 2$

c)

$y = x^3 - 7x^2 - 1$

Q4 Water is poured into a bowl. The volume (v) of water in the bowl (in ml) after t seconds is given by the function: $v = 3t^2 + 4$. (MODELLING)
a) How much water is in the bowl initially?
b) Find the rate at which water is being poured into the bowl when $t = 4$ seconds.

Q5 Find the equations of the tangent and the normal to the curve $y = \sqrt{x^3} - 3x - 10$ at $x = 16$.

Q6 Find the equation of the tangent to the curve $y = x^3 + \frac{4}{x} + 2\sqrt{x}$ at $x = 1$.

Q7 Show that the graphs of $y = \frac{x^3}{3} - 2x^2 - 4x + \frac{86}{3}$ and $y = \sqrt{x}$ both go through the point (4, 2), and are perpendicular at that point. (PROBLEM SOLVING)

Q8 Consider the curve C given by the equation $y = x^2 - 6$ and the line L given by the equation $y = 3$.
a) Find the coordinates of the points, A and B, where C and L intersect.
b) Find the gradient of C at points A and B.
c) Find the equations of the normals to C at A and B.
d) The normals at points A and B meet the point D. Find the coordinates of the point D.

Q9 Consider the curve C given by the equation $y = x^3 - 2x^2 + 1$, $x > 0$, and the line L given by the equation $y = 1$.
a) Write down the gradient of the line L for any x.
b) Find the point at which the curve C has the same gradient as the line L.
c) Hence give the equation of the tangent to C at this point.

Review Exercises
Mixed questions covering the whole chapter, with solutions at the back of the book.

Modelling
Modelling questions involve using maths to represent real-life situations. Examples and questions that include modelling are indicated with stamps.

Problem Solving
Problem solving examples and questions are also marked with stamps. These questions involve skills such as combining different areas of maths or interpreting information given to identify what's being asked for.

Chapter 1 — Algebra

This chapter will cover some of the basic algebra skills that you'll need throughout the course — so make sure you're completely comfortable with everything here. The good news is you should have seen a lot of it before.

1. Proof

Simple proofs — odd and even numbers

These are the 'proper' definitions for **odd** and **even numbers**:

> Any **even** number can be written as $2a$, where a is an integer.
>
> Any **odd** number can be written as $2b + 1$, where b is an integer.

Tip: Remember, integers are just whole numbers. They can be positive, negative or 0.

In the proofs below, $2j + 1$ and $2k + 1$ represent any two **odd numbers**, and $2l$ and $2m$ represent any two **even numbers** (where j, k, l and m are integers).

  a) **Prove that the sum of two even numbers is even.**

$$2l + 2m = 2(l + m) = \text{even, so } \textbf{even + even = even}$$

b) **Prove that the sum of an odd number and an even number is odd.**

$$(2j + 1) + (2l) = 2j + 2l + 1 = 2(j + l) + 1 = \text{odd, so } \textbf{odd + even = odd}$$

c) **Prove that the product of two odd numbers is odd.**

$$(2j + 1)(2k + 1) = 4jk + 2j + 2k + 1 = 2(2jk + j + k) + 1 = \text{odd, so } \textbf{odd} \times \textbf{odd = odd}$$

Proof by deduction

A **proof by deduction** is when you use **known facts** to build up your argument and show a statement **must** be true.

  A rational number is 'a number that can be written as a quotient of two integers, where the denominator is non-zero'. Use this to prove that the product of two rational numbers is always a rational number.

- Express two rational numbers using the definition given in the question:

  Take any two rational numbers, a and b. Then $a = \dfrac{p}{q}$ and $b = \dfrac{r}{s}$, where p, q, r and s are integers, and q and s are non-zero.

- Find their product.

  $ab = \dfrac{p}{q} \times \dfrac{r}{s} = \dfrac{pr}{qs}.$

- pr and qs are the products of integers, so are also integers. q and s are non-zero, so qs is also non-zero.

  ab is a quotient of two integers and has a non-zero denominator, so by definition, ab is rational. **Hence the original statement is true.**

Proof by exhaustion

In **proof by exhaustion** you break things down into two or more **cases**. You have to make sure that your cases cover **all possible situations**, then prove separately that the statement is true for **each case**.

 Prove the following statement:
"*For any integer x, the value of f(x) = x³ + x + 1 is an odd integer.*"

To prove the statement, split the situation into two cases:
(i) x is an even integer, and (ii) x is an odd integer.

(i)   If x is an even integer, then it can be written as $x = 2n$, for some integer n.
Substitute $x = 2n$ into the function:
$f(2n) = (2n)^3 + 2n + 1 = 8n^3 + 2n + 1 = 2(4n^3 + n) + 1$
n is an integer $\Rightarrow (4n^3 + n)$ is an integer
$\qquad\qquad\qquad\quad \Rightarrow 2(4n^3 + n)$ is an even integer
$\qquad\qquad\qquad\quad \Rightarrow 2(4n^3 + n) + 1$ is an odd integer

So f(x) is odd when x is even.

(ii)   If x is an odd integer, then it can be written as $x = 2m + 1$, for some integer m.
Substitute $x = 2m + 1$ into the function:
$f(2m + 1) = (2m + 1)^3 + 2m + 1 + 1$
$\qquad\qquad = (8m^3 + 12m^2 + 6m + 1) + 2m + 1 + 1$
$\qquad\qquad = 8m^3 + 12m^2 + 8m + 3 = 2(4m^3 + 6m^2 + 4m + 1) + 1$
m is an integer $\Rightarrow (4m^3 + 6m^2 + 4m + 1)$ is an integer
$\qquad\qquad\qquad\quad \Rightarrow 2(4m^3 + 6m^2 + 4m + 1)$ is an even integer
$\qquad\qquad\qquad\quad \Rightarrow 2(4m^3 + 6m^2 + 4m + 1) + 1$ is an odd integer

So f(x) is odd when x is odd.

So f(x) is odd when x is even and when x is odd. As any integer x must be either odd or even, you have therefore shown that f(x) is odd for any integer x. **The statement is true.**

Disproof by counter-example

Disproof by counter-example is the easiest way to show a mathematical statement is **false**.
All you have to do is find **one case** where the statement doesn't hold.

 Disprove the following statement:
"*For any pair of integers x and y, if x > y, then x² + x > y² + y.*"

▪ To disprove the statement, find just one example of x and y where $x > y$, but $x^2 + x \le y^2 + y$.
Let $x = 2$ and $y = -4$, then $2 > -4 \Rightarrow x > y$.
But $x^2 + x = 2^2 + 2 = 6$ and $y^2 + y = (-4)^2 + (-4) = 12$, so $x^2 + x < y^2 + y$.

▪ So when $x = 2$ and $y = -4$, the first part of the statement holds, but the second part doesn't.
So the statement is not true.

Exercise 1.1

Q1   a) Prove that the sum of two odd numbers is even.

      b) Prove that the product of two even numbers is even.

      c) Prove that the product of an odd number and an even number is even.

Q2   By finding a counter-example, disprove the statement: "If p is a non-zero integer, then $\dfrac{1}{p^2} < \dfrac{1}{p}$."

Q3   Prove that, for any integer x, $(x + 5)^2 + 3(x - 1)^2$ is always divisible by four.

Q4   Prove by exhaustion that the product of any three consecutive integers is even.

Q5   Disprove the following statement: "$n^2 - n - 1$ is a prime number for any integer $n > 2$."

Q6   Disprove the following: $\sqrt{x^2 + y^2} < x + y$.

Q7   Prove that the sum of two rational numbers is also a rational number.

Q8   a) Prove the statement: "For any integer n, $n^2 - n - 1$ is always odd."

      b) Hence prove that $(n^2 - n - 2)^3$ is always even.

2. Algebraic Expressions

Expanding brackets

Examples

a)   **Expand $3xy(x^2 + 2x - 8)$.**

Multiply each term inside the brackets by the bit outside — separately.

$(3xy \times x^2) + (3xy \times 2x) + (3xy \times (-8)) = (3x^3y) + (6x^2y) + (-24xy)$

$$= 3x^3y + 6x^2y - 24xy$$

b)   **Expand $(2y^2 + 3x)^2$.**

You can expand squared brackets using the formula $(a + b)^2 = a^2 + 2ab + b^2$:

You could also just write this as two sets ⟶ $(2y^2 + 3x)^2 = (2y^2)^2 + 2(2y^2)(3x) + (3x)^2$
of brackets and multiply out as normal. a^2 $2ab$ b^2

$$= 4y^4 + 12xy^2 + 9x^2$$

c)   **Expand $(2x^2 + 3x - 6)(4x^3 + 6x^2 + 3)$.**

Multiply each term in the first set of brackets by the whole second set of brackets:

$(2x^2 + 3x - 6)(4x^3 + 6x^2 + 3) = 2x^2(4x^3 + 6x^2 + 3) + 3x(4x^3 + 6x^2 + 3) + (-6)(4x^3 + 6x^2 + 3)$

Multiply out each of these sets of brackets and simplify by collecting like terms:

$$= (8x^5 + 12x^4 + 6x^2) + (12x^4 + 18x^3 + 9x) + (-24x^3 - 36x^2 - 18)$$
$$= 8x^5 + 24x^4 - 6x^3 - 30x^2 + 9x - 18$$

d)   **Expand $(2x + 5)(x + 2)(x - 3)$.**

Start by multiplying the first two sets of brackets:
    $(2x + 5)(x + 2)(x - 3)$
$$= (2x^2 + 4x + 5x + 10)(x - 3)$$
$$= (2x^2 + 9x + 10)(x - 3)$$

Multiply the long bracket by the final set of brackets: $= 2x^2(x - 3) + 9x(x - 3) + 10(x - 3)$
Expand the single brackets and simplify: $= (2x^3 - 6x^2) + (9x^2 - 27x) + (10x - 30)$
$$= 2x^3 + 3x^2 - 17x - 30$$

Exercise 2.1

Q1 Expand the brackets in these expressions:

a) $5(x + 4)$ b) $a(4 - 2b)$ c) $-2(x^2 + y)$ d) $6mn(m + 1)$

e) $-4ht(t^2 - 2ht - 3h^3)$ f) $7z^2(2 + z)$ g) $4(x + 2) + 3(x - 5)$ h) $p(3p^2 - 2q) + (q + 4p^3)$

i) $7xy(x^2 + z^2)$ j) $x(2x + 3) - 3x^2$ k) $st(t - s) - s(5 + t^2)$ l) $2x(2 + 3xy) - xy(5x + 4)$

Q2 Expand and simplify:

a) $(x + 5)(x - 3)$ b) $(2z + 3)(3z - 2)$ c) $(u + 8)^2$ d) $(ab + cd)(ac + bd)$

e) $(10 + f)(2f^2 - 3g)$ f) $(7 + q)(7 - q)$ g) $(2 - 3w)^2$ h) $(4rs^2 + 3)^2$

i) $(5k^2l - 2kn)^2$ j) $(3gh + 2h)(3gh - 4)$ k) $(2yz + 7)(7y - 2z)$ l) $(5c^2 - c)(c^2 + 4c)$

Q3 Expand and simplify the following expressions:

a) $(l + 5)(l^2 + 2l + 3)$ b) $(2 + q)(3 - q + 4q^2)$ c) $(m + 1)(m + 2)(m - 4)$ d) $(r + s)^3$

e) $(4 + x + y)(1 - x - y)$ f) $(2c^2 - cd + d)(2d - c - 5c^2)$ g) $(2x - 3y)^2(xy + 4y)$

Q4 Carole's garden is a square with sides of length x metres. Mark's garden is a rectangle. One side of the rectangle is 3 metres longer than the side of the square and the other is twice as long as the side of the square, plus an extra metre. Find the difference in area between Mark's garden and Carole's. Give your answer in terms of x.

Factorising

A **common factor** which is in every term of an expression can be '**taken out**' and put outside brackets to simplify the expression. When you've taken out **all** possible factors, the expression is **factorised**.

 Factorise $2x^3z + 4x^2yz + 14x^2y^2z$ completely.

Look for any factors that are in each term.

Numbers: 2 divides into 2, 4 and 14, so it's a common factor.
Variables: There's at least an x^2 in each term and there's a z in each term.

There's a common factor of $2x^2z$, so write each term as $2x^2z \times$ something:

$$2x^3z + 4x^2yz + 14x^2y^2z = 2x^2z \cdot x + 2x^2z \cdot 2y + 2x^2z \cdot 7y^2$$
$$= 2x^2z(x + 2y + 7y^2)$$

The terms in the brackets have no common factors — so this expression is completely factorised.

Difference of two squares

If you expand brackets of the form $(a - b)(a + b)$, the 'ab' terms cancel and you're left with one square minus another. This result is called the **difference of two squares**: $a^2 - b^2 = (a - b)(a + b)$.

 a) Factorise $x^2 - 36y^2$.

36 is a square number so $36y^2$ can be written as a square:

$$x^2 - 36y^2 = x^2 - 6^2y^2 = x^2 - (6y)^2 = (x - 6y)(x + 6y)$$

b) Factorise $x^2 - 5$.

5 isn't a square number but you can write it as a square: $x^2 - 5 = x^2 - (\sqrt{5})^2 = (x - \sqrt{5})(x + \sqrt{5})$

Exercise 2.2

Q1 Factorise the following expressions completely:

a) $9k + 15l$

b) $u^2 - uv$

c) $10w + 15$

d) $2x^2y - 12xy^2$

e) $f^2g^2 - fg$

f) $3u^2v^2 + 5u^4v^4 + 12u^2v$

g) $p^3 + 3pq^3 + 2p$

h) $abcde - bcdef - cdefg$

i) $11xy^2 - 11x^2y - 11x^2y^2$

j) $mnp^2 + 7m^2np^3$

k) $2ab^4 + 3a^3b^2 - 4ab$

l) $36xyz - 8x^2z^2 + 20y^2z^2$

Q2 Write the following expressions as products of factors:

a) $x^2 - y^2$

b) $9a^2 - 4b^2$

c) $25x^2 - 49z^2$

d) $a^2c - 16b^2c$

e) $y^2 - 2$

f) $4x^2 - 3$

Q3 Express the following as the product of factors.

a) $(4 - z)^2(2 - z) + p(2 - z)$

b) $(r - d)^3 + 5(r - d)^2$

c) $(b + c)^5(a + b) - (b + c)^5$

d) $l^2m(a - 2x) + rp^2(2x - a)$

e) $(h - 4g)^2 + h - 4g$

f) $2(x^2 + y) + x^3 + xy$

Q4 Simplify each expression, leaving your answer in its factorised form.

a) $(p + q)^2 + 2q(p + q)$

b) $2(2x - y)^2 - 6x(2x - y)$

c) $(r + 6s)^2 - (r + 6s)(r - s)$

d) $(l + w + h)^2 - l(l + w + h)$

e) $x^2(1 - y)^2 + x(2 - 2y)$

f) $b(a + b)^3 + 3a(a + b)^2$

Q5 Simplify these expressions by expanding brackets, factorising or both.

a) $(m + 5)(m^2 - 5m + 25)$

b) $(p - 2q)(p^2 + 2pq + 4q^2)$

c) $(u - v)(u + v) - (u + v)^2$

d) $(c + d)^3 - c(c + d)^2 - d(c + d)^2$

e) $s(2 + r)^2 + r^2(s - 2) + 2(r - s)(r + s)$

f) $[(2x + y)(y - 2x)]^2 - (4x^2 + y^2 + 2z^2)^2$

Algebraic fractions

If you're **adding fractions** and they all have the same **denominator**, you can just add the **numerators**.

$$\frac{a}{x} + \frac{b}{x} + \frac{c}{x} \equiv \frac{a + b + c}{x} \qquad x \text{ is the } \mathbf{common\ denominator}$$

Tip: This equals sign with 3 lines $\equiv$ means it's true for all values of a, b, c or x — this is called an **identity**.

If the fractions you want to add don't have a common denominator you can 'find' one — **rewrite** the fractions so that the denominators are the same by multiplying **top** and **bottom** by the same thing.

> **Example**   Simplify $\dfrac{3}{x + 2} + \dfrac{5}{x - 3}$.
>
> - The first step is to rewrite the fractions so that they have a common denominator.
>
> - You need an expression that both $(x + 2)$ and $(x - 3)$ divide into — you can get one by multiplying the denominators together to give a common denominator of $(x + 2)(x - 3)$.
>
> - Make the denominator of each fraction into the common denominator.
>
> Multiply the top and bottom of each fraction by whatever makes the bottom line equal to the common denominator. $\longrightarrow \dfrac{3(x - 3)}{(x + 2)(x - 3)} + \dfrac{5(x + 2)}{(x + 2)(x - 3)}$
>
> All the bottom lines are the same, so add the top lines. $\longrightarrow = \dfrac{3(x - 3) + 5(x + 2)}{(x + 2)(x - 3)}$
>
> Now tidy up the top. $\longrightarrow = \dfrac{3x - 9 + 5x + 10}{(x + 2)(x - 3)} = \dfrac{8x + 1}{(x + 2)(x - 3)}$

Algebraic fractions can sometimes be simplified by cancelling **factors** that appear in both the numerator and denominator.

 Simplify $\dfrac{ax + ay}{az}$.

You can either... ▪ Factorise — then cancel.

... Or ▪ Split into two fractions — then cancel.

Factorise the top line. Cancel the 'a'.

$$\frac{ax + ay}{az} = \frac{a(x + y)}{az} = \frac{\cancel{a}(x + y)}{\cancel{a}z} = \frac{x + y}{z}$$

$$\frac{ax + ay}{az} = \frac{ax}{az} + \frac{ay}{az} = \frac{\cancel{a}x}{\cancel{a}z} + \frac{\cancel{a}y}{\cancel{a}z} = \frac{x}{z} + \frac{y}{z} = \frac{x + y}{z}$$

Exercise 2.3

Q1 Express each of these as a single fraction.

a) $\dfrac{x}{3} + \dfrac{x}{4}$

b) $\dfrac{2}{t} + \dfrac{13}{t^2}$

c) $\dfrac{1}{2p} - \dfrac{1}{5q}$

d) $\dfrac{ab}{c} + \dfrac{bc}{a} + \dfrac{ca}{b}$

e) $\dfrac{2}{mn} - \dfrac{3m}{n} + \dfrac{n^2}{m}$

f) $\dfrac{2}{ab^3} - \dfrac{9}{a^3 b}$

g) $\dfrac{1}{x} + \dfrac{2x}{y} + \dfrac{4}{x^2}$

h) $2 + \dfrac{a^2}{b} - \dfrac{2b}{a^2}$

Q2 Express the following as single fractions in their simplest form.

a) $\dfrac{5}{y - 1} + \dfrac{3}{y - 2}$

b) $\dfrac{7}{r - 5} - \dfrac{4}{r + 3}$

c) $\dfrac{8}{p} - \dfrac{1}{p - 3}$

d) $\dfrac{w}{2(w - 2)} + \dfrac{3w}{w - 7}$

e) $\dfrac{z + 1}{z + 2} - \dfrac{z + 3}{z + 4}$

f) $\dfrac{1}{q + 1} + \dfrac{3}{q - 2}$

g) $\dfrac{x}{x + z} + \dfrac{2z}{x - z}$

h) $\dfrac{y}{2x + 3} - \dfrac{2y}{3 - x}$

Q3 Simplify these expressions.

a) $\dfrac{2x + 10}{6}$

b) $\dfrac{6a - 12b - 15c}{3}$

c) $\dfrac{np^2 - 2n^2 p}{np}$

d) $\dfrac{4st + 6s^2 t + 9s^3 t}{2t}$

e) $\dfrac{10yz^3 - 40y^3 z^3 + 60y^2 z^3}{10z^2}$

f) $\dfrac{12cd - 6c^2 d + 3c^3 d^2}{12c^2 de}$

g) $\dfrac{2x + x^2 y - x^2}{x^2 + 3x}$

h) $\dfrac{4g^2 - 4h^2}{g^2 + gh}$

3. Laws of Indices

The laws of indices are a set of simple rules for manipulating expressions involving indices (powers).

$$a^m \times a^n = a^{m+n} \qquad \frac{a^m}{a^n} = a^{m-n} \qquad (a^m)^n = a^{mn} \qquad a^1 = a$$

$$a^{\frac{1}{m}} = \sqrt[m]{a} \qquad a^{-m} = \frac{1}{a^m} \qquad a^{\frac{m}{n}} = \sqrt[n]{a^m} = (\sqrt[n]{a})^m \qquad a^0 = 1$$

Examples **Simplify the following:**

a) $(ab^2)^4$

$(ab^2)^4 = a^4 (b^2)^4 = \mathbf{a^4 b^8}$

b) $9^{\frac{3}{2}}$

$9^{\frac{3}{2}} = (9^{\frac{1}{2}})^3 = (\sqrt{9})^3 = 3^3 = \mathbf{27}$

c) 2^{-3}

$2^{-3} = \dfrac{1}{2^3} = \dfrac{1}{8}$

Example — Express $\dfrac{(7^{\frac{1}{3}})^6 \times (7^{-1})^4}{(7^{-4})^{-2}}$ as 7^k, where k is an integer.

This one looks really complicated, but it's just a series of easy steps.

$$\frac{(7^{\frac{1}{3}})^6 \times (7^{-1})^4}{(7^{-4})^{-2}} = \frac{7^{\frac{6}{3}} \times 7^{-1 \times 4}}{7^{-4 \times -2}} \quad\longleftarrow\quad (a^m)^n = a^{mn}$$

$$= \frac{7^2 \times 7^{-4}}{7^8}$$

$$= \frac{7^{2-4}}{7^8} \quad\longleftarrow\quad a^m \times a^n = a^{m+n}$$

$$= \frac{7^{-2}}{7^8}$$

You could also write this as $\dfrac{1}{7^{10}}$.

$$= 7^{-2-8} \quad\longleftarrow\quad \frac{a^m}{a^n} = a^{m-n}$$

$$= 7^{-10}$$

Exercise 3.1

Q1 Simplify the following, leaving your answer as a power:

a) 10×10^4

b) $y^{-1} \times y^{-2} \times y^7$

c) $5^{\frac{1}{2}} \times 5^3 \times 5^{\frac{-3}{2}}$

d) $6^5 \div 6^2$

e) $3^4 \div 3^{-1}$

f) $\dfrac{6^{11}}{6}$

g) $\dfrac{r^2}{r^6}$

h) $(3^2)^3$

i) $(k^{-2})^5$

j) $(z^4)^{-\frac{1}{8}}$

k) $(8^{-6})^{-\frac{1}{2}}$

l) $\dfrac{p^5 q^4}{p^4 q}$

m) $\dfrac{c^{-1} d^{-2}}{c^2 d^4}$

n) $(ab^2)^2$

o) $\dfrac{12yz^{-\frac{1}{2}}}{4yz^{\frac{1}{2}}}$

p) $(mn^{\frac{1}{2}})^4$

Q2 Evaluate:

a) $4^{\frac{1}{2}} \times 4^{\frac{3}{2}}$

b) $\dfrac{2^3 \times 2}{2^5}$

c) $\dfrac{7^5 \times 7^3}{7^6}$

d) $(3^2)^5 \div (3^3)^3$

e) $(4^{-\frac{1}{2}})^2 \times (4^{-3})^{-\frac{1}{3}}$

f) $\dfrac{(2^{\frac{1}{2}})^6 \times (2^{-2})^{-2}}{(2^{-1})^{-1}}$

g) 1^0

h) $\left(\dfrac{4}{5}\right)^0$

i) $(-5.726324)^0$

Q3 Express the following as negative or fractional powers or both:

a) $\dfrac{1}{p}$

b) $\sqrt{q}$

c) $\sqrt{r^3}$

d) $\sqrt[4]{s^5}$

e) $\dfrac{1}{\sqrt[3]{t}}$

f) $\left(\dfrac{1}{\sqrt[3]{x}}\right)^4$

Q4 Evaluate: a) $9^{\frac{1}{2}}$ b) $8^{\frac{1}{3}}$ c) $4^{\frac{3}{2}}$ d) $27^{-\frac{1}{3}}$ e) $16^{-\frac{3}{4}}$

Q5 If $p = \dfrac{1}{16}q^2$, write the following expressions in terms of q:

a) $p^{\frac{1}{2}}$

b) $2p^{-1}$

c) $p^{\frac{1}{2}} \div 2p^{-1}$

d) $p^2 q$

e) $\dfrac{4p}{q^3}$

f) $\dfrac{q^2}{4p^2}$

Q6 Find the value of x for each of the following:

a) $4^x = \sqrt[3]{16}$

b) $9^x = \dfrac{1}{3}$

c) $\sqrt{5} \times 5^x = \dfrac{1}{25}$

d) $(16^x)^2 = \dfrac{1}{4}$

e) $x^{-3} = -8$

f) $\sqrt{100^x} = 0.001$

4. Surds

The laws of surds

Numbers like $\sqrt{2}$ that can only be written exactly using roots are called **surds**. Surds are **irrational**. There are four rules you'll need to know to be able to use surds properly:

$$\sqrt{ab} = \sqrt{a}\sqrt{b} \qquad \sqrt{\frac{a}{b}} = \frac{\sqrt{a}}{\sqrt{b}} \qquad a = (\sqrt{a})^2 = \sqrt{a}\sqrt{a} \qquad (\sqrt{a}+\sqrt{b})(\sqrt{a}-\sqrt{b}) = a-b$$

Simplifying surds usually means making the number in the $\sqrt{}$ sign smaller or getting rid of a fraction inside the $\sqrt{}$ sign.

Examples

a) **Simplify** $\sqrt{\frac{3}{16}}$

$$\sqrt{\frac{3}{16}} = \frac{\sqrt{3}}{\sqrt{16}} = \frac{\sqrt{3}}{4}$$

b) **Find** $(2\sqrt{5} + 3\sqrt{6})^2$

$$(2\sqrt{5}+3\sqrt{6})^2 = (2\sqrt{5}+3\sqrt{6})(2\sqrt{5}+3\sqrt{6})$$
$$= (2\sqrt{5})^2 + (2\times(2\sqrt{5})\times(3\sqrt{6})) + (3\sqrt{6})^2$$
$$= (2^2 \times \sqrt{5^2}) + (2\times2\times3\times\sqrt{5}\times\sqrt{6}) + (3^2\times\sqrt{6^2})$$

$= 4 \times 5 = 20 \quad\quad = 20 + 12\sqrt{30} + 54 \quad = 12\sqrt{5}\sqrt{6} = 12\sqrt{30} \quad = 9\times6 = 54$

$$= 74 + 12\sqrt{30}$$

c) **Express** $\sqrt{63} - \sqrt{28}$ **in the form** $k\sqrt{x}$ **where** k **and** x **are integers.**

Try to write both numbers as 'a square number' $\times x$. Here x is 7.

$$\sqrt{63} - \sqrt{28} = \sqrt{9\times7} - \sqrt{4\times7}$$
$$= \sqrt{9}\sqrt{7} - \sqrt{4}\sqrt{7}$$
$$= 3\sqrt{7} - 2\sqrt{7} = \sqrt{7}$$

Exercise 4.1

Q1 Simplify the following surds:

a) $\sqrt{8}$ b) $\sqrt{24}$ c) $\sqrt{50}$ d) $\sqrt{63}$ e) $\sqrt{72}$ f) $\sqrt{\frac{5}{4}}$ g) $\sqrt{\frac{7}{100}}$ h) $\sqrt{\frac{11}{9}}$

Q2 Evaluate the following. Give your answer as either a whole number or a surd.

a) $2\sqrt{3} \times 4\sqrt{3}$ b) $\sqrt{5} \times 3\sqrt{5}$ c) $(\sqrt{7})^2$ d) $2\sqrt{2} \times 3\sqrt{5}$ e) $(2\sqrt{11})^2$

f) $5\sqrt{8} \times 2\sqrt{2}$ g) $4\sqrt{3} \times 2\sqrt{27}$ h) $2\sqrt{6} \times 5\sqrt{24}$ i) $\frac{\sqrt{10}}{6} \times \frac{12}{\sqrt{5}}$ j) $\frac{\sqrt{12}}{3} \times \frac{2}{\sqrt{27}}$

Q3 Express the following in the form $k\sqrt{x}$, where k and x are integers and x is as small as possible.

a) $\sqrt{20} + \sqrt{5}$ b) $\sqrt{32} - \sqrt{8}$ c) $\sqrt{27} + 4\sqrt{3}$

d) $2\sqrt{8} - 3\sqrt{2}$ e) $3\sqrt{10} + \sqrt{250}$ f) $4\sqrt{27} + 2\sqrt{48} + 5\sqrt{108}$

Q4 Expand the following expressions. Give your answers in the simplest form.

a) $(1+\sqrt{2})(2+\sqrt{2})$ b) $(3+4\sqrt{3})(2-\sqrt{3})$ c) $(\sqrt{11}+2)(\sqrt{11}-2)$

d) $(9-2\sqrt{5})(9+2\sqrt{5})$ e) $(\sqrt{3}+2)^2$ f) $(3\sqrt{5}-4)^2$

Q5 Triangle ABC is right-angled with angle ABC = 90°. Side AC has length $5\sqrt{2}$ cm and side AB has length $\sqrt{2}$ cm. Find the length of side BC in the form $k\sqrt{3}$ cm, where k is an integer.

Rationalising the denominator

'**Rationalising the denominator**' means removing surds from the denominator of a fraction. To do this, multiply **top and bottom** of the fraction by an **expression** that will get rid of surds in the denominator.
If the denominator is of the form $a + \sqrt{b}$, multiply by $a - \sqrt{b}$ to get rid of the surd.

Examples

a) **Show that** $\dfrac{9}{\sqrt{3}} = 3\sqrt{3}$.

To get rid of the surd, multiply top and bottom by $\sqrt{3}$:

$$\frac{9}{\sqrt{3}} = \frac{9 \times \sqrt{3}}{\sqrt{3} \times \sqrt{3}} = \frac{9\sqrt{3}}{3} = 3\sqrt{3}$$

Cancelling 3 from top and bottom.

b) **Rationalise the denominator of** $\dfrac{7 + \sqrt{5}}{3 + \sqrt{5}}$.

$$\frac{7 + \sqrt{5}}{3 + \sqrt{5}} \times \frac{3 - \sqrt{5}}{3 - \sqrt{5}} = \frac{(7 + \sqrt{5})(3 - \sqrt{5})}{(3 + \sqrt{5})(3 - \sqrt{5})}$$

Multiply top and bottom by $3 - \sqrt{5}$.

$$= \frac{(7 \times 3) - 7\sqrt{5} + 3\sqrt{5} - (\sqrt{5})^2}{3^2 - 3\sqrt{5} + 3\sqrt{5} - (\sqrt{5})^2}$$

The surds cancel each other out.

$$= \frac{21 - 4\sqrt{5} - 5}{9 - 5}$$

Now cancel 4 from each term.

$$= \frac{16 - 4\sqrt{5}}{4} = 4 - \sqrt{5}$$

Exercise 4.2

Q1 Simplify the following, giving your answers in the form $p\sqrt{q}$, where p and q are integers:

a) $\dfrac{6}{\sqrt{3}}$ b) $\dfrac{21}{\sqrt{7}}$ c) $\dfrac{30}{\sqrt{5}}$ d) $\sqrt{45} + \dfrac{15}{\sqrt{5}}$ e) $\dfrac{\sqrt{54}}{3} - \dfrac{12}{\sqrt{6}}$ f) $\dfrac{\sqrt{300}}{5} + \dfrac{30}{\sqrt{12}}$

Q2 Express the following in the form $a + b\sqrt{k}$, where a, b and k are integers:

a) $\dfrac{4}{1 + \sqrt{3}}$ b) $\dfrac{8}{-1 + \sqrt{5}}$ c) $\dfrac{18}{\sqrt{10} - 4}$ d) $\dfrac{\sqrt{6}}{2 - \sqrt{6}}$

Q3 Express the following in the form $p + q\sqrt{r}$, where r is an integer, and p and q are integers or fractions:

a) $\dfrac{\sqrt{2} + 1}{\sqrt{2} - 1}$ b) $\dfrac{\sqrt{5} + 3}{\sqrt{5} - 2}$ c) $\dfrac{3 - \sqrt{3}}{4 + \sqrt{3}}$ d) $\dfrac{3\sqrt{5} - 1}{2\sqrt{5} - 3}$

e) $\dfrac{\sqrt{2} + \sqrt{3}}{3\sqrt{2} - \sqrt{3}}$ f) $\dfrac{2\sqrt{7} - \sqrt{5}}{\sqrt{7} + 2\sqrt{5}}$ g) $\dfrac{2\sqrt{2} + \sqrt{3}}{\sqrt{3} - \sqrt{12}}$ h) $\dfrac{\sqrt{3} + 3}{\sqrt{5} + \sqrt{15}}$

Q4 Express the following in the form $k(\sqrt{x} \pm \sqrt{y})$, where x and y are integers and k is an integer or fraction.

a) $\dfrac{4}{\sqrt{7} - \sqrt{3}}$ b) $\dfrac{24}{\sqrt{11} - \sqrt{17}}$ c) $\dfrac{2}{\sqrt{13} + \sqrt{5}}$ d) $\dfrac{\sqrt{3}}{\sqrt{21} - 3\sqrt{5}}$

Q5 Solve the equation $8 = (\sqrt{5} - 1)x$, giving your answer in the form $a + b\sqrt{5}$ where a and b are integers.

Q6 Solve $5 + \sqrt{7} = (3 - \sqrt{7})y$. Give your answer in the form $p + q\sqrt{7}$, where p and q are integers.

Q7 A rectangle has an area of $(2 + \sqrt{2})$ cm² and a width of $(3\sqrt{2} - 4)$ cm. Find the length of the rectangle. Give your answer in the form $a + b\sqrt{2}$ where a and b are integers.

Review Exercise — Chapter 1

Q1 Prove that when an odd number is subtracted from an even number, the result is always odd.

Q2 Prove that the difference between any two rational numbers is also a rational number.

Q3 Disprove the following statement:
"When one rational number is divided by another rational number, the result is always rational."

Q4 Remove the brackets and simplify the following expressions:
a) $(a + b)(a - b)$
b) $(a + b)(a + b)$
c) $35xy + 25y(5y + 7x) - 100y^2$
d) $(x + 3y + 2)(3x + y + 7)$
e) $(c + 2d)(c - d)(2d - 3c)$
f) $[(s - 2t)(s + 2t)]^2$

Q5 The length of the longest side of a cuboid-shaped box is x cm.
The shortest side of the box is 10 cm shorter than the longest side, and the other side is 8 cm shorter than the longest side.
Find an expression for the total volume of 5 of these boxes, in terms of x.
Your final answer should contain no brackets.

Q6 Fully factorise each of the following expressions:
a) $2x^2y + axy + 2xy^2$
b) $a^2x + a^2b^2x^2$
c) $16y + 8yx + 56x$
d) $24s + 60st + 15s^2t^2$
e) $27c - 9c^3d - 45cd^2$
f) $x^2y^2z^2 + x^3y^3 - x^2yz$

Q7 Write each of the following expressions as a product of factors:
a) $(x + 1) - y(x + 1)$
b) $z^4 + z^2(3 - z)$
c) $(x + y)^2 + x(x + y)$
d) $x(x - 2) + 3(2 - x)$
e) $25 - x^4$
f) $9b^2c^4 - 4c^2d^6$

Q8 Put the following expressions over a common denominator:
a) $\dfrac{2x}{3} + \dfrac{y}{12} + \dfrac{x}{5}$
b) $\dfrac{5}{xy^2} - \dfrac{2}{x^2y}$
c) $\dfrac{1}{x} + \dfrac{x}{x + y} + \dfrac{y}{x - y}$
d) $\dfrac{a}{b} + \dfrac{4}{a} - \dfrac{7}{a^2}$
e) $3x - \dfrac{4}{3xy}$
f) $\dfrac{2s}{t^2} + \dfrac{5}{2t} - \dfrac{t}{s^2}$

Q9 Simplify these expressions:
a) $\dfrac{2a}{b} - \dfrac{a}{2b}$
b) $\dfrac{2p}{p + q} + \dfrac{2q}{p - q}$
c) $\dfrac{c + d}{(c - d)^2} + \dfrac{1}{c + d}$
d) $\dfrac{1}{1 + x} - \dfrac{1 - x}{2x^2}$
e) $\dfrac{2k}{k^2 - 1} + \dfrac{k^2}{k - 1}$
f) $\dfrac{4}{z + 1} + \dfrac{2}{y + z} - \dfrac{6}{y - 1}$

Q10 The diagram on the right shows part of a garden.
The combined area of the lawn and flower bed is $3x^2$ m².
The area of the flower bed is x^2 m².
Show that y can be expressed as:

$$y = \dfrac{x^2(2x - 15)}{(x + 6)(x - 3)}$$

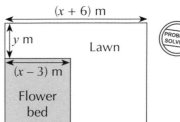

Q11 Simplify:

a) $x^3 \cdot x^5$

b) $a^7 \cdot a^8$

c) $\dfrac{x^8}{x^2}$

d) $(a^2)^4$

e) $(xy^2) \cdot (x^3yz)$

f) $\dfrac{a^2 b^4 c^6}{a^3 b^2 c}$

Q12 Simplify:

a) $g^2 \times g^{-5}$

b) $p^4 r^2 \div p^5 r^{-6}$

c) $\left(k^{\frac{1}{3}}\right)^6$

d) $(mn^8 \times m^4 n^{-11})^{-2}$

e) $s^4 t^3 \times \left(\dfrac{1}{s^2 t^5}\right)^{-3}$

f) $\dfrac{a^2}{b^2 c} \times \dfrac{b^6}{a^4 c^{-2}} \div \dfrac{c^2}{a^3 b}$

Q13 Work out the following:

a) $16^{\frac{1}{2}}$

b) $8^{\frac{1}{3}}$

c) $16^{\frac{3}{4}}$

d) x^0

e) $49^{-\frac{1}{2}}$

f) $\dfrac{1}{27^{-\frac{2}{3}}}$

Q14 Simplify:

a) $\sqrt{28}$

b) $\sqrt{\dfrac{5}{36}}$

c) $\sqrt{18}$

d) $\sqrt{\dfrac{9}{16}}$

Q15 Simplify the following expressions by writing them in the form $k\sqrt{x}$, where k and x are integers and x is as small as possible.

a) $\sqrt{3} - \sqrt{12}$

b) $3\sqrt{5} + \sqrt{45}$

c) $\sqrt{7} + \sqrt{448}$

d) $\sqrt{52} + \sqrt{117}$

e) $4\sqrt{150} + \sqrt{54} - \sqrt{5}\sqrt{120}$

Q16 The diagram on the right shows a shape which has been made by cutting a small square from one corner of a larger square. The area of the larger square was 1920 cm². The area of the smaller square was 1080 cm². Find the value of a. Give your answer in the form $k\sqrt{x}$, where k and x are integers and x is as small as possible.

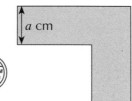

PROBLEM SOLVING

Q17 Show that:

a) $\dfrac{8}{\sqrt{2}} = 4\sqrt{2}$

b) $\dfrac{\sqrt{2}}{2} = \dfrac{1}{\sqrt{2}}$

Q18 Find $\left(6\sqrt{3} + 2\sqrt{7}\right)^2$.

Q19 Rationalise the denominator of $\dfrac{2}{3 + \sqrt{7}}$.

Q20 Write the following in the form $p + q\sqrt{r}$, where r is an integer, and p and q are integers or fractions:

a) $\dfrac{11 + \sqrt{13}}{5 - \sqrt{13}}$

b) $\dfrac{2\sqrt{7} + 9}{3 - \sqrt{7}}$

c) $\dfrac{3\sqrt{5} + \sqrt{15}}{\sqrt{60} - \sqrt{20}}$

Chapter 2 — Quadratics and Cubics

Quadratic equations are ones with an x^2 term (and no higher powers of x). Cubic equations have an x^3 term (and no higher powers of x). In this chapter, you'll see how to factorise both types of equation.

1. Quadratic Equations

Factorising a quadratic

Quadratic equations are equations of the general form $ax^2 + bx + c = 0$, where a, b and c are constants (i.e. numbers) and $a \neq 0$.

Example   **Solve $x^2 - 8 = 2x$ by factorising.**

1. Rearrange into standard $ax^2 + bx + c = 0$ form. $x^2 - 2x - 8 = 0$

2. Write down the two brackets with x's in. $x^2 - 2x - 8 = (x \quad)(x \quad)$

3. Find two numbers that multiply together to make c 2 and 4 multiply to give 8 and
    but which also add or subtract to give b.   add / subtract to give 6 and 2.

4. Find the signs — c is negative, so the signs must be opposite. $x^2 - 2x - 8 = (x + 2)(x - 4)$

5. The factors multiply to give 0, so one of them must be 0. $x + 2 = 0$ or $x - 4 = 0$
    $$\Rightarrow x = -2 \text{ or } x = 4$$

Example   **Factorise $3x^2 + 4x - 15$.**

1. As before, write down two brackets — but now $3x^2 + 4x - 15 = (3x \quad)(x \quad)$
    you need two things that will multiply to give $3x^2$.

2. Find two numbers that multiply together to make 15 $(3x \quad 5)(x \quad 3) \Rightarrow 5x$ and $9x$
    — but which will give you $4x$ when you multiply them   which then add or subtract
    by x and $3x$, and then add / subtract them.   to give $14x$ and $4x$.

3. Find the signs — c is negative, so the signs must be opposite. $3x^2 + 4x - 15 = (3x - 5)(x + 3)$

Tip: For some questions you might need to try a few possible pairs of values before you find the right one.

Exercise 1.1

Q1   Factorise the following expressions.
     a) $x^2 - 6x + 5$ b) $x^2 - 3x - 18$ c) $x^2 + 22x + 121$ d) $x^2 - 12x$
     e) $y^2 - 13y + 42$ f) $x^2 + 51x + 144$ g) $x^2 - 121$ h) $x^2 - 35x + 66$

Q2   Factorise the following expressions.
     a) $4x^2 - 4x - 3$ b) $2x^2 + 23x + 11$ c) $7x^2 - 19x - 6$ d) $-x^2 - 5x + 36$
     e) $6x^2 - 7x - 3$ f) $2x^2 - 2$ g) $3x^2 - 3$ h) $-x^2 + 9x - 14$

Q3 Solve the following equations.
a) $x^2 - 2x - 8 = 0$
b) $2x^2 + 2x - 40 = 0$
c) $p^2 + 21p + 38 = 0$
d) $x^2 - 15x + 54 = 0$
e) $x^2 + 18x = -65$
f) $x^2 - x = 42$
g) $x^2 + 1100x + 100\,000 = 0$
h) $3x^2 - 3x - 6 = 0$
i) $5x^2 - 21x + 4 = 0$

Q4 Solve the following equations.
a) $-5x^2 - 22x + 15 = 0$
b) $32x^2 + 60x + 13 = 0$
c) $5a^2 + 12a = 9$
d) $8x^2 + 22x + 15 = 0$
e) $4q^2 + 6 = 11q$
f) $24y^2 + 23y - 12 = 0$

Q5 Solve $(x - 1)(x - 2) = 37 - x$.

Q6 $f(x) = -x^2 + 7x + 30$. Find the x coordinates of the point or points at which the graph of $f(x)$ meets the x-axis.

Q7 In a scientific experiment, the temperature, $T\,°C$, is modelled by the equation $T = -2h^2 + 13h - 20$, where h is the time in hours from the start of the experiment. Find both times at which the temperature is $0\,°C$.

Q8 Factorise $x^2 + 6xy + 8y^2$.

The quadratic formula

You can find the **solutions** of a quadratic equation, even if it won't factorise, with the **quadratic formula**.

$$\text{If } ax^2 + bx + c = 0 \text{ then: } x = \frac{-b \pm \sqrt{b^2 - 4ac}}{2a}$$

Example

Solve the quadratic equation $2x^2 = 4x + 3$, leaving your answer in the form $p \pm q\sqrt{r}$ where p, q and r are whole numbers or fractions.

1. Rearrange into standard $ax^2 + bx + c = 0$ form. $\quad 2x^2 - 4x - 3 = 0$

2. Plug $a = 2$, $b = -4$ and $c = -3$ into the quadratic formula. $\quad x = \dfrac{-(-4) \pm \sqrt{(-4)^2 - 4 \times 2 \times (-3)}}{2 \times 2}$

3. Simplify as much as possible. $\quad = 1 \pm \dfrac{1}{2}\sqrt{10}$

Exercise 1.2

Q1 Solve the following equations using the quadratic formula, giving your answers in surd form where necessary.
a) $x^2 - 4x = -2$
b) $x^2 - 2x - 44 = 0$
c) $x^2 + 3x = 12$
d) $x^2 - 14x + 42 = 0$
e) $4x^2 + 4x - 1 = 0$
f) $-x^2 + 4x - 3 = 0$
g) $x^2 - \frac{5}{6}x + \frac{1}{6} = 0$
h) $x^2 - x - \frac{35}{2} = 0$
i) $x^2 - 2\sqrt{11}x + 11 = 0$

Q2 a) Multiply out $(x - 2 + \sqrt{5})(x - 2 - \sqrt{5})$.
b) Solve the equation $x^2 - 4x - 1 = 0$ using the quadratic formula.
c) How does your answer to b) relate to the expression given in a)?

Q3 The roots of the equation $x^2 + 8x + 13 = 0$ can be written in the form $x = A \pm \sqrt{B}$ where A and B are integers. Find A and B.

Q4 Solve the following equations, giving your answers in surd form where necessary.
a) $x^2 + x + \frac{1}{4} = 0$
b) $x^2 - \frac{7}{4}x + \frac{2}{3} = 0$
c) $25x^2 - 30x + 7 = 0$
d) $60x - 5 = -100x^2 - 3$
e) $2x(x - 4) = 7 - 3x$
f) $(3x - 5)(x + 2) = 3x - 2$

Completing the square

Completing the square just means writing a quadratic expression $ax^2 + bx + c$ in the form

$$a(x + \text{something})^2 + d$$

The '**something**' is chosen so that the '**square**' bit gives the correct x^2 and x terms.

You '**complete**' it by adding a number to make it the **same** as the original quadratic.

Tip: The 'something' is always $\frac{b}{2a}$. When $a = 1$, the 'something' is just $\frac{b}{2}$ — i.e. half the coefficient of x.

Example   Solve $x^2 + 6x + 3 = 0$ by completing the square.

1. Write down the square bit: $a = 1$, so the 'something' is $\frac{b}{2} = \frac{6}{2} = 3$. $(x + 3)^2$

2. Multiply out the square. $(x + 3)^2 = x^2 + 6x + 9$

3. The constant term has to be $+3$, so subtract 6 from the square. $x^2 + 6x + 3 = (x + 3)^2 - 6$

4. Set this equal to zero and rearrange to find x. $(x + 3)^2 - 6 = 0 \Rightarrow x + 3 = \pm\sqrt{6}$

$$\Rightarrow x = -3 \pm \sqrt{6}$$

Exercise 1.3

Q1 Solve the following equations, leaving your answer in surd form where appropriate:
a) $(x + 4)^2 = 25$ b) $(2x + 5)^2 = 9$ c) $(5x - 3)^2 = 21$ d) $(3x - 1)^2 = 32$

Q2 Rewrite the following expressions in the form $(x + p)^2 + q$:
a) $x^2 + 6x + 8$ b) $x^2 + 8x - 10$ c) $x^2 - 3x - 10$ d) $x^2 - 20x + 15$
e) $x^2 + 9x - 2$ f) $x^2 - 5x + 7$ g) $x^2 - 2mx + n$ h) $x^2 + 6rx + s$

Q3 Solve the following equations by completing the square:
a) $x^2 - 6x - 16 = 0$ b) $x^2 + 4x - 8 = 0$ c) $x^2 - 4x + 3 = 0$ d) $x^2 + 24 = 10x$
e) $p^2 - 10p = 200$ f) $x^2 + 2x + k = 0$ g) $q^2 + 3q = -2$ h) $x^2 - 4x + k = 0$

It's a bit more complicated in cases where a is **not** 1. You have to put a **outside** of the squared bracket, and allow for this when choosing the number to go inside the bracket — basically by dividing by a.

Example   Rewrite $2x^2 + 3x - 5$ by completing the square.

1. The square will be of the form $2(x + \text{something})^2$:
   $a = 2$, so the 'something' is $\frac{b}{2a} = \frac{3}{2 \times 2} = \frac{3}{4}$.

   $2\left(x + \frac{3}{4}\right)^2$

2. Multiply out the square.

   $2\left(x + \frac{3}{4}\right)^2 = 2x^2 + 3x + \frac{9}{8}$

3. The constant term has to be -5, so subtract the $\frac{9}{8}$ and then 'add on' -5 to the square.

   $2x^2 + 3x - 5 = 2\left(x + \frac{3}{4}\right)^2 - \frac{9}{8} - 5$

   $= 2\left(x + \frac{3}{4}\right)^2 - \frac{49}{8}$

Solve $3 - 4x - x^2 = 0$ **by completing the square.**

1. The square will be of the form $-(x + \text{something})^2$:

    $a = -1$, so the 'something' is $\dfrac{b}{2a} = \dfrac{-4}{2 \times -1} = 2$ $-(x + 2)^2$

2. Multiply out the square. $-(x + 2)^2 = -x^2 - 4x - 4$

3. The constant term has to be $+3$, so add 7 to the square. $3 - 4x - x^2 = -(x + 2)^2 + 7$

4. Set this equal to zero and rearrange. $-(x + 2)^2 + 7 = 0 \Rightarrow (x + 2)^2 = 7$

    $\Rightarrow \boldsymbol{x = -2 \pm \sqrt{7}}$

Exercise 1.4

Q1   Rewrite the following expressions in the form $p(x + q)^2 + r$:

a) $3x^2 - 12x + 7$ b) $2x^2 + 16x + 5$ c) $5x^2 + 20x - 2$ d) $2x^2 - 4x - 3$

e) $6x^2 + 30x - 20$ f) $-x^2 - 9x + 9$ g) $4x^2 - 22x + 5$ h) $-3x^2 + 9x + 1$

Q2   Solve the following equations by completing the square:

a) $4x^2 + 24x - 13 = 0$ b) $9x^2 + 18x = 16$ c) $2x^2 - 12x + 9 = 0$ d) $2x^2 - 12x - 54 = 0$

e) $5x^2 + 10x = 1$ f) $-3x^2 - 18x + 2 = 0$ g) $3x^2 + 2x = \dfrac{7}{6}$ h) $5x^2 - 3x + \dfrac{2}{5} = 0$

Q3   By completing the square, show that the solutions to $ax^2 + bx + c = 0$

are found at $x = \dfrac{-b \pm \sqrt{b^2 - 4ac}}{2a}$.

Quadratics involving functions of x

An equation might involve different powers of x, or functions like $\sin x$ or e^x. However, as long as it's in the form $a(\textbf{something})^2 + b(\textbf{something}) + c$, you can use **substitution** to turn it into a normal quadratic.

Example   **Solve the equation** $x^{\frac{2}{3}} + 3x^{\frac{1}{3}} - 40 = 0.$

1. Use $u = x^{\frac{1}{3}}$ (since $\left(x^{\frac{1}{3}}\right)^2 = x^{\frac{2}{3}}$) to make a quadratic in u. $u^2 + 3u - 40 = 0$

2. Now solve the quadratic. $(u + 8)(u - 5) = 0 \Rightarrow u = -8$ or $u = 5$

3. Substitute $x^{\frac{1}{3}}$ back into the equation and solve for x. $x^{\frac{1}{3}} = -8$, so $x = (-8)^3 = \boldsymbol{-512}$ or

    $x^{\frac{1}{3}} = 5$, so $x = 5^3 = \boldsymbol{125}$

Exercise 1.5

Q1   Find an expression for u, in terms of x, that allows you to write each equation below in the form $au^2 + bu + c = 0$. You do **not** need to solve the resulting equations.

a) $2x + 4x^{\frac{1}{2}} - 7 = 0$ b) $e^x(e^x - 6) = 8$ c) $5^x + 5^{2x} = 4$ d) $2 \cos^2 x + 3 = 5 \cos x$

Q2   Solve the equation $\dfrac{3}{(5x + 2)^2} + \dfrac{1}{5x + 2} = 10$.

2. Quadratic Functions and Roots

The roots of a quadratic function

The **roots** of a quadratic function are the values of x where the function $f(x)$ is equal to **zero** — i.e. where the graph **crosses the x-axis**.

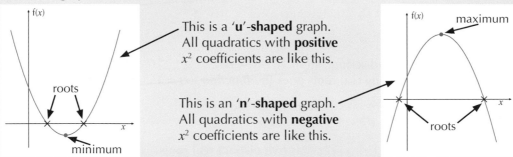

This is a 'u'-shaped graph. All quadratics with **positive** x^2 coefficients are like this.

This is an 'n'-shaped graph. All quadratics with **negative** x^2 coefficients are like this.

The completed square, $f(x) = p(x + q)^2 + r$, tells you lots about the function.

- If p is **positive**, the graph will be **u-shaped** and have a **minimum**.
  If p is **negative**, the graph will be **n-shaped** and have a **maximum**.

- The **minimum** or **maximum** is $(-q, r)$ — so there is a **line of symmetry** at $x = -q$.

- If p and r have **different signs**, the function has **two** real roots.
  If $r = 0$ then the function has **one** real root. The graph would just **touch** the x-axis at the root.
  If p and r have the **same sign**, the function has **no** real roots. The graph **wouldn't touch** the x-axis.

Tip: In some areas of maths, you can actually take the square root of negative numbers and get 'imaginary' or 'complex' numbers. You won't need to do that in this course, but that's why you have to say no 'real' roots.

Example **How many real roots does the quadratic function $f(x) = x^2 + 4x + 7$ have?**

Write in the form $f(x) = p(x + q)^2 + r$ by completing the square. $f(x) = (x + 2)^2 + 3$

$p = 1$ and $r = 3$ are of the same sign, so the function has **no real roots**.

Exercise 2.1

Q1 How many real roots does each quadratic function have?

a)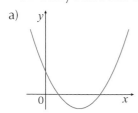

b)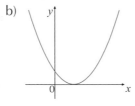

c)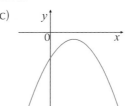

d)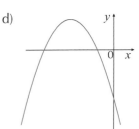

Q2 Express $f(x) = x^2 + 6x + 10$ in the form $f(x) = (x + q)^2 + r$, where q and r are positive or negative constants. Using your answer, state whether $f(x)$ has any real roots and give the equations of any lines of symmetry of the graph of $f(x)$.

Q3 The function $f(x) = -x^2 - 7x - 6$ can be expressed in the form $f(x) = -\left(x + \frac{7}{2}\right)^2 + \frac{25}{4}$
Does this function have any real roots? Explain your answer.

Using the discriminant

The $b^2 - 4ac$ part of the quadratic formula is called the **discriminant**.

- If the discriminant is **positive**, the formula will give you **two** different values for x.

- If it's **zero**, you'll only get **one** value for x, since adding and subtracting zero gets the same value.

- If it's **negative**, you don't get any (real) values for x.

 Example

Find the discriminant of $15 - x - 2x^2$.
How many real roots does the function $f(x) = 15 - x - 2x^2$ have?

Put $a = -2$, $b = -1$ and $c = 15$ into the formula for the discriminant.
$b^2 - 4ac = (-1)^2 - (4 \times -2 \times 15) = 1 + 120 = \textbf{121}$

The discriminant is > 0, so $15 - x - 2x^2$ has **two distinct real roots**.

Example

Find the range of values of k for which the function
$f(x) = 3x^2 + 2x + k$ has no real roots.

Put $a = 3$, $b = 2$ and $c = k$ into the formula for the discriminant. $\quad b^2 - 4ac = 2^2 - 4 \times 3 \times k$
$= 4 - 12k$

No roots means $b^2 - 4ac < 0$. $\quad 4 - 12k < 0 \Rightarrow 4 < 12k \Rightarrow \boldsymbol{k > \dfrac{1}{3}}$

Exercise 2.2

Q1 Find the discriminant, and hence the number of real roots, for each of the following:

a) $x^2 + 8x + 15$
b) $x^2 + 2\sqrt{3}x + 3$
c) $(2x + 1)(5x - 3)$
d) $-3x^2 - \dfrac{11}{5}x - \dfrac{2}{5}$

e) $9x^2 + 20x$
f) $\dfrac{19}{16}x^2 - 4$
g) $13x^2 + 8x + 2$
h) $\dfrac{x^2}{3} + \dfrac{5}{2}x + 3$

Q2 The discriminant of the equation $15x^2 + bx = 2$ is 169, where b is an integer.
Find all possible values of b.

Q3 The equation $0 = ax^2 + 7x + \dfrac{1}{4}$ has one real root. Find a.

Q4 Find the range of values of p for which $x^2 - 12x + 27 + p = 0$ has two distinct real roots.

Q5 Find the range of values of q for which $10x^2 - 10x + \dfrac{q}{2} = 0$ has two distinct real roots.

Q6 The equation $2x^2 + (10p + 1)x + 5 = 0$ has no real roots. Show that p satisfies $p(5p + 1) < \dfrac{39}{20}$.

Q7 The equation $x^2 + (k + 5)x + \dfrac{k^2}{4} = 0$, where k is a constant, has no real roots.
a) Show that k satisfies $10k + 25 < 0$.
b) Find the range of possible values of k.

PROBLEM SOLVING

Q8 For what values of k would the equation $\left(k - \dfrac{6}{5}\right)x^2 + \sqrt{k}\,x + \dfrac{5}{4} = 0$ have:

a) one real root?
b) no real roots?
c) two distinct real roots?

3. Quadratic Graphs

Sketching a quadratic graph

Shape — if the coefficient of x^2 is **positive** — the graph will be **u-shaped**.
— if the coefficient of x^2 is **negative** — the graph will be **n-shaped**.

Intersection points — to find the **y-intercept**, let $x = 0$ and calculate the value of y.
— to find the **x-intercepts**, let $y = 0$ and solve the equation $0 = ax^2 + bx + c$ to find the value or values of x.

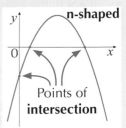

Example **Sketch the graph of the quadratic function $f(x) = x^2 - 4x + 3$, including any points of intersection with the axes.**

1. Decide on the shape of the graph. The coefficient of x^2 is positive, so the graph is u-shaped.

2. Find the y-intercept ($x = 0$). $y = f(0) = (0)^2 - 4(0) + 3 = 3$

3. Find the x-intercepts ($y = 0$). $x^2 - 4x + 3 = 0 \Rightarrow (x - 3)(x - 1) = 0$
$\Rightarrow x = 3$ or $x = 1$

4. Sketch the graph.

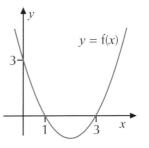

Exercise 3.1

Q1 Sketch the following graphs on the same set of axes, indicating the x-intercepts of each.
a) $y = x^2 - 1$ b) $y = x^2 - 9$ c) $y = x^2$

Q2 a) Factorise the expression $f(x) = x^2 - 10x + 9$.
b) Use your answer to a) to sketch the graph of $f(x)$, showing the points where it crosses both axes.
c) Sketch the graph of $-f(x)$ on the same axes.

Q3 Sketch the following graphs, showing any intersections with the axes:
a) $y = x^2 - 2x + 1$ b) $y = x^2 + x - 1$ c) $y = 2x^2 + 5x + 2$
d) $y = x^2 - 9x + 18$ e) $y = -x^2 + 3$ f) $y = 2x^2 - 5x - 1$

Q4 a) What are the roots of the quadratic function shown in the graph on the right?
b) The quadratic can be written in the form $y = -x^2 + px + q$ where p and q are integers. Use your answer to part a) to find p and q.

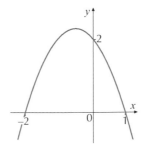

Q5 The height of an aeroplane stunt, h m, is modelled by the equation $h = 0.5t^2 - 13t + 100$, where t is the time in seconds. The stunt is completed when the aeroplane returns to the starting height.

a) Sketch a graph of aeroplane's flight showing the time taken to complete the stunt.

b) Find the minimum height that the aeroplane reaches.

4. Factorising Cubics

Factorising a cubic (when x is a factor)

For a cubic of the form $ax^3 + bx^2 + cx$, **take out x** as your first factor as follows:

$$ax^3 + bx^2 + cx = x(ax^2 + bx + c)$$

Then you can just deal with the **quadratic** inside the brackets to find any other factors (or solutions).

Examples **Solve the following cubic equations.**

a) $x^3 - 2x^2 - 24x = 0$

Take out x as a factor and then factorise the quadratic.

$$x^3 - 2x^2 - 24x = x(x^2 - 2x - 24)$$
$$= x(x - 6)(x + 4)$$

Solve the equation in the usual way.

$$x(x - 6)(x + 4) = 0$$
$$\Rightarrow x = 0, x = 6 \text{ and } x = -4$$

b) $-4x^3 - 4x^2 + x = 0$

Take out $-x$ as a factor.

$$-4x^3 - 4x^2 + x = 0$$
$$-x(4x^2 + 4x - 1) = 0$$

Use the quadratic formula to solve the quadratic.

$$x = \frac{-b \pm \sqrt{b^2 - 4ac}}{2a}$$

$$= \frac{-4 \pm \sqrt{4^2 - 4 \times 4 \times (-1)}}{2 \times 4} = -\frac{1}{2} \pm \frac{1}{2}\sqrt{2}$$

So the solutions are $x = 0$, $x = -\frac{1}{2} + \frac{1}{2}\sqrt{2}$ and $x = -\frac{1}{2} - \frac{1}{2}\sqrt{2}$.

Exercise 4.1

Q1 Factorise the following cubic expressions:

a) $x^3 + 5x^2 + 6x$
b) $x^3 + 6x^2 - 7x$
c) $x^3 - 18x^2 + 81x$
d) $x^3 + 7x^2 + 10x$

e) $x^3 + 4x^2 + 3x$
f) $x^3 + 2x^2 - 35x$
g) $x^3 - 6x^2 - 16x$
h) $-x^3 + 4x^2 - 3x$

i) $-x^3 - 3x^2 + 4x$
j) $2x^3 + 15x^2 + 25x$
k) $2x^3 - 7x^2 + 6x$
l) $4x^3 + 13x^2 - 12x$

m) $x^3 - 36x$
n) $x^3 - \frac{4}{25}x$
o) $x^3 - 49x$
p) $x^3 - \frac{9}{4}x$

Q2 Solve the following cubic equations:

a) $-x^3 + 2x^2 + 24x = 0$
b) $-x^3 - 4x^2 + 21x = 0$
c) $2x^3 + 9x^2 + 4x = 0$

d) $3x^3 + 26x^2 - 9x = 0$
e) $x^3 + \frac{2}{3}x^2 - \frac{8}{9}x$
f) $x^3 - \frac{7}{9}x^2 + \frac{10}{81}x = 0$

g) $3x^3 - 3x^2 + 4x = 0$
h) $4x - x^3 = 0$
i) $5x^3 + 7x^2 - 3x = 0$

j) $x^2(4x + 3) = x$
k) $2x^3 + 8x^2 = -3x$
l) $2x^3 + 3x = x^2$

The Remainder Theorem

For a polynomial f(x), the **Remainder Theorem** says:

> When you divide f(x) by (x − a), the remainder is f(a).
>
> When you divide f(x) by (ax − b), the remainder is $f\left(\frac{b}{a}\right)$.

 Find the remainder when you divide $2x^3 - 3x^2 - 3x + 7$ by the following polynomials.

a) $x - 2$

$a = 2$ so the remainder is f(2). $\qquad$ $f(2) = (2 \times 8) - (3 \times 4) - (3 \times 2) + 7 = \textbf{5}$

b) $2x - 1$

$a = 2$ and $b = 1$ so the remainder is $f\left(\frac{1}{2}\right)$. $\qquad$ $f\left(\frac{1}{2}\right) = 2\left(\frac{1}{8}\right) - 3\left(\frac{1}{4}\right) - 3\left(\frac{1}{2}\right) + 7 = \textbf{5}$

Exercise 4.2

Q1 Use the Remainder Theorem to work out the remainder in each of the following divisions:

a) $2x^3 - 3x^2 - 39x + 20$ divided by $(x - 1)$ $\qquad$ b) $x^3 - 3x^2 + 2x$ divided by $(x + 1)$

c) $6x^3 + x^2 - 5x - 2$ divided by $(x + 1)$ $\qquad$ d) $x^3 + 2x^2 - 7x - 2$ divided by $(x + 3)$

e) $4x^3 - 6x^2 - 12x - 6$ divided by $(2x + 1)$ $\qquad$ f) $x^3 - 3x^2 - 6x + 8$ divided by $(2x - 1)$

Q2 Find the remainder when $f(x) = x^4 - 3x^3 + 7x^2 - 12x + 14$ is divided by:

a) $x + 2$ $\qquad$ b) $2x + 4$ $\qquad$ c) $x - 3$ $\qquad$ d) $2x - 6$

Q3 Find the remainder when $f(x) = x^4 - 3x^3 + 4x^2 + 5x - 7$ is divided by:

a) $x - 3$ $\qquad$ b) $2x + 1$ $\qquad$ c) $x - 1$ $\qquad$ d) $3x - 2$

Q4 The remainder when $x^3 + cx^2 + 17x - 10$ is divided by $(x + 3)$ is −16.
Use the Remainder Theorem to find the value of c.

Q5 The remainder when $x^3 + px^2 - 10x - 19$ is divided by $(x + 2)$ is 5.
Use the Remainder Theorem to find the value of p.

Q6 When $x^3 - dx^2 + dx + 1$ is divided by $(x + 2)$ the remainder is −25.
Use the Remainder Theorem to find the value of d.

Q7 When $x^3 - 2x^2 + 7x + k$ is divided by $(x + 1)$ the remainder is −8. Find the value of k.

Q8 $f(x) = x^4 - 3x^3 + px - 5$. The remainder when f(x) is divided by $(x - 1)$ is the same as the remainder when f(x) is divided by $(x + 1)$. Use the Remainder Theorem to find the value of p.

Q9 $f(x) = x^4 + 5x^3 + qx + 156$. The remainder when f(x) is divided by $(x - 2)$ is the same as the remainder when f(x) is divided by $(x + 1)$. Use the Remainder Theorem to find the value of q.

Algebraic division

Once you've found one linear factor of a cubic, you can use **algebraic long division** to find the quadratic factor. This uses the same method that you'd use for numbers.

Tip: If the cubic has any missing terms, you'll need to add in a term in the correct place with a coefficient of 0.

Example $x - 2$ is a factor of the cubic $f(x) = 2x^3 - 5x - 6$. Use algebraic long division to write $f(x)$ as the product of a linear factor and a quadratic factor.

1. Start by dividing the first term in the cubic ($2x^3$) by the first term of the divisor (x): $2x^3 \div x = 2x^2$. Write this answer above the cubic.

$$\begin{array}{r} 2x^2 + 4x + 3 \\ x-2{\overline{\smash{\big)}\,2x^3 + 0x^2 - 5x - 6}} \\ -\ (2x^3 - 4x^2) \\ \hline 4x^2 - 5x \end{array}$$

2. Multiply the divisor ($x - 2$) by this answer ($2x^2$) to get $2x^3 - 4x^2$ and write this under the first two terms of the cubic.

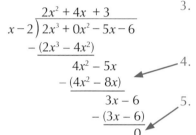

3. Subtract $2x^3 - 4x^2$ from the main expression to get $4x^2$. Bring down the $-5x$ term just to make things clearer for the next subtraction.

4. Repeat this process until you are left with a constant — divide $4x^2$ by x to get $4x$, etc...

5. The remainder of 0 means that the divisor is a factor (this won't always be the case).

So $f(x) = (x - 2)(2x^2 + 4x + 3)$

Exercise 4.5

Q1 Use algebraic long division and the given factors to fully factorise the following cubic expressions:

     a) $x^3 - 2x^2 - 15x + 36$, factor: $(x - 3)$ b) $x^3 - x^2 - 11x - 10$, factor: $(x + 2)$

     c) $2x^3 + 11x^2 - 23x - 14$, factor: $(x - 2)$ d) $x^3 + 10x^2 + 31x + 30$, factor: $(x + 5)$

Q2 Write $x^3 - 5x + 4$ as the product of a linear factor and a quadratic factor using long division.

Q3 a) Using algebraic long division, find the remainder when you divide $f(x) = x^3 - 2x^2 + x - 1$ by $(x + 3)$.

     b) Use the Remainder Theorem to show that your answer to part a) is correct.

Q4 $f(x) = x^3 + 2x^2 - 7x - 2$. Use algebraic long division to express $f(x)$ in the form $(x - 2)g(x)$, where $g(x)$ is a quadratic.

Q5 $f(x) = x^3 - 7x - 6$ and $f(-2) = 0$. Use algebraic long division to find all the solutions of $f(x) = 0$.

Q6 Write $x^3 + x^2 - 12$ as the product of a linear factor and a quadratic factor using long division.

Q7 a) Use algebraic division to find the remainder when $f(x) = x^3 - 8x^2 + 20x - 3$ divided by $(x - 2)$.

     b) Hence find the solutions to $f(x) - 13 = 0$.

Review Exercise — Chapter 2

Q1 Factorise the following expressions:

a) $x^2 + 2x + 1$
b) $x^2 - 13x + 30$
c) $x^2 - 4$
d) $3 + 2x - x^2$
e) $2x^2 - 7x - 4$
f) $5x^2 + 7x - 6$

Q2 Solve the following equations:

a) $x^2 - 3x + 2 = 0$
b) $x^2 + x - 12 = 0$
c) $2 + x - x^2 = 0$
d) $x^2 + x - 16 = x$
e) $3x^2 - 15x - 14 = 4x$
f) $4x^2 - 1 = 0$
g) $6x^2 - 11x + 9 = 2x^2 - x + 3$
h) $4 - 9x^2 = 0$
i) $3x^2 + 10x - 8 = 2 - x - 3x^2$

Q3 Solve these quadratic equations, leaving your answers in surd form where necessary.

a) $3x^2 - 7x + 3 = 0$
b) $2x^2 - 6x - 2 = 0$
c) $x^2 + 4x + 6 = 12$

Q4 a) Rewrite the expression $x^2 + 6x + 7$ in the form $(x + m)^2 + n$.

b) Hence solve the equation $(2x + 1)^2 + 6(2x + 1) + 7 = 0$. Leave your answers in surd form.

Q5 Find all four solutions to the equation $x^4 - 17x^2 + 16 = 0$.

Q6 If the quadratic equation $x^2 + kx + 4 = 0$ has two distinct real roots, what are the possible values of k?

Q7 Rewrite these quadratics by completing the square. Then state their maximum or minimum value and the value of x where this occurs. Also, say if and where their graphs cross the x-axis.

a) $x^2 - 4x - 3$
b) $x^2 + 5x + 8$
c) $3 - 3x - x^2$
d) $2x^2 - 4x + 11$
e) $4x^2 - 28x + 48$
f) $14 + 12x - 3x^2$

Q8 How many roots do these quadratic equations have?
Sketch the graph of each quadratic function.

a) $x^2 - 2x - 3 = 0$
b) $x^2 - 6x + 9 = 0$
c) $2x^2 + 4x + 3 = 0$

Q9 a) Find the coordinates of the points of intersection of the graphs of $y = f(x)$ and $y = g(x)$, where $f(x) = 5x^3 - 13x^2 + 6x$ and $g(x) = -5x^3 + 7x^2 + 6x$.

b) Using your answer to part a) or otherwise, express $f(x) = 5x^3 - 13x^2 + 6x$ as the product of three factors.

Q10 A car travels through a multistorey car park. It starts above ground level, then goes underground. The first 10 seconds of the car's vertical path are modelled by the equation $h = 0.25t^2 - 2.75t + 6$, where h is the height in metres above the ground and t is the time in seconds.

a) Sketch a graph showing the height of the car during the first 10 seconds.

b) For the first 10 seconds of the car's journey, use your graph to find:

(i) the initial height of the car.

(ii) the lowest point of the car.

(iii) how long the car is underground for.

Exercise 1.1

Q1 Find the set of values for x which satisfy:

a) $2x - 1 < x + 4$ b) $4 - 3x \geq 10 - 5x$ c) $5x + 7 > 3x + 1$ d) $3 - 2x \leq 5x - 4$

e) $9 - x \geq 7x + 5$ f) $12x - 9 \leq 4x + 11$ g) $3x - 6 > 6 - 3x$ h) $-4x < 16 - 7x$

Q2 Find the set of values for x which satisfy the inequalities below. Give your answers in set notation.

a) $2(x + 3) > 3(x + 2)$ b) $5(1 + 3x) \leq 7$ c) $12 \geq 2(5 - 2x)$

Q3 Find the set of values for x which satisfy:

a) $\dfrac{6 - 5x}{2} < \dfrac{4 - 8x}{3}$ b) $\dfrac{3x - 1}{4} \geq 2x$ c) $\dfrac{x - 2}{2} - \dfrac{2x + 3}{3} < 7$

Q4 Find the set of values for x which satisfy the inequalities below. Give your answers in set notation.

a) $-5 < 2x - 3 < 15$ b) $-5 \leq 4 - 3x < 19$ c) $5 \leq 7 + 6x \leq 11$

Q5 Solve the following inequalities, and represent the solutions on a number line:

a) $2x \geq 3 - x$ b) $5x - 1 < 3x + 5$ c) $2x + 1 \geq 3x + 2$

d) $3(x - 3) \leq 5(x - 1)$ e) $9 - x \leq 3 - 4x$ f) $\dfrac{2(x - 3)}{3} + 1 < \dfrac{2x - 1}{2}$

Q6 Find the set of values of x for which $7 \leq 3x - 2 < 16$.

Q7 Find the set of values for x which satisfy **both** $4 - 2x < 10$ and $3x - 1 < x + 7$. Give your answer in set notation.

Q8 Find the values of x which satisfy both inequalities:

a) $2x \geq 3x - 5$ and $3x - 2 \geq x - 6$ b) $5x + 1 \leq 11$ and $2x - 3 < 5x - 6$

c) $2x - 1 \leq 3x - 5$ and $5x - 6 > x + 22$ d) $3x + 5 < x + 1$ and $6x - 1 \geq 3x + 5$

Quadratic inequalities

When solving inequalities, it's important that you **don't divide** or **multiply** by **variables**.

- The variable might be **negative** — so the inequality sign may end up pointing in the wrong direction.

- The variable could be equal to **zero** — you can't divide something by zero.

> **Example**   **Find the values of x which satisfy $2x^2 + 2x - 5 > 3x - 2$.**
> **Give your answer in set notation.**
>
> - First rewrite the inequality with zero on one side. $2x^2 - x - 3 > 0$
>
> - Then draw the graph of $y = 2x^2 - x - 3$.
>   Factorise the quadratic to find where it crosses the x-axis: $\Rightarrow$ $2x^2 - x - 3 = 0$
> $(2x - 3)(x + 1) = 0$
> $\Rightarrow$ $x = \dfrac{3}{2}$ and $x = -1$
>
> - The coefficient of x^2 is positive, so the graph is u-shaped and looks like this:
>
> - $2x^2 - x - 3 > 0$ is true when the graph is **positive**.
>   The graph shows that this is true when $x < -1$ or $x > \dfrac{3}{2}$.
>
> - So the solution is: $x < -1$ or $x > \dfrac{3}{2}$
>
> - In set notation, this is: $\{x : x < -1\} \cup \left\{x : x > \dfrac{3}{2}\right\}$
>
> $y = 2x^2 - x - 3$

You may be asked to find the set of values for x which satisfy **both** a quadratic inequality and a linear inequality. To do this, work out the solution of each inequality separately and then use a **graph** to help you find the solution that satisfies both.

Examples   Find the set of values of x which satisfy: a) $5x - 10 > 4x - 7$

- Solve in the usual way: $5x - 10 > 4x - 7 \implies 5x > 4x + 3 \implies x > 3$

b) $2x^2 - 11x + 5 < 0$

- Factorise the quadratic to find where the graph crosses the x-axis:

$$2x^2 - 11x + 5 = 0 \implies (2x - 1)(x - 5) = 0 \implies x = \frac{1}{2} \text{ and } x = 5$$

- The coefficient of x^2 is positive, so the graph is u-shaped. It looks like this:

- You're interested in when this is negative, i.e. below the x-axis.

- From the graph, this is when x is between $\frac{1}{2}$ and 5.

- So $2x^2 - 11x + 5 < 0$ when: $\frac{1}{2} < x < 5$

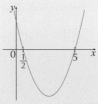

$y = 2x^2 - 11x + 5$

c) both $5x - 10 > 4x - 7$ and $2x^2 - 11x + 5 < 0$

- You already know the solutions to both inequalities.

- Add the line $x = 3$ to your graph.

- You're now interested in when the curve is negative, **and** when the x values are greater than 3.

- So both inequalities are satisfied when: $3 < x < 5$

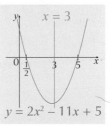

$y = 2x^2 - 11x + 5$

Exercise 1.2

Q1 Use the graphs given to solve the following quadratic inequalities:

a) $x^2 + 2x - 3 < 0$

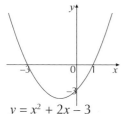

$y = x^2 + 2x - 3$

b) $4x - x^2 < 0$

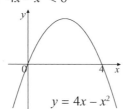

$y = 4x - x^2$

c) $2x^2 \geq 5 - 9x$

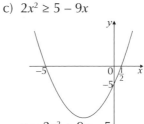

$y = 2x^2 + 9x - 5$

d) $x^2 - 2x - 5 > 0$

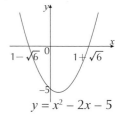

$y = x^2 - 2x - 5$

Q2 Use the graphs given to solve the quadratic inequalities below. Give your answers in set notation.

a) $x^2 \leq 4$

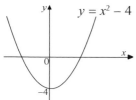

$y = x^2 - 4$

b) $13x < 3x^2 + 4$

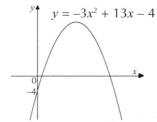

$y = -3x^2 + 13x - 4$

c) $x^2 + 4 < 6x$

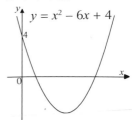

$y = x^2 - 6x + 4$

Q3 Find the ranges of values of x which satisfy the following quadratic inequalities.
Include a sketch of the graph for each answer.

a) $x^2 + 5x - 6 \geq 0$ b) $x^2 - 3x + 2 < 0$ c) $6 - 5x > 6x^2$

d) $x^2 - 5x + 24 \leq 5x + 3$ e) $36 - 4x^2 \leq 0$ f) $x^2 - 6x + 3 > 0$

g) $x^2 - x + 3 > 0$ h) $6 \geq 5x^2 + 13x$ i) $2x^2 > 3(x + 3)$

j) $(x + 4)^2 \leq 5x$ k) $x^2 + 5x < \dfrac{1}{2}$ l) $\dfrac{3}{4}x^2 \geq 1 + \dfrac{1}{4}x$

Q4 A rectangular office is to be built, measuring $(x - 9)$ metres wide and $(x - 6)$ metres long.
Given that at least 28 m² of floor space is required, find the set of possible values of x.

Q5 a) Find the set of values of k for which $kx^2 - 6x + k = 0$ has two distinct real solutions.

b) Find the set of values for k which gives the equation $x^2 - kx + k = 0$ no real roots.
Give your answer in set notation.

Q6 Find the values of x which satisfy both:

a) $4(3 - x) \geq 13 - 5x$ and $7x + 6 \geq 3x^2$ b) $x^2 > 5x - 3$ and $2(x + 3) \leq 10x$

Graphing inequalities

You can also show **regions** on a graph that satisfy **inequalities** in **two variables** (x and y).

The method has four steps:

> 1. Write each inequality as an equation.
> 2. Draw the graph for each equation.
> 3. Work out which side of each line you want.
> 4. Label the correct region.

Example   **Graph the following inequalities and label the region that satisfies all three:**
$$2x + y > 4 \qquad x - y < 1 \qquad y \leq 3$$

- Change these into equations:
$$y = 4 - 2x \qquad y = x - 1 \qquad y = 3$$

- Plot the lines on your graph — use dotted lines for > or <
inequalities and solid lines for ≥ or ≤ inequalities.

- Decide which side of each line you want.
Try the origin (0, 0) in each inequality.

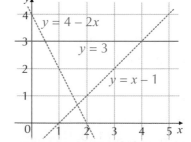

- $2x + y > 4 \Rightarrow 0 + 0 > 4$ which is false. The origin
is on the wrong side of the line, so shade this side.

- $x - y < 1 \Rightarrow 0 - 0 < 1$ which is true. The origin is on
the correct side of the line, so shade the other side.

- $y \leq 3 \Rightarrow 0 \leq 3$ which is true. The origin is on the
correct side of the line, so shade the other side.

This unshaded region is the area you want —
it satisfies all three inequalities. Don't forget to
label the correct region — this one is labelled R.

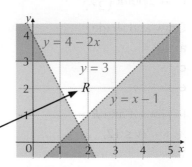

Example **Draw and label the region that satisfies the following inequalities:**
$$y > x^2 - x - 2 \qquad y \geq 4 + 7x - 2x^2$$

- First, write the inequalities as equations:
$$y = x^2 - x - 2 = (x + 1)(x - 2)$$
$$y = 4 + 7x - 2x^2 = (4 - x)(1 + 2x)$$

- Now draw the graphs of these equations, using a dotted line for $y = x^2 - x - 2$ and a solid line for $y = 4 + 7x - 2x^2$:

- Now try the origin in each inequality:
$y > x^2 - x - 2 \Rightarrow 0 > 0 - 0 - 2$ which is true. The origin is on the correct side of the line, so shade the other side.

- $y \geq 4 + 7x - 2x^2 \Rightarrow 0 \geq 4 + 0 - 0$ which is false. The origin is on the wrong side of the line, so shade this side.

- So you get an unshaded region that looks like this:

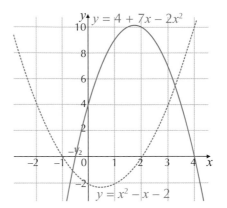

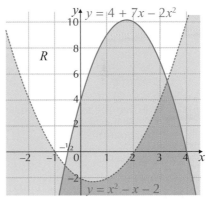

Exercise 1.3

Q1 Work out whether the following statements are true or false:
   a) The point $(2, 4)$ is in the region that satisfies $3y > 8x - 3$.
   b) The point $(-3, -5)$ lies outside the region that satisfies $4y + x^2 \leq 3$.
   c) The point $(8, -4)$ is in the region that satisfies $y^2 + (x + 6)^2 \geq 68$.
   d) The point $(1, 3)$ is in the region that satisfies $x + 2y > 4$ and $3x^2 > 20 - 4y$.
   e) The point $\left(\frac{1}{2}, \frac{3}{2}\right)$ lies outside the region that satisfies $y^2 < 10 - 8x^2$ and $3x + 4y \geq 6$.

Q2 Draw and shade the regions that satisfy the following sets of inequalities:
   a) $x + y < 5$, $2x + y \geq 4$, $x + 2y > 6$ b) $x \leq 4$, $y \leq 7$, $x + y > 4$
   c) $y > x^2$, $x - y \geq -3$ d) $y - 2 \leq x^2$, $2x^2 - y < 2$
   e) $4x^2 > y - 5$, $3x + 5y \leq 40$ f) $2y + 4x^2 < 6x + 10$, $5y > 2x + 5$

Q3 Regions A and B are described by the sets of inequalities below:
   A: $x + 2y \leq 12$, $2y - 3x \leq 4$, $y \geq 2$ B: $x \geq 3$, $2x \leq y + 9$, $x + 3y \leq 15$
   Which region has the greater area?

Q4   A bakery is running out of ingredients and wants to see how many sponge cakes and baguettes they can make. A cake requires 1 lb of flour and 3 eggs, and a baguette requires 2 lb of flour and 1 egg. The bakery can make x cakes and y baguettes. They have 24 lb of flour remaining, which can be represented by the inequality $x + 2y \leq 24$.

a) They only have 42 eggs left. Use this information to form another inequality in x and y.

b) On a graph, draw and label the region that satisfies both of these inequalities.

c) A customer requests 8 cakes and 10 baguettes for a fête.
Can the bakery meet their order? If not, what ingredient(s) do they not have enough of?

2. Simultaneous Equations

Simultaneous equations — both linear

You can solve two linear simultaneous equations by **elimination**.
This method involves **four** steps:

> 1. **Match the coefficients**
> 2. **Eliminate to find one variable**
> 3. **Find the other variable (that you eliminated)**
> 4. **Check your answer**

Example   Solve the simultaneous equations $3x + 5y = -4$ and $-2x + 3y = 9$.

- Number your equations 1 and 2.

  ① $3x + 5y = -4$
  ② $-2x + 3y = 9$

  Number the new equations.

- Match the coefficients:
  To get the x's to match, multiply equation 1 by 2 and equation 2 by 3.

  ①×2 $6x + 10y = -8$ ⟶ ③
  ②×3 $-6x + 9y = 27$ ⟶ ④

- Eliminate to find one variable: Add the new equations together to eliminate the x's.

  ③+④ $19y = 19 \Rightarrow y = 1$

- Find the variable you eliminated:
  Put $y = 1$ into one of the equations to find x.

  $y = 1$ in ① $\Rightarrow$ $3x + 5 = -4$
  $\qquad\qquad\qquad 3x = -9$
  $\qquad\qquad\qquad x = -3$

- So the solution is:

  $\mathbf{x = -3, \ y = 1}$

- Check your answer:
  Put these values into the other equation.

  $-2x + 3y = 9$ ⟵ If these two numbers are the same, then the values you've got for the variables are right.
  $x = -3, \ y = 1$
  $\Rightarrow -2 \times (-3) + 3 \times 1 = 6 + 3 = 9$

Tip: If you drew the **graph** of each equation you'd get two straight lines.
The point where these two lines **intersect** gives the **solution** to the two simultaneous equations.

Exercise 2.1

Q1   Solve the following simultaneous equations:

a) $2x - 3y = 3$, $\ x + 3y = 6$

b) $3x + 2y = 7$, $\ 7x - y = -12$

c) $4x + 3y = -4$, $\ 6x - 4y = 11$

d) $7x - 6y = 4$, $\ 11x + 9y = -6$

e) $6x + 2y - 8 = 0$, $\ 4x + 3 = -3y$

f) $2x + 18y - 21 = 0$, $\ -14y = 3x + 14$

g) $2x + 16y = 10$, $\ 64y - 5 + 3x = 0$

h) $4x - 3y = 15$, $\ 5y - 12 = 9x$

Q2 Find the point of intersection of each pair of straight lines.

a) $y = 2x - 3$, $y = \frac{1}{2}x + 3$

b) $y = -\frac{2}{3}x + 7$, $y = \frac{1}{2}x + \frac{21}{2}$

c) $x + 2y + 5 = 0$, $3x - 5y - 7 = 0$

d) $2x - 3y = 7$, $5x - \frac{15}{2}y = 9$

e) $8x = -3y + 10$, $9y = 3 - 6x$

f) $7x - 5y = 15$, $2x - 9 = 3y$

g) $6x + 3y = 10$, $-9 = 8y - 4x$

h) $10y = 3 - x$, $5y = 6x + 5$

i) $\frac{7}{3}x = 2 + \frac{5}{3}y$, $y = \frac{3}{4}x + \frac{1}{3}$

j) $\frac{3}{4}y = \frac{9}{5}x - 10$, $-\frac{3}{5}y + \frac{3}{2}x + 10 = 0$

Q3 Three roads on a map are modelled (in (x, y) coordinates) by the following equations:

A: $5x + 2y = -11$ B: $2x = y + 1$ C: $5y = 13 + x$

Signposts are placed at every intersection of the roads.
Find the coordinates of all of these signposts.

Simultaneous equations — if one is not linear

The other main method for solving simultaneous equations is substitution.
When one of the equations has quadratic terms, you can **only** use the **substitution** method.
This method also has **four** steps:

> 1. **Isolate variable in linear equation**
> 2. **Substitute into the quadratic equation**
> 3. **Solve to get values for one variable**
> 4. **Put these values in the linear equation**

Example **Solve the simultaneous equations $-x + 2y = 5$ and $x^2 + y^2 = 25$.**

- Start by labelling the two equations.

  ① $-x + 2y = 5$
  ② $x^2 + y^2 = 25$

- Rearrange the linear equation so that either x or y is on its own on one side of the equals sign.

  ① $-x + 2y = 5 \Rightarrow x = 2y - 5$

- Substitute this expression into the quadratic...   Sub into ②

  $x^2 + y^2 = 25$
  $\Rightarrow (2y - 5)^2 + y^2 = 25$

- ...and then rearrange this into the form $ax^2 + bx + c = 0$, so you can solve it — either by factorising or using the quadratic formula.

  $\Rightarrow (4y^2 - 20y + 25) + y^2 = 25$
  $\Rightarrow 5y^2 - 20y = 0$
  $\Rightarrow 5y(y - 4) = 0$
  $\Rightarrow y = 0$ or $y = 4$

- Finally put both values back into the linear equation to find the corresponding values for x:

  When $y = 0$:   When $y = 4$:
  ① $-x + 2y = 5$ ① $-x + 2y = 5$
  $\Rightarrow x = -5$ $-x + 8 = 5$
                        $\Rightarrow x = 3$

- Solving these simultaneous equations has produced a **pair** of solutions:

  $x = -5, y = 0$ and $x = 3, y = 4$

Example — Find any points of intersection of the graphs $y = x^2 - 4x + 5$ and $y = 2x - 4$.

- Label the two equations:
  - (1) $y = x^2 - 4x + 5$
  - (2) $y = 2x - 4$

- Substitute (2) in (1): $2x - 4 = x^2 - 4x + 5$

- Rearrange and solve: $x^2 - 6x + 9 = 0$

  $(x - 3)^2 = 0$ ⟵ Double root — i.e. you only get 1 solution from the quadratic equation.

  $x = 3$

- In Equation (2) this gives: $y = 2 \times 3 - 4 = 2$

- So there's one solution: **$x = 3, y = 2$**

- Since the equations have only one solution, the two graphs only meet at one point: (3, 2).

- The straight line is actually a **tangent** to the curve.

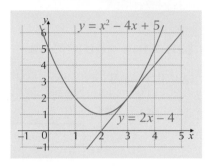

Tip: Some sets of simultaneous equations have no solutions. This means the graphs of the equations never meet.

Exercise 2.2

Q1   Solve the following simultaneous equations using substitution:
   a) $y = 4x + 3$, $2y - 3x = 1$
   b) $5x + 2y = 16$, $2y - x - 4 = 0$

Q2   Solve the following simultaneous equations:
   a) $y = 2x + 5$, $y = x^2 - x + 1$
   b) $y = 2x^2 - 3$, $y = 3x + 2$
   c) $2x^2 - xy = 6$, $y - 3x + 7 = 0$
   d) $xy = 6$, $2y - x + 4 = 0$
   e) $y = x^2 - 2x - 3$, $y + x + 8 = 0$
   f) $y = 2x^2 - 3x + 5$, $5x - y = 3$
   g) $2x^2 + 3y^2 + 18x = 347$, $4x + y = 7$
   h) $2y = 2x^2 + x + 1$, $y + 2x = 2$
   i) $x^2 + 4x = 4y + 40$, $12y + 5x + 30 = 0$
   j) $y - x = x + 2$, $\frac{1}{4}y^2 + 25 = 3x^2 + 11x$

Q3   Find the points of intersection of the following curves and straight lines:
   a) $y = \frac{1}{2}x^2 + 4x - 8$, $y = 4 + \frac{3}{2}x$
   b) $y = 2x^2 + x - 6$, $5x - y + 10 = 0$
   c) $x^2 + y^2 = 50$, $x + 2y = 5$
   d) $2x^2 - y + 3x + 1 = 0$, $y - x - 5 = 0$
   e) $3x^2 + 9x + 1 = 6y$, $2x + 3y = \frac{11}{2}$
   f) $4x - y + 10 = 0$, $2y - 19 = 4x^2 + 8x$

Q4   a) Solve the simultaneous equations $x^2 + y^2 = 10$ and $x - 3y + 10 = 0$.
   b) Say what your answer to part a) means geometrically.

Q5   Without drawing the graphs, determine whether the following curves and lines intersect at one or two points, or do not intersect at all:

   a) $y = x^2 + 6x - 7$ and $y = 2x - 3$
   b) $3x^2 + 4y^2 + 6x = 9$ and $x + 2y = 3$
   c) $xy + 2x - y = 8$ and $x + y = 1$

Review Exercise — Chapter 3

Q1 Solve:

a) $7x - 4 > 2x - 42$ b) $12y - 3 \leq 4y + 4$

c) $9y - 4 \geq 17y + 2$ d) $x + 6 < 5x - 4$

e) $4x - 2 > x - 14$ f) $7 - x \leq 4 - 2x$

g) $11x - 4 < 4 - 11x$ h) $1 + 10y \geq 7y - 12$

Q2 Find the set of values for x that satisfy the following inequalities:

a) $3x^2 - 5x - 2 \leq 0$ b) $x^2 + 2x + 7 > 4x + 9$

c) $3x^2 + 7x + 4 \geq 2(x^2 + x - 1)$ d) $x^2 + 3x - 1 \geq x + 2$

e) $2x^2 > x + 1$ f) $3x^2 - 12 < x^2 - 2x$

g) $3x^2 + 6x \leq 2x^2 + 3$ h) $(x + 2)(x - 3) \geq 8 - 3x^2$

Q3 Draw and shade the region which satisfies each of the following sets of inequalities.

a) $8 \leq y - x$, $y < 12 - x$, $9x + 2y < -4$

b) $x + 3y > 15$, $3x + y < 12$, $4y \leq x + 36$

c) $x + 4y \geq 4$, $y < 6 + x - x^2$

d) $2y \geq 3x + 4$, $2y < 28 - x$, $2y > x^2 - 10x + 9$

e) $10y + 10x > x^2$, $y < -x^2 + 8x - 12$

Q4 Solve these sets of simultaneous equations:

a) $3x - 4y = 7$ and $-2x + 7y = -22$ b) $2x - 3y = \frac{11}{12}$ and $x + y = -\frac{7}{12}$

c) $2x + 3y = 8$ and $6y = 5 - 4x$ d) $11y = 9x + 4$ and $3x - 2y = 7$

e) $\frac{1}{2}x + \frac{1}{3}y = 50$ and $x + 4y = 25$ f) $x + 4y = \frac{1}{4}$ and $y + 2x = \frac{1}{5}$

Q5 Find where the following lines meet:

a) $y = 3x - 4$ and $y = 7x - 5$ b) $y = 13 - 2x$ and $7x - y - 23 = 0$

c) $2x - 3y + 4 = 0$ and $x - 2y + 1 = 0$ d) $5x - 7y = 22$ and $3y - 4x - 13 = 0$

e) $9 - 8y = \frac{2}{3}x$ and $\frac{1}{3}x + \frac{2}{3}y = 10$ f) $24x + 15y = 2$ and $18x + 36y = 5$

Q6 Find, where possible, the solutions to these sets of simultaneous equations. Interpret your answers geometrically.

a) $y = x^2 - 7x + 4$ and $2x - y - 10 = 0$ b) $y = 30 - 6x + 2x^2$ and $y = 2(x + 11)$

c) $2x^2 + 2y^2 - 3 = 0$ and $y = x + 4$ d) $4y + 3x = 8$ and $2y - 2x^2 - 4x = 7$

e) $\frac{1}{4}x^2 + 3x + 15 = 4y$ and $2y = 3x + 3$ f) $(x - 3)^2 + (y + 4)^2 = 25$ and $x - 7y = 6$

Q7 Without drawing the graphs, decide whether the curve $y = x^2 - 2x - 3$ and the line $y = 3x + 11$ intersect at one or two points, or do not intersect at all.

Q7 Find the gradient and y-intercept of the following lines:

a) $6x - 2y + 3 = 0$

b) $-9x + 3y - 12 = 0$

c) $-x - 4y - 2 = 0$

d) $7x + 8y + 11 = 0$

e) $2x - 14y + 1 = 0$

f) $-3x + 28y - 16 = 0$

g) $0.1x + 0.2y + 0.3 = 0$

h) $-10x + 0.1y + 11 = 0$

i) $\frac{6}{7}x - 3y + \frac{3}{4} = 0$

j) $4 - 2x = 18y$

k) $6(1 - y) = 0.5x$

l) $3(x - 3y + 2) = \frac{1}{3}(2y - 2x + 1)$

Q8 A straight line has gradient 3 and passes through the point $(2, -7)$.
State which of the following coordinates are points on the line.

a) $(1, -10)$ b) $(-2, -7)$ c) $(5, 2)$ d) $(0.5, 2.5)$ e) $(7, 8)$ f) $(0, -12)$

Q9 A straight line passes through the points $(6, 6)$ and $(-1, 20)$.
Which of the following coordinates are also on the line?

a) $(2, 14)$ b) $(-4, -24)$ c) $(10, -2)$ d) $(26, -34)$ e) $(-34, 88)$ f) $(2.5, 13)$

Q10 The distance travelled by a car is modelled by a straight line graph. At time $t = 0$ hours, it starts at distance $d = 0$ kilometres, and its speed (the gradient) is a constant 32 km/h throughout the journey.

a) Give the equation of the line in the form $d = mt + c$

b) How long does it take the car to travel a distance of 9.6 km? Give your answer in minutes.

c) Give one criticism of this model.

Q11 At a cafe, a small cup of coffee costs £x and a large cup of coffee costs £y.
Robert buys 3 small cups and 4 large cups for £18.

a) Write this as an equation in the form $ax + by + c = 0$, where a, b and c are all integers.

b) Draw the straight line graph of this equation.

c) Amani buys 1 small cup and 2 large cups for £8. Write a second equation (in the same form) to represent this and plot the graph on the same set of axes.

d) Write down the cost of a small cup of coffee and the cost of a large cup of coffee.

Line segments

You can find the **midpoint** of a line segment (i.e. the point that lies exactly halfway between the two ends) using the following formula:

$$\text{Midpoint (AB)} = \left(\frac{x_A + x_B}{2}, \frac{y_A + y_B}{2} \right)$$

 Points A $(1, a)$ and B $(b, 1)$ lie on the line $4x + 3y + 5 = 0$.
Find the midpoint of the line segment AB.

1. Start by finding the missing coordinates:

Point A: $4(1) + 3a + 5 = 0 \Rightarrow 3a = -9 \Rightarrow a = -3$

Point B: $4b + 3(1) + 5 = 0 \Rightarrow 4b = -8 \Rightarrow b = -2$

2. So A is at $(1, -3)$ and B is at $(-2, 1)$. Now you can use the midpoint formula:

$$\text{Midpoint} = \left(\frac{1 + (-2)}{2}, \frac{(-3) + 1}{2} \right) = \left(\frac{-1}{2}, \frac{-2}{2} \right) = (-0.5, -1)$$

To find the **length** of a line segment (the **distance between two points**), use Pythagoras' theorem:

$$\text{Length (AB)} = \sqrt{(x_B - x_A)^2 + (y_B - y_A)^2}$$

Example

Find the length of the segment of the line with equation $y = 5x - 2$ between $x = 3$ and $x = 4$.

1. First, find the y-coordinates at $x = 3$ and $x = 4$:

   When $x = 3$, $y = 5(3) - 2 = 13$

   When $x = 4$, $y = 5(4) - 2 = 18$

2. Now substitute these values into the formula:

   $$\text{Length} = \sqrt{(4-3)^2 + (18-13)^2} = \sqrt{1+25} = \sqrt{26}$$

Exercise 1.2

Q1 For the line segments below, find: (i) the midpoint, (ii) the exact length of the line segment.

a) $(0, 0)$ to $(2, 5)$

b) $(4, 7)$ to $(-3, 8)$

c) $(1, -8.8)$ to $(-11, 0.2)$

d) $\left(5, \frac{1}{3}\right)$ to $\left(-10, \frac{10}{3}\right)$

e) $y = 2x + 6$ between $x = 1$ and $x = 5$

f) $3x + 2y + 1 = 0$ between $x = 2$ and $x = 4$

g) $y = -4x - 11$ between $x = -3$ and $x = 2$

h) $x - \frac{1}{2}y - 3 = 0$ between $x = -4$ and $x = -1$

Q2 For the given segments of the straight lines, find: (i) the midpoint, (ii) the exact length of AB.

a) Line: $y = 3x - 5$, $\quad$ A $= (1, a)$, $\quad$ B $= (b, 1)$

b) Line: $-2x - y + 11 = 0$, $\quad$ A $= (a, 3)$, $\quad$ B $= (4.5, b)$

c) Line: $y = -\frac{2}{5}x + 1$, $\quad$ A $= (5, a)$, $\quad$ B $= (b, 7)$

d) Line: $\frac{1}{4}x - \frac{1}{3}y - \frac{1}{2} = 0$, A $= (a, 12)$, B $= (b, b)$

Q3 An orienteering group are following a straight path from point A to point B. On their map, point A has coordinates $(0.8, 1.1)$, and point B has coordinates $(2.3, 0.5)$, where 1 unit is 1 km. The group have travelled for 700 m when one of them slips and injures their leg. Which is shorter: to return to point A or continue on to point B?

Q4 a) The line segment between the points A $(2a, a)$ and B $(b, b + 3)$ has a gradient of 2 and a midpoint of $(4, 5)$. Find the exact distance between A and B.

b) The points A (a, a) and B $(b, 3)$ are joined by a line segment with a gradient of $-\frac{1}{5}$. Given that the midpoint of AB is at $(c, 1)$, find the exact distance between A and B.

Q5 The line segment CD has midpoint $(1, 2)$, gradient $\frac{3}{4}$ and length 5. Find the coordinates of the end points C and D.

2. Parallel and Perpendicular Lines

Parallel lines

Parallel lines have **equal gradient** — that's what makes them parallel. So when finding the equation of a line parallel to a line with a given equation, you know the gradient will be the same for both.

Example **Find the line parallel to $2x - 8y + 11 = 0$ that passes through the point $(3, -1)$. Give your equation in the form $ax + by + c = 0$, where a, b and c are integers.**

1. First, put the given line in a more useful form, i.e. $y = mx + c$.

$$2x - 8y + 11 = 0 \Rightarrow -8y = -2x - 11 \Rightarrow y = \frac{1}{4}x + \frac{11}{8}$$

2. The gradient of the given line is $\frac{1}{4}$, so that's also the gradient of the parallel line you want.

$$y = \frac{1}{4}x + c$$

$$x = 3 \text{ and } y = -1 \Rightarrow -1 = \frac{1}{4}(3) + c \Rightarrow c = -\frac{7}{4}$$

3. So $y = \frac{1}{4}x - \frac{7}{4}$ which rearranges to: $x - 4y - 7 = 0$

Exercise 2.1

Q1 State which of the following straight lines are parallel to $y = -3x - 1$.
a) $2y = -6x + 2$
b) $y - 3x - 1 = 0$
c) $6y + 18x = 7$
d) $\frac{1}{3}(y + 1) = x$
e) $-9y - 2 = 27x$
f) $4y = 12x$

Q2 Find the equations of the parallel lines shown in blue.
Write them in the form $ax + by + c = 0$, where a, b and c are integers.
a) $y = 4x - 1$

$(3, 2)$
b) $(-4, -5)$
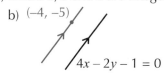
$4x - 2y - 1 = 0$

Q3 State whether the following pairs of lines are parallel.
a) $y = 2x + 1$
   $y + \frac{1}{2}x = 1$
b) $2x - 3y + 1 = 0$
   $y = \frac{2}{3}x + 2$
c) $-5x + 4y + 3 = 0$
   $8y = 10x$

Q4 Line A passes through the point $(4, 3)$ and is parallel to the line $2x - 4y + 3 = 0$.
Find the equation of line A in the form: a) $y = mx + c$ b) $ax + by + c = 0$.

Q5 Find the equations of the lines which are parallel to each of the following lines and pass through the points given. Give your answers in the form $ax + by + c = 0$, where a, b, and c are integers.
a) $y = 2x - 1$, $(2, 1)$
b) $5x + y - 11 = 0$, $(3, -1)$
c) $3y = \frac{1}{3}x + 2$, $(-6, 2)$
d) $x - \frac{1}{4}y + 1 = 0$, $(-6, -5)$
e) $x - y = 13$, $(0, 0)$
f) $100 = y + \frac{1}{5}x$, $(50, 50)$
g) $0.5x + 2.2y - 12 = 0$, $(4, 8)$
h) $3(x + 1) - 2(y - 1) = 4$, $(-2, 2)$
i) $\frac{y - 3x}{2} = \frac{4 + y}{3}$, $(2, 3)$

Perpendicular lines

Finding the equations of **perpendicular** lines (or '**normals**') is just as easy as finding the equations of parallel lines — you just need to know one key fact:

> The gradients of perpendicular lines **multiply to give –1**.

Which means:

> Gradient of the perpendicular line =
> **–1 ÷ the gradient of the other one**.

 Example

Find the equation of the line perpendicular to $7x - 3y + 5 = 0$ that passes through the point (–3, –11).

1. Start by converting the equation into a more useful form:

$$7x - 3y + 5 = 0 \implies -3y = -7x - 5 \implies y = \frac{7}{3}x + \frac{5}{3}$$

2. Now use the gradient rule: gradient of perpendicular line $= -1 \div \frac{7}{3} = -\frac{3}{7} \implies y = -\frac{3}{7}x + c$

3. Substitute in the coordinates (–3, –11) to find c: $-11 = -\frac{3}{7}(-3) + c \implies c = -11 - \frac{9}{7} = -\frac{86}{7}$

4. So the perpendicular line has equation: $y = -\frac{3}{7}x - \frac{86}{7} \implies \mathbf{3x + 7y + 86 = 0}$

Exercise 2.2

Q1 Find the equations of the dotted lines. Give your answers in the form $y = mx + c$.

a) (–2, 5)   b) (5, 2)

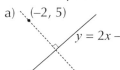

$y = 2x - 3$

$x - 5y - 30 = 0$

Q2 Find the equations of the lines which are perpendicular to each of the following lines and pass through the points given. Give your answers in the form $ax + by + c = 0$, where a, b, and c are integers.

a) $y = \frac{1}{4}x - 1$, (–1, 2)

b) $2x + 3y - 1 = 0$, (–3, –1)

c) $y = \frac{3}{2}x + 2$, (2, 1)

d) $5x - 10y + 1 = 0$, (6, –5)

e) $-4x + 21y = 2$, (0.5, 7)

f) $5(2 - x + 3y) = 2$, (–5, –1)

g) $7y + 1 = \frac{2x - 3}{8}$, (7, 8)

h) $y = 2(2x + 0.1y) + 1$, (3, 4.4)

i) $72x - 96y = -0.5$, (27, 36)

Q3 Triangle ABC has vertices at A(0, 2), B(4, 3) and C(5, –1).

a) Find the equations of the line segments AB, BC and AC in the form $y = mx + c$.

b) What type of triangle is ABC? Explain why.

Q4 Line A passes through the point (a, b) and is perpendicular to the line $3x - 2y = 6$. Find an equation of line A in terms of a and b.

Q5 The perpendicular bisector of a line segment AB is the line that is perpendicular to AB, passing through its midpoint. Find the equation of the perpendicular bisector of the line segment AB, where A = (1, 4) and B = (5, 2).

When you're sketching cubics and quartics, watch out for any **repeated roots**.
These occur when a **factor** is repeated (i.e. when a bracket is squared, cubed, etc.).

- A **squared** bracket means it's a **double root**, and the graph will only **touch** the x-axis, not cross it.
- A **cubed** bracket means a **triple root**, which still crosses the x-axis, but **flattens out** as it does so.

Example **Sketch the graph of $y = (2 - x)^3$.**

1. Expanding the brackets gives: $y = 8 - 12x + 6x^2 - x^3$

2. This time, the coefficient of x^3 is negative, so the graph will have a top-left to bottom-right shape.

3. $x = 0$ gives a y-intercept of 8.

4. The function is zero only once, at $x = 2$ — this is a triple root (you know this because the $(2 - x)$ bracket is cubed).

5. So the graph looks like this:

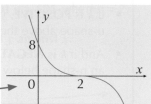

Exercise 4.1

Q1 The diagram shows four graphs, A, B, C and D.
State which graph would represent each of the following functions.
a) $y = -1.5x^4$ b) $y = 0.5x^3$ c) $y = 2x^6$ d) $y = -3x^3$

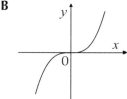
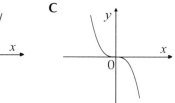
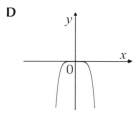

Q2 a) Factorise completely $x^3 - 7x^2 + 12x$.
b) Hence sketch the graph of $y = x^3 - 7x^2 + 12x$, showing where the graph meets the coordinate axes.

Q3 Sketch the graphs of the functions, showing clearly where they meet the x-axis.
a) $y = x(x + 2)(x - 3)$
b) $y = (x + 1)(2x - 1)(x - 3)$
c) $y = x(x + 1)(2 - x)$
d) $y = x^2(2x - 5)$
e) $y = x(5 - x)^2$
f) $y = (1 - x)(2 - x)^2$
g) $y = -5x^2(3x - 2)$
h) $y = (7 - x)(9 - 2x)(3 - x)$
i) $y = (4 + x)^3$
j) $y = x^3 - 16x$
k) $y = 2x^3 - 12x^2 + 18x$
l) $y = -3x^2 - x^3$

Q4 Sketch the graphs of the following quartics:
a) $y = 3x(x - 4)^2(2x - 1)$
b) $y = -3x^2(2x - 7)^2$
c) $(4 - x)(x + 2)^3$
d) $y = x^2(x^2 - 9x + 14)$
e) $y = (x + 1)(2 - 3x)(4x^2 - 9)$
f) $y = (x - 5)(2x^3 + 5x^2 - 3x)$

Q5 Sketch the graph of $y = x^4 - 10x^3 + 35x^2 - 50x + 24$, given that its roots are all positive integers.

Reciprocal functions and negative powers

Reciprocal functions are those of the form $y = \dfrac{k}{x}$ (or $y = kx^{-1}$) where k is a constant.

In general, for any graph in the form $y = \dfrac{k}{x^n}$ or kx^{-n}:

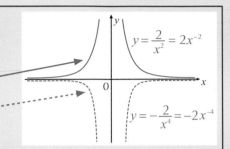

EVEN

- **When n is EVEN,** you get a graph with two bits next to each other.

- If k is **POSITIVE**, both parts of the graph are above the x-axis

- And if k is **NEGATIVE**, the graph is below the x-axis.

$$y = \frac{2}{x^2} = 2x^{-2}$$

$$y = -\frac{2}{x^4} = -2x^{-4}$$

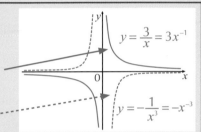

ODD

- **When n is ODD,** you get a graph with two bits opposite each other.

- If k is **POSITIVE**, the graph is in the top-right and bottom-left quadrants.

- And if k is **NEGATIVE**, it's in the top-left and the bottom-right.

$$y = \frac{3}{x} = 3x^{-1}$$

$$y = -\frac{1}{x^3} = -x^{-3}$$

Tip: Graphs of reciprocal functions always have **asymptotes** — lines which the curve gets infinitely close to, but **never** touches. For all of these graphs, the asymptotes have equations $x = 0$ and $y = 0$.

Exercise 4.2

Q1 The diagram shows four graphs, A, B, C and D.
State which graph would represent each of the following functions:

a) $y = x^{-2}$ b) $y = -3x^{-3}$ c) $y = -\dfrac{3}{x^4}$ d) $y = 2x^{-5}$

A 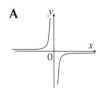   **B** 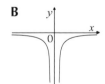   **C** 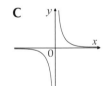   **D**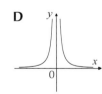

Q2 Sketch the graphs of the following reciprocal functions, showing the points where $x = 1$ and $x = -1$:

a) $y = 1.5x^{-5}$ b) $y = 7x^{-2}$ c) $y = -\dfrac{6}{x}$ d) $y = -1.2x^{-4}$

e) $y = \dfrac{3}{x^3}$ f) $y = \dfrac{1}{2}x^{-6}$ g) $y = \dfrac{1}{3x^2}$ h) $y = \dfrac{4}{5x^{11}}$

Q3 a) Sketch the graphs of $y = 3x^{-2}$ and $y = -x^3 - 2x^2$ on the same axes.

b) Find the number of real roots of $3x^{-2} = -x^3 - 2x^2$.

Q4 a) Use graph paper to draw the graphs of $y = -\dfrac{2}{x}$ and $y = 4 - x^2$ on the same axes for $-3 \le x \le 3$.
Use a scale of 2 cm for 1 unit.

b) Use your answer to part a) to estimate the solutions to $-\dfrac{2}{x} = 4 - x^2$.

5. Graph Transformations

Translations

Translating the graph of a function means moving it either **horizontally** or **vertically**. The shape of the graph itself doesn't change, it just moves. There are two types of translation:

$y = f(x) + a$
Adding a number to the **whole function** translates the graph in the **y-direction**.
If $a > 0$, the graph goes **upwards**.
If $a < 0$, the graph goes **downwards**.
This can be described by a **column vector**: $\begin{pmatrix} 0 \\ a \end{pmatrix}$.

$y = f(x + a)$
Writing '$x + a$' instead of 'x' translates the graph in the **x-direction**.
If $a > 0$, the graph goes to the **left**.
If $a < 0$, the graph goes to the **right**.
As a **column vector**, this would be $\begin{pmatrix} -a \\ 0 \end{pmatrix}$.

Examples   The diagram shows the graph of $y = f(x)$, where $f(x) = x(x + 2)(x - 2)$.

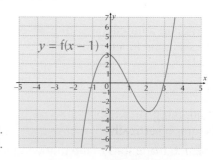

a) **Sketch the graph $y = f(x) + 2$.**

1. 2 has been added to the whole function, so $a = 2$.

2. So the graph will be translated 2 units in the y-direction, i.e. upwards by 2.

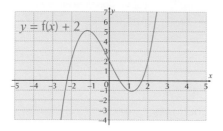

The point $(0, 0)$ on $f(x)$ has become the point $(0, 2)$.

The other roots of $f(x)$, $(-2, 0)$ and $(2, 0)$, have become $(-2, 2)$ and $(2, 2)$.

b) **Sketch the graph $y = f(x - 1)$.**

1. Here, it's of the form $y = f(x + a)$ so it's a translation in the x-direction.

2. $a = -1$, so it's a translation to the **right** by 1 unit.

1 is added to the x-coordinate of every point. E.g. $(-2, 0)$ becomes $(-1, 0)$.

Exercise 5.1

Q1   The diagram shows the graph of $y = f(x)$.

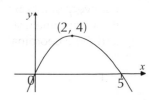

a) Sketch the graph of $y = f(x) + 2$, labelling the coordinates of the maximum and where the curve meets the y-axis.

b) Sketch the graph of $y = f(x + 2)$ labelling the points where the curve meets the x-axis and the maximum.

Q2 If $g(x) = -\dfrac{2}{x}$, sketch these graphs and write down the equations of the asymptotes for each.

    a) $y = g(x)$ b) $y = g(x + 3)$ c) $y = g(x) + 3$

Q3 Given the graph of $y = x^2(x - 4)$, describe the translation that would give the graph of:

    a) $x^2(x - 4) + 1$ b) $y = (x - 2)^2(x - 6)$ c) $y = x(x + 4)^2$

Q4 Explain how the graph of $y = x^3 + 3x + 7$ can be translated to give the graph of $y = x^3 + 3x + 2$. Include a column vector in your answer.

Q5 Find the equation (in its simplest form) of the graph obtained by translating $y = x^2 - 3x + 7$ by:

    a) $\begin{pmatrix} 0 \\ 6 \end{pmatrix}$ b) $\begin{pmatrix} 0 \\ -5 \end{pmatrix}$ c) $\begin{pmatrix} -1 \\ 0 \end{pmatrix}$ d) $\begin{pmatrix} 3 \\ 0 \end{pmatrix}$

Q6 The diagram shows the graph of $y = f(x)$. The graph has a maximum at (5, 3), crosses the x-axis at (3, 0) and (6, 0) and crosses the y-axis at (0, –1).

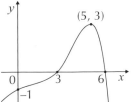

    a) Sketch the graph of $y = f(x) - 2$.

    b) Label the coordinates of the maximum and the point where the graph meets the y-axis.

Q7 a) Sketch the graph of $y = (x - 1)(2x - 3)(4 - x)$ and label the points where the graph meets the coordinate axes.

    b) The graph in part a) is translated by the vector $\begin{pmatrix} 2 \\ 0 \end{pmatrix}$. Give the equation of the translated graph in its factorised form.

    c) On separate axes, sketch the graph of the equation from part b), labelling all the points where the graph meets the x-axis.

Q8 a) The graph of $f(x) = x^2 + 5$ is translated to the left by 3 to give the graph of $g(x)$. Find the equation of $g(x)$ in its simplest form.

    b) The graph of $g(x)$ is then translated downwards by 4 to give the graph of $h(x)$. Find the equation of $h(x)$ in its simplest form.

Q9 Give the equations of the asymptotes of the following graphs:

    a) $y = \dfrac{1}{x} - 4$ b) $y = \dfrac{1}{x + 3}$ c) $y = \dfrac{1}{x - 1} + 7$

Stretches and reflections

The graph of a function can be stretched, squashed or reflected by **multiplying** the whole function or the x's in the function by a number. The result you get depends on what you multiply and whether the number is positive or negative.

$y = af(x)$
Multiplying the **whole function** by a stretches the graph **vertically** by a scale factor of a.
• If $a > 1$ or $a < -1$, the graph is **stretched**.
• If $-1 < a < 1$, the graph is **squashed**.
• If a is **negative**, the graph is **also reflected** about the x-**axis**.
For every point on the graph, the x-coordinate stays the same and the y-coordinate is multiplied by a.

$y = f(ax)$
Writing 'ax' instead of 'x' stretches the graph **horizontally** by a scale factor of $\dfrac{1}{a}$.
• If $a > 1$ or $a < -1$, the graph is **squashed**.
• If $-1 < a < 1$, the graph is **stretched**.
• If a is **negative**, the graph is **also reflected** about the y-**axis**.
For every point on the graph, the y-coordinate stays the same and the x-coordinate is multiplied by $\dfrac{1}{a}$.

Tip: Don't describe a transformation as a "squash" in your answers — call it a "stretch with a scale factor of...".

6. Circles

You can describe a circle with **radius r** and **centre (a, b)** with the equation:

$$(x - a)^2 + (y - b)^2 = r^2$$

Example

Circle C has its centre at (6, 4) and a radius of 3.
Show that C is given by the equation $(x - 6)^2 + (y - 4)^2 = 9$.

1. Join a point P (x, y) on the circumference of the circle to the centre (6, 4), creating a right-angled triangle.

2. The hypotenuse of this right-angled triangle has length 3, and the other sides have length $(x - 6)$ and $(y - 4)$.

3. Now use Pythagoras' theorem: $(x - 6)^2 + (y - 4)^2 = 3^2$

     or: $(x - 6)^2 + (y - 4)^2 = 9$ as required.

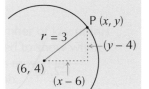

Example

What is the centre and radius of the circle with equation $(x - 2)^2 + (y + 3)^2 = 16$?

1.   Compare the equation with the general form: $(x - 2)^2 + (y + 3)^2 = 16$

     $(x - a)^2 + (y - b)^2 = r^2$

2.   So, $a = 2$, $b = -3$ and $r = 4$.   The centre (a, b) is **(2, –3)** and the radius (r) is **4**.

Exercise 6.1

Q1   Find an equation for a circle with centre (0, 0) and radius:

   a) 5   b) 7   c) $\sqrt{23}$ d) $3\sqrt{2}$ e) $36\sqrt{6}$

Q2   Find the equation for each of the following circles:

   a) centre (2, 5), radius 3   b) centre (–3, 2), radius 5   c) centre (–2, –3), radius 7

   d) centre (3, 0), radius 4   e) centre (5, 3), radius 8   f) centre (3, 1), radius $\sqrt{31}$

   g) centre (–3, –2), radius $\sqrt{5}$ h) centre (–10, 7), radius 11   i) centre (8, 0), radius $\sqrt{17}$

Q3   Find the centre and radius of the circles with the following equations (giving your answer in its simplest form):

   a) $(x - 1)^2 + (y - 5)^2 = 4$ b) $(x - 3)^2 + (y - 5)^2 = 64$ c) $(x - 3)^2 + (y + 2)^2 = 25$

   d) $(x - 6)^2 + (y - 4)^2 = 20$ e) $(x + 8)^2 + (y + 1)^2 = 27$ f) $x^2 + (y - 12)^2 = 147$

Q4   Circle C has its centre at (3, 5) and passes through the point (10, 4).
   Find the exact radius of the circle and hence give the equation of C.

Q5   A circle has its centre at a point A and passes through the origin. Find the equation of the circle if:

   a) A = (1, 1)   b) A = (–7, 13)   c) A = (8, –6)   d) A = (14, 22)

Rearranging circle equations

Sometimes you'll be given an equation for a circle that doesn't look much like $(x - a)^2 + (y - b)^2 = r^2$ — e.g. $x^2 + y^2 + 8x + 6y + 3 = 0$. The general form of this type of equation is:

$$x^2 + y^2 + 2fx + 2gy + c = 0$$

In this form, you can't tell what the **radius** is or where the **centre** is. To find them, **rearrange** into the form $(x - a)^2 + (y - b)^2 = r^2$ — you'll normally have to **complete the square**.

Example

The equation of a circle is $x^2 + y^2 - 6x + 4y + 4 = 0$.
Find the centre of the circle and the radius.

1. You need to get the equation into the form $(x - a)^2 + (y - b)^2 = r^2$.

2. Group the x's and the y's together:
    $$x^2 - 6x + y^2 + 4y + 4 = 0$$

3. Complete the square for the x-terms and the y-terms.
    $$(x - 3)^2 - 9 + (y + 2)^2 - 4 + 4 = 0$$

4. Rearrange to get it into the form $(x - a)^2 + (y - b)^2 = r^2$.
    $$(x - 3)^2 + (y + 2)^2 = 9$$

5. This is the recognisable form:
    The centre is **(3, −2)** and the radius is $\sqrt{9}$ = **3**.

Exercise 6.2

Q1 A circle has the equation $x^2 + y^2 + 2x - 4y - 3 = 0$.
a) Find the coordinates of the centre of the circle.
b) Find the radius of the circle. Give your answer in the form $k\sqrt{2}$.

Q2 A circle has the equation $x^2 + y^2 - 3x + 1 = 0$.
a) Find the coordinates of the centre of the circle.
b) Find the radius of the circle. Simplify your answer as much as possible.

Q3 For each of the following circles, find the exact radius and the coordinates of the centre.
a) $x^2 + y^2 + 2x - 6y - 6 = 0$
b) $x^2 + y^2 - 2y - 4 = 0$
c) $x^2 + y^2 - 6x - 4y = 12$
d) $x^2 + y^2 - 10x + 6y + 13 = 0$
e) $x^2 + y^2 + 14x - 8y - 1 = 0$
f) $x^2 + y^2 - 4x + y = 3.75$
g) $x^2 + y^2 + 2x + 3y - 1.25 = 0$
h) $(x - 2)^2 + y^2 + 2x + 4y - 12 = 0$
i) $2x^2 + 2y^2 + 16x - 8y - 2$

Q4 A circle has centre $(0, -3)$ and radius $\sqrt{10}$. Find the equation of the circle in the form $x^2 + y^2 + 2fx + 2gy + c = 0$ and give the values of f, g and c.

Q5 A circle has centre $(-4, 2)$ and passes through the origin. Find the equation of the circle in the form $x^2 + y^2 + 2fx + 2gy + c = 0$ and give the values of f, g and c.

Q6 a) Show that the circle with equation $x^2 + y^2 + 2fx + 2gy + c = 0$, where f, g and c are constants, has its centre at $(-f, -g)$ and a radius of $\sqrt{f^2 + g^2 - c}$.
b) Hence find the centre and radius of the circle given by the equation $x^2 + y^2 - 5x - 5y + 10 = 0$.

Exercise 6.3

Q1 The circle shown has the equation $(x - 3)^2 + (y - 1)^2 = 10$.
The line shown is a tangent to the circle and touches it at point A (4, 4).

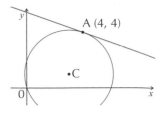

a) Find the centre of the circle, C.

b) Work out the gradient of the radius at (4, 4).

c) Find the equation of the tangent at A in the form $ax + by = c$.

Q2 Find the equation of the tangent to each circle below at the point given.
Give your answers in the form $ax + by + c = 0$, where a, b and c are integers.

a) $(x + 1)^2 + (y - 2)^2 = 13$, (−3, −1)

b) $x^2 + y^2 + 2x - 7 = 0$, (−3, 2)

c) $x^2 + y^2 + 2x + 4y = 5$, (0, −5)

d) $(x - 6)^2 + (y - 6)^2 = 20$, (10, 4)

e) $(x - 4)^2 + (y + 2)^2 = 26$, (9, −3)

f) $x^2 + y^2 + 16x - 6y + 28 = 0$, (−11, 9)

g) $(x + 3)^2 + (y + 1)^2 = 13$, (−5, −4)

h) $x^2 + y^2 - 14x - 12y = 61$, (−4, 1)

Q3 A circle with centre (−2, 4) passes through the point A $(n, 1)$.
Given that the tangent to the circle at A has a gradient of $\frac{5}{3}$, find the value of n.

Q4 The circle shown is centred at C. Points A and B lie on the circle.
Point A has coordinates (−3, 7). The midpoint of the line segment AB,
M, has coordinates (−1, 1). Line l passes through both C and M.

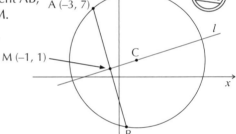

a) Use the information above to find an equation for the line l.

b) The coordinates of C are (2, 2).
Find an equation for the circle.

Q5 The points A (−2, 12), B (4, 14) and C (8, 2) all lie on the circle shown in the diagram below.

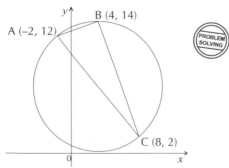

a) Prove that the line segment AC is a diameter of the circle.

b) Hence find the equation of the circle.

Q6 Find the equation of the circle that passes through the points
A = (2, 11), B = (−9, 0) and C = (6, 5).

Q7 Find the equation of the circumcircle of the triangle XYZ, where:

a) X = (8, 2), Y = (−4, −4), Z = (2, 8)

b) X = (2, 6), Y = (5, 9), Z = (−5, 9)

c) X = (14, 14), Y = (22, 6), Z = (22, 10)

d) X = (17, −14), Y = (−7, 10), Z = (−11, −2)

Review Exercise — Chapter 4

Q1 Find the equations of the straight lines that pass through the following pairs of points. Write each of them in the forms:

(i) $y - y_1 = m(x - x_1)$ (ii) $y = mx + c$ (iii) $ax + by + c = 0$, where a, b and c are integers

a) $(2, -1)$ and $(-4, -19)$ b) $\left(0, -\frac{1}{3}\right)$ and $\left(5, \frac{2}{3}\right)$ c) $(8, 7)$ and $(-7, -2)$

d) $(5, 5)$ and $\left(2, \frac{5}{2}\right)$ e) $(1.3, 2)$ and $(1.8, 0)$ f) $(4.6, -2.3)$ and $(-5.4, -0.3)$

Q2 a) The line l_1 has equation $y = \frac{3}{2}x - \frac{2}{3}$. Find the equation of the line parallel to l_1, passing through the point with coordinates $(4, 2)$.

b) The line l_2 passes through the point $(6, 1)$ and is perpendicular to $2x - y - 7 = 0$. What is the equation of l_2?

Q3 The coordinates of points R and S are $(1, 9)$ and $(10, 3)$ respectively. Find the equation of the line perpendicular to RS, passing through the point $(1, 9)$.

Q4 For each equation below, explain whether $y \propto x$:

a) $y = 7x + 2$ b) $y = ax - bx$ (a and b constants)

c) $y = 2x + 2x^2 - 2 - x - 2x^2$ d) $y = (x + 3)^2 - (x - 3)^2$

Q5 Siobhan is modelling the motion of a sliding box. She finds that the frictional force on the box is directly proportional to its mass. If the frictional force, F, is 15 N when its mass, m, is 12 kg, estimate the frictional force when the mass of the box is increased to 18 kg.

(MODELLING)

Q6 Given that s is inversely proportional to t^3, and that $s = 18$ when $t = 6$, find:

a) s when $t = 3$ b) s when $t = 0.5$ c) t when $s = 486$

Q7 Draw rough sketches of the following curves:

a) $y = -2x^4$ b) $y = \frac{7}{x^2}$ c) $y = -5x^3$ d) $y = -\frac{2}{x^5}$

e) $y = \frac{2}{3}x^5$ f) $y = -4x^{-4}$ g) $y = \frac{x^2}{2}$ h) $y = \frac{4}{5x^6}$

Q8 Sketch these cubic graphs:

a) $y = (x - 4)^3$ b) $y = (3 - x)(x + 2)^2$ c) $y = (1 - x)(x^2 - 6x + 8)$

d) $y = (x - 1)(x - 2)(x - 3)$ e) $y = 3x^3 - 6x^2$ f) $y = x^3 - x^2 - 12x$

Q9 Sketch the graphs of the following quartic functions:

a) $y = (x - 4)^4$ b) $y = -(x + 1)^2(x - 1)^2$ c) $y = x^4 + 2x^3$

d) $y = x^2(x^2 - 16)$ e) $y = (x + 5)^3(x + 6)$ f) $y = (x^2 + 2x - 15)(9x^2 - 6x + 1)$

Q10 Given that $a > 1$, use the graph of f(x) to sketch the graph of:

a) $y = \text{f}(ax)$ b) $y = \text{f}\left(\frac{1}{a}x\right)$

c) $y = a\text{f}(x)$ d) $y = \frac{1}{a}\text{f}(x)$

e) $y = \text{f}(x + a)$ f) $y = \text{f}(x - a)$

g) $y = \text{f}(x) + a$ h) $y = \text{f}(x) - a$

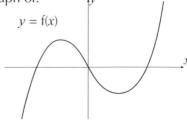
$y = \text{f}(x)$

Exercise 1.1

Q1   Use Pascal's triangle to expand $(1 + x)^4$.

Q2   Use your calculator to work out the following:

a) $^6C_2$ b) $\binom{12}{5}$ c) $\dfrac{30!}{4!26!}$ d) $^8C_8$

Q3   Without using a calculator, work out the following:

a) $\dfrac{9!}{4!5!}$ b) $^{10}C_3$ c) $\dfrac{15!}{11!4!}$ d) $\binom{8}{6}$ e) $^{100}C_{99}$

Q4   Find the first 4 terms, in ascending powers of x, of the binomial expansion of $(1 + x)^{10}$. Give each term in its simplest form.

Q5   Write down the full expansion of $(1 + x)^6$.

Q6   Find the first 4 terms in the expansion of $(1 + x)^7$ in ascending powers of x.

Q7   Find the first three terms, in ascending powers of x, of the binomial expansion of:
a) $(1 + x)^{11}$ b) $(1 + x)^{12}$ c) $(1 + x)^{15}$ d) $(1 + x)^{30}$

Expansions of the form $(1 + ax)^n$

When the **coefficient of x** in your binomial **isn't 1**, e.g. $(1 + 2x)^6$, you have to substitute the **whole x term** (e.g. $2x$) into the **binomial formula**:

$$(1 + ax)^n = 1 + \binom{n}{1}(ax) + \binom{n}{2}(ax)^2 + \binom{n}{3}(ax)^3 + ... + (ax)^n$$

Find the coefficient of x^2 in the expansion of $(1 + 6x)^4(1 - 2x)^6$.

1. To find the x^2 term in the combined expansion you'll need to find all the terms up to x^2 in both expansions and then multiply together:

    $$(1 + 6x)^4 = 1 + \binom{4}{1}(6x) + \binom{4}{2}(6x)^2 + \dots = 1 + 24x + 216x^2 + \dots$$

    $$(1 - 2x)^6 = 1 + \binom{6}{1}(-2x) + \binom{6}{2}(-2x)^2 = 1 - 12x + 60x^2 - \dots$$

2. So: $(1 + 6x)^4(1 - 2x)^6 = (1 + 24x + 216x^2 + \dots)(1 - 12x + 60x^2 - \dots)$
    $= 1 - 12x + 60x^2 - \dots + 24x - 288x^2 + 1440x^3 - \dots + 216x^2 - 2592x^3 + 12\,960x^4 - \dots$
    $= 1 + 12x - 12x^2 + (higher\ power\ terms) + \dots$

3. So the coefficient of x^2 is: **−12**

Exercise 1.2

Q1 Find the full expansions of:

a) $(1 + 3x)^4$
b) $(1 - x)^4$
c) $(1 - x)^6$
d) $(1 - 2x)^5$
e) $(1 - 4x)^3$
f) $(1 - 5x)^5$
g) $(1 + 2x)^6$
h) $(1 + x)^9 - (1 - x)^9$

Q2 Find the first 3 terms, in ascending powers of x, in the expansion of $(1 + x)^3(1 - x)^4$.

Q3 Find the coefficient of x^3y^2 in the expansion of $(1 + x)^5(1 + y)^7$.

Q4 Find the first 4 terms, in ascending powers of x, of the binomial expansion of $(1 + kx)^8$, where k is a non-zero constant.

Q5 In the expansion of $(1 - kx)^6$, the coefficient of x^2 is 135.
Use this information to find the value of k, given that k is positive.

Expansions of the form $(a + b)^n$

When your binomial is of the form $(a + b)^n$ (e.g. $(2 + 3x)^7$, where $a = 2$ and $b = 3x$), you can use a slightly **different formula**:

$$\boxed{(a + b)^n = a^n + \binom{n}{1}a^{n-1}b + \binom{n}{2}a^{n-2}b^2 + \dots + \binom{n}{n-1}ab^{n-1} + b^n}$$

Tip: The powers of a decrease as the powers of b increase. The sum of the powers of a and b in each term is always n.

Give the first three terms, in ascending powers of x, of the expansion of $(4 - 5x)^7$.

Use the formula with $a = 4$, $b = -5x$ and $n = 7$:

$$(4 + (-5x))^7 = 4^7 + \left(\binom{7}{1} \times 4^6 \times (-5x)\right) + \left(\binom{7}{2} \times 4^5 \times (-5x)^2\right) + \dots$$

$$= 16\,384 + (7 \times 4096 \times -5x) + (21 \times 1024 \times 25x^2) + \dots$$

$$= \mathbf{16\,384 - 143\,360x + 537\,600x^2 + \dots}$$

Your other option with expansions of $(a + b)^n$ is to **factorise** the binomial so you get $a^n\left(1 + \frac{b}{a}\right)^n$, then plug $\frac{b}{a}$ into the **original binomial formula** (as you did with $(1 + ax)^n$ expansions in the last section).

> **Example** **What is the coefficient of x^4 in the expansion of $(2 + 5x)^7$?**
>
> 1. Factorise: $(2 + 5x) = 2\left(1 + \frac{5}{2}x\right) \Rightarrow (2 + 5x)^7 = 2^7\left(1 + \frac{5}{2}x\right)^7$
>
> 2. Find the coefficient of x^4 in the expansion of $\left(1 + \frac{5}{2}x\right)^7$. The term is:
>
> $\binom{7}{4} \times \left(\frac{5}{2}x\right)^4 = \frac{7 \times 6 \times 5 \times 4}{1 \times 2 \times 3 \times 4} \times \frac{5^4}{2^4}x^4 = 35 \times \frac{5^4}{2^4}x^4 = \frac{21875}{16}x^4 \Rightarrow$ the coefficient is $\frac{21875}{16}$
>
> 3. Multiply this by 2^7 to get the coefficient for the original binomial: $2^7 \times \frac{21875}{16} = \mathbf{175\,000}$

Exercise 1.3

Q1 Find the first 4 terms, in ascending powers of x, of the binomial expansion of $(3 + x)^6$.

Q2 Find the full expansion of: a) $(2 + x)^4$ b) $(2 + 2x)^4$ c) $(2 - 2x)^4$ d) $\left(\frac{1}{2} + \frac{1}{2}x\right)^4$

Q3 In the expansion of $(1 + \lambda x)^8$, the coefficient of x^5 is 57 344.
   a) Work out the value of λ.   b) Find the first 3 terms of the expansion in ascending powers of x.

Q4 Find the first 4 terms in the expansion of $(3 + 5x)^7$ in ascending powers of x.

Q5 Find the first 5 terms, in ascending powers of x, of $(1 + x)(3 + 2x)^6$.

Q6 The term in x^2 for the expansion of $(1 + x)^n$ is $231x^2$.
   a) What is the value of n?   b) What is the term in x^3?

Q7 Find the coefficient of x^2 in the following binomial expansions:
   a) $(4 + 2x)^5$ b) $(2 - 5x)^8$ c) $2x\left(1 + \frac{1}{2}x\right)^7$ d) $(5 + x)(3x - 1)^9$

Q8 Find the full expansion of:
   a) $(1 + 3x)(2 - x)^5$ b) $(1 + 3x)^5(2 - x)$ c) $(1 + 3x)^2(2 - x)^4$ d) $(1 + 3x)^3(2 - x)^3$

Q9 In the expansion of $(a + 3x)^8$, the coefficient of x^2 is $\frac{32}{27}$ times the coefficient of x^5. What is the value of a?

Q10 In the expansion of $(1 + 2x)^5(3 - x)^4$, what is the coefficient of x^3?

Q11 In the expansion of $(1 + x)^n$, the coefficient of x^3 is 3 times the coefficient of x^2.
   a) Calculate the value of n.
   b) If the coefficient of x^2 is a times the coefficient of x, what is a?

Q12 In the expansion of $(2 + \mu x)^8$, where μ is a constant, the coefficient of x^2 is 87 808. What are the possible values of μ?

Q13 Find the coefficient of x^2 in the expansion of $[(x + 2)^3(x + 3)^2]^2$.

Approximations

You can use a binomial expansion to find **approximations** of a number raised to a power.
Approximations are most accurate when x is small, so that you can **ignore high powers** of x.
For example, to approximate 3.001^6 you can substitute $x = 0.001$ into the expansion of $(3 + x)^6$.

 Find the first 3 terms of the expansion of $(1 - x)^9$,
and use this to estimate the value of 0.998^9.

1. Use the formula: $(1 - x)^9 = 1 + \binom{9}{1}(-x) + \binom{9}{2}(-x)^2 + \ldots = 1 - 9x + 36x^2 - \ldots$

2. $(0.998)^9 = (1 - 0.002)^9 = (1 - x)^9$ when $x = 0.002$.

    So substitute $x = 0.002$ into the expansion you've just found:
    $$(0.998)^9 = (1 - 0.002)^9 \approx 1 - 9(0.002) + 36(0.002)^2 = 1 - 0.018 + 0.000144 = \mathbf{0.982144}$$

You can also use an expansion to approximate more complicated expressions:

 Show that, for small x, $(2 - x)(1 + 2x)^7 \approx 2 + 27x + 154x^2$.
You can assume that terms in x^3 or higher powers can be ignored.

1. Find the first few terms of the expansion of $(1 + 2x)^7$:
    $$(1 + 2x)^7 = 1 + {}^7C_1(2x) + {}^7C_2(2x)^2 + {}^7C_3(2x)^3 + \ldots$$
    $$= 1 + 7(2x) + 21(4x^2) + 35(8x^3) + \ldots$$
    $$= 1 + 14x + 84x^2 + 280x^3 + \ldots$$

2. Multiply your expansion through by $(2 - x)$, ignoring any x^3 or higher power terms:
    $$(2 - x)(1 + 2x)^7 \approx (2 - x)(1 + 14x + 84x^2)$$
    $$= 2 + 28x + 168x^2 - x - 14x^2 - 84x^3$$
    $$= 2 + 27x + 154x^2 - 84x^3 \approx \mathbf{2 + 27x + 154x^2} \text{ as required}$$

Exercise 1.4

Q1 a) Find the first 3 terms in the expansion of $(2 + x)^6$ in ascending powers of x.
   b) Use this expansion to find an approximation for:
      (i) 2.01^6 (ii) 2.1^6 (iii) 2.2^6 (iv) 2.5^6 (v) 1.9^6 (vi) 1.99^6

Q2 Use the expansion of $(4 - x)^7$ up to the x^3 term to estimate to 1 d.p.:   a) 3.9^7 b) 3.99^7 c) 3.999^7

Q3 a) Find, in their simplest form, the first 5 terms in the expansion of $\left(1 + \frac{x}{2}\right)^{12}$ in ascending powers of x.
   b) Use the expansion to estimate the value of 1.005^{12} to 7 d.p.

Q4 If x is small, so that x^2 and higher powers can be ignored, show that $(1 + x)(1 - 3x)^6 \approx 1 - 17x$.

Q5 Use the terms up to x^3 of the expansion of $(3 - 2x)^7$ to give an approximate value to 2 d.p. of:
   a) 2.998^7 b) 2.8^7 c) 2.94^7 d) 3.002^7 e) 3.03^7

Q6 Marc finds the expansion of $(1 + x)^{10}$ up to the term in x^3. He wants to substitute $x = 1.6$
   into this expression to approximate 2.6^{10}. Explain why this will not be a good approximation.

Review Exercise — Chapter 5

Q1 Give, in their simplest form, the first four terms in the binomial expansion of $(1 + x)^{12}$ in ascending powers of x.

Q2 Find the first 3 terms, in ascending powers of x, of the binomial expansion of:
a) $(1 + x)^{40}$ b) $(1 - x)^{20}$ c) $(1 + 3x)^{20}$ d) $(2 - x)^{10}$ e) $(2 + 3x)^{10}$

Q3 What is the term in x^4 in the expansion of $(1 - 2x)^{16}$?

Q4 a) Find the first 4 terms of the expansion of $\left(1 + \frac{x}{3}\right)^9$ in ascending powers of x, giving each term in its simplest form.
b) Use your expansion to estimate the value of $(1.003)^9$, giving your answer to 6 decimal places.

Q5 Give the full expansion of the binomial $(1 + 3x)^5$.

Q6 a) Find the first 5 terms, in ascending powers of x, of the expansion of $(1 + ax)^8$, where a is a non-zero constant.
b) Given that the coefficient of x^2 in this expansion is double the coefficient of x^3, find the value of a and the coefficient of x.

Q7 Find the first 3 terms, in ascending powers of x, of the binomial expansion of $(4 - 5x)^7$. Give each term in its simplest form.

Q8 Find the coefficient of x^2 in the expansion of $(2 + 3x)^5$.

Q9 a) Find the first 5 terms, in ascending powers of x, of the expansion of $\left(3 + \frac{x}{4}\right)^{11}$. Give each term in its simplest form.
b) Use your expansion to find an estimate for the value of $(3.002)^{11}$. Give your answer to 3 decimal places.

Q10 a) Find the first 3 terms, in ascending powers of x, of the binomial expansion of $(2 + kx)^{13}$, where k is a non-zero constant.
b) Given that the coefficient of x in this expansion is $\frac{1}{6}$ of the coefficient of x^2, find the value of k.

Q11 Use the terms up to x^3 of the binomial expansion of $(1 - 3x)^8$ to approximate the value of 0.97^8 to 3 decimal places.

Q12 a) Find the first four terms, in ascending powers of x, of the binomial expansion of $\left(\frac{x}{3} - 2\right)^6$.
b) Given that terms in x^3 or higher powers can be ignored, find an approximation of:
(i) $4x\left(\frac{x}{3} - 2\right)^6$ (ii) $(3 - x)\left(\frac{x}{3} - 2\right)^6$ (iii) $\left(\frac{x}{3} - 2\right)^6 (x + 1)^{16}$

Q13 a) Find the first 5 terms, in ascending powers of x, of the expansion of $(1 + x)^{15}$.
b) Explain why this would not give an accurate estimate of the value of 2.01^{15}.

Q14 a) Approximate the value of 2.5^6 using the terms up to x^3 of the following binomial expansions:
(i) $(2 + x)^6$ (ii) $(3 - x)^6$
b) Given that the actual value of 2.5^6 is 244.14 (2 d.p.), which expansion provides the best approximation?

Chapter 6 — Trigonometry

You came across trigonometry at GCSE, so some parts of this chapter will be a recap of things you already know. You need to be really happy with the basics of trig as you'll see some harder topics in Chapter 18.

1. The Sine and Cosine Rules

Make sure you can remember SOHCAHTOA (for right-angled triangles):

$$\sin x = \frac{\text{opp}}{\text{hyp}}, \quad \cos x = \frac{\text{adj}}{\text{hyp}}, \quad \tan x = \frac{\text{opp}}{\text{adj}}$$

The table shows some useful common trig values:

Tip: If you rationalise the denominator of $\frac{1}{\sqrt{2}}$, you get $\frac{\sqrt{2}}{2}$.

x	0°	30°	45°	60°	90°	180°
$\sin x$	0	$\frac{1}{2}$	$\frac{1}{\sqrt{2}}$	$\frac{\sqrt{3}}{2}$	1	0
$\cos x$	1	$\frac{\sqrt{3}}{2}$	$\frac{1}{\sqrt{2}}$	$\frac{1}{2}$	0	−1
$\tan x$	0	$\frac{1}{\sqrt{3}}$	1	$\sqrt{3}$	—	0

Trig values from the unit circle

You can find trig values from the **unit circle** — a circle with **radius 1**, centred on the **origin**. Take a point on the unit circle and make a right-angled triangle:

From this you know that:

$$\sin \theta = \frac{\text{opp}}{1} = \text{opp} = y \quad \text{and} \quad \cos \theta = \frac{\text{adj}}{1} = \text{adj} = x$$

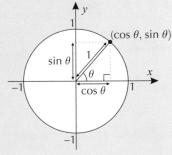

So on the unit circle, the y-coordinate is **sin θ** and the x-coordinate is **cos θ**.

For any point on the unit circle, the coordinates are (cos θ, sin θ), where θ is the angle measured from the **positive** x-axis in an **anticlockwise** direction.

This is true for **all** values of θ, including values greater than 90°.

Example

Find the coordinates of the point A on the unit circle, shown on the diagram to the right. Give your answer to 2 d.p.

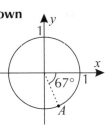

1. You need the angle from the positive x-axis in an anticlockwise direction, so subtract from 360°:   360° − 67° = 293°

2. Find the sin and cos values of 293°:   cos 293° = 0.3907...
                                sin 293° = −0.9205...

So the coordinates of A are **(0.39, −0.92) to 2 d.p**.

Exercise 1.1

Q1 Find the coordinates of points P, Q and R on the unit circle. Give your answers to 3 significant figures.

Q2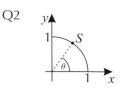

The sketch on the left shows a point S on the unit circle. Find the value of θ in degrees to 3 s.f. if the coordinates of S are:

a) (0.899, 0.438)

b) (0.669, 0.743)

c) (0.089, 0.996)

The sine and cosine rules

For any triangle *ABC*:

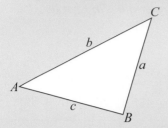

The Sine Rule
$\dfrac{a}{\sin A} = \dfrac{b}{\sin B} = \dfrac{c}{\sin C}$

Area of any triangle
Area $= \dfrac{1}{2}\, ab \sin C$

The Cosine Rule
$a^2 = b^2 + c^2 - 2bc \cos A$

You can use the **sine rule** if you know **any two angles** and a **side**.

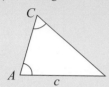

You can **sometimes** use the **sine rule** if you know **two sides** and an **angle that isn't between them**:

This doesn't always work though — sometimes there are **2 possible** triangles:

 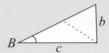

You can use the **cosine rule** if:

- You know **all three** sides...

- ...or you know **two sides** and the **angle** that's **between** them.

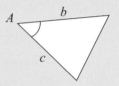

Tip: You can also rearrange the cosine rule into the form $\cos A = \dfrac{b^2 + c^2 - a^2}{2bc}$ to find an angle.

Example

Find the missing sides and angles for $\triangle ABC$, in which $A = 40°$, $a = 27$ m and $B = 73°$. Then find the area of the triangle.

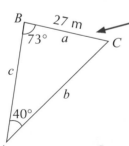

1. Start by **sketching** the triangle.

2. Here you have 2 angles and a side, so you can use the **sine rule**.

3. Start by finding angle *C* (using the fact that the angles in a triangle add up to 180°):
   $\angle C = 180° - 73° - 40° = \mathbf{67°}$

4. Now use the sine rule to find the other sides one at a time:

$$\frac{a}{\sin A} = \frac{b}{\sin B} \Rightarrow \frac{27}{\sin 40°} = \frac{b}{\sin 73°} \qquad \frac{c}{\sin C} = \frac{a}{\sin A} \Rightarrow \frac{c}{\sin 67°} = \frac{27}{\sin 40°}$$

$$\Rightarrow b = \frac{27 \times \sin 73°}{\sin 40°} \qquad\qquad\qquad \Rightarrow c = \frac{27 \times \sin 67°}{\sin 40°}$$

$$= \mathbf{40.2\ m\ (1\ d.p.)} \qquad\qquad\qquad = \mathbf{38.7\ m\ (1\ d.p.)}$$

5. Now you've found the missing values, you can find the area using the formula:
   Area of $\triangle ABC = \dfrac{1}{2}\, ab \sin C = \dfrac{1}{2} \times 27 \times 40.169... \times \sin 67° = \mathbf{499.2\ m^2\ (1\ d.p.)}$

Example Find the values of X, Y and Z.

1. You've been given all three sides but none of the angles, so use the cosine rule. It's best to start with the largest angle, which in this case is Y:

$$a^2 = b^2 + c^2 - 2bc \cos A \Rightarrow \cos A = \frac{b^2 + c^2 - a^2}{2bc}$$

$$\cos Y = \frac{6^2 + 6.5^2 - 10^2}{2 \times 6 \times 6.5} = -0.278...$$

$$\Rightarrow Y = \cos^{-1}(-0.278...) = 106.191...° = \mathbf{106.2°} \text{ (1 d.p.)}$$

2. Use the cosine rule again to find the value of another angle:

$$\cos Z = \frac{10^2 + 6.5^2 - 6^2}{(2 \times 10 \times 6.5)} = 0.817... \Rightarrow Z = \cos^{-1}(0.817...) = 35.183...° = \mathbf{35.2°} \text{ (1 d.p.)}$$

3. Now that you have two of the angles, you can find the other by subtracting them from 180°:

$$X = 180° - 106.191...° - 35.183...° = 38.624...° = \mathbf{38.6°} \text{ (1 d.p.)}$$

Tip: The sine rule always gives an acute angle. If you have a choice of rules, you should use the cosine rule to find the largest angle first, in case it's obtuse (the largest angle is the one opposite the longest side). After that, you can use whichever rule you prefer, since a triangle can only have one obtuse angle.

Exercise 1.2

Give all answers to 3 significant figures unless otherwise stated.

Q1   a) Use the cosine rule to find the length QR.   b) Use the sine rule to find the length TW.

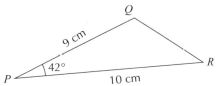   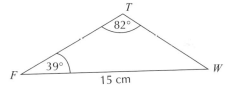

Q2   a) Find the size of angle D.   b) Find the size of angle V.

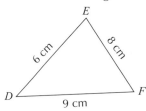   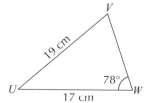

Q3   In triangle JKL: $JL = 24$ cm, $KL = 29$ cm and angle $L = 62°$. Find the length JK.

Q4   In triangle PQR: $PR = 48$ m, angle $P = 38°$ and angle $R = 43°$. Find the length PQ.

Q5   In triangle ABC: $AB = 14$ cm, angle $A = 67°$ and angle $B = 49°$. Find the length BC.

Q6   In triangle DEF: $DE = 8$ cm, $EF = 11$ cm and $DF = 16$ cm. Find the smallest angle.

Q7   The vertices of triangle XYZ have coordinates X: (–2, 2), Y: (5, 8) and Z: (3, –2). Find the angle XYZ. (PROBLEM SOLVING)

Q8 Find the area of each triangle.

a)

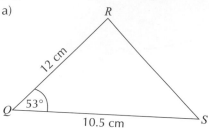

b)

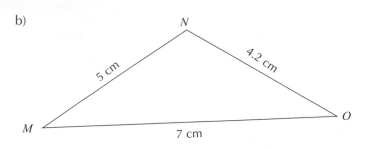

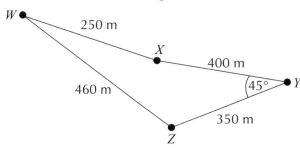

Exercise 1.3

Give all answers to 3 significant figures unless otherwise stated.

Q1 A building has a wall that forms an angle of 81° when measured from the horizontal ground inside the building. A safety inspector calculates that a ladder leaning against the outside of the wall must be at an angle of 78° to the ground. What distance up the wall would a 5 m ladder safely reach?

Q2 Two points, A and B, are both at sea level and on opposite sides of a mountain. The distance between them is 5 km, and the top of the mountain lies on the direct line between them. From A, the angle of elevation of the top of the mountain (M) is 21°, and from B, the angle of elevation is 17°.

a) Find the distance BM.

b) Hence find the height of the mountain to the nearest metre.

Q3   A ship sails 8 km on a bearing of 070°
and then changes direction to sail 10
km on a bearing of 030°.

a) Draw a diagram to represent the situation.

b) What is the ship's distance
from its starting position?

c) On what bearing must it now sail to
get back to its starting position?

Q4   Find the area of the quadrilateral
ABCD shown in the diagram below.

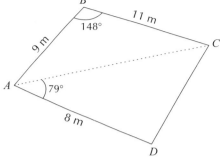

2. Trig Identities

There are **two trig identities** you need to know:

$$\tan \theta \equiv \frac{\sin \theta}{\cos \theta}$$

$$\sin^2 \theta + \cos^2 \theta \equiv 1$$

Tip: The '≡' means that the relation is true for all values of θ. An identity is just a relation which contains a '≡' sign — see p.6.

Example   Show that $\dfrac{\cos^2 \theta}{1 + \sin \theta} \equiv 1 - \sin \theta$.

1. Start with the left-hand side. You know there's a trig identity with a $\cos^2 \theta$ in it, so start by rearranging the identity to get it in terms of $\cos^2 \theta$.

$$\sin^2 \theta + \cos^2 \theta \equiv 1$$
$$\Rightarrow \cos^2 \theta \equiv 1 - \sin^2 \theta$$

2. Replace the $\cos^2 \theta$ on the top of the fraction:

$$\frac{\cos^2 \theta}{1 + \sin \theta} \equiv \frac{1 - \sin^2 \theta}{1 + \sin \theta}$$

3. The top of the fraction is a difference of two squares:

$$\equiv \frac{(1 + \sin \theta)(1 - \sin \theta)}{1 + \sin \theta}$$

4. Finally, cancel $(1 + \sin \theta)$ from the top and bottom of the fraction:

$$\equiv 1 - \sin \theta \text{ as required}$$

Example   Find the exact value of $\sin \theta$ if $\cos \theta = \dfrac{2}{3}$, given that θ is an acute angle.

1. The identity to use here is:

$$\sin^2 \theta + \cos^2 \theta \equiv 1$$

2. Rearranging this gives:

$$\sin^2 \theta \equiv 1 - \cos^2 \theta$$

3. Then put in the value of $\cos \theta$ in the question and take the square root of each side. θ is acute, so $\sin \theta$ is positive (have a look at the graph on p.70), so you can ignore the negative square root.

$$\sin \theta = \sqrt{1 - \left(\frac{2}{3}\right)^2} = \sqrt{\frac{5}{9}} = \frac{\sqrt{5}}{3}$$

Exercise 2.1

Q1 Use the identity $\tan \theta \equiv \dfrac{\sin \theta}{\cos \theta}$ to show that $\dfrac{\sin \theta}{\tan \theta} - \cos \theta \equiv 0$.

Q2 Use the identity $\sin^2 \theta + \cos^2 \theta \equiv 1$ to show that $\cos^2 \theta \equiv (1 - \sin \theta)(1 + \sin \theta)$.

Q3 Given that x is acute, find the exact value of $\cos x$ if $\sin x = \dfrac{1}{2}$.

Q4 Show that $4 \sin^2 x - 3 \cos x + 1 \equiv 5 - 3 \cos x - 4 \cos^2 x$.

Q5 Given that x is acute, find the exact value of $\tan x$ if $\sin^2 x = \dfrac{3}{4}$.

Q6 Show that $(\tan x + 1)(\tan x - 1) \equiv \dfrac{1}{\cos^2 x} - 2$.

Q7 A student is asked to solve the equation $\sin \theta = \dfrac{1}{2} \tan \theta$, where $0° \leq \theta \leq 90°$.
Their working is shown below:

$$\sin \theta = \frac{1}{2} \tan \theta \implies \sin \theta = \frac{1}{2} \times \frac{\sin \theta}{\cos \theta}$$

$$\implies \cos \theta \sin \theta = \frac{1}{2} \sin \theta \implies \cos \theta = \frac{1}{2} \implies \theta = 60°$$

Find the error they made and explain how this has resulted in an incomplete solution.

Q8 Show that $\tan x + \dfrac{1}{\tan x} \equiv \dfrac{1}{\sin x \cos x}$.

Q9 Show that $4 + \sin x - 6 \cos^2 x \equiv (2 \sin x - 1)(3 \sin x + 2)$.

Q10 Show that $\sin^2 x \cos^2 y - \cos^2 x \sin^2 y \equiv \cos^2 y - \cos^2 x$.

Q11 Use the identity $\sin^2 \theta + \cos^2 \theta \equiv 1$ to prove Pythagoras' theorem.

---

3. Trig Graphs

You should be able to draw the graphs of **sin x**, **cos x** and **tan x** — including all the important points, like where the graphs cross the **axes** and their **maximum** and **minimum** points.

sin x

- The graph of $y = \sin x$ is **periodic** — it repeats itself every 360° (you say it has a period of 360°). So $\sin x = \sin (x + 360°) = \sin (x + 720°) = \sin (x + 360n°)$, where n is an integer.

- It bounces between $y = -1$ and $y = 1$, and it can **never** have a value outside this range.

- It goes through the **origin** (as $\sin 0° = 0$) and then crosses the x-axis every **180°**.

- $\sin (-x) = -\sin x$. The graph has **rotational symmetry** about the origin, so you could rotate it 180° about (0, 0) and it would look the same.

- The graph of $y = \sin x$ looks like this:

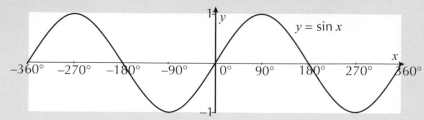

cos x

- The graph of $y = \cos x$ is also **periodic** with period 360°.
  $\cos x = \cos (x + 360°) = \cos (x + 720°) = \cos (x + 360n°)$, where n is an integer.

- It also bounces between $y = -1$ and $y = 1$, and it can **never** have a value outside this range.

- It crosses the y-axis at $y = 1$ (as $\cos 0° = 1$) and the x-axis at ±90°, ±270° etc.

- $\cos (-x) = \cos x$. The graph is **symmetrical** about the **y-axis**, so you could reflect it in the y-axis and it would look the same.

- The graph of $y = \cos x$ looks like this:

Tip: The graphs of sin x and cos x are the same shape but shifted 90° along the x-axis.

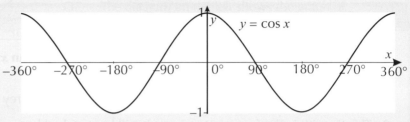

tan x

- The graph of $y = \tan x$ is also **periodic**, but this time it repeats itself every 180°.
  So $\tan x = \tan (x + 180°) = \tan (x + 360°) = \tan (x + 180n°)$, where n is an integer.

- It takes values between $-\infty$ and ∞ in each **180° interval**.

- It goes through the **origin** (as $\tan 0° = 0$).

- It's **undefined** at ±90°, ±270°, ±450°... — at these points it **jumps** from ∞ to $-\infty$ or vice versa. The lines $x = \pm90°$, ±270° etc. are **asymptotes** — the graph never touches them, but gets infinitely close.

- The graph of $y = \tan x$ looks like this:

Tip: $y = \tan x$ is undefined at the asymptotes because you're dividing by zero. Remember that $\tan x \equiv \dfrac{\sin x}{\cos x}$, so when $\cos x = 0$, $\tan x$ is undefined, and $\cos x = 0$ when $x = 90°$, 270° etc.

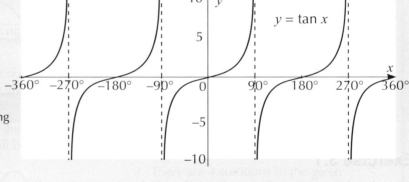

You can apply the different types of **transformations** (see p.48-50) to the trig graphs as well.

Example) On the same axes, sketch the graphs of $y = \cos x$ and $y = -2 \cos x$ in the range $-360° \le x \le 360°$.

1. Start by sketching the graph of cos x (the grey line on the graph on the next page).

2. The transformation is in the form $y = n \cos x$, so it will be stretched vertically.

3. $n = -2$, so it will be stretched by a factor of 2. As n is negative, it will also be reflected in the x-axis. Use this information to sketch the graph (see next page).

Changing the interval

Solving equations of the form sin kx = n

- **Multiply** the **interval** you're looking for solutions in by k. E.g. for the equation sin $2x = n$ in the interval $0° \leq x \leq 360°$, you'd look for solutions in the interval $0° \leq 2x \leq 720°$. Then **solve** the equation over the new interval.

- This gives you solutions for kx, so you then need to **divide** each solution by k to find the values of x.

You can either **sketch the graph** over the new interval (this will show you **how many** solutions there are) or you can use the **CAST method** to find solutions between $0°$ and $360°$ then add on multiples of $360°$ until you have all the solutions in the new interval.

Example   Solve cos $4x = 0.6$ for $0° \leq x \leq 360°$. Give your answers to 1 d.p.

1. First, change the interval. $k = 4$, so multiply the whole interval by 4: $0° \leq 4x \leq 1440°$

2. Then solve the equation to find the solutions for $4x$.

3. Find the first solution using a calculator:
   cos $4x = 0.6 \Rightarrow 4x = 53.13°$ (2 d.p.)

4. You want the quadrants where cos is positive, so the other solution between $0°$ and $360°$ is:
   $4x = 360° - 53.13° = 306.87°$ (2 d.p.)

5. Now add on multiples of $360°$ to find all the solutions in the interval $0° \leq 4x \leq 1440°$ (to 2 d.p.):
   $53.13°, 306.87°, 413.13°, 666.87°, 773.13°, 1026.87°, 1133.13°, 1386.87°$

6. These are solutions for $4x$. To find the solutions for x, divide through by 4. So the solutions to cos $4x = 0.6$ in the interval $0° \leq x \leq 360°$ (to 1 d.p.) are:
   13.3°, 76.7°, 103.3°, 166.7°, 193.3°, 256.7°, 283.3°, 346.7°

Example   Solve sin $3x = -\dfrac{1}{\sqrt{2}}$ for $0° \leq x \leq 360°$.

1. $k = 3$, which means the interval you need to find solutions in is: $0° \leq 3x \leq 1080°$
   So sketch the graph of $y = \sin x$ between $0°$ and $1080°$ (see next page).

2. Find a solution: $3x = -45°$. This is outside the interval for $3x$, so use the pattern of the graph to find a solution in the interval: $-45° + 360° = 315°$

3. Use the symmetry of the graph to find the other solution between $0°$ and $360°$:
   $180° + 45° = 225°$

4. The graph repeats every $360°$, so add on lots of $360°$ to these values to find the other solutions between $0°$ and $1080°$: $3x = 585°, 675°, 945°, 1035°$

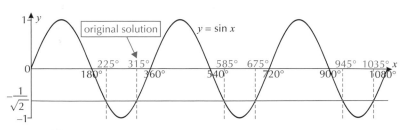

5. Now you have 6 solutions for $3x$, so divide them all by 3 to get the solutions for x:

$x = 75°, 105°, 195°, 225°, 315°, 345°$

Exercise 4.3

In this exercise, give all answers to 1 d.p.

Q1 Solve the following equations in the interval $0° \leq x \leq 360°$:

    a) $\sin 2x = 0.6$ b) $\tan 4x = 4.6$ c) $\cos 3x = -0.24$

    d) $\sin 3x = 0.94$ e) $\cos 5x = 0.5$ f) $\tan 2x = -6.7$

Q2 Find all the solutions to $\cos 2x = 0.72$ in the interval $0 \leq x \leq 360°$.

Q3 Find all the solutions to $\frac{1}{2}\sin 3x - 0.61 = -0.75$ in the interval $0 \leq x \leq 360°$.

Q4 Solve $\tan \frac{x}{2} = 2.1$ in the interval $0° \leq x \leq 360°$.

Q5 Solve $\cos \frac{x}{3} = \frac{\sqrt{3}}{2}$ in the interval $-180° \leq x \leq 180°$.

Solving equations of the form $\sin (x + c) = n$

Here, instead of multiplying the interval, you have to add or subtract the value of c.

- **Add** (or **subtract**) the value of c to the **whole interval** — so the interval $0° \leq x \leq 360°$
  becomes $c \leq x + c \leq 360° + c$.

- Now **solve** the equation over the **new interval** — either sketch a graph or use a CAST diagram.

- Finally, **subtract** (or **add**) c from your solutions to give the values for x.

Example

Solve $\tan (x - 75°) = 2$ for $0° \leq x \leq 360°$.
Give your answers to 1 d.p.

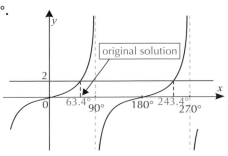

1. Find the new interval. Subtract 75° from each bit
   of the interval: $-75° \leq x - 75° \leq 285°$
   You'll need to sketch $\tan x$ over this interval.

2. Use your calculator to find a solution:
   $\tan (x - 75°) = 2 \Rightarrow x - 75° = 63.4°$ (1 d.p.)

3. Use the pattern of the graph to find the other solution in the interval —
   add on 180° to the solution you've already found: 63.4° + 180° = 243.4° (1 d.p.)

4. Finally, add on 75° to find the solutions in the interval 0° ≤ x ≤ 360° (to 1 d.p.):
   x = 138.4°, 318.4°

Example **Solve 2 sin (x + 60°) + $\sqrt{3}$ = 0 for 0° ≤ x ≤ 720°.**

1. First, rearrange: $2 \sin (x + 60°) + \sqrt{3} = 0 \Rightarrow 2 \sin (x + 60°) = -\sqrt{3} \Rightarrow \sin (x + 60°) = -\frac{\sqrt{3}}{2}$

2. Then add 60° to each bit of the interval: $60° \leq x + 60° \leq 780°$

3. $\sin 60° = \frac{\sqrt{3}}{2}$, so put 60° into the CAST diagram:

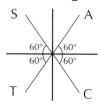

sin x is negative in the 3rd and 4th quadrants, so the solutions between 0° and 360° are:
x + 60° = 180° + 60° = 240° and x + 60° = 360° − 60° = 300°

4. To find the other solutions, just add 360° to these solutions:
   x + 60° = 600°, 660°

5. Finally, subtract 60° from each solution: **x = 180°, 240°, 540°, 600°**

Exercise 4.4

In this exercise, give all answers to 1 d.p.

Q1   Find all the solutions to cos (x − 27°) = 0.64 in the interval 0° ≤ x ≤ 360°.

Q2   Solve tan (x − 140°) = −0.76 in the interval 0° ≤ x ≤ 360°.

Q3   Find all the solutions to sin (x + 36°) = 0.45 in the interval 0° ≤ x ≤ 360°.

Q4   Find all the solutions to tan (x + 73°) = 1.84 in the interval 0° ≤ x ≤ 360°.

Q5   Find all the solutions to sin (x − 45°) = −0.25 in the interval −180 ≤ x ≤ 360°.

Q6   Solve cos (x + 22.5°) = 0.13 in the interval 0 ≤ x ≤ 360°.

Using trig identities to solve equations

Remember the **trig identities** from p.69: $\tan x \equiv \frac{\sin x}{\cos x}$ and $\sin^2 x + \cos^2 x \equiv 1$

You can use them to help solve complicated-looking trig equations — e.g. ones that contain two **different** trig functions. If you're left with a **quadratic equation** (e.g. one that contains both $\sin^2 x$ and $\sin x$), you might need to factorise before you solve it — see p.16).

Example   Solve $6 \cos^2 x + \cos x \tan x = 5$ for $0° \le x \le 360°$. **PROBLEM SOLVING**
Give any non-exact answers to 1 d.p.

1. Use the identity for tan to replace the tan term:
$$6 \cos^2 x + \cos x \tan x = 5 \implies 6 \cos^2 x + \cos x \frac{\sin x}{\cos x} = 5$$

2. Cancel the cos term:
$$\implies 6 \cos^2 x + \sin x = 5$$

3. Replace the $\cos^2 x$ with $1 - \sin^2 x$:
$$\implies 6(1 - \sin^2 x) + \sin x = 5$$

4. Rearrange to form a quadratic equation in terms of $\sin x$:
$$\implies 6 \sin^2 x - \sin x - 1 = 0$$

5. Factorise the quadratic:
$$\implies (2 \sin x - 1)(3 \sin x + 1) = 0$$

   Tip: Use the substitution $y = \sin x$ to help factorise if you need to.

6. Solve the quadratic equation to get solutions for $\sin x$:
$$2 \sin x - 1 = 0 \implies \sin x = \frac{1}{2} \quad \text{or} \quad 3 \sin x + 1 = 0 \implies \sin x = -\frac{1}{3}$$

7. One solution for $\sin x = \frac{1}{2}$ is: $x = 30°$

   Use a CAST diagram to find the other solution — you want a positive solution, so look at the second quadrant: $180° - 30° = 150°$

8. One solution for $\sin x = -\frac{1}{3}$ is: $x = -19.47...°$
   Use a CAST diagram to find the solutions in the given interval — you need a negative solution for $\sin x$, so look at the 3rd and 4th quadrants:
   $180° + 19.47...° = 199.47...°$ and $360° - 19.47...° = 340.52...°$

   You now have all the solutions:
   $x = 30°, 150°, 199.5°$ and $340.5°$ (to 1 d.p.)

Exercise 4.5

 PROBLEM SOLVING

In this exercise, give any non-exact answers to 1 d.p.

Q1 Solve each of the following equations for values of x in the interval $0° \le x \le 360°$:

a) $(\tan x - 5)(3 \sin x - 1) = 0$ b) $5 \sin x \tan x - 4 \tan x = 0$

c) $\tan^2 x = 9$ d) $4 \cos^2 x = 3 \cos x$

e) $3 \sin x = 5 \cos x$ f) $5 \tan^2 x - 2 \tan x = 0$

g) $6 \cos^2 x - \cos x - 2 = 0$ h) $7 \sin x + 3 \cos x = 0$

Q2 Find the solutions to each of the following equations in the given interval:

a) $\tan x = \sin x \cos x$ $0° \le x \le 360°$

b) $5 \cos^2 x - 9 \sin x = 3$ $-360° \le x \le 720°$

c) $2 \sin^2 x + \sin x - 1 = 0$ $-360° \le x \le 360°$

Q3 a) Show that the equation $4 \sin^2 x = 3 - 3 \cos x$ can be written as $4 \cos^2 x - 3 \cos x - 1 = 0$.

b) Hence solve the equation $4 \sin^2 x = 3 - 3 \cos x$ in the interval $0° \le x \le 360°$.

Q4 Find all the solutions of the equation $9 \sin^2 2x + 3 \cos 2x = 7$ in the interval $0° \le x \le 360°$.

Q5 Find all the solutions of the equation $\frac{\cos x}{\tan x} + \sin x = 3$ in the interval $-360° \le x \le 360°$.

Review Exercise — Chapter 6

Q1 Write down the exact values of cos 30°, sin 30°, tan 30°, cos 45°, sin 45°, tan 45°, cos 60°, sin 60° and tan 60°.

Q2 The points below lie on the unit circle. For each point, if a line from the origin to the point makes an angle of θ when measured in an anticlockwise direction from the positive x-axis, find the exact value of θ, where $0 \le \theta \le 180°$.

    a) $\left(\dfrac{1}{2}, \dfrac{\sqrt{3}}{2}\right)$ b) $\left(\dfrac{\sqrt{3}}{2}, \dfrac{1}{2}\right)$ c) $(-1, 0)$

Q3 For triangle $\triangle ABC$, in which $A = 30°$, $C = 25°$ and $b = 6$ m:

    a) Find all the sides and angles of the triangle.

    b) Find the area of the triangle.

Q4 For triangle $\triangle PQR$, in which $p = 13$ km, $q = 23$ km and $R = 20°$:

    a) Find all the sides and angles of the triangle.

    b) Find the area of the triangle.

Q5 Find all the angles in the triangle below in degrees to 1 d.p.

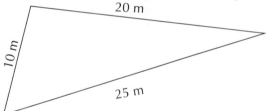

Q6 Find the missing sides and angles for the 2 possible triangles $\triangle ABC$ which satisfy $b = 5$, $a = 3$, $A = 35°$.

Q7 Show that $\tan x - \sin x \cos x \equiv \sin^2 x \tan x$.

Q8 Show that $\tan^2 x - \cos^2 x + 1 \equiv \tan^2 x(1 + \cos^2 x)$.

Q9 Simplify: $(\sin y + \cos y)^2 + (\cos y - \sin y)^2$.

Q10 Show that $\dfrac{\sin^4 x + \sin^2 x \cos^2 x}{\cos^2 x - 1} \equiv -1$.

Q11 Sketch the following graphs in the interval $-360° \le x \le 360°$, making sure you label all of the key points.

    a) $y = \cos x$ b) $y = \sin x$ c) $y = \tan x$

Q12 Below is the graph of $y = \cos x$ and a transformation of the graph.
What is the equation of the transformed graph?

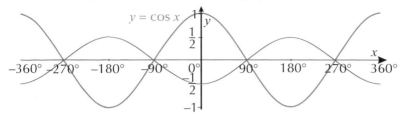

Q13 Below is a graph of $y = \sin x$ and a transformation of the graph.
What is the equation of the transformed graph?

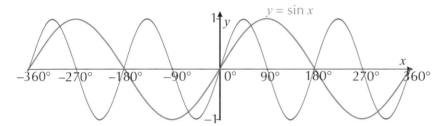

Q14 Sketch the following pairs of graphs on the same axes:

a) $y = \cos x$ and $y = \frac{1}{2} \cos x$ (for $0° \le x \le 360°$)

b) $y = \sin x$ and $y = \sin (x + 30°)$ (for $0° \le x \le 360°$)

c) $y = \tan x$ and $y = \tan 3x$ (for $0° \le x \le 180°$)

Q15 a) Solve each of these equations for $0° \le \theta \le 360°$:

(i) $\sin \theta = \frac{\sqrt{3}}{2}$ (ii) $\tan \theta = -1$ (iii) $\cos \theta = -\frac{1}{\sqrt{2}}$

b) Solve each of these equations for $-180° \le \theta \le 180°$ (giving your answers to 1 d.p.):

(i) $\cos 4\theta = -\frac{2}{3}$ (ii) $\sin (\theta + 35°) = 0.3$ (iii) $\tan \frac{\theta}{2} = 500$

Q16 Find all the solutions to $6 \sin^2 x = \cos x + 5$ in the interval $0° \le x \le 360°$
giving your answers to 1 d.p. where appropriate.

Q17 Solve $3 \tan x + 2 \cos x = 0$ for $-90° \le x \le 90°$.

Q18 Find all the solutions of the equation $8 \sin^2 x + 2 \sin x - 1 = 0$ in the interval $0° \le x \le 360°$,
giving your answers to 1 d.p. where appropriate.

Q19 Find all the solutions of the equation $\tan x - 3 \sin x = 0$ in the interval $0° \le x \le 720°$,
giving your answers to 1 d.p.

Example £350 is initially paid into a bank account that pays 3% interest per year. No further money is deposited or withdrawn. Create a model to show how much money will be in the account after t years and use it to calculate how many whole years it will be before there is over £1000 in the account.

1. After t years, there will be: £350 × 1.03^t

2. Find t when 350 × 1.03^t > 1000: $350 \times 1.03^t > 1000 \Rightarrow 1.03^t > \frac{20}{7}$

3. Take logs: $\log 1.03^t > \log \frac{20}{7} \Rightarrow t \log 1.03 > \log \frac{20}{7}$

$$\Rightarrow t > \frac{\log \frac{20}{7}}{\log 1.03} \Rightarrow t > 35.516...$$

4. So there will be over £1000 in the account after **36 years**.

Exercise 5.1

Q1 A radioactive substance has a half-life of 10 years. Its decay is modelled by the equation $A = A_0 e^{-kt}$, where A is the activity in Bq (becquerel) after t years and A_0 and k are constants.

a) After how many years will the substance be reduced to a quarter of its original activity?

b) Find the original activity if the activity after 5 years is 200 grams.

c) Find the activity remaining after 15 years.

Q2 An oven is turned on at 12:00. After t minutes its temperature, $T\,°C$, is given by the formula:
$$T = 225 - 207\,e^{-\frac{t}{8}}$$

a) What was the initial temperature of the oven?

b) What was the temperature after 5 minutes?

c) At what time does the oven reach a temperature of 190 °C?

d) Sketch the graph of T against t.

e) Explain how the model restricts the temperature from rising indefinitely.

Q3 A woman is prescribed a medicine, and the concentration of the medicine in her bloodstream is monitored. Initially the concentration in her bloodstream is 3 mg per litre of blood (mg/l). After t hours, the concentration of the drug is N mg/l, where $N = Ae^{-t}$.

a) What is the concentration after 30 minutes?

b) How long does it take for the level to reduce to 0.1 mg/l?

c) Sketch the graph of N against t.

d) What is the gradient of the graph in terms of t?

Q4 The value of a car (£V) t years after purchase can be modelled by the formula: $V = 1500 + 9000\,e^{-\frac{t}{3}}$.

a) Explain the significance of the negative coefficient of t.

b) What was its price when new?

c) What was its value after 5 years?

d) After how many whole years will it be worth less than £2500?

e) Sketch the graph of V against t.

f) A different car's value is modelled by the formula $V = 16000\,e^{-0.6t}$. Compare the two models.

Limitations of modelling

The real world can't always be simplified to a couple of variables — it's usually much more **complicated** than that. Models **ignore** most factors, leaving only the ones you're interested in. This simplification means that models aren't spot on — they have **drawbacks**.

For example, an exponential model may only match the real-world scenario within a **certain range**, beyond which the numbers get too big or too small. In such cases, an **upper limit** can applied.

The penguin population of a small island is surveyed.
The population, P, can be modelled by the formula $P = 5000e^{0.1t}$,
where t is the number of years after the initial survey.

Explain why this model may not be appropriate for the long term.

After 60 years ($t = 60$), the penguin population is over 2 million. This seems unrealistic — it's much too large a population. The model doesn't take into account other factors (e.g. predators, food supply) and allows the population to grow infinitely.

Exercise 5.2

Q1 A fungus is being grown under controlled conditions in a laboratory. Initially, it covers an area of 4 mm². After t hours, its area is F mm², where $F = F_0e^{gt}$ (F_0 and g are constants). After 6 hours its area is 10 mm².

a) Find the values of F_0 and g.   b) Predict the area of the fungus after 12 hours.

c) How long will it take for the fungus to grow to 15 mm²?

d) Describe one limitation of the model used.

Q2 A forest fire spreads in such a way that the burnt area (H hectares) after t hours is given by the relation $H = 20e^{bt}$. Assume that the fire burns unchecked.

a) Interpret the value 20 used in the model.   b) If $e^b = 1.8$, find b.

c) Find the area burnt after 3 hours.

d) How long would it take to burn an area of 500 hectares?

e) What constant factor is the burnt area multiplied by every hour?
What percentage does the burnt area increase by each hour?

f) Describe one limitation of the model.

6. Using Logarithmic Graphs

You can use **logs** to convert an equation of the form $y = ax^n$ to linear form — you can then plot this as a **straight line graph**, which is much easier to work with.

To convert $y = ax^n$ to linear form, just **take logs** of both sides and rearrange:

$$y = ax^n \Rightarrow \log y = \log ax^n \Rightarrow \log y = \log a + \log x^n \Rightarrow \log y = n\log x + \log a$$

This is now in "$y = mx + c$" straight-line form (where n is the gradient and $\log a$ is the vertical intercept). So to draw the graph, plot the values of **log y** against **log x** and label the axes accordingly.

Review Exercise — Chapter 7

Q1 The graph on the right shows the equation $y = Ae^{kx}$, where A and k are constants.

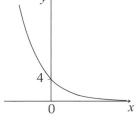

a) Which of the following is the equation of the graph?

$y = -4e^{-3x}$ $\qquad\qquad$ $y = 4e^{3x}$ $\qquad\qquad$ $y = 4e^{-3x}$

b) Use your answer to part a) to find the exact gradient of the graph at the following points:

$\quad$ (i) $x = -1$ $\qquad\quad$ (ii) $x = 0$ $\qquad\qquad$ (iii) $x = 4$

Q2 Write the following using log notation:

a) $4^2 = 16$ $\qquad\qquad$ b) $216^{\frac{1}{3}} = 6$ $\qquad\qquad$ c) $3^{-4} = \dfrac{1}{81}$

Q3 Write down the values of the following:

a) $\log_3 27$ $\qquad\qquad$ b) $\log_3\left(\dfrac{1}{27}\right)$ $\qquad\qquad$ c) $\log_3 18 - \log_3 2$

Q4 Simplify the following:

a) $\log 3 + 2\log 5$ $\qquad\qquad$ b) $\dfrac{1}{2}\log 36 - \log 3$ $\qquad\qquad$ c) $\log 2 - \dfrac{1}{4}\log 16$

Q5 Simplify $\log_b (x^2 - 1) - \log_b (x - 1)$.

Q6 Prove that $\dfrac{2 + \log_a 4}{\log_a 2a} = 2$.

Q7 Find the value of the following, giving your answers to 3 s.f.:

a) $\log_7 12$ $\qquad\qquad$ b) $\log_5 8$ $\qquad\qquad$ c) $\log_{16} 125$

Q8 a) Copy and complete the table for the function $y = 4^x$:

x	-3	-2	-1	0	1	2	3
y							

b) Plot a graph of $y = 4^x$ for $-3 \le x \le 3$.

c) Use the graph to solve the equation $4^x = 20$.

d) Solve the equation $4^x = 20$ algebraically, giving your answer to 3 s.f.

Q9 Solve the following, giving your answer to 3 s.f.:

a) $10^x = 240$ $\qquad$ b) $\log_{10} x = 5.3$ $\qquad$ c) $10^{2x+1} = 1500$ $\qquad\qquad$ d) $4^{(x-1)} = 200$

Q10 Find the value of x, to 4 decimal places, when:

a) $e^{2x} = 6$ $\qquad$ b) $\ln(x + 3) = 0.75$ $\qquad$ c) $3e^{-4x+1} = 5$ $\qquad$ d) $\ln x + \ln 5 = \ln 4$.

Q11 Solve the following equations, giving your solutions as exact values:

a) $2\ln x - \ln(2x) = 2$ $\qquad\qquad\qquad\quad$ b) $\ln(2x - 7) + \ln 4 = -3$

c) $2e^{2x} + e^x = 3$ $\qquad\qquad\qquad\qquad\quad$ d) $e^{8x} - e^{4x} - 6 = 0$

Q12 Find the exact solutions of $2(10^{2x}) - 7(10^x) + 5 = 0$.

Q13 Find the smallest integer P such that $1.5^P > 1\,000\,000$.

Q14 Scientists are monitoring the population of curly-toed spiders at a secret location. It appears to be dropping at a rate of 25% a year. When the population has dropped below 200, the species will be in danger of extinction. At the moment the population is 2000. In which year will the spiders be in danger of extinction?

Q15 The value of a motorbike (£V) varies with age (in t years from new) according to $V = 7500e^{-0.2t}$.
    a) What is its value after 10 years (to the nearest £)?
    b) After how many years will the motorbike's value have fallen below £500?
    c) Sketch a graph showing how the value of the motorbike varies with age, labelling all key points.

Q16 A nature reserve has a population of 20 leopards in 2010. The number of leopards in the nature reserve can be modelled by the formula $L = L_0 e^{\frac{t}{12}}$ where L is the number of leopards in the population, L_0 is the initial population size and t is the time in years.
    a) How many leopards does the model predict the nature reserve will have after 10 years?
    b) The reserve has enough space for 60 leopards.
        How long will it be until the reserve runs out of space?

    When a number of leopards are released into the wild, the wild population can be modelled by the formula $W = W_0 e^{-\frac{t}{3}}$ where W is the population, t is the time in years and W_0 is the initial population.
    c) If the zoo releases a population of 15 leopards into the wild, predict how many will be in this population after 5 years in the wild.

Q17 The spread of a zombie apocalypse through a population can be modelled by the exponential formula: $Z = 10 + 20e^t$ where Z is the number of zombies and t is the time in weeks.
    a) How many zombies were there initially?
    b) Predict how many people will have become zombies after 2 weeks if it spreads according to the model.
    c) How many weeks will have passed before there are 60 million zombies?

Q18 The rules of a sport say that the length, l m, and the width, w m, of the rectangular playing field can be any value, as long as the area is 120 m^2. Use logs to model the relationship between l and w as a straight line and show this graphically.

Q19 The populations (y) of red and grey squirrels in a forest over time (t months) are modelled using the graph on the right. Grey squirrels were introduced to the forest at time $t = 0$.
    a) Find an exponential equation for the population of red squirrels in the forest.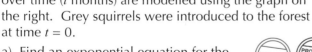
    b) Find an exponential equation for the population of grey squirrels in the forest.
    c) The population of red squirrels is considered critical when there are fewer than 20 left in the forest. In which month will the population reach a critical level?
    d) Explain why this model may not be suitable to predict the number of red and grey squirrels over a long timescale.

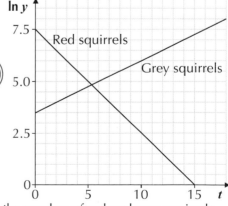

Chapter 8 — Differentiation

Differentiation is an algebraic process that finds the gradient of a curve (remember that the gradient of a curve is how steep it is). It's useful for finding out how fast one thing changes with respect to another.

1. The Gradient of a Curve

The **derivative** of a function y with respect to x is written $\dfrac{dy}{dx}$ (the derivative of f(x) with respect to x can be written **f'(x)**). The derivative of a function is its **gradient** (as a function of x). You can find it using the following formula:

$$f'(x) = \lim_{h \to 0}\left[\frac{f(x+h) - f(x)}{(x+h) - x}\right]$$

Tip: $\lim\limits_{h \to 0}$ in front of the function just means 'what the function goes towards as h goes towards zero'.

Using this formula is called **differentiating from first principles**.

Example

Find an expression for the gradient of the function f(x) = x^2 by differentiating from first principles.

1. Write down the formula for differentiating from first principles. $\quad f'(x) = \lim\limits_{h \to 0}\left[\dfrac{f(x+h) - f(x)}{(x+h) - x}\right]$

2. Substitute f(x) = x^2. $\quad\quad = \lim\limits_{h \to 0}\left[\dfrac{(x+h)^2 - x^2}{(x+h) - x}\right]$

3. Multiply out and simplify. $\quad\quad = \lim\limits_{h \to 0}\left[\dfrac{x^2 + 2xh + h^2 - x^2}{x+h-x}\right]$

$\quad\quad = \lim\limits_{h \to 0}\left[\dfrac{2xh + h^2}{h}\right]$

4. Finally, decide what will happen as h gets close to 0 — in this case, $2x + h$ gets close to $2x$. $\quad\quad = \lim\limits_{h \to 0}[2x + h] = \mathbf{2x}$

Exercise 1.1

Q1 The curve C is given by $y = $ f(x) where f(x) = x^3.

a) Find the gradient of the straight line joining the point on the curve where $x = 1$ and the point on the curve where:
(i) $x = 2$ $\quad\quad$ (ii) $x = 1.5$ $\quad\quad$ (iii) $x = 1.1$

b) The gradient of the curve at the point (1, 1) is 3. What do you notice about the gradient of the straight lines in part a) as the value of x moves closer to 1?

Q2 Derive from first principles expressions for the gradients of the following curves:
a) $y = x$ $\quad\quad$ b) f(x) = x^3 $\quad\quad$ c) f(x) = $2x$ $\quad\quad$ d) f(x) = $2x^2$

Q3 For the functions below, find the derivative of y with respect to x by differentiating from first principles.
a) $y = 5x^2 + 1$ $\quad\quad$ b) $y = x - x^2$ $\quad\quad$ c) $y = 3x^3$ $\quad\quad$ d) $y = 2x^3 + 3x$

2. Differentiating $y = f(x)$

Differentiating x^n

Expressions are much easier to **differentiate** when they're written using **powers of x** — like writing $\sqrt{x}$ as $x^{\frac{1}{2}}$ or $\frac{3}{x^2}$ as $3x^{-2}$. When you've done this, you can use this **formula** to differentiate:

$$\text{If } y = x^n, \text{ then } \frac{dy}{dx} = nx^{n-1}$$

Tip: If there's a number in front of the x^n term, multiply the derivative by it. So if $y = ax^n$, then $\frac{dy}{dx} = anx^{n-1}$.

Examples   **Using the formula for powers of x:**

a) **Differentiate $y = \sqrt{x}$.**

Write the square root as a fractional power of x
($n = \frac{1}{2}$).

$$y = x^{\frac{1}{2}}$$
$$\frac{dy}{dx} = nx^{n-1} = \frac{1}{2}x^{\left(-\frac{1}{2}\right)} = \frac{1}{2\sqrt{x}}$$

b) **Differentiate $y = \frac{1}{x^2}$.**

Write the fraction as a negative power of x
($n = -2$).

$$y = x^{-2}$$
$$\frac{dy}{dx} = nx^{n-1} = -2x^{-3} = -\frac{2}{x^3}$$

c) **Differentiate $y = 4x^3$.**

This is just a normal power with $n = 3$, but there's a constant (a number) in front of it.

$$y = 4x^3$$
$$\frac{dy}{dx} = 4(nx^{n-1}) = 4(3x^2) = \mathbf{12x^2}$$

d) **Find the gradient of the curve $y = x^2$ at $x = -2$.**

- You need the gradient of the graph of $y = x^2$, so differentiate.

$$\frac{dy}{dx} = 2x$$

- Now just put in the x-value to find the gradient of the graph at that point.

$$\text{When } x = -2, \frac{dy}{dx} = \mathbf{-4}$$

Exercise 2.1

Q1   Differentiate to find $\frac{dy}{dx}$ for:

    a) $y = x^6$ b) $y = x^{-2}$ c) $y = 3x^2$ d) $y = 7x$ e) $y = 3\sqrt{x}$ f) $y = 2x^{-1}$

Q2   Differentiate to find $f'(x)$ for:

    a) $f(x) = x^7$ b) $f(x) = x^{-4}$ c) $f(x) = 4x^3$ d) $f(x) = 3\sqrt[3]{x}$ e) $f(x) = -7$ f) $f(x) = 4x^{-2}$

Q3   Find the gradient of each of the following functions:

    a) $y = 2x^2$ when $x = 4$ b) $y = x^{-1}$ when $x = 2$ c) $y = -4x^5$ when $x = 1$

    d) $f(x) = 2\sqrt{x}$ at the point $(9, 6)$ e) $f(x) = x^4$ at the point $(-2, 16)$ f) $f(x) = -2x^3$ when $f(x) = -250$

Differentiating functions

If there are lots of terms in the expression, just differentiate each bit **separately**. Formally, this means:

$$\frac{d}{dx}(x^m + x^n) = \frac{d}{dx}(x^m) + \frac{d}{dx}(x^n)$$

Simplify a function before you differentiate it by multiplying out **brackets** or simplifying **fractions**. You might have to split a fraction up into separate terms to simplify it.

Examples a) Find $\dfrac{d}{dx}\left(6x^2 + \dfrac{4}{\sqrt[3]{x}} - \dfrac{2}{x^2} + 1\right)$.

Tip: This notation just means the derivative with respect to x of the thing in the brackets.

1. Rewrite the function as powers of x: $6x^2 + \dfrac{4}{\sqrt[3]{x}} - \dfrac{2}{x^2} + 1 = 6x^2 + 4x^{-\frac{1}{3}} - 2x^{-2} + 1$

2. Then differentiate each term: $\dfrac{d}{dx}\left(6x^2 + \dfrac{4}{\sqrt[3]{x}} - \dfrac{2}{x^2} + 1\right) = 6(2x) + 4\left(-\dfrac{1}{3}x^{-\frac{4}{3}}\right) - 2(-2x^{-3}) + 0$

$$= 12x - \dfrac{4}{3\sqrt[3]{x^4}} + \dfrac{4}{x^3}$$

b) **Differentiate the function** $f(x) = \dfrac{x^3 + 4x + 1}{2x^2}$.

1. The numerator won't factorise, so split the fraction up into three fractional terms.

$$f(x) = \dfrac{x^3 + 4x + 1}{2x^2} = \dfrac{x^3}{2x^2} + \dfrac{4x}{2x^2} + \dfrac{1}{2x^2}$$

$$= \dfrac{x}{2} + \dfrac{2}{x} + \dfrac{1}{2x^2}$$

2. Write each term as a power of x.

$$= \dfrac{1}{2}x^1 + 2x^{-1} + \dfrac{1}{2}x^{-2}$$

3. Then differentiate each term.

$$f'(x) = \dfrac{1}{2} + 2(-x^{-2}) + \dfrac{1}{2}(-2x^{-3}) = \dfrac{1}{2} - 2x^{-2} - x^{-3}$$

$$= \dfrac{1}{2} - \dfrac{2}{x^2} - \dfrac{1}{x^3}$$

Exercise 2.2

Q1 Differentiate these functions:

a) $y = 4x^3 - x^2$

b) $y = x + \dfrac{1}{x}$

c) $y = 3x^2 + \sqrt{x} - 5$

d) $f(x) = -2x^5 + 4x - \dfrac{1}{x^2}$

e) $f(x) = \sqrt{x^3} - x$

f) $f(x) = 5x - \dfrac{2}{x^3} + \sqrt[3]{x}$

Q2 Find:

a) $\dfrac{d}{dx}(x(x^6 - 1))$

b) $\dfrac{d}{dx}((x - 3)(x + 4))$

c) $\dfrac{d}{dx}(x(x - 1)(x - 2))$

d) $\dfrac{d}{dx}((x - 3)(x + 4)(x - 1))$

e) $\dfrac{d}{dx}(x^2(x - 4)(3 - x^3))$

f) $\dfrac{d}{dx}((x - 3)^2(x^2 - 2))$

Q3 Find the gradient of each of the following curves:

a) $y = x^4 - x^2 + 2$ when $x = 3$

b) $y = 2x^5 + \dfrac{1}{x}$ when $x = -2$

c) $y = x(x - 1)(x - 2)$ when $x = -3$

d) $y = 5(x^2 - 1)(3 - x)$ when $x = 0$

e) $y = \sqrt{x}(x - 1)$ at $(4, 6)$

f) $f(x) = x^3(x^2 - 5)$ at $(-1, 4)$

g) $f(x) = \dfrac{1}{x^2}(x^3 - x)$ at $x = 5$

h) $f(x) = \dfrac{3x^3 + 18x^2 + 24x}{x + 4}$ at $(-2, 0)$

Q4   For each of the following curves, sketch the graph of $y = f'(x)$.

    a) $f(x) = (x + 3)(x + 4)$

    b) $f(x) = \dfrac{x^3 - 3x^2 + 2x}{x - 1}$

    c) $f(x) = x^4 - 4x^3 + 4x^2 - 9$

    d) $f(x) = (x - 1)^2(x + 5)$

Q5   For each of the following functions, find the coordinates of the point or points where the gradient is 0:

    a) $y = x^2 - 2x$

    b) $y = 3x^2 + 4x$

    c) $y = 5x^2 - 3x$

    d) $y = 9x - 3x^3$

    e) $y = 2x^3 - x^2$

    f) $y = 2x^3 + 3x^2 - 12x$

Q6   Differentiate these functions:

    a) $y = \dfrac{x^2 - 3x - 4}{x + 1}$

    b) $f(x) = \dfrac{x^4 - 9}{x^2 + 3}$

    c) $f(x) = \dfrac{x^5 - 16x^3}{x + 4}$

    d) $y = \dfrac{1}{x}(x - 3)(x - 4)$

    e) $y = \sqrt{x}(x^3 - \sqrt{x})$

    f) $f(x) = \dfrac{3 - \sqrt{x}}{\sqrt{x}}$

    g) $f(x) = \dfrac{x + 5\sqrt{x}}{\sqrt{x}}$

    h) $f(x) = \dfrac{x - 3\sqrt{x} + 2}{\sqrt{x} - 1}$

    i) $y = \dfrac{4 - x}{2 + \sqrt{x}}$

Finding tangents and normals

A **tangent** is a straight line that just **touches** the curve and has the **same gradient** at that point.

A **normal** is a straight line that is **perpendicular** (at right angles) to the curve at a particular point.

Tangents and normals are perpendicular to each other — their gradients **multiply to give –1**.

To find the equation of the tangent or normal to a curve at a point:

- Differentiate the function and find the gradient of the curve at that point.

- Use this to deduce the gradient, m, of the tangent or normal:

    | gradient of tangent = gradient of curve | | gradient of normal = $\dfrac{-1}{\text{gradient of the curve}}$ |

- Write the equation of the tangent or normal in the form $y = mx + c$.

- Work out the constant value c in the equation by using the coordinates of the point you know.

Example

Find the equation of the tangent to the curve $y = (4 - x)(x + 2)$ at the point (2, 8), giving your answer in the form $ax + by + c = 0$, where a, b and c are integers.

1. Write the curve in a form you can differentiate...

    $y = (4 - x)(x + 2) = 4x + 8 - x^2 - 2x$
    $= 8 + 2x - x^2$

    ...and differentiate it.

    $\dfrac{dy}{dx} = 0 + 2 - 2x = 2 - 2x$

2. Find the gradient of the curve at (2, 8):

    $x = 2 \Rightarrow \dfrac{dy}{dx} = 2 - (2 \times 2) = 2 - 4 = -2$
    gradient of tangent = gradient of curve, so $m = -2$.

3. So the equation of the tangent is:

    $y = -2x + c$.

4. Use the point (2, 8) to work out the value of c:

    $x = 2, y = 8 \Rightarrow 8 = -4 + c \Rightarrow c = 12$

    So the tangent has equation:

    $y = -2x + 12$

5. Rearrange into the form $ax + by + c = 0$:

    $2x + y - 12 = 0$

> **Example**
>
> Find the equation of the normal to the curve $y = x(x - 3)(x + 2)$ at the point $(2, -8)$, giving your answer in the form $y = mx + c$.
>
> 1. Simplify and differentiate:
>
> $$y = x(x - 3)(x + 2) = x^3 - x^2 - 6x$$
> $$\frac{dy}{dx} = 3x^2 - 2x - 6$$
>
> 2. Find the gradient of the curve at $(2, -8)$:
>
> $$x = 2 \Rightarrow \frac{dy}{dx} = 3(2^2) - 2(2) - 6 = 2$$
>
> 3. Find the gradient of the normal at $(2, -8)$:
>
> $$m = \frac{-1}{\text{gradient of the curve at } (2, -8)} = -\frac{1}{2}$$
>
> 4. So the equation of the normal is:
>
> $$y = -\frac{1}{2}x + c$$
>
> 5. Use the point $(2, -8)$ to work out the value of c: $x = 2$, $y = -8 \Rightarrow -8 = -1 + c \Rightarrow c = -7$
>
> 6. So the equation of the normal is:
>
> $$y = -\frac{1}{2}x - 7$$

Exercise 2.3

Q1 Find the equation of the tangent to each of these curves at the given point. Give your answer in the form $y = mx + c$.

a) $y = 9x - 2x^2$, $(1, 7)$

b) $y = x^3 - 2x + 3$, $(2, 7)$

c) $y = (x + 2)(2x - 3)$, $(2, 4)$

d) $y = x(x - 1)^2$, $(-1, -4)$

e) $y = x^2(x + 3) - 10$, $(2, 10)$

f) $y = x(2x + 4)(x - 3)$, $(-1, 8)$

Q2 Find the tangent to each of these curves at the given point, giving your answer in the form $ax + by + c = 0$, where a, b and c are integers.

a) $y = \frac{1}{x} + x + 3$, $\left(2, 5\frac{1}{2}\right)$

b) $y = 4x^2 - 3\sqrt{x}$, $(1, 1)$

c) $y = \frac{3}{x} + 2\sqrt{x}$, $\left(4, 4\frac{3}{4}\right)$

d) $y = \frac{1}{x} + \frac{4}{x^2}$, $\left(2, 1\frac{1}{2}\right)$

e) $y = \frac{1}{3}x^2 - 4\sqrt{x} - \frac{1}{3}$, $(4, -3)$

f) $y = x - \frac{2}{x} + \frac{3}{x^2}$, $(-3, -2)$

Q3 Find the normal to each of these curves at the given point, giving your answer in the form $ax + by + c = 0$, where a, b and c are integers.

a) $y = 3x^2 - 4x + 2$, $(2, 6)$

b) $y = x^2(x + 4) - 5x$, $(-1, 8)$

c) $y = x(x - 1)(x - 2)$, $(3, 6)$

d) $y = x(x - 3)(x + 4) - 10$, $(-2, 10)$

e) $y = \frac{x^3 - 5x^2 - 14x}{x + 2}$, $(5, -10)$

Q4 Find the normal to each of these curves at the given point, giving your answer in an appropriate form.

a) $y = \frac{2x^5 - 2x^4}{3x^3}$, $(-2, 4)$

b) $y = \frac{5x^2 - 2x + 3}{x^2}$, $\left(2, 4\frac{3}{4}\right)$

c) $y = \frac{3x - x^2}{\sqrt{x}}$, $(4, -2)$

d) $y = \frac{1}{x} - \frac{3}{x^2} - \frac{4}{x^3} + \frac{7}{4}$, $(-2, 1)$

e) $y = x + \frac{2}{\sqrt{x}}$, $(4, 5)$

f) $y = \frac{x^3 - 5x^2 - 4x}{x\sqrt{x}}$, $(4, -4)$

Q5 Consider the curve with equation $y = f(x)$ where $f(x) = x^3 - 3x^2 + 3$.

a) Find the coordinates of the point where $f'(x) = 9$ and $x > 0$.

b) Find the equation of the tangent to the curve at this point, giving your answer in the form $y = mx + c$.

c) Find the equation of the normal to the curve at this point, giving your answer in the form $ax + by + c = 0$, where a, b and c are integers.

Q6 a) Show that the curve $y = \frac{x^3 + x^2 + x + 5}{x^2}$ passes through the point $\left(-2, -\frac{1}{4}\right)$.

b) Find the equation of the tangent to the curve at this point, giving your answer in the form $ax + by + c = 0$, where a, b and c are integers.

c) Find the equation of the normal to the curve at this point, giving your answer in the form $ax + by + c = 0$, where a, b and c are integers.

3. Second Order Derivatives

If you differentiate y with respect to x, you get the derivative $\frac{dy}{dx}$.

If you then differentiate $\frac{dy}{dx}$ with respect to x, you get the **second order derivative**, denoted $\frac{d^2y}{dx^2}$.

The second derivative gives the **rate of change** of the **gradient** of the curve with respect to x.
In function notation, the **second derivative** is written $f''(x)$.

> **Example**   For the function $f(x) = 2x^3 + 4x^2 + x$, find $f'(x)$ and $f''(x)$.
>
> 1.   Differentiate to find $f'(x)$. $f'(x) = 2(3x^2) + 4(2x) + 1 = \mathbf{6x^2 + 8x + 1}$
>
> 2.   Differentiate again to get the second derivative. $f''(x) = 6(2x) + 8 = \mathbf{12x + 8}$

Exercise 3.1

Q1   Find $\frac{dy}{dx}$ and $\frac{d^2y}{dx^2}$ for each of these functions:

    a) $y = x^3$ b) $y = x^5$ c) $y = x^4$ d) $y = x$

    e) $y = \dfrac{1}{x}$ f) $y = \sqrt{x}$ g) $y = \dfrac{1}{x^2}$ h) $y = x\sqrt{x}$

Q2   Find $f'(x)$ and $f''(x)$ for each of these functions:

    a) $f(x) = x(4x^2 - x)$ b) $f(x) = (x^2 - 3)(x - 4)$ c) $f(x) = \dfrac{4x^5 + 12x^3 - 40x}{4(x^2 + 5)}$

    d) $f(x) = 3\sqrt{x} + x\sqrt{x}$ e) $f(x) = \dfrac{1}{x}(3x^4 - 2x^3)$ f) $f(x) = \dfrac{x^2 - x\sqrt{x} + 7x}{\sqrt{x}}$

Q3   Find the value of the second derivative at the given value for x.

    a) $f(x) = x^3 - x^2$, $x = 3$ b) $y = x\sqrt{x} - \dfrac{1}{x}$, $x = 4$ c) $f(x) = x^2(x - 5)(x^2 + x)$, $x = -1$

    d) $y = \dfrac{x^5 + 4x^4 - 12x^3}{x + 6}$, $x = 5$ e) $f(x) = \dfrac{9x^2 + 3x}{3\sqrt{x}}$, $x = 1$ f) $y = \left(\dfrac{1}{x^2} + \dfrac{1}{x}\right)(5 - x)$, $x = -3$

4. Derivatives and Graphs

Stationary points

Stationary points occur when the **gradient** of a graph is **zero**, so you can use **differentiation** to find them:

1. Differentiate $f(x)$.

2. Set $f'(x) = 0$.

3. Solve $f'(x) = 0$ to find the x-values.

4. Put the x-values back into the original equation to find the y-values.

There are three types of stationary point, as shown on the graph:

Tip: Some stationary points are called **local** maximum or minimum points because the function takes on higher or lower values in other parts of the graph. The maximum and minimum points shown here are both local.

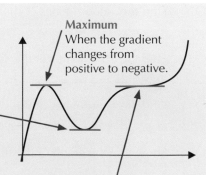

Maximum
When the gradient changes from positive to negative.

Minimum
When the gradient changes from negative to positive.

Point of inflection
When the gradient doesn't change sign either side of the stationary point.

Example Below is a sketch of the graph of $y = x^3(x^2 + x - 3)$. One stationary point occurs at $(-1.8, 9.1)$. Show that the other two occur when $x = 0$ and when $x = 1$, and find their coordinates.

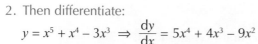
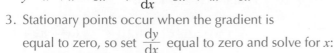

1. Start by multiplying out the brackets:
   $y = x^3(x^2 + x - 3) = x^5 + x^4 - 3x^3$

2. Then differentiate:
   $y = x^5 + x^4 - 3x^3 \Rightarrow \dfrac{dy}{dx} = 5x^4 + 4x^3 - 9x^2$

3. Stationary points occur when the gradient is
   equal to zero, so set $\dfrac{dy}{dx}$ equal to zero and solve for x:
   $$5x^4 + 4x^3 - 9x^2 = 0 \Rightarrow x^2(5x^2 + 4x - 9) = 0$$
   $$\Rightarrow x^2(5x + 9)(x - 1) = 0$$
   $$\Rightarrow x = 0,\ x = -\frac{9}{5} = -1.8 \text{ (given above) and } x = 1.$$

4. So the other two stationary points occur at $x = 0$ and $x = 1$. To find the coordinates
   of these points, just put the x-values into the original equation:

   $x = 0 \Rightarrow y = x^3(x^2 + x - 3)$ $\qquad\qquad$ $x = 1 \Rightarrow y = x^3(x^2 + x - 3)$
   $\qquad\qquad = 0^3(0^2 + 0 - 3) = 0(-3) = 0$ $\qquad\qquad = 1^3(1^2 + 1 - 3) = 1(-1) = -1$

   The coordinates of the other stationary points are **(0, 0)** and **(1, –1)**.

Exercise 4.1

Q1 Without doing any calculations, say how many stationary points the graphs below have
in the intervals shown.

a) 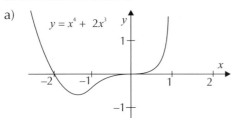   b)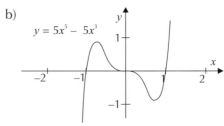

Q2 Find the x-coordinates of the stationary points of the curves with the following equations:
a) $y = x^2 + 3x + 2$ $\qquad$ b) $y = (3 - x)(4 + 2x)$ $\qquad$ c) $y = x^3 + 4x^2 - 3x$ $\qquad$ d) $y = x^4 - 12x^3$

Q3 Find the coordinates of the stationary points of the curves with the following equations:
a) $y = 2x^2 - 5x + 2$ $\qquad$ b) $y = -x^2 + 3x - 4$ $\qquad$ c) $y = 7 - 6x - 3x^2$ $\qquad$ d) $y = (x - 1)(2x + 3)$

Q4 Find the coordinates of the stationary points of the curves with the following equations:
a) $y = x^3 - 3x + 2$ $\qquad$ b) $y = 4x^3 + 5$ $\qquad$ c) $y = 3x^3 + 6x^2$ $\qquad$ d) $y = 4x^3 + 12x^2 + 8$

Q5 Show that the graph of the function given by $f(x) = x^5 + 3x + 2$ has no stationary points.

Q6 a) Differentiate $y = x^3 - 7x^2 - 5x + 2$.
b) Hence find the coordinates of the stationary points of the curve with equation $y = x^3 - 7x^2 - 5x + 2$.

Q7 A graph is given by the function $f(x) = x^3 + kx$, where k is a constant.
Given that the graph has no stationary points, find the range of possible values for k.

Maximum and minimum points

You might be asked to decide if a stationary point is a **maximum** or **minimum**.

To do this, **differentiate again** to find $\dfrac{d^2y}{dx^2}$ or $f''(x)$ (see p.101).

Tip: Maximum and minimum points are also known as **turning points**.

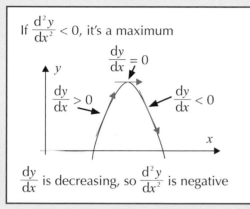

If $\dfrac{d^2y}{dx^2} < 0$, it's a maximum

$\dfrac{dy}{dx} = 0$

$\dfrac{dy}{dx} > 0$ $\dfrac{dy}{dx} < 0$

$\dfrac{dy}{dx}$ is decreasing, so $\dfrac{d^2y}{dx^2}$ is negative

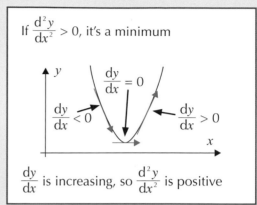

If $\dfrac{d^2y}{dx^2} > 0$, it's a minimum

$\dfrac{dy}{dx} = 0$

$\dfrac{dy}{dx} < 0$ $\dfrac{dy}{dx} > 0$

$\dfrac{dy}{dx}$ is increasing, so $\dfrac{d^2y}{dx^2}$ is positive

---

Example Find the coordinates of the stationary points of the function $y = 2x^3 - 3x^2 - 12x + 5$ and determine their nature.

1. Start by differentiating the function: $y = 2x^3 - 3x^2 - 12x + 5 \Rightarrow \dfrac{dy}{dx} = 6x^2 - 6x - 12$

2. Set the derivative equal to zero and solve the resulting equation:
$$6x^2 - 6x - 12 = 0 \Rightarrow \quad x^2 - x - 2 = 0$$
$$(x + 1)(x - 2) = 0$$
$$x = -1 \text{ and } x = 2$$

3. These are the x-values of the stationary points. Put these values into the original equation to find the coordinates:
When $x = -1$, $y = 12$ and when $x = 2$, $y = -15$

4. So the coordinates of the stationary points are: **(–1, 12) and (2, –15)**

5. To determine the nature of the stationary points, differentiate again:
$$\dfrac{dy}{dx} = 6x^2 - 6x - 12 \Rightarrow \dfrac{d^2y}{dx^2} = 12x - 6$$

6. Then just put in the x-values of the coordinates of the stationary points.

7. At $x = -1$, $\dfrac{d^2y}{dx^2} = -18$, which is negative — so **(–1, 12) is a maximum**

8. And at $x = 2$, $\dfrac{d^2y}{dx^2} = 18$, which is positive — so **(2, –15) is a minimum**

Exercise 4.2

Q1   The diagram on the right shows a sketch of the graph of $y = f(x)$. For each turning point, say whether $f''(x)$ would be positive or negative.

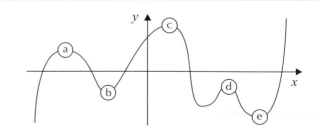

Q2 For each function, find its second derivative and say whether the given point is a maximum or a minimum:
a) $y = x^3 - 12x + 4$ has a stationary point at $(2, -12)$.
b) $y = 2x^4 - 16x^3 + 900$ has a stationary point at $(6, 36)$.
c) $y = 4x^5 + 15x^4 - 250$ has a stationary point at $(-3, -7)$.
d) $y = x^5 - 5x^4 + 5x^2 - 40x + 400$ has a stationary point at $(4, 64)$.

Q3 A function $y = f(x)$ is such that $f(1) = 3$, $f'(1) = 0$ and $f''(1) = 7$.
a) Give the coordinates of one of the turning points of $f(x)$.
b) Determine the nature of this turning point, explaining your answer.

Q4 Find the stationary points on the graphs of the following functions and say whether they're maximum or minimum turning points:
a) $y = 5 - x^2$
b) $y = 2x^3 - 6x + 2$
c) $y = x^3 - 3x^2 - 24x + 15$
d) $f(x) = x^4 + 4x^3 + 4x^2 - 10$
e) $f(x) = 8x^3 + 16x^2 + 8x + 1$
f) $f(x) = \dfrac{27}{x^3} + x$

Q5 a) Given that $f(x) = x^3 - 3x^2 + 4$, find $f'(x)$ and $f''(x)$.
b) Hence find the coordinates of any stationary points on the graph $f(x)$ and say whether they're maximum or minimum turning points.

Q6 A function is given by $y = x^2 + \dfrac{2000}{x}$.
a) Find the value of x at which y is stationary.
b) Is this a minimum or maximum point?

Q7 The curve given by $f(x) = x^3 + ax^2 + bx + c$ has a stationary point with coordinates $(3, 10)$. If $f''(x) = 0$ at $(3, 10)$, find a, b and c.

Q8 a) The equation $y = x^4 + kx^3 + x^2 + 17$ has only one stationary point. Show that $k^2 < \dfrac{32}{9}$.
b) Find the coordinates of the stationary point and say whether it's a maximum or a minimum point.

Increasing and decreasing functions

You can use differentiation to find if a function is **increasing** or **decreasing** at a given point. This can help you to **sketch** the function and determine the nature of **turning points**.

A function is **increasing** when the gradient is **positive**.
y gets bigger...
$\dfrac{dy}{dx} > 0$
...as x gets bigger

A function is **decreasing** when the gradient is **negative**.
y gets smaller...
$\dfrac{dy}{dx} < 0$
...as x gets bigger

You can also tell how **quickly** a function is increasing or decreasing by looking at the size of the gradient — the **bigger** the gradient (positive or negative), the **faster** the function is increasing or decreasing.

A big increase in x and a small increase in y means a **small positive** gradient.

A small increase in x and a big increase in y means a **large positive** gradient.

A big increase in x and a small decrease in y means a **small negative** gradient.

A small increase in x and a big decrease in y means a **large negative** gradient.

Find the values of x for which the function $y = x^3 - 6x^2 + 9x + 3$ is increasing.

1. Start by differentiating:
$$y = x^3 - 6x^2 + 9x + 3 \implies \frac{dy}{dx} = 3x^2 - 12x + 9$$

2. The function is increasing when the derivative is greater than zero, so form an inequality and solve it:
$$\frac{dy}{dx} > 0 \implies 3x^2 - 12x + 9 > 0$$
$$\implies x^2 - 4x + 3 > 0$$
$$\implies (x-3)(x-1) > 0$$

3. For the inequality to be true, either both brackets must be positive or both brackets must be negative:
$$x - 1 > 0 \text{ and } x - 3 > 0 \implies x > 1 \text{ and } x > 3 \implies x > 3$$
$$\text{or } x - 1 < 0 \text{ and } x - 3 < 0 \implies x < 1 \text{ and } x < 3 \implies x < 1$$

Tip: This is a different method for solving quadratic inequalities from the one on p.30 — either is fine.

4. So the function is increasing when: $\quad x < 1 \text{ and } x > 3$

Tip: You could also look at the nature of the stationary points. If you work out $\frac{d^2y}{dx^2}$ at the points where $\frac{dy}{dx} = 0$, you'll find that there's a maximum at $x = 1$ and a minimum at $x = 3$. So the function is increasing before $x = 1$, then decreasing until it reaches $x = 3$ where it starts increasing again. Or, using inequalities, it's increasing for $x < 1$ and $x > 3$.

Exercise 4.3

Q1 For each of these functions, calculate the first derivative and use this to find the range of values for which the function is increasing.
a) $y = x^2 + 7x + 5$
b) $y = 5x^2 + 3x - 2$
c) $y = 2 - 9x^2$

Q2 For each of these functions, find $f'(x)$ and find the range of values of x for which $f(x)$ is decreasing.
a) $f(x) = 16 - 3x - 2x^2$
b) $f(x) = (6 - 3x)(6 + 3x)$
c) $f(x) = (1 - 2x)(7 - 3x)$

Q3 Calculate $\frac{dy}{dx}$ for each of these functions and state the range of values for which the function is increasing.
a) $y = x^3 - 6x^2 - 15x + 25$
b) $y = x^3 + 6x^2 + 12x + 5$
c) $y = x^2 + \sqrt{x}, x > 0$
d) $y = 4x^2 + \frac{1}{x}, x \neq 0$

Q4 Find the first derivative of each function and state the range of values for which the function is decreasing.
a) $f(x) = x^3 - 3x^2 - 9x + 1$
b) $f(x) = x^3 - 4x^2 + 4x + 7$
c) $f(x) = 2x^4 + x$
d) $f(x) = x^4 - 2x^3 - 5x^2 + 6$

Q5 Use differentiation to explain why $f(x) = x^3 + x$ is an increasing function for all real values of x.

Q6 Is the function $f(x) = 3 - 3x - x^3$ an increasing or decreasing function? Explain your answer.

Q7 The function $y = 5 - 3x - ax^5$ is a decreasing function for all real values of x. Find the range of possible values for a.

Q8 The function $y = x^k + x$, where k is a positive integer, is an increasing function for all real values of x. Find all possible values of k.

Curve sketching

Curve sketching was covered in Chapter 4, but you can also use **differentiation** to find out more about the **shape** of the graph and to work out some **key points** like the turning points. Use the following **step-by-step** method to get all the information you need to draw an accurate sketch:

1. **Find where the curve crosses the axes.**
   - To find where it crosses the **y-axis**, just put $x = 0$ into the function and find the value of y.
   - To find where it crosses the **x-axis**, set the function equal to zero and solve for x.
2. **Decide on the shape of the graph.**
   Look at the **highest power** of x and its **coefficient** — this determines the overall **shape** of the graph. The most common ones are **quadratics**, **cubics** (see p.45) and **reciprocals** (see p.47).
3. **Differentiate to find the stationary points.**
   - Find the **stationary points** by **differentiating** and setting $f'(x) = 0$.
   - Then **differentiate again** to decide whether these points are **maximums** or **minimums**.

Tip: You could also find where the function is increasing or decreasing.

Example | Sketch the curve of the equation $y = f(x)$, where $f(x) = x^3 - 4x^2 + 4x$.

1. Start by finding where the curve crosses the axes. When $x = 0$, $y = 0$, so the curve goes through the origin. Find where it meets the x-axis by solving the equation $f(x) = 0$:
$$x^3 - 4x^2 + 4x = 0 \Rightarrow x(x^2 - 4x + 4) = 0$$
$$\Rightarrow x(x - 2)(x - 2) = 0$$
$$\Rightarrow x = 0 \text{ and } x = 2$$

2. Next find the stationary points on the graph by finding $f'(x)$ and solving $f'(x) = 0$:
$$f(x) = x^3 - 4x^2 + 4x \Rightarrow f'(x) = 3x^2 - 8x + 4$$
$$f'(x) = 0 \Rightarrow 3x^2 - 8x + 4 = 0$$
$$\Rightarrow (3x - 2)(x - 2) = 0$$
$$\Rightarrow x = 2 \text{ and } x = \frac{2}{3}$$
when $x = 2$, $y = 0$ and when $x = \frac{2}{3}$, $y = \frac{32}{27}$ (≈ 1.2)

3. Differentiate again to find out if these are maximums or minimums:
$$f''(x) = 6x - 8$$
At $x = 2$, $f''(x) = 4$, so there is a minimum at $(2, 0)$.
At $x = \frac{2}{3}$, $f''(x) = -4$, so there is a maximum at $\left(\frac{2}{3}, \frac{32}{27}\right)$.

Tip: If you find it helpful, you can also work out where the graph is increasing and decreasing — it's increasing when $x < \frac{2}{3}$ and when $x > 2$, and decreasing when $\frac{2}{3} < x < 2$.

4. It's a cubic equation with a positive coefficient of x^3, so the graph will go from bottom left to top right.

5. Notice that the x-intercept $x = 2$ is also the minimum.

6. Now you have all the information you need to sketch the graph:

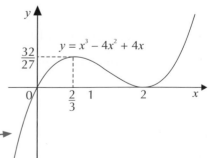

Exercise 4.4

Q1 For the graph $y = x^3 - 2x^2$:
 a) Find the coordinates of the points at which it crosses each axis.
 b) Find $\frac{dy}{dx}$ and hence the coordinates of the points where $\frac{dy}{dx} = 0$.
 c) Identify whether the stationary points are maximums or minimums.
 d) Sketch the graph of $y = x^3 - 2x^2$.

Q2 a) Solve the equation $x^3 + x^2 = 0$.
 b) Find the stationary points of the graph of $f(x) = x^3 + x^2$ and say whether they're maximum or minimum points.
 c) Use your answers to parts a) and b) to sketch the graph of $f(x) = x^3 + x^2$, labelling the coordinates of the stationary points and places where the curve meets the axes.

Q3 For the graph $y = x^4 - 2x^2$:
 a) Find the coordinates of the points at which it crosses each axis.
 b) Find the coordinates of the stationary points.
 c) Identify whether the stationary points are maximums or minimums.
 d) Sketch the graph of $y = x^4 - 2x^2$.

Q4 a) Find the first and second derivatives of the function $f(x) = x^4 - x^3$.
 b) Write down the ranges of values of x for which $f(x)$ is increasing and decreasing.
 c) Sketch the graph of $y = f(x)$, labelling the coordinates of all stationary points and the points where the curve crosses the axes.

Q5 Sketch the graphs of the equations below, labelling the coordinates of any stationary points and the points where the curves cross the axes.
 a) $y = 3x^3 + 3x^2$　　　　b) $y = -x^3 + 9x$　　　　c) $y = x^4 - x^2$　　　　d) $y = x^4 + x^2$

Q6 Given that $x^3 - x^2 - x + 1 = (x + 1)(x - 1)^2$, sketch the graph of $y = x^3 - x^2 - x + 1$, labelling the coordinates of all the stationary points and the points where the curve crosses the axes.

Q7 a) Show that $x^3 - 4x = 0$ when $x = -2$, 0 and 2.
 b) Use first and second derivatives to show that the graph of $y = x^3 - 4x$ has a minimum at $(1.2, -3.1)$ and a maximum at $(-1.2, 3.1)$, where all coordinates are given to 1 d.p.
 c) Use your answers to parts a) and b) to sketch the graph of $y = x^3 - 4x$, labelling the coordinates of the stationary points and the points at which the curve crosses the axes.

Q8 a) Show that the graph of $f(x) = x + \frac{1}{x}$, $x \neq 0$ has 2 stationary points.
 b) Calculate the coordinates of these stationary points and say whether they're maximum or minimum points.
 c) Describe what happens to $f(x)$ as $x \to 0$ from both sides.
 d) Describe what happens to $f(x)$ as $x \to \infty$ and $x \to -\infty$.
 e) Hence sketch the graph of the function $x + \frac{1}{x}$.

Q9 a) Show that for the graph of $y = x^4 + \frac{8}{\sqrt{x}}$, $x > 0$, $\frac{dy}{dx} = 0$ when $x = 1$.
 b) Sketch the graph of $y = x^4 + \frac{8}{\sqrt{x}}$, $x > 0$, labelling the coordinates of the stationary point.

5. Real-Life Problems

Velocity and acceleration problems

Until now, all the examples have been about differentiating functions of x to find gradients of curves. But **real life** examples often involve a function of t, time, and you'll need to differentiate to find the **rate of change** over time. The maths is **the same**, the **letters** are just different.

 A car pulls off from a junction and drives away, travelling x metres in t seconds. For the first 10 seconds, its journey can be modelled by the equation $x = 2t^2$.

a) Use this model to find the velocity of the car after 8 seconds.

1. Velocity is the rate of change of displacement with respect to time (see Chapter 15) — it can be found by differentiating the expression for displacement with respect to time.

2. So to work out the velocity as a function of t, differentiate x to find $\frac{dx}{dt}$:
$$x = 2t^2 \implies \frac{dx}{dt} = 4t$$

3. You've got velocity as a function of t, so put $t = 8$ seconds into the expression:
$$\text{When } t = 8, \frac{dx}{dt} = \textbf{32 ms}^{-1}$$

b) Find the car's acceleration during this period.

1. Acceleration is the rate of change of velocity with respect to time — it can be found by differentiating the expression for velocity with respect to time.

2. The velocity is $\frac{dx}{dt}$ so differentiate again to get the second derivative $\frac{d^2x}{dt^2}$:
$$\frac{dx}{dt} = 4t \implies \frac{d^2x}{dt^2} = \textbf{4 ms}^{-2}$$

Exercise 5.1

Q1 A particle moves along a path described by the equation $x = 3t^2 - 7t$, where t is the time in seconds and x is the displacement in metres.

a) Find the velocity, $\frac{dx}{dt}$, of the particle as a function of t.

b) What is the velocity of the particle in ms^{-1} at: (i) $t = 2$ seconds?   (ii) $t = 5$ seconds?

c) Find the value of t when the velocity is 17 ms^{-1}.

d) Find the acceleration $\frac{d^2x}{dt^2}$ of the particle as a function of t.

Q2 A particle moves along a path described by the equation $x = 2t^3 - 4t^2$, $t > 0$, where t is the time in seconds and x is the displacement in metres.

a) Find the velocity of the particle after t seconds.

b) Find x and t when the velocity is 30 ms^{-1}.

c) Find the acceleration of the particle after t seconds.

d) Find the acceleration at $t = 5$ seconds in ms^{-2}.

e) Find the velocity when the acceleration is 16 ms^{-2}.

Length, area and volume problems

Differentiation can be used in **real-life problems** to maximise a quantity subject to certain factors, e.g. maximising the volume of a box that can be made with a set amount of cardboard.

To find the maximum value of something, all you need is an equation **in terms of only one variable** (e.g. x) — then just **differentiate as normal**. Often there will be too many variables in the question, so you've got to know how to manipulate the information to get rid of the unwanted variables.

Example A farmer wants to build a rectangular sheep pen with length x m and width y m. She has 20 m of fencing in total, and wants the area inside the pen to be as large as possible. How long should each side of the pen be, and what will the area inside the pen be?

1. Start by writing down an expression for the area of the pen: Area = length × width = xy m²

2. This has too many variables, so find an expression for y in terms of x. Find an expression for the amount of fencing available in terms of x and y and rearrange it to make y the subject:
$$\text{Perimeter} = 20 \text{ m} = 2x + 2y \Rightarrow y = \frac{20 - 2x}{2} = 10 - x$$

3. Substitute this into the expression for the area and use differentiation to maximise it:
$$A = xy = x(10 - x) = 10x - x^2, \text{ so } A = 10x - x^2 \Rightarrow \frac{dA}{dx} = 10 - 2x$$

4. Set $\frac{dA}{dx} = 0$ and solve for x: $\frac{dA}{dx} = 0 \Rightarrow 10 - 2x = 0$, so $x = 5 \Rightarrow y = 10 - x = 5$

5. To check that this value of x gives a maximum for A, differentiate again:
$$\frac{d^2A}{dx^2} = -2, \text{ which is negative, so this will give a maximum for } A$$

6. So both x and y should be **5 m** and the total area inside the pen will be $5 \times 5 =$ **25 m²**.

Example A cylindrical pie tin is t cm high with a diameter of d cm. The volume of the pie tin is 1000 cm³. Show that the surface area of the tin is given by $A = \frac{\pi}{4} d^2 + \frac{4000}{d}$ and find the minimum surface area.

1. Find an expression for the surface area:
$$A = \text{area of tin's base} + \text{area of tin's curved face} = \pi\left(\frac{d}{2}\right)^2 + (\pi d \times t) = \frac{\pi d^2}{4} + \pi d t$$

2. Find an equation for the volume and rearrange it to make t the subject, then substitute that into the equation for surface area: $V = \pi\left(\frac{d}{2}\right)^2 t = 1000$
$$\Rightarrow t = \frac{1000}{\pi\left(\frac{d}{2}\right)^2} = \frac{4000}{\pi d^2} \Rightarrow A = \frac{\pi d^2}{4} + \pi d t = \frac{\pi d^2}{4} + (\pi d \times \frac{4000}{\pi d^2}) = \frac{\pi d^2}{4} + \frac{4000}{d}$$

3. Differentiate with respect to d and find the values of d that make $\frac{dA}{dd} = 0$:
$$\frac{dA}{dd} = \frac{\pi d}{2} - \frac{4000}{d^2}, \text{ so when } \frac{dA}{dd} = 0, \frac{\pi d}{2} - \frac{4000}{d^2} = 0 \Rightarrow d^3 = \frac{2 \times 4000}{\pi} \Rightarrow d = \frac{20}{\sqrt[3]{\pi}}$$

4. Check to see if this value of d gives a minimum for A:
$$\frac{d^2A}{dd^2} = \frac{\pi}{2} + \frac{8000}{d^3} = \frac{\pi}{2} + \frac{8000}{\left(\frac{8000}{\pi}\right)} = \frac{3\pi}{2}, \text{ so it's a minimum}$$

5. Now calculate the surface area for that value of d: $A = \frac{\pi}{4}\left(\frac{20}{\sqrt[3]{\pi}}\right)^2 + \frac{4000}{\left(\frac{20}{\sqrt[3]{\pi}}\right)} =$ **439 cm²** (to 3 s.f.)

Exercise 5.2

Q1 A farmer wants to enclose a rectangular area of 100 m² with a fence.
Find the minimum length of fencing he needs to use.

Q2 A ball is catapulted vertically with an initial speed of 30 ms⁻¹. After t seconds, the height, h, of the ball, in m, is given by $h = 30t - 4.9t^2$. Use calculus to find the maximum height the ball reaches.

Q3 A rectangular vegetable patch is enclosed by a wall on one side and fencing on three sides as shown in the diagram.

Use calculus to show that the maximum possible area that can be enclosed by 66 m of fencing is 544.5 m².

Q4 A pet food manufacturer designs tins of cat food of capacity 500 cm³ as shown. The radius of the tin is r cm and the height is h cm.

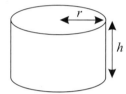

a) Show that the surface area A of the tin is given by $A = 2\pi r^2 + \dfrac{1000}{r}$.

b) Find the value of r which minimises the surface area (to 3 s.f.).

c) Find the minimum possible surface area for the tin (to 3 s.f.).

Q5 A child makes a box by taking a piece of card measuring 40 × 40 cm and cutting squares with side length x cm, as shown in the diagram. The sides are then folded up to make a box.

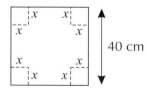

a) Write down a formula for the volume of the box, V.

b) Find the maximum possible volume of the box to 3 s.f.

Q6 A chocolate manufacturer designs a new box which is a triangular prism as shown in the diagram. The cross-section of the prism is a right-angled triangle with sides of length x cm, x cm and h cm. The length of the prism is l cm and the volume is 300 cm³.

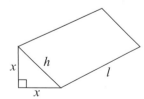

a) Show that the surface area of the prism is given by $A = x^2 + \dfrac{600(2 + \sqrt{2})}{x}$.

b) Show that the value of x which minimises the surface area of the box is $\sqrt[3]{600 + 300\sqrt{2}}$.

Review Exercise — Chapter 8

Q1 Differentiate the following functions from first principles:

    a) $y = x + 1$
                b) $y = 4x^2$
                    c) $y = \dfrac{3}{x}$

Q2 Differentiate these functions with respect to x:

    a) $y = x^2 + 2$
            b) $y = x^4 + \sqrt{x}$
          c) $y = \dfrac{7}{x^2} - \dfrac{3}{\sqrt{x}} + 12x^3$

Q3 Find the gradients of these graphs at $x = 2$:

a)
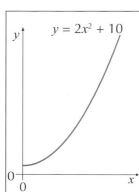
$y = 2x^2 + 10$

b)
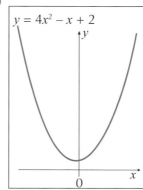
$y = 4x^2 - x + 2$

c)
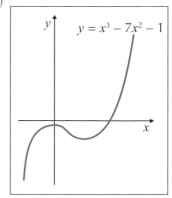
$y = x^3 - 7x^2 - 1$

Q4 Water is poured into a bowl. The volume (v) of water in the bowl (in ml) after t seconds is given by the function: $v = 3t^2 + 4$.

    a) How much water is in the bowl initially?

    b) Find the rate at which water is being poured into the bowl when $t = 4$ seconds.

Q5 Find the equations of the tangent and the normal to the curve $y = \sqrt{x^3} - 3x - 10$ at $x = 16$.

Q6 Find the equation of the tangent to the curve $y = x^3 + \dfrac{4}{x} + 2\sqrt{x}$ at $x = 1$.

Q7 Show that the graphs of $y = \dfrac{x^3}{3} - 2x^2 - 4x + \dfrac{86}{3}$ and $y = \sqrt{x}$ both go through the point (4, 2), and are perpendicular at that point.

Q8 Consider the curve C given by the equation $y = x^2 - 6$ and the line L given by the equation $y = 3$.

    a) Find the coordinates of the points, A and B, where C and L intersect.

    b) Find the gradient of C at points A and B.

    c) Find the equations of the normals to C at A and B.

    d) The normals at points A and B meet the point D. Find the coordinates of the point D.

Q9 Consider the curve C given by the equation $y = x^3 - 2x^2 + 1$, $x > 0$, and the line L given by the equation $y = 1$.

    a) Write down the gradient of the line L for any x.

    b) Find the point at which the curve C has the same gradient as the line L.

    c) Hence give the equation of the tangent to C at this point.

Q10 Find the equations of the tangent and the normal to the curve $y = 1 + \sqrt{x^3}$ at $x = 16$.

Q11 Consider the curve with equation $y = f(x)$, where $f(x) = x^3 - 3x$.
   a) Work out the gradient of this curve when $x = -1$.
   b) Show that $2f''(x) - 3f'(x) + f(x) = x^3 + 9(1 + x - x^2)$.

Q12 Let $f(x) = x^4$. Find $f''(x) + 2f'(x) - 4f(x)$.

Q13 Find the coordinates of the stationary points of the graph of $y = x^3 - 6x^2 - 63x + 21$.

Q14 a) Find the stationary points of the graph of the function $y = x^3 + \dfrac{3}{x}$.
   b) Work out whether each stationary point is a maximum or a minimum.

Q15 Find all the stationary points of the graph of $y = 2x^4 - x^2 + 4$ and determine their nature.

Q16 Find when each of the functions below are increasing and decreasing:
   a) $y = 6(x + 2)(x - 3)$
   b) $y = \dfrac{1}{x^2}$

Q17 Sketch the graph of $y = 3x^3 - 16x$, clearly showing the coordinates of any turning points.

Q18 Sketch the graph of $y = -3x^3 + 6x^2$, clearly showing the coordinates of any turning points.

Q19 Given that $xy = 20$ and that both x and y are positive, find the least possible value of $x^2 + y^2$.

Q20 A particle moves along a path described by the equation $x = t^3 - 8t$, $t > 0$, where t is the time in seconds and x is the displacement in metres.
   a) Find $\dfrac{dx}{dt}$, the velocity of the particle as a function of t.
   b) Find x and t when the velocity is 19 ms^{-1}.
   c) Find the acceleration $\dfrac{d^2x}{dt^2}$ of the particle as a function of t.
   d) Find the acceleration, in ms^{-2}, after 2 seconds.
   e) Find the velocity, in ms^{-1}, when the acceleration is 18 ms^{-2}.

Q21 The height (h m) a firework can reach is related to the mass (m g) of fuel it carries as shown:
$$h = \frac{m^2}{10} - \frac{m^3}{800}$$

   Find the mass of fuel required to achieve the maximum height and state what the maximum height is to 3 s.f.

Q22 The diagram shows a box with dimensions x cm, $2x$ cm and y cm, and volume 200 cm^3.
   a) Show that the surface area A of the box is given by $A = 4x^2 + \dfrac{600}{x}$.
   b) Use calculus to find the value of x that gives the minimum value of A (to 3 s.f.).
   c) Hence find the minimum possible surface area of the box, correct to 3 s.f.

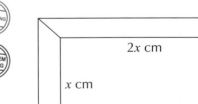

Chapter 9 — Integration

Integration is the 'opposite' of differentiation. When you integrate something, you're trying to find a function that returns to what you started with when you differentiate it. This function is called an integral.

1. Indefinite Integration

Integrating x^n

The integral of a **function** f(x) with respect to x is written $\int f(x)\,dx$.
The formula below tells you how to integrate **any power of x** (except x^{-1}).

$\int$ means **the integral of**.

dx means
with respect to x.

$$\int x^n\,dx = \frac{x^{n+1}}{n+1} + C$$

Increase the power by one
— then divide by it.

Add a **constant**.

If a term is multiplied by a **constant**, take it **outside** the integral: $\int ax^n\,dx = a\int x^n\,dx$

Examples   **Find the following integrals:**

a) $\int x^3\,dx$ Increase the power to 4...

$$\int x^3\,dx = \frac{x^4}{4} + C$$ ...and add a constant of integration.

...divide by 4...

b) $\int \frac{2}{x^3}\,dx$ Take the 2 outside...   ...increase the power by 1 to –2...

$$\int \frac{2}{x^3}\,dx = \int 2x^{-3}\,dx = 2\int x^{-3}\,dx = 2\left(\frac{x^{-2}}{-2}\right) + C = -\frac{1}{x^2} + C$$

Don't forget to
add the constant.

...and divide by –2.

c) $\int 4\,dx$ Increase the power from 0 to 1.

$$\int 4\,dx = \int 4x^0\,dx = \frac{4x^1}{1} + C = 4x + C$$ Add a constant.

Divide by the power.

Exercise 1.1

Q1   Find an expression for y when $\frac{dy}{dx}$ is the following:

a) x^7 b) $2x^3$ c) $8x$ d) $-5x^4$ e) $200x^{99}$ f) x^{-3}

g) $4x^{-4}$ h) $-6x^{-5}$ i) -12 j) $x^{\frac{1}{2}}$ k) $x^{\frac{1}{3}}$ l) $12\sqrt{x^3}$

Q2   Find the following:

a) $\int x^{\frac{2}{3}}\,dx$ b) $\int 7x^{\frac{4}{3}}\,dx$ c) $\int x^{-\frac{1}{2}}\,dx$ d) $\int 2x^{-\frac{1}{3}}\,dx$

e) $\int 14x^{0.4}\,dx$ f) $\int -1.2x^{-0.6}\,dx$ g) $\int -2x^{-\frac{5}{4}}\,dx$ h) $\int -\frac{3}{2}x^{-\frac{1}{2}}\,dx$

i) $\int -\frac{4}{3}x^{-\frac{4}{3}}\,dx$ j) $\int \frac{1}{2}\sqrt{x^5}\,dx$ k) $\int \frac{2}{3}x^{\frac{7}{5}}\,dx$ l) $\int 50.5x^{0.01}\,dx$

Integrating functions

If there are **lots of terms** in an expression, you can just integrate each bit **separately**.

Examples   a) Find $\int \left(3x^2 - \dfrac{2}{\sqrt{x}} + \dfrac{7}{x^2}\right) dx$.

Write as powers of x.

Integrate each term separately.

$\int \left(3x^2 - \dfrac{2}{\sqrt{x}} + \dfrac{7}{x^2}\right) dx = \int (3x^2 - 2x^{-\frac{1}{2}} + 7x^{-2})\, dx$

Take the constants outside the integral.

$= 3\int x^2\, dx - 2\int x^{-\frac{1}{2}}\, dx + 7\int x^{-2}\, dx$

$= \dfrac{3x^3}{3} - \dfrac{2x^{\frac{1}{2}}}{\left(\frac{1}{2}\right)} + \dfrac{7x^{-1}}{-1} + C = x^3 - 4\sqrt{x} - \dfrac{7}{x} + C$

Just add one constant of integration.

b) **Find y if $\dfrac{dy}{dx} = \dfrac{(x-1)^2}{\sqrt{x}}$.**

$\int \left(\dfrac{(x-1)^2}{\sqrt{x}}\right) dx = \int \left(\dfrac{x^2 - 2x + 1}{x^{\frac{1}{2}}}\right) dx = \int \left(\dfrac{x^2}{x^{\frac{1}{2}}} - \dfrac{2x}{x^{\frac{1}{2}}} + \dfrac{1}{x^{\frac{1}{2}}}\right) dx$

Expand the bracket...

...split into separate terms...

...and write as powers of x.

Do each of these bits separately.

$= \int (x^{\frac{3}{2}} - 2x^{\frac{1}{2}} + x^{-\frac{1}{2}})\, dx$

$= \int x^{\frac{3}{2}}\, dx - 2\int x^{\frac{1}{2}}\, dx + \int x^{-\frac{1}{2}}\, dx$

$= \dfrac{x^{\frac{5}{2}}}{\left(\frac{5}{2}\right)} - \dfrac{2x^{\frac{3}{2}}}{\left(\frac{3}{2}\right)} + \dfrac{x^{\frac{1}{2}}}{\left(\frac{1}{2}\right)} + C = \dfrac{2(\sqrt{x})^5}{5} - \dfrac{4(\sqrt{x})^3}{3} + 2\sqrt{x} + C$

Exercise 1.2

Q1 Find $f(x)$ when $f'(x)$ is given by the following:

a) $5x + 3x^{-4}$

b) $4x(x^2 - 1)$

c) $(x - 3)^2$

d) $x\left(6x + \dfrac{4}{x^4}\right)$

e) $\left(x + \dfrac{2}{x}\right)^2$

f) $x\left(3x^{\frac{1}{2}} - \dfrac{2}{x^{\frac{4}{3}}}\right)$

g) $6\sqrt{x} - \dfrac{1}{x^2}$

h) $\dfrac{2}{\sqrt{x}} - 7x^2\sqrt{x}$

i) $5(\sqrt{x})^3 - \dfrac{3x}{\sqrt{x}}$

j) $\sqrt{x}\,(1 - x)$

k) $3\sqrt[6]{x} - \dfrac{\sqrt{x}}{\sqrt[3]{x}}$

l) $\dfrac{x^3 - 2x^2}{\sqrt{x}}$

Q2 Find the following integrals:

a) $\int (0.55x^{0.1} - 3x^{-1.5}x)\, dx$

b) $\int \left(8x^3 - \dfrac{2}{\sqrt{x}} + \dfrac{5}{x^2}\right) dx$

c) $\int \left((\sqrt{x})^5 + \dfrac{1}{2\sqrt{x}}\right) dx$

d) $\int \left(\sqrt{x}\left(7x^2 - 1 - \dfrac{2}{x}\right)\right) dx$

e) $\int (3x - 5\sqrt{x})^2\, dx$

f) $\int \left(\dfrac{2x^3 - \sqrt{x}}{x}\right) dx$

g) $\int \left(\dfrac{(5x - 3)^2}{\sqrt{x}}\right) dx$

h) $\int (x^{\frac{1}{2}} + 1)(x^{-\frac{1}{2}} - 3)\, dx$

i) $\int x(2x + \sqrt{x})^2\, dx$

Q3 a) Given that $\dfrac{dy}{dx} = 1.5x^2 - \dfrac{4}{x^3}$, find y.

b) Given that $f'(x) = \dfrac{4}{3\,(x^{\frac{1}{3}})^4} + 5x^{\frac{3}{2}}$, find $f(x)$.

Q4 Find: a) $\int \left(\dfrac{(\sqrt{x} + 3)(\sqrt{x} - 1)}{\sqrt{x}}\right) dx$

b) $\int \left(\sqrt{x}\left(\sqrt{x} - \dfrac{1}{\sqrt{x}}\right)^2\right) dx$

Integrating to find equations of curves

Differentiating the equation of a curve gives its **gradient**. **Integrating** the gradient of a curve does the **opposite** — it gives you the **equation** of the curve. To find the equation of a **particular curve** by integration, you need to know the coordinates of **one point** on it, which you can use to find C.

> **Example** The curve $y = f(x)$ goes through the point (2, 8) and $f'(x) = 6x(x - 1)$. Find $f(x)$.
>
> 1. Integrate $f'(x)$ to find $f(x)$:
> $$f'(x) = 6x(x - 1) = 6x^2 - 6x$$
> $$f(x) = \int (6x^2 - 6x)\,dx = \frac{6x^3}{3} - \frac{6x^2}{2} + C = 2x^3 - 3x^2 + C$$
>
> 2. Find C using the point (2, 8). Put $x = 2$ and $y = 8$ into $f(x)$:
> $$8 = (2 \times 2^3) - (3 \times 2^2) + C \implies 8 = 16 - 12 + C \implies C = 4$$
>
> 3. So the equation is: $f(x) = 2x^3 - 3x^2 + 4$

Exercise 1.3

Q1 For each of the following, the curve $y = f(x)$ passes through the given point. Find $f(x)$.

a) $f'(x) = 4x^3$, (0, 5)

b) $f'(x) = 3x^2 - 4x + 3$, (1, –3)

c) $f'(x) = 6x(x + 2)$, (–1, 1)

d) $f'(x) = \frac{5}{x^2} + 2x$, (5, 4)

e) $f'(x) = 3x^2(x - 4)$, (2, –10)

f) $f'(x) = (3x + 1)(x - 1)$, (3, –3)

g) $f'(x) = x(x + \frac{3}{x^3})$, (–3, 5)

h) $f'(x) = \frac{9x^3 + 2x^{-2}}{x}$, (–1, 2)

i) $f'(x) = \sqrt{x}(3 - x)$, (1, 4)

Q2 A curve $y = f(x)$ that passes through the point (4, 9) has gradient function $f'(x) = \frac{3}{\sqrt{x}} + 2x$. Find the equation of the curve.

Q3 The gradient function of a curve is given by $\frac{dy}{dx} = 3\sqrt{x} + \frac{1}{x^2}$. Find the equation of the curve if it passes through the point (1, 7).

Q4 Consider $\frac{dy}{dt} = (\sqrt{t} - 3)^2$. Given that $y = 9$ when $t = 4$, find y as a function of t.

Q5 The curve $y = f(x)$ goes through the point $(1, \frac{1}{3})$ and $f'(x) = \sqrt{x}(5x - 1)$. Find $f(x)$.

Q6 The curve $y = f(x)$ has derivative $f'(x) = x^2 + \frac{2}{x^{\frac{3}{2}}}$ and passes through the point $(1, -\frac{5}{3})$. Find the equation of the curve.

Q7 The gradient function of a curve is given by $\frac{dy}{dx} = \frac{x - 6}{x^3} + 2$. Find the equation of the curve if it passes through the point (3, –1).

Q8 An object is moving such that its acceleration, in ms^{-2}, is given by the function $\frac{dv}{dt} = 6t - t^2$, for $0 \le t \le 10$, (t = time, measured in seconds). Given that the object comes to rest ($v = 0$ ms^{-1}) at $t = 10$ seconds, find its initial velocity (v, when $t = 0$).

Q9 A function has a gradient given by $f'(x) = 3x^2 + kx - k$, where k is a constant. Given that $f(x)$ passes through the point (2, 7) with a gradient of 18, find the value of k, and hence find the equation of $f(x)$.

2. Definite Integration

Evaluating definite integrals

Definite integrals have **limits** (little numbers) next to the integral sign — they tell you the **range of x-values** to integrate between. To find a definite integral, integrate the function as normal, but **don't** add a **constant of integration**. Work out the **value** of the definite integral by **putting in the limits**:

If you know that the integral of f(x) is $\int f(x)\, dx = g(x) + C$ then:

upper limit $\int_a^b f(x)\, dx = [g(x)]_a^b = g(b) - g(a)$ — **Subtract** the value of g at the **lower** limit from the value of g at the **upper** limit.

lower limit

Example Evaluate $\int_1^3 (x^2 + 2)\, dx.$

1. Find the integral in the normal way but use the notation above:

$$\int_1^3 (x^2 + 2)\, dx = \left[\frac{x^3}{3} + 2x\right]_1^3$$

2. Put in the limits: $\left[\frac{x^3}{3} + 2x\right]_1^3 = \left(\frac{3^3}{3} + 6\right) - \left(\frac{1^3}{3} + 2\right) = 15 - \frac{7}{3} = \frac{38}{3}$

Example Find the possible values for A that satisfy $\int_1^4 \left(\frac{3}{7}x^2 + \frac{2A}{\sqrt{x}}\right)dx = 5A^2.$ (PROBLEM SOLVING)

1. First, evaluate the integral. Treat the A as a constant for now.

$$\int_1^4 \left(\frac{3}{7}x^2 + 2Ax^{-\frac{1}{2}}\right)dx = \left[\frac{1}{7}x^3 + 4Ax^{\frac{1}{2}}\right]_1^4 = \left(\frac{64}{7} + 8A\right) - \left(\frac{1}{7} + 4A\right) = \frac{63}{7} + 4A = 9 + 4A$$

2. You know that this is equal to $5A^2$ from the question, so form a quadratic in A and solve it:

$$9 + 4A = 5A^2 \implies 5A^2 - 4A - 9 = 0 \implies (5A - 9)(A + 1) = 0$$

3. So the solutions are: $A = \frac{9}{5}$ or -1

Exercise 2.1

Q1 Find the value of the following, giving exact answers:

a) $\int_{-2}^0 (4x^3 + 2x)\, dx$

b) $\int_{-2}^5 (x^3 + x)\, dx$

c) $\int_{-5}^{-2} (x + 1)^2\, dx$

d) $\int_3^4 (6x^{-4} + x^{-2})\, dx$

e) $\int_1^2 \left(x^2 + \frac{1}{x^2}\right)dx$

f) $\int_1^4 (3x^{-4} + \sqrt{x})\, dx$

g) $\int_0^1 ((2x + 3)(x + 2))\, dx$

h) $\int_1^4 \left(\frac{x^2 + 2}{\sqrt{x}}\right)dx$

i) $\int_4^9 \left(\frac{1}{x} + \sqrt{x}\right)^2 dx$

j) $\int_4^{16} \left(\frac{\sqrt{x} - 1}{x^2}\right)dx$

k) $\int_1^9 x^{\frac{1}{2}}(5x - x^{-\frac{1}{2}})\, dx$

l) $\int_1^4 (1 + x^2)(1 + \sqrt{x})\, dx$

Q2 Integrate the function $4x - 5x^3 + 7$ between the limits $x = -1$ and $x = 3$.

Q3 Find the integral of f(x) between $x = 0$ and $x = 1$, if $f(x) = 3 - 4\sqrt{x} + \frac{1}{2}x^2$

Q4 Find a, where $a > 0$, given that:

a) $\int_0^a x^3 \, dx = 64$

b) $\int_0^a 2x^4 = 4a^4$

Q5 Find the possible values of A that satisfy:

a) $\int_2^3 (1 - 2Ax) \, dx = 6A^2$

b) $\int_{-2}^2 \left(\frac{21}{8} x^2 + \frac{A}{x^2} \right) dx = 3A^2$

Q6 Find the possible values of a if the integral of ax^a with respect to x between $x = 0$ and $x = 1$ is equal to:

a) $\frac{2}{3}$

b) $\frac{3}{2}$

c) $(a + 4)$

d) $(4a + 1)$

The area under a curve

The value of a **definite integral** represents the **area** between the x-axis and the graph of the function you're integrating between the two limits. If the area lies **below** the x-axis, it'll give a **negative** value — in this case, you'll need to make your answer **positive** at the end, as you can't have **negative area**.

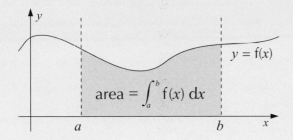

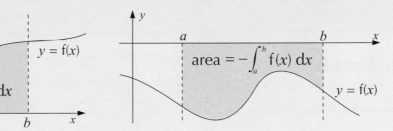

Example Find the area between the graph of $y = x^2$, the x-axis and the lines $x = -1$ and $x = 2$.

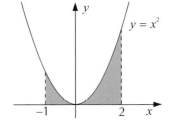

Integrate the function $f(x) = x^2$ between -1 and 2 with respect to x.

$$\int_{-1}^2 x^2 \, dx = \left[\frac{x^3}{3} \right]_{-1}^2 = \left(\frac{2^3}{3} \right) - \left(\frac{(-1)^3}{3} \right) = \frac{8}{3} + \frac{1}{3} = \frac{9}{3} = 3$$

Example Find the area between the graph of $y = 4x - 3x^2 - x^3$ and the x-axis between $x = -4$ and $x = 0$.

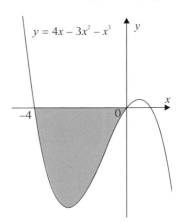

1. You can see from the sketch of the graph that the area you're trying to find lies below the x-axis. So the integral will come out negative:

$$\int_{-4}^0 (4x - 3x^2 - x^3) \, dx = \left[2x^2 - x^3 - \frac{x^4}{4} \right]_{-4}^0$$

$$= (0) - \left(2(-4)^2 - (-4)^3 - \frac{(-4)^4}{4} \right)$$

$$= 0 - (32 + 64 - 64) = -32$$

2. So the area between the curve and the x-axis is: **32**

To find the area for a portion of a curve which lies both **above** and **below** the x-axis, find the areas above and below **separately** and add them up at the end so that the negative and positive integrals don't **cancel each other out**.

 Find the area between the graph of $y = x^3$, the x-axis and the lines $x = -2$ and $x = 2$.

1. Split up the integral into two parts — one where the area is above the x-axis (A), and one where the area is below the x-axis (B):

$$A: \int_0^2 x^3 = \left[\frac{x^4}{4}\right]_0^2 = \frac{1}{4}[x^4]_0^2 = \frac{1}{4}(2^4 - 0^4) = \frac{16}{4} = 4$$

$$B: \int_{-2}^0 x^3 = \left[\frac{x^4}{4}\right]_{-2}^0 = \frac{1}{4}[x^4]_{-2}^0 = \frac{1}{4}(0^4 - (-2)^4) = -\frac{16}{4} = -4$$

2. So the total area is: $4 + 4 = \textbf{8}$

Tip: If you tried integrating this normally, the negative area would cancel out the positive area: $4 + (-4) = 0$.

Exercise 2.2

Q1 Calculate the exact shaded area in the following diagrams:

a) 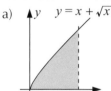 $y = x + \sqrt{x}$

b) 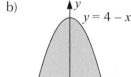 $y = 4 - x^2$

c) 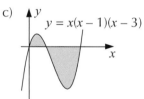 $y = x(x - 1)(x - 3)$

Q2 Find the area enclosed by the curve with equation $y = (x - 1)(3x + 9)$, the x-axis and the lines:

a) $x = 1$ and $x = 5$ b) $x = -3$ and $x = -4$ c) $x = -2$ and $x = 2$

Q3 Find the area enclosed by the graph of $y = \frac{20}{x^5}$, the x-axis and the lines $x = 1$ and $x = 2$.

Q4 Calculate the area enclosed by the line $y = 3x$, the curve $y = (x - 6)^2$ and the x-axis.

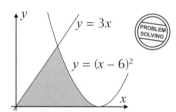

Q5 By first sketching the graph, find the total area between the graph of $y = x^3 + 4x^2 + 3x$ and the x-axis between $x = 0$ and $x = -2$.

Q6 The area under a velocity-time graph gives the distance travelled. An object's motion is tracked as it speeds up, and then slows to rest. Its velocity, v m/s, at time t s is modelled by the function $v = 10t - t^2$. How far does the object travel:

a) between $t = 1$ and $t = 3$?

b) in total over its 10 seconds of motion?

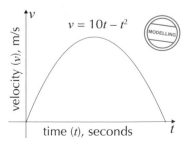

Review Exercise — Chapter 9

Q1 Find f(x) in each case below. Give each term in its simplest form.

    a) $f'(x) = x^{-\frac{1}{2}} + 4 - 5x^3$ b) $f'(x) = 2x + \dfrac{3}{x^2}$ c) $f'(x) = 6x^2 - \dfrac{1}{3\sqrt{x}}$

Q2 Integrate with respect to x:

    a) $\dfrac{5}{7}x^4 + \dfrac{2}{3}x + \dfrac{1}{4}$ b) $\dfrac{1}{\sqrt{x}} + \sqrt{x}$ c) $\dfrac{3}{x^2} + \dfrac{3}{\sqrt[3]{x}}$

Q3 a) Find $\displaystyle\int \left(4x^2 + \dfrac{3}{\sqrt{x}} - 2\right) dx$ b) Find $\displaystyle\int \left(3\sqrt{x} + 3\right)^2 dx$

Q4 Work out the equation of the curve that has derivative $\dfrac{dy}{dx} = 6x - 7$
and goes through the point $(1, 0)$.

Q5 The gradient function of a curve is given by $\dfrac{dy}{dx} = 2(3x - 6.5)$.
The curve passes through the point $(1, 2)$.

    a) Find the equation of the curve.

    b) Sketch the curve, stating the coordinates of the points where the curve crosses the axes.

Q6 A curve $y = f(x)$ that passes through the origin has derivative $f'(x) = 6x^2 + 6x - 5$.

    a) Find the equation of the curve.

    b) Factorise and hence sketch the curve, showing the points where the curve cuts the axes.

Q7 The gradient of a curve C is given by $\dfrac{dy}{dx} = \dfrac{(x+2)(x-2)}{\sqrt{x}}$, $x > 0$.

    a) Show that $\dfrac{dy}{dx}$ can be written in the form $Ax^{\frac{3}{2}} + Bx^{-\frac{1}{2}}$, where A and B are integers.

    b) The point $\left(1, \dfrac{7}{5}\right)$ lies on C. Find the equation of C.

Q8 The curve C with equation $y = f(x)$ has derivative $f'(x) = 6x^2 - 12 - \dfrac{8}{x^2}$, $x > 0$
and passes through the point P with coordinates $(-2, 5)$.
Find the equation of the curve C.

Q9 The curve $y = f(x)$ passes through the point P with coordinates $(1, -9)$.
Given that $f'(x) = \dfrac{5x^2 + 1}{x^{\frac{1}{2}}} - 10$, $x > 0$, find the equation of the curve.

Q10 Evaluate the following definite integrals:

    a) $\displaystyle\int_0^1 (4x^3 + 3x^2 + 2x + 1)\, dx$ b) $\displaystyle\int_1^6 \dfrac{3}{x^2}\, dx$ c) $\displaystyle\int_1^2 \left(\dfrac{8}{x^5} + \dfrac{3}{\sqrt{x}}\right) dx$

    d) $\displaystyle\int_4^9 \sqrt{x}\left(1 - 2\sqrt{x}\right) dx$ e) $\displaystyle\int_1^4 \dfrac{3\sqrt{x} + 2x^4}{x^2}\, dx$ f) $\displaystyle\int_{-1}^{0.5} \dfrac{2x^5 + 4x^4}{5x^3}\, dx$

Q11 a) Evaluate $\displaystyle\int_{-3}^{3} (9 - x^2)\, dx$.

    b) Sketch the area represented by this integral.

Q12 Find the possible values of A that satisfy:

a) $\int_4^5 (2A^2 - 6x^2)\, dx = 120A$

b) $\int_1^4 (A - 2\sqrt{x})^2\, dx = 10 - A^2$

Q13 Find the shaded area in the diagrams below:

a)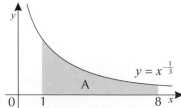

b) $y = x^2 + 8x + 7$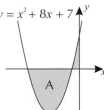

c) $y = x^2 + x - 6$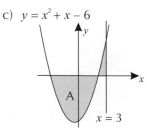

Q14 Use integration to find the shaded area in each of these graphs:

a)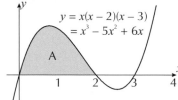

b)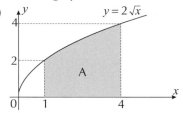

c)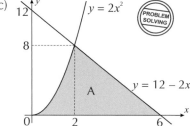

d)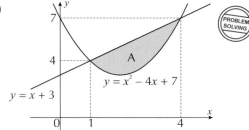

Q15 Find the total shaded area on each of the following graphs:

a)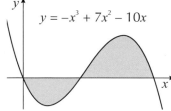

b)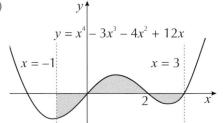

Q16 The graph of $y = 2x^3 - 15x^2 + 36x - 28$ has a double root at $x = a$, where a is a positive integer. Find the value of a and hence find the area bounded by the graph, the x-axis, the y-axis and the line $x = a$.

Q17 An architect is designing a floor plan for a new art gallery. He sketches the plan on a set of axes, with the x- and y-axes forming two walls and the third given by the function $y = 9 - \frac{1}{3}\sqrt{x^3}$ for $0 \le x \le 9$, measured in metres.

a) The room needs at least 40 m² of floor space. Does the plan meet this requirement?

b) An area bounded by the x-axis, the y-axis and the curve $y = 2 - \frac{1}{2}x^2$, $0 \le x \le 2$, is reserved for an information kiosk. How much floor space is left?

Chapter 10 — Vectors

You'll have seen vectors before at GCSE — they've got a size and a direction.
In this section you'll see how they work and what you can do with them.

1. Vectors

Introducing vectors

Scalars are quantities **without a direction** — e.g. a speed of 2 ms⁻¹.	**Vectors** have both **size and direction** — e.g. a velocity of 2 ms⁻¹ on a bearing of 050°.

- Vectors are written using either a **lowercase bold** letter or a **lowercase underlined** letter, e.g. **v** or v̲.
  The vector from **point A** to **point B** is written $\overrightarrow{AB}$.
- You can **add vectors** together by drawing the arrows nose to tail. The single vector that
  goes from the start to the end of the combined vectors is called the **resultant vector**.

Tip: −**a** is the vector **a** with its direction reversed. Subtracting a vector is the same as adding the negative vector.

 Find $\overrightarrow{WZ}$ and $\overrightarrow{ZX}$ in terms of **p, q** and **r**.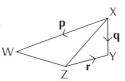

Describe the route from one point to another.
If you go backwards, subtract the vector.

$$\overrightarrow{WZ} = -\mathbf{p} + \mathbf{q} + (-\mathbf{r}) = -\mathbf{p} + \mathbf{q} - \mathbf{r} \qquad \overrightarrow{ZX} = \mathbf{r} - \mathbf{q}$$

Exercise 1.1

Q1 State whether each of these real world examples refers to a scalar quantity, a vector quantity or neither.

a) A pilot flies due south for a distance of 200 kilometres.

b) The time taken to travel from London to Exeter is 3 hours.

c) A force of 20 newtons is required to pull a sledge up the steepest section of a hill —
the slope is at an angle of 5° to the horizontal.

Q2 Vectors **a** and **b** are represented by the lines below:

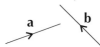

Draw and label sketches that represent the following vectors:
a) −**a**   b) 2**b**   c) **a** + **b**   d) **a** − **b**.

Q3 For the rectangle ABCD shown on the right,
write down single vectors that are equivalent to:
a) $\overrightarrow{AB} + \overrightarrow{BC}$ b) $\overrightarrow{BC} + \overrightarrow{CD} + \overrightarrow{DA}$ c) $\overrightarrow{DC} - \overrightarrow{BC}$

Q4 In the triangle XYZ the vector **p** represents $\overrightarrow{XZ}$ and the vector **q** represents $\overrightarrow{YX}$.
Express the following in terms of **p** or **q** or both:
a) $\overrightarrow{XY}$ b) $\overrightarrow{YZ}$ c) $\overrightarrow{ZY}$

Q5   In triangle DEF, J and L are midpoints of ED and FD respectively.

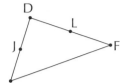

Given that $\vec{EF} = \mathbf{f}$ and $\vec{ED} = \mathbf{d}$, prove that $\vec{JL} = \frac{1}{2}\mathbf{f}$.

Scalar multiplication

When you multiply a vector by a **scalar**, the vector's **length changes** but its **direction** stays the **same**.

All **parallel** vectors are **scalar multiples** of each other, so showing that one vector is a scalar multiple of another is the same as showing they're parallel.

 $\vec{CA} = \mathbf{p}$, $\vec{CB} = \mathbf{q}$, point M lies halfway along $\vec{CB}$, point N lies halfway along $\vec{AB}$. Show that $\vec{MN}$ is parallel to $\vec{CA}$.

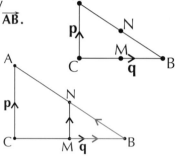

Find $\vec{MN}$ in terms of $\vec{CA}$:

$\vec{MN} = \vec{MB} + \vec{BN} = \frac{1}{2}\vec{CB} + \frac{1}{2}\vec{BA}$

$\vec{BA} = -\mathbf{q} + \mathbf{p}$ and $\vec{CB} = \mathbf{q}$

$\vec{MN} = \frac{1}{2}\mathbf{q} + \frac{1}{2}(-\mathbf{q} + \mathbf{p}) = \frac{1}{2}\mathbf{p} = \frac{1}{2}\vec{CA}$

$\vec{MN}$ is a scalar multiple of $\vec{CA}$, so they're **parallel**.

Tip: Vectors of the same size which are parallel and pointing in the same direction are the same vector.

Exercise 1.2

Q1   Give two vectors that are parallel to $3\mathbf{t} - 2\mathbf{u}$.

Q2   Group the following into sets of parallel vectors:

$2\mathbf{a} + \mathbf{b}$ $2\mathbf{p} + \mathbf{q}$ $2\mathbf{a} - \mathbf{b}$ $4\mathbf{b} + 8\mathbf{a}$ $10\mathbf{a} - 5\mathbf{b}$ $-\mathbf{b} - 2\mathbf{a}$ $\frac{1}{2}\mathbf{q} + \mathbf{p}$

Q3   ABCD is a parallelogram.
The vector $\vec{BA} = \mathbf{n}$ and $\vec{BD} = \mathbf{m}$.
Find $\vec{BC}$ in terms of $\mathbf{n}$ and $\mathbf{m}$.

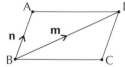

Q4   In the rectangle ABCD, E is the midpoint of AD and F divides DC in the ratio 2:1.

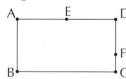

If $\vec{AB} = \mathbf{b}$ and $\vec{AD} = \mathbf{d}$, find the following vectors in terms of $\mathbf{b}$ and $\mathbf{d}$.
a) $\vec{DF}$ b) $\vec{BE}$ c) $\vec{EF}$

Q5 $\overrightarrow{XY} = \mathbf{a}$, $\overrightarrow{XZ} = \mathbf{b}$. P is the midpoint of $\overrightarrow{YZ}$, and Q is the midpoint of $\overrightarrow{XY}$.
Show that $\overrightarrow{PQ}$ is parallel to $\overrightarrow{XZ}$.

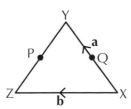

Q6 Given that $\overrightarrow{TU} = \mathbf{v} - \mathbf{w}$ and $\overrightarrow{ST} = 2\mathbf{v} + \mathbf{w}$, show that $\overrightarrow{US}$ is parallel to $\mathbf{v}$.

Q7 Given that $\overrightarrow{XY} = 3\mathbf{a} - 4\mathbf{b} + 2\mathbf{c}$ and $\overrightarrow{XZ} = \mathbf{a} - 2\mathbf{b} - 2\mathbf{c}$, show that $\overrightarrow{YZ}$ is parallel to $\mathbf{a} - \mathbf{b} + 2\mathbf{c}$.

Collinear points

Three or more points are **collinear** if they all lie on a **single straight line**.

If vectors $\overrightarrow{AB}$ and $\overrightarrow{BC}$ are **parallel**, then the points A, B and C must lie on a straight line, i.e. they are **collinear**.

 Example $\overrightarrow{AP} = \mathbf{m}$, $\overrightarrow{AQ} = \mathbf{m} + 2\mathbf{n}$, $\overrightarrow{AR} = \mathbf{m} + 6\mathbf{n}$. Show that P, Q and R are collinear.

Sketch a diagram. Use the diagram to find $\overrightarrow{PQ}$ and $\overrightarrow{QR}$:

$\overrightarrow{PQ} = -\overrightarrow{AP} + \overrightarrow{AQ} = -\mathbf{m} + \mathbf{m} + 2\mathbf{n} = 2\mathbf{n}$

$\overrightarrow{QR} = -\overrightarrow{AQ} + \overrightarrow{AR} = -\mathbf{m} - 2\mathbf{n} + \mathbf{m} + 6\mathbf{n}$
$\qquad = 4\mathbf{n} = 2(2\mathbf{n}) = 2(\overrightarrow{PQ})$

$\overrightarrow{QR}$ is a scalar multiple of $\overrightarrow{PQ}$ so the vectors are parallel, meaning the points **P, Q and R lie on a straight line**.

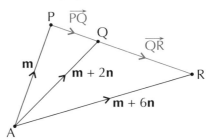

Exercise 1.3

Q1 $\overrightarrow{XY} = \mathbf{t} + \mathbf{u}$, $\overrightarrow{AY} = -\mathbf{t}$, $\overrightarrow{AZ} = \mathbf{u}$. Show that X, Y and Z are collinear.

Q2 $\overrightarrow{OA} = \mathbf{a}$, $\overrightarrow{OB} = \mathbf{b}$, $\overrightarrow{OC} = 5\mathbf{a} - 4\mathbf{b}$. Show that A, B and C are collinear.

Q3 $\overrightarrow{PQ} = -(\mathbf{m} + \frac{9}{2}\mathbf{n})$, $\overrightarrow{PR} = \mathbf{m} - \frac{3}{2}\mathbf{n}$, $\overrightarrow{PS} = 2\mathbf{m}$.
Show that Q, R and S are collinear.

Q4 In the diagram on the right, $\overrightarrow{OB} = 4\mathbf{a}$, $\overrightarrow{AB} = 2\mathbf{b}$, $\overrightarrow{BD} = 4\mathbf{a} - \mathbf{b}$ and $\overrightarrow{DC} = -\frac{5}{2}\mathbf{b} - \mathbf{a}$. Show that OAC is a straight line.

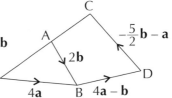

Q5 ABCD is a quadrilateral. X is the midpoint of the line AC.
$\overrightarrow{DA} = \mathbf{a} - \mathbf{b}$, $\overrightarrow{AB} = 3\mathbf{a} - 2\mathbf{b}$ and $\overrightarrow{XC} = \mathbf{a}$. Is DXB a straight line?
Give reasons for your answer.

PROBLEM SOLVING

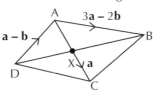

Position vectors

A **position vector** $\overrightarrow{OA}$ describes the **position** of a point A in relation to the origin O.

You can write the vector from one point
to another in terms of their position vectors: $\overrightarrow{AB} = -\overrightarrow{OA} + \overrightarrow{OB} = \overrightarrow{OB} - \overrightarrow{OA} = \mathbf{b} - \mathbf{a}$

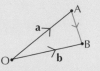

Expressing vectors as components

A **unit vector** is any vector with a **length of 1 unit**. The vectors **i** and **j** are **standard unit vectors** — **i** is in the direction of the **positive x-axis**, and **j** is in the direction of the **positive y-axis**.

All vectors in two dimensions are made up of **horizontal** and **vertical** components, so you can express them as a sum of **i** and **j** unit vectors, e.g. $4\mathbf{i} + 3\mathbf{j}$.

Column vectors can also be used to show these components of a vector — $x\mathbf{i} + y\mathbf{j} = \begin{pmatrix} x \\ y \end{pmatrix}$.

 The coordinate grid on the right shows points A and B.

a) Write down the position vectors of A and B in i + j form.

- Point A lies 5 units to the right and 7 units above the origin. $\overrightarrow{OA} = 5\mathbf{i} + 7\mathbf{j}$

- Point B lies 4 units to the right and 1 units above the origin. $\overrightarrow{OB} = 4\mathbf{i} + \mathbf{j}$

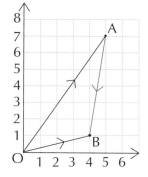

b) Hence find $\overrightarrow{AB}$ in terms of i and j.

- You know that $\overrightarrow{AB} = -\overrightarrow{OA} + \overrightarrow{OB} = \overrightarrow{OB} - \overrightarrow{OA}$

- Add or subtract the **i** and **j** components separately. $\overrightarrow{AB} = (4\mathbf{i} + \mathbf{j}) - (5\mathbf{i} + 7\mathbf{j}) = -\mathbf{i} - 6\mathbf{j}$

c) Write $\overrightarrow{AB}$ as a column vector.

- To write a vector in column form, remember that $x\mathbf{i} + y\mathbf{j} = \begin{pmatrix} x \\ y \end{pmatrix}$. $-\mathbf{i} - 6\mathbf{j} = \begin{pmatrix} -1 \\ -6 \end{pmatrix}$

Exercise 1.4

Q1 On a map, Jack's house has coordinates (2, 3) and his school has coordinates (4, −5). Write down the position vectors of Jack's house and school as column vectors.

Q2 Given that $\mathbf{a} = \begin{pmatrix} -1 \\ -2 \end{pmatrix}$, $\mathbf{b} = \begin{pmatrix} 3 \\ -2 \end{pmatrix}$ and $\mathbf{c} = \begin{pmatrix} 4 \\ 3 \end{pmatrix}$, calculate the following:

a) $\mathbf{a} + \mathbf{b} + \mathbf{c}$ b) $\mathbf{c} - 2\mathbf{b}$ c) $3\mathbf{a} - \mathbf{b} + 2\mathbf{c}$ d) $5\mathbf{a} - 5\mathbf{c}$

Q3 C has position vector $-\mathbf{i} + 2\mathbf{j}$ and D has position vector $4\mathbf{i} - 3\mathbf{j}$.

a) What are the Cartesian coordinates of the points C and D?

b) Write the vectors $\overrightarrow{CD}$ and $\overrightarrow{DC}$ in **i** and **j** vector form.

Q4 Given that $\mathbf{p} = \begin{pmatrix} -1 \\ -2 \end{pmatrix}$, $\mathbf{q} = \begin{pmatrix} 3 \\ -2 \end{pmatrix}$ and $\mathbf{r} = \begin{pmatrix} -4 \\ 5 \end{pmatrix}$, show that $\mathbf{p} + 3\mathbf{q} + \mathbf{r}$ is parallel to $12\mathbf{i} - 9\mathbf{j}$.

Q5   ABCD is a square. A has position vector –4**i** + 6**j**, C has position vector 3**i** – **j**.
        Find the position vectors of B and D.

Q6   M is the midpoint of the line PQ, where P has position vector –3**i** + **j**
        and M has position vector 2**i** – 5**j**. What is the position vector of Q?

Q7   Triangle ABC is shown below. Find the vectors $\overrightarrow{AB}$, $\overrightarrow{BC}$ and $\overrightarrow{CA}$
        in terms of unit vectors **i** and **j**.

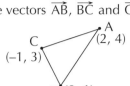

Q8   A robotic vacuum cleaner models a room using a quadrilateral DEFG,
        with vertices at the points D (–7, –2), E (–3, –1), F (–1, 5) and G (–3, 10).

        a) Give the column vectors for the room's walls $\overrightarrow{DE}$, $\overrightarrow{EF}$, $\overrightarrow{FG}$ and $\overrightarrow{GD}$.
        b) The vacuum cleaner follows the wall from D to E, then E to F. Give a single column
           vector that the vacuum cleaner could have followed to get from D to F more efficiently.

Q9   PQR is a triangle. Given that $\overrightarrow{OQ} = \begin{pmatrix} 3 \\ 3 \end{pmatrix}$, $\overrightarrow{OP} = \begin{pmatrix} 3 \\ 0 \end{pmatrix}$ and $\overrightarrow{PR} = \begin{pmatrix} 4 \\ 7 \end{pmatrix}$,

        find the Cartesian coordinates of R and give the vector $\overrightarrow{QR}$.

2. Calculating with Vectors

Magnitude of a vector

The **magnitude** (or **modulus**) $|\mathbf{a}|$ of a vector **a** is the distance between its start point and end point.
It's calculated using Pythagoras's Theorem.

To find a **unit vector** in the direction of a vector you just **divide** the vector by its **magnitude.**

So the unit vector in the direction of the vector **a** is: $\frac{1}{|\mathbf{a}|}\mathbf{a} = \frac{\mathbf{a}}{|\mathbf{a}|}$.

Example   **Find the magnitude of the vector a = 5i + 3j.**

1. You know the length of two sides of the right-angled triangle
   formed by **a** and its horizontal and vertical components.

2. So find $|\mathbf{a}|$ using Pythagoras. $\longrightarrow$ $|\mathbf{a}| = \sqrt{5^2 + 3^2} = \sqrt{34} = \mathbf{5.83}$ (3 s.f.)

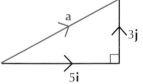

Exercise 2.1

Q1   Find the exact magnitude of the following vectors:

    a) 6**i** + 8**j**   b) 12**i** – 5**j**   c) $\begin{pmatrix} 2 \\ 4 \end{pmatrix}$ d) $\begin{pmatrix} -3 \\ -1 \end{pmatrix}$ e) $\begin{pmatrix} 24 \\ -7 \end{pmatrix}$ f) $\begin{pmatrix} -\sqrt{13} \\ 6 \end{pmatrix}$

    g) 3**i** + $\sqrt{7}$**j**   h) –7**j**   i) $\begin{pmatrix} \sqrt{2} \\ -\sqrt{3} \end{pmatrix}$ j) 3(2**i** + $\sqrt{5}$**j**)   k) **a** = $\begin{pmatrix} 2 \\ -1 \end{pmatrix}$ + 2$\begin{pmatrix} -3 \\ 1 \end{pmatrix}$

Q2   S has position vector 10**i** + 5**j**. Find the exact length of the line that joins point S to the origin.

Q3   For each of the following pairs of points, find the distance between them using position vectors:
a) (0, 1) and (2, 2)   b) (–3, 2) and (4, 3)   c) (–1, –1) and (0, 4)

Q4   For each of the pairs of vectors given below, find the exact magnitude of the resultant when the two vectors are added together.

a) **a** = 2**i** + **j** and **b** = 2**i** – 4**j**   b) **u** = –5**i** + **j** and **v** = 9**i** – 5**j**   c) **f** = $\begin{pmatrix} 7 \\ 2 \end{pmatrix}$ and **g** = $\begin{pmatrix} 17 \\ -12 \end{pmatrix}$

d) **d** = $\begin{pmatrix} 4 \\ -2 \end{pmatrix}$ and **e** = $\begin{pmatrix} -1 \\ -4 \end{pmatrix}$ e) **s** = 3**i** – 4**j** and **t** = –(3**i** + **j**)   f) **w** = $\begin{pmatrix} -3 \\ -5 \end{pmatrix}$ and **x** = $\begin{pmatrix} -6 \\ 5 \end{pmatrix}$

Q5   For each of the following vectors, give the unit vector in the same direction

a) 3**i**   b) $\begin{pmatrix} 1 \\ 2 \end{pmatrix}$ c) 5**i** – 4**j**   d) $\begin{pmatrix} -2 \\ -6 \end{pmatrix}$

Q6 $\overrightarrow{AB}$ = 3**i** – 2**j** and $\overrightarrow{BC}$ = **i** + 5**j**. Find the unit vector in the direction of $\overrightarrow{AC}$.

Q7   Point A has position vector 2**i** – **j**, and point B has position vector 7**i** – 13**j**. Find the unit vector in the direction of $\overrightarrow{BA}$.

Q8 $\overrightarrow{OP} = \begin{pmatrix} 3 \\ 5 \end{pmatrix}$, $\overrightarrow{OQ} = \begin{pmatrix} -2 \\ b \end{pmatrix}$. Given that $|\overrightarrow{PQ}| = \sqrt{29}$ and $|\overrightarrow{OQ}| = \sqrt{13}$, find b.

Direction of a vector

The **direction** of a vector **a** is the **angle** between a line parallel to the x-axis and **a**. It is usually measured **anticlockwise** from the positive x-axis.

If you know the **i** and **j** components of a vector, then you can find the direction of the vector by using **trigonometry**.

Examples   a) **The diagram shows the vector a = 2i + 3j. Find the direction of the vector.**

1. The vector forms the hypotenuse of a right-angled triangle of height 3 units and base width 2 units.

2. Use trigonometry to find the angle θ.
$\tan \theta = \frac{3}{2} \Rightarrow \theta = \tan^{-1}\left(\frac{3}{2}\right) = \mathbf{56.3°}$ (1 d.p.)

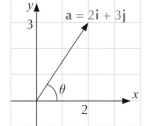

b) **Find the direction of the vector** $\begin{pmatrix} -3 \\ -2 \end{pmatrix}$.

1. Draw a diagram. The vector forms the hypotenuse of a triangle with height 2 units and base 3 units.

2. Use trigonometry to find the angle θ.
$\tan \theta = \frac{2}{3} \Rightarrow \theta = \tan^{-1}\left(\frac{2}{3}\right) = 33.690...°$

3. The direction is measured anticlockwise from the positive x-axis, so add an extra 180° onto θ:
$180° + \tan^{-1}\left(\frac{2}{3}\right) = \mathbf{213.7°}$ (1 d.p.)

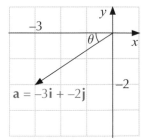

Similarly, if you know the **magnitude** and **direction** of a vector then you can use **trigonometry** to calculate its horizontal and vertical components.

Tip: This is how to convert a vector from **magnitude/direction form** to **component form**.

Example Given a vector **v** = a**i** + b**j**, with direction 30° and magnitude | **v** | = 5, calculate a and b.

Using trigonometry, find a and b:

$\cos 30° = \dfrac{a}{5}$ so $a = 5 \cos 30°$

$\sin 30° = \dfrac{b}{5}$ so $b = 5 \sin 30°$

So, **v** = (5 cos 30°)**i** + (5 sin 30°)**j** = $\dfrac{5\sqrt{3}}{2}$ **i** + $\dfrac{5}{2}$ **j**

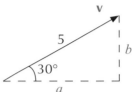

Exercise 2.2

Q1 Find the direction of the following vectors to 2 d.p:

a) 6**i** + 8**j**   b) 12**i** – 5**j**   c) $\begin{pmatrix} 2 \\ 4 \end{pmatrix}$ d) $\begin{pmatrix} -3 \\ -1 \end{pmatrix}$ e) $\begin{pmatrix} 24 \\ -7 \end{pmatrix}$

f) $\begin{pmatrix} -\sqrt{13} \\ 6 \end{pmatrix}$ g) 3**i** + $\sqrt{7}$ **j**   h) –7**j**   i) 3**i** – 2**j**   j) $\begin{pmatrix} -7 \\ -6 \end{pmatrix}$

Q2 By finding the horizontal and vertical components, express the following vectors in exact **i**, **j** form:

a) **a** has direction 45° and magnitude $\sqrt{2}$.   b) **b** has direction 60° and magnitude $\sqrt{7}$.

c) **c** has direction 33° and magnitude 3.   d) **d** has direction 76° and magnitude 5.

e) **e** has direction 117° and magnitude 6.   f) **f** has direction 155° and magnitude 7.

Q3 Vector **s** is parallel to **t**. Given that **t** has direction 60° and | **s** | = $\sqrt{38}$, express **s** in exact **i**, **j** form.

Q4 Given that **a** = $\begin{pmatrix} -5 \\ 2 \end{pmatrix}$ and **h** = $\begin{pmatrix} 2 \\ 2 \end{pmatrix}$, find the magnitude and direction of **a** + **b** to one decimal place.

Q5 The vector **c** has the same direction as vector **d**. Given that **d** = 8**i** – 6**j** and |**c**| = 70, find vector **c**.

Q6 The vector **q** = 5**i** + y**j** and has direction 44°. Find |**q**| to 2 d.p.

Q7 The vector **v** = x**i** – 4**j** makes an angle of 51° below the x-axis. Find |**v**| to 2 d.p.

Q8 The quadrilateral ABCD is used to model a plane's flight path as it circles near an airport.

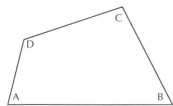

$\overrightarrow{OA}$ = **i** + **j**, $\overrightarrow{OB}$ = 11**i** + **j**, $\overrightarrow{OC}$ = 8**i** + 7**j** and $\overrightarrow{OD}$ = 2**i** + 5**j**, where **i** and **j** have a length of one kilometre. Calculate, to the nearest km, the distance the plane travels if it circles three times.

Angle between two vectors

The **angle between** two vectors **a** and **b** can be calculated by constructing a triangle with **a** and **b** as two of its sides and using the **cosine rule**.

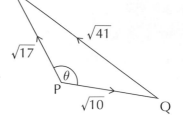

Example   **Find the angle θ between the vectors $\overrightarrow{PQ} = 3\mathbf{i} - \mathbf{j}$ and $\overrightarrow{PR} = -\mathbf{i} + 4\mathbf{j}$.**

1. $\overrightarrow{PQ}$ and $\overrightarrow{PR}$ form two sides of a triangle PQR.

2. Calculate the length of these sides.
$$|\overrightarrow{PQ}| = \sqrt{3^2 + (-1)^2} = \sqrt{10} \text{ and } |\overrightarrow{PR}| = \sqrt{(-1)^2 + 4^2} = \sqrt{17}.$$

3. Work out the other side of the triangle using known vectors.
$$\overrightarrow{QR} = \overrightarrow{PR} - \overrightarrow{PQ} = -\mathbf{i} + 4\mathbf{j} - (3\mathbf{i} - \mathbf{j}) = -4\mathbf{i} + 5\mathbf{j}$$
Its length is $|\overrightarrow{QR}| = \sqrt{(-4)^2 + 5^2} = \sqrt{41}$.

4. Use the cosine rule to find angle θ.
$$\cos\theta = \frac{(\sqrt{10})^2 + (\sqrt{17})^2 - (\sqrt{41})^2}{2 \times \sqrt{17} \times \sqrt{10}} = \frac{-14}{2\sqrt{170}} = \frac{-7}{\sqrt{170}}. \text{ So, } \theta = \cos^{-1}\left(\frac{-7}{\sqrt{170}}\right) = \mathbf{122.5°} \text{ (1 d.p.)}$$

Exercise 2.3

Q1   Find, to 2 d.p., the angles between the following pairs of vectors:

   a) $\mathbf{a} = \mathbf{i} + \mathbf{j}$ and $\mathbf{b} = -\mathbf{i} + 2\mathbf{j}$ b) $\mathbf{c} = 3\mathbf{i} - 2\mathbf{j}$ and $\mathbf{d} = -2\mathbf{i}$ c) $\mathbf{e} = \mathbf{i} - 3\mathbf{j}$ and $\mathbf{f} = 2\mathbf{i} + \mathbf{j}$

   d) $\mathbf{g} = \begin{pmatrix} 7 \\ -1 \end{pmatrix}$ and $\mathbf{h} = \begin{pmatrix} -3 \\ -2 \end{pmatrix}$ e) $\mathbf{k} = \begin{pmatrix} \sqrt{2} \\ -1 \end{pmatrix}$ and $\mathbf{l} = \begin{pmatrix} -4 \\ 2 \end{pmatrix}$ f) $\mathbf{m} = \begin{pmatrix} -2 \\ \sqrt{3} \end{pmatrix}$ and $\mathbf{n} = \begin{pmatrix} 5 \\ 4 \end{pmatrix}$

Q2   Two boats set off from a harbour. Each boat's course is modelled by a vector.

   Boat A's course is given by the column vector $\mathbf{a} = \begin{pmatrix} 3 \\ 3 \end{pmatrix}$.

   Boat B's course is given by the column vector $\mathbf{b} = \begin{pmatrix} -2 \\ 5 \end{pmatrix}$.

   What is the angle between the two boats' courses? Give your answer to 2 decimal places.

Q3 $|\overrightarrow{AB}| = 12$ and $|\overrightarrow{BC}| = 14$. The angle between vectors $\overrightarrow{AB}$ and $\overrightarrow{BC}$ is 115°. Find $|\overrightarrow{CA}|$ to 2 d.p.

Q4 $|\overrightarrow{EF}| = 2.6$ and $|\overrightarrow{EG}| = 3.3$. The angle between vectors $\overrightarrow{EF}$ and $\overrightarrow{EG}$ is 23°. Find $|\overrightarrow{GF}|$ to 2 d.p.

Q5   A drone's flight is modelled with vectors, as shown on the right.
First it travels along the vector $\mathbf{a} = 4\mathbf{i} + 3\mathbf{j}$. Then it turns left along vector $\mathbf{b}$, at an angle of 110° to **a**.
It returns along vector **c** to where it took off.
Given that $|\mathbf{b}| = 7$ m, find $|\mathbf{c}|$ to 2 d.p.

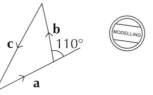

Q6   The diagram to the right shows a parallelogram WXYZ.

   Given that $\overrightarrow{WX} = 2\mathbf{i} + 5\mathbf{j}$, and $\overrightarrow{WZ} = 8\mathbf{i}$, what is angle θ (to 1 d.p.)?

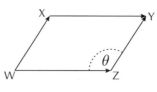

3. Modelling with Vectors

An object's **motion** will have a **magnitude** and **direction**, so can be modelled using vectors:

- **Displacement** is the **distance** an object has travelled in a given **direction**.
- **Velocity** is the **speed** of an object with a **direction**.
- **Acceleration** is the rate at which an object's **velocity changes**.

   a) **The acceleration of a particle is given by the vector a = (6i − 2j) ms⁻².**
Find the magnitude of the acceleration, and the angle this
vector makes with the horizontal axis.

1. Draw a diagram.

2. Use Pythagoras' theorem to find the magnitude:
   $|\mathbf{a}| = \sqrt{6^2 + (-2)^2} = \sqrt{40} = $ **6.32** ms⁻² (3 s.f.)

3. Use trigonometry to find the angle θ:
   $\tan \theta = \dfrac{2}{6} \Rightarrow \theta = \tan^{-1}\left(\dfrac{2}{6}\right) = $ **18.4°** (3 s.f.)

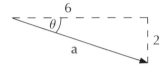

b) **A ship travels 75 km on a bearing of 140°. Express the ship's**
displacement from its starting position as a column vector.

1. Draw a diagram. This shows you that the
   angle **d** makes with the positive x-axis is 50°.

2. Using trigonometry:
   $\cos 50° = \dfrac{x}{75} \Rightarrow x = 75 \cos 50° = 48.21$ (to 2 d.p.)
   $\sin 50° = \dfrac{y}{75} \Rightarrow y = 75 \sin 50° = 57.45$ (to 2 d.p.)

3. The vertical component of the vector is negative, so: $\mathbf{d} = \begin{pmatrix} 48.21 \\ -57.45 \end{pmatrix}$ km

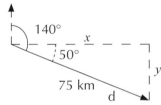

Exercise 3.1

Q1 The acceleration of various particles are given by the vectors below.
Calculate the exact magnitude of each particle's acceleration.
- a) $\mathbf{a} = (\mathbf{i} + 2\mathbf{j})$ ms⁻²
- b) $\mathbf{b} = (-\mathbf{i} - \mathbf{j})$ ms⁻²
- c) $\mathbf{c} = (3\mathbf{i} + 2\mathbf{j})$ ms⁻²
- d) $\mathbf{d} = (-2\mathbf{i} + 3\mathbf{j})$ ms⁻²

Q2 The velocity of a fish swimming in the horizontal plane is modelled by the vector $\mathbf{v} = 2t(2\mathbf{i} - \mathbf{j})$ ms⁻¹.
- a) State the fish's velocity after 2 seconds.
- b) Calculate the fish's exact speed after 3 seconds.
- c) Find the angle that $\mathbf{v}$ makes with $\mathbf{i}$.

Q3 A firework's displacement is modelled by the vector $\mathbf{s} = 2t^2(-\mathbf{i} + 7\mathbf{j})$ m,
where t is time in seconds, $\mathbf{i}$ is horizontal and $\mathbf{j}$ is vertical (pointing upwards).
- a) Find the firework's displacement after 1.5 seconds.
- b) Calculate, to 3 s.f., the firework's angle to the horizontal.

The firework explodes after 2.5 seconds.
- c) What is the firework's vertical distance from the ground when it goes off?

Q4 A roller coaster is accelerating at 30 m/s⁻² at an angle of 35° below the positive horizontal. Express this acceleration as a vector of the form $\mathbf{a} = x\mathbf{i} + y\mathbf{j}$.

Q5 A simple mathematical model of a ball bouncing off the side of a pool table is constructed using vectors. The ball's velocity has vector $\mathbf{v_1} = \begin{pmatrix} 3 \\ -2 \end{pmatrix}$ before it hits the side, and vector $\mathbf{v_2} = \begin{pmatrix} 1 \\ 3 \end{pmatrix}$ afterwards. Find the acute angle θ between $\mathbf{v_1}$ and $\mathbf{v_2}$. Give your answer to 2 d.p.

The effect of **two forces** working together can also be modelled by vectors.

These two vectors will often form a triangle **without** a **right angle**, so you will need to use the **sine rule** and **cosine rule** (see p.66) for the trigonometry involved.

 Two tug boats are pulling a ship with an angle of 30° between them. One tug boat exerts a force of 10 kN and is modelled with vector a. The other boat exerts a force of 12 kN and is modelled with vector b.

The resultant force on the ship, r, is the resultant vector of these two forces. Calculate the size of the resultant force.

1. $\mathbf{r}$ is the resultant of $\mathbf{a}$ and $\mathbf{b}$, so $\mathbf{r} = \mathbf{a} + \mathbf{b}$. Draw the vectors end to end.

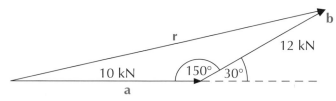

2. Use trigonometry to calculate the size of $\mathbf{r}$.

The angle opposite $\mathbf{r}$ is $180° - 30° = 150°$

Using the cosine rule: $|\mathbf{r}|^2 = 10^2 + 12^2 - (2 \times 10 \times 12 \times \cos 150°) = 244 - 240 \cos 150°$

$|\mathbf{r}| = \sqrt{244 - 240 \cos 150°} = \mathbf{21.3\ kN}$ (3 s.f.)

Exercise 3.2

Q1 An aircraft tries to fly due north at 600 km/h, but there is a wind from the west at 75 km/h. The aircraft's actual course is modelled by the resultant of these two vectors. Calculate:

a) the actual bearing the plane is flying on to the nearest degree.

b) the aircraft's resultant speed in km/h (to 2 d.p.).

Q2 Two lumberjacks are pulling ropes attached to a tree. The angle between the ropes is 100°. One lumberjack exerts a force of 250 N and the other exerts a force of 210 N. The resultant force $\mathbf{f}$ is modelled by the resultant of these two vectors. Calculate the magnitude of $\mathbf{f}$.

Q3 Ray is attempting to paddle his canoe due north at 4 ms⁻¹, but there is a current travelling west at 3 ms⁻¹. Ray's actual course is modelled by the resultant of these two vectors. Calculate:

a) The actual bearing Ray is travelling on.

b) Ray's resultant speed in ms⁻¹.

Vectors can be used to model **lines** and the **sides of polygons** when investigating problems in geometry.

Tip: 'X divides BC in the ratio 2:5' means X is $\frac{2}{7}$ of the way from B to C.

'X divides CB in the ratio 2:5' would mean X is $\frac{2}{7}$ of the way from C to B.

 The routes from Ayeside to Beesville ($\overrightarrow{AB}$) and to Ceeston ($\overrightarrow{AC}$) are modelled by the vectors **p** and **q** respectively. Xander's house lies between Beesville and Ceeston such that its position, X, divides the line BC in the ratio 2:5.

Find the vector $\overrightarrow{AX}$ in terms of p and q.

1. $\overrightarrow{AX} = \overrightarrow{AB} + \overrightarrow{BX}$. You know $\overrightarrow{AB} = \mathbf{p}$, so you just need to find $\overrightarrow{BX}$ in terms of **p** and **q**.

2. X divides BC in the ratio 2:5, so BX is $\frac{2}{2+5} = \frac{2}{7}$ of BC:

   $\overrightarrow{BX} = \frac{2}{7}\overrightarrow{BC}$

3. Now find $\overrightarrow{BC}$ in terms of **p** and **q**:

   $\overrightarrow{BC} = \overrightarrow{BA} + \overrightarrow{AC} = -\overrightarrow{AB} + \overrightarrow{AC} = -\mathbf{p} + \mathbf{q}$

4. Plugging all this back into your equation for $\overrightarrow{AX}$ gives:

   $\overrightarrow{AX} = \overrightarrow{AB} + \overrightarrow{BX} = \overrightarrow{AB} + \frac{2}{7}\overrightarrow{BC} = \mathbf{p} + \frac{2}{7}(-\mathbf{p} + \mathbf{q}) = \frac{5}{7}\mathbf{p} + \frac{2}{7}\mathbf{q}$

Exercise 3.3

Q1 The quadrilateral ABCD is used to model a garden.
There is a straight path that crosses the garden.
Its start point divides $\overrightarrow{AB}$ in the ratio 7:3, and it ends at the midpoint of $\overrightarrow{CD}$.

The path is modelled by vector $\mathbf{p} = \begin{pmatrix} x \\ y \end{pmatrix}$.
Calculate x and y.

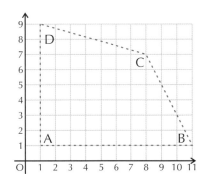

Q2 A park is modelled as a quadrilateral EFGH, with sides given by the following vectors:
$\overrightarrow{EF} = 2\mathbf{i} + 3\mathbf{j}$, $\overrightarrow{FG} = \mathbf{i} - \frac{1}{2}\mathbf{j}$, $\overrightarrow{GH} = -\mathbf{i} - \frac{3}{2}\mathbf{j}$ and $\overrightarrow{HE} = -2\mathbf{i} - \mathbf{j}$.

Show that the park is a trapezium.

Q3 The position vectors of the vertices of the parallelogram PQRS are:
$\overrightarrow{OP} = 2\mathbf{i} + 3\mathbf{j}$, $\overrightarrow{OQ} = 7\mathbf{i} + 4\mathbf{j}$, $\overrightarrow{OR} = 6(\mathbf{i} + \mathbf{j})$ and $\overrightarrow{OS} = \mathbf{i} + 5\mathbf{j}$.

What are the exact lengths of this parallelogram's diagonals?

Q4 In the diagram below, W divides QR in the ratio $a:b$.
Given that $\overrightarrow{PW} = \frac{5}{9}\mathbf{s} + \frac{4}{9}\mathbf{t}$, find a and b.

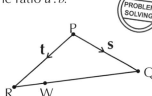

Review Exercise — Chapter 10

Q1 Vectors **a** and **b** are represented by the lines below:

Draw and label sketches that represent the following vectors:

a) –**b** b) 3**a** c) **a** + **b** d) 2**a** – **b**. e) **b** – **a**

Q2 Give two vectors that are parallel to each of the following:

a) 2**a** b) 3**i** + 4**j** c) 3**i** – **j** d) $\begin{pmatrix} 3 \\ 5 \end{pmatrix}$

Q3 $\overrightarrow{XY}$ = 2**b** – **a**, $\overrightarrow{OY}$ = 2**b**, $\overrightarrow{OZ}$ = 2(**a** – **b**). Show that X, Y and Z are collinear.

Q4 $\overrightarrow{OA}$ = 3**p**, $\overrightarrow{OB}$ = **q**, $\overrightarrow{OC}$ = 4**q** – 9**p**. Show that A, B and C are collinear.

Q5 Using the diagram on the right find these vectors in terms of vectors **a**, **b** and **c**.

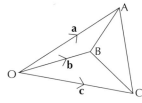

a) $\overrightarrow{AB}$ b) $\overrightarrow{BA}$ c) $\overrightarrow{CB}$ d) $\overrightarrow{AC}$

Q6 CDEFGH is a regular hexagon whose centre is O.

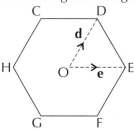

If $\overrightarrow{OE}$ = **e** and $\overrightarrow{OD}$ = **d**, express in terms of **e** and **d**:

a) $\overrightarrow{HE}$ b) $\overrightarrow{DG}$ c) $\overrightarrow{ED}$ d) $\overrightarrow{CE}$ e) $\overrightarrow{DF}$

Q7 Give, in **i** and **j** form, the position vectors of the following points:

a) (2, –4) b) (–1, –2) c) (5, 7) d) (–8, –6) e) (3, –7)

Q8 X is the point (6, –1) and Y is the point (–4, 7).
Write the vectors $\overrightarrow{XO}$ and $\overrightarrow{YO}$ in **i** and **j** form and in column vector form.

Q9 Find **a** + 2**b** – 3**c** where **a** = 3**i** + 7**j**, **b** = –2**i** + 2**j**, and **c** = **i** – 3**j**.

Q10 Given that $\mathbf{d} = \begin{pmatrix} 3 \\ 2 \end{pmatrix}$, $\mathbf{e} = \begin{pmatrix} -1 \\ -2 \end{pmatrix}$, and $\mathbf{f} = \begin{pmatrix} 3 \\ -1 \end{pmatrix}$, find the following vectors:

a) $2\mathbf{d} - \mathbf{f}$ b) $\mathbf{d} - \mathbf{e} - \mathbf{f}$ c) $\mathbf{f} - 3\mathbf{d} + \mathbf{e}$ d) $-2\mathbf{e} + \mathbf{d} - \mathbf{f}$

Q11 R has position vector $\begin{pmatrix} 3 \\ -1 \end{pmatrix}$ and S has position vector $\begin{pmatrix} -5 \\ -7 \end{pmatrix}$. Find the magnitude of $\overrightarrow{RS}$.

Q12 a) On a grid, draw the vectors $\mathbf{u} = 2\mathbf{i} - \mathbf{j}$ and $\mathbf{v} = -\mathbf{i} - \mathbf{j}$.

b) Draw the following vectors:

(i) $2\mathbf{u}$ (ii) $-\mathbf{v}$ (iii) $\mathbf{v} - \mathbf{u}$ (iv) $2(\mathbf{u} + \mathbf{v})$

c) Find the magnitude of $\mathbf{u}$.

d) Find the direction of $2(\mathbf{u} + \mathbf{v})$.

Q13 If $\mathbf{p} = 5\mathbf{i} - 12\mathbf{j}$ and vector $\mathbf{q}$ is parallel to $\mathbf{p}$ with magnitude 65, find the vector $\mathbf{q}$.

Q14 A has position vector $\begin{pmatrix} 2 \\ -3 \end{pmatrix}$ and B has position vector $\begin{pmatrix} x \\ 1 \end{pmatrix}$.
Given that $|\overrightarrow{AB}| = 5$, and the direction of $\overrightarrow{OB}$ is less than $90°$, find x.

Q15 $\mathbf{v} = 4\mathbf{i} - 6\mathbf{j}$ and $\mathbf{u} = -\mathbf{i} - 3\mathbf{j}$. Find the angle between $\mathbf{v}$ and $\mathbf{u}$ to two decimal places.

Q16 A man wants to swim across a river. The current is flowing at 1.8 ms⁻¹ parallel to the riverbank. Find the speed and direction that he needs to swim at for his resultant speed to be 1.2 ms⁻¹ perpendicular to the riverbank.

Q17 A girl cycles along a bearing of 171° with speed 16 kmh⁻¹. Find her velocity in terms of $\mathbf{i}$ and $\mathbf{j}$, where $\mathbf{i}$ and $\mathbf{j}$ are the unit vectors directed due east and due north respectively.

Q18 The position vectors of the vertices of the quadrilateral ABCD are:
$\overrightarrow{OA} = \mathbf{i} - \mathbf{j}$, $\overrightarrow{OB} = -4\mathbf{j}$, $\overrightarrow{OC} = 4\mathbf{i} - 2\mathbf{j}$ and $\overrightarrow{OD} = 3\mathbf{i} + \mathbf{j}$.
What are the exact lengths of this quadrilateral's diagonals?

Q19 STU is a triangle, where $\overrightarrow{ST} = 4\mathbf{a}$ and $\overrightarrow{UT} = 3\mathbf{b} - \mathbf{a}$.
Point M is the midpoint of line ST and point P divides line SU in the ratio 3:1.
Find the vector $\overrightarrow{PM}$ in terms of $\mathbf{a}$ and $\mathbf{b}$.

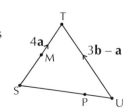

Chapter 11 — Sampling, Data Presentation and Interpretation

Everything in statistics focuses on data. This chapter covers methods of collecting data, ways of presenting it graphically and how to interpret your findings and draw conclusions.

1. Populations and Sampling

For any statistical investigation, there will be a **group** of something (e.g. people, items, animals, etc.) that you want to **find out about**. This **whole group** is called the **population**. Populations are **finite** if the members are **countable** (in practice, not just in theory), and **infinite** if they are **uncountable**.

To collect information about your population, you can carry out a **survey**. This means **questioning** the people or **examining** the items.

Censuses and Sampling

When you collect information from **every member** of a population, it's called a **census** — it's a **survey** of the **whole population**. It's easier to carry out if the population is fairly **small** and **easily accessible**.

<u>Advantage</u>	<u>Disadvantages</u>
It's an **accurate representation** of the population because every member has been surveyed — it's **unbiased**.	• For **large** populations, it takes a lot of **time** and **effort** (and possibly **money**) to carry out.
	• It can be difficult to make sure **all** members are surveyed. If some are missed, the survey may be **biased**.
	• If the tested items are **used up** or **damaged** in some way by doing a census, a census is **impractical**.

If doing a census is **impossible** or **impractical**, you can find out about a population by questioning or examining a **selected group** of the people or items — called a **sample**.

<u>Advantages</u>	<u>Disadvantages</u>
• Sample surveys are **quicker** and **cheaper** than a census, and it's easier to get hold of all the required information.	• Each possible sample will give **different** results, so you could just happen to select one which doesn't **accurately reflect** the population.
• It's the only option when surveyed items are **used up** or **damaged**.	• Samples can easily be affected by sampling bias.

It's important that the sample is as similar to the population as possible so that it is **representative**. Otherwise, it may be **biased**, and conclusions about the population based on your sample may not be correct.

To avoid sampling bias:

• Select from the **correct population** and make sure no member of the population is **excluded**.

• Select your sample at **random** — if members are linked in some way, it can cause bias.

• Make sure all your sample members **respond**.

Exercise 1.1

Q1 For each population described say whether it is finite or infinite.

    a) The grains of sand on a beach.   b) The 2016 Olympic gold medallists.

    c) The stars in the Milky Way galaxy.   d) The cells in a human body.

    e) The members of the Ulverston Musical Appreciation Society.

    f) The jalapeño chilli plants on sale at Church Lane Garden Centre.

Q2 Members of a local book club have to be consulted about the next book they'll read.

    a) What is the population?   b) Explain whether a census or a sample survey should be used.

Q3 For each situation below, explain whether a census or a sample survey should be done:

    a) Marcel is in charge of a packaging department of 8 people.
       He wants to know the average number of items a person packs per day.

    b) A toy manufacturer produces batches of 500 toys. As part of a safety check,
       they want to test the toys to work out the strength needed to pull them apart.

    c) Tara has a biased dice. She wants to find the proportion of dice rolls that will result in a 'three'.

Q4 Pooja is doing a survey on whether people buy ethically-sourced products. She asked her mother to hand out questionnaires to 20 of her friends. Why might this sample be biased?

Sampling Methods

Simple random sampling

Simple random sampling is where every person or item in the population has an **equal chance** of being in the sample, and each selection is **independent** of the others.

To choose a simple random sample:	

To choose a simple random sample:

- Give a **number** to each population **member**, from a **full list** of the population.

- Generate a list of **random numbers** and **match** them to the numbered members to select your sample.

Advantage

Every member of the population has an **equal chance** of being selected, so it's **completely unbiased**.

Disadvantage

It can be **inconvenient** if the population is spread over a **large area** — it might be difficult to track down the selected members (e.g. in a nationwide sample).

 A zoo has 80 cotton-top tamarins. Describe how the random-number table given could be used to select a sample of five of them, for a study on tail lengths.

8330	3992	1840
0330	1290	3237
9165	4815	0766

1. Draw up a list of the 80 cotton-top tamarins, and give each tamarin a unique 2-digit number between 01 and 80.

2. Use the random-number table to choose five numbers.
    Five random numbers can be chosen by reading off every two digits that give a unique number between 01 and 80.
    The first five numbers are: ~~83~~ (too big), 30, 39, ~~92~~ (too big), 18, 40, 03

3. Select the cotton-top tamarins with the numbers **30, 39, 18, 40** and **03**.

Systematic sampling

Systematic sampling selects **every n^{th} member** from the population you're investigating.

To choose a systematic sample:	Advantages
• **Number** each member of the population from a **full list**. • Calculate a **regular interval** to use by dividing the population size by the sample size. • Generate a **random** starting point to choose the **first member** of your sample. • Keep **adding** the interval to the starting point to select your sample.	• It can be used for quality control on a production line — a **machine** can be set up to sample every n^{th} item. • It should give an **unbiased sample**. **Disadvantage** If the interval coincides with a **pattern** in the population, the sample could be biased.

Example

50 000 fans attended a football match. Describe how systematic sampling could be used to select a sample of 100 people.

1. Give each fan a 5-digit number between 00 001 and 50 000.

2. 50 000 ÷ 100 = 500, so select every 500th fan.

3. Use a calculator to randomly generate a starting point between 1 and 500.

4. Keep adding 500 to the starting point to find the rest of the sample.

     E.g. if 239 is randomly generated, then select the fans numbered:
          00 239, 00 739, 01 239, ... , 48 739, 49 239, 49 739

Exercise 1.2

Q1   The animals in a zoo are given a unique 3-digit ID number between 001 and 500. Describe how you could use a random number generator to choose a simple random sample of 20 of the zoo's animals.

Q2   A teacher wants to interview a sample of 10 students from his school of 700 students.
      He picks 10 classes at random, and then selects a random student from within each class.

      a) Explain why this is not a simple random sample.

      b) The teacher has a list of every student in the school, sorted by age.
         Describe how he could use this list to select a systematic sample of 10 students.

      c) Give an advantage of the sampling method described in part b) over his original sampling method.

Q3   All dogs which are admitted to the Graymar Animal Sanctuary are microchipped with a unique identification number. 108 of the dogs at the sanctuary were admitted between 2015 and 2016.
      A sample of 12 of these dogs is selected for long-term monitoring.

      a) What is the population?

      b) Explain how to select this sample using: (i) simple random sampling   (ii) systematic sampling

Q4   A high-street store is investigating the number of customers they get each day over the course of one year. They record how many people make a purchase from their shop per day, on each of 50 days during the year. They use systematic sampling to choose which 50 days to sample.
      Explain why this sampling method might lead to bias in their data.

Stratified sampling

If a population is divided into **categories** (e.g. age or gender), you can use a stratified sample — this uses the same proportion of each category in the sample as there is in the population.

To choose a stratified sample:
▪ Divide the population into **categories**.
▪ Calculate the number needed for each category in the sample using the formula: $\dfrac{\text{size of category in pop.}}{\text{total size of pop.}} \times \text{total sample size}$
▪ **Randomly** select the sample for each category.

Advantages
▪ If the categories are **disjoint** (i.e. there is **no overlap**, e.g. age groups), this should give a **representative** sample.
▪ It's useful when results may **vary** depending on categories.
Disadvantage
The extra detail needed can make it **expensive**.

 A teacher takes a sample of 20 pupils from her school, stratified by year group. The table below shows the number of pupils in each year group. Calculate how many pupils from each year group should be in her sample.

The population is split into five categories, based on year group.
Find the number needed for each, rounding to the nearest whole number.

Year Group	No. of pupils
7	120
8	80
9	95
10	63
11	42

Total population = $120 + 80 + 95 + 63 + 42 = 400$

Year 7 = $\dfrac{120}{400} \times 20 =$ **6**   Year 8 = $\dfrac{80}{400} \times 20 =$ **4**

Year 9 = $\dfrac{95}{400} \times 20 = 4.75 \approx$ **5**   Year 10 = $\dfrac{63}{400} \times 20 = 3.15 \approx$ **3**

Year 11 = $\dfrac{42}{400} \times 20 = 2.1 \approx$ **2**   (check: $6 + 4 + 5 + 3 + 2 =$ **20**)

Quota sampling

Quota sampling is often used in market research. The interviewer will be given a quota of people in each category to interview (e.g. 20 men and 20 women). They then choose people to interview until the quotas are fulfilled.

To choose a quota sample:
▪ Divide the population into **categories**.
▪ Give each category a **quota** (number of members to sample).
▪ Collect data until the quotas are met in **all** categories (**without** using random sampling).

Advantages
▪ It is **easy** for the interviewer as they don't need **access** to the whole population, or a **list** of every member.
▪ The interviewer continues to sample until all the quotas are met, so **non-response** is less of a problem.
Disadvantage
It can be **biased** by the interviewer — selection isn't random, so they might **exclude** some of the population.

 A video-game company wants to gather opinions on a new game. The interviewer is asked to interview 75 people aged under 30, and 25 people aged 30+. Give one advantage and one disadvantage of this quota sample.

Advantage: The company doesn't have a full list of everyone who has played the game, so random sampling isn't possible.

Disadvantage: People with strong views on the game are more likely to respond to the interviewer, which may cause sampling bias.

Exercise 1.3

Q1   A sports centre selects a sample of 10 members, stratified by age.
The table shows the total number of members in each age group.

Age (a)	Under 20	20 to 40	41 to 60	Over 60
No. of members	45	33	15	57

Calculate how many people from each age group should be sampled.

Q2   Martin is investigating the heights of athletes at a competition. He wants to measure 10 males and 10 females taking part in each of the high jump, the long jump and the pole vault.
Give one advantage and one disadvantage of using quota sampling in this situation.

Q3   Numbria council wants to collect residents' opinions on public transport, using a stratified sample of 200 residents. The table shows the number of residents, to the nearest 100, in each area:

Area	Addspatria	Lessmorland	Conicston	Logby Bridge	Angleside	Gradesbeck
No. of residents	7000	8600	4200	6800	5400	8000

a) Explain why stratified sampling might be better than simple random sampling in this case.

b) Calculate how many residents from each area should be in the sample.

c) They use a simple random sample to select the required number of residents in each area, and send them a survey through the post, asking them to fill it in and send it back.
Suggest why this could lead to bias in the sample.

Opportunity sampling

Opportunity (or convenience) sampling is where the sample is chosen from a section of the population that is most **convenient** for the sampler.

To choose an opportunity sample:

Choose members of the population that are the **easiest** to sample —
e.g. ask the first people you meet or sample whatever products you can find.

Advantage
Data can be gathered very **quickly** and **easily**.

Disadvantage
It **isn't random** and can be **very biased** — there's no attempt to make the sample representative.

 Examples   **Mel thinks that most people watch her favourite television programme.
She asks 20 friends whether they watch the television programme.**

a) **Name the sampling method Mel used.**

Mel asked her friends because they're easily available to sample, so:

Opportunity (or **convenience**) **sampling**

b) **Give two reasons why Mel's sample may biased.**

1.   Mel's friends could be of a similar age or the same gender, which is not representative of the whole population.

2.   Because this is Mel's favourite television programme, she might have encouraged her friends to watch it too.

Exercise 1.4

Q1 James wants to find out what colour of car is most common. He stands by a busy road and records the colour of the first 100 cars that pass by. Give an advantage and a disadvantage of this sampling method.

Q2 A biologist is collecting data on the butterflies in a forest. She needs to capture 30 butterflies and measure their wingspan. Suggest why opportunity sampling might be appropriate in this case.

Q3 Hattie has a biased coin. To investigate the probability of getting heads, she takes the results of the first 50 times she flips the coin. Is this data likely to be biased? Explain your answer.

Q4 For a school project, Neville is investigating the types of music people in the UK like to listen to. He collects data by asking friends from his year group. Is this sample likely to be representative of the population? Give one way in which the sample could be improved.

Cluster sampling

Cluster sampling is another method that's useful when the population can be divided into **distinct groups**. The clusters should be groups that you expect to give **similar** results to each other.

To choose a cluster sample:	Advantages
• Divide the population into **clusters** covering the **whole population**, where **no member** of the population belongs to **multiple clusters**. • **Randomly** select clusters to use in the sample, based on the required sample size. • Either use **all** the members of the selected clusters (a **one-stage** cluster sample), or **randomly sample** within each cluster to form the sample (a **two-stage** cluster sample).	• It can be more **practical** (e.g. quicker or cheaper) in certain situations. • You can incorporate **other** sampling methods, making it quite **adaptable**. **Disadvantages** • Because you only sample certain clusters, the results could be **less representative**. • It's not always possible to separate a population into clusters in a natural way.

You can use **any** of the **other sampling techniques** for **either stage** of the sample (selecting the clusters or choosing which members of the cluster to use in the sample), depending on the **circumstances**.

 A researcher wants to conduct a taste test of a new energy drink on university students in the UK.

a) **Explain why a cluster sample might be suitable in this situation.**

Taking universities in the UK as the clusters, all university students are included, and you can assume that no student belongs to multiple universities. You would also expect different universities to give similar results.

Universities in the UK form clusters that are disjoint and cover the whole population, and that would be expected to give similar results to each other. Using a cluster sample would also be convenient in this situation, as the researcher would only need to visit a few universities, rather than every one.

b) **Explain whether a one-stage or a two-stage cluster sample would be more appropriate.**

Conducting a taste test on every student at a university would be expensive and difficult to organise. It would be better to take a sample of the students and conduct the test on them, so a **two-stage cluster sample** would be more appropriate.

Exercise 1.5

Q1 Will wants to know about the number of people that cycle to work across his company.
He suggests using a one-stage cluster sample, with the different departments as the clusters.

a) Give a possible reason why Will's suggested method may not be suitable in this situation.

b) Suggest a different sampling method Will could use and give one advantage of this method.

Q2 A manufacturing company makes machines that produce widgets. They have a list of all of the machines that they have made, and the addresses of the companies that own them. They want to collect data on the proportion of misshapen widgets that their machines produce, minimising the amount of time spent travelling from site to site while still getting a representative sample.

Describe how a cluster sample could be used to collect this data, stating whether a one-stage or a two-stage cluster sample would be more appropriate.

Self-selection sampling

Self-selection (or volunteer) sampling is where people **choose** to be part of the sample — e.g. they choose to complete a questionnaire or volunteer to take part in a study.

To create a self-selection sample:	Advantages
<ul><li>**Advertise** or appeal to the whole population for participation in the sample (possibly offering payment).</li><li>Either use everyone who responds as the sample, or take a sample of them to best represent the population.</li></ul>	<ul><li>It requires **little time** or **effort** in finding sample members, as they contact you.</li><li>People who have **volunteered** are **less likely** not to respond.</li><li>It could be the **only way** to get people to take part in a study, or to find members of a population.</li></ul> **Disadvantage** There can easily be **trends** within the respondents, such as people having **strong opinions**, which would lead to bias.

 A website puts an advert on their home page, asking visitors to complete a short survey about the site for a payment of £20. Give three ways that this sampling method could cause bias in their results.

1. People who are willing to complete the survey might have stronger opinions than other visitors, which would introduce bias into the results.

2. Certain people might not see the advert if the website does not display properly for them, or if they block adverts through their browser, which would exclude parts of the population from the sample, making it less representative.

3. Since the website is offering money for responses, people might be more likely to try to fill out the survey multiple times or not take the questions seriously, which would make the responses less representative of the views of all of their visitors.

Exercise 1.6

Q1 The manager of a park wants to collect opinions from visitors about a potential building project.
Describe how she could use self-selection sampling to do this and give an advantage of this method.

Q2 David gives out a questionnaire about reading habits to the students in his year group at school.
He gets 70 responses from boys and 40 from girls. As his sample, he decides to use all of the responses from the girls, and 40 randomly selected responses from the boys, to match the proportion of boys and girls in his year group. Give an advantage and a disadvantage of this method.

2. Representing Data

Data basics

Data consists of **observations** (or **measurements**), each recording a value of a particular **variable**.

- Variables that take **non-numerical** values (e.g. names, colours) are called **qualitative** variables.
- Variables that take **numerical** values (e.g. height, age) are called **quantitative** variables.

There are two different types of **quantitative** variables.

- A **discrete** variable can take only **certain values** (e.g. number of people or shoe size) — this means there are 'gaps' between possible values (you can't take size 9.664 shoes, for example).
- A **continuous** variable can take **any value** within a particular range (e.g. height or mass) — there are no gaps between possible values.

Data can be shown in a **table**. When the variable is quantitative, the data is often **grouped** into **classes**, particularly if it is continuous. The **upper** and **lower class boundaries** are the largest and smallest data values that would be included in that class.

Tip: For **continuous** data, the **upper** class boundary of a class will be **the same** as the **lower** class boundary of the **next** one, since there are **no gaps** in the possible values the variable can take.

For grouped data, you can find the **class width** and the **midpoint** of a class using these formulas:

$$\text{class width} = \text{upper class boundary} - \text{lower class boundary}$$

$$\text{midpoint} = \frac{\text{lower class boundary} + \text{upper class boundary}}{2}$$

 A researcher measures the length of 40 cars (to the nearest 10 cm). Her results are shown in the table. Add columns to the table to show the lower and upper class boundaries, the class widths and the class midpoints.

Length (cm)	Frequency
250-350	5
360-410	11
420-450	17
460-500	7

1. The shortest car that measures 250 cm to the nearest 10 cm is 245 cm long. So the lower class boundary of the 250-350 class is 245 cm.

2. The upper class boundary of the 250-350 class is 355 cm (even though a car measuring 355 cm would actually go into the 360-410 class).

3. Use the formulas above to find the class widths and the midpoints.

Length (cm)	Frequency	Lower class boundary (cm)	Upper class boundary (cm)	Class width (cm)	Midpoint (cm)
250-350	5	245	355	110	300
360-410	11	355	415	60	385
420-450	17	415	455	40	435
460-500	7	455	505	50	480

You can represent data using different diagrams, depending on whether the data is discrete or continuous. **Frequency polygons** are one type that are used for continuous data.

Example

The table shows the maximum daily temperature (°C) in a town over 180 days.

Maximum daily temperature, t (°C)	$10 < t \leq 15$	$15 < t \leq 20$	$20 < t \leq 25$	$25 < t \leq 30$
Frequency	21	98	56	5

Draw a frequency polygon to show the data.

1. Find the midpoint of each class using the formula on p.141.

Class	$10 < t \leq 15$	$15 < t \leq 20$	$20 < t \leq 25$	$25 < t \leq 30$
Midpoint	12.5	17.5	22.5	27.5

2. Plot the midpoints on the horizontal axis and the frequencies on the vertical axis.

3. Join the points with straight lines.

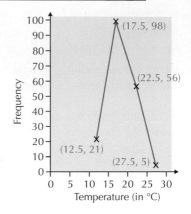

Exercise 2.1

Q1 A mechanic collects the following information about cars he services:

Make, Mileage, Colour, Number of doors, Cost of service

Write down all the variables from this list that are: a) qualitative b) quantitative

Q2 Amy is an athletics coach. She records the following information about each of the athletes she trains:

Number of medals won last season, Height, Mass, Shoe size

Write down all the variables from this list that are examples of:

a) discrete quantitative variables b) continuous quantitative variables

Q3 A group of 50 people were given 30 seconds to see how many words they could make out of a set of 10 letters. The bar chart shows the results.

a) Is the data discrete or continuous?

b) How many people found at least 11 words?

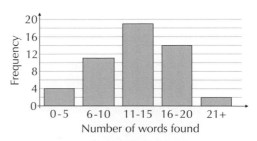

Q4 The heights of the members of a history society are shown in the table.

a) Explain why 'height' is a continuous variable.

b) For each class, find:

   (i) the lower class boundary (ii) the upper class boundary

   (iii) the class width (iv) the class midpoint

c) Show the information in the table in a frequency polygon.

Height, h (cm)	Number of members
$140 \leq h < 150$	3
$150 \leq h < 160$	9
$160 \leq h < 170$	17
$170 \leq h < 180$	12
$180 \leq h < 190$	5
$190 \leq h < 200$	1

Histograms

Histograms look like bar charts. However, as they're used for **continuous variables**, there are **no gaps** between the bars, and the heights of the bars show **frequency density**, rather than frequency, where:

$$\text{Frequency density} = \frac{\text{frequency}}{\text{class width}}$$

> **Example**
>
> **The masses (to the nearest 100 g) of 1000 parcels are given in the table below. Draw a histogram to show this data.**
>
> | Mass of parcel (to nearest 100 g) | 100-200 | 300-400 | 500-700 | 800-1100 |
> |---|---|---|---|---|
> | Number of parcels | 100 | 250 | 600 | 50 |
>
> 1. Draw a table showing the class boundaries, class width and frequency density.
>
> | Mass of parcel (g) | Lower class boundary (g) | Upper class boundary (g) | Class width | Frequency | Frequency density |
> |---|---|---|---|---|---|
> | 100 - 200 | 50 | 250 | 200 | 100 | 0.5 |
> | 300 - 400 | 250 | 450 | 200 | 250 | 1.25 |
> | 500 - 700 | 450 | 750 | 300 | 600 | 2 |
> | 800 - 1100 | 750 | 1150 | 400 | 50 | 0.125 |
>
> 2. Draw the histogram — plot frequency density on the vertical axis and mass along the horizontal axis.
>
>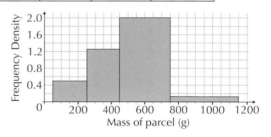

On a histogram, the frequency in a class is proportional to the **area** of its bar.
In other words, **frequency = k × area of bar** (where k is a number).

> **Examples**
>
> **The histogram shows the heights of a group of people. There were 12 people between 155 cm and 160 cm tall.**
>
>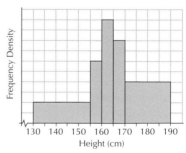
>
> **a) How many people in the group are between 130 cm and 155 cm tall?**
>
> 1. Use the bar for 155-160 cm to find k.
>   Area of 155-160 cm bar = 1 × 6 = 6 squares
>   Frequency = k × area $\Rightarrow$ $k = 12 \div 6 = 2$
>
> 2. Now find the area of the 130-155 cm bar and multiply by k to get the frequency.
>   Area of 130-155 cm bar = 5 × 2 = 10 $\Rightarrow$ frequency = 2 × 10 = **20 people**
>
> **b) Estimate the number of people in the group who are over 175 cm tall.**
>
> Assuming that the heights are evenly spread throughout the 170-190 cm class, three-quarters of the people in the class would be over 175 cm tall.
> Area of 170-190 cm bar = 4 × 4 = 16 $\Rightarrow$ frequency = k × area = 2 × 16 = 32 people
> The estimated number over 175 cm = $32 \times \frac{3}{4} =$ **24 people**

If you **divide** the **area** of a bar by the **total area** of all the bars, you get the **proportion** of data values in that class. This also tells you the **probability** of a randomly chosen data value being in that class.

The histogram below shows the speeds of a number of cars, measured along a particular stretch of road.

One of the cars is chosen at random.

a) **Find the probability that it was travelling at between 16 and 24 miles per hour.**

   1. Find the total area of all the bars.
       $8 + 16 + 36 + 38 + 32 + 20 = 150$

   2. Divide the area of the 16-24 mph bar by the total area.
       $16 \div 150 = \mathbf{0.107}$ (3 s.f.)

b) **Estimate the probability that it was travelling at less than 28 miles per hour.**

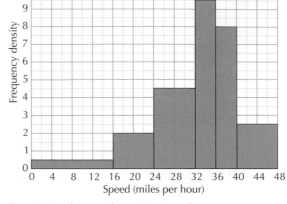

   1. The area that represents a speed of less than 28 miles per hour is given by the 0-16 bar, the 16-24 bar and half of the 24-32 bar. $8 + 16 + \left(\frac{1}{2} \times 36\right) = 42$

   2. Divide this by the total area. $42 \div 150 = \mathbf{0.28}$

Exercise 2.2

Q1 The table shows the percentage of water remaining in a cyclist's bottle after their first lap, over 20 races. Draw a histogram to show the data.

Water remaining, w (%)	f
$60 \leq w < 80$	2
$80 \leq w < 85$	5
$85 \leq w < 95$	9
$95 \leq w \leq 100$	4

Q2 The histogram shows the audition times (in seconds) for contestants applying for a place on a television talent show. The auditions for 54 contestants lasted between 30 and 45 seconds.

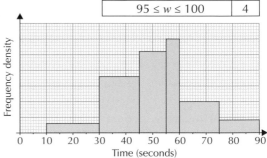

   a) Work out the number of contestants whose auditions lasted less than 30 seconds.

   b) How many contestants auditioned altogether?

   c) Estimate the number of contestants whose auditions lasted less than 40 seconds.

   d) A contestant is chosen at random. Find the probability that their audition lasted at least one minute.

   e) Estimate the probability that a randomly chosen contestant's audition lasted less than 25 seconds.

Q3 A butterfly enthusiast measures the wingspans (w, in mm), to the nearest millimetre, of a sample of tortoiseshell butterflies. She groups her measurements and displays the data in a histogram. The group containing butterflies with $44.5 \leq w < 47.5$ has a frequency of 12. This group is represented on the histogram by a bar of width 1.5 cm and height 9 cm.

   a) Show that each butterfly is represented on the histogram by an area of 1.125 cm².

   b) The bar representing the butterflies with $51.5 \leq w < 53.5$ has an area of 22.5 cm².
      Work out the frequency for this group.

   c) The frequency for butterflies with $53.5 \leq w < 58.5$ is 14.
      Work out the width and the height of the bar used to represent this group.

Stem and leaf diagrams

Stem and leaf diagrams are another way to represent data.
Each value is split into a 'stem' and a 'leaf', like this:

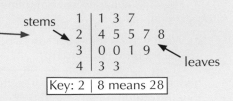

A stem and leaf diagram always needs a **key** to tell you what the
stems and leaves represent. In this example, the stems represent
the 'tens', so the first row shows the values 11, 13 and 17.
The leaves in each row should be **sorted** from **lowest** to **highest**.

stems 1 | 1 3 7
2 | 4 5 5 7 8
3 | 0 0 1 9   leaves
4 | 3 3

Key: 2 | 8 means 28

**The lengths, in m, of cars in a car park were measured to the nearest 10 cm.
The results were: 2.9, 3.5, 4.0, 2.8, 4.1, 2.7, 3.1, 3.6, 3.8 and 3.7.
Draw a stem and leaf diagram to show the data.**

1. Use the numbers before the decimal point as the stems,
   and the numbers after the decimal point as the leaves.

   2 | 9 8 7
   3 | 5 1 6 8 7
   4 | 0 1

2. Put the leaves in order and add a key.

   2 | 7 8 9
   3 | 1 5 6 7 8
   4 | 0 1

   Key 2|9 means 2.9 m

A **back-to-back** stem and leaf diagram is two normal stem and leaf diagrams drawn either side of the
same stems. The left-hand diagram is read 'backwards' because the stems are on the opposite side.

**The heights of boys and girls in a Year 11 class
are given to the nearest cm in the back-to-back
stem and leaf diagram on the right.
Write out the data in full.**

Boys		Girls
	15	9
8	16	1 5 9
9 8 1	17	0 2 3 5
5 2	18	0
1	19	

Key: 1|17|0
means 171 for Boys
and 170 for Girls

1. The boys' heights are read backwards,
   so the first value, 8|16|, is a height of 168 cm.

   The boys' heights in cm are: **168, 171, 178, 179, 182, 185, 191**

2. The first value for the girls, |15|9, is a height of 159 cm.

   The girls' heights in cm are: **159, 161, 165, 169, 170, 172, 173, 175, 180**

Exercise 2.3

Q1 The stem and leaf diagram shows the number of members
in each of the choirs taking part in a choir competition.
a) How many choirs were competing in this competition altogether?
b) How many choirs had 45 members?
c) How many choirs had more than 52 members?
d) What was the size of the largest choir?

1 | 2 6 7 9
2 | 1 2 2 2 5 6 7 8
3 | 0 3 6 7 9
4 | 1 4 5 5 7 8
5 | 0 1 3 3 9
6 |
7 | 1 3

Key: 1 | 2 = 12 members

Q2 Construct a stem and leaf diagram for the following data:

289, 275, 303, 289, 273, 290, 290, 271, 275, 289, 310, 303, 272, 275, 301, 319, 316,
282, 307, 306, 303, 295, 283, 302, 317, 297, 280, 280, 285, 272, 301, 275, 279, 287

Q3 The stem and leaf diagram shows the minimum recorded temperature
(to the nearest 0.1 °C) in 24 towns on a June night.

a) How many towns had a minimum temperature below 10 °C?

b) Which temperature was recorded most frequently?

c) What was the difference between the highest and lowest temperatures
recorded in these towns?

```
 8 | 2 5
 9 | 4 7 8 9 9
10 | 1 3 7 7 7 9
11 | 0 4 5 8
12 | 1 3 6 8
13 | 2 6 7
```
Key: 8 | 2 = 8.2 °C

Q4 Sixteen children belong to an orchestra. The distances (in kilometres)
that the children live from the practice hall are shown below.

2.4	4.3	1.5	0.8	2.7	5.6	1.6	1.2
3.7	2.6	3.5	2.9	2.1	4.0	2.5	6.4

a) Draw a stem and leaf diagram to show this information.

b) (i) Find the furthest distance that a child lives from the practice hall.

(ii) How many children live less than 2 km from the practice hall?

Q5 Freddie has a collection of films on DVD.
The back-to-back stem and leaf diagram shows the
running times (to the nearest minute) of these films.

a) What is the running time of the shortest comedy film?

b) How many of his dramas last more than 90 minutes?

c) How many of his films last between 70 and 80 minutes?

```
  Comedies  |    | Dramas
 7 5 3 1 0  |  6 |
9 6 5 4 2 2 |  7 | 6
8 8 7 4 1 1 |  8 | 7 9
    8 6 5 0 |  9 | 1 2 4 7
        4 2 | 10 | 2 4 4 5 5 7 8
          4 | 11 | 1 1 4 5 6 7
```
Key: 1 | 8 | 7 = 81 minutes for comedies
and 87 minutes for dramas

Describing distributions

There are a number of terms you can use to describe the distribution of a quantitative data set:

- **Symmetrical**: the data is symmetrical about the mean and median, which are roughly equal.
- **Positively Skewed**: the data is concentrated in the lower part of the range (on the left).
- **Negatively Skewed**: the data is concentrated in the upper part of the range (on the right).
- **Unimodal**: the data has one point where the distribution 'peaks'.
- **Bimodal**: the data has two points where the distribution 'peaks'.

 Describe the distributions shown in the following diagrams:

a)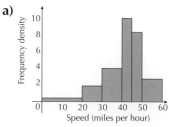

b)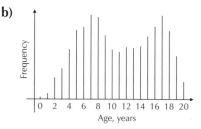

c)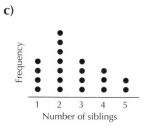

a) ▪ The data is **unimodal** — it has one peak at 40-45 mph.
▪ The graph shows **negative skew** — the data is concentrated in the upper part of the range.

b) ▪ The data is **bimodal** — there are two peaks, one at 7 years and one at 17 years.
▪ The data appears to be relatively **symmetrical**, with slight negative skew if any.

c) ▪ The data is **unimodal** — it has one peak at 2.
▪ There is **positive skew** — the data is concentrated in the lower part of the range.

Exercise 2.4

Q1 The diagram to the right shows the number of pets in each house in two different neighbourhoods, A and B. For each neighbourhood, is the data positively skewed, negatively skewed, or symmetrical?

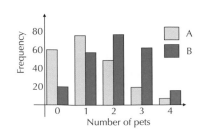

Q2 A company collects data on the heights of 1000 40-year-olds (500 men and 500 women). They plot a histogram to show the data, which appears to be bimodal. Explain why this might be the case.

3. Location: Mean, Median and Mode

Measures of location (or of **central tendency**) summarise where the 'centre' of the data lies. The most common measure of location is the **mean** — the formula for the mean ($\overline{x}$, said 'x-bar') is:

$$\text{Mean} = \overline{x} = \frac{\sum x}{n} \text{ or } \frac{\sum fx}{\sum f}$$

where each x is a **data value**, f is the **frequency** of each x (the number of times it occurs), and n is the **total number** of data values.

The $\sum$ (sigma) means "sum" (see p.293) — so $\sum x$ means add up all the values of x, and $\sum f = n$.

 A scientist counts the number of eggs in some song thrush nests. His data is shown in this table. Calculate the mean number of eggs in these nests.

Number of eggs, x	2	3	4	5	6
Number of nests, f	4	9	16	8	3

1. Add a row showing the values of fx and a column showing the totals $\sum f$ and $\sum fx$ to the table.

x	2	3	4	5	6	Total
f	4	9	16	8	3	40
fx	8	27	64	40	18	157

2. Now use the formula for the mean.

$$\overline{x} = \frac{\sum fx}{\sum f} = \frac{157}{40} = \textbf{3.925 eggs}$$

If you know a data set of size n_1 has mean $\overline{x}_1$ and another data set of size n_2 has mean $\overline{x}_2$, then the combined mean is:

$$\overline{x} = \frac{n_1 \overline{x}_1 + n_2 \overline{x}_2}{n_1 + n_2}$$

 A scientist is looking at the amount of rainfall over a week. The mean of the first 5 days is $\overline{x}_1 = 4.1$ mm and the mean of the next 2 days is $\overline{x}_2 = 19.9$ mm. Find the combined mean ($\overline{x}$) of the rainfall over the week.

$$\overline{x} = \frac{n_1 \overline{x}_1 + n_2 \overline{x}_2}{n_1 + n_2} = \frac{(5 \times 4.1) + (2 \times 19.9)}{5 + 2} = \frac{60.3}{7} = 8.6142... = \textbf{8.61 mm} \text{ (3 s.f.)}$$

Exercise 3.1

Q1 Katia visits 12 shops and records the price of a loaf of bread. Her results are given below:
£1.08, £1.15, £1.25, £1.19, £1.26, £1.24, £1.15, £1.09, £1.16, £1.20, £1.05, £1.10
Work out the mean price of a loaf of bread in these shops.

Q2 In a competition, the 7 members of team A scored a mean of 35 points, and the 6 members of team B scored 252 points altogether. Find the combined mean score.

Q3 The total number of goals scored in 20 football matches are shown in the table. Calculate the mean number of goals scored in these matches.

Number of goals, x	0	1	2	3	4
Frequency, f	5	7	4	3	1

Q4 A drama group has 15 members. The mean age of the members is 47.4 years.
a) A 17-year-old leaves the drama group. Find the new mean age.
b) A new member then joins, making the mean age 47.6 years. How old is the new member?

There are two other important measures of location — the **median** and the **mode**.

> **Median** = value in the middle of the data set when all the data values are placed in order of size.

To find the median, put the n data values **in order**, then:

- if $\frac{n}{2}$ is **not** a **whole number**, **round it up** to find the position of the median.
- if $\frac{n}{2}$ is a **whole number**, the median is **halfway** between the value in **this** position and the **next** value.

> **Mode** = most frequently occurring data value.

Tip: A data set can have multiple modes — if it only has one, it's called **unimodal**, and if it has two, it's **bimodal**. If each data value occurs **only once** (common when the data is continuous), the data set has **no mode**.

Example

Find the median and mode of the following data set:

4, 3, 11, 4, 8, 9, 3, 8, 7, 8

1. Put the data in order and use the rule for $\frac{n}{2}$
   — it's 5, so the median is halfway between the 5th and 6th values.

   3, 3, 4, 4, 7, 8, 8, 8, 9, 11
   $\frac{n}{2} = \frac{10}{2} = 5$
   Median $= (7 + 8) \div 2 = \mathbf{7.5}$

2. Read off the mode.

   Mode = **8**

Finding the mode and median for data in a **frequency table** is easy, as long as the data **isn't grouped**.

Examples

The table shows the number of letters received one day in a sample of houses.

No. of letters	No. of houses
0	11
1	25
2	27
3	21

a) **Find the modal number of letters.**

The modal number of letters is the one received by the most houses.   Mode = **2 letters**

b) **Find the median number of letters.**

1. Add a column for the cumulative frequency (see p.154) — a running total of the frequency.

2. Find $\frac{n}{2}$: $n = 84$, so $\frac{n}{2} = \frac{84}{2} = 42$

   The median is halfway between the 42nd and 43rd data values.

No. of letters	No. of houses (frequency)	Cumulative frequency
0	11	11
1	25	36
2	27	63
3	21	84

3. Using the cumulative frequency, you can see that the data values in positions 37 to 63 are all 2, so: Median = **2 letters**

Exercise 3.2

Q1 Seventeen friends took part in a charity fun run. Below is the amount, in £, that each friend raised.

250, 19, 500, 123, 185, 101, 45, 67, 194, 77, 108, 110, 187, 216, 84, 98, 140

a) Find the median amount of money raised by these friends.

b) Explain why it is not possible to find the mode for this data.

Q2 A financial adviser records the interest rates charged by 12 different banks to customers taking out a loan. His findings are below.

6.2%, 6.9%, 6.9%, 8.8%, 6.3%, 7.4%, 6.5%, 6.4%, 9.9%, 6.2%, 6.4%, 6.9%

Find the modal interest rate and the median interest rate charged by these banks.

Q3 An online seller has received the ratings shown in the table. Find the modal and the median customer rating.

Rating	1	2	3	4	5
No. of customers	7	5	25	67	72

Q4 A theatre stages 35 performances of its pantomime one year. The stem and leaf diagram shows the number of empty seats for each performance.

a) Write down the value of the modal number of empty seats.

b) Work out the median number of empty seats.

```
0 | 0 3 5 5 5 6 6 8 9 9
1 | 1 2 2 3 5 7 8
2 | 0 2 3 4 4 5
3 | 1 4 5 6 8 8 9
4 | 3 5 5 7
5 | 7
```

Key: 3 | 1 = 31 empty seats

Q5 Kwasi and Ben each check the download speeds on their computers on a number of different occasions. Their results are shown in the back-to-back stem and leaf diagram. Find the modal and the median download speeds for:

a) Kwasi   b) Ben

```
        Kwasi         Ben
                  3 | 5 7 8
        7 4 2 1 0 0 | 4 | 0 2 6 6 8
          8 8 4 3 0 | 5 | 1 3 5 9
        9 9 8 7 6 1 | 6 | 1 2 2 4 5 7
              9 2 | 7 | 4 7 8
```

Key: 3 | 5 | 9 means 5.3 Mbit/s for Kwasi and 5.9 Mbit/s for Ben.

Averages of grouped data

You can only **estimate** the mean and median for **grouped** data, since you no longer have the exact data values. Instead of the mode, you can only find the **modal class**.

- The **modal class** is the class with the **highest frequency density** (see p.143). If all the classes are the same width, then this will just be the class with the **highest frequency**.

- To estimate the **mean**, assume that every reading takes the value of its class **midpoint** (see p.141). Then you can use the formula $\bar{x} = \dfrac{\sum fx}{\sum f}$, where x is now the midpoint of each class.

- To estimate the **median**, find **which class** the median is in, using the value of $\frac{n}{2}$, then use **linear interpolation** — see the next example for the method.

The table shows the heights of a number of trees in a park.

Height of tree to nearest m	0-5	6-10	11-15	16-20
Number of trees	26	17	11	6

a)   Estimate the mean height of the trees.

1.   Add the class midpoints (x) and the values of fx to the table.

Height of tree to nearest m	0-5	6-10	11-15	16-20	Totals
Class midpoint, x	2.75	8	13	18	—
Number of trees, f	26	17	11	6	60
fx	71.5	136	143	108	458.5

2.   Use the formula: Mean $= \dfrac{\sum fx}{\sum f} = \dfrac{458.5}{60} =$ **7.64 m** (3 s.f.)

b)   Estimate the median height of the trees.

1.   Draw a table showing the cumulative frequency for each class.

Height of tree to nearest m	0-5	6-10	11-15	16-20
Number of trees, f	26	17	11	6
Cumulative frequency	26	43	54	60

2. $\dfrac{n}{2} = 30$, so there are 30 values that are less than or equal to the median.

   $\dfrac{n}{2} = 30$, so the median is in the 6-10 class

3.   Use what you know to draw a diagram.

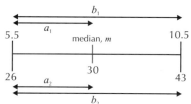

   Class boundaries: lower = 5.5, upper = 10.5
   Cumulative frequency at lcb = 26, at ucb = 43
   Cumulative frequency at median = 30

4.   Assuming the values are evenly spread, $\dfrac{a_1}{b_1} = \dfrac{a_2}{b_2}$.

   $\dfrac{a_1}{b_1} = \dfrac{a_2}{b_2} \implies \dfrac{m-5.5}{10.5-5.5} = \dfrac{30-26}{43-26} \implies \dfrac{m-5.5}{5} = \dfrac{4}{17}$

   $\implies m = 5 \times \dfrac{4}{17} + 5.5 =$ **6.68 m** (3 s.f.)

Exercise 3.3

Q1   A postman records the number of letters delivered to each of 50 houses one day.
The results are shown in the table.

a) State the modal class.

No. of letters	0-2	3-5	6-8	9-11	12-14
No. of houses	20	16	7	5	2

b) Estimate the mean number of letters delivered to these houses.

Q2   The time that 60 students took to change after PE is shown below.

Time (t, mins)	Frequency, f	Cumulative frequency	Midpoint, x	fx
$3 \le t < 4$	7	7	3.5	24.5
$4 \le t < 5$	14	21	4.5	
$5 \le t < 6$	24			
$6 \le t < 8$	10			
$8 \le t < 10$	5			

a) Copy and complete the table.

b) Work out estimates of the mean and the median time it took these students to change.

Q3   The table below shows the times that a random sample of 60 runners took to complete a marathon.

Time (t, mins)	$180 \leq t < 240$	$240 \leq t < 270$	$270 \leq t < 300$	$300 \leq t < 360$	$360 \leq t < 480$
Frequency, f	8	19	21	9	3

    a) Estimate the mean time of these runners (you may use $\sum fx = 16\,740$, where x is the class midpoint).

    b) Calculate an estimate for the median time it took these runners to complete the marathon.

Comparing measures of location

The mean, the median and the mode are all useful for different kinds of data:

Mean

- The mean is a good average as it uses **all** of the data.
- It can be heavily affected by **extreme values / outliers** (see p.155) and by **skew** (see p.146).
- It can only be used with **quantitative** data (i.e. numbers).

Median

- The median is **not** affected by **extreme** values or by data that is **skewed**.
- Estimating the median for **grouped** data requires a lot of work.

Mode

- The mode can be used with **qualitative** (non-numerical) data.
- Data can have **more than one** mode, and if every value occurs only once then there is **no mode**.

Exercise 3.4

Q1   Explain whether the mean, median or mode would be most suitable
     as a summary of each of the following data sets.

    a) Salaries of each employee at a company.

    b) Length of adult female adder snakes.

    c) Make of cars parked in a car park.

    d) Weight of all newborn full-term babies born one year at a hospital.

    e) Distance a firm's employees travel to work each morning.

Q2   Hosi records the number of bedrooms in the houses lived in by a sample of 10 adults.
     His results are shown in the table.

Number of bedrooms	1	2	3	4	5	6	7	8
Frequency	1	2	4	2	0	0	0	1

    Explain why the mean may not be the most suitable measure of location for the data.

4. Dispersion

Range, interquartile range and interpercentile range

Dispersion measures how **spread out** the data values are. The simplest measure of dispersion is **range**:

> Range = highest value – lowest value

Tip: The **midrange** (halfway between the highest and lowest values) is another **measure of location**.

Another measure of dispersion is the **interquartile range**. **Quartiles** divide the data into four quarters. 25% of the data is less than or equal to the **lower quartile** (Q_1), 50% of the data is less than or equal to the **median** (Q_2), and 75% of the data is less than or equal to the **upper quartile** (Q_3).

To find Q_1 and Q_3, find their **position** in the ordered list of the data:

- For Q_1, work out $\frac{n}{4}$ and for Q_3, work out $\frac{3n}{4}$.
- If this value is **not** a **whole number**, **round it up** to find the position of the quartile.
- If it **is** a whole number, the quartile is **halfway** between the value in **this** position and the **next** value.

You can then find the **interquartile range** using the formula:

> Interquartile range (IQR) = upper quartile (Q_3) – lower quartile (Q_1)

Example

Find the median and interquartile range of the following data set:
2, 5, 3, 11, 6, 8, 3, 8, 1, 6, 2, 23, 9, 11, 18, 19, 22, 7

1. Put the list in order.   1, 2, 2, 3, 3, 5, 6, 6, 7, 8, 8, 9, 11, 11, 18, 19, 22, 23

2. Find the position of the median. $\frac{n}{2} = \frac{18}{2} = 9$, so the median is halfway between the 9th and 10th values. Median = $(7 + 8) \div 2 = $ **7.5**

3. Find the positions of Q_1 and Q_3. $\frac{n}{4} = \frac{18}{4} = 4.5$, so $Q_1 = $ the 5th value = 3

   $\frac{3n}{4} = \frac{54}{4} = 13.5$, so $Q_3 = $ the 14th value = 11

4. Subtract Q_1 from Q_3.   IQR = $Q_3 - Q_1 = 11 - 3 = $ **8**

To **estimate** quartiles for **grouped** data, use **linear interpolation**.

Example

Estimate the interquartile range for the tree heights in this table.

Height of tree to nearest m	0-5	6-10	11-15	16-20
Number of trees	26	17	11	6

1. Add the cumulative frequencies to the table.

Height (m)	0-5	6-10	11-15	16-20
No. of trees	26	17	11	6
Cumulative frequency	26	43	54	60

2. Draw a diagram showing the position of Q_1.

   Cumulative frequency at $Q_1 = \frac{n}{4} = 15$, so Q_1 is in the 0-5 class.

   Class boundaries: lower = 0, upper = 5.5

   Cumulative frequency at lcb = 0, at ucb = 26

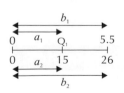

3. Solve $\frac{a_1}{b_1} = \frac{a_2}{b_2}$ to find Q_1.

   $\frac{a_1}{b_1} = \frac{a_2}{b_2} \Rightarrow \frac{Q_1 - 0}{5.5 - 0} = \frac{15 - 0}{26 - 0} \Rightarrow Q_1 = 5.5 \times \frac{15}{26} = 3.1730...$ m

4. Draw another diagram showing the position of Q_3.

   Cumulative frequency at $Q_3 = \frac{3n}{4} = 45$, so Q_3 is in the 11-15 class.
   Class boundaries: lower = 10.5, upper = 15.5
   Cumulative frequency at lcb = 43, at ucb = 54

5. Solve $\frac{a_1}{b_1} = \frac{a_2}{b_2}$ to find Q_3.

   $\frac{a_1}{b_1} = \frac{a_2}{b_2} \Rightarrow \frac{Q_3 - 10.5}{15.5 - 10.5} = \frac{45 - 43}{54 - 43} \Rightarrow Q_3 = 5 \times \frac{2}{11} + 10.5 = 11.409... \text{ m}$

6. Find the interquartile range: $IQR = Q_3 - Q_1 = 11.409... - 3.1730... = \textbf{8.24 m}$ (3 s.f.)

Percentiles are similar to quartiles, but they divide the data into **100 parts**.

> The **position** of the xth percentile (P_x) is $\frac{x}{100} \times$ total frequency (n).

Tip: The median is the 50th percentile, Q_1 is the 25th percentile, etc.

Use **linear interpolation** to estimate percentiles for **grouped data**, just like for quartiles.

You can find **interpercentile ranges** by subtracting two percentiles.

> The $a\%$ **to** $b\%$ **interpercentile range** is $P_b - P_a$.

Example

A reptile specialist records the mass (m, in kilograms) of 150 tortoises. Her results are shown in the table.

Estimate the 10th percentile for this data.

Mass (kg)	Frequency	Cumulative frequency
$0.2 \le m < 0.6$	27	27
$0.6 \le m < 1.0$	43	70
$1.0 \le m < 1.4$	35	105
$1.4 \le m < 1.8$	31	136
$1.8 \le m < 2.2$	14	150

1. Draw a diagram showing the position of P_{10}.

   Cumulative frequency at $P_{10} = \frac{10n}{100} = 15$,
   so P_{10} is in the $0.2 \le m < 0.6$ class.
   Class boundaries: lower = 0.2, upper = 0.6
   Cumulative frequency at lcb = 0, at ucb = 27

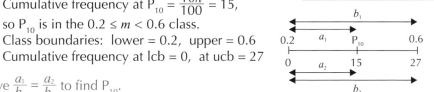

2. Solve $\frac{a_1}{b_1} = \frac{a_2}{b_2}$ to find P_{10}.

   $\frac{a_1}{b_1} = \frac{a_2}{b_2} \Rightarrow \frac{P_{10} - 0.2}{0.6 - 0.2} = \frac{15 - 0}{27 - 0} \Rightarrow P_{10} = 0.4 \times \frac{15}{27} + 0.2 = \textbf{0.422 kg}$ (3 s.f.)

Exercise 4.1

Q1 Find the range and interquartile range of the following data set:

   41, 49, 26, 20, 31, 9, 32, 39, 4, 21, 9, 12, 48, 23, 26, 10

Q2 The diameters (in miles) of the eight planets in the Solar System are given below:

   3032, 7521, 7926, 4222, 88 846, 74 898, 31 763, 30 778

   For this data set, calculate: a) the range   b) the upper and lower quartiles   c) the interquartile range

Q3 The data sets below show the speeds (in mph) of 18 different cars observed at the given time and place.

In town at 8:45 am: 14, 16, 15, 18, 15, 17, 16, 16, 18, 16, 15, 13, 15, 14, 16, 17, 18, 15

In town at 10:45 am: 34, 29, 36, 32, 31, 38, 30, 35, 39, 31, 29, 30, 25, 29, 33, 34, 36, 31

On the motorway at 1 pm: 67, 76, 78, 71, 73, 88, 74, 69, 75, 76, 95, 71, 69, 78, 73, 76, 75, 74

For each set of data, calculate:

a) the range and the interquartile range   b) the 30% to 70% interpercentile range

c) the 10% to 90% interpercentile range   d) the 45% to 55% interpercentile range

Q4 The lengths (l) of a zoo's beetles measured to the nearest mm are shown in the table below. Estimate:

a) the interquartile range

b) the 20% to 80% interpercentile range

c) the 5% to 95% interpercentile range

d) the 40% to 60% interpercentile range

e) the 1% to 99% interpercentile range

Length (l)	Number of beetles
0-5	82
6-10	28
11-15	44
16-30	30
31-50	16

Cumulative frequency diagrams

A **cumulative frequency diagram** plots the **running total** of the frequencies at each upper class boundary. It makes it easy to read off the **median** and the **quartiles**.

 a) **Draw a cumulative frequency diagram for the data below.**

Age in years	11-12	13-14	15-16	17-18
Number of students	50	65	58	27
Cumulative frequency	50	115	173	200

1. There are 0 students under the age of 11, so the first point is (11, 0). Plot the point (upper class boundary, cumulative frequency) for each class:
   (11, 0), (13, 50), (15, 115), (17, 173) and (19, 200)

2. Join up the points with straight lines.

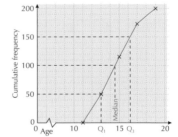

b) **Estimate the median and interquartile range from the graph.**

$n = 200$, so Q_1, Q_2 and Q_3 will be in the 50th, 100th and 150th positions respectively. Read these off the graph.

$Q_1 = 13$, $Q_2 \approx 14.5$, $Q_3 \approx 16.2 \Rightarrow$ Median $\approx$ **14.5 years**, IQR $\approx 16.2 - 13 =$ **3.2 years**

Exercise 4.2

Q1 The weights of a group of boys were measured and summarised in the cumulative frequency diagram. Estimate how many of the boys weigh:

a) Less than 55 kg

b) More than 73 kg

c) Explain why your answers are estimates.

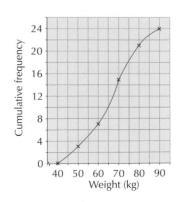

Q2 Draw a cumulative frequency diagram for the data given below.

Distance walked, d (km)	$0 < d \leq 2$	$2 < d \leq 4$	$4 < d \leq 6$	$6 < d \leq 8$
Number of walkers	1	10	7	2

Use your diagram to estimate the median and interquartile range.

Q3 The cumulative frequency diagram shows the monthly earnings of some sixteen-year-olds.

a) How many people were sampled?

b) Estimate the median earnings.

c) Estimate the interquartile range.

d) Estimate how many earned:
  (i)   less than £84
  (ii) at least £94
  (iii) between £46 and £84

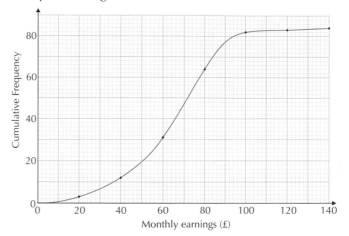

Outliers and box plots

An **outlier** is a piece of data that lies a **long way** from the majority of the readings in a data set. To decide whether a reading is an outlier, you have to **test** whether it falls **outside** certain limits, called **fences**. It's common to use the fences $Q_1 - (1.5 \times IQR)$ and $Q_3 + (1.5 \times IQR)$.

A **box plot** is a 'visual summary' of a data set — it shows the **median**, **quartiles** and **outliers**:

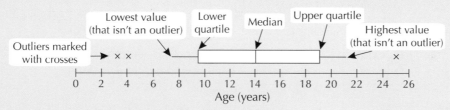

 The stem and leaf diagram shows the IQs of Year 11 students at a high school.

Draw a box plot to represent this data, using the fences $Q_1 - 1.5 \times IQR$ and $Q_3 + 1.5 \times IQR$ to identify outliers.

9	3
10	5 8 9
11	0 2 3 5 6 8 9
12	0 0 1 3 4 6 8
13	2 4
14	4

1. Find the quartiles:

$n = 21 \Rightarrow \frac{n}{4} = 5.25, \frac{n}{2} = 10.5, \frac{3n}{4} = 15.75$

Key: 10 | 5 means an IQ of 105

Q_1 is the 6th value = 112, Q_2 is the 11th value = 119, Q_3 is the 16th value = 124

2. Find the fences: IQR = 124 − 112 = 12
   Lower fence = 112 − (1.5 × 12) = 94, upper fence = 124 + (1.5 × 12) = 142

3. Check for outliers: 93 < 94 so 93 is an outlier, 144 > 142 so 144 is an outlier

4. Draw the box plot:

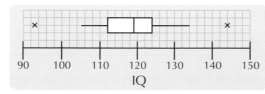

Exercise 4.3

In this exercise use the fences $Q_1 - (1.5 \times IQR)$ and $Q_3 + (1.5 \times IQR)$ to test for outliers.

Q1 The lower and upper quartiles of a data set are 19 and 31. Are the data values 4 and 52 outliers?

Q2 A set of data was analysed and the following values were found.

minimum value = 4, maximum value = 49, $Q_1 = 16$, median = 24, $Q_3 = 37$

a) Find the interquartile range.   b) Are there any outliers in this data set?

c) Draw a box plot to illustrate the data set.

Q3 The numbers of items of junk mail received in six months by people living in the towns of Goossea and Pigham are shown.

a) Are any of the data values from Pigham outliers?

b) Draw a box plot to illustrate the data from Pigham.

c) Draw a box plot to illustrate the data from Goossea.

Goossea

0, 2, 6, 13, 15, 17, 19, 24, 27, 28, 28, 31, 32, 35, 41, 44, 50, 75

Pigham

14, 17, 20, 20, 23, 26, 32, 33, 35, 35, 39, 41, 42, 46, 48, 52, 54, 55

Variance and standard deviation

Variance and **standard deviation** are two related measures of **dispersion** — the bigger they are, the more **spread out** the data values are from the mean. For a set of n x-values with mean $\bar{x}$:

$$\text{variance} = \frac{\sum(x - \bar{x})^2}{n} = \frac{\sum x^2}{n} - \bar{x}^2$$

$$\text{standard deviation} = \sqrt{\text{variance}}$$

Tip: The variance can also be written as $\frac{S_{xx}}{n}$, where $S_{xx} = \sum(x - \bar{x})^2$.

Tip: The standard deviation has the same units as the data, and the variance has squared units.

You can use the **standard deviation** to check for **outliers** (see p.155) — some commonly used fences are ($\bar{x} \pm 2$ standard deviations) and ($\bar{x} \pm 3$ standard deviations).

Examples

a) **Find the variance and standard deviation of the following data set:**

2, 3, 4, 4, 6, 11, 12

1. Find the mean: $\bar{x} = \dfrac{\sum x}{n} = \dfrac{42}{7} = 6$

2. Find $\sum x^2$: $\sum x^2 = 4 + 9 + 16 + 16 + 36 + 121 + 144 = 346$

3. Use the variance formula: $\text{variance} = \dfrac{\sum x^2}{n} - \bar{x}^2 = \dfrac{346}{7} - 6^2 = 13.428... = \mathbf{13.4}$ (3 s.f.)

4. Take the square root: $\text{standard deviation} = \sqrt{13.428...} = \mathbf{3.66}$ (3 s.f.)

b) **Use the fences ($\bar{x} \pm 2$ standard deviations) to check the data for outliers.**

Find the fences: $\bar{x} + 2$ s.d. $= 6 + 7.32... = 13.3$ (1 d.p.)

$\bar{x} - 2$ s.d. $= 6 - 7.32... = -1.3$ (1 d.p.)

All of the data is between these fences, so there are **no outliers**.

For data in a **frequency table**, the variance formula can be written:

$$\text{variance} = \frac{\sum fx^2}{\sum f} - \bar{x}^2, \text{ where } \bar{x} = \frac{\sum fx}{\sum f}$$

Find the variance and standard deviation of the data in this table.

x	2	3	4	5	6	7
frequency, f	2	5	5	4	1	1

1. Add rows to the table for fx, x^2 and fx^2, and a column for the totals.

x	2	3	4	5	6	7	Total
f	2	5	5	4	1	1	18
fx	4	15	20	20	6	7	72
x^2	4	9	16	25	36	49	—
fx^2	8	45	80	100	36	49	318

2. Find the mean: $\bar{x} = \dfrac{\sum fx}{\sum f} = \dfrac{72}{18} = 4$

3. Use the formula: variance $= \dfrac{\sum fx^2}{\sum f} - \bar{x}^2 = \dfrac{318}{18} - 4^2 = 1.666... = \mathbf{1.67}$ (3 s.f.)

4. Take the square root: standard deviation $= \sqrt{1.666...} = \mathbf{1.29}$ (3 s.f.)

Exercise 4.4

Q1 The attendance figures (x) for Wessex Football Club's first six matches of the season were:
$$756, 755, 764, 778, 754, 759.$$
a) Find the mean ($\bar{x}$) of these attendance figures.
b) Calculate the sum of the squares of the attendance figures, $\sum x^2$.
c) Use your answers to find the variance and standard deviation of the attendance figures.

Q2 The figures for the number of TVs (x) in the households of 20 students are shown in the table.
a) Find the mean number of TVs ($\bar{x}$) in the 20 households.
b) By adding rows showing x^2 and fx^2 to the table, find $\sum fx^2$.
c) Calculate the variance and standard deviation for the data.

x	1	2	3	4
frequency, f	7	8	4	1

Q3 A data set is summarised as follows: $n = 10$, $\sum x = 29$ and $\sum x^2 = 95.03$
a) Find the standard deviation for this data.
b) The lowest value in the data set is 0.35. Use the fence ($\bar{x} - 3$ standard deviations) to determine whether or not this value is an outlier.

Q4 Su and Ellen are collecting data on the durations of the eruptions of the volcano in their garden. Between them, they have recorded the duration of the last 60 eruptions.
- Su has timed 23 eruptions, with average duration 3.42 minutes and s.d. 1.07 minutes.
- Ellen has timed 37 eruptions, with average duration 3.92 minutes and s.d. 0.97 minutes.

(PROBLEM SOLVING)

a) Calculate the combined mean duration of all the observed eruptions.
b) Find the variance and standard deviation of the combined set of 60 eruptions.

If you're asked to find the **sample variance**, you need a slightly different formula. ⟶

The **sample standard deviation** is the square root of the sample variance.

Sample variance $= \dfrac{\sum (x - \bar{x})^2}{n-1} = \dfrac{\sum x^2 - n\bar{x}^2}{n-1}$

For data in a frequency table, use: $\dfrac{\sum fx^2 - (\sum f)\bar{x}^2}{(\sum f) - 1}$

Tip: Sample variance can also be written as $\dfrac{S_{xx}}{n-1}$, where $S_{xx} = \sum (x - \bar{x})^2$.

Tip: The sample standard deviation is often written as s, and the sample variance as s^2.

Find the sample standard deviation of the following data.
15, 33, 31, 24, 30, 28, 14, 19, 22, 18, 39, 27

1. Find the mean and $\sum x^2$: $\quad \bar{x} = \dfrac{\sum x}{n} = \dfrac{300}{12} = 25$, $\quad \sum x^2 = 8150$

2. Use the formula: sample variance $= \dfrac{\sum x^2 - n\bar{x}^2}{n-1} = \dfrac{8150 - 12 \times 25^2}{11} = \dfrac{8150 - 7500}{11} = 59.09...$

3. Take the square root: sample standard deviation $= \sqrt{59.09...} = \textbf{7.69}$ (3 s.f.)

Exercise 4.5

Q1 A student asks a sample of 21 people in his year group how many contacts they have on their mobile phone. The 21 responses can be summarised by $\sum x = 946$ and $\sum x^2 = 50\,290$, where x is the number of contacts. Calculate the mean and sample standard deviation of x.

Q2 Calculate the sample variance and sample standard deviation for the data in the table.

x	0	5	10	15	20	25
frequency, f	4	9	13	11	7	2

You can only **estimate** the variance and standard deviation of **grouped** data.
Assume that each data value is equal to the **class midpoint** and use the formula on p.156.

The heights of sunflowers in a garden were measured, and are recorded in the table below.

Height of sunflower, h (cm)	$150 \leq h < 170$	$170 \leq h < 190$	$190 \leq h < 210$	$210 \leq h < 230$
Frequency, f	5	10	12	3

Estimate the variance and the standard deviation of the heights.

1. Add extra rows for the class midpoint (x), fx, x^2 and fx^2, and a totals column:

Height of sunflower, h (cm)	$150 \leq h < 170$	$170 \leq h < 190$	$190 \leq h < 210$	$210 \leq h < 230$	Total
Frequency, f	5	10	12	3	30
Class midpoint, x	160	180	200	220	—
fx	800	1800	2400	660	5660
x^2	25 600	32 400	40 000	48 400	—
fx^2	128 000	324 000	480 000	145 200	1 077 200

2. Estimate the mean: $\quad \bar{x} = \dfrac{\sum fx}{\sum f} = \dfrac{5660}{30}$

3. Use the formula: $\quad$ variance $= \dfrac{\sum fx^2}{\sum f} - \bar{x}^2 = \dfrac{1\,077\,200}{30} - \left(\dfrac{5660}{30}\right)^2 = 311.55...$
$$= \textbf{312 cm}^2 \text{ (3 s.f.)}$$

standard deviation $= \sqrt{311.55...} = \textbf{17.7 cm}$ (3 s.f.)

Exercise 4.6

Q1 The yields (w, in kg) of potatoes from a number of allotments is shown in the grouped frequency table on the right.

a) Estimate the variance and standard deviation for this data.

b) Explain why your answers to a) are estimates.

Yield, w (kg)	Frequency
$50 \leq w < 60$	23
$60 \leq w < 70$	12
$70 \leq w < 80$	15
$80 \leq w < 90$	6
$90 \leq w < 100$	2

Q2 Estimate the standard deviation for the data in the following table:

p	$0 \leq p < 0.3$	$0.3 \leq p < 0.5$	$0.5 \leq p < 0.6$	$0.6 \leq p < 0.75$	$0.75 \leq p < 1$
frequency	31	68	132	97	22

Comparing measures of dispersion

The range, interquartile range, variance and standard deviation have advantages and disadvantages:

Range

- The range is the **easiest** measure of dispersion to calculate.
- It's heavily affected by even a **single** extreme value / outlier, and it depends on only **two** data values — it **doesn't** tell you anything about how spread out the rest of the values are.

Interquartile range

- It's **not** affected by **extreme values** — so if the data contains **outliers**, then the interquartile range is a good measure of dispersion to use.
- It can be fairly **difficult** to calculate, particularly for grouped data.

Variance

- The variance depends on **all** the data values, but it's **difficult** to calculate, and is affected by **outliers**.
- It's also expressed in **different units** from the actual data values, so it can be difficult to interpret.

Standard deviation

- Like the variance, the standard deviation depends on **all** the data values, but is **difficult** to calculate, and is affected by **extreme values**.
- It has the **same units** as the data values so it is easier to interpret.

Exercise 4.7

Q1 Catherine is examining data on the number of court cases that have occurred each year for the past 20 years. Give one advantage of using the interquartile range as a measure of dispersion.

Q2 A TV channel wants to evaluate some data that they have collected on the amount of time that people spend watching TV per week. They anticipate that there will be a number of extreme values in the data. Which would be a better measure of dispersion: the standard deviation or the interquartile range?

Coding

Coding is a way of making the numbers in a data set **easier** to work with, by doing one or both of:

- **adding** a number to (or **subtracting** a number from) all your readings,
- **multiplying** (or **dividing**) all your readings by a number.

You have to change your **original** variable, x, to a **different** one, such as y.
An original data value x will be related to a **coded** data value y by an equation of the form $y = \dfrac{x-a}{b}$ where a and b are numbers you choose.

The mean and standard deviation of the original data values will then be related to the mean and standard deviation of the coded data values by the following equations:

$$\overline{y} = \frac{\overline{x} - a}{b}, \text{ where } \overline{x} \text{ and } \overline{y} \text{ are the means of variables } x \text{ and } y$$

$$\text{standard deviation of } y = \frac{\text{standard deviation of } x}{b}$$

Example

Find the mean and standard deviation of:
1 862 020, 1 862 040, 1 862 010 and 1 862 050.

1. All of the values start with 1862..., so subtract 1 862 000: $x - 1\,862\,000$: {20, 40, 10, 50}

2. All of these results can be divided by 10: $\frac{x - 1\,862\,000}{10}$: {2, 4, 1, 5}

3. Define your coded variable: $y = \frac{x - 1\,862\,000}{10}$

4. Find the mean and s.d. of the coded data: $\overline{y} = \frac{2 + 4 + 1 + 5}{4} = \frac{12}{4} = 3$

   s.d. of $y = \sqrt{\frac{2^2 + 4^2 + 1^2 + 5^2}{4} - 3^2} = \sqrt{\frac{46}{4} - 9} = \sqrt{2.5} = 1.5811...$

5. Use the formula and rearrange for x: $\overline{y} = \frac{\overline{x} - a}{b} \Rightarrow \overline{x} = a + b\overline{y} \Rightarrow \overline{x} = 1\,862\,000 + 10 \times 3$
   $= \mathbf{1\,862\,030}$

   s.d. of $y = \frac{\text{s.d. of } x}{b} \Rightarrow \textbf{s.d. of } \boldsymbol{x} = b \times \text{s.d. of } y$
   $= 10 \times 1.5811... = \mathbf{15.8}$ (3 s.f.)

With **grouped** data, you assume that all of the data values are equal to their **class midpoint**, so this is the x-value that you use with the coding equation $y = \frac{x - a}{b}$.

Example Estimate the mean and standard deviation of this data using $y = \frac{x - 15.5}{10}$.

Number of beans	11-20	21-30	31-40	41-50
Frequency, f	17	21	27	15

1. Add to the table.

2. Find the mean and s.d. of y:

   $\overline{y} = \frac{\sum fy}{\sum f} = \frac{120}{80} = 1.5$

   s.d. of $y = \sqrt{\frac{\sum fy^2}{\sum f} - \overline{y}^2}$

   $= \sqrt{\frac{264}{80} - 1.5^2} = \sqrt{1.05} = 1.0246...$

Number of beans	11-20	21-30	31-40	41-50	Total
Frequency, f	17	21	27	15	80
Class midpoint, x	15.5	25.5	35.5	45.5	—
Coded value, y	0	1	2	3	—
fy	0	21	54	45	120
y^2	0	1	4	9	—
fy^2	0	21	108	135	264

3. Uncode the data: $\overline{y} = \frac{\overline{x} - 15.5}{10} \Rightarrow \overline{x} = 10\overline{y} + 15.5 = \mathbf{30.5 \text{ beans}}$

   s.d. of $y = \frac{\text{s.d. of } x}{10} \Rightarrow \textbf{s.d. of } \boldsymbol{x} = 10 \times \text{s.d. of } y = 10 \times 1.0246... = \mathbf{10.2 \text{ beans}}$ (3 s.f.)

Exercise 4.8

Q1 A set of data values (x) are coded using $y = \frac{x - 20\,000}{15}$.
The mean of the coded data ($\overline{y}$) is 12.4, and the standard deviation of the coded data is 1.34.
Find the mean and standard deviation of the original data set.

Q2 The widths (in cm) of 10 sunflower seeds in a packet are given below.

0.61, 0.67, 0.63, 0.63, 0.66, 0.65, 0.64, 0.68, 0.64, 0.62

a) Code the data (x) to form a new data set consisting of integer values (y) between 1 and 10.

b) Find the mean and standard deviation of the original values (x).

Q3 The table below shows the weight, x, of 12 items on a production line.

Weight (to nearest g)	100-104	105-109	110-114	115-119
Frequency	2	6	3	1

Use the coding $y = x - 102$ to estimate the mean and standard deviation of the items' weights.

Q4 Twenty pieces of data (x) have been summarised as follows: $\sum(x + 2) = 7$ and $\sum(x + 2)^2 = 80$
Calculate the mean and standard deviation of the data.

Comparing distributions

You can **compare** two distributions by comparing measures of **location** (mean, median, midrange, mode) or measures of **dispersion** (range, interquartile range, standard deviation, etc.). It's important to **relate** these back to the **context** of the data in order to **draw conclusions** about the distributions.

 The table summarises the marks obtained by a group of students in Maths 'Calculator' and 'Non-calculator' papers.
Compare the location and dispersion of the distributions.

Calculator paper		Non-calculator paper
58	Median, Q_2	42
30	Interquartile range	21
55	Mean	46
21.2	Standard deviation	17.8

Location: The mean and the median are both higher for the Calculator paper, so **scores are generally higher on the Calculator paper**.

Dispersion: The IQR and standard deviation are higher for the Calculator paper, so **scores on the Calculator paper are more spread out than those for the Non-calculator paper**.

 The box plots below show how the masses (in g) of the tomatoes in two harvests were distributed. Compare the distributions of the two harvests.

Location: The midrange is about the same for both harvests, but the median is higher for Harvest 1, so **the tomatoes in Harvest 1 were generally heavier**.

Dispersion: The interquartile range (IQR) and the range for Harvest 1 are higher than those for Harvest 2, so **the masses of the tomatoes in Harvest 1 were more varied than the masses of the tomatoes in Harvest 2**.

Exercise 4.9

Q1 The box plots show the prices of shoes (in £) from two different shops.

Compare the location and dispersion of the two shops' prices.

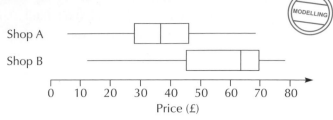

Shop A

Shop B

Price (£)

Q2 10 men and 10 women were asked how many hours of sleep they got on a typical night.
The results are as follows: Men: 6, 7, 9, 8, 8, 6, 7, 7, 10, 5
                               Women: 9, 9, 7, 8, 5, 11, 10, 8, 10, 8

Compare the location and dispersion of the two data sets.

5. Correlation and Regression

Scatter diagrams and correlation

Data made up of pairs of values (x, y) is called **bivariate data**. You can plot bivariate data on a **scatter diagram** — where each variable is plotted along one of the axes. Scatter diagrams are helpful for recognising when data is **correlated** — the closer the data points are to forming a straight line, the **stronger** the correlation is. You may have to identify **outliers** — these could be values that **don't fit the pattern**, or **measurement errors**.

Examples Describe the correlation shown in each scatter diagram:

a)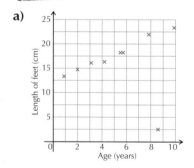

b)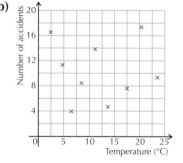

c)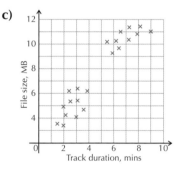

a) Most of the data points lie very close to a straight line with positive gradient, so the diagram shows **strong positive** correlation.

The point at (8.5, 2.5) appears to be a measurement error.

b) The data does not seem to form any line, so there is **no** correlation between the variables.

c) Overall, the data seems to trend towards a line with positive gradient, so the diagram shows **positive** correlation overall.

However, the data forms two clusters, which both show only weak positive correlation.

Although two variables might be **correlated**, this does not mean that a change in one **causes** a change in the other. They could be linked by another factor — for example, sales of barbecues and sales of ice cream might be correlated, but they're both affected by another factor (temperature).

Exercise 5.1

Q1 8 runners participating in a 1 km race were asked how many hours of exercise they did per week. Their responses, and their race times in minutes, are shown in the table below:

Exercise, hours	17	15	5	12	2	2	10	7.5
Race time, mins	6.7	6.8	9.5	6.1	11.5	6.3	8	9.9

a) Plot a scatter diagram to show this data.

b) Describe any correlation shown, and identify any results that appear to be outliers.

Q2 Zoe lives near a beach. She records the number of seagulls and the number of people flying kites she sees each day, over the course of one month. She finds negative correlation in the data, and concludes that seagulls must be scared off by kites. Explain whether the data supports this conclusion.

Q3 This table shows the average length and the average circumference of eggs for several species of bird, measured in cm.

Length	5.9	2.1	3.4	5.1	8.9	6.6	7.2	4.5	6.8
Circumference	19.6	6.3	7.1	9.9	3.5	21	18.7	8.3	18.4

a) Plot a scatter diagram to show this data.   b) Describe any trends in the data.

c) One of the measurements was recorded incorrectly. Use your scatter diagram to determine which.

Linear regression

If two variables are correlated, you can draw a **'line of best fit'** through the data on the scatter diagram. **Linear regression** is a process that is used to find the equation of this line, called the **regression line**. In order to interpret a regression line, you need to decide which is the explanatory variable and which is the response variable.

- The **explanatory variable** (or **independent variable**) is the variable you can directly control, or the one that you think is **affecting** the other — it is always drawn along the **horizontal axis**.

- The **response variable** (or **dependent variable**) is the variable you think is **being affected** — it is always drawn up the **vertical axis**.

 For each situation below, explain which quantity would be the explanatory variable, and which would be the response variable.

a) **A scientist is investigating the relationship between the amount of fertiliser applied to a tomato plant and the eventual yield.**

1. The scientist can directly control the amount of fertiliser they give each plant, so **'amount of fertiliser' is the explanatory variable**.

2. The scientist measures the effect this has on the plant's yield, so **'yield' is the response variable**.

b) **A researcher is examining how a town's latitude and the number of days when the temperature rose above 10 °C are linked.**

Although the researcher can't control the latitude of towns, it would be the difference in latitude that leads to a difference in temperature, and not the other way around. So **'town's latitude' is the explanatory variable**, and **'number of days when the temperature rose above 10 °C' is the response variable**.

The **regression line of y on x** is a line of the form: $\boxed{y = a + bx}$ where a and b are constants.

The '**...of y on x**' part means that x is the explanatory variable, and y is the response variable.

 Example
A company is collecting data on the fuel efficiency of a type of lorry. They compare the load on a lorry, x (in tonnes), with the fuel efficiency, y (in km per litre), and calculate the regression line of y on x to be: $y = 12.5 - 0.8x$. Interpret the values of a and b in this context. MODELLING

1. The value of **a** tells you that **a load of 0 tonnes corresponds to a fuel efficiency of 12.5 km per litre** — this is the fixed fuel efficiency of the lorry before you have even loaded anything on it.

2. The value of **b** tells you that **for every extra tonne carried, you'd expect the lorry's fuel efficiency to fall by 0.8 km per litre** (since when x increases by 1, y falls by 0.8).

You can use a regression line to **predict** values of your **response variable**.
There are two forms of this — **interpolation** and **extrapolation**.

- **Interpolation** is when you use the regression line to predict values of the response variable for values of the explanatory variable that are **within** the range of your collected data. This is usually **reliable** since the observed data supports the prediction.

- **Extrapolation** is when you predict values of the response variable for values of the explanatory variable that are **outside** the range of the collected data. This is a lot more **unreliable**, as the data only provides evidence that the regression line is accurate for values within the observed range. Outside of this range, the relationship could **change** in a way that the data does not show.

 Examples
The length of a spring (y, in cm) when loaded with different masses (m, in g) has the regression line of y on m: $y = 7.8 + 0.01043m$

a) **Estimate the length of the spring when loaded with a mass of:** (i) 370 g (ii) 670 g

(i) $m = 370$, so: $y = 7.8 + 0.01043 \times 370 = $ **11.7 cm** (1 d.p.)

(ii) $m = 670$, so: $y = 7.8 + 0.01043 \times 670 = $ **14.8 cm** (1 d.p.)

b) **The smallest value of m used to find the regression line was 200 g, and the largest value of m was 500 g. Comment on the reliability of the estimates in part a).**

1. $m = 370$ falls within the range of the original data for m, so this is an interpolation. This means **the result should be fairly reliable**.

2. But $m = 670$ falls outside the range of the original data for m, so this is an extrapolation. This means the regression line may not be valid, and **the estimate of y should be treated with caution**.

Exercise 5.2

Q1 For each pair of variables, state which is the explanatory variable, and which is the response variable:

a) 'time spent practising the piano in a week' and 'number of mistakes made in a test at the end of the week'

b) 'age of a second-hand car' and 'value of the car'

c) 'number of phone calls made in a town in a week' and 'population of the town'

d) 'growth rate of a plant in an experiment' and 'amount of sunlight falling on the plant'

Q2 The equation of the regression line of y on x is $y = 1.67 + 0.107x$.
  a) Which variable is the response variable?
  b) Find the predicted value of y corresponding to: (i) $x = 5$ (ii) $x = 20$

Q3 A volunteer counted the number of spots (s) on an area of skin after d days of acne treatment, where d had values 2, 6, 10, 14, 18 and 22. The equation of the regression line of s on d is $s = 58.8 - 2.47d$.
  a) Estimate the number of spots the volunteer had on day 7.
     Comment on the reliability of your answer.
  b) She forgot to count how many spots she had before starting to use the product. Estimate this number. Comment on your answer.
  c) The volunteer claims that the regression equation must be wrong, because it predicts that after 30 days she should have a negative number of spots. Comment on this claim.

Non-linear regression

When the relationship between two variables is **non-linear** (i.e. they don't form a straight line), the 'best fit' of the data can be described by a non-linear function, such as a quadratic, trigonometric, logarithmic or exponential function.

 A concert venue collects data on the number of tickets sold for an event, y, and the amount they spend on advertising for the event, £x. They calculate that the regression curve of y on x is: $y = 0.002x^2 + 55$

a) **The venue has budgeted to spend £500 on advertising for a particular event. How many tickets do they expect to sell?**

Set $x = 500$: $y = 0.002 \times 500^2 + 55 = $ **555 tickets**

b) **The venue has 1500 seats. One of the staff members claims that, if they want to sell out the event, they should spend £850 on advertising. Comment on the validity of this claim.**

  1. This claim is trying to predict the amount they should spend based on the number of tickets they want to sell — i.e. predict the explanatory variable from the response variable. The regression curve should only be used to predict the value of the response variable, so **this claim is not reliable**.

  2. If 1500 is the maximum number of tickets the venue can sell, then they may not have a lot of data to support the claim and it could be extrapolated from their collected data — this is another reason why it might be **unreliable**.

Exercise 5.3

Q1 The scatter diagram shows a bivariate data set (x, y).
   Which of the following types of function would be
   the most appropriate as a best fit model for this data?
       linear   quadratic   cubic   sine   exponential

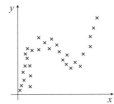

Q2 A bivariate data set (s, t) is summarised as follows:
       number of pairs of data values: 5   range of s: 1.6 to 7.9   regression curve of t on s: $t = 2e^{0.3s}$
   Predict the value of t when $s = 2$, and comment on the validity of this estimate.

Q1 The manager of a tennis club wants to know if members are happy with the facilities provided.

a) Identify the population the manager is interested in.

b) Is this population finite or infinite?

Q2 A teacher is investigating whether a student's ability to memorise a random string of letters is related to their ability to spell. He plans to ask students from his school, which has 1200 pupils, to do a standard spelling test and then to memorise a random string of 20 letters.

a) What is the population?

b) Give two reasons why he should use a sample survey rather than carry out a census.

Q3 The houses on Park Road are numbered from 1 to 173. Forty households are to be chosen to take part in a council survey. Describe a method for choosing an unbiased sample.

Q4 A school uniform manufacturer wants to collect data on the heights of teenagers at the schools in their county. Describe a suitable sampling method for this situation.

Q5 For each of the following situations, name the sampling method used and give one disadvantage of using this sampling method:

a) A tea company is investigating tea-drinking habits of its customers. The interviewer is asked to sample exactly 60 women and 40 men using a non-random sampling method.

b) After a concert, a band is looking for feedback from their fans. Using the ticket numbers, they select every 100th fan to complete a survey.

c) A student is researching shopping habits in the UK. He records how many people enter his local shopping centre between 9 am and 5 pm on a Monday.

Q6 Twenty phone calls were made by a householder one evening. The lengths of the calls (in minutes to the nearest minute) are recorded in the table below.

Length of calls	0 - 2	3 - 5	6 - 8	9 - 15
Number of calls	10	6	3	1

Show this data on: a) a frequency polygon,   b) a histogram.

Q7 The histogram represents the number of people working at a company, grouped by age.

a) Find the percentage of people aged between 26 and 29.

b) Find the probability that a randomly-chosen person is aged 36 or over.

c) Estimate the percentage of people aged 35 or over.

d) Explain why your answer in part c) is only an estimate.

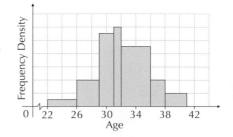

Q8 The stem and leaf diagram on the right represents the lengths (in cm) of 15 bananas. Write down the original data as a list.

```
12 | 8
13 | 2 5
14 | 3 3 6 8
15 | 2 9
16 | 1 1 2 3
17 | 0 2
```

Key: 12|8 means 12.8 cm

Q9   Describe the distribution of the data shown by each
      of the three curves on the diagram, stating any skewness
      and whether the data appears to be unimodal or bimodal.

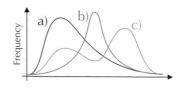

Q10   Calculate the mean, median and mode of the data in the table.

x	0	1	2	3	4
f	5	4	4	2	1

Q11   The speeds of 60 cars travelling in a 40 mph speed limit area were measured to the nearest mph.
      The data is summarised in the table. Estimate the mean and median, and state the modal class.

Speed (mph)	30 - 34	35 - 39	40 - 44	45 - 50
Frequency	12	37	9	2

Q12   Two data sets, A and B, are given below:
      A: 16, 41, 28, 23, 7, 11, 37, 16, 9, 21, 26, 18, 14, 31, 8
      B: 33, 38, 25, 15, 42, 12, 6, 24, 30, 15, 19, 15, 40, 36, 24
      Calculate: a) the range of B   b) the interquartile range of A
                    c) the 20% to 80% interpercentile range of B

Q13   a) Draw a cumulative frequency diagram for the following data:

r	$0 \leq r < 2$	$2 \leq r < 4$	$4 \leq r < 6$	$6 \leq r < 8$	$8 \leq r < 10$
Frequency	2	6	7	4	1

      b) Use your cumulative frequency diagram to estimate the number of r-values that are:
         (i) less than 3   (ii) more than 5   (iii) between 3.5 and 7
      c) Use your cumulative frequency diagram to estimate:
         (i) the interquartile range   (ii) the 10% to 90% interpercentile range

Q14   A company is testing a new video game. In the game, each level lasts for 200 seconds,
      after which the next level starts immediately. 100 people played the game,
      and the level they reached before losing is shown in the table:

Level reached	3	4	5	6	7	8	9	10
Frequency, f	6	11	14	28	22	10	7	2

      a) Draw a grouped frequency table with 8 classes showing how long the games lasted, in seconds.
      b) Draw a cumulative frequency diagram for the data in your new table.
      c) Use your cumulative frequency diagram to estimate the number of games that lasted:
         (i) less than 500 seconds,   (ii) more than 1500 seconds.
      d) Use linear interpolation to estimate the interquartile range of the games' durations.

Q15   Two workers iron 10 items of clothing and record the time, to the nearest minute, that each takes:
          Worker A: 3 5 2 7 10 4 5 5 4 12   Worker B: 4 4 8 6 7 8 9 10 11 9
      a) For worker A's times, find: (i) the median   (ii) the lower and upper quartiles
         (iii) whether there are any outliers, using the fences $Q_1 - 1.5 \times$ IQR and $Q_3 + 1.5 \times$ IQR.
      b) Draw two box plots, using the same scale, to represent the times of each worker.
      c) Make one statement comparing the two sets of data.
      d) Which worker would be better to employ? Give a reason for your answer.

Q16 Find the mean and standard deviation of the following numbers: 11, 12, 14, 17, 21, 23, 27

Q17 The scores in an IQ test for 50 people are recorded in the table below.

Score	100 - 106	107 - 113	114 - 120	121 - 127	128 - 134
Frequency	6	11	22	9	2

Estimate the mean and variance of the distribution.

Q18 For a set of data, $n = 100$, $\sum(x - 20) = 125$, and $\sum(x - 20)^2 = 221$.

a) Find the mean and standard deviation of x.

b) Use the fences ($\bar{x} \pm 2$ standard deviations) to test whether the value $x = 19.6$ is an outlier.

Q19 The time taken (to the nearest minute) for a commuter to travel to work on 20 consecutive work days is recorded in the table. Use the coding $y = x - 35.5$ to estimate the mean and standard deviation of the times, where x is the class midpoint.

Time	Frequency, f
30 - 33	3
34 - 37	6
38 - 41	7
42 - 45	4

Q20 A travel agent is collecting data on two islands, A and B. She records the maximum daily temperature on 100 days. The cumulative frequency curves for her results are shown on the graph.

Compare the location and dispersion of the data for the two islands.

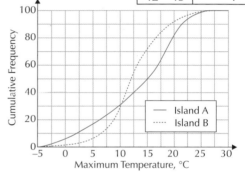

Q21 The table below shows the results of some measurements concerning alcoholic cocktails. Here, x = total volume in ml, and y = percentage alcohol concentration by volume.

x	90	100	100	150	160	200	240	250	290	300
y	40	35	25	30	25	25	20	25	15	7

a) Draw a scatter diagram representing this information.

b) Does the data suggest any correlation?

Q22 For each pair of variables below, state which would be the explanatory variable and which would be the response variable.

a) 'number of volleyball-related injuries in a year' and 'number of sunny days that year'

b) 'number of rainy days in a year' and 'number of board game-related injuries that year'

c) 'a person's disposable income' and 'amount they spend on luxuries'

d) 'number of trips to the loo in a day' and 'number of cups of tea drunk that day'

e) 'number of festival tickets sold' and 'number of pairs of Wellington boots bought'

Q23 The radius in mm, r, and the mass in grams, m, of 10 randomly selected blueberry pancakes are given in the table below.

r	48.0	51.0	52.0	54.5	55.1	53.6	50.0	52.6	49.4	51.2
m	100	105	108	120	125	118	100	115	98	110

The regression line of m on r has equation $m = 3.94r - 94$

a) Use the regression line to estimate the mass of a blueberry pancake of radius 60 mm.

b) Comment on the reliability of your estimate, giving a reason for your answer.

Chapter 12 — Probability

Probability is a measure of how likely events are to happen. You'll have seen the topics in this chapter at GCSE, but you'll build on them here with trickier A-Level questions.

1. Elementary Probability

If **all the possible outcomes** (the different things that can happen) are **equally likely**, you can work out the **probability of an event** using this formula:

$$P(\text{event}) = \frac{\text{Number of outcomes where event happens}}{\text{Total number of possible outcomes}}$$

Tip: 'P(event)' is short for 'the probability of an event' — it's always between 0 (impossible) and 1 (certain).

The **sample space** (called S) is the set of **all possible outcomes** of a trial. Drawing a **diagram** of the sample space can help you to count the outcomes you're interested in.

Example

Two bags each contain five cards. Bag A contains cards numbered 1, 3, 3, 4 and 5, and bag B contains cards numbered 1, 2, 4, 4 and 5. A card is selected at random from each bag and the numbers on the two cards are added together to give a total score.

Use a sample-space diagram to find the probability that the total score is no more than 6.

1. Draw a sample-space diagram showing all the possible total scores.
   Circle all the scores of 6 or less. ⟶

2. Now use the probability formula.
   There are 25 equally likely outcomes in total, and 12 outcomes where the event 'total score is no more than 6' happens.

P(total score is no more than 6) $= \dfrac{12}{25}$

The **expected frequency** of an event A in n trials is given by:

Expected frequency $= n \times P(A)$

Exercise 1.1

Q1 One card is selected at random from a standard pack of 52 playing cards. Find the probability of selecting each of the following:

   a) the 7 of diamonds   b) the queen of spades   c) a 9 of any suit   d) a heart or a diamond

Q2 A dice game involves rolling two standard dice and calculating the product of the two scores.

   a) Draw a sample-space diagram to show all the possible outcomes.

   b) Find the probability that the product is a prime number.

   c) Find the probability that the product is less than 7.

   d) Find the expected frequency of 'a multiple of 10', if the game is played 60 times.

Q3 A game involves picking a card at random from 10 cards, numbered 1 to 10, and tossing a coin.

   a) Draw a sample-space diagram to show all the possible outcomes.

   b) Find the probability that the card selected shows an even number and the coin shows 'tails'.

Q4 Martha rolls two fair six-sided dice and calculates a score by subtracting the smaller result from the larger (the score is zero if the two results are the same).

a) Draw a sample-space diagram to show all the possible outcomes.

b) Find P(the score is zero).

c) Find P(the score is greater than 5).

d) What is the most likely score? And what is its probability?

Q5 Spinner 1 has five equal sections, labelled 2, 3, 5, 7 and 11, and spinner 2 has five equal sections, labelled 2, 4, 6, 8 and 10. If each spinner is spun once, find the probability that the number on spinner 2 is greater than the number on spinner 1.

2. Solving Probability Problems

Venn diagrams

You can use a Venn diagram to help you **find probabilities** — each **circle** represents an **event** in the sample space. The Venn diagram below represents the events A and B.

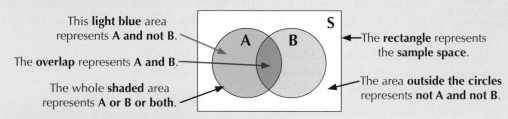

This **light blue** area represents **A and not B**.

The **overlap** represents **A and B**.

The whole **shaded** area represents **A or B or both**.

The **rectangle** represents the **sample space**.

The area **outside the circles** represents **not A and not B**.

- The **total probability** in S equals **1**.
- The area **outside a circle** represents the event **not happening**, e.g. **not A**, written **A′**. P(A′) = 1 − P(A).

Examples **There are 30 pupils in a class. 14 of the pupils are girls and 11 of the pupils have brown hair. Of the pupils with brown hair, 6 are boys.**

a) **Show this information on a Venn diagram.**

- Draw a Venn diagram with circles BH for 'brown hair' and G for 'girls'.
- Label it with the numbers of pupils in each part of the diagram.

1. 6 boys have brown hair, so 6 pupils have brown hair but aren't girls.

2. 11 pupils have brown hair, so: 11 − 6 = 5 girls have brown hair.

3. There are 14 girls in total, so: 14 − 5 = 9 girls don't have brown hair.

4. There are 30 pupils in total, so: 30 − (9 + 5 + 6) = 10 boys don't have brown hair.

BH   G   S
6   5   9
10

b) **A girl is selected at random from the class. Find the probability that she has brown hair.**

Use the probability formula for equally likely outcomes. You already know that the pupil is a girl, so there are 14 possible outcomes. And there are 5 girls who have brown hair.

P(the girl selected has brown hair) = $\frac{5}{14}$

In the next example, the Venn diagram shows the **proportion** in each group.

 A survey was done to find out which of cats (C), dogs (D) and gerbils (G) people like. The diagram shows the proportion who like each animal.

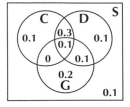

One person who completed the survey is chosen at random. Find the probability that this person likes dogs or cats (or both).

- 'Likes dogs or cats or both' is shown by the area that's in C or D or both.

- The probability of the person being in this area is equal to the proportion of people in the area.

P(likes dogs, cats or both)
= 0.1 + 0.3 + 0 + 0.1 + 0.1 + 0.1
= **0.7**

Tip: You could also do P(likes dogs, cats or both) = 1 − (0.2 + 0.1) = 0.7, since the total probability is 1.

Exercise 2.1

Q1 For events A and B, P(A) = 0.4, P(B) = 0.5 and P(A and B) = 0.15.

    a) Draw a Venn diagram to represent events A and B.

    b) Find P(A and not B)   c) Find P(B and not A)

    d) Find P(A or B)   e) Find P(neither A nor B)

Q2 Use the Venn diagram to find the following probabilities:

    a) P(L and M)   b) P(L and N)

    c) P(N and not L)   d) P(neither L nor M nor N)

    e) P(L or M)   f) P(not M)

    g) P(L and M and N)   h) P(M and not L)

Q3 Two hundred people were asked which of Italy, France and Germany they have visited. The results are shown in the diagram.

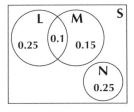

    Find the probability that a randomly selected person has been to:

    a) none of the three countries

    b) Germany, given that they have been to France

    c) Italy, but not France

    d) France, but not Italy

Q4 1000 football supporters were asked if they go to home league matches, away league matches, or cup matches. 560 go to home matches, 420 go to away matches, and 120 go to cup matches. 240 go to home and away matches, 80 go to home and cup matches, and 60 go to away and cup matches. 40 go to all 3 types of match.

    Find the probability that a randomly selected supporter goes to:

    a) exactly two types of match   b) exactly one type of match   c) at least one type of match

Two-way tables

Another sort of diagram you can use to represent probability problems is a **two-way table**.
The **whole table** represents the **sample space** and the **cells** represent different **events** that can happen.

Tip: The totals of the rows and columns should each add up to the number in the bottom right-hand cell.

 A shop sells balloons in three colours (red, blue and silver), and three designs (plain, stars and spots). The table shows the shop's sales of balloons for one day.

	Red	Blue	Silver	Total
Plain	11	21	13	45
Stars	43	29	48	120
Spots	45	20	20	85
Total	99	70	81	250

Each customer bought one balloon. Use the table to find the probability that a randomly-chosen customer bought a balloon that was blue or had spots.

1. Find the total number of possible outcomes. This is the total number of customers — i.e. the total number of balloons sold.

   250 possible outcomes

2. Now find the number of outcomes matching the event 'customer bought a blue or spotty balloon'. It's the total number of blue balloons, plus the number of red and silver balloons with spots.

   $70 + 45 + 20 = 135$ outcomes match the event 'blue or spotty'

3. Use the formula for equally likely outcomes.

   P(blue or spotty balloon) $= \dfrac{135}{250} = \dfrac{27}{50}$

Tip: You can't just add the totals for 'blue' and 'spots', as that would count the 'blue and spotty' ones twice.

 In any week, Carmelita goes to a maximum of two evening classes. She goes to a dance class, to a knitting class, to both classes, or to neither class. The probability, P(D), that she attends the dance class is 0.6, the probability, P(K), that she attends the knitting class is 0.3, and the probability that she attends both classes is 0.15.

By showing this information in a two-way table, find the probability that in a given week Carmelita attends at least one evening class.

1. Draw a two-way table showing the events D, D', K and K'.
   - Fill in the probabilities you know:
     P(D) = 0.6, P(K) = 0.3 and P(D and K) = 0.15.
     The total probability of 1 goes in the bottom-right cell.
   - Use the row and column totals to fill in the gaps.

   P(D and K)

	D	D'	Total
K	0.15	0.15	0.30	◀ P(K)
K'	0.45	0.25	0.70
Total	0.60	0.40	1.00

   P(D)   Total probability

2. Now find the probability that Carmelita attends either the dance class or the knitting class, or both — P(D or K). This is made up of the probabilities in column D or row K, or both.

   P(D or K) = 0.15 + 0.45 + 0.15 = **0.75**

   Tip: You could also do 1 − P(D' and K')
   = 1 − 0.25 = 0.75

Exercise 2.2

Q1 The table shows information on the ladybirds being studied by a scientist. Find the probability that a randomly selected ladybird:

a) is red or orange

b) is yellow or has fewer than 10 spots

Number of spots	Colour of ladybird		
	Red	Yellow	Orange
fewer than 10	20	9	1
10 or more	15	3	2

Q2 Rich only ever buys two brands of tea, 'BC Tops' and 'Cumbria Tea', and two brands of coffee, 'Nenco' and 'Yescafé'. On his weekly shopping trip, Rich buys either one brand of tea or no tea, and either one brand of coffee, or no coffee.

a) Copy and complete the two-way table below, which shows the probabilities for each combination of tea and coffee Rich might buy in any one week.

	BC Tops	Cumbria	No tea	Total
Nenco	0.16	0.07		
Yescafé	0.11			0.18
No coffee		0.12	0.14	
Total	0.51		0.27	1

b) Find the probability that, on any given shopping trip:

(i) Rich buys Cumbria Tea and Yescafé

(ii) Rich buys coffee

(iii) Rich buys tea but no coffee

(iv) Rich doesn't buy Nenco

Q3 A sixth form college has 144 students.
46 of the students study maths, 38 study physics and 19 study both.

a) Represent the information given above using a two-way table.

b) Find the probability that a randomly selected student from the college studies at least one of either maths or physics.

c) What is the probability that a randomly chosen maths student also studies physics?

3. Laws of Probability

The addition law

For **two events**, A and B:

$$P(A \text{ or } B) = P(A) + P(B) - P(A \text{ and } B)$$

Tip: In probability, "A or B" means "A or B or both"

The addition law is **really useful** for finding missing probabilities — as long as you know three of the values in the formula, you can **rearrange** the formula to find the remaining probability.

Tip: You can use this law with any pair of events, including A' and B'.

 Examples On any given day, the probability that Jason eats an apple is 0.6, the probability that he eats a banana is 0.3, and the probability that he eats both an apple and a banana is 0.2. Use the addition law to find:

a) **the probability that he eats an apple or a banana (or both).**

- Let A be the event 'eats an apple' and B be the event 'eats a banana'.
- Find P(A or B) using the addition law.

$$P(A \text{ or } B) = P(A) + P(B) - P(A \text{ and } B)$$
$$= 0.6 + 0.3 - 0.2 = \mathbf{0.7}$$

b) **the probability that he either doesn't eat an apple, or doesn't eat a banana.**

- You want to find P(A' or B').
- Use the addition law but replace A with A' and B with B'.

$$P(A' \text{ or } B') = P(A') + P(B') - P(A' \text{ and } B')$$
$$= [1 - P(A)] + [1 - P(B)] - [1 - P(A \text{ or } B)]$$
$$= (1 - 0.6) + (1 - 0.3) - (1 - 0.7)$$
$$= 0.4 + 0.7 - 0.3 = \mathbf{0.8}$$

Tip: (A' and B') is the complement of (A or B), so P(A' and B') = 1 − P(A or B).

Exercise 3.1

Q1 If P(A) = 0.3, P(B) = 0.5 and P(A and B) = 0.15, find:

    a) P(A′)   b) P(A or B)   c) P(A′ and B′)

Q2 If P(A′) = 0.36, P(B) = 0.44 and P(A and B) = 0.27, find:

    a) P(B′)   b) P(A or B)   c) P(A and B′)   d) P(A or B′)

Q3 A car is selected at random from a car park. The probability of the car being blue is 0.25 and the probability of it being an estate is 0.15. The probability of the car being a blue estate is 0.08.

    a) What is the probability of the car not being blue?

    b) What is the probability of the car being blue or being an estate?

    c) What is the probability of the car being neither blue nor an estate?

Q4 If P(X or Y) = 0.77, P(X) = 0.43 and P(Y) = 0.56, find:

    a) P(Y′)   b) P(X and Y)   c) P(X′ and Y′)   d) P(X′ or Y′)

Q5 If P(C′ or D) = 0.65, P(C) = 0.53 and P(D) = 0.44, find:

    a) P(C′ and D)   b) P(C′ and D′)   c) P(C′ or D′)   d) P(C and D)

Q6 The probability that a student has read 'To Kill a Mockingbird' is 0.62.
The probability that a student hasn't read 'Animal Farm' is 0.66.
The probability that a student has read at least one of these two books is 0.79. Find:

    a) The probability that a student has read both the books.

    b) The probability that a student has read 'Animal Farm' but hasn't read 'To Kill a Mockingbird'.

    c) The probability that a student has read neither of the books.

Mutually exclusive events

Events which have **no outcomes** in common **can't happen** at the same time. These events are called **mutually exclusive** (or just 'exclusive'). If A and B are mutually exclusive events, then **P(A and B) = 0**, so the **addition law** becomes:

$$P(A \text{ or } B) = P(A) + P(B)$$

For n mutually exclusive events $A_1, A_2, ..., A_n$: **$P(A_1 \text{ or } A_2 \text{ or ... or } A_n) = P(A_1) + P(A_2) + ... + P(A_n)$**.

**A card is selected at random from a standard pack of 52 cards.
Find the probability that the card is either a picture card
(a Jack, Queen or King), or the 7, 8 or 9 of clubs.**

Let A be the event 'select a picture card' and B be the event 'select the 7, 8 or 9 of clubs'.
You want to find the probability of A or B. The card can't be both a picture card and the 7, 8, or 9 of clubs, so A and B are mutually exclusive, which means that P(A or B) = P(A) + P(B).

1.   Find the probabilities of events A and B using the formula for equally likely outcomes. $P(A) = \frac{12}{52}$ and $P(B) = \frac{3}{52}$

2.   Put these probabilities into the addition law. $P(A \text{ or } B) = P(A) + P(B) = \frac{12}{52} + \frac{3}{52} = \mathbf{\frac{15}{52}}$

To show that events A and B are **mutually exclusive**, you just need to show **P(A and B) = 0**.
(Or to show they're **not** mutually exclusive, you can show P(A and B) ≠ 0.)

Tip: You can also prove that A and B are **not** mutually exclusive by showing that P(A or B) ≠ P(A) + P(B).

[Example]   **For two events, A and B, P(A) = 0.38, P(B) = 0.24 and P(A or B) = 0.6.**
            Show whether or not events A and B are mutually exclusive.

Use the addition law to find P(A and B).

   P(A or B) = P(A) + P(B) − P(A and B)
   ⇒ P(A and B) = P(A) + P(B) − P(A or B) = 0.38 + 0.24 − 0.6 = 0.02
   So P(A and B) ≠ 0, which means A and B are **not mutually exclusive**.

Exercise 3.2

Q1   If X and Y are mutually exclusive events, with P(X) = 0.48 and P(Y) = 0.37, find:
   a) P(X and Y)   b) P(X or Y)   c) P(X′ and Y′)

Q2   P(L) = 0.28, P(M) = 0.42 and P(N) = 0.33. If the pairs of events (L and M) and
   (L and N) are mutually exclusive, and P(M and N) = 0.16, find:
   a) P(L or M)   b) P(L or N)   c) P(M or N)   d) P(L and M and N)
   e) Draw and label a Venn diagram to show events L, M and N.

Q3   Kwame is planning his evening. The probabilities that he will go bowling, to the cinema or out for
   dinner are 0.17, 0.43 and 0.22 respectively. Given that he only has time to do one activity, find:
   a) The probability that he either goes bowling or to the cinema.
   b) The probability that he doesn't do any of the 3 activities.

Q4   For events A, B and C, P(A) = 0.28, P(B) = 0.66, P(C) = 0.49, P(A or B) = 0.86,
   P(A or C) = 0.77 and P(B or C) = 0.92. Find each of the probabilities below
   and say whether or not each pair of events is mutually exclusive.
   a) P(A and B)   b) P(A and C)   c) P(B and C)

Q5   For events C and D, P(C′) = 0.6, P(D) = 0.25 and P(C and D′) = 0.4.
   a) Show that C and D are mutually exclusive.   b) Find P(C or D)

Q6   A box contains 50 biscuits. Of the biscuits, 20 are chocolate-coated and the rest are plain.
   Half of all the biscuits are in wrappers. One biscuit is selected at random from the box.
   If P is the event 'the biscuit is plain', and W is the event 'the biscuit is in a
   wrapper', show that events P and W are not mutually exclusive.

Independent events

If the probability of an event B happening **doesn't depend** on whether an event A has happened or not,
events A and B are **independent**. The **product law** for **independent events** A and B is:

$$P(A \text{ and } B) = P(A)P(B)$$

Examples Rick and Nick each have their own biased coin. The probability of Rick getting tails is 0.2, and the probability of Nick getting tails is 0.6.

a) **Find the probability that both Rick and Nick get tails.**

The coins don't have any affect on each other — so the two coin tosses are independent.

Use the product law for independent events.   P(Rick gets tails and Nick gets tails)
= P(Rick gets tails) × P(Nick gets tails)
= 0.2 × 0.6 = **0.12**

b) **Find the probability that Rick or Nick (or both) get tails.**

You know all the probabilities   P(Rick gets tails or Nick gets tails)
you need to use the addition law.   = P(Rick gets tails) + P(Nick gets tails) – P(Both get tails)
= 0.2 + 0.6 – 0.12 = **0.68**

To show that events A and B are independent, you just need to show that P(A) × P(B) = P(A and B).

Example For events A and B, P(A) = 0.4, P(A and B) = 0.1 and P(A′ and B) = 0.2. Say whether or not A and B are independent.

1. Find P(B).

P(B) = P(A and B) + P(A′ and B)
= 0.1 + 0.2 = 0.3

2. Compare P(A) × P(B) to P(A and B).

P(A) × P(B) = 0.4 × 0.3 = 0.12
≠ P(A and B) = 0.1

So A and B are **not independent**.

Exercise 3.3

Q1   If X and Y are independent events, with P(X) = 0.62 and P(Y) = 0.32, calculate P(X and Y).

Q2   P(A and B) = 0.45 and P(B′) = 0.25. If A and B are independent events, what is P(A)?

Q3   X, Y and Z are independent events, with P(X) = 0.84, P(Y) = 0.68 and P(Z) = 0.48.
Find the following probabilities:

a) P(X and Y)   b) P(Y′ and Z′)   c) P(X and Z′)   d) P(Y′ and Z)

Q4   Events M and N are independent, with P(M) = 0.4 and P(N) = 0.7. Calculate the following probabilities:

a) P(M and N)   b) P(M or N)   c) P(M and N′)

Q5   A card is picked at random from a standard pack of 52 cards.
The card is replaced and the pack is shuffled, before a second card is picked at random.

a) What is the probability that both cards picked are hearts?

b) Find the probability that the ace of hearts is chosen both times.

Q6   For events A, B and C: $P(A) = \frac{3}{11}$, $P(B) = \frac{1}{3}$, $P(C) = \frac{15}{28}$, $P(A \text{ and } B) = \frac{1}{11}$,

$P(A \text{ and } C) = \frac{2}{15}$ and $P(B \text{ and } C) = \frac{5}{28}$.

Show whether or not each of the pairs of events (A and B), (A and C) and (B and C) are independent.

Q7   Simran, Mikhail and Lucy go shopping independently.
The probabilities that they will buy a DVD are 0.66, 0.5 and 0.3 respectively.

a) What is the probability that all three of them buy a DVD?

b) What is the probability that at least two of them buy a DVD?

Tree diagrams

Tree diagrams are used to show probabilities when **two or more events** occur.

- Each set of branches represents one **trial**. Each individual **branch** is a **possible result**.
- To find the **probability** of a combination of events, you **multiply along the branches** representing those events. The probabilities of **all combinations** added together is always **1**.

 A bag contains 10 balls, 6 of which are red and 4 of which are purple. One ball is selected from the bag at random, then replaced. A second ball is then selected at random.

a) **Draw a tree diagram to show this information.**

There are two trials — '1st ball selection' and '2nd ball selection', each with two possible results — 'red' and 'purple'.

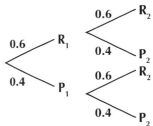

b) **Find the probability that one ball is red and the other is purple.**

1. There are 2 'paths' along the branches that give 'red and purple' — (R_1 and P_2) or (P_1 and R_2).

   $P(R_1 \text{ and } P_2) = 0.6 \times 0.4 = 0.24$
   $P(P_1 \text{ and } R_2) = 0.4 \times 0.6 = 0.24$

2. Find the probability of (R_1 and P_2) or (P_1 and R_2) by adding these two probabilities together.

   $P(1 \text{ red and } 1 \text{ purple})$
   $= P(R_1 \text{ and } P_2) + P(P_1 \text{ and } R_2)$
   $= 0.24 + 0.24 = \textbf{0.48}$

Events are **dependent** if the probability of one event happening is **affected** by whether or not the other happens. For dependent events, the probabilities on the second set of branches **depend** on the result of the first set.

Tip: Watch out for questions where the selection is 'without replacement' — this will give you dependent events.

 A box of 6 biscuits contains 5 chocolate biscuits and 1 lemon biscuit. George takes out a biscuit at random and eats it. He then takes out another biscuit at random.

a) **Draw a tree diagram to show this information.**

- There are two trials — '1st biscuit selection' and '2nd biscuit selection', with results 'chocolate' and 'lemon'.
- George eats the first biscuit, so the probabilities for the second biscuit depend on the first pick.

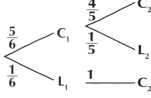

b) **Find the probability that the second biscuit he takes is chocolate.**

1. There are 2 'paths' along the branches that give 'second biscuit is chocolate' — (C_1 and C_2) or (L_1 and C_2).

   $P(C_1 \text{ and } C_2) = \dfrac{5}{6} \times \dfrac{4}{5} = \dfrac{2}{3}$
   $P(L_1 \text{ and } C_2) = \dfrac{1}{6} \times 1 = \dfrac{1}{6}$

2. Add the probabilities for the two 'paths' together.

   $P(2\text{nd biscuit is chocolate})$
   $= P(C_1 \text{ and } C_2) + P(L_1 \text{ and } C_2) = \dfrac{2}{3} + \dfrac{1}{6} = \dfrac{5}{6}$

Exercise 3.4

Q1 The probability that Jake will win two consecutive darts matches is shown on the tree diagram.

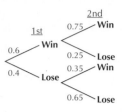

a) Explain whether the events 'wins 1st match' and 'wins 2nd match' are independent.

b) Find the probability that Jake will win:

   (i) both matches   (ii) at least one match

Q2 A game involves rolling a fair, six-sided dice and tossing a fair coin. A player wins if they roll a '6' and the coin shows 'tails'.

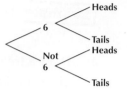

a) Complete the tree diagram by showing the probability on each branch.

b) Find the probability that a person wins the game.

c) Find the probability that a person doesn't win the game.

Q3 The probability that a randomly selected Year 13 student has passed their driving test is 0.3. The probability that they intend to go to university is 0.75.

a) Assuming that 'passed driving test' and 'intends to go to university' are independent, draw a tree diagram to show this information.

b) Find the probability that a randomly selected student has passed their driving test and intends to go to university.

c) Find the probability that a randomly selected student hasn't passed their driving test and does not intend to go to university.

Q4 A restaurant has found that if a diner orders a roast dinner, the probability that they order apple pie for pudding is 0.72. If they order a different main course, they order apple pie with probability 0.33. The probability that a diner orders a roast dinner is 0.56.

By drawing a tree diagram, find the probability that a randomly selected diner will order apple pie for pudding.

Q5 A game involves picking two balls at random from a bag containing 12 balls — 5 red, 4 yellow and 3 green — where the first ball isn't replaced. A player wins if they pick two balls of the same colour.

a) Draw a tree diagram to show the possible results of each pick.

b) Find the probability that a player picks two red balls.

c) Find the probability that a player wins the game.

d) The game changes so that the first ball is replaced before the second one is picked. Is a player more or less likely to win now?

Q6 Juan and Callum write movie reviews for every movie they watch. For any given movie, Juan and Callum give it a positive review with independent probabilities 0.4 and 0.3 respectively. Using tree diagrams or otherwise, find the probability that exactly one positive review is written, if:

a) Juan and Callum watch a movie together.

b) Callum watches two movies on his own.

c) Juan watches three movies on his own.

d) Juan and Callum watch a movie together, then Callum watches another movie on his own.

e) Juan watches two movies on his own, then Callum watches a movie on his own.

Review Exercise — Chapter 12

Q1 A fair, six-sided dice and a fair coin are thrown and a score is recorded.
If a head is thrown, the score is double the number on the dice.
If a tail is thrown, the score is the number on the dice plus 4.

    a) Draw a sample-space diagram to represent all the possible outcomes.

    b) What is the probability of scoring 8?

    c) What is the probability of scoring more than 5?

    d) If a tail is thrown, what is the probability that the score is an even number?

Q2 Half the students in a sixth-form college eat sausages for dinner and 20% eat chips.
2% eat sausages and chips together.

    a) Draw a Venn diagram to show this information.

    b) Find the percentage of students who eat chips but not sausages.

    c) Find the percentage of students who eat either chips or sausages but not both.

    d) Find the probability that a randomly selected student eats sausages but not chips.

    e) Find the probability that a randomly selected student eats neither sausages nor chips.

    f) Find the probability that a randomly selected student who eats chips also eats sausages.

Q3 A travel company asked 100 people which of activity, beach and skiing holidays
they enjoy. Each person asked enjoys at least one of these types of holiday.

10 people enjoy all three types of holiday. 25 people enjoy both activity and
beach holidays, 22 people enjoy both activity and skiing holidays, and 21
people enjoy both beach and skiing holidays. 41 people enjoy activity holidays,
59 people enjoy beach holidays, and 58 people enjoy skiing holidays.

One person is selected at random. Find the probability that they
like beach holidays but don't like skiing holidays.

Q4 The hot-beverage choices of a company's 30 workers are shown in the table below.

	Milk or sugar			
	Only milk	Only sugar	Both	Neither
Tea	7	4	6	1
Coffee	5	3	2	2

(Drink)

If one worker is selected at random, find the probability that he or she:

a) drinks coffee

b) drinks milky tea without sugar

c) either drinks tea or takes only sugar

Q5　On any shopping trip, the probability that Aiden buys clothes is 0.7, the probability that he buys music is 0.4 and the probability that he buys both clothes and music is 0.2.

Find the probability that:

a) He buys clothes or music or both.

b) He buys neither clothes nor music.

c) He either doesn't buy clothes or doesn't buy music.

Q6　For a certain biased dice, P(roll a 1) = 0.3 and P(roll a 3) = 0.2. This dice is rolled once.

a) Find the probability that a 1 or a 3 is rolled.

b) Find the probability that neither a 1 nor a 3 is rolled.

c) The dice is rolled twice. Find the probability of rolling:

　　(i) two 1s,　　　　(ii) a 1, then a 3,　　　　(iii) a 3, then neither a 1 nor a 3.

Q7　R and S are independent events with P(R) = 0.9 and P(S) = 0.8. Find:

a) P(R and S)　　　　　　b) P(R or S)

c) P(R′ and S′)　　　　　d) P(R′ or S′)

Q8　Hafsa rolls two fair, six-sided dice and calculates her score by adding the two results together.

a) What is the probability that her score is a prime number?

b) What is the probability that her score is a square number?

Let P be the event 'Hafsa's score is a prime number' and S be the event 'Hafsa's score is a square number'.

c) Explain whether or not the events P and S are mutually exclusive.

d) Find P(P or S).

Hafsa carries out the experiment twice. Let S_1 be the event 'score from first pair of rolls is a square number' and S_2 be the event 'score from second pair of rolls is a square number'.

e) Explain whether or not the events S_1 and S_2 are independent.

f) Find P(S_1 and S_2).

Q9　Kai plays either football or rugby every Saturday.
The tree diagram on the right shows the probabilities that he plays football (F) or rugby (R) on each of the next two Saturdays.

1st Sat　2nd Sat
0.6 F
0.35 F
R
R
0.6 F
R

a) Fill in the three missing probabilities to complete the tree diagram.

b) Find the probability that Kai plays football on at least one of the next two Saturdays.

c) Find the probability that Kai plays the same sport on both of the next two Saturdays.

Chapter 13 — Statistical Distributions

This chapter introduces probability distributions for discrete random variables, including the binomial distribution. The normal distribution for continuous random variables is covered later, in Chapter 28.

1. Probability Distributions

Probability distributions and functions

A **discrete random variable** can take a certain number of different values with different probabilities. A **table** showing all the possible values it can take and the probability that it takes each value is called the **probability distribution**.

A **discrete random variable** is usually represented by an **upper case** letter such as X. The **particular values** that X can take are represented by the **lower case** letter x.

 Draw the probability distribution table for X, where X is the score on a fair, six-sided dice.

X can take the values 1, 2, 3, 4, 5 and 6, each with probability $\frac{1}{6}$.

x	1	2	3	4	5	6
$P(X = x)$	$\frac{1}{6}$	$\frac{1}{6}$	$\frac{1}{6}$	$\frac{1}{6}$	$\frac{1}{6}$	$\frac{1}{6}$

A **probability function** is a formula that generates the probability of X taking the value x, or every possible x. It is written $P(X = x)$ or sometimes just $p(x)$.

Examples **For the situations below, write down the probability function of X.**

a) **A fair coin is tossed once and the number of tails, X, is counted.**

The outcome can either be heads or tails.
So X can either take the value 0 (if it lands on heads) or 1 (if it lands on tails) — each with probability $\frac{1}{2}$.

$$P(X = x) = \frac{1}{2} \quad x = 0, 1$$

b) **A biased coin, for which the probability of heads is $\frac{3}{4}$ and tails is $\frac{1}{4}$, is tossed once and the number of tails, X, is counted.**

- X can either be 0 (for heads) or 1 (for tails).

- $P(X = 0)$ is $\frac{3}{4}$ and $P(X = 1)$ is $\frac{1}{4}$.

- There are different probabilities, so use a different 'formula' for each x value. Write the probability function as a bracket.

$$P(X = x) = \begin{cases} \dfrac{3}{4} & x = 0 \\ \dfrac{1}{4} & x = 1 \end{cases}$$

Exercise 1.1

Q1 For each of the following situations, identify the discrete random variable, X, and all possible values, x, that X can take.

a) Tossing a fair coin 4 times and recording the number of tails.

b) Tossing a fair coin 6 times and recording the number of heads.

c) Rolling a fair four-sided dice (numbered 1, 2, 3 and 4) twice, and recording the sum of the scores.

Q2 Draw a table showing the probability distribution for each of the following probability functions:

a) $P(X = x) = \frac{x}{10}$, $x = 1, 2, 3, 4$

b) $p(x) = 0.55 - 0.1x$, $x = 0, 3, 4, 5$

c) $p(x) = 0.2$, $x = 10, 20, 30, 40, 50$

d) $P(X = x) = 0.01x^2$, $x = 1, 3, 4, 5, 7$

Q3 A fair six-sided dice is rolled. Write the probability distribution for the following random variables:

a) A = 'score rolled on the dice plus 1'.

b) B = '1 if the score is even, 0 otherwise'.

c) C = '5 times the score rolled on the dice'.

d) D = '1 if the score is a prime number, 0 otherwise'.

Q4 A biased coin, for which the probability of heads is $\frac{2}{3}$ and tails is $\frac{1}{3}$, is tossed once and the number of heads, X, is counted. Write down the probability function of X.

Q5 A game is played with a standard pack of playing cards. A card is drawn at random, and a score, X, is awarded according to the following rules:

    If the card has an even number, the score is half of that number.

    If the card has an odd number, the score is that number.

    If the card is an Ace, Jack, Queen or King, the score is 1.

Draw a table showing the probability distribution of the score, X.

The **probabilities** of **all** the possible values that a discrete random variable can take **add up to 1**.
For a discrete random variable X:

$$\sum_{\text{all } x} P(X = x) = 1$$

Examples

The number of hot beverages drunk by GP Pits Tea staff each day is modelled by the discrete random variable X, which has the probability distribution:

x	0	1	2	3	4 or more
$P(X = x)$	0.1	0.2	0.3	0.2	a

a) Find the value of a.

Use $\sum_{\text{all } x} P(X = x) = 1$. $0.1 + 0.2 + 0.3 + 0.2 + a = 1 \Rightarrow 0.8 + a = 1 \Rightarrow a = 0.2$

b) Find $P(2 \leq X < 4)$.

Just add up the required probabilities. $P(2 \leq X < 4) = P(X = 2 \text{ or } 3) = P(X = 2) + P(X = 3)$
                                          $= 0.3 + 0.2 = 0.5$

c) Find the mode.

It's the most likely value, so it has the highest probability.   **mode = 2**

Exercise 1.2

Q1 The number of items bought, X, in the 'less than five items' queue at a shop is modelled as a random variable with the probability distribution shown on the right.

x	1	2	3	4
$P(X = x)$	0.2	0.4	0.1	a

    a) Find a.   b) Find $P(X \geq 2)$.   c) Find $P(X < 2)$.

Q2 For each of the probability functions in a) to c) below:
    (i) Find k.   (ii) Write down the probability distribution of X.   (iii) Find $P(X \leq 2)$.

    a) $P(X = x) = kx^2$ $x = 1, 2, 3$ b) $P(X = x) = \dfrac{k}{x}$ $x = 1, 2, 3$ c) $P(X = x) = \begin{cases} kx & x = 1, 2, 3, 4 \\ k(8 - x) & x = 5, 6, 7 \end{cases}$

Q3 In a game, the score is recorded from rolling a fair 20-sided dice that has sides numbered 0, 2, 5 or 10. The probability of scoring 2 is three times the probability of scoring 5. The probability of scoring anything else is $\dfrac{1}{10}$. The random variable X represents the score on the dice for one roll.
Write down the probability distribution of X and find $P(X > 0)$.

Q4 Liam is designing a game where the possible outcomes are "wins two prizes", "wins one prize" and "wins no prizes". He sets it up so that the probability of winning two prizes is half of the probability of winning one prize, which is half of the probability of winning no prizes. Draw a table showing the probability distribution of the number of prizes won, X, and find the probability of winning at least one prize.

When it's not clear what the probability distribution or function should be, it can be helpful to draw a **sample-space diagram** (see p.169) of all the **possible outcomes** and work it out from that.

 A game involves rolling two fair dice. If the sum of the scores is greater than 10 then the player wins 50p. If the sum is between 8 and 10 (inclusive) then they win 20p. Otherwise they get nothing.

a) **If X is the random variable 'amount player wins', find the probability distribution of X.**

    1. X can take values 0, 20 and 50. Find the probability of each value by drawing a sample-space diagram showing all the possible sums of scores.

Score on dice 1

+	1	2	3	4	5	6
1	2	3	4	5	6	7
2	3	4	5	6	7	8
3	4	5	6	7	8	9
4	5	6	7	8	9	10
5	6	7	8	9	10	11
6	7	8	9	10	11	12

(left axis: Score on dice 2)

$P(X = 0) = P(\text{Sum of scores} < 8) = \dfrac{21}{36} = \dfrac{7}{12}$

$P(X = 20) = P(8 \leq \text{Sum of scores} \leq 10) = \dfrac{12}{36} = \dfrac{1}{3}$

$P(X = 50) = P(\text{Sum of scores} > 10) = \dfrac{3}{36} = \dfrac{1}{12}$

    2.   Draw the probability distribution.

x	0	20	50
$P(X = x)$	$\dfrac{7}{12}$	$\dfrac{1}{3}$	$\dfrac{1}{12}$

b) **The game costs 15p to play. Find the probability of making a profit.**

A player makes a profit if they win more than 15p.

$P(X > 15) = P(X = 20) + P(X = 50) = \dfrac{1}{3} + \dfrac{1}{12} = \dfrac{5}{12}$

A random variable where every value of X is **equally likely** follows a **uniform** distribution. For example, rolling a normal, unbiased dice gives you a **discrete uniform distribution**.

 A lottery involves a ball being picked at random from a box of 30 balls numbered from 11 to 40. The random variable X represents the number on the first ball to be picked. Write down the probability function of X, and find P($X < 20$).

1. Each ball has a probability of $\frac{1}{30}$ of being picked first. $\quad$ **P($X = x$) $= \frac{1}{30}$, $\quad x = 11, 12, ..., 40$**

2. Add up the probabilities. $\quad$ P($X < 20$) = P($X = 19$) + P($X = 18$) + ... + P($X = 11$)

$$= \frac{1}{30} + \frac{1}{30} + ... + \frac{1}{30} = \frac{9}{30} = \frac{3}{10}$$

Exercise 1.3

Q1 An unbiased four-sided dice with possible scores 1, 2, 3 and 4 is rolled twice. X is the random variable 'product of the two scores on the dice'. Find P($3 < X \leq 10$).

Q2 Tatiana is playing a game involving a fair four-sided dice with sides numbered 1 to 4. The dice is rolled twice, then the score is found using the table on the right. If X is the random variable 'number of points scored', find the following probabilities:

a) P($X = 5$)   b) P($X \leq 5$)
c) P($X \geq 5$)   d) P($X > 6$)

		Result of first roll		
	1	2	3	4
1	4	5	6	2
2	5	4	5	8
3	6	5	4	7
4	2	8	7	4

(Result of second roll labels rows 1–4)

Q3 A game involves rolling two fair six-sided dice. If the difference between the two scores is 0, then the player scores 10 points. If the difference is 1 or 2, then they score 5 points. Otherwise they score zero points. X is the random variable 'number of points scored'.
a) Find the probability distribution of X.   b) Find P($X > 0$).

Q4 A random variable, X, has a discrete uniform distribution and can take consecutive integer values between 12 and 15 inclusive. Draw a table showing the distribution of X, and find P($X \leq 14$).

Q5 Yuki sells pieces of square turf. The size of turf (in m²), X, requested by each of his customers is modelled as a random variable with the probability distribution shown.

x	1	4	9	16	25	36
P($X = x$)	k	k	k	k	k	k

a) Find k b) Find P($X \geq 5$)   c) Find P($X \geq 10$)
d) Find P($3 \leq X \leq 15$)   e) Find P(X is divisible by three)

Q6 In a raffle, the winning ticket is randomly picked from a box of 150 tickets, numbered from 1 to 150. The random variable Y represents the number on the winning ticket. Write down the probability function of Y, and find P($60 < Y \leq 75$).

Q7 A random variable X has the probability function p(x) = $k(x^3 - 6x^2 + 11x)$ for $x = 1, 2, 3$. Show that X has a discrete uniform distribution and find the value of k.

The cumulative distribution function

The **cumulative distribution function**, written **F(x)**, gives the probability that X will be **less than or equal to** a particular value, x. It's like a **running total** of probabilities.

To find $F(x_0)$ for a given value x_0, you **add up** all of the probabilities of the values X can take which are less than or equal to x_0.

$$F(x_0) = P(X \leq x_0) = \sum_{x \leq x_0} P(X = x)$$

 The probability distribution of the discrete random variable H is given in the table on the right.

h	0.1	0.2	0.3	0.4
$P(H = h)$	$\frac{1}{4}$	$\frac{1}{4}$	$\frac{1}{3}$	$\frac{1}{6}$

Draw a table to show the cumulative distribution function F(h).

1. Find the probability that H is less than or equal to each of the four values of h in turn.

$F(0.1) = P(H \leq 0.1) = P(H = 0.1) = \frac{1}{4}$

$F(0.2) = P(H \leq 0.2) = P(H = 0.1) + P(H = 0.2) = \frac{1}{4} + \frac{1}{4} = \frac{1}{2}$

$F(0.3) = P(H \leq 0.3) = P(H = 0.1) + P(H = 0.2) + P(H = 0.3) = \frac{1}{4} + \frac{1}{4} + \frac{1}{3} = \frac{5}{6}$

$F(0.4) = P(H \leq 0.4) = P(H = 0.1) + P(H = 0.2) + P(H = 0.3) + P(H = 0.4) = \frac{1}{4} + \frac{1}{4} + \frac{1}{3} + \frac{1}{6} = 1$

2. Put these values into a table.

h	0.1	0.2	0.3	0.4
$F(h) = P(H \leq h)$	$\frac{1}{4}$	$\frac{1}{2}$	$\frac{5}{6}$	1

Exercise 1.4

Q1 Each of a)-d) shows the probability distribution for a discrete random variable, X. Draw up a table to show the cumulative distribution function F(x) for each one.

a)
x	1	2	3	4	5
$p(x)$	0.1	0.2	0.3	0.2	0.2

b)
x	1	2	3	4
$p(x)$	0.3	0.2	0.3	0.2

c)
x	−2	−1	0	1	2
$p(x)$	$\frac{1}{5}$	$\frac{1}{5}$	$\frac{1}{5}$	$\frac{1}{5}$	$\frac{1}{5}$

d)
x	2	4	8	16	32	64
$p(x)$	$\frac{1}{2}$	$\frac{1}{4}$	$\frac{1}{8}$	$\frac{1}{16}$	$\frac{1}{32}$	$\frac{1}{32}$

Q2 Each of a)-b) shows the probability distribution for a discrete random variable, X. For each part, draw a table showing the cumulative distribution function, F(x), and use it to find the required probabilities.

a)
x	1	2	3	4
$p(x)$	0.3	0.1	0.45	0.15

Find (i) $P(X \leq 3)$
(ii) $P(1 < X \leq 3)$

b)
x	−2	−1	0	1	2
$p(x)$	$\frac{1}{10}$	$\frac{2}{5}$	$\frac{1}{10}$	$\frac{1}{5}$	$\frac{1}{5}$

Find (i) $P(X \leq 0)$
(ii) $P(X > 0)$

Q3 The discrete random variable X has probability function: $P(X = x) = \frac{1}{8}$, $x = 1, 2, 3, 4, 5, 6, 7, 8$

a) Draw up a table showing the cumulative distribution function, F(x).

b) Find (i) $P(X \leq 3)$ (ii) $P(3 < X \leq 7)$

2. Binomial Distributions

Counting arrangements

Some discrete random variables follow a **binomial distribution**. To use the binomial distribution, you need to be able to work out the number of **different orders** in which things can be **arranged**.

Say you have **n different** objects — these can be arranged in **n!** ('n factorial') different orders, where $n! = n \times (n-1) \times (n-2) \times \ldots \times 3 \times 2 \times 1$. If **x** of the objects are **the same**, then:

> **n** objects, of which **x** are **identical**, can be arranged in $\dfrac{n!}{x!}$ orders.

Example

In how many different orders can 7 objects be arranged if 4 of those objects are identical?

Use the result above with $n = 7$ and $x = 4$.
$$\frac{n!}{x!} = \frac{7!}{4!} = \frac{7 \times 6 \times 5 \times \cancel{4} \times \cancel{3} \times \cancel{2} \times \cancel{1}}{\cancel{4} \times \cancel{3} \times \cancel{2} \times \cancel{1}} = \textbf{210 orders}$$

Tip: If there is another group of y identical objects, then divide $n!$ by $y!$ too — i.e. there would be $\dfrac{n!}{x!y!}$ orders.

Exercise 2.1

Q1 For each word below, find the number of different orders in which the letters can be arranged.

a) RANDOM   b) STARLING   c) TART   d) START

e) STARLINGS   f) SASSIEST   g) STARTER   h) STRESSLESS

If there are only **two** types of object, then:

> **x** objects of one type and $(n - x)$ objects of another type can be arranged in $\dfrac{n!}{x!(n-x)!}$ different orders.

$\dfrac{n!}{x!(n-x)!}$ is a **binomial coefficient** (see p.59), which can also be written $\dbinom{n}{x}$ or ^nC_x.

Example

In how many different orders can 8 identical blue books and 5 identical green books be arranged on a shelf?

The two different types of object are blue books and green books.

$$n = 13,\ x = 8 \text{ and } n - x = 5, \text{ so } \binom{13}{8} = \frac{13!}{8!5!} = \textbf{1287 orders}$$

If a trial results in either **success** or **failure**, and you carry out n trials, then you can find the number of ways to arrange **x successes** and $(n - x)$ **failures** using the **binomial coefficient** $\dbinom{n}{x}$.

15 coins are tossed. How many ways are there to get 9 heads and 6 tails?

Each coin toss is a trial, 'heads' is 'success' and 'tails' is 'failure'.

$$n = 15, x = 9 \text{ and } n - x = 6, \text{ so } \binom{15}{9} = \frac{15!}{9!6!} = \mathbf{5005}$$

Exercise 2.2

Q1   A school football squad consists of 20 players.
How many different ways are there for the coach to choose 11 players out of 20?

Q2   Ten 'success or failure' trials are carried out.
In how many different ways can the following be arranged:
  a) 3 successes and 7 failures?   b) 5 successes and 5 failures?   c) 7 successes and 3 failures?

Q3   Twenty 'success or failure' trials are carried out.
In how many different ways can the following be arranged:
  a) 10 successes and 10 failures?   b) 14 successes and 6 failures?   c) 2 successes and 18 failures?

Q4   A coin is tossed 11 times. How many ways are there to get:
  a) 4 heads?   b) 6 heads?   c) 8 heads?   d) 11 heads?   e) 5 tails?

The binomial distribution

A random variable X follows a **binomial distribution** as long as these 5 conditions are satisfied:

> 1.   There is a **fixed** number (n) of trials.
> 2.   Each trial involves either '**success**' or '**failure**'.
> 3.   All the trials are **independent**.
> 4.   The probability of 'success' (p) is the **same** in each trial.
> 5.   The variable is the **total** number of **successes** in the n trials.

When X follows a binomial distribution, you can write $X \sim \mathbf{B}(n, p)$, where n and p are the **parameters**.

 For each random variable described below, say if it would follow a binomial distribution. If so, state the distribution's parameters, n and p.

a)   **The number of times (T) I have to toss a coin before I get 'heads'.**
The number of trials isn't fixed.   **Not binomial**

b)   **The number of red cards (R) drawn from a standard, shuffled 52-card pack in 10 picks, replacing the card each time.**

There's a fixed number (10) of independent trials with two possible results ('red' or 'black/not red') and a constant probability 0.5 of success, as the cards are replaced.   **Binomial: $R \sim \mathbf{B}(10, 0.5)$**

State any assumptions that would need to be made in order for N to be modelled by a binomial distribution, where N is the total number of defective widgets produced by a machine in a day, if it produces 5000 widgets every day.

There's a fixed number (5000) of trials, and each trial has two possible results ('defective' or 'not defective'). N is the number of 'successes' over the trials. That leaves two conditions to satisfy.

Assumptions — **the trials are independent** (one defective widget doesn't lead to another)
— **the probability of a defective widget being produced is always the same**.

Exercise 2.3

Q1 In each of the following situations, explain whether or not the random variable follows a binomial distribution. For those that follow a binomial distribution, state the parameters n and p.

   a) The number of spins (X) of a fair five-sided spinner (numbered 1-5) until a 3 is obtained.

   b) The number of defective light bulbs (X) in a batch of 2000 new bulbs, where 0.5% of light bulbs are randomly defective.

   c) The number of boys (Y) out of the next 10 children born in a town, assuming births are equally likely to produce a girl or a boy.

Q2 A sewing machine operator sews buttons onto jackets. The probability that a button sewed by this operator falls off a jacket before it leaves the factory is 0.001. On one particular day, the sewing machine operator sews 650 buttons, and X is the number of these buttons that fall off a jacket before it leaves the factory. Can X be modelled by a binomial distribution? State any assumptions you make and state the value of any parameters.

Q3 Kaitlin believes that it is sunny in Philadelphia on 30% of the days in a year. She claims that the number of sunny days in any given week, X, can be modelled by the binomial distribution $X \sim B(7, 0.3)$. Explain why this model may not be accurate.

Q4 A circus performer successfully completes his circus act on 95% of occasions. He will perform his act on 15 occasions and X is the number of occasions on which he successfully completes the act. State the assumptions that would need to be made in order for X to be modelled by a binomial distribution.

Q5 Ahmed picks 10 cards from a standard, shuffled pack of 52 cards. If X is the number of picture cards (i.e. jacks, queens or kings), state the conditions under which X would follow a binomial distribution, giving the parameters of this distribution.

Using the binomial probability function

If a random variable X follows a binomial distribution, it has the **probability function** below.

For a random variable X, where $X \sim B(n, p)$:

$$P(X = x) = \binom{n}{x} \times p^x \times (1-p)^{n-x} \text{ for } x = 0, 1, 2,..., n.$$

Tip: You might see this formula written:

$$^nC_x \, p^x \, q^{n-x}, \text{ where } ^nC_x = \binom{n}{x} \text{ and } q = 1 - p$$

Tip: You can find $P(X = x)$ on a calculator, if it has a binomial probability distribution function.

**I spin the fair spinner on the right 7 times.
Find the probability that I spin:**

a) **2 fives**

Call 'spin a five' a success, and
'spin anything other than a five' a failure.
The number of fives spun follows a
binomial distribution with $n = 7$ and $p = \frac{1}{5}$.

$$P(2 \text{ fives}) = \binom{7}{2} \times \left(\frac{1}{5}\right)^2 \times \left(\frac{4}{5}\right)^5$$

$$= \frac{7!}{2!5!} \times \frac{1}{25} \times \frac{1024}{3125} = \mathbf{0.275 \text{ (3 s.f.)}}$$

b) **4 numbers less than three**

Call 'spin a one or a two' a success,
and 'spin a three, four or five' a failure.
The number of 'ones or twos' spun follows a
binomial distribution with $n = 7$ and $p = \frac{2}{5}$.

$$P(4 \text{ numbers less than three})$$

$$= \binom{7}{4} \times \left(\frac{2}{5}\right)^4 \times \left(\frac{3}{5}\right)^3$$

$$= \frac{7!}{4!3!} \times \frac{16}{625} \times \frac{27}{125} = \mathbf{0.194 \text{ (3 s.f.)}}$$

You might need to find several individual probabilities and then **add** the results together.

Example If $X \sim B(6, 0.32)$, find $P(2 \leq X < 4)$.

1. If $2 \leq X < 4$, then X can be 2 or 3. So you need to find $P(X = 2)$ and $P(X = 3)$.

$$P(X = 2) = \binom{6}{2} \times 0.32^2 \times (1 - 0.32)^{6-2} \qquad P(X = 3) = \binom{6}{3} \times 0.32^3 \times (1 - 0.32)^{6-3}$$

$$= \frac{6!}{2!4!} \times 0.32^2 \times 0.68^4 = 0.3284... \qquad = \frac{6!}{3!3!} \times 0.32^3 \times 0.68^3 = 0.2060...$$

2. Add the probabilities together. $\qquad P(2 \leq X < 4) = P(X = 2) + P(X = 3)$

$$= 0.3284... + 0.2060... = \mathbf{0.534 \text{ (3 s.f.)}}$$

Exercise 2.4

Q1 Find the probabilities below. Give your answers to 3 significant figures.
   a) For $X \sim B(10, 0.14)$:   (i) $P(X = 2)$ (ii) $P(X = 4)$ (iii) $P(X = 5)$
   b) For $X \sim B(8, 0.27)$:   (i) $P(X = 3)$ (ii) $P(X = 5)$ (iii) $P(X = 7)$
   c) For $X \sim B(22, 0.55)$:   (i) $P(X = 10)$ (ii) $P(X = 15)$ (iii) $P(X = 20)$

Q2 Find the probabilities below. Give your answers to 3 significant figures.
   a) For $X \sim B(12, 0.7)$:   (i) $P(X \geq 11)$ (ii) $P(8 \leq X \leq 10)$ (iii) $P(X > 9)$
   b) For $X \sim B(20, 0.16)$:   (i) $P(X < 2)$ (ii) $P(X \leq 3)$ (iii) $P(1 < X \leq 4)$
   c) For $X \sim B(30, 0.88)$:   (i) $P(X > 28)$ (ii) $P(25 < X < 28)$ (iii) $P(X \geq 27)$

Q3 A fair, six-sided dice is rolled 5 times. Find the probability of rolling:
   a) exactly 2 sixes   b) exactly 1 three   c) fewer than 3 fours
   d) 1 to 5 odd numbers (inclusive)   e) more than 3 ones   f) fewer than 2 prime numbers

Sometimes it's easier to find the probability of the 'other' result, and subtract it from 1.

Example | A drug with a success rate of 83% is tested on 8 people. X, the number of people the drug is successful on, can be modelled by the binomial distribution $X \sim \text{B}(8, 0.83)$. Find $P(X \le 6)$.

1. Use the fact that $P(X \le 6) = 1 - P(X > 6)$. $P(X \le 6) = 1 - P(X > 6) = 1 - P(X = 7) - P(X = 8)$

2. Find $P(X = 7)$ and $P(X = 8)$.

$$P(X = 7) = \binom{8}{7} \times 0.83^7 \times (1 - 0.83)^{8-7}$$

$$= \frac{8!}{7!1!} \times 0.83^7 \times 0.17^1 = 0.3690...$$

$$P(X = 8) = \binom{8}{8} \times 0.83^8 \times (1 - 0.83)^{8-8}$$

$$= \frac{8!}{8!0!} \times 0.83^8 \times 0.17^0 = 0.2252...$$

3. Subtract these probabilities from 1.

$P(X \le 6) = 1 - P(X = 7) - P(X = 8) = 1 - 0.3690... - 0.2252... = \mathbf{0.406}$ **(3 s.f.)**

The **mean** or **expected value** of a random variable is the value you'd expect it to take **on average** if you repeated the experiment lots of times.

> If $X \sim \text{B}(n, p)$, then: Mean or Expected Value $E(X) = np$

Example | I roll a fair 6-sided dice 30 times. Find the expected number of sixes rolled.

Let the random variable X represent the number of sixes in 30 rolls. Then $X \sim \text{B}(30, \frac{1}{6})$.

Work out the expected value. $E(X) = np = 30 \times \frac{1}{6} = \mathbf{5}$

Example | If $X \sim \text{B}(20, 0.2)$, find $E(X)$.

Use the formula with $n = 20$ and $p = 0.2$. $E(X) = np = 20 \times 0.2 = \mathbf{4}$

Exercise 2.5

Q1   Find the probabilities below. Give your answers to 3 significant figures.

    a) For $X \sim \text{B}(5, \frac{1}{2})$:   (i) $P(X \le 4)$ (ii) $P(X > 1)$ (iii) $P(1 \le X \le 4)$

    b) For $X \sim \text{B}(8, \frac{2}{3})$:   (i) $P(X < 7)$ (ii) $P(X \ge 2)$ (iii) $P(0 \le X \le 8)$

Q2   A multiple-choice test has three possible answers to each question, only one of which is correct. A student guesses the answer to each of the twelve questions at random. The random variable X is the number of correct answers.

    a) State the distribution of X and explain why this model is suitable.

    b) Find the probability that the student gets fewer than three questions correct.

    c) Find the number of answers you'd expect the student to get correct.

Q3   A discrete random variable X follows the binomial distribution $X \sim B(25, p)$.
Given that the mean of X is 10, find $P(X = 10)$.

Q4   5% of the items made using a particular production process are defective.
A quality control manager samples 15 items at random.
What is the probability that there are between 1 and 3 defective items (inclusive)?

Q5   For each dart thrown by a darts player, the probability that it scores 'treble-20' is 0.75.
a) The player throws 3 darts. Find the probability that he gets a 'treble-20' with at least 2 darts.
b) He throws another 30 darts for a charity challenge. If he gets a 'treble-20' with at least 26 of the 30 darts, he wins the charity a prize. What is the probability that he wins the prize?
c) How many 'treble-20s' would you expect the darts player to get from the 30 darts?

3. The Binomial Cumulative Distribution Function

Finding probabilities

If the probability you're trying to find involves a range of values, it's often quicker to use the
binomial cumulative distribution function (c.d.f.). This gives you **$P(X \leq x)$**, for $X \sim B(n, p)$.

You can use either the **binomial tables** (see p.468-472) or a **calculator** to find these probabilities.

1. To use the binomial tables first find the table with the correct **value of n**.
Then find the correct **value of p** across the top of the table.

For example, suppose that $X \sim B(12, 0.35)$, and you need to find $P(X \leq 2)$:

① Find n...   **Binomial Cumulative Distribution Function**   ② ...then find p.
Values show $P(X \leq x)$, where $X \sim B(n, p)$

	$p =$	0.05	0.10	0.15	0.20	0.25	0.30	0.35	0.40	0.45	0.50
$n = 12$, $x =$	0	0.5404	0.2824	0.1422	0.0687	0.0317	0.0138	0.0057	0.0022	0.0008	0.0002
	1	0.8816	0.6590	0.4435	0.2749	0.1584	0.0850	0.0424	0.0196	0.0083	0.0032
	2	0.9804	0.8891	0.7358	0.5583	0.3907	0.2528	0.1513	0.0834	0.0421	0.0193
	3	0.9978	0.9744	0.9078	0.7946	0.6488	0.4925	0.3467	0.2253	0.1345	0.0730
	4	0.9998	0.9957	0.9761	0.9274	0.8424	0.7237	0.5833	0.4382	0.3044	0.1938
	5	1.0000	0.9995	0.9954	0.9806	0.9456	0.8822	0.7873	0.6652	0.5269	0.3872

Read across from $x = 2$ to get $P(X \leq 2) = 0.1513$.

2. To find probabilities on a calculator you usually have to go into the **distribution** mode
and choose the **binomial c.d.f.** Then enter the values of n, p and x.

So if you wanted to find $P(X \leq 2)$ for the binomial distribution above, you'd input the values
$n = 12$, $p = 0.35$ and $x = 2$ into the binomial c.d.f.

This gives $P(X \leq 2) = 0.151287... = 0.1513$ (4 d.p.) — i.e. the same value as the table (to 4 d.p.)

Tip: The values of p in the tables only go as high as $p = 0.5$ in steps of 0.05 and n only goes up to 50.
For a binomial distribution with a value of p or n that's not in the tables, use your calculator.

   **I have an unfair coin. When I toss this coin, the probability of getting
heads is 0.55. Find the probability that it will land on heads fewer than
6 times when I toss it 10 times in total.**

There are 10 trials and   If X is the number of heads in 10 tosses, $X \sim B(10, 0.55)$.
$p = P(\text{heads}) = 0.55$.   So $P(X < 6) = P(X \leq 5) = \mathbf{0.4956}$ **(4 d.p.)**

Exercise 3.1

Q1 The random variable $X \sim B(10, 0.25)$. Find:
   a) $P(X \leq 2)$ b) $P(X \leq 7)$ c) $P(X \leq 9)$ d) $P(X < 10)$
   e) $P(X < 5)$ f) $P(X < 4)$ g) $P(X < 6)$ h) $P(X < 2)$

Q2 The random variable $X \sim B(12, 0.8)$. Find:
   a) $P(X < 10)$ b) $P(X \leq 6)$ c) $P(X \leq 7)$ d) $P(X < 12)$
   e) $P(X < 8)$ f) $P(X < 5)$ g) $P(X \leq 5)$ h) $P(X < 9)$

Q3 The random variable $X \sim B(20, 0.5)$. Find:
   a) $P(X \leq 15)$ b) $P(X < 11)$ c) $P(X \leq 14)$ d) $P(X < 5)$
   e) $P(X \leq 13)$ f) $P(X < 13)$ g) $P(X < 17)$ h) $P(X < 4)$

Q4 The random variable $X \sim B(50, 0.35)$. Find:
   a) $P(X < 14)$ b) $P(X < 24)$ c) $P(X \leq 9)$ d) $P(X \leq 17)$
   e) $P(X \leq 28)$ f) $P(X \leq 18)$ g) $P(X < 22)$ h) $P(X \leq 11)$

Q5 The probability that a randomly selected 8-year-old in a particular region has green eyes
    is 0.18. A sample of thirty 8-year-olds from the region is chosen at random.
    Find the probability that fewer than ten of them have green eyes.

Q6 In a production process it is known that approximately 5% of items are faulty.
    In a random sample of 25 objects, estimate the probability that fewer than 6 are faulty.

For trickier questions, you have to work out how to use the c.d.f. to get to the answer.

  If $X \sim B(12, 0.45)$, find $P(5 < X \leq 8)$.

1. The largest value satisfying the inequality $5 < X \leq 8$ is $X = 8$.
    So you need to find $P(X \leq 8)$. $P(X \leq 8) = 0.9644...$

2. Since $X = 5$ doesn't satisfy the inequality $5 < X \leq 8$,
    and neither does any value smaller than 5,
    you need to find $P(X \leq 5)$ and subtract it from $P(X \leq 8)$. $P(X \leq 5) = 0.5269...$

   So $P(5 < X \leq 8) = P(X \leq 8) - P(X \leq 5) = 0.9644... - 0.5269... = \mathbf{0.4375}$ **(4 d.p.)**

  The probability of this spinner landing on blue is 0.7.
It is spun 12 times, and the random variable X represents the
number of times the spinner lands on blue. Find $P(X > 8)$.

Use the fact that $P(X > 8) = 1 - P(X \leq 8)$. $X \sim B(12, 0.7)$
                               $P(X > 8) = 1 - P(X \leq 8)$
                                        $= 1 - 0.5074... = \mathbf{0.4925}$ **(4 d.p.)**

Exercise 3.2

Q1 The random variable $X \sim B(15, 0.4)$. Find:
- a) $P(X > 3)$
- b) $P(X > 6)$
- c) $P(X > 10)$
- d) $P(X \geq 5)$
- e) $P(X \geq 3)$
- f) $P(X \geq 13)$

Q2 The random variable $X \sim B(20, 0.35)$. Find:
- a) $P(X = 7)$
- b) $P(X = 12)$
- c) $P(2 < X \leq 4)$
- d) $P(10 < X \leq 15)$
- e) $P(7 \leq X \leq 10)$
- f) $P(3 \leq X < 11)$

Q3 The random variable $X \sim B(25, 0.8)$. Find:
- a) $P(X \geq 17)$
- b) $P(X \geq 20)$
- c) $P(X > 14)$
- d) $P(X = 21)$
- e) $P(3 \leq X < 14)$
- f) $P(12 \leq X < 18)$

Q4 The random variable $X \sim B(29, 0.42)$. Find:
- a) $P(X \leq 15)$
- b) $P(X > 10)$
- c) $P(X \geq 18)$
- d) $P(13 < X < 17)$.

Q5 I have an unfair coin. When I toss this coin, the probability of getting heads is 0.85. If I toss it 15 times, find the probability that it will land on heads at least 11 times but fewer than 14 times.

Q6 A shop delivers newspapers to a customer 7 days a week. The probability that any random newspaper is undelivered is known to be 0.05. If the customer has more than one paper undelivered in a week they get free newspapers for that week. The number of newspapers undelivered in a week, X, can be modelled by a binomial distribution.

Find the probability that the customer gets free newspapers for the week, in any random week.

Using the binomial cumulative distribution function 'backwards'

You could be **given a probability** (for example, $P(X \leq x) = 0.5$) and asked to **find the value of x**. You can use either the **binomial tables** or a **calculator**:

1. If you're using the tables, find the **table for n** and go down the **column for p** until you find the **probability** you're looking for. Read off the corresponding **value of x** on the left-hand side.

2. On a calculator you can use **trial and error** — try **different values of x** until you find the right probability. Or you might be able to **generate a table** of values and read off the value you need.

Examples The random variable X has the distribution $X \sim B(30, 0.4)$.

a) **Find the maximum value a such that $P(X \leq a) < 0.05$.**

You're looking for x where $P(X \leq x) < 0.05$ and $P(X \leq x + 1) \geq 0.05$.
To 4 d.p. $P(X \leq 6) = 0.0172$, $P(X \leq 7) = 0.0435$, $P(X \leq 8) = 0.0940$
So the maximum value a such that $P(X \leq a) < 0.05$ is $a = 7$.

b) **Find the minimum value b such that $P(X > b) < 0.05$.**

If $P(X > b) < 0.05$, then $P(X \leq b) > 0.95$. So you're looking
for x where $P(X \leq x) > 0.95$ and $P(X \leq x - 1) \leq 0.95$.

$P(X \leq 15) = 0.9029$, $P(X \leq 16) = 0.9519$, $P(X \leq 17) = 0.9788$
So the minimum value of b with $P(X \leq b) > 0.95$ is $b = 16$.
This means that the minimum value of b with $P(X > b) < 0.05$ must also be $b = 16$.

Exercise 3.3

Q1 The random variable $X \sim B(8, 0.35)$. Find the values of a, b, c and d such that, to 4 d.p.:

a) $P(X \leq a) = 0.4278$ b) $P(X < b) = 0.9747$

c) $P(X > c) = 0.8309$ d) $P(X \geq d) = 0.1061$

Q2 The random variable $X \sim B(50, 0.3)$. Find the values of a, b, c and d such that, to 4 d.p.:

a) $P(X \leq a) = 0.9877$ b) $P(X < b) = 0.0183$

c) $P(X > c) = 0.8610$ d) $P(X \geq d) = 0.3161$

Q3 A teacher is writing a multiple-choice test, with 4 options for each of the 30 questions. He wants the probability of someone passing the test by guessing the answer to each question to be 10% or less.

a) What is the lowest score that should be set as the pass mark?

b) Another teacher says the probability of passing by guessing should be less than 1%. What should the minimum pass score be now?

Q4 In a fairground competition, a fair coin is tossed 20 times by a contestant. If the contestant scores x heads or more, they win a prize. If the random variable X represents the number of heads obtained, find the minimum number of heads that are needed to win if the probability of winning is to be kept below 0.05.

4. Modelling Real Problems

Modelling real problems with B(n, p)

The first step with a real-world problem is to **model** it using a sensible probability distribution. To use a **binomial distribution**, you need to check that all the conditions are satisfied (see p.187).

When you've decided how to model the situation, you can 'do the maths'. Don't forget to include units in your answer where necessary. You may then need to **interpret** your solution — saying what your answer means in the **context** of the question.

 A double-glazing salesman is handing out leaflets in a busy shopping centre. He knows that the probability of a passing person taking a leaflet is always 0.3. During a randomly chosen one-minute interval, 30 people passed him.

a) **Suggest a suitable model to describe the number of people (X) who take a leaflet.**

There's a fixed number (30) of independent trials with two possible results ('take a leaflet' and 'doesn't take a leaflet') and a constant probability of success (0.3). X is the total number of people taking leaflets.

All the conditions for a **binomial distribution** are satisfied. So $X \sim B(30, 0.3)$.

b) **What is the probability that more than 10 people take a leaflet?**

You can find this probability from the binomial tables or a calculator.

$$P(X > 10) = 1 - P(X \leq 10)$$
$$= 1 - 0.7303...$$
$$= \mathbf{0.2696 \ (4 \ d.p.)}$$

Examples   **I am tossing a coin that I know is three times as likely to land on heads as it is on tails.**

a) **What is the probability that it lands on tails for the first time on the third toss?**

1. Find the probabilities for heads and tails.

P(heads) = 3 × P(tails).
And P(heads) + P(tails) = 1.
So P(heads) = 0.75 and P(tails) = 0.25.

2. If it lands on tails for the first time on the third toss, then the first two tosses must've been heads. All the tosses are independent so multiply the probabilities.

P(lands on tails for the first time on the third toss)
= 0.75 × 0.75 × 0.25 = **0.141 (3 s.f.)**

b) **What is the probability that in 10 tosses, it lands on heads at least 7 times?**

1. Define your random variable, and state how it is distributed.

If X represents the number of heads in 10 tosses, then $X \sim B(10, 0.75)$.

2. Use the fact that all the probabilities add up to 1.

$P(X \geq 7) = 1 - P(X < 7) = 1 - P(X \leq 6)$
$= 1 - 0.2241...$
= **0.7759 (4 d.p.)**

Exercise 4.1

Q1 A hairdresser hands out leaflets. She knows there is always a probability of 0.25 that a passer-by will take a leaflet. During a five-minute period, 50 people pass the hairdresser.

a) Suggest a suitable model for X, the number of passers-by who take a leaflet in the five-minute period. Explain why this is a suitable model.

b) What is the probability that more than 4 people take a leaflet?

c) What is the probability that exactly 10 people take a leaflet?

Q2 Jasmine plants 15 randomly selected seeds in each of her plant trays. She knows that 35% of this type of plant grow with yellow flowers, while the remainder grow with white flowers. All her seeds grow successfully, and Jasmine counts how many plants in each tray grow with yellow flowers.

a) Find the probability that a randomly selected tray has exactly 5 plants with yellow flowers.

b) Find the probability that a randomly selected tray contains more plants with yellow flowers than plants with white flowers.

Q3 Simon tries to solve the crossword puzzle in his newspaper every day for 18 days. He either succeeds or fails to solve the puzzle.

a) Simon believes that the number of successes, X, can be modelled by a random variable following a binomial distribution. State two conditions needed for this to be true.

b) He believes that the situation has distribution $X \sim B(18, p)$, where p is the probability Simon successfully completes the crossword. If $P(X = 4) = P(X = 5)$, find p.

Q4 A roulette wheel has 37 pockets numbered 0 to 36. In each game, the wheel is spun and a small ball is thrown onto it, which is equally likely to land in each pocket. Ricky always bets that it will land in the pocket numbered 21, as this is his favourite number. One day, Ricky plays 74 times.

a) The random variable X, 'the number of times Ricky wins', can be modelled with a binomial distribution. Give the parameters of this distribution.

b) Find the probability that Ricky wins at least twice.

c) Ricky bets £5 on each game, and for each win he gets his bet back plus £175. Show that Ricky can expect to make a loss over the course of the 74 games.

Q1 The probability distribution of Y is:

y	0	1	2	3
$P(Y = y)$	0.5	k	k	$3k$

a) Find the value of k.   b) Find $P(Y < 2)$.

Q2 A game is played by rolling a fair, six-sided dice twice. If the sum of the two results is a multiple of 3, then the player scores 3 points. If the sum is a multiple of 5, they score 5 points, and if the sum is a multiple of 7, they score 7 points. Otherwise, they score 2 points. X is the random variable 'number of points scored'.

Draw a table showing the probability distribution of X and find $P(X \leq 5)$.

Q3 The probability distribution for the random variable W is given in the table. Draw up a table to show the cumulative distribution function.

w	0.2	0.3	0.4	0.5
$P(W = w)$	0.2	0.2	0.3	0.3

Q4 Each probability function below describes a discrete random variable, X. In each case, draw a table showing the cumulative distribution function, and use it to find the required probabilities.

a) $P(X = x) = \dfrac{(x + 2)}{25}$ $x = 1, 2, 3, 4, 5$ Find (i) $P(X \leq 3)$ (ii) $P(1 < X \leq 3)$

b) $P(X = x) = \dfrac{1}{6}$ $x = 1, 2, 3, 4, 5, 6$ Find (i) $P(X \leq 3)$ (ii) $P(3 < X < 6)$

Q5 In how many different orders can the following be arranged?
a) 15 identical red balls, plus 6 other balls, all of different colours.
b) 4 red counters, 4 blue counters, 4 yellow counters and 4 green counters.
c) 7 green counters and 5 blue counters.
d) 3 'heads' and 4 'tails' in seven coin tosses.

Q6 Which of the following would follow a binomial distribution? Explain your answers.
a) The number of prime numbers you throw in 30 throws of a standard dice.
b) The number of people in a particular class at a school who get 'heads' when they flip a coin.
c) The number of aces in a 7-card hand dealt from a standard pack of 52 cards.
d) The number of shots I have to take before I score from the free-throw line in basketball.

Q7 Use the binomial probability function to find the probability of the following.
a) Getting exactly 5 heads when you spin a fair coin 10 times.
b) Getting exactly 9 heads when you spin a fair coin 10 times.
c) Getting at least 5 heads when you spin a fair coin 10 times.
d) Getting at least 9 heads when you spin a fair coin 10 times.

Q8   If $X \sim B(14, 0.27)$, find:

a) $P(X = 4)$ b) $P(X < 2)$ c) $P(5 < X \leq 8)$ d) $P(X \geq 11)$

Q9   Find the mean of each of the following random variables.

a) $X \sim B(20, 0.4)$ b) $X \sim B(40, 0.15)$ c) $X \sim B(25, 0.45)$ d) $X \sim B(50, 0.8)$

e) $X \sim B(30, 0.7)$ f) $X \sim B(45, 0.012)$ g) $X \sim B(15, 0.4)$ h) $X \sim B(25, 0.414)$

Q10   If $X \sim B(25, 0.15)$ and $Y \sim B(15, 0.65)$ find:

a) $P(X \leq 3)$ b) $P(X \leq 7)$ c) $P(X \leq 15)$ d) $P(2 < X < 8)$

e) $P(Y \leq 3)$ f) $P(Y \leq 7)$ g) $P(Y \leq 15)$ h) $P(8 \leq Y < 13)$

Q11   Find the required probability for each of the following binomial distributions.

a) $P(X \leq 15)$ if $X \sim B(20, 0.4)$ b) $P(X < 4)$ if $X \sim B(40, 0.15)$ c) $P(X > 7)$ if $X \sim B(25, 0.45)$

d) $P(X \geq 40)$ if $X \sim B(50, 0.8)$ e) $P(X = 20)$ if $X \sim B(30, 0.7)$ f) $P(X = 7)$ if $X \sim B(10, 0.75)$

Q12   If $X \sim B(30, 0.35)$, find:

a) a if $P(X \leq a) = 0.8737$ b) b if $P(X \geq b) = 0.8762$

c) the maximum value c such that $P(X \leq c) < 0.05$.

Q13   If $X \sim B(25, 0.25)$, find:

a) a if $P(X \leq a) = 0.0962$ b) b if $P(X \geq b) = 0.4389$

c) the minimum value c such that $P(X > c) < 0.1$.

Q14   A takeaway shop sends vouchers to people. The owners know that there is always a probability of 0.15 that a person uses the voucher they receive. During a two-hour period, 40 people are each sent one voucher.

a) Suggest a suitable model for X, the number of people who use the voucher they received in this two-hour period. Explain why this is a suitable model.

b) Find the probability that at least 10 people use the voucher.

c) Find the probability that exactly 6 people use the voucher.

Q15   A chocolate shop sells selection boxes of 12 chocolates, where each chocolate is randomly selected from all the varieties of chocolates they sell. Forrest likes 70% of the varieties the shop sells and dislikes the rest. He buys one of the selection boxes at random.

a) Find the probability that Forrest's selection box contains exactly 10 chocolates that he likes.

b) Find the probability that his selection box contains more chocolates that he likes than chocolates that he dislikes.

Q16   A teacher is writing a multiple-choice test, with 5 options for each of the 20 questions. She wants the probability of someone passing the test by guessing all the answers to be 10% or less. How high should the pass mark be to give a student guessing the answer to every question less than a 10% probability of passing the test?

Q17   During a football match, Messy tries to dribble past a certain player 11 times. He either succeeds or fails to dribble past the player.

a) Messy believes that the number of successes, X, can be modelled by a random variable following a binomial distribution. State two conditions needed for this to be true.

b) He believes that the situation has distribution $X \sim B(11, p)$, where p is the probability that Messy successfully dribbles past the player. If $P(X = 3) = P(X = 4)$, find p.

Chapter 14 — Statistical Hypothesis Testing

Hypothesis testing (or significance testing) uses data from a sample to test whether a statement about a whole population is believable or not. In this chapter, you'll carry out hypothesis tests using the binomial distribution.

1. Hypothesis Tests

Null and alternative hypotheses

Parameters are quantities that **describe** the characteristics of a **population** — e.g. the **mean** (μ), **variance** (σ^2), or a **proportion** (p).

A **hypothesis** (plural: **hypotheses**) is a claim or a statement that **might** be true, but which might **not** be.

A **hypothesis test** is a method of testing a hypothesis about a population using **observed data** from a **sample**. You need **two** hypotheses for every test — a **null** hypothesis and an **alternative** hypothesis.

Null hypothesis

- The **null hypothesis** (H_0) is a statement about the **value** of a population parameter. It always gives a **specific value** to the parameter (e.g. H_0: $p = 0.5$).

- Depending on your data, there are **two** possible results of a hypothesis test:
  a) **Fail to reject H_0**: the data provides **no evidence** to think that your null hypothesis is **untrue**.
  b) **Reject H_0**: the data provides evidence to think that your null hypothesis is **unlikely to be true**.

Alternative hypothesis

Your **alternative hypothesis** (H_1) is what you're going to conclude if you end up rejecting H_0 — i.e. what you're rejecting H_0 in favour of. There are **two kinds** of alternative hypothesis:

- A **one-tailed** alternative hypothesis specifies whether the parameter you're investigating is **greater than** or **less than** the value you used in H_0 (e.g. H_1: $p > 0.5$).

- A **two-tailed** alternative hypothesis **doesn't specify** whether the parameter is greater than or less than the value in H_0 — all it says is that it's **not equal** to the value in H_0 (e.g. H_1: $p \neq 0.5$).

Tip: You say that you're carrying out a **one-tailed hypothesis test** or a **two-tailed hypothesis test**.

 Examples
> **The average probability over the course of a day that a customer entering a particular post office has to queue for more than 2 minutes is 0.6.**
> **The manager wants to test whether the probability of having to queue for more than 2 minutes is different between the hours of 1 pm and 2 pm.**
> *(MODELLING)*

a) **Write down a suitable null hypothesis.**

   Let p be the probability of having to queue for more than 2 minutes between 1 pm and 2 pm.

   $$H_0\text{:}\ p = 0.6$$

b) **Write down a suitable alternative hypothesis.**

   The manager wants to test for any difference in the value of p.

   $$H_1\text{:}\ p \neq 0.6$$

c) **State whether this test is one- or two-tailed.**

   The alternative hypothesis only specifies that p is not equal to 0.6. **The test is two-tailed**.

Exercise 1.1

Q1 Over the last few years Jules has had a 90% success rate in germinating her geranium plants. This year she has bought an improved variety of seeds and hopes for even better results.

a) Which quantity is Jules investigating?

b) What value has this quantity taken over the last few years?

c) Write down a suitable: (i) null hypothesis, (ii) alternative hypothesis.

d) State whether this test is one- or two-tailed.

Q2 The local council found that only 16% of residents were aware that grants were available to help pay to insulate their houses. The council ran a campaign to publicise the grants, and now want to test whether there is an increased awareness in the area. Write down suitable null and alternative hypotheses involving the proportion of residents aware of the grants.

Q3 In a village shop, 3% of customers buy a jar of chilli chutney. The owner has changed the packaging of the chutney and wants to know if the proportion of customers buying a jar of chilli chutney has changed. Write down suitable null and alternative hypotheses.

Q4 It is claimed that the proportion of members of a gym who watch Australian soaps is 40%. Boyd wants to test his theory that the proportion is higher. Write down suitable null and alternative hypotheses.

2. Hypothesis Tests for a Binomial Distribution

Setting up the test

To set up a hypothesis test for a **binomial** distribution:

1. Define the **population parameter** in **context** — for a binomial distribution it's always p, a **probability** of success, or **proportion** of a population.

2. Write down the **null** hypothesis (H_0) — $H_0: p = a$ for some constant a.

3. Write down the **alternative** hypothesis (H_1) — H_1 will either be $H_1: p < a$ or $H_1: p > a$ (one-tailed test) or $H_1: p \neq a$ (two-tailed test).

4. State the **test statistic**, X.

> A **test statistic** for a hypothesis test is a statistic calculated from **sample data**, which is used to **decide** whether or not to reject H_0.

For a binomial distribution it's always the **number of 'successes'** in the sample.

5. Write down the **probability distribution** of the test statistic under H_0 — $X \sim B(n, p)$ where n is the sample size.

6. State the **significance level**, α — you'll usually be given this.

> The **significance level** of a test (α) determines **how unlikely** your data needs to be under the null hypothesis (H_0) before you reject H_0.

E.g. a significance level of $\alpha = 0.05$ would mean that you would **only** reject H_0 if your observed data fell into the **most extreme 5%** of possible outcomes.

Cleo wants to test whether a coin is more likely to land on heads than tails. She plans to flip it 15 times and record the results. Write down suitable null and alternative hypotheses. Define the test statistic, X, and give its probability distribution under the null hypothesis.

- Define your population parameter.   Let p be the probability of the coin landing on heads.

- The null hypothesis will be that the coin is unbiased. H_0: $p = 0.5$

- Cleo believes the coin is more likely to land on heads. H_1: $p > 0.5$

- Each 'heads' is a success.   **X = the number of heads in the sample of 15 throws**

- Under H_0, $p = 0.5$ and $n = 15$. $X \sim B(15, 0.5)$

Exercise 2.1

MODELLING

Q1   For each hypothesis test described below, write down suitable null and alternative hypotheses, define the test statistic, X, and give its probability distribution under the null hypothesis.

a) Callie believes a 10-sided spinner is biased towards landing on 7.
   She plans to test this by spinning the spinner 50 times and recording the results.

b) The probability of being stopped at a particular set of traffic lights is thought to be 0.25.
   Eli thinks he is less likely to be stopped. He passes the lights once a day for 2 weeks
   and records whether or not he has to stop.

c) A taxi company's drivers get lost on average on 1 in every 40 journeys.
   The company employs some new drivers and wants to test whether this
   proportion has changed, using a random sample of 100 journeys.

d) A school health team checks teenagers for the presence of an antibody before vaccinating them.
   Usually 35% of teenagers have the antibody present. The team is to select a random sample of 40
   teenagers from a remote Scottish island where they think that this proportion may be different.

e) Lucy believes that only 50% of students in her school will have seen a particular film. Rahim thinks
   that a higher proportion of students will have seen the film, so asks a random sample of 30 students.

f) Each day, the probability that a cat catches a mouse is 0.7. The cat's owner has put a bell on its
   collar and wants to test if it now catches fewer mice. She records whether a mouse is caught every
   day for 3 weeks after attaching the bell.

Testing for significance

- To test an observed value for significance, work out the **p-value** — the probability of X being **at least as extreme** as this value, x, under H_0. To do this, use the **binomial cumulative distribution function**, $P(X \leq x)$ — either use your calculator or the binomial tables (see p.468 for the tables).

- Then **compare** the p-value to the **significance level** and write your **conclusion**. If the p-value is **less** than the significance level α, for a one-tailed test, or $\frac{\alpha}{2}$, for a two-tailed test, **reject** H_0.

Ed believes that a five-sided spinner is biased towards landing on 5. He spins the spinner 20 times and it lands on 5 ten times. Using a 5% level of significance, test the hypothesis that the spinner is biased towards landing on 5.

1. Identify the population parameter. p = the probability of the spinner landing on 5

2. Formulate the null and alternative hypotheses for p.
   The null hypothesis is that the spinner is not biased $H_0: p = 0.2$
   and the alternative hypothesis is that the spinner is more likely to land on 5. $H_1: p > 0.2$

3. State the test statistic X and its probability distribution under H_0.
   Let X = number of times the spinner lands on a 5 in the sample. Under H_0, $X \sim B(20, 0.2)$.

4. State the significance level of the test. $\alpha = 0.05$

5. The observed value is 10, so find the probability of X being 10 or more, under the null hypothesis.
$$P(X \geq 10) = 1 - P(X < 10) = 1 - P(X \leq 9)$$
$$= 1 - 0.9974... = 0.0026 \ (4 \text{ d.p.})$$
Since $0.0026 < 0.05$, the result is significant.

6. Write your conclusion.
   There is evidence at the 5% level of significance to reject H_0 and to support Ed's claim that the spinner is biased towards landing on 5.

Exercise 2.2

MODELLING

Q1 Charlotte claims she can read Milly's mind. To test this claim, Milly thinks about a number from 1 to 5 while Charlotte attempts to read her mind. Charlotte is right on 4 out of 10 occasions.

   a) Write down the population parameter and suitable null and alternative hypotheses.

   b) Define the test statistic and write down its sampling distribution under the null hypothesis.

   c) Are these results significant at a 5% level of significance?

Q2 Last year 45% of students said that the chicken dinosaurs in the school canteen were good value. After this year's price increase Ellen says fewer people think they are good value. She asked 50 people and found only 16 said that chicken dinosaurs were good value. Test Ellen's claim at the 10% level.

Q3 Pete's Driving School advertises that 70% of its clients pass the driving test at their first attempt. Hati and three of her friends failed. Four other friends did pass first time. She complained that the advertisement was misleading and that the percentage was actually lower. Test whether there is evidence to support Hati's complaint at the 1% level.

 A wildlife photographer is taking photographs of a rare glass frog. He's found over time that the probability that he'll sight a glass frog during any day of searching is 0.05. He moves to another part of the rainforest where he claims the probability will be different. During his first 6 days searching he spots the frog on 3 of the days. Use a 1% level of significance to test his claim.

1. Identify the population parameter.
   Let p = probability that the wildlife photographer will spot a glass frog in a day of searching.

2. Formulate the hypotheses. $H_0: p = 0.05$, $H_1: p \neq 0.05$

3. State the test statistic.

Let X = number of sampled days that he spots a frog. Under H_0, $X \sim B(6, 0.05)$

4. State the significance level.

$\alpha = 0.01$, so $\frac{\alpha}{2} = 0.005$

5. The test is two-tailed, so you need to work out which 'tail' you are working in.
   Find the number of days on which the photographer expects to see a glass frog.

Under H_0, the photographer believes he'll see a glass frog on 5% of days when he looks. So in 6 days, he'd expect to see a glass frog on $0.05 \times 6 = 0.3$ days.

The observed number of days (3) is greater than this expected value under H_0, so you're in the upper tail. So find $P(X \geq 3)$.

$$P(X \geq 3) = 1 - P(X < 3) = 1 - P(X \leq 2)$$
$$= 1 - 0.9977... = 0.0022 \text{ (4 d.p.)}$$

Since $0.0022 \leq 0.005$, the result is significant.

6. Write your conclusion.

There is sufficient evidence at the 1% level of significance to reject H_0 in favour of the wildlife photographer's claim that the probability of sighting a glass frog is different in the other part of the rainforest.

Exercise 2.3

Q1 In the past, 25% of John's violin pupils have gained distinctions in their exams. He's using a different examination board and wants to know if the percentage of distinctions will be significantly different. His first 12 exam candidates gained 6 distinctions. Test whether the percentage of distinctions is significantly different at the 1% level.

Q2 Jin is a keen birdwatcher. Over time he has found that 15% of the birds he sees are classified as 'rare'. He has bought a new type of birdseed and is not sure whether it will attract more or fewer rare birds. On the first day only 2 out of 40 of the birds were rare. Test whether the percentage of rare birds is significantly different at the 10% level.

Q3 10% of customers at a village newsagent's buy Pigeon Spotter Magazine. The owner has just opened a new shop in a different village and wants to know whether this proportion will be different in the new shop. One day 8 out of a random sample of 50 customers bought Pigeon Spotter Magazine. Is this significant at the 5% level?

Critical regions

Instead of finding the *p*-value, you can test for significance by finding the **critical region**.

> The **critical region** (CR) is the **set** of all values of the **test statistic** that would cause you to **reject H_0**.

- **One-tailed tests** have a **single** critical region, at one end of the distribution. **Two-tailed** tests have a critical region split into **two**, with a bit at each end.

- Find the critical region for your significance level α. For a **one-tailed** test, the probability of rejection in the tail will be **less than or equal to** α. It the test is **two-tailed**, you could either be asked to make the probability of rejection in the tails **less than** $\frac{\alpha}{2}$, or **as close** to $\frac{\alpha}{2}$ as possible. Then see if the **observed** value (x) **lies in** the critical region — if it **does**, **reject** H_0.

- The set of all the values of the test statistic for which you **wouldn't** reject H$_0$ (i.e. the values not in the critical region) is known as the **acceptance region**.

- The value at the **edge** of a critical region is called a **critical value**.

> The **actual significance level** of a test is the **probability** of **rejecting H$_0$** when it is true — the probability of **incorrectly rejecting H$_0$**.

You find the actual significance level by calculating the **probability** of X taking a value in the **critical region** (assuming H$_0$ is true).

 Examples   **Records show that the proportion of trees in a wood that suffer from a particular leaf disease is 15%. Hasina thinks that recent weather conditions might have affected this proportion. She examines a random sample of 20 of the trees.**

a) **Using a 10% level of significance, find the critical region for a two-tailed test of Hasina's theory. The probability of rejection in each tail should be as close to 0.05 as possible.**

   1. Define the population parameter.   Let p = proportion of trees with the leaf disease.

   2. Formulate the hypotheses.   H$_0$: $p = 0.15$,   H$_1$: $p \neq 0.15$

   3. Define the test statistic and state its probability distribution.
          Let X = number of sampled trees with the disease.   Under H$_0$, $X \sim B(20, 0.15)$

   4. State the significance level of the test. $\alpha = 0.1$, so $\frac{\alpha}{2} = 0.05$

   5. The lower tail of the critical region is the set of 'low' values of X with a total probability as close to 0.05 as possible. The upper tail is the set of 'high' values of X with a total probability as close to 0.05 as possible.
          Lower tail: $P(X \leq 0) = 0.0388 < 0.05$, $P(X \leq 1) = 0.1756 > 0.05$
                      0.0388 is closer to 0.05, so the lower tail is $X \leq 0$.
          Upper tail: $P(X \geq 6) = 1 - P(X \leq 5) = 1 - 0.9327 = 0.0673 > 0.05$
                      $P(X \geq 7) = 1 - P(X \leq 6) = 1 - 0.9781 = 0.0219 < 0.05$
                      0.0673 is closer to 0.05, so the upper tail is $X \geq 6$.
       So the critical region is $X = 0$ or $X \geq 6$.

    Tip: If the question didn't specify that each tail should be as close to 0.05 as possible, the lower tail would be $X = 0$ and the upper tail would be $X \geq 7$.

b) **Find the actual significance level of a test based on your critical region from part a).**

   Add the probabilities (under H$_0$) of the test statistic falling in each part of the critical region.
                 $P(X = 0) + P(X \geq 6) = 0.0388 + 0.0673 = \textbf{0.1061}$ (4 d.p.) (or **10.61%**)

c) **Hasina finds that 8 of the sampled trees have the leaf disease. Comment on this finding.**

         The observed value of 8 is in the critical region. So there is evidence at the 10% level of significance to reject H$_0$ and to support Hasina's theory that there has been a change in the proportion of affected trees.

Exercise 2.4

Q1 A primary school hopes to increase the percentage of pupils reaching the top level in reading from its current value of 25% by limiting the time pupils spend playing games online. Twenty parents will be limiting their child's use of online games.

   a) Using a 5% level, find the critical region for a one-tailed test of whether the proportion of pupils reaching the top reading level has increased.

   b) State the actual significance level.

   c) Write down the acceptance region for this test.

Q2 Miss Cackle wishes to decrease the percentage of pupils giving up her potion-making class after year 9 from its current level of 20%. Over the last 3 years she has tried a new teaching method in one of her classes of 30 pupils. Using a 10% significance level, find the critical region for a test of whether the number of pupils giving up potions after year 9 has decreased. State the actual significance level.

Q3 Politicians are testing for a difference in local councils' rubbish collection service between the North and the South. They've found that 40% of the northern councils provide a weekly service. They have randomly chosen 25 councils in the south of the country to investigate. Find the critical region for a test of whether the number of councils providing weekly collections is significantly different in the south at the 5% level. The probability of each tail should be as close to 2.5% as possible. State the actual significance level.

Q4 A travel agent thinks that fewer people are booking their holidays early this year. In the past, 35% have booked their summer holiday by February 1st. She intends to ask 15 people on 2nd February whether they have booked their summer holiday.

   a) Find the critical region for a test at the 5% level of whether fewer people are booking their holidays early this year.

   b) State the actual significance level.

   c) The travel agent finds that 3 of the people she asked had already booked their summer holiday. Is this result significant at the 5% level?

Q5 A new drug is to be tested on 50 people to see if they report an improvement in their symptoms. In the past it has been found that with a placebo treatment, 15% of people report an improvement, so the new drug has to be significantly better than this. Find the critical region for a test at the 1% level of significance of whether the new drug is significantly better than a placebo. State the actual significance level.

Q6 Tests conducted on five-year-old girls have found that 5% of them believe that they have magical powers. A group of 50 five-year-old boys are to be tested to see if the same proportion of boys believe that they have magical powers. Find the critical region for a test at the 10% level of whether the proportion of boys who believe they have magical powers is different from that of girls. The probability of each tail should be less than or equal to 5%. Calculate the actual significance level.

Q7 The British Furniture Company's top salesman has persuaded 60% of customers to take out a loyalty card. He has been on a motivational course and aims to improve even further. On his first day's work after the course he serves 12 customers.

   a) Using a 5% level of significance, find the critical region for a test of whether the salesman has improved.

   b) State the actual significance level.

   c) He persuades 10 customers to take out a loyalty card. Is this result significant at the 5% level?

   d) Repeat parts a)-c) for a 10% level of significance.

Review Exercise — Chapter 14

Q1 The probability that one brand of watch battery lasts for more than 18 months is 0.64.
Elena thinks that a new brand of watch battery is more likely to last for more than
18 months. Write down suitable null and alternative hypotheses and state whether
her test is one-tailed or two-tailed.

Q2 Salma thinks a coin might be biased. She wants to find out about p, the proportion
of coin tosses that result in 'heads'. State whether a one-tailed or two-tailed hypothesis
test should be used. Define suitable null and alternative hypotheses for her test.

Q3 The probability that each item a machine produces is faulty is thought to be 0.05.
The manager takes a sample of 50 items to check this claim. Write down suitable
null and alternative hypotheses for his test, define the test statistic and give its
probability distribution under the null hypothesis.

Q4 Milo correctly answers 84% of questions in a quiz. Tina claims that she is better
at quizzes than Milo. In a sample of 10 questions, she answers 9 questions correctly.

a) Write down the population parameter and appropriate hypotheses to test Tina's claim.

b) What is the test statistic? What is its probability distribution under the null hypothesis?

c) Test Tina's claim at the 5% significance level.

Q5 Carry out the following tests of the binomial parameter p.
Let X represent the number of successes in a random sample of size 20:

a) Test $H_0: p = 0.2$ against $H_1: p < 0.2$, at the 5% significance level, using $x = 2$.

b) Test $H_0: p = 0.4$ against $H_1: p > 0.4$, at the 1% significance level, using $x = 15$.

Q6 A writer finds that, on average, 1 out of every 20 pages in his previous book contains an error.
For his new book, he uses a different proofreader. He checks 50 pages, and finds that 2 of them
contain errors. Test whether the detected error rate is significantly different at the 5% level.

Q7 The owner of a restaurant wants to improve its reviews on a website.
Currently, the restaurant has 45% positive reviews. After changing the menu
and carrying out staff training, the owner wants to know if the proportion of positive reviews
has increased. He checks a random sample of 20 new reviews on the website.

a) Find the critical region for a hypothesis test at the 1% significance level.

b) Find the actual significance level.

c) Find the acceptance region.

Q8 Find the critical region for the following test where $X \sim B(10, p)$:
Test $H_0: p = 0.3$ against $H_1: p < 0.3$, at the 5% significance level.

Q9 85% of students are happy with the service their bus company provides. 100 randomly-selected
students from another school are asked if they are happy with their bus company.

a) Find the critical region for a hypothesis test at the 10% significance level
of whether the proportion of 'happy' students is different at the second school.
The probability in each tail should be as close to 5% as possible.

b) Find the actual significance level.

c) 75 students from the second school are happy with the bus company.
Is this result significant at the 10% level?

Chapter 15 — Kinematics

Kinematics is the study of the motion of objects. In kinematics, objects are described in terms of their displacement, velocity and acceleration (usually by an equation or on a graph).

1. Motion Graphs

Displacement-time graphs

Displacement is an object's **distance from a particular point** (often its starting point) measured in a straight line. It's not necessarily the same as the total distance travelled.

- A **displacement-time (*x-t*) graph** shows how an object's **displacement** from a particular point changes over time.

- The **gradient** of the graph at a particular point gives the object's **velocity** at that time.

 A girl goes for a run along a straight path. Her journey is detailed below:
- **She runs 1.5 km in 5 minutes, then rests for 2 minutes.**
- **She then jogs 0.5 km in 4 minutes, in the same direction as before.**
- **Finally, she runs 2.5 km back in the direction she came, passing her starting point along the way.**
- **She finishes 20 minutes after she first set off.**

Show her journey on a displacement-time graph.

1. The graph starts at (0, 0), then increases to a height of 1.5 km over 5 minutes.

2. The girl rests for 2 minutes, so this is a horizontal line.

3. The girl jogs from a displacement of 1.5 km to 2 km, over 4 minutes.

4. Finally, she travels in the opposite direction for 2.5 km, finishing at (20, –0.5).

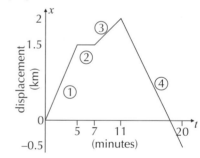

Tip: In a distance-time graph, the graph only goes upwards, since distance travelled can't go down with time.

Exercise 1.1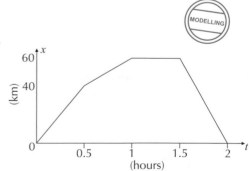

Q1 The displacement-time graph on the right shows the journey of a car travelling in a straight line. Calculate the velocity of the car during each stage of the journey.

Q2 A man walks with velocity u ms^{-1} for 500 m, then with velocity $-2u$ ms^{-1} for 700 m. He then walks 600 m with velocity $1.5u$ ms^{-1}.

a) Find the man's final displacement.

b) Show his journey on a displacement-time graph.

c) Find his total journey time. Give your answer in terms of u.

d) Find his average speed in terms of u.

Q3　A man leaves his house at 13:00. He walks in a straight line at a speed of 5 mph for one hour, then at a speed of 3 mph in the same direction for the next hour. He then rests for an hour. The man's wife leaves their house at 14:30 and travels at a constant speed to meet him at 15:30.

Draw a displacement-time graph to show the two journeys.

Q4　A coach travels in a straight line between three coach stops, *A*, *B* and *C*. Its journey is as follows:

- Leaves *A* at midday, travels 30 km at a constant speed to *B* in one hour and then stops for 30 minutes.

- Leaves *B* and travels 60 km at a constant speed to point *C* in the same direction as before, moving at a constant speed of 40 kmh^{-1}, and then stops for 30 minutes.

- Leaves *C* and returns to *A* at a constant speed, arriving at 18:00.

a) Draw a displacement-time graph to show the coach's journey.

b) Find the velocity of the coach during the final stage of the journey.

c) Find the average speed of the coach over the whole journey.

Q5　A car travels in a straight line with speed *u* ms^{-1} for *t* seconds, stops for 100 seconds, then returns back the way it came with speed 2*u* ms^{-1}.

a) Draw a displacement-time graph to show the movement of the car.

b) Find an expression in terms of *u* and *t* for the total distance travelled by the car.

c) Find the average speed of the car (including its rest time). Give your answer in terms of *u* and *t*.

Velocity-time graphs

A **velocity-time (*v-t*) graph** shows how an object's **velocity** changes over time.
Velocity is different from **speed** because it takes into account the direction of movement.

- The **gradient** of a velocity-time graph gives the object's **acceleration**.
- The **area** under the graph gives the object's **displacement**.

[Example]　**A car starts from rest and reverses in a straight line with constant acceleration to a velocity of –5 ms^{-1} in 12 seconds.**

Still reversing, it then decelerates to rest in 3 seconds and remains stationary for another 3 seconds.

The car then moves forward along the same straight line as before (but in the opposite direction), accelerating uniformly to a velocity of 8 ms^{-1} in 6 seconds. It maintains this speed for 6 seconds.

Show the car's movement on a velocity-time graph.

1. The graph starts at (0, 0) (*t* = 0 s, *v* = 0 ms^{-1}), then decreases to –5 ms^{-1} over 12 seconds.

2. The graph returns to 0 ms^{-1} in 3 seconds.

3. The car is then stationary, so the graph remains at 0 ms^{-1} for 3 seconds.

4. The graph increases to 8 ms^{-1} in 6 seconds.

5. Finally, the car travels at a constant velocity for 6 seconds — shown by a horizontal line.

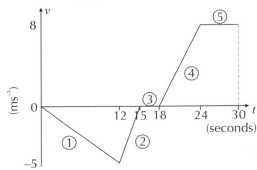

> **Example** For the example on the previous page, find the car's final displacement.

1. Using the graph, find the area below the horizontal axis. $\text{Area} = \frac{1}{2} \times 15 \times -5 = -37.5$ m

2. Find the area above the horizontal axis —
   using the formula for the area of a trapezium. $\text{Area} = \frac{1}{2}(6 + 12) \times 8 = 72$ m

3. Add these together to find the final displacement. $\text{Displacement} = -37.5 + 72 = \textbf{34.5 m}$

Speed-time graphs are very similar, but they show how an object's **speed** changes over time.

- The **gradient** of the graph gives the **magnitude** of its **acceleration**.
- The **area** under the graph is the **distance travelled**.

> **Example** A bus is travelling at speed V ms⁻¹. When it reaches point A it accelerates uniformly for 4 s, reaching a speed of 21 ms⁻¹ as it passes point B.
> At point B, the driver brakes uniformly until the bus comes to a halt 7 s later. The rate of deceleration is twice the rate of acceleration.
> **Draw a speed-time graph of the motion and find the value of V.**

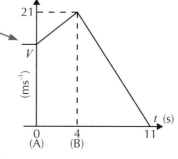

1. Use the information from the question to draw the graph.

2. Calculate the acceleration for the first 4 s
   by finding the gradient.

   $\text{Acceleration} = \dfrac{21 - V}{4}$ ms⁻²

3. Calculate the deceleration between 4 s and 11 s
   (deceleration is negative acceleration).

   $\text{Acceleration} = \dfrac{0 - 21}{11 - 4} = -3$ ms⁻², so the deceleration is 3 ms⁻².

4. Rate of deceleration is twice the rate of acceleration. $3 = 2 \times \dfrac{21 - V}{4} \Rightarrow 6 = 21 - V$

   $\Rightarrow \textbf{V = 15 ms⁻²}$

Exercise 1.2

(MODELLING)

Q1 The speed-time graph below shows a bus journey.

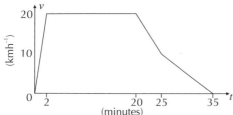

Describe the motion of the bus, given that it travels in a straight line.

Q2 The velocity-time graph on the right shows the motion of a particle travelling in a straight line. Find the particle's acceleration:
a) during the first 5 seconds of motion.
b) between 40 and 60 seconds.
c) during the final 10 seconds of motion.

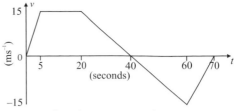

Q3 A particle is travelling in a straight line. It passes point A with velocity 10 ms⁻¹. Immediately after passing A, it accelerates at 4 ms⁻² for x metres up to a velocity of 50 ms⁻¹, then decelerates at 10 ms⁻² for y metres to point B. It passes B with velocity 10 ms⁻¹. The particle takes T seconds to travel between A and B.
a) Show the particle's motion between A and B on a velocity-time graph.
b) Find the area under the graph in terms of T.
c) Calculate the values of x, y and T.

Q4 A train is travelling at a steady speed of 30 ms⁻¹ along a straight track. As it passes a signal box, it begins to decelerate steadily, coming to rest at a station in 20 seconds. The train remains stationary for 20 seconds, then sets off back in the direction it came with an acceleration of 0.375 ms⁻². It reaches a speed of 15 ms⁻¹ as it passes the signal box.
a) Draw a velocity-time graph to show the motion of the train after it first passes the signal box. How long after leaving the station does the train reach the signal box again?
b) Find the train's deceleration as it comes into the station.
c) Find the distance between the signal box and the station.

Q5 A stone is held out over the edge of a cliff and thrown vertically upwards with a speed of 9.8 ms⁻¹. It decelerates until its velocity becomes zero at its highest point, 1 second after being thrown, then begins to fall back down. It lands in the sea below the cliff edge with speed 29.4 ms⁻¹, 4 seconds after it was thrown.
a) Draw a velocity-time graph to show the motion of the stone.
b) Find the distance the stone travels before it reaches its highest point,
c) Find the distance the stone travels from its highest point to the sea,
d) Find the height of the cliff above the sea.

Other motion graphs

An **acceleration-time (a-t) graph** shows how an object's acceleration changes over time.
The **area** under a portion of the graph gives the object's change in **velocity** during that time.

  The acceleration of a parachutist who jumps from a plane is modelled by the *a-t* graph below. Describe the motion of the parachutist and find her velocity when she is no longer accelerating.

1. Describe the motion of the parachutist — be careful with the negative part of the graph.

   She falls with an acceleration of 10 ms⁻² for 7.5 s. Then there's a deceleration (the parachute opens) of 5 ms⁻² for 12.5 s. After 20 s the acceleration is zero, so she falls with constant velocity.

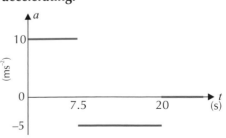

2. Find the area under the graph — let A be the area
   for the first 7.5 s and B be area from 7.5 s to 20 s.   Area A: $10 \times 7.5 = 75$ ms⁻¹

   Area B: $-5 \times 12.5 = -62.5$ ms⁻¹

3. Add A and B to get the velocity when the acceleration is zero. $75 + -62.5 =$ **12.5 ms⁻¹**

It can be easy to get different types of motion graph mixed up — remember:

▪ **Displacement**, **velocity** and **acceleration** are **vector** quantities
  — they have a magnitude and a direction (see p.121).

▪ **Distance**, **speed** and **magnitude of acceleration** are **scalar** quantities — they only have magnitudes.

> E.g. 1   Bicycle A has velocity 6 ms⁻¹ and Bicycle B has velocity –6 ms⁻¹. They have the
> same speed, but different velocities as they're travelling in opposite directions.
>
> E.g. 2   In the car example on p.207-208 you found the car's final displacement.
> Finding the final distance travelled would be different — you would add
> the magnitudes of the displacements to get $37.5 + 72 = 109.5$ m

▪ Motion graphs for vector quantities **can go below** the horizontal axis — e.g. the acceleration of
  –5 ms⁻² in the parachute example is an acceleration in the direction opposite to travel (upwards).

▪ Motion graphs for scalar quantities **can't go below** the horizontal axis.

Exercise 1.3

MODELLING

Q1 The motion of a remote-controlled car, starting from rest,
follows the *a-t* graph to the right. Find the velocity when:

a) $t = 5$

b) $t = 12$

c) $t = 16$

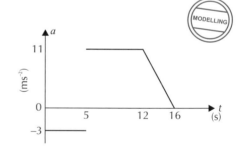

Q2 A train starts from rest at station A and travels with constant acceleration for 30 s. It then travels with
constant speed V ms⁻¹ for 3 minutes. It then decelerates with constant deceleration for
1 minute before coming to rest at station B. The total distance between stations A and B is 6.3 km.

a) Sketch a speed-time graph for the motion of the train between stations A and B.

b) Hence or otherwise find the value of V.

c) Calculate the distance travelled by the train while decelerating.

d) Sketch an acceleration-time graph for the train's motion.

Q3 The carriage on a theme park ride moves vertically up
and down in a straight line. The ride lasts 30 seconds and
the carriage goes above and below the ground.
The displacement-time graph on the right shows the motion
of the ride. Sketch a distance-time graph of the motion
and find the distance travelled by the carriage.

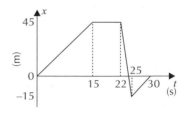

There are five **constant acceleration equations** — these are used to find out information about objects which are **accelerating** (or decelerating) **uniformly**. For **displacement** s, **initial velocity** u, **final velocity** v, **acceleration** a and **time** t the constant acceleration equations (also known as '*suvat*' equations) are:

$$v = u + at \qquad s = ut + \frac{1}{2}at^2 \qquad s = \left(\frac{u+v}{2}\right)t \qquad v^2 = u^2 + 2as \qquad s = vt - \frac{1}{2}at^2$$

Tip: To choose the right equation, use the values you know and the variable you need to find.

 A particle accelerates from rest for 8 seconds at a rate of 12 ms⁻².
The particle's motion is restricted to a straight path.

a) **Find the velocity of the particle at the end of the 8 seconds.**

    1.   List the variables involved. $u = 0, \ v = ?, \ a = 12, \ t = 8$

    2.   Substitute the values into $v = u + at$
         (the equation with u, v, a and t in it). $v = 0 + (12 \times 8) = \mathbf{96 \ ms^{-1}}$

b) **Find the displacement of the particle at the end of the 8 seconds.**

    Substitute the values into $s = ut + \frac{1}{2}at^2$. $s = (0 \times 8) + \frac{1}{2}(12 \times 8^2) = \mathbf{384 \ m}$

Exercise 2.1

Q1   A car travels along a straight horizontal road.
        It accelerates uniformly from rest to a velocity of 12 ms⁻¹ in 5 seconds.
        a) Find the car's acceleration.   b) Find the total displacement of the car.

Q2   A cyclist travelling at 18 kmh⁻¹ brakes steadily, coming to rest in 50 m.
        a) Calculate the cyclist's initial velocity in ms⁻¹ .
        b) Find the time it takes the cyclist to come to rest.   c) Find the cyclist's deceleration.

Q3   A skier accelerates from 5 ms⁻¹ to 25 ms⁻¹ over a distance of 60 m.
        a) Find the skier's acceleration.   b) What modelling assumptions have you made?

Q4   A car travels with uniform acceleration between three lamp posts, equally spaced at 18 m apart.
        It passes the second post 2 seconds after passing the first post, and passes the third post 1 second later.
        a) Find the car's acceleration.
        b) Calculate the car's velocity when it passes the first post.

Q5   A bus is approaching a tunnel. At time $t = 0$ seconds, the driver begins slowing down steadily from a
        speed of U ms⁻¹ until, at $t = 15$ s, he enters the tunnel, travelling at 20 ms⁻¹. The driver maintains this
        speed while he drives through the tunnel. After emerging from the tunnel at $t = 40$ s,
        he accelerates steadily, reaching a speed of U ms⁻¹ at $t = 70$ s.
        a) Calculate the length of the tunnel.
        b) Given that the total distance travelled by the bus is 1580 m, find the value of U.

Gravity

An object moving through the air will experience an **acceleration** towards the centre of the earth due to **gravity**.

- Acceleration due to gravity is denoted by the letter **g**. You can usually assume that $g = \textbf{9.8 ms}^{-2}$, unless a question tells you to use a different value.

- Acceleration due to gravity always acts **vertically downwards**.

- For an object moving freely under gravity, you can use the *suvat* equations to find information such as the **speed of projection** (initial speed), **time of flight**, **greatest height** and **landing speed**.

 A ball is projected vertically upwards at 3 ms⁻¹ from a point 1.5 m above the ground.

a) **How long does it take to reach its maximum height?**

   1. List the variables, taking up as the positive direction (*a* is negative since *g* always acts downwards).
                $u = 3,\ v = 0,\ a = -9.8,\ t = ?$

   2. Use $v = u + at$.
                $0 = 3 + (-9.8 \times t) \Rightarrow t = \dfrac{3}{9.8} = \textbf{0.306 s (3 s.f.)}$

b) **What is the ball's speed when it hits the ground?**

   1. List the variables (the ball lands on the ground 1.5 m below the point of projection, so *s* = –1.5).
                $v = ?,\ u = 3,\ a = -9.8,\ s = -1.5$

   2. Use $v^2 = u^2 + 2as$.
                $v^2 = 3^2 + 2(-9.8 \times -1.5) = 38.4 \Rightarrow v = \pm\sqrt{38.4}$

   3. For speed, ignore the negative root.   Speed $= \sqrt{38.4} = \textbf{6.20 ms}^{-1}$ **(3 s.f.)**

 A particle is fired vertically upwards from ground level with speed 49 ms⁻¹. Assuming that air resistance can be ignored, find the amount of time that the particle is over 78.4 m above the ground.

   1. List the variables, taking up as the positive direction. $s = 78.4,\ u = 49,\ a = -9.8,\ t = ?$

   2. Using $s = ut + \dfrac{1}{2}at^2$. $78.4 = 49t - 4.9t^2 \Rightarrow t^2 - 10t + 16 = 0$
                           $(t - 2)(t - 8) = 0 \Rightarrow t = 2, t = 8$

   3. The particle is above 78.4 m between 2 seconds and 8 seconds. $8 - 2 = \textbf{6 seconds}$

Exercise 2.2

In this exercise, assume all objects can be modelled as particles and do not experience any resistance forces.

Q1 A pebble is dropped down a hole to see how deep it is. It reaches the bottom of the hole after 3 seconds. How deep is the hole?

Q2 An orange is thrown vertically upwards with initial speed 14 ms⁻¹. How long does it take to reach its maximum height?

Q3 A ball is dropped from a second floor window that is 5 metres from the ground.
 a) How long will it take to reach the ground?
 b) At what speed will it hit the ground?

Q4 An arrow is projected vertically upwards from ground level with a speed of 30 ms⁻¹.
 a) Find the maximum height reached by the arrow.
 b) Find the time it takes the arrow to reach the ground.
 c) Find the arrow's speed and direction 2 seconds after launch.

Q5 A particle is projected vertically upwards with a speed u ms⁻¹ from a point d metres above the ground. After 3 seconds the particle hits the ground with a speed of 20 ms⁻¹.
 a) Calculate the value of u.
 b) Calculate the value of d.

Q6 An apple is thrown vertically upwards with speed 8 ms⁻¹ from a height of 5 metres above the ground.
 a) Calculate the apple's maximum height above the ground.
 b) For how long is the apple 8 m or more above the ground?

Q7 A decorator is painting the frame of a fifth floor window and catapults a brush up to his mate exactly three floors above him. He catapults it vertically with a speed of 12 ms⁻¹, and it is at its maximum height when his mate catches it.
 a) Find the distance between the decorator and his mate.
 b) For how long is the brush in the air?

 He later catapults a tub of putty vertically at the same speed but his mate fails to catch it. The floors of the building are equally spaced apart, and the decorator is positioned at the base of the fifth floor.
 c) At what speed does it hit the ground?

Q8 The displacement-time graph on the right shows the motion of an object fired vertically upwards with speed 24.5 ms⁻¹ over the edge of a cliff. The object travels in a vertical line and hits the ground below (at $x = 0$).
 a) Find the value of p.
 b) Find the value of q.
 c) Find the value of r.

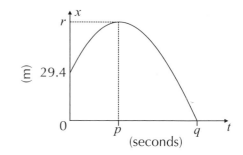

Q9 A projectile is fired from a point 50 m below ground level vertically upwards. It passes a target 100 m above ground level and 3 seconds later passes another target which is 220 m above ground level.

 a) Find the speed of projection of the projectile.
 b) Find the maximum height above the ground reached by the projectile.
 c) Find the time taken by the projectile to reach the first target.

Q10 On a theme park ride, the carriage is fired vertically downwards from a height of 20 m above ground level. The carriage is modelled as a particle and moves freely under gravity before the brakes are applied, 10 m below ground level. When the brakes are applied, the carriage is travelling at 25 ms⁻¹.
 a) Find the speed of projection of the carriage.
 b) Find the time taken for the carriage to reach ground level.
 c) Suggest one reason why this may not be a suitable model.

Example

A car, *A*, travelling along a straight road at a constant 30 ms⁻¹, passes point *R* at time *t* = 0. Exactly 2 seconds later, a second car, *B*, passes point *R* with velocity 25 ms⁻¹, moving in the same direction as car *A*. Car *B* accelerates at a constant 2 ms⁻².

Find the time when the two cars are level.

1. Draw a diagram to help to picture what's going on.

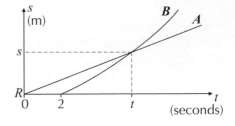

2. For each car, there are different *suvat* variables, so write separate lists and separate equations (*s* is the same for both cars because they're level).

   Car A: $s_A = s$, $u_A = 30$, $v_A = 30$, $a_A = 0$, $t_A = t$

   Car B: $s_B = s$, $u_B = 25$, $v_B = v$, $a_B = 2$, $t_B = (t - 2)$

3. Use $s = ut + \frac{1}{2}at^2$.

   Car A: $s = 30t + \left(\frac{1}{2} \times 0 \times t^2\right) = 30t$

   Car B: $s = 25(t - 2) + \left(\frac{1}{2} \times 2 \times (t - 2)^2\right) = 25t - 50 + (t^2 - 4t + 4)$

   $s = t^2 + 21t - 46$

4. Make the expressions for *s* equal to each other (because the cars have travelled the same distance). $30t = t^2 + 21t - 46 \Rightarrow t^2 - 9t - 46 = 0$

5. Use the quadratic formula to solve for *t*. $t = \dfrac{-b \pm \sqrt{b^2 - 4ac}}{2a} = \dfrac{9 \pm \sqrt{9^2 - (4 \times 1 \times (-46))}}{2 \times 1}$

   $\Rightarrow t = 12.639...$ or $t = -3.639...$

6. Time must be positive.   The cars are level **12.6 seconds (3 s.f.)** after car *A* passes *R*.

You can **derive** the *suvat* equations from motion graphs (see pages 206-210) or from each other.

Examples

A particle moves with constant acceleration *a*.
The particle will accelerate from an initial velocity *u* to a final velocity *v*.
As it accelerates, it will cover a distance *s* over time *t*.

a) **Derive $v = u + at$ using a velocity-time graph.**

   1. Sketch the *v-t* graph (this is a straight line).

   2. The acceleration of the particle is given by the gradient of the graph. $a = \dfrac{v - u}{t - 0}$

   $\Rightarrow at = v - u$

   $\Rightarrow v = u + at$

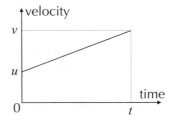

b) **Use $v = u + at$ and $s = \left(\dfrac{u + v}{2}\right)t$ to derive $s = ut + \frac{1}{2}at^2$.**

   Substitute $v = u + at$ into $s = \left(\frac{u + v}{2}\right)t$. $s = \left(\dfrac{u + u + at}{2}\right)t = \left(u + \dfrac{1}{2}at\right)t \Rightarrow \boldsymbol{s = ut + \frac{1}{2}at^2}$

Exercise 2.3

Q1 A particle moves with constant acceleration a. The particle will accelerate from an initial velocity u to a final velocity v. As it accelerates, it will cover a distance s over time t.

a) Derive $s = \left(\dfrac{u+v}{2}\right)t$ using a velocity-time graph.

b) Use $s = \left(\dfrac{u+v}{2}\right)t$ and $v = u + at$ to derive $v^2 = u^2 + 2as$.

Q2 At time $t = 0$, an object passes point W with velocity 2 ms⁻¹. It travels at this constant velocity for 8 seconds, until it reaches point X. Immediately after passing X, the object accelerates uniformly to point Y, 28 m away. The object's velocity at Y is 6 ms⁻¹. Immediately after passing Y, the object decelerates uniformly to V ms⁻¹ (where $V > 2$) in 5 seconds. The object's total displacement is 67 m.

a) Find the time taken for the object to travel between X and Y.

b) Draw a velocity-time graph to show the motion of the object.

c) Find the value of V.

Q3 A van is travelling at a velocity of 14 ms⁻¹ along a straight road. At time $t = 0$, the van passes a car, which then sets off from rest travelling in the same direction as the van. The car accelerates uniformly to a velocity of 18 ms⁻¹ in 20 seconds, then maintains this speed.   (MODELLING)

a) Draw a velocity-time graph to show the motion of the two vehicles.

b) How long after setting off does the car overtake the van?

Q4 Two remote-controlled cars, X and Y, lie on a straight line 30 m apart. At time $t = 0$, they are moving towards each other. X has initial speed 15 ms⁻¹ and accelerates at a rate of 1 ms⁻². Y has initial speed 20 ms⁻¹ and accelerates at a rate of 2 ms⁻².   (MODELLING) (PROBLEM SOLVING)

a) Calculate the time taken for the cars to collide.

b) Calculate the speed of each car when they collide.

c) How far from the initial position of X do the two cars collide?

Q5 A particle travels between three points on a line, P, Q and R. At time $t = 0$, the particle passes P with velocity 15 ms⁻¹. Immediately after passing P, the particle accelerates uniformly at 3 ms⁻² for 4 seconds, until it reaches Q with velocity U ms⁻¹. It then travels at this constant velocity for 6 seconds to point R. Immediately after passing R, the particle decelerates uniformly for T seconds until it comes to rest.

a) Draw a velocity-time graph to show the particle's motion.

b) Find the value of U.

c) Given that the total displacement of the particle is 405 m, find how long after passing P the particle comes to rest.

d) Find the deceleration of the particle in coming to rest.

Q6 At time $t = 0$, a ball is rolled across a mat with velocity 5 ms⁻¹. It decelerates at a rate of 0.5 ms⁻² until it comes to rest. 3 seconds later, a second ball is rolled along a smooth floor, in the same direction as the first, travelling with a constant velocity of 4 ms⁻¹. The starting points of the two balls are side-by-side.

a) How long after the first ball is rolled does the second ball pass the first ball?

b) Find the displacement of each ball when the second ball passes the first ball.   (MODELLING) (PROBLEM SOLVING)

c) How far ahead of the first ball is the second ball, 15 seconds after the first ball is rolled?

Q7 At time $t = 0$, particle A is dropped from a bridge 40 m above the ground. One second later, particle B is projected vertically upwards with speed 5 ms⁻¹ from a point 10 m above the ground.

a) Find the distance travelled by A when B is at the highest point in its motion.   (PROBLEM SOLVING)

b) How long after A is dropped do the two particles become level?

c) How far from the ground are they at this time?

3. Non-Uniform Acceleration

Differentiating displacement and velocity equations

So far, you've seen situations where acceleration is constant. But when it **isn't**, the *suvat* equations **won't work**. You'll need a different method for solving these problems. If you're given an equation for *s* in terms of *t*, then you can use **differentiation** (see Chapter 8) to find the velocity and acceleration.

$$v = \frac{ds}{dt} \text{ and } a = \frac{dv}{dt} = \frac{d^2 s}{dt^2}$$

Examples

An object has displacement *s* (in miles) at time *t* (in hours) given by:

$$s = \frac{1}{9}t^4 - t^3 + 12t, \text{ where } t \geq 0.$$

a) Calculate the object's initial velocity.

1. Differentiate to find the equation for velocity. $v = \frac{ds}{dt} = \frac{4}{9}t^3 - 3t^2 + 12$

2. Initial velocity is when $t = 0$. $v = \frac{4}{9}(0)^3 - 3(0)^2 + 12 = \textbf{12 miles/hour}$

b) Find its acceleration at time *t* = 3.

1. Differentiate the equation for velocity to find the equation for acceleration (so you will have differentiated the displacement twice). $v = \frac{4}{9}t^3 - 3t^2 + 12$

   $a = \frac{dv}{dt} = \frac{4}{3}t^2 - 6t$

2. Substitute $t = 3$. $a = \frac{4}{3}(3)^2 - 6(3) = 12 - 18 = \textbf{-6 miles/hour}^2$

Exercise 3.1

Q1 An object's displacement in metres at *t* seconds is given by the function: $s = 2t^3 - 4t^2 + 3$.

a) Calculate the object's displacement at time $t = 3$.

b) Find the object's velocity equation.

c) What is its velocity at time $t = 3$?

Q2 An object's displacement in metres at *t* seconds is given by the function: $s = \frac{1}{3}t^4 - 2t^3 + 3t^2$.

a) Find the object's displacement at time $t = 4$.

b) Find the object's acceleration at time $t = 3$.

Q3 An object's displacement in metres at *t* seconds is given by the function: $s = \sin(2t) - t^3 + 4t^2 + 2$. The input of the sine function is in degrees.

a) Find the object's velocity at time $t = 0$.

b) Find the object's acceleration at time $t = 1$.

Q4 At time $t = 0$, a dog breaks its lead and runs along a straight path, until it is caught again at $t = 4$. Its displacement in metres at time *t* seconds while it is running free is modelled by the equation:

$$s = \frac{1}{5}t^5 - 2t^4 + 7t^3 - 10t^2 + 5t$$

a) Calculate the dog's initial velocity.

b) What is the dog's acceleration at time $t = 2$?

Integrating acceleration and velocity equations

You can use **integration** (see Chapter 9) to find an equation for an object's displacement from its velocity (or to find its velocity from its acceleration).

$$s = \int v \, \mathrm{d}t \quad \text{and} \quad v = \int a \, \mathrm{d}t$$

You'll always get a **constant of integration**, C, when you integrate.
Because of this, you'll often be given a **condition** so you can find C.

Examples   **The acceleration of an object in km h^{-2} at time t hours is given by:**
$$a = 20t^3 + 18t - 2$$

a) **Given that its initial velocity is 1 km h^{-1}, find the equation for its velocity in terms of t.**

   1. Integrate the acceleration. $\quad v = \int (20t^3 + 18t - 2) \, \mathrm{d}t = 20\left(\frac{t^4}{4}\right) + 18\left(\frac{t^2}{2}\right) - 2t + C$
      $$= 5t^4 + 9t^2 - 2t + C$$

   2. Using the condition that $v = 1$ when $t = 0$, find C. $\quad 1 = 0 + C \Rightarrow C = 1$

   3. Write out the equation for the velocity. $\quad \boldsymbol{v = 5t^4 + 9t^2 - 2t + 1}$

b) **After 1 hour, the object's displacement is 4 km. Find its displacement after 2 hours.**

   1. Integrate the velocity. $\quad s = \int (5t^4 + 9t^2 - 2t + 1) \, \mathrm{d}t = t^5 + 3t^3 - t^2 + t + C$

   2. Using the condition that $s = 4$ when $t = 1$, find C. $\quad 4 = 1^5 + 3(1)^3 - 1^2 + 1 + C \Rightarrow C = 0$

   3. Substitute $t = 2$ into the equation. $\quad s = t^5 + 3t^3 - t^2 + t = 2^5 + 3(2)^3 - 2^2 + 2$
      $$= 32 + 24 - 4 + 2 = \textbf{54 km}$$

Exercise 3.2

Q1 The velocity (in cm s^{-1}) of a particle, t seconds after a chemical reaction, is found to be:
$$v = 1 + 6t + 6t^2 - 4t^3$$
a) Given that the particle starts at $s = 0$, give an equation for its displacement.
b) Find the displacement and velocity of the particle at $t = 2$.

Q2 The velocity (in m s^{-1}) of a particle, after t seconds, is given by the equation $v = 12t^3 - 18t^2 + 2t$.
a) Given that the particle starts at $s = 2$, give an equation for its displacement.
b) Find the displacement and velocity of the particle at $t = 2$.

Q3 A shuttlecock is hit horizontally from a height of 3 m. The shuttlecock's vertical velocity is 0 m s^{-1} at time $t = 0$ seconds. The wind affects its motion such that its vertical acceleration is given by the function $a = -6t^2 + 6t - 6$ (where upwards is the positive direction). Find the vertical velocity of the shuttlecock at time $t = 1$.

Q4 A paper aeroplane is thrown from a height of 2 m. The plane's vertical velocity is 0 m s^{-1} at time $t = 1$ second. The wind affects its motion such that its vertical acceleration is given by the function $a = -3t^2 + 6t - 4$. Find the formula for the plane's vertical displacement, measured in metres above the ground (upwards is the positive direction).

Maximum and minimum points

You can also find **local maximum** and **minimum points** of these functions, just like on p.103. This means finding the maximum (or minimum) displacement, velocity or acceleration that an object reaches. For example, you can find an object's maximum velocity by **investigating** the points where $\frac{dv}{dt}$ (i.e. its acceleration) is **zero**. You should also check the values at the **boundaries** of t — the lower boundary is usually $t = 0$, and if no upper boundary is given, check the value as $t \to \infty$.

Example

At time t (s), an object's displacement (cm) follows the function:

$$s = 10 + 36t + t^3 - \frac{1}{6}t^4, \ 0 \le t \le 6$$

Find the object's maximum velocity during this period.

1. Find an equation for the object's velocity.

$$v = \frac{ds}{dt} = 36 + 3t^2 - \frac{2}{3}t^3$$

2. The local maximum(s) will happen when $\frac{dv}{dt} = 0$, so differentiate and set it equal to zero.

$$\frac{dv}{dt} = 6t - 2t^2 = 0 \Rightarrow 2t(3 - t) = 0$$
$$\Rightarrow t = 0 \text{ or } t = 3$$

3. So there are three points to investigate: $t = 0$, $t = 3$ and $t = 6$. Calculate v at each of these points.

At $t = 0$, $v = 36 + 3(0) - \frac{2}{3}(0) = 36$ ms⁻¹

At $t = 3$, $v = 36 + 3(9) - \frac{2}{3}(27) = 45$ ms⁻¹

At $t = 6$, $v = 36 + 3(36) - \frac{2}{3}(216) = 0$ ms⁻¹

4. The largest of these is at $t = 3$, so:

The object's maximum velocity is **45 ms⁻¹**.

Tip: You could also find $\frac{d^2v}{dt^2}$ to check that $t = 3$ is a maximum point.

Exercise 3.3

Q1 The velocity of a cat (in ms⁻¹) at time t (seconds) over a period of three seconds is approximated by the function $v = t^3 - 6t^2 + 9t$.

a) Find the time at which the cat is travelling at the greatest velocity.

b) The cat's displacement at $t = 0$ is 5 metres. What is its displacement at $t = 2$ (assuming that its motion is in a straight line)?

Q2 Given that s is measured in metres and t in seconds, find the maximum velocity of an object whose displacement is given by:

a) $s = 15t + 6t^2 - t^3, \ 0 \le t \le 5$

b) $s = \frac{-t^5}{20} + \frac{t^4}{4} - \frac{t^3}{3} + 11t, \ 0 \le t \le 4$

Q3 A computer is used to track the motion of a lizard, running back and forth along a track. The computer logs its position over a 7 second interval and computes that its displacement can be approximated by the following quartic function:

$$s = \frac{1}{6}t^4 - 2t^3 + 5t^2 + 2t \ \text{ for } 0 \le t \le 7$$

where s is measured in metres and t in seconds. Calculate the lizard's greatest speed (i.e. the velocity of greatest magnitude) over these 7 seconds.

Q4 An object leaves $s = 0$ m at $t = 0$ s, travelling in the positive direction, then returns to $s = 0$ m at $t = 1$ s. Given that the object's acceleration is given by $a = (6t - 4)$ ms⁻², find the maximum displacement that it reaches in this one second period.

Q1 The displacement-time graph on the right shows a motorcycle journey. Find the velocity of the motorcycle during each stage of the journey.

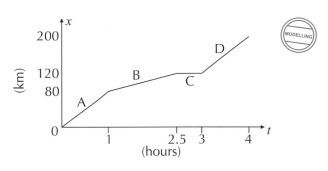

Q2 A runner starts from rest and accelerates at 0.5 ms^{-2} for 5 seconds. She then maintains a constant velocity for 20 seconds before decelerating to a stop at 0.25 ms^{-2}. Draw a velocity-time graph to show the motion and find the distance the runner travels.

Q3 A journey is shown on the speed-time graph on the right.

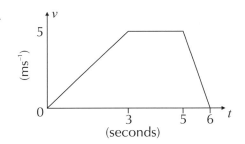

a) Find the acceleration during the first 3 seconds of motion.

b) Find the deceleration during the final 1 second of motion.

c) Find the distance travelled between $t = 3$ and $t = 6$.

Q4 The acceleration of a parachutist who jumps from a plane is modelled by the *a-t* graph on the right. Describe the motion of the parachutist and find his velocity when he is no longer accelerating.

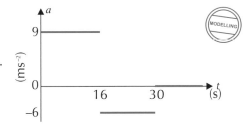

Q5 A motorcyclist accelerates uniformly from 3 ms^{-1} to 9 ms^{-1} in 2 seconds. What is the distance travelled by the motorcyclist during this acceleration?

Q6 A runner accelerates at a rate of 0.2 ms^{-2} along a straight road. At the start of the road, her velocity is 6 ms^{-1}. It takes her 20 seconds to run the length of the road.

a) How long is the road?

b) What is her velocity as she reaches the end of the road?

Q7 A horse runs directly towards the edge of a cliff with velocity 11 ms^{-1}. The horse begins to decelerate at a rate of 3.8 ms^{-2} when it is a distance of 25 m from the cliff edge. Will the horse stop before it reaches the cliff edge?

Q8 A particle is projected vertically upwards with velocity 35 ms^{-1}.

a) Find the maximum height reached by the particle.

b) Find the time the particle is in the air before it lands again.

Q9 A projectile is fired from a point 10 m below ground level vertically upwards. It passes a target 20 m above ground level and 2 seconds later passes another target which is 50 m above ground level. Assume that air resistance can be ignored.

a) Find the speed of projection of the projectile.

b) Find the maximum height above the ground reached by the projectile.

c) Find the time taken by the projectile to reach the first target.

Q10 A swimmer and a fish set off from the same place at the same time. The swimmer swims in a straight line with constant velocity 1 ms^{-1}. The fish accelerates uniformly from rest to U ms^{-1} in 2 seconds, then maintains this speed. It moves in a straight line throughout its motion, and overtakes the swimmer 5 seconds after they set off.

a) Draw a velocity-time graph to show the motion of the swimmer and the fish. (MODELLING)

b) Use your graph to find the value of U.

Q11 At time $t = 0$, particle A is dropped from a crane 35 m above the ground. Two seconds later, particle B is projected vertically upwards with speed 3 ms^{-1} from a point 5 m above the ground.

a) Find the distance travelled by A when B is at the highest point in its motion.

b) How long after A is dropped do the two particles become level? (MODELLING)

c) How far from the ground are they at this time?

Q12 An object's displacement in metres at t seconds is given by the function: $s = \frac{1}{4}t^4 - t^3 - t^2$.

a) Find the object's displacement at time $t = 5$.

b) Find the object's acceleration at time $t = 2$.

Q13 The velocity (in cm s^{-1}) of a particle, t seconds after a chemical reaction, is found to be:
$$v = 3 + 5t + 4t^2 - 3t^3$$

a) Given that the particle starts at $s = 0$, give an equation for its displacement.

b) Find the displacement and velocity of the particle at $t = 2$.

Q14 Find the maximum positive displacement of the objects whose displacement functions are given below (where displacement, s, is measured in metres, and time, t, is measured in seconds):

a) $s = 2 + 3t - 2t^2$

b) $s = t^2 + t^3 - 1.25t^4$

c) $s = -3t^4 + 8t^3 - 6t^2 + 16$

Q15 The displacement of a yo-yo is measured as it extends out as far as the string allows and then retracts. The motion is modelled by the function:
$$s = 2t^4 - 8t^3 + 8t^2, \quad 0 \leq t \leq 2$$
where t is measured in seconds and s is measured in feet from the starting point. (MODELLING)

a) What happens at the limits $t = 0$ and $t = 2$?

b) Find the length of the string (i.e. the maximum displacement of the yo-yo).

Q16 An athlete's displacement during a training exercise can be modelled by the following quartic function:
$$s = \frac{1}{40}t^4 + \frac{1}{15}t^3 - 2t^2 \quad \text{for } 0 \leq t \leq 6,$$ (MODELLING)
where s is measured in metres and t in seconds.
Calculate the athlete's greatest speed over the 6 second interval.

Chapter 16 — Forces and Newton's Laws

A force is an influence which can change the motion of a body (i.e. cause an acceleration). It can also be thought of as a 'push' or a 'pull' on an object. All forces are vectors, so the stuff you learnt about vectors in Chapter 10 should come in useful in this chapter.

1. Understanding Units

S.I. units

The International System of Units (S.I.) was developed so that measurements could be consistent. Some S.I. units (including the **metre**, the **kilogram** and the **second**) are referred to as **base** units. **All** quantities can be measured in units **derived** from the base S.I. units — for example, the **Newton** (the unit of **force**) can be written in terms of the kilogram, metre and second.

> **Example**   Derive the S.I. units of velocity and acceleration.
>
> 1. Velocity is the change in displacement divided by the time taken. Displacement is measured in metres, and time in seconds. $m \div s = \textbf{ms}^{-1}$ (or **m/s**)
>
> 2. Similarly, acceleration is the change in velocity over time. $ms^{-1} \div s = \textbf{ms}^{-2}$ (or **m/s²**)

Exercise 1.1

Q1   Give the derived units of the following measurements using the S.I. base units kg, m and s:

a) Volume = length × width × height
b) Density = mass ÷ volume
c) Momentum = mass × velocity
d) Force = mass × acceleration
e) Energy = force × distance
f) Pressure = force ÷ area

2. Models in Mechanics

Modelling

Models are used to **simplify** complex real-life situations by making certain assumptions. In mechanics, the words below refer to **specific assumptions** that a model makes.

Light — the body has negligible mass.
Static — the body is not moving.
Rough — a body in contact with the surface will experience a frictional force which will act to oppose motion.
Smooth — a body in contact with the surface won't experience a frictional force.
Rigid — the body does not bend.
Thin — the body has negligible thickness.

Particle — a body whose mass acts at a point, so its dimensions don't matter.
Plane — a flat surface.
Lamina — a flat, thin, two-dimensional body.
Beam or **Rod** — a long, thin, straight, rigid body.
Wire — a thin, inextensible, rigid, light body.
String — a thin, inextensible and light body.
Peg — a fixed support which a body can hang from or rest on.
Pulley — a fixed and smooth wheel, over which a string passes.

You need to understand what each **type** of force is and be able to label it on a diagram.

- **Weight** (W) is due to the particle's mass, m, and the acceleration due to gravity, g: $W = mg$ — weight always acts **downwards**.

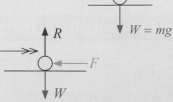

- The **Normal Reaction** (R or N) from a surface. Reaction is always at **90° to the surface**.

- **Friction** (F) is due to **roughness** between a body and surface. Always acts **against motion**, or likely motion.

- **Tension** (T) is the force in a **taut** string, wire, or rod. Prevents two objects from moving further apart.

- **Thrust** (or **compression**) is the force in a **rod** (not a string). Prevents two objects from moving closer together.

Examples   Draw a diagram to model each of the following situations. In each case, state the assumptions you have made.

a)   A book is put flat on a table. One end of the table is slowly lifted and the angle to the horizontal is measured when the book starts to slide.

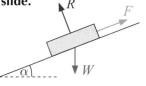

Assumptions — the book is a particle,
— the book is rigid, so it doesn't bend or open,
— the surface of the table is rough,
— there are no other external forces acting.

b)   A ball is held by two strings, A and B, at angles α and β to the vertical.

Assumptions — the ball is a particle,
— the strings are light,
— the strings are inextensible.

Exercise 2.1

For the following questions, draw a diagram to model the situation and state any assumptions you have made.

Q1   An apple falls from a tree.

Q2   A conker hangs vertically in equilibrium from a shoelace that is threaded through the conker.

Q3   A sledge is steadily pulled up an icy hill by a rope.

Q4   a) A wooden box is pushed across a polished marble floor.
      b) A crate is pulled across a carpeted floor by a horizontal rope.

Q5   A person pushes a small package along the road with a stick. The stick makes an angle of 20° with the horizontal.

Q6 a) A car is driven up a hill. b) A car is driven down a hill.

Q7 a) A strongman pulls a lorry along a horizontal road by a rope parallel to the road.
b) A strongman pushes a lorry along a horizontal road with a rod parallel to the road.

Q8 A weight is attached to the bottom of a rod which is held at an angle of 30° to the vertical.

3. Forces

- Forces are **vectors** — they have a **magnitude** (size) and a **direction** that they act in.
- A **component of a force** is the part of the force that acts in a **particular direction**.
- You can describe forces using the **unit vectors i** and **j**. The number in front of the **i** is the horizontal force component, and the number in front of the **j** is the vertical force component.

 A force $F = 3i - 2j$ N acts on a particle P. Find the magnitude and direction of the force.

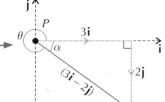

1. Draw a diagram of the force acting on the particle to get a clear idea of what's going on:

2. The force and its **i** and **j** components form a right-angled triangle, so you can use Pythagoras' theorem to find the magnitude of the force:
   Magnitude of $F = \sqrt{3^2 + 2^2} = \sqrt{13} = $ **3.61 N** (3 s.f.)

3. Use trigonometry to find the acute angle α:
   $$\tan \alpha = \frac{2}{3} \Rightarrow \alpha = \tan^{-1}\left(\frac{2}{3}\right) = 33.690...°$$
   $\theta = 360 - \alpha$, so $\theta = $ **326°** (3 s.f.)

Exercise 3.1

Q1 Find the magnitude and direction of the following forces. Give your answers to 3 s.f. where appropriate:

a) 7**i** N b) 2**i** + 2**j** N c) 3**i** + 4**j** N d) −3**i** + 4**j** N e) 12**i** − 5**j** kN

Q2 Find the magnitude and direction of each force below, giving your answers to 3 s.f. where appropriate:

a) $\begin{pmatrix} 3 \\ 1 \end{pmatrix}$ N b) $\begin{pmatrix} -4 \\ -2 \end{pmatrix}$ N c) $\begin{pmatrix} 12 \\ -3 \end{pmatrix}$ N d) $\begin{pmatrix} -0.5 \\ 0.5 \end{pmatrix}$ kN e) $\begin{pmatrix} 0 \\ -11 \end{pmatrix}$ N

Q3 Find the direction of the force $(i + \sqrt{3} j)$ N.

Q4 The force $\begin{pmatrix} 56a \\ -42a \end{pmatrix}$ N (where a is a constant) has a magnitude of 35 N. Find the value of a.

Q5 The forces $\begin{pmatrix} 3 \\ 4 \end{pmatrix}$ N and $\begin{pmatrix} 4 \\ 3 \end{pmatrix}$ N act at the same point. Find the angle between these two forces.

Resultant Forces and Equilibrium

The **resultant force** on an object is the **single** force that has the **same effect** as all the forces acting on the object combined.

To calculate the resultant force on an object, you need to **add the components** of the forces acting on the object in each direction. This is often called **resolving** the forces in each direction.

 Two forces, given by the vectors 3i – j N and –2i + 4j N, act on an object. Calculate the resultant force on the object in both the i- and j-directions.

Resolve the forces in each direction. ——→ i: 3**i** + (–2**i**) = **i**
j: (–**j**) + 4**j** = 3**j**

When the resultant force on an object is **zero** (usually when all the forces on the object **cancel** each other out), the object is in **equilibrium**.

 A particle is suspended in equilibrium by three light, inextensible strings. The diagram shows all of the forces acting on the particle (in N). Find the missing force F.

1. The particle is in equilibrium, so both the horizontal and vertical components of the forces must add to zero.

2. Resolve the horizontal and vertical forces:

$-2 + 0 + x = 0 \implies x = 2$ $1 - 3 + y = 0 \implies y = 2$

So the missing force F is given by $\begin{pmatrix} 2 \\ 2 \end{pmatrix}$.

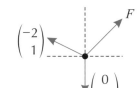

Exercise 3.2

Q1 An object hangs in equilibrium on a string, as shown in the diagram. Find the tension in the string, T.

Q2 Find the resultant of each of these pairs of forces:
   a) $8\mathbf{i} + 5\mathbf{j}$ N and $3\mathbf{i} - 2\mathbf{j}$ N.   b) $2\mathbf{i} - \mathbf{j}$ N and $-\mathbf{i} + 3\mathbf{j}$ N.   c) $-\mathbf{i} - 3\mathbf{j}$ N and $5\mathbf{i} + 4\mathbf{j}$ N.

Q3 An object is held in equilibrium by three forces: $3\mathbf{i} + 2\mathbf{j}$ N, $x\mathbf{i} - 4\mathbf{j}$ N and $-5\mathbf{i} + 2\mathbf{j}$ N. Find the value of the constant x.

Q4 As part of an experiment on magnetism, a magnetic stone is held in place on a table, while some students hold two magnets on the table. The forces exerted on the stone by the magnets are given by $\mathbf{i}$ N and $-5\mathbf{i} - 2\mathbf{j}$ N respectively.

   a) Draw a diagram showing the stone and the magnetic forces acting on it.

   b) Find the resultant magnetic force acting on the stone.

   Another two magnets are added, resulting in two new forces on the stone given by $4\mathbf{i} + \mathbf{j}$ N and F N respectively.

   c) Given that the magnetic forces now hold the stone in equilibrium, find the force F.

4. Newton's Laws of Motion

Newton's first law:

> A body will stay at **rest** or maintain a **constant velocity** unless a **resultant force** acts on the body.

Newton's second law:

> The **overall resultant force** (F_{net}) acting on a body is equal to the **mass** of the body multiplied by the body's **acceleration**.

A body's mass, its acceleration and the resultant force acting on it are related by the following formula, sometimes called the **equation of motion**: ———→ $\boxed{F_{net} = ma}$

Tip: $F = ma$ gives the equation for an object's weight W:
$W = mg$, where g is the acceleration due to gravity, approximately 9.8 ms^{-2}.

Newton's third law:

> For **two bodies**, A and B, **in contact** with each other, the force exerted by A on B is **equal in magnitude** but **opposite in direction** to the force exerted by B on A.

Examples   A particle of mass 12 kg is attached to the end of a light, vertical string. The particle is accelerating vertically downwards at a rate of 7 ms^{-2}.

a) **Find W, the weight of the particle.**

Use the formula for weight — $W = mg$: $12 \times 9.8 = \textbf{117.6 N}$

b) **Find T, the tension in the string.**

Resolve the forces vertically ($\downarrow$): $F_{net} = ma$, so $117.6 - T = 12 \times 7$
                                $T = 117.6 - 84 = \textbf{33.6 N}$

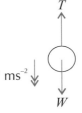

c) **Find the resultant force acting horizontally on the particle.**

The particle isn't accelerating horizontally, so by Newton's first law, there is no resultant force acting horizontally on the particle.

A particle of weight 30 N is being accelerated across a rough horizontal plane by a force of 6 N acting parallel to the horizontal. The particle experiences a constant resistance force of 2.5 N. Given that the particle starts from rest, find its speed after 4 s.

1. Calculate the mass: $W = mg \implies m = \dfrac{W}{g} \implies m = \dfrac{30}{9.8} = \textbf{3.061... kg}$

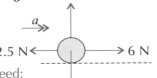

2. Resolve horizontally ($\rightarrow$): $F_{net} = ma \implies 6 - 2.5 = 3.061... \times a$
                        $\implies a = 3.5 \div 3.061... = \textbf{1.143... ms}^{-2}$

3. Use one of the constant acceleration equations (p.211) to find the speed:

$u = 0, \quad v = ?, \quad a = 1.143..., \quad t = 4$
$v = u + at \implies v = 0 + 1.143... \times 4 = \textbf{4.57 ms}^{-1}$ (3 s.f.)

A particle of mass m kg is acted upon by a force F of $(-8\mathbf{i} + 6\mathbf{j})$ N, resulting in an acceleration of magnitude 8 ms⁻².

a) Find the value of m.

   1. F_{net} = magnitude of $F = \sqrt{(-8)^2 + 6^2} = \sqrt{100} = 10$ N

   2. Use Newton's second law to find m. $F_{net} = ma$: $10 = 8m \Rightarrow m = $ **1.25 kg**

b) The force on the particle changes to a force of $4\mathbf{i} + 7\mathbf{j}$.
Find the new acceleration of the particle in vector form.

You can use Newton's second law with vectors to get the acceleration:

$F_{net} = ma$: $(4\mathbf{i} + 7\mathbf{j}) = 1.25a$
$$\Rightarrow a = (4 \div 1.25)\mathbf{i} + (7 \div 1.25)\mathbf{j}$$
$$= 3.2\mathbf{i} + 5.6\mathbf{j} \text{ N}$$

Exercise 4.1

Q1   A particle with mass 15 kg is accelerating at 4 ms⁻².
Find the magnitude of the resultant force acting on the particle.

Q2   A particle with mass 300 g is accelerating at 5 ms⁻².
Find the magnitude of the resultant force acting on the particle.

Q3   A block of mass 5 kg is acted on by a resultant force of 10 N. Find:

a) the acceleration of the block,

b) the speed of the block after 8 s (given that it starts from rest).

Q4   A particle of mass 18 kg is attached to the end of a taut, vertical string. Given that the particle is accelerating vertically upwards at 0.4 ms⁻², find T, the tension in the string.

Q5   A particle of mass 2 kg is attached to the end of a taut, vertical string. Given that the particle is accelerating vertically downwards at 2 ms⁻², find T, the tension in the string.

Q6   A model car, initially at rest on a horizontal plane, is acted on by a resultant horizontal force of magnitude 18 N, causing it to accelerate at 5 ms⁻². Find:

a) the mass of the model car,

b) the car's speed after 4 seconds,

c) the magnitude of the normal reaction from the plane.

Q7   A sack of flour of mass 55 kg is attached to the end of a light vertical rope.
The sack starts from rest and accelerates vertically upwards at a constant
rate so that after 4 seconds it is moving with speed 2.5 ms⁻¹.

a) Find the magnitude of the acceleration of the sack of flour.

b) Assuming that the sack experiences a non-gravitational constant resistance
to motion of magnitude 120 N, find the tension in the rope.

Q8   A stone of mass 300 grams is dropped from the top of a mine shaft and falls vertically
down the shaft. It hits the bottom 12 seconds after being released from rest. Assuming
that the stone experiences a constant resistance of 1.5 N, find the depth of the mine shaft.

Q9   A particle of mass 10 kg is acted on by a force of $(8\mathbf{i} - 2\mathbf{j})$ N.

    a) Find the acceleration of the particle in vector form.

    b) Find the magnitude of the acceleration.

    c) Assuming that the particle is initially at rest,
       find the speed of the particle after 6 seconds have elapsed.

Q10   A particle of mass m kg is acted on by a force of $(8\mathbf{i} + 6\mathbf{j})$ N. Given that the particle is initially
at rest and accelerates to a velocity of $(32\mathbf{i} + 24\mathbf{j})$ ms^{-1} in 2 seconds, find the value of m.

Q11   Two constant forces are acting on a body of mass 2 kg. 10 seconds after starting to
accelerate from rest, the velocity of the body is given by $(30\mathbf{i} + 20\mathbf{j})$ ms^{-1}.

    a) Calculate the resultant force acting on the body. Give your answer in vector form.

    b) If one of the forces is given by $(10\mathbf{i} - 3\mathbf{j})$ N, what is the magnitude of the other force?

Q12   Two constant forces act on a body of mass x kg. 3 seconds after starting to accelerate
from rest, the velocity of the body is given by $(6\mathbf{i} - 9\mathbf{j})$ ms^{-1}.

    a) Given that the resultant force is $10\mathbf{i} - 15\mathbf{j}$, find x.

    b) One of the forces is given by $(\mathbf{i} + 7\mathbf{j})$ N. Calculate the magnitude of the other force.

Connected Particles

In situations where you have two (or more) particles **joined together**, you can still consider the motion of each **individually** and resolve the forces acting on each particle separately.

However, if the connection between the particles is **light, inextensible** and remains **taut**, and the particles are moving in the **same straight line**, they can also be considered to be moving as **one particle** with the **same acceleration**.

 A person of mass 70 kg is standing in a lift of mass 500 kg. The lift is attached to a vertical light, inextensible cable, as shown. By modelling the person as a particle, and given that the lift is accelerating vertically upwards at a rate of 0.6 ms^{-2}, find:

a) **T, the tension in the cable.**

    Resolve vertically ($\uparrow$) for the whole system
    treating the lift and person as one particle:

    $F_{net} = ma$: $T - 570g = 570 \times 0.6$
                    $\Rightarrow T = (570 \times 0.6) + (570 \times 9.8) = \mathbf{5928}$ **N**

b) **The magnitude of the force exerted
by the person on the floor of the lift.**

  1. Sketch a diagram showing the forces acting on the person.

  2. Resolve vertically ($\uparrow$) for the person in the lift:

    $F_{net} = ma$: $R - 70g = 70 \times 0.6$ $\Rightarrow$ $R = 42 + 70g = \mathbf{728}$ **N**

    By Newton's 3rd law, the force exerted by the person on
    the floor of the lift is equal to the reaction from the lift.

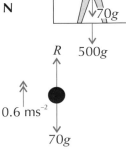

When two objects are **connected** by a **light**, **taut** and **inextensible string**, the string exerts an equal **tension** force at both ends, usually (but not always) in **opposite directions**. For example, if the string passes over a **pulley**, then the tension forces will both act **towards the pulley** (see next page).

Thrust (or **compression**) is the opposite effect, where a **rigid rod** pushes on two connected objects with equal force. For example, the legs of a **table** could be modelled as rigid rods, exerting a thrust force on both the **tabletop** and the **floor**.

 A 30-tonne locomotive engine is pulling a single 10-tonne carriage, as shown. They are accelerating at 0.3 ms⁻² due to the force P generated by the engine. The coupling between the engine and the carriage can be modelled as light and inextensible. It is assumed that there are no forces resisting the motion.

a) **Find the magnitude of the driving force P.**

Consider the engine and the carriage as a single particle, and resolve horizontally ($\rightarrow$):

$F_{net} = ma$, so $P = 40\,000 \times 0.3 = $ **12 000 N**

b) **Find the magnitude of the tension in the coupling.**

Resolving horizontally ($\rightarrow$), consider only the forces acting on the carriage:

$F_{net} = ma$, so $T = 10\,000 \times 0.3 = $ **3000 N**

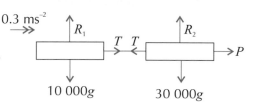

c) **When the engine and carriage are travelling at 15 ms⁻¹, the coupling breaks. Given that the driving force remains the same, find the distance travelled by the engine in the first 5 seconds after the coupling breaks.**

1. Resolve horizontally ($\rightarrow$), considering only the forces acting on the engine to find its new acceleration:

   $F_{net} = ma$: $P = 30\,000 \times a$
   $\Rightarrow a = 12\,000 \div 30\,000 = $ **0.4 ms⁻²**

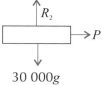

2. Now use a constant acceleration equation to find the distance travelled:
   $s = s$ $u = 15$ $a = 0.4$ $t = 5$

   $s = ut + \dfrac{1}{2}at^2$ $\Rightarrow$ $s = (15 \times 5) + \left(\dfrac{1}{2} \times 0.4 \times 5^2\right) = $ **80 m**

Exercise 4.2

Q1 A lift of mass 2000 kg is carrying a load of weight 4000 N.

a) Calculate the tension in the lift cable, given that the lift is accelerating vertically upwards at 0.2 ms⁻² and that the cable is light, inextensible and vertical.

b) Find the reaction force between the floor of the lift and the load.

Q2 A lift is being tested for safety. The lift has a mass of 1000 kg and contains a load of mass 1400 kg. The lift is attached to a vertical light, inextensible cable.

a) Calculate the tension in the cable given that the lift is accelerating vertically downwards at a rate of 1.5 ms⁻².

b) Find the reaction force between the floor of the lift and the load.

c) The lift is raised to a height of 30 m above the ground.
The cable is cut and the lift falls freely from rest to the ground.
Find the speed of the lift as it hits the ground.

Q3   A tractor of mass 2 tonnes is pulling a trailer of mass 1.5 tonnes by means of a light, rigid coupling, as shown. The tractor applies its brakes and both tractor and trailer decelerate at a rate of 0.3 ms⁻².

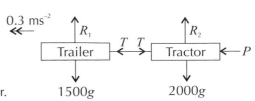

a) Calculate the braking force, P, generated by the tractor.

b) Find the magnitude of T, the thrust in the coupling between the tractor and the trailer.

c) State an assumption that has been made in this model of the motion of the tractor and trailer.

Q4   A car is towing a caravan along a level road. The car has mass 1200 kg and the caravan has mass 800 kg. Resistance forces of magnitude 600 N and 500 N act on the car and the caravan respectively. The acceleration of the car and caravan is 0.2 ms⁻².

a) Calculate the driving force of the car.

b) Find the tension in the tow bar.

c) The car and caravan are travelling at a speed of 20 ms⁻¹ when the tow bar breaks.
Given that the resistance forces remain constant, how long does the caravan take to come to rest?

Pegs and pulleys

Particles connected by a string which passes over a **peg** or **pulley** will move with the **same magnitude of acceleration** as each other (as long as the string is inextensible). However, the two connected particles **cannot** be treated as one because they will be moving in different directions.

If the peg or pulley is **smooth**, then the **magnitude** of the **tension** in the string connecting the particles will be the **same** either side of the peg or pulley.

 Masses A and B, of 3 kg and 5 kg respectively, are connected by a light, inextensible string and hang vertically either side of a smooth, fixed pulley. They are released from rest.

a) **Find the magnitude of the acceleration of each mass.**

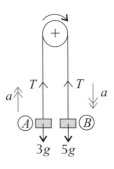

1. Resolve vertically (↑) for A:

    $F_{net} = ma$: $T - 3g = 3a$ — call this equation ①

2. Resolve vertically (↓) for B:

    $F_{net} = ma$: $5g - T = 5a \Rightarrow T = 5g - 5a$ — call this equation ②

3. Substitute equation ② into equation ①:

    $(5g - 5a) - 3g = 3a \Rightarrow 2 \times 9.8 = 8a \Rightarrow a = 2.45$ ms⁻²

b) **Find the time it takes for each mass to move 40 cm.**

Use one of the constant acceleration equations:

$s = ut + \frac{1}{2}at^2$: $0.4 = (0 \times t) + \left(\frac{1}{2} \times 2.45 \times t^2\right)$

$\Rightarrow 0.4 = 1.225t^2 \Rightarrow t = \sqrt{\frac{0.4}{1.225}} = \mathbf{0.571}$ **s** (3 s.f.)

Example

Particle A, of mass 3 kg, is placed on a smooth, horizontal table. A light, inextensible string connects it over a smooth, fixed peg to particle B of mass 5 kg which hangs vertically.

Find the tension in the string if the system is released from rest.

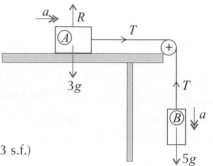

1. Resolve horizontally ($\rightarrow$) for A:

$F_{net} = ma$: $T = 3a \Rightarrow a = \dfrac{T}{3}$ — call this equation ①

2. Resolve vertically ($\downarrow$) for B:

$F_{net} = ma$: $5g - T = 5a$ — call this equation ②

Substitute equation ① into equation ②:

$5g - T = 5 \times \dfrac{T}{3}$ $\Rightarrow$ $\dfrac{8}{3}T = 5g$ $\Rightarrow$ $T = \textbf{18.4 N}$ (3 s.f.)

Exercise 4.3

Q1 Two particles, A and B, of mass 3 kg and 2 kg respectively, are joined by a light inextensible string which passes over a fixed, smooth pulley. Initially, both particles are held at rest with particle A 60 cm higher than particle B. Both particles are then released from rest.

a) Draw a diagram showing the forces acting on the masses.

b) How long is it after the particles are released before they are level?

Q2 Particle A, mass 35 kg, and particle B, mass M kg ($M < 35$), are connected by a light, inextensible rope which passes over a fixed, smooth peg, as shown. Initially both particles are level and they are released from rest.

a) Calculate T, the tension in the rope, given that the particles move 5 m vertically in the first 2 seconds after they are released.

b) Find M.

Q3 Particles A and B, of mass 5 kg and 7 kg respectively, are connected by a light, inextensible string which passes over a fixed, smooth pulley. Particle A is resting on a smooth horizontal surface and particle B is hanging vertically. The system is released from rest.

a) Find the magnitude of the acceleration of the particles.

b) Find the tension in the string.

c) What assumptions have you made in your model?

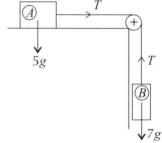

Q4 A bucket of stones with mass 50 kg is attached to one end of a light inextensible rope, and the other end is attached to a counterweight of 10 kg. The rope passes over a smooth fixed pulley. The bucket is raised from rest on the ground to a height of 12 m in 20 s by the addition of a constant force F acting vertically downwards on the counterweight.

a) Draw a diagram to show the forces acting on this system.

b) Calculate the tension in the rope.

c) Find the magnitude of F.

When the bucket is 12 m above the ground, the stones are removed and the force F stops acting on the counterweight.

d) Given that the bucket weighs 11 kg and the system is released from rest, find the speed of the bucket as it hits the ground.

Q5 A particle of mass 2 kg is placed on a smooth, horizontal table. A light, inextensible horizontal string connects it over a smooth peg, fixed to the edge of the table, to a particle of mass M kg which hangs vertically. Given that the tension in the string is 16 N when the system is released from rest, calculate M to two decimal places.

Q6 Two particles, A and B, of mass 15 kg and 12 kg respectively, are attached to the ends of a light inextensible string which passes over a fixed, smooth pulley. The particles are held at rest so that the string is taut and they are both 6 m above the horizontal ground, as shown.

a) Find the acceleration of the particles immediately after they are released from rest.

b) Find the magnitude of the force which the string exerts on the pulley.

c) Particle A strikes the ground without rebounding. Particle B then moves freely under gravity without striking the pulley. Find the time between particle A hitting the ground and particle B coming to rest for the first time.

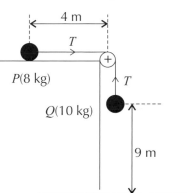

Q7 Two particles, P and Q, of mass 8 kg and 10 kg respectively, are attached to the ends of a light, inextensible string which passes over a fixed, smooth pulley. P is held at rest on a smooth horizontal surface, 4 m from the pulley, and Q hangs vertically, 9 m above the horizontal ground, as shown.

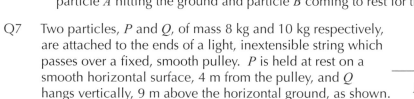

The system is released from rest and P begins to accelerate towards the pulley. At the instant P hits the pulley, the string breaks and Q then moves freely under gravity until it hits the ground.

Find the time between the instant the particles are released from rest and the instant when Q hits the ground.

Problems can also include resistance forces, such as the friction on a table.

 A block, A, of mass 6 kg, is placed on a rough horizontal table. A light inextensible string connects A to a second block, B, of mass 12 kg. The string passes over a fixed, smooth peg and B hangs vertically, as shown. The system is released from rest. Given that A experiences a fixed resistance force F of 30 N, find the tension in the string.

1. Resolve horizontally for A ($\rightarrow$):

Using $F_{net} = ma$: $T - F = 6a$

$\Rightarrow a = \frac{1}{6}(T - 30)$ — call this equation ①

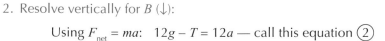

2. Resolve vertically for B ($\downarrow$):

Using $F_{net} = ma$: $12g - T = 12a$ — call this equation ②

3. Substitute equation ① into equation ②:

$12g - T = 12 \times \frac{1}{6}(T - 30) \quad \Rightarrow \quad 12g - T = 2T - 60$

$\Rightarrow 3T = 117.6 + 60 = 177.6 \quad \Rightarrow \quad T = \textbf{59 N}$ (2 s.f.)

Exercise 4.4

Q1 Two particles A and B, of mass 6 kg and M kg respectively, are joined by a light, inextensible string which passes over a fixed, smooth pulley.

The particles are held at rest with A on a rough, horizontal surface and B hanging vertically, as shown to the right.

Given that A experiences a constant resistance force, F, of 10 N and that the tension in the string has magnitude 12 N, find:

a) the acceleration of A immediately after the particles are released,

b) the value of M.

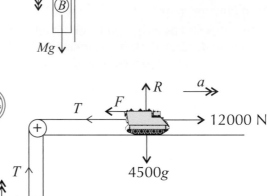

Q2 A 4500 kg buggy is lifting a 300 kg stone slab using a light, inextensible rope which passes over a fixed, smooth pulley, as shown. Initially, the slab is at rest on the ground below the pulley and the rope is taut. The buggy produces a driving force of 12 000 N and is slowed by a constant resistance force of F N.

The slab reaches 2 ms⁻¹ after 6 seconds. Find the magnitude of the resistance force F N.

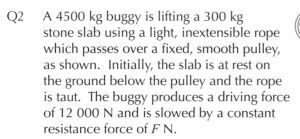

Q3 A 4000 kg truck is lifting a 250 kg crate of building materials, using a light inextensible rope which passes over a fixed smooth pulley, as shown. Initially, the crate is at rest on the ground below the pulley and the rope is taut. The truck produces a driving force of D newtons and is slowed by a constant resistance force F of 500 N.

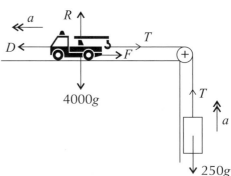

a) The crate reaches 3 ms⁻¹ after 5 seconds. Find the magnitude of the driving force, D.

b) When the crate reaches 3 ms⁻¹, the rope snaps. Given that the driving force remains the same, what is the truck's new acceleration?

c) After the rope snaps, the crate travels freely, experiencing no resistance forces. How much time elapses between the moment when the rope snaps, and when the crate hits the ground?

d) Give a possible improvement that could be made to this model.

Q1 Give the derived units of the following measurements using the S.I. base units kg, m, s and A — A is amperes, the S.I. measure of electrical current.

a) speed = distance ÷ time

b) volume = length × width × height

c) jerk = acceleration ÷ time

d) current density = current ÷ area

Q2 Draw a diagram to model the following situations and state any assumptions you have made.

a) A brick is resting flat on a horizontal table.

b) A golf ball is dropped from a tall building.

c) A sledge is steadily pulled along the horizontal ground by a small child with a rope.

d) A toboggan travels down an icy slope, at an angle α to the horizontal.

e) A pendulum on a string is pushed by a rod, so that it is at an angle α to the vertical.

Q3 A force $(x\mathbf{i} + y\mathbf{j})$ N, with direction parallel to the vector $(2\mathbf{i} + 7\mathbf{j})$ N, acts on a particle, P. Find the angle between the vector $\mathbf{j}$ and the force.

Q4 Find the magnitude and direction of the resultant force in each of the following:

a)

b)

c)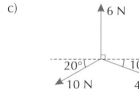

d)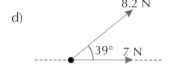

e)

f)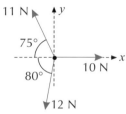

Q5 A horizontal force of 2 N acts on a 1.5 kg particle which is initially at rest on a smooth horizontal plane. Find the speed of the particle 3 seconds after it is released from rest.

Q6 A horizontal force of F N acts on a 7 kg particle which is initially at rest on a smooth horizontal plane. After 6 seconds the particle is travelling at 3 ms^{-1}. Find the force F.

Q7

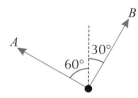

A particle of mass M kg is suspended in equilibrium by two light wires A and B, with angles 60° and 30° to the vertical, as shown. The tension in wire A is 20 N. Find:

a) the magnitude of the tension in wire B,

b) the value of M.

Q8 A force of magnitude 18 N acts on a particle at 60° above the positive horizontal. A force of magnitude 16 N also acts vertically upwards on the particle.

a) Draw a diagram to illustrate the forces acting on the particle.

b) Find the magnitude and direction of the resultant of the two forces.

Q9 Particles A and B, of mass 3 kg and 4 kg respectively, are connected by a light, inextensible string which passes over a fixed, smooth pulley. Particle A is resting on a smooth horizontal surface and particle B is hanging vertically. The system is released from rest.

a) Find the magnitude of the acceleration of the particles.

b) Find the tension in the string.

c) What assumptions have you made in your model?

Q10 Two forces act on a particle of mass 8 kg which is initially at rest on a smooth horizontal plane. The two forces are $(24\mathbf{i} + 18\mathbf{j})$ N and $(6\mathbf{i} + 22\mathbf{j})$ N (with $\mathbf{i}$ and $\mathbf{j}$ being perpendicular unit vectors in the plane). Find:

a) the magnitude and direction of the resulting acceleration of the particle,

b) the particle's distance from its starting point after 3 seconds.

Q11 A tractor of mass 2 tonnes experiences a resistance force of 1000 N whilst driving along a straight horizontal road. If the tractor engine provides a forward force of 1500 N and it's pulling a trailer of mass 1 tonne, and given that the tractor is accelerating at 0.05 ms⁻², find:

a) the resistance force acting on the trailer,

b) the tension in the coupling between the tractor and trailer.

Q12 Two particles are connected by a light, inextensible string and hang in a vertical plane either side of a fixed, smooth pulley. When released from rest the particles accelerate at 1.2 ms⁻². Given that the heavier particle has mass 4 kg, find the mass of the other particle.

Q13 A light, inextensible string passing over a smooth pulley connects boxes A and B, of mass 10 kg and 8 kg respectively, as shown in the diagram. The system is released from rest and the boxes begin to accelerate at a rate of 0.5 ms⁻². Box A experiences a constant frictional force F. Find the magnitude of F.

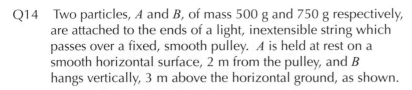

Q14 Two particles, A and B, of mass 500 g and 750 g respectively, are attached to the ends of a light, inextensible string which passes over a fixed, smooth pulley. A is held at rest on a smooth horizontal surface, 2 m from the pulley, and B hangs vertically, 3 m above the horizontal ground, as shown.

The system is released from rest and B begins to accelerate towards the ground. At the instant A hits the pulley, the string breaks and B then moves freely under gravity until it hits the ground.

Find the time between the instant the particles are released from rest and the instant when B hits the ground.

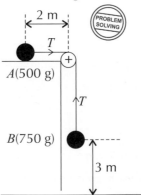

Chapter 17 — Algebra and Functions

This chapter covers the more advanced algebra skills you need for Year 2. It builds on a lot of the skills from Chapter 1, so make sure you're completely comfortable with everything there.

1. Proof By Contradiction

Here's another type of proof to add to the ones on p.2-3. To prove a statement by **contradiction**, you start by saying "suppose the statement **isn't true**...". You then show that this would mean that something **impossible** would have to be true, which means that the initial statement has to be wrong.

Examples   a) **Prove that $\sqrt{2}$ is irrational.**

Assume that $\sqrt{2}$ can be written as $\frac{a}{b}$ with a and b both non-zero integers.
You can also assume that a and b do not have any common factors.

If $\sqrt{2} = \frac{a}{b}$, then $\sqrt{2}b = a$. Squaring both sides gives you $2b^2 = a^2$ — so a^2 is an even number.

If a^2 is even, then a must be even as well. So replace a with $2k$ for some integer k:
$$2b^2 = (2k)^2 = 4k^2 \implies b^2 = 2k^2$$

This tells you that b must be even (since b^2 is even). However, we assumed at the start that a and b had no common factors, so this contradicts our initial assumption.

Therefore $\sqrt{2}$ cannot be written as a fraction $\frac{a}{b}$, so it is irrational.

b) Prove by contradiction that there are infinitely many prime numbers.

Assume that there are a finite number of primes (say n), and list them all:
$p_1 = 2, p_2 = 3, p_3 = 5, \dots , p_{n-1}, p_n$.

Now multiply all of these together: $p_1 p_2 p_3 \dots p_{n-1} p_n$ — call this number P.

Because of how it is defined, P is a multiple of every prime number.

Dividing $P + 1$ by p_1, gives: $(P + 1) \div p_1 = (p_1 p_2 p_3 \dots p_{n-1} p_n + 1) \div p_1$
$$= p_2 p_3 \dots p_{n-1} p_n \text{ remainder } 1$$

Dividing $(P + 1)$ by any prime number gives a remainder of 1, so $(P + 1)$ isn't divisible by any of the prime numbers in the list. So either it is also a prime number, or it is a product of some other prime numbers that are not on the list.

Either way, there is at least one prime number that is not on the list, which contradicts the assumption that the list contained all of them, so there must be infinitely many prime numbers.

Exercise 1.1

Q1   Prove, by contradiction, that there is no largest multiple of 3.

Q2   Prove that if x^2 is odd, then x must be odd.

Q3   a) Prove that the product of a non-zero rational number and an irrational number is always irrational.
b) Disprove that the product of an irrational number and an irrational number is always irrational.

Q4   Prove that there is no smallest positive rational number.

Q5   Prove that $1 + \sqrt{2}$ is irrational.

Q6   a) Prove by exhaustion that if x is an integer and x^2 is a multiple of 3, then x must be a multiple of 3.
b) Hence prove that $\sqrt{3}$ is irrational.

Algebraic fractions should be simplified as much as possible. This makes them easier to work with.

If there's a **fraction** in the numerator or denominator, **multiply** the whole algebraic fraction by the same factor to get rid of it.

Look for **common factors** in the numerator and denominator — **factorise** top and bottom and see if there's anything you can **cancel**.

Tip: There's more about simplifying algebraic fractions back on p.6-7.

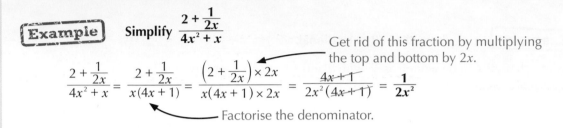

Example Simplify $\dfrac{2 + \frac{1}{2x}}{4x^2 + x}$

Get rid of this fraction by multiplying the top and bottom by $2x$.

$$\frac{2 + \frac{1}{2x}}{4x^2 + x} = \frac{2 + \frac{1}{2x}}{x(4x+1)} = \frac{\left(2 + \frac{1}{2x}\right) \times 2x}{x(4x+1) \times 2x} = \frac{4x+1}{2x^2(4x+1)} = \frac{1}{2x^2}$$

Factorise the denominator.

Exercise 2.1

Q1 Simplify the following:

a) $\dfrac{3x + 6}{x^2 + 3x + 2}$

b) $\dfrac{x^2 + 3x}{x^2 + x - 6}$

c) $\dfrac{2x - 6}{x^2 - 9}$

d) $\dfrac{5x^2 - 20x}{2x^2 - 5x - 12}$

e) $\dfrac{3x^2 - 7x - 6}{2x^2 - x - 15}$

f) $\dfrac{x^3 - 4x^2 - 19x - 14}{x^2 - 6x - 7}$

g) $\dfrac{x^3 - 2x^2}{x^3 - 4x}$

h) $\dfrac{1 + \frac{1}{x}}{x + 1}$

i) $\dfrac{3 + \frac{1}{x}}{2 + \frac{1}{x}}$

j) $\dfrac{1 + \frac{1}{2x}}{2 + \frac{1}{x}}$

k) $\dfrac{\frac{1}{3x} - 1}{3x^2 - x}$

l) $\dfrac{2 + \frac{1}{x}}{6x^2 + 3x}$

m) $\dfrac{\frac{3x}{x+2}}{\frac{x}{x+2} + \frac{1}{x+2}}$

n) $\dfrac{2 + \frac{1}{x+1}}{3 + \frac{1}{x+1}}$

o) $\dfrac{1 - \frac{2}{x+3}}{x+2}$

p) $\dfrac{4 - \frac{1}{x^2}}{2 - \frac{1}{x} - \frac{1}{x^2}}$

Adding and subtracting algebraic fractions

Before you can add or subtract two fractions, they need to have a **common denominator**.

Tip: The common denominator should be the lowest common multiple (LCM) of all the denominators.

Example Simplify: $\dfrac{2y}{x(x+3)} + \dfrac{1}{y^2(x+3)} - \dfrac{x}{y}$

The common denominator is $xy^2(x+3)$.

$$\frac{2y \times y^2}{x(x+3) \times y^2} + \frac{1 \times x}{y^2(x+3) \times x} - \frac{x \times xy(x+3)}{y \times xy(x+3)} = \frac{2y^3 + x - x^2y(x+3)}{xy^2(x+3)} = \frac{2y^3 + x - x^3y - 3x^2y}{xy^2(x+3)}$$

Exercise 2.2

Q1 Simplify the following:

a) $\dfrac{3}{x+1} + \dfrac{2}{x+2}$

b) $\dfrac{4}{x-3} - \dfrac{1}{x+4}$

c) $\dfrac{6}{x+2} + \dfrac{6}{x-2}$

d) $\dfrac{3}{x-2} - \dfrac{5}{2x+3}$

e) $\dfrac{3}{x+2} + \dfrac{x}{x+1}$

f) $\dfrac{5x}{(x+1)^2} - \dfrac{3}{x+1}$

g) $\dfrac{5}{x(x+3)} + \dfrac{3}{x+2}$

h) $\dfrac{3x}{4} - \dfrac{2x-1}{5x}$

i) $\dfrac{x}{x^2-4} - \dfrac{1}{x+2}$

j) $\dfrac{3}{x+1} + \dfrac{6}{2x^2+x-1}$

k) $\dfrac{2}{x} + \dfrac{3}{x+1} + \dfrac{4}{x+2}$

l) $\dfrac{3}{x+4} - \dfrac{2}{x+1} + \dfrac{1}{x-2}$

m) $2 - \dfrac{3}{x+1} + \dfrac{4}{(x+1)^2}$

n) $\dfrac{2x^2-x-3}{x^2-1} + \dfrac{1}{x(x-1)}$

Multiplying and dividing algebraic fractions

You **multiply** algebraic fractions in exactly the same way that you multiply normal fractions.

To **divide** by an algebraic fraction, you just **multiply** by its reciprocal.

Examples a) Simplify $\dfrac{x^2-2x-15}{2x+8} \times \dfrac{x^2-16}{x^2+3x}$

$$\dfrac{x^2-2x-15}{2x+8} \times \dfrac{x^2-16}{x^2+3x} = \dfrac{\cancel{(x+3)}(x-5)}{2\cancel{(x+4)}} \times \dfrac{\cancel{(x+4)}(x-4)}{x\cancel{(x+3)}} = \dfrac{(x-5)(x-4)}{2x} \left(= \dfrac{x^2-9x+20}{2x} \right)$$

b) Simplify $\dfrac{3x}{5} \div \dfrac{3x^2-9x}{20}$

$$\dfrac{3x}{5} \div \dfrac{3x^2-9x}{20} = \dfrac{\cancel{3x}}{\cancel{5}} \times \dfrac{\cancel{20}^{\,4}}{\cancel{3x}(x-3)} = \dfrac{4}{x-3}$$

Exercise 2.3

Q1 Simplify the following:

a) $\dfrac{2x}{3} \times \dfrac{5x}{4}$

b) $\dfrac{6x^3}{7} \times \dfrac{2}{x^2}$

c) $\dfrac{8x^2}{3y^2} \times \dfrac{x^3}{4y}$

d) $\dfrac{8x^4}{3y} \times \dfrac{6y^2}{5x}$

e) $\dfrac{x}{3} \div \dfrac{3}{x}$

f) $\dfrac{4x^3}{3} \div \dfrac{x}{2}$

g) $\dfrac{3}{2x} \div \dfrac{6}{x^3}$

h) $\dfrac{2x^3}{3y} \div \dfrac{4x}{y^2}$

i) $\dfrac{x+2}{4} \times \dfrac{x}{3x+6}$

j) $\dfrac{4x}{5} \div \dfrac{4x^2+8x}{15}$

k) $\dfrac{2x^2-2}{x} \times \dfrac{5x}{3x-3}$

l) $\dfrac{2x^2+8x}{x^2-2x} \times \dfrac{x-1}{x+4}$

m) $\dfrac{x^2-4}{9} \div \dfrac{x-2}{3}$

n) $\dfrac{2}{x^2+4x} \div \dfrac{1}{x+4}$

o) $\dfrac{x^2+4x+3}{x^2+5x+6} \times \dfrac{x^2+2x}{x+1}$

p) $\dfrac{x^2+5x+6}{x^2-2x-3} \times \dfrac{3x+3}{x^2+2x}$

q) $\dfrac{x^2-4}{6x-3} \times \dfrac{2x^2+5x-3}{x^2+2x}$

r) $\dfrac{x^2+7x+6}{4x-4} \div \dfrac{x^2+8x+12}{x^2-x}$

s) $\dfrac{x^2+4x+4}{x^2-4x+3} \times \dfrac{x^2-2x-3}{2x^2-2x} \times \dfrac{4x-4}{x^2+2x}$

t) $\dfrac{x}{6x+12} \div \dfrac{x^2-x}{x+2} \times \dfrac{3x-3}{x+1}$

Q2 Write $\dfrac{x^2+5x}{2x^2+7x+3} \times \dfrac{2x+1}{x^3-x^2} \div \dfrac{x+5}{x^2+x-6}$ as a single fraction.

Algebraic division

A polynomial $f(x)$ can be written in the form: $\mathbf{f(x) \equiv q(x)d(x) + r(x)}$
where $q(x)$ is the **quotient**, $d(x)$ is the **divisor** and $r(x)$ is the **remainder**.

This formula can be used to do algebraic division.

> - First, you have to work out the **degree** of the **quotient**, which will depend on the degree of the polynomial $f(x)$: **deg q(x) = deg f(x) − 1**. The **remainder** will have degree **0**.
>
> - Write out the division using the formula, but replace $q(x)$ and $r(x)$ with **general polynomials**. For example, a general polynomial of degree 2 is $Ax^2 + Bx + C$, where A, B and C are constants to be found. A general polynomial of degree 0 is just a constant, e.g. D.
>
> - The next step is to work out the values of the **constants** (A, B, etc.). You do this by substituting in values for x to make bits disappear, and by **equating coefficients**. It's best to start with the **constant term** and work **backwards** from there.
>
> - Finally, write out the division again, replacing A, B, C, etc. with the values you've found.

Example   Divide $x^4 - 3x^3 - 3x^2 + 10x + 5$ by $x - 2$.

1. First, work out the degrees of the quotient and remainder:

    $f(x)$ has degree 4, so the quotient $q(x)$ has degree $4 - 1 = 3$. The remainder $r(x)$ has degree 0.

2. Write out the division in the form $f(x) \equiv q(x)d(x) + r(x)$,
   replacing $q(x)$ and $r(x)$ with general polynomials of degree 3 and 0:

    $$x^4 - 3x^3 - 3x^2 + 10x + 5 \equiv (Ax^3 + Bx^2 + Cx + D)(x - 2) + E$$

3. Substitute $x = 2$ into the identity to make the $q(x)d(x)$ bit disappear:

    $$16 - 3(8) - 3(4) + 10(2) + 5 = 0 + E$$
    $$16 - 24 - 12 + 20 + 5 = E \implies E = 5$$

4. So now the identity looks like this:

    $$x^4 - 3x^3 - 3x^2 + 10x + 5 \equiv (Ax^3 + Bx^2 + Cx + D)(x - 2) + 5$$

5. Now substitute $x = 0$ into the identity:

    when $x = 0$, $5 = -2D + 5 \implies D = 0$

6. So now you have:

    $$x^4 - 3x^3 - 3x^2 + 10x + 5 \equiv (Ax^3 + Bx^2 + Cx)(x - 2) + 5$$

7. For the remaining terms, equate the coefficients on both sides. Expanding the brackets on the RHS and collecting terms gives:

    $$x^4 - 3x^3 - 3x^2 + 10x + 5 \equiv Ax^4 + (B - 2A)x^3 + (C - 2B)x^2 - 2Cx + 5$$

8. The coefficient of x^4 is A on the RHS and 1 on the LHS, so A = 1.
   Similarly, comparing the coefficients of x^3 gives $B - 2A = -3$ (so B = −1) and comparing the coefficients of x gives $-2C = 10$ (so C = −5). So the identity looks like this:

    $$x^4 - 3x^3 - 3x^2 + 10x + 5 \equiv (x^3 - x^2 - 5x)(x - 2) + 5$$
    So, $(x^4 - 3x^3 - 3x^2 + 10x + 5) \div (x - 2) = \mathbf{x^3 - x^2 - 5x}$ **remainder 5**.

- You know from the Remainder Theorem (see p.23) that the remainder when f(x) is divided by $(x - a)$ is equal to f(a).

- So, if the remainder is zero (it divides exactly) then f(a) = 0, i.e. a is a solution of f(x) = 0. You can use this to find the roots of polynomials of higher degree.

Examples a) **Divide $x^3 + 5x^2 - 18x - 18$ by $x - 3$.**

1. f(x) has degree 3, so q(x) has degree 3 − 1 = 2.

2. Write out the division in the form $f(x) \equiv q(x)d(x) + r(x)$:

$$x^3 + 5x^2 - 18x - 18 \equiv (Ax^2 + Bx + C)(x - 3) + D$$

3. Putting $x = 3$ into the identity gives D = 0, so: $x^3 + 5x^2 - 18x - 18 \equiv (Ax^2 + Bx + C)(x - 3)$

4. Now, setting $x = 0$ gives the equation −18 = −3C, so C = 6.

$$x^3 + 5x^2 - 18x - 18 \equiv (Ax^2 + Bx + 6)(x - 3)$$

5. Equating the coefficients of x^3 and x^2 gives A = 1 and B − 3A = 5, so B = 8. So:

$$x^3 + 5x^2 - 18x - 18 \equiv (x^2 + 8x + 6)(x - 3), \text{ so } (x^3 + 5x^2 - 18x - 18) \div (x - 3) = \boldsymbol{x^2 + 8x + 6}$$

b) **Hence solve $x^3 + 5x^2 - 18x - 18 = 0$.**

$x^3 + 5x^2 - 18x - 18 \equiv (x^2 + 8x + 6)(x - 3)$, so set each bracket equal to 0 and find the solutions:

$$(x - 3) = 0 \Rightarrow \boldsymbol{x = 3} \qquad x^2 + 8x + 6 = 0 \Rightarrow \boldsymbol{x = -4 \pm \sqrt{10}}$$

Exercise 2.4

Q1 Use the formula $f(x) \equiv q(x)d(x) + r(x)$ to divide the following expressions. In each case, state the quotient and remainder.

a) $(x^3 - 14x^2 + 6x + 11) \div (x + 1)$

b) $(2x^3 + 5x^2 - 8x - 17) \div (x - 2)$

c) $(6x^3 + x^2 - 11x - 5) \div (2x + 1)$

d) $(x^3 - 14x^2 + 6x + 11) \div (x + 1)$

e) $(x^3 + 10x^2 + 15x - 13) \div (x + 3)$

f) $(2x^3 + 5x^2 - 8x - 17) \div (x - 2)$

g) $(3x^3 - 78x + 9) \div (x + 5)$

h) $(x^4 - 1) \div (x - 1)$

i) $(8x^3 - 6x^2 + x + 10) \div (2x - 3)$

j) $(10x^3 + 7x^2 - 5x + 21) \div (2x + 1)$

k) $(3x^3 - 8x^2 + 15x - 12) \div (x - 2)$

l) $(16x^4) \div (2x - 3)$

Q2 Write $3x^4 - 8x^3 - 6x - 4$ in the form $(Ax^3 + Bx^2 + Cx + D)(x - 3) + E$, and hence state the result when $3x^4 - 8x^3 - 6x - 4$ is divided by $x - 3$.

Q3 Divide $2x^3 - 5x^2 - 21x + 36$ by $2x - 3$, and hence solve $2x^3 - 5x^2 - 21x + 36 = 0$.

Q4 Divide $x^4 + 3x^3 + x^2 + 1$ by $x + 1$, hence give one solution to $x^4 + 3x^3 + x^2 = -1$.

Q5 Divide $3x^4 + x^3 - 5x^2 - 4x + 4$ by $3x - 2$.

Q6 Divide $3x^4 + 7x^3 - 22x^2 - 8x$ by $x - 2$, and hence solve the equation $3x^4 + 7x^3 - 22x^2 - 8x = 0$.

3. Mappings and Functions

A **mapping** is an operation that takes one number and transforms it into another. For example, 'multiply by 5', 'square root' and 'divide by 7' are all mappings. The set of numbers you start with is called the **domain**, and the set of numbers they become is called the **range** (or **image**).

A **function** is a mapping that takes every number in the domain to exactly **one** number in the range.

Functions are written using the following notation:

$$f(x) = 5x + 1 \quad \text{or} \quad f : x \rightarrow 5x + 1$$

A function is **one-to-one** if each value in the **range** corresponds to **exactly one** value in the **domain**.

A function is **many-to-one** if some values in the **range** correspond to **more than one** value in the **domain**.

The domain and/or range will often be the set of **real numbers**, $\mathbb{R}$.
A real number is any positive or negative number (or 0) — including fractions, decimals, integers and surds. If x can take any real value, it's usually written as $x \in \mathbb{R}$. Other sets of numbers include $\mathbb{Z}$, the set of **integers**, and $\mathbb{N}$, the set of **natural numbers** (positive integers, not including 0).

Tip: The symbol $\in$ means "belongs to" or "is a member of the set"— so $x \in \mathbb{R}$ means that x belongs to the set of real numbers. You can also give domains and ranges using set notation, e.g. $\{x : x > 0\}$ or $\{x : x \in \mathbb{Z}\}$.

Examples

a) **Give the value of f(–2) for the function f(x) = x^2 – 1.**

Just replace each x in the function with –2 and calculate the answer:

$f(-2) = (-2)^2 - 1 = 4 - 1 = \mathbf{3}$

b) **Find the value of x for which f(x) = 12 for the function f : $x \rightarrow 2x - 3$.**

Solve this like a normal equation: $2x - 3 = 12 \Rightarrow 2x = 15 \Rightarrow x = \mathbf{7.5}$

Functions can also be given in **several parts** (known as '**piecewise**' functions).
Each part of the function will act over a different domain. For example:

$$f(x) = \begin{cases} 2x + 3 & x \leq 0 \\ x^2 & x > 0 \end{cases}$$

So f(2) is $2^2 = 4$ (because $x > 0$),
but f(–2) is $2(-2) + 3 = -1$ (because $x \leq 0$).

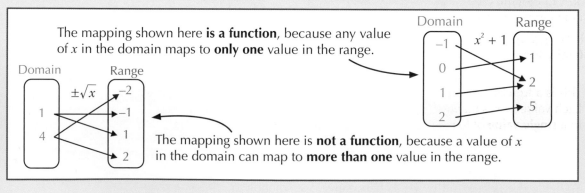

The mapping shown here **is a function**, because any value of x in the domain maps to **only one** value in the range.

The mapping shown here is **not a function**, because a value of x in the domain can map to **more than one** value in the range.

Exercise 3.1

Q1   Draw a mapping diagram for the mapping "multiply by 6" acting on the domain {1, 2, 3, 4}.

Q2 $y = x + 4$ is a mapping with domain $\{x \in \mathbb{N}, x \leq 7\}$. Draw the mapping diagram.

Q3   Complete the mapping diagrams below:

a)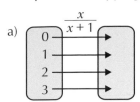

b)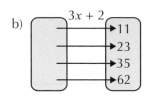

Q4   For the function $g : x \to \dfrac{1}{2x+1}$, $x > -\dfrac{1}{2}$, evaluate $g(0)$ and $g(2)$.

Q5   f defines a function $f : x \to \dfrac{1}{2 + \log_{10} x}$ for the domain $x > 0.01$. Evaluate $f(1)$ and $f(100)$.

Q6   a) Find the range of the function $h(x) = \sin x$, $0° \le x \le 180°$.
      b) Find the range of $j(x) = \cos x$ on the same domain.

Q7   State the largest possible domain and range of each function:
      a) $f(x) = 3^x - 1$ b) $g(x) = (\ln x)^2$

Q8   State whether or not each of the mapping diagrams below
      shows a function, and if not, explain why.

a)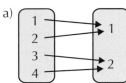

b)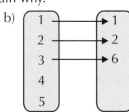

c)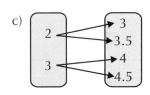

Graphs of functions

Mappings and functions with a **continuous**
domain can be drawn as **graphs**.

For each value of x in the **domain**
(which goes along the horizontal x-axis)
you can plot the corresponding value of $f(x)$
in the **range** (up the vertical y-axis).

Drawing graphs can make it easier to
identify functions.

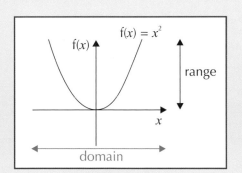

This is a **function.**
Each value of x is mapped
to a **single value** of $f(x)$.

This is **not a function.**
Some values of x
are mapped to **two
different values** of $f(x)$.

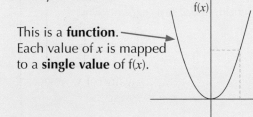

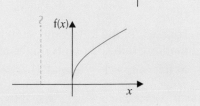

The graph on the right isn't a function for $x \in \mathbb{R}$ because $f(x)$ is **not
defined** for $x < 0$. This just means that when x is negative there is
no real value that $f(x)$ can take.

a) State the range for the function
$f(x) = x^2 - 5,\ x \in \mathbb{R}.$

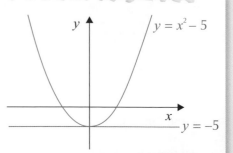

1. The smallest possible value of x^2 is 0.

2. So the smallest possible value of $x^2 - 5$ must be -5.

3. So the range is $f(x) \geq -5$.

4. This can be shown by sketching a graph of $y = f(x)$:

b) State the domain for $f(x) = \sqrt{(x-4)}$.

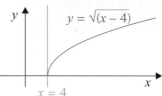

1. There are no real solutions for the square root of a negative number.

2. This means there is a limit on the domain so that $x - 4 \geq 0$.

3. This gives a domain of $x \geq 4$.

4. Again, this can be demonstrated by sketching a graph of $y = f(x)$:

Some mappings that aren't functions can be turned into functions by **restricting their domain**.

For example, consider the graph of the mapping $y = \dfrac{1}{x-1}$ for $x \in \mathbb{R}$:

1. This is **not** a function, because it's not defined at $x = 1$.

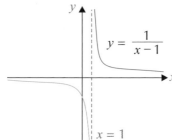

2. If you change the domain to $x > 1$, the mapping is now a function:

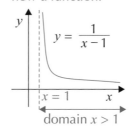

Tip: You could also restrict the domain by giving values that x **can't** be equal to, e.g. $x \neq 1$.

In this case the graph would be in two parts like in the first diagram.

Exercise 3.2

Q1 State whether or not each of the graphs below shows a function, and if not, explain why.

a)

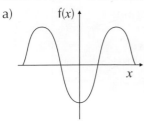

b)

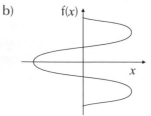

Q2 For each of the following functions, sketch the graph of the function for the given domain, marking relevant points on the axes, and state the range.

a) $f(x) = 3x + 1$ $\quad x \geq -1$

b) $f(x) = x^2 + 2$ $\quad -3 \leq x \leq 3$

c) $f(x) = \cos x$ $\quad 0° \leq x \leq 360°$

d) $f(x) = \begin{cases} 5 - x & 0 \leq x < 5 \\ x - 5 & 5 \leq x \leq 10 \end{cases}$

Q3 State the domain and range for the following functions:

a)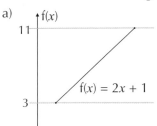

b)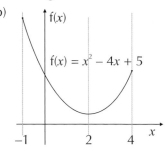

Q4 The graph on the right shows the function $f(x) = \dfrac{x+2}{x+1}$, defined for the domain $x \geq 0$. State the range.

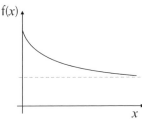

Q5 The diagram shows the function $f(x) = \dfrac{1}{x-2}$ drawn over the domain $x > a$. State the value of a.

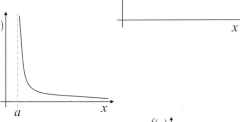

Q6 The diagram shows the function $f(x) = \sqrt{9-x^2}$ for $x \in \mathbb{R},\ a \leq x \leq b$. State the values of a and b.

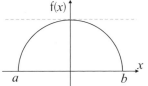

Q7 $h(x) = \sqrt{x+1}$, $x \in \mathbb{R}$. Give a restricted domain which would make $h(x)$ a function.

Q8 $k : x \to \tan x$, $x \in \mathbb{R}$. Give an example of a domain which would make k a function.

Q9 $m(x) = \dfrac{1}{x^2-4}$. What is the largest continuous domain which would make $m(x)$ a function?

Q10 The diagram on the right shows the graph of $y = f(x)$.
a) Explain why f is not a function on the domain $x \in \mathbb{R}$.
b) State the largest possible domain that would make f a function.

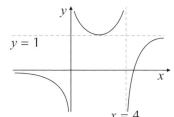

4. Composite Functions

If you have two functions f and g, you can combine them to make a **composite function**.

Composite functions are written **fg(x)**. This means 'do **g first**, then **f**'.

The **order** is really important — usually fg(x) ≠ gf(x).

If you get a composite function that's written f²(x), it means ff(x). This just means you have to do f **twice**.

For the functions f : $x \rightarrow 2x^3$, $x \in \mathbb{R}$ and g : $x \rightarrow x - 3$, $x \in \mathbb{R}$, find fg(4).

1. Remember that you work from right to left, so do g first. Substitute 4 in for x in g(x):

$$g(4) = 4 - 3 = 1$$

2. Now, substitute in g(4) = 1 for x in f(x): $\quad$ f(g(4)) = f(1) = 2×1^3 = **2**

For a composite function fg(x), the domain can also be found by putting the **range** of **g(x)** into **f(x)**. If the domain of f(x) does not fully include the range of g(x) then the domain of g(x) will have to be **restricted further.**

Find the domain of fg(x), where f(x) = $\sqrt{x}$, $x \geq 0$, and g(x) = $x + 5$, $x \in \mathbb{R}$.

1. The range of g(x) is g(x) $\in \mathbb{R}$. This is bigger than the domain of f(x), so the domain of g(x) will need to be restricted.

2. The input into f needs to be ≥ 0. Since for fg(x) the input into f is g(x) (i.e. $x + 5$): $x + 5 \geq 0 \Rightarrow x \geq -5$.

So the largest possible domain for fg(x) is $x \geq -5$.

Tip: If the domain in the example above was not restricted, fg(x) would be undefined in places, e.g. fg(-6) = f($-6 + 5$) = f(-1) = $\sqrt{-1}$ (which is undefined).

Exercise 4.1

Q1 $\quad$ f : $x \rightarrow x^2$, $x \in \mathbb{R}$ and g : $x \rightarrow 2x + 1$, $x \in \mathbb{R}$. Find the values of:
a) fg(3) $\qquad$ b) gf(3) $\qquad$ c) $f^2(5)$ $\qquad$ d) $g^2(2)$

Q2 $\quad$ f(x) = $\sin x$, $x \in \mathbb{R}$ and g(x) = $2x$, $x \in \mathbb{R}$. Evaluate fg($90°$) and gf($90°$).

Q3 $\quad$ f : $x \rightarrow \dfrac{3}{x + 2}$, $x > -2$ and g : $x \rightarrow 2x$, $x \in \mathbb{R}$.
a) Find the values of gf(1), fg(1) and $f^2(4)$. $\qquad$ b) Explain why fg(-1) is undefined.

Q4 $\quad$ f(x) = $\cos x$, $x \in \mathbb{R}$ and g(x) = $2x$, $x \in \mathbb{R}$. Find the functions:
a) fg(x) $\qquad$ b) gf(x)

Q5 $\quad$ f(x) = $2x - 1$, $x \in \mathbb{R}$ and g(x) = 2^x, $x \in \mathbb{R}$. Find the functions:
a) fg(x) $\qquad$ b) gf(x) $\qquad$ c) $f^2(x)$

Q6 $\quad$ f(x) = $\dfrac{2}{x - 1}$, $x > 1$ and g(x) = $x + 4$, $x \in \mathbb{R}$. Find the functions fg(x) and gf(x), writing them as single fractions in their simplest forms.

Q7 $\quad$ f(x) = $\dfrac{x}{1 - x}$, $x \in \mathbb{R}$, $x \neq 1$ and g(x) = x^2, $x \in \mathbb{R}$. Find $f^2(x)$ and gfg(x).

Q8 $\quad$ f(x) = x^2 with domain $x \in \mathbb{R}$, and g(x) = $2x - 3$ also with $x \in \mathbb{R}$.
a) Find fg(x) and write down its range. $\qquad$ b) Find gf(x) and write down its range.

Q9 $f(x) = \frac{1}{x}$ and $g(x) = \ln(x + 1)$, both with domain $x > 0$.

a) Find gf(x) and write down its range and largest possible domain.

b) Find fg(x) and write down its range and largest possible domain.

Q10 Given that $f(x) = 3x + 2$, $g(x) = 5x - 1$, and $h(x) = x^2 + 1$ (all with domains $x \in \mathbb{R}$), find fgh(x).

Solving composite function equations

If you're asked to **solve** an equation such as fg(x) = 8, the best way to do it is to work out what fg(x) is, then **rearrange** fg(x) = 8 to make **x** the subject.

Example For the functions $f : x \to \sqrt{x}$ with domain $x \geq 0$ and $g : x \to \frac{1}{x-1}$ with domain $x > 1$, solve the equation $fg(x) = \frac{1}{2}$. Also, state the range of fg(x).

1. First, find fg(x):

$$fg(x) = f\left(\frac{1}{x-1}\right) = \sqrt{\frac{1}{x-1}} = \frac{1}{\sqrt{x-1}}$$

So $\frac{1}{\sqrt{x-1}} = \frac{1}{2}$

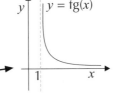

2. Rearrange this equation to find x:

$$\frac{1}{\sqrt{x-1}} = \frac{1}{2} \Rightarrow \sqrt{x-1} = 2 \Rightarrow x - 1 = 4 \Rightarrow x = 5$$

3. To find the range, draw the graph of fg(x).

4. From the graph you can see that: The range is **fg(x) > 0**.

   You can also see the domain of fg(x) is $x > 1$ (though the question doesn't ask for this).

Exercise 4.2

Q1 For the following functions, solve the given equations:

a) $f(x) = 2x + 1$, $x \in \mathbb{R}$ $g(x) = 3x - 4$, $x \in \mathbb{R}$ fg(x) = 23

b) $f(x) = \frac{1}{x}$, $x \neq 0$ $g(x) = 2x + 5$, $x \in \mathbb{R}$ gf(x) = 6

c) $f(x) = x^2$, $x \in \mathbb{R}$ $g(x) = \frac{x}{x-3}$, $x \neq 3$ gf(x) = 4

d) $f(x) = x^2 + 1$, $x \in \mathbb{R}$ $g(x) = 3x - 2$, $x \in \mathbb{R}$ fg(x) = 50

e) $f(x) = \frac{x^2}{16}$, $x \in \mathbb{R}$ $g(x) = 2x$, $x \in \mathbb{R}$ fg(x) = 5

f) $f(x) = 2x + 1$, $x \in \mathbb{R}$ $g(x) = \sqrt{x}$, $x \geq 0$ fg(x) = 17

g) $f(x) = \log_{10} x$, $x > 0$ $g(x) = 3 - x$, $x \in \mathbb{R}$ fg(x) = 0

h) $f(x) = 2^x$, $x \in \mathbb{R}$ $g(x) = x^2 + 2x$, $x \in \mathbb{R}$ fg(x) = 8

i) $f(x) = \frac{x}{x+1}$, $x \neq -1$ $g(x) = 2x - 1$, $x \in \mathbb{R}$ fg(x) = gf(x)

j) $f(x) = 3x^3$, $x \in \mathbb{R}$ $g(x) = 2x$, $x \in \mathbb{R}$ fg(x) = gf(x)

k) $f(x) = \frac{7}{3-x}$, $x \neq 3$ $g(x) = x^2 + 3$, $x \in \mathbb{R}$ fg(x) = -14

Q2 $f : x \to x^2 + b$, $x \in \mathbb{R}$ and $g : x \to b - 3x$, $x \in \mathbb{R}$ (b is a constant).

a) Find fg and gf and give the range of each in terms of b.

b) Given that gf(2) = -8, find the value of fg(2).

5. Inverse Functions

An **inverse function** does the **opposite** to the function.

An inverse function maps an element in the **range** to an element in the **domain** — the opposite of a function. This means that only **one-to-one** functions have inverses, as the inverse of a many-to-one function would be one-to-many, which isn't a function.

The inverse of a function is its **reflection** in the line $y = x$.

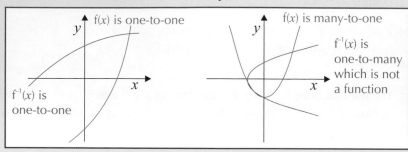

For any inverse $f^{-1}(x)$: $\boxed{f^{-1}f(x) = x = ff^{-1}(x)}$

The **domain** of the inverse is the **range** of the function, and the **range** of the inverse is the **domain** of the function.

Here's a general method for finding the inverse of a given function:

- **Replace $f(x)$ with y** to get an equation for **y in terms of x**.
- **Rearrange** the equation to make x the subject.
- **Replace x with $f^{-1}(x)$ and y with x** — this is the **inverse function**.
- **Swap** round the **domain** and **range** of the function.

Examples

a) **Find the inverse of the function $f(x) = \sqrt{2x - 1}$, with domain $x \geq \dfrac{1}{2}$ and range $f(x) \geq 0$. State the domain and the range of the inverse.**

1. Replace $f(x)$ with y.

$$y = \sqrt{2x - 1}$$

2. Rearrange to make x the subject:

$$y^2 = 2x - 1 \implies x = \frac{y^2 + 1}{2}$$

3. Replace x with $f^{-1}(x)$ and y with x.

$$f^{-1}(x) = \frac{x^2 + 1}{2}$$

4. Swap round the domain and range. **domain: $x \geq 0$ range: $f^{-1}(x) \geq \dfrac{1}{2}$**

b) **Sketch the graph of the inverse of the function $f(x) = x^2 - 8$ with domain $x \geq 0$.**

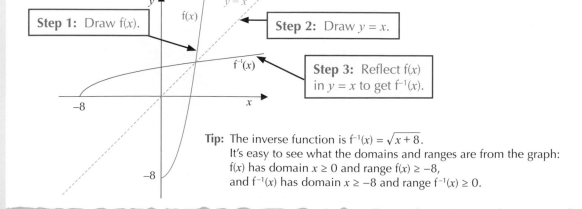

Step 1: Draw $f(x)$.

Step 2: Draw $y = x$.

Step 3: Reflect $f(x)$ in $y = x$ to get $f^{-1}(x)$.

Tip: The inverse function is $f^{-1}(x) = \sqrt{x + 8}$.
It's easy to see what the domains and ranges are from the graph:
$f(x)$ has domain $x \geq 0$ and range $f(x) \geq -8$,
and $f^{-1}(x)$ has domain $x \geq -8$ and range $f^{-1}(x) \geq 0$.

Exercise 5.1

Q1 Do the functions shown in the diagrams below have inverses? Justify your answers.

a)

b)

Q2 For the following functions, explain whether or not an inverse f^{-1} exists:

a) $f(x) = \sin x$, $x \in \mathbb{R}$ 　　　b) $f(x) = x^2 + 3$, $x \in \mathbb{R}$ 　　　c) $f(x) = (x - 4)^2$, $x \geq 4$

Q3 Find the inverse of each of the following functions, stating the domain and range:

a) $f(x) = 3x + 4$, $x \in \mathbb{R}$ 　　　b) $f(x) = 5(x - 2)$, $x \in \mathbb{R}$

c) $f(x) = \dfrac{1}{x + 2}$, $x > -2$ 　　　d) $f(x) = x^2 + 3$, $x > 0$

Q4 $f(x) = \dfrac{3x}{x + 1}$, $x > -1$.

a) Find $f^{-1}(x)$, stating the domain and range. 　　b) Evaluate $f^{-1}(2)$. 　　c) Evaluate $f^{-1}\left(\dfrac{1}{2}\right)$.

Q5 $f(x) = \dfrac{x - 4}{x + 3}$, $x > -3$.

a) Find $f^{-1}(x)$, stating the domain and range. 　　b) Evaluate $f^{-1}(0)$. 　　c) Evaluate $f^{-1}\left(-\dfrac{2}{5}\right)$.

Q6 Find the domain and range of $f^{-1}(x)$ for the following functions:

a) $f(x) = \log_{10}(x - 3)$, $x > 3$ 　　　b) $f(x) = 4x - 2$, $1 \leq x \leq 7$ 　　　c) $f(x) = \dfrac{x}{x - 2}$, $x < 2$

d) $f(x) = 3^{x-1}$, $x \geq 2$ 　　　e) $f(x) = \tan x$, $0° \leq x < 90°$ 　　　f) $f(x) = \ln(x^2)$, $3 \leq x \leq 4$

Q7 Find the inverse $f^{-1}(x)$ for the following functions, giving the domain and range:

a) $f(x) = e^{x+1}$, $x \in \mathbb{R}$ 　　　b) $f(x) = x^3$, $x < 0$

c) $f(x) = 2 - \log_2(x)$, $x \geq 1$ 　　　d) $f(x) = \dfrac{1}{x - 2}$, $x \neq 2$

Q8 $f(x) = 2x + 3$, $x \in \mathbb{R}$. Sketch $y = f(x)$ and $y = f^{-1}(x)$ on the same set of axes, marking the points where the functions cross the axes.

Q9 $f(x) = x^2 + 3$, $x > 0$.

a) Sketch the graphs of $f(x)$ and $f^{-1}(x)$ on the same set of axes.

b) State the domain and range of $f^{-1}(x)$.

Q10 $f(x) = \dfrac{1}{x + 1}$, $x > -1$.

a) Sketch the graphs of $f(x)$ and $f^{-1}(x)$ on the same set of axes.

b) Explain how your diagram shows that there is just one solution to the equation $f(x) = f^{-1}(x)$.

Q11 $f(x) = \dfrac{1}{x - 3}$, $x > 3$.

a) Find $f^{-1}(x)$ and state its domain and range. 　　b) Sketch $f(x)$ and $f^{-1}(x)$ on the same set of axes.

c) How many solutions are there to the equation $f(x) = f^{-1}(x)$? 　　d) Solve $f(x) = f^{-1}(x)$.

6. Modulus

The modulus function

The modulus of a number is its size — it doesn't matter if it's positive or negative.

> The modulus of a number, x, is written $|x|$.
> In general terms, for $x \geq 0$, $|x| = x$ and for $x < 0$, $|x| = -x$.

Functions can have a modulus too:

> $|f(x)| = f(x)$ when $f(x) \geq 0$ and $|f(x)| = -f(x)$ when $f(x) < 0$.

If the modulus is inside the brackets in the form $f(|x|)$, then you make the x-value positive before applying the function. So $f(|-2|) = f(2)$.

Examples

Draw the graphs of $y = |f(x)|$ and $y = f(|x|)$ for $f(x) = 5x - 5$. State the range of each.

$y = |f(x)|$:

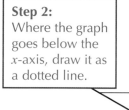

Step 2:
Where the graph goes below the x-axis, draw it as a dotted line.

$y = |f(x)| = |5x - 5|$

Step 1:
Draw the graph of $y = 5x - 5$.

Step 3:
Reflect the negative (dotted) part of the line in the x-axis.

The range of this is $|f(x)| \geq 0$.

$y = f(|x|)$:

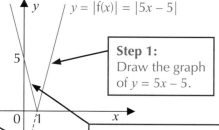

$y = f(|x|) = 5|x| - 5$

Step 2:
For negative x-values, reflect the part of the line where x is positive in the y-axis.

Step 1:
Draw the graph of $y = 5x - 5$ as before.

The range of this is $f(|x|) \geq -5$.

Exercise 6.1

Q1 Sketch the following graphs and state the range of each:

a) $y = |x + 3|$ b) $y = |5 - x|$ c) $y = |3x - 1|$ d) $y = |x| - 9$ e) $y = 2|x| + 5$

Q2 For each of the following functions, sketch the graph of $y = |f(x)|$:

a) $f(x) = 2x + 3$ b) $f(x) = 4 - 3x$ c) $f(x) = -4x$ d) $f(x) = 7 - \frac{1}{2}x$ e) $f(x) = -(x + 2)$

Q3 Match up each graph (1-4) with its correct equation (a-d):

a) $y = |x| + 4$
b) $y = |2x - 10|$
c) $y = |x + 1|$
d) $y = |2x| - 2$

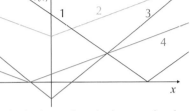

Q4 For each of the graphs below, sketch the graph of $y = |f(x)|$:

a) 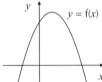 b) 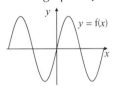 c)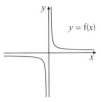

Q5 Draw the graph of the function $f(x) = \begin{cases} |2x + 4| & x < 0 \\ |x - 4| & x \geq 0 \end{cases}$

Q6 For the function $f(x) = 3x - 5$:

a) Draw, on the same axes, the graphs of $y = f(x)$ and $y = |f(x)|$.

b) How many solutions are there to the equation $|3x - 5| = 2$?

Q7 For the function $f(x) = 4x + 1$:

a) Draw accurately the graph of $y = |f(x)|$. b) Use your graph to solve the equation $|f(x)| = 3$.

Solving modulus equations and inequalities

You might be asked to substitute a modulus value into an expression
to find the possible values that the expression could take.

Examples a) If $|x| = 2$, what are the possible values of $5x - 3$?

1. If $|x| = 2$, then either $x = 2$ or $x = -2$. So substitute these two values into the expression:

If $x = 2$, then $5x - 3 = 5(2) - 3 = 10 - 3 = \textbf{7}$

If $x = -2$, then $5x - 3 = 5(-2) - 3 = -10 - 3 = \textbf{-13}$

b) Find all of the possible values of $|3x - 4|$ when $|x| = 6$.

1. $|x| = 6$ means $x = 6$ or $x = -6$.

2. Substituting $x = 6$ into $|3x - 4|$ gives: $|3(6) - 4| = |18 - 4| = |14| = \textbf{14}$

3. Substituting $x = -6$ gives: $|3(-6) - 4| = |-18 - 4| = |-22| = \textbf{22}$

The method for solving equations of the form $|f(x)| = n$ is shown below.
Solving $|f(x)| = g(x)$ is exactly the same — just replace n with $g(x)$.

- **Step 1:** Sketch the functions $y = |f(x)|$ and $y = n$ on the same axes.
  The solutions you're trying to find are where they **intersect**.

- **Step 2:** From the graph, work out the ranges of x for which $f(x) \geq 0$ and $f(x) < 0$:
  e.g. $f(x) \geq 0$ for $x \leq a$ or $x \geq b$ and $f(x) < 0$ for $a < x < b$.
  These ranges should 'fit together' to cover **all** possible x-values.

- **Step 3:** Use this to write **two new equations**, one true for each range of x:
  ① $f(x) = n$ for $x \leq a$ or $x \geq b$ ② $-f(x) = n$ for $a < x < b$

- **Step 4:** Solve each equation and check that any solutions are **valid**. Get rid of
  any solutions outside the range of x you have for that equation.

- **Step 5:** Look at the graph and **check** that your solutions look right.

Example   **Solve $|2x - 4| = 5 - x$.** ← This is an example of $|f(x)| = g(x)$,
where $f(x) = 2x - 4$ and $g(x) = 5 - x$.

1. Sketch $y = |2x - 4|$ and $y = 5 - x$. The graphs cross twice.

2. Looking at where $f(x) \geq 0$ and
   where $f(x) < 0$ gives:

   ① $2x - 4 = 5 - x$ for $x \geq 2$ $2x - 4 < 0$ when $x < 2$
   ② $-(2x - 4) = 5 - x$ for $x < 2$.

3. Solving these gives:

   ① $3x = 9 \Rightarrow x = 3$ and   ② $-x = 1 \Rightarrow x = -1$

4. Checking against the graph, there are two solutions and they're where we expected.

Exercise 6.2

Q1   Solve the following equations:

    a) $|x - 2| = 6$ b) $|4x + 2| = 10$ c) $2 - |3x - 4| = 1$ d) $9 - |x + 3| = 0$

    e) $|2x + 3| = 1$ f) $|2 - x| = 1$ g) $1 + |4 - 2x| = 7$ h) $3 + |2x| = 6$

Q2   If $|x| = 5$, find the possible values of $|3x + 2|$.

Q3   If $|x| - 2 = -1$, find the possible values of $|7x - 1|$.

Q4   If $|x| = 3$, find the possible values of $|-2x + 1|$.

Q5   a) On the same axes sketch the graphs of $|f(x)|$ and $g(x)$, where: $f(x) = 2x + 3$ and $g(x) = x - 1$.
     b) Hence find any solutions of the equation $|f(x)| = g(x)$.

Q6   If $|4x + 1| = 3$, find the possible values of $2|x - 1| + 3$

When using **graphs** to solve functions of the form $|f(x)| = |g(x)|$ you have to do a bit more work at the start to identify the different areas of the graph. There could be regions where:

- $f(x)$ and $g(x)$ are **both** positive or **both** negative — you need to solve the equation $f(x) = g(x)$.
- One function is **positive** and the other is **negative** — you need to solve the equation $-f(x) = g(x)$.

There is also an **algebraic** method for solving equations of this type:

> If $|a| = |b|$ then $a^2 = b^2$. So if $|f(x)| = |g(x)|$ then $[f(x)]^2 = [g(x)]^2$.

This is true because squaring gives the **same answer** whether the value is **positive** or **negative**. You'll usually be left with a **quadratic** to solve.

Example Solve $|x - 2| = |3x + 4|$.

1. Square both sides to give:
$$(x - 2)^2 = (3x + 4)^2$$
$$x^2 - 4x + 4 = 9x^2 + 24x + 16$$
$$8x^2 + 28x + 12 = 2x^2 + 7x + 3 = 0$$

2. Factorise and solve: $2x^2 + 7x + 3 = (2x + 1)(x + 3) = 0$. So $x = -\frac{1}{2}$ and $x = -3$.

Inequalities with a modulus can be a bit nasty to solve. In general, for $a > 0$:

> $|x| < a \implies -a < x < a$ $|x| > a \implies x > a$ or $x < -a$

Using this, you can **rearrange** more complicated inequalities like $|x - a| \leq b$. From the method above, this means that $-b \leq x - a \leq b$, so **adding** a to **each bit** of the inequality gives $a - b \leq x \leq a + b$.

Example Solve $|x - 4| < 7$.

1. Using the theory above: $|x - 4| < 7 \implies -7 < x - 4 < 7$

2. Now add 4 to each bit: $-7 + 4 < x < 7 + 4$, so $-3 < x < 11$

Tip: For inequalities of the form $|f(x)| > |g(x)|$ or $|f(x)| < |g(x)|$, it often helps to draw a graph like the one on the previous page, then you can see where one function is greater than the other.

Exercise 6.3

Q1 a) On the same axes sketch the graphs of $|f(x)|$ and $|g(x)|$, where $f(x) = 5x + 10$ and $g(x) = x + 1$
b) Hence find any solutions of the equation $|f(x)| = |g(x)|$.

Q2 Solve, either graphically or otherwise:
a) $|x + 2| = |2x|$ b) $|4x - 1| = |2x + 3|$ c) $|3x - 6| = |10 - 5x|$

Q3 Solve the following inequalities:
a) $|x| < 8$ b) $|x| \geq 5$ c) $|2x| > 12$ d) $|4x + 2| \leq 6$ e) $3 \geq |3x - 3|$
f) $6 - 2|x + 4| < 0$ g) $3x + 8 < |x|$ h) $2|x - 4| \geq x$ i) $|x - 3| \geq |2x + 3|$

Q4 Give the solutions of $x + 6 \leq |3x + 2|$ in set notation.

Q5 Find the possible values of $|5x + 4|$, given that $|1 + 2x| \leq 3$.

7. Transformations of Graphs

The transformations you've met before are translations (a vertical or horizontal shift), stretches (either vertical or horizontal) and reflections in the *x*- or *y*- axis:

y = f(x + a):	For $a > 0$: f(x + a) is f(x) translated a **left**, f(x − a) is f(x) translated a **right**.
y = f(x) + a:	For $a > 0$: f(x) + a is f(x) translated a **up**, f(x) − a is f(x) translated a **down**.
y = af(x):	The graph of af(x) is f(x) **stretched** parallel to the **y-axis** (i.e. vertically) by a factor of a. And if **a < 0**, the graph is also **reflected** in the **x-axis**.
y = f(ax):	The graph of f(ax) is f(x) **stretched** parallel to the **x-axis** (i.e. horizontally) by a factor of $\frac{1}{a}$. And if **a < 0**, the graph is also **reflected** in the **y-axis**.

For more on these four transformations, see p.48.

You need to be able to do combinations of these transformations. Don't try and do all the transformations at once — break it up into the separate bits and draw a graph for each stage.

Example

The graph below shows the function $y = \sin x$, $0° \leq x \leq 360°$. Draw the graph of $y = 2 - \sin 2x$, $0° \leq x \leq 360°$.

The turning points are at (90°, 1) and (270°, −1). The y-intercept is (0, 0).

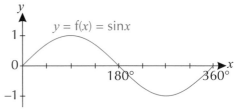

1. This is a lot easier to deal with if you rearrange the function from $y = 2 - \sin 2x$ to $y = -\sin 2x + 2$. This gets it in the form $y = -f(2x) + 2$.

   So we need a horizontal stretch by a factor of $\frac{1}{2}$, followed by a vertical stretch by a factor of −1, followed by a vertical translation by 2 up (in the positive *y*-direction).

2. First draw the graph of $y = \sin 2x$, by squashing the graph horizontally by a factor of 2 (i.e. a stretch by a factor of $\frac{1}{2}$).

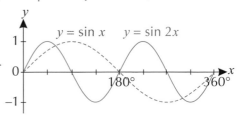

The turning points have been squashed up in the *x*-direction, so halve the *x*-coordinates: (45°, 1) and (135°, −1).

There are also now an extra two within the domain, each one occurring a further 90° along the *x*-axis: (225°, 1) and (315°, −1).

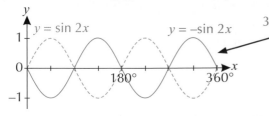

3. From there, draw the graph of $y = -\sin 2x$, by reflecting in the *x*-axis.

   This transformation flips the turning points, so multiply the *y*-coordinates by −1. They're now at (45°, −1), (135°, 1), (225°, −1) and (315°, 1).

4. Finally, translate the graph of $y = -\sin 2x$ up by 2 to get the graph of $y = -\sin 2x + 2$ (or $y = 2 - \sin 2x$).

Add 2 to the y-coordinates of the turning points to give $(45°, 1)$, $(135°, 3)$, $(225°, 1)$ and $(315°, 3)$.

The y-intercept is also translated up by 2: it's at $(0, 2)$.

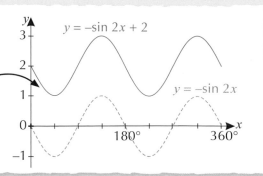

Exercise 7.1

Q1 Given that $f(x) = x^2$, sketch the following graphs on the same axes:

a) $y = f(x)$ b) $y = f(x) + 3$ c) $y = f(x - 2)$ d) $y = f(x + 4) - 1$

In each case, write down the coordinates of the turning point, and in parts b)-d), give the translation as a column vector.

Q2 The graph of $f(x) = x^3$ is translated to form the graph of $g(x) = f(x - 1) + 4$.

a) Sketch the graphs of $y = f(x)$ and $y = g(x)$. b) Give this translation as a column vector.

c) What is the equation of $g(x)$?

Q3 Given that $f(x) = |x|$, sketch the following graphs on the same axes:

a) $y = f(x)$ b) $y = f(x) + 2$ c) $y = f(x - 4)$ d) $y = 2f(x + 1)$

Q4 Let $f(x) = |2x - 6|$. On the same axes sketch the graphs of:

a) $y = f(x)$ b) $y = f(-x)$ c) $y = f(-x) + 2$

Q5 Let $f(x) = \dfrac{1}{x}$. On the same axes sketch the graphs of:

a) $y = f(x)$ b) $y = -f(x)$ c) $y = -f(x) - 3$

Q6 a) Let $f(x) = \cos x$. Sketch the graph $y = f(x)$ for $0° \le x \le 360°$.

b) On the same axes sketch the graph of $y = f(2x)$.

c) On the same axes sketch the graph of $y = 1 + f(2x)$.

d) State the coordinates of the minimum point(s) of the graph $y = \cos 2x + 1$, in the interval $0° \le x \le 360°$.

Q7 The graph $y = \cos x$ is translated by vector $\begin{pmatrix} 90° \\ 0 \end{pmatrix}$ and stretched by scale factor $\dfrac{1}{2}$ parallel to the y-axis.

a) Sketch the new graph for $0 \le x \le 360°$. b) Write down its equation.

Q8 Complete the following table for the function $f(x) = x^3$:

Transformed function	New equation	Coordinates of point of inflection
$f(x - 2)$		
$-f(x) - 3$		
$f(-x) + 4$		

Q9 a) Sketch the graph of $y = f(x)$ where $f(x) = \dfrac{1}{x}$.

b) Write down the sequence of transformations needed to map $f(x)$ on to $g(x) = 3 - \dfrac{1}{x}$.

c) Sketch the graph of $y = g(x)$.

Q10 Complete the following table:

Original graph	New graph	Sequence of transformations
$y = x^3$	$y = (x - 4)^3 + 5$	
$y = 4^x$	$y = 4^{3x} - 1$	
$y = |x + 1|$	$y = 1 - |2x + 1|$	
$y = \sin x$	$y = -3\sin 2x + 1$	

Q11　a) Write $y = 2x^2 - 4x + 6$ in the form $y = a[(x + b)^2 + c]$.

　　b) Hence list the sequence of transformations that will map $y = x^2$ on to $y = 2x^2 - 4x + 6$.

　　c) Sketch the graph of $y = 2x^2 - 4x + 6$.

　　d) Write down the coordinates of the minimum point of the graph.

Q12　Starting with the curve $y = \cos x$, state the sequence of transformations which could be used to sketch the following curves:

　　a) $y = 4 \cos 3x$　　　　b) $y = 4 - \cos 2x$　　　　c) $y = 2 \cos(x - 60°)$

Q13　The diagram shows $y = f(x)$ with a minimum point, P, at $(2, -3)$.
　　Copy the diagram and sketch each of the following graphs.
　　In each case state the new coordinates of the point P.

　　a) $y = f(x) + 5$　　　　b) $y = f(x + 4)$　　　　c) $y = -f(x)$

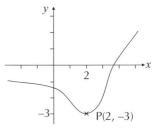

8. Partial Fractions

You can split a fraction with **more than one linear factor** in the denominator into **partial fractions**.

This means writing it as a **sum** of two or more **simpler fractions**.

Finding the value of the numerators is the tricky bit.

Write out the expression as an identity, e.g.　　　$\dfrac{7x - 7}{(2x + 1)(x - 3)} \equiv \dfrac{A}{(2x + 1)} + \dfrac{B}{(x - 3)}$

Add the partial fractions together, and then **cancel** the denominators from both sides.

This will give you an **identity** for A and B, for example:　　$7x - 7 \equiv A(x - 3) + B(2x + 1)$

Use the **Substitution** method or the **Equating Coefficients** method:

Substitution	Equating Coefficients
Substitute a number for x to leave you with just one constant on the right hand side.	Equate the constant terms, coefficients of x and coefficients of x^2, then solve the equations simultaneously.

 Express $\dfrac{7x - 1}{(x - 3)(x - 1)(x + 2)}$ **in partial fractions.**

1. Write it out as an identity:　　　$\dfrac{7x - 1}{(x - 3)(x - 1)(x + 2)} \equiv \dfrac{A}{(x - 3)} + \dfrac{B}{(x - 1)} + \dfrac{C}{(x + 2)}$

2. Add the partial fractions — this means writing them over a common denominator:

$$\frac{A}{(x-3)} + \frac{B}{(x-1)} + \frac{C}{(x+2)} \equiv \frac{A(x-1)(x+2) + B(x-3)(x+2) + C(x-3)(x-1)}{(x-3)(x-1)(x+2)}$$

3. Cancel the denominators from both sides of the original identity, so the numerators are equal:

$$7x - 1 \equiv A(x-1)(x+2) + B(x-3)(x+2) + C(x-3)(x-1)$$

Substitution Method

Substituting $x = 3$ gets rid of B and C:

$$21 - 1 = A(3-1)(3+2) + 0 + 0$$
$$20 = 10A \implies A = 2$$

Substituting $x = 1$ gets rid of A and C:

$$7 - 1 = 0 + B(1-3)(1+2) + 0$$
$$6 = -6B \implies B = -1$$

Substituting $x = -2$ gets rid of A and B:

$$-14 - 1 = 0 + 0 + C(-2-3)(-2-1)$$
$$-15 = 15C \implies C = -1$$

Equating Coefficients Method

Compare coefficients:

$$7x - 1 \equiv A(x-1)(x+2) + B(x-3)(x+2) + C(x-3)(x-1)$$
$$\equiv A(x^2 + x - 2) + B(x^2 - x - 6) + C(x^2 - 4x + 3)$$
$$\equiv (A + B + C)x^2 + (A - B - 4C)x + (-2A - 6B + 3C)$$

Equating x^2 coefficients: $0 = A + B + C$

Equating x coefficients: $7 = A - B - 4C$

Equating constant terms: $-1 = -2A - 6B + 3C$

Solving these equations simultaneously gives: $A = 2$, $B = -1$ and $C = -1$

4. Replace A, B and C in the original identity: $\dfrac{7x-1}{(x-3)(x-1)(x+2)} \equiv \dfrac{2}{(x-3)} - \dfrac{1}{(x-1)} - \dfrac{1}{(x+2)}$

Exercise 8.1

Q1 Express $\dfrac{3x+3}{(x-1)(x-4)}$ in the form $\dfrac{A}{x-1} + \dfrac{B}{x-4}$.

Q2 Express $\dfrac{5x-1}{x(2x+1)}$ in the form $\dfrac{A}{x} + \dfrac{B}{2x+1}$.

Q3 Find the values of the constants A and B in the identity $\dfrac{3x-2}{x^2+x-12} \equiv \dfrac{A}{x+4} + \dfrac{B}{x-3}$.

Q4 Write $\dfrac{2}{x^2-16}$ in partial fractions.

Q5 Factorise $x^2 - x - 6$ and hence express $\dfrac{5}{x^2-x-6}$ in partial fractions.

Q6 Write $\dfrac{11x}{2x^2+5x-12}$ in partial fractions.

Q7 a) Factorise $x^3 - 9x$ fully.   b) Hence write $\dfrac{12x+18}{x^3-9x}$ in partial fractions.

Q8 Write $\dfrac{3x+9}{x^3-36x}$ in the form $\dfrac{A}{x} + \dfrac{B}{x+6} + \dfrac{C}{x-6}$.

Q9 a) Use the Factor Theorem to factorise $x^3 - 7x - 6$.   b) Hence write $\dfrac{6x+2}{x^3-7x-6}$ in partial fractions.

Q10 Express $\dfrac{6x+4}{(x+4)(x-1)(x+1)}$ in partial fractions.

Q11 Express $\dfrac{15x-27}{x^3-6x^2+3x+10}$ in partial fractions.

Repeated factors

If the denominator of an algebraic fraction has **repeated linear factors,** the partial fractions will take a slightly **different form:**

> The **power** of the repeated factor tells you **how many** times that factor should appear in the partial fractions.
>
> $$\frac{7x-3}{(x+1)^2(x-4)} \text{ is written as } \frac{A}{(x+1)} + \frac{B}{(x+1)^2} + \frac{C}{(x-4)}$$
>
> A factor that's **squared** in the original denominator will appear in the denominator of **two** of your partial fractions — once squared and once just as it is.
>
> $$\frac{32x-14}{x^2(2x+7)} \text{ is written as } \frac{A}{x} + \frac{B}{x^2} + \frac{C}{(2x+7)}$$

Example Express $\dfrac{4x+15}{(x+2)^2(3x-1)}$ in partial fractions.

1. Write the identity: $\dfrac{4x+15}{(x+2)^2(3x-1)} \equiv \dfrac{A}{(x+2)} + \dfrac{B}{(x+2)^2} + \dfrac{C}{(3x-1)}$

2. Add the fractions: $\dfrac{A}{(x+2)} + \dfrac{B}{(x+2)^2} + \dfrac{C}{(3x-1)} \equiv \dfrac{A(x+2)(3x-1) + B(3x-1) + C(x+2)^2}{(x+2)^2(3x-1)}$

3. Cancel the denominators from both sides: $4x+15 \equiv A(x+2)(3x-1) + B(3x-1) + C(x+2)^2$.

4. Substituting $x = -2$ gets rid of A and C: $-8+15 = 0 + B(-6-1) + 0 \Rightarrow 7 = -7B \Rightarrow B = -1$

5. Substituting $x = \frac{1}{3}$ gets rid of A and B: $\frac{4}{3} + 15 = 0 + 0 + C\left(\frac{1}{3} + 2\right)^2 \Rightarrow \frac{49}{3} = \frac{49}{9}C \Rightarrow C = 3$

6. There's no value of x you can substitute to get rid of B and C to just leave A, so try equating coefficients instead:

7. Equate coefficients of x^2: $\qquad 0 = 3A + C$
   You know $C = 3$, so: $\qquad -3 = 3A \Rightarrow A = -1$

8. Replace A, B and C in the original identity: $\dfrac{4x+15}{(x+2)^2(3x-1)} \equiv -\dfrac{1}{(x+2)} - \dfrac{1}{(x+2)^2} + \dfrac{3}{(3x-1)}$

Exercise 8.2

Q1 Express $\dfrac{3x}{(x+5)^2}$ in the form $\dfrac{A}{(x+5)} + \dfrac{B}{(x+5)^2}$.

Q2 Write $\dfrac{5x+2}{x^2(x+1)}$ in the form $\dfrac{A}{x} + \dfrac{B}{x^2} + \dfrac{C}{(x+1)}$.

Q3 Write the following in partial fractions.

   a) $\dfrac{2x-7}{(x-3)^2}$
   b) $\dfrac{6x+7}{(2x+3)^2}$
   c) $\dfrac{7x}{(x+4)^2(x-3)}$
   d) $\dfrac{11x-10}{x(x-5)^2}$
   e) $\dfrac{x+5}{(x-1)^2x}$

Q4 Express $\dfrac{5x+10}{x^3-10x^2+25x}$ in partial fractions.

Q5 Express $\dfrac{3x+2}{(x-2)(x^2-4)}$ in partial fractions.

Q6 Find the value of c such that $\dfrac{x+17}{(x+1)(x+c)^2} = \dfrac{1}{x+1} - \dfrac{1}{x+c} + \dfrac{5}{(x+c)^2}$

Review Exercise — Chapter 17

Q1 Prove that if x^3 is odd, then x must be odd.

Q2 Simplify the following:

a) $\dfrac{4x^2 - 25}{6x - 15}$

b) $\dfrac{2x + 3}{x - 2} \times \dfrac{4x - 8}{2x^2 - 3x - 9}$

c) $\dfrac{x^2 - 3x}{x + 1} \div \dfrac{x}{2}$

Q3 Write the following as a single fraction:

a) $\dfrac{x}{2x + 1} + \dfrac{3}{x^2} + \dfrac{1}{x}$

b) $\dfrac{2}{x^2 - 1} - \dfrac{3x}{x - 1} + \dfrac{x}{x + 1}$

c) $\dfrac{2}{(x + 1)^2} - \dfrac{x}{x + 1} + \dfrac{1}{3x}$

Q4 Write $2x^3 + 8x^2 + 7x + 8$ in the form $(Ax^2 + Bx + C)(x + 3) + D$.
Using your answer, state the result when $2x^3 + 8x^2 + 7x + 8$ is divided by $(x + 3)$.

Q5 Divide $x^4 + x^3 - 5x^2 - 7x - 2$ by $x + 1$, hence find a solution to $x^4 + x^3 - 5x^2 - 7x = 2$.

Q6 For the following mappings, state the range and say whether or not the mapping is a function.
If not, explain why, and if so, say whether the function is one-to-one or many-to-one.

a) $f(x) = x^2 - 16, \; x \geq 0$

b) $f : x \to x^2 - 7x + 10, \; x \in \mathbb{R}$

c) $f(x) = \sqrt{x}, \; x \in \mathbb{R}$

Q7 $f(x) = \dfrac{5}{2x + 1}$ defines a mapping.

a) Evaluate $f(0)$ and $f(\tfrac{1}{2})$.

b) Draw the mapping diagram for the domain $x \in \mathbb{N}$, $x < 6$ and list the range.

c) Is the mapping a function for the domain $x \in \mathbb{Z}$? If not, explain why not.

d) Is the mapping a function for the domain $x \in \mathbb{R}$? If not, explain why not.

Q8 a) Sketch the graph of the function $f(x) = \begin{cases} x^2 - 2 & -2 < x < 2 \\ 2 & \text{otherwise} \end{cases}$

b) State the range of the function.

Q9 For each pair of functions f and g, find $fg(2)$, $gf(1)$ and $fg(x)$.

a) $f(x) = \dfrac{3}{x}, \; x > 0$ and $g(x) = 2x + 3, \; x \in \mathbb{R}$

b) $f(x) = 3x^2, \; x \geq 0$ and $g(x) = x + 4, \; x \in \mathbb{R}$

Q10 $f(x) = \log_{10} x$ and $g(x) = 10^{x+1}$.

a) Find the values of $fg(1)$, $gf(1)$, $f^2(10)$ and $g^2(-1)$.

b) Explain why $f^2(1)$ is undefined.

Q11 $f(x) = 3x$ and $g(x) = x + 7$, both with domain $x \in \mathbb{R}$.
Find the composite functions $fg(x)$, $gf(x)$ and $g^2(x)$.

Q12 A one-to-one function f has domain $x \in \mathbb{R}$ and range $f(x) \geq 3$.
Does this function have an inverse? If so, state its domain and range.

Q13 Using algebra, find the inverse of the function $f(x) = \sqrt{2x - 4}, \; x \geq 2$.
State the domain and range of the inverse.

Q14 $f(x) = \cos x, \; 0 \leq x \leq \dfrac{\pi}{2}$. Does the inverse function $f^{-1}(x)$ exist? Justify your answer.

Q15 The function $f(x) = \dfrac{x}{x - 1}, \; x < 1$. Show that $f(x) = f^{-1}(x)$, hence find $f^2(x)$.

Q16 $f(x) = \log_{10}(x + 4)$, $x > -4$. Find $f^{-1}(x)$.

Q17 The graph below shows the function $y = \cos x$, $0 \le x \le 360°$.
Sketch the graph of $y = -\cos 2x + 1$.

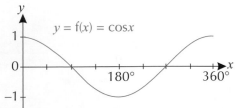

$y = f(x) = \cos x$

Q18 For the function $f(x) = 2x - 1$ $\{ x \in \mathbb{R} \}$, sketch the graphs of:
a) $|f(x)|$
b) $f(|x|)$

Q19 Solve the equation $|3x - 1| = |4 - x|$.

Q20 $f(x) = x^2 - 2x - 8$.
a) On the same axes sketch the graphs of $|f(x)|$ and $f(|x|)$.
b) Use your graphs to help you solve the equation $f(|x|) = -5$.

Q21 Sketch the graphs of:
a) $y = 3x + 2$
b) $y = |3x + 2|$
c) $y = -|3x + 2|$

Q22 Write $\dfrac{2x}{(x-5)(x+5)}$ as partial fractions in the form $\dfrac{A}{(x-5)} + \dfrac{B}{(x+5)}$.

Q23 Find the values of the constants A and B in the identity $\dfrac{2-x}{(3x+2)(x+1)} \equiv \dfrac{A}{(3x+2)} + \dfrac{B}{(x+1)}$.

Q24 Find the values of the constants A and B in the identity $\dfrac{x-3}{x^2+3x+2} \equiv \dfrac{A}{(x+1)} + \dfrac{B}{(x+2)}$.

Q25 Express the following as partial fractions:

a) $\dfrac{4}{x^2+x}$
b) $\dfrac{4x+5}{(x+4)(2x-3)}$
c) $\dfrac{5x}{x^2+x-6}$

d) $\dfrac{10x}{(x+3)(2x+4)}$
e) $\dfrac{6x+10}{(2x+1)(2-3x)}$
f) $\dfrac{2x+1}{x^2+3x}$

Q26 Show that $\dfrac{2x-5}{(x-5)^2}$ can be written in the form $\dfrac{A}{(x-5)} + \dfrac{B}{(x-5)^2}$.

Q27 Express the following as partial fractions.

a) $\dfrac{2x+2}{(x+3)^2}$
b) $\dfrac{-18x+14}{(2x-1)^2(x+2)}$
c) $\dfrac{x-5}{x^3-x^2}$

Q28 Find the value of b such that $\dfrac{bx+7}{(x+1)^2(x+2)} = \dfrac{3}{x+1} + \dfrac{2}{(x+1)^2} - \dfrac{3}{x+2}$. (PROBLEM SOLVING)

Chapter 18 — Trigonometry 2

You came across some trigonometry in Chapter 6, but there's quite a bit more here. One key difference in Year 2 trigonometry is that you don't just work in degrees — you have to work with radians too.

1. Arcs and Sectors

Radians

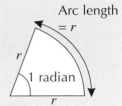

Arc length = r

1 radian

- A **radian** (rad) is just another unit of measurement for an angle.
- **1 radian** is the angle formed in a **sector** that has an **arc length** that is the same as the **radius**. In other words, if you have a **sector** with an angle of **1 radian**, then the **length** of the **arc** will be exactly the **same length** as the **radius** r.
- This is how **radians relate to degrees**:

   $360°$ (a complete circle) $= 2\pi$ radians $180° = \pi$ radians   1 radian $\approx 57°$

- To **convert** from **radians to degrees**, divide by π, then multiply by 180.
- To **convert** from **degrees to radians**, divide by 180, then multiply by π.
- Here's a table of some of the useful **common angles**, in degrees and radians:

Degrees	0	30	45	60	90	120	180	270	360
Radians	0	$\frac{\pi}{6}$	$\frac{\pi}{4}$	$\frac{\pi}{3}$	$\frac{\pi}{2}$	$\frac{2\pi}{3}$	π	$\frac{3\pi}{2}$	2π

Example   Convert $\frac{\pi}{15}$ into degrees.

- To convert from radians to degrees, divide by π... $\dfrac{\pi}{15} \div \pi = \dfrac{1}{15}$

- ... then multiply by 180... $\dfrac{1}{15} \times 180 = \mathbf{12°}$

Exercise 1.1

Q1   Convert the angles below into radians. Give your answers in terms of π.
   a) 180°   b) 135°   c) 270°   d) 70°   e) 150°   f) 75°

Q2   Convert the angles below into degrees.
   a) $\frac{\pi}{4}$ b) $\frac{\pi}{2}$ c) $\frac{\pi}{3}$ d) $\frac{5\pi}{2}$ e) $\frac{3\pi}{4}$ f) $\frac{7\pi}{3}$

Arc length and sector area

A **sector** is part of a circle formed by **two radii** and part of the **circumference**. The **arc** of a sector is the **curved** edge of the sector. You can work out the **length** of the **arc** or the **area** of the sector if you know the **angle** at the **centre** (θ) and the **length** of the **radius** (r).

Tip: When working out arc length and sector area you **always** work in radians.

For a circle with **radius r** and a sector with **angle θ** (measured in **radians**), its **arc length**, s, is given by: $\boxed{s = r\theta}$

For the same sector, its **area**, A, is given by: $\boxed{A = \dfrac{1}{2}r^2\theta}$

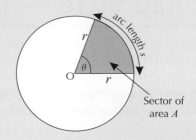

Sector of area A

Tip: If you put $\theta = 2\pi$ in either formula (and so make the sector equal to the whole circle), you get the normal circumference and area formulas.

Examples a) **Find the exact length L and area A in the diagram to the right.**

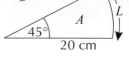

1. Convert the angle to radians: $45° = \dfrac{45 \times \pi}{180} = \dfrac{\pi}{4}$ radians

2. Then put everything in the formulas: $L = r\theta = 20 \times \dfrac{\pi}{4} = \mathbf{5\pi}$ **cm**

$A = \dfrac{1}{2}r^2\theta = \dfrac{1}{2} \times 20^2 \times \dfrac{\pi}{4} = \mathbf{50\pi}$ **cm²**

b) **Find the exact value of θ in the diagram to the left.**

Use the formula for the arc length: $s = r\theta \implies 4\pi = 20\theta$

$\theta = \dfrac{4\pi}{20} = \dfrac{\pi}{5}$ **radians**

Exercise 1.2

Q1 The diagram to the right shows a sector OAB. The centre is at O and the radius is 6 cm. The angle AOB is 2 radians. Find the arc length and area of this sector.

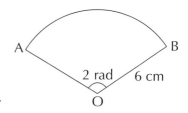

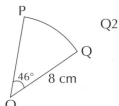

Q2 The diagram to the left shows a sector OPQ. The centre is at O and the radius is 8 cm. The angle POQ is 46°. Find the arc length and area of this sector to 1 d.p.

Q3 A sector of a circle of radius 4 cm has an area of 6π cm². Find the exact value of the angle θ.

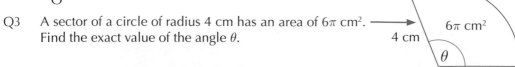

Q4 The diagram below shows a sector of a circle with a centre O and radius r cm. The angle AOB shown is θ.

For each of the following values of θ and r, give the arc length and the area of the sector. Where appropriate give your answers to 3 s.f.

a) $\theta = 1.2$ radians, $r = 5$ cm

b) $\theta = 0.6$ radians, $r = 4$ cm

c) $\theta = 80°$, $r = 9$ cm

d) $\theta = \dfrac{5\pi}{12}$, $r = 4$ cm

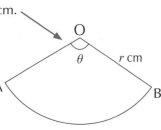

Q5 The diagram to the right shows a sector ABC of a circle, where the angle BAC is 0.9 radians. Given that the area of the sector is 16.2 cm², find the arc length *s*.

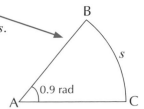

Q6 A circle C has a radius of length 3 cm with centre O.
A sector of this circle is given by angle AOB which is 20°.
Find the length of the arc AB and the area of the sector.
Give your answer in terms of π.

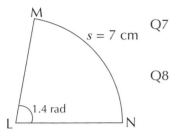

Q7 The sector shown on the left has an arc length of 7 cm.
The angle MLN is 1.4 rad. Find the area of the sector.

Q8 A circle of radius *r* contains a sector of area 80π cm².
Given that the arc length of the sector is 16π cm, find the angle of the sector (θ) and the value of *r*, giving your answers to 3 s.f.

Q9 The diagram to the right shows a semicircle of radius 2 cm, with a smaller sector of radius 1 cm removed.
Given that the area of the sector A and the area of B are equal, find the exact value of θ.

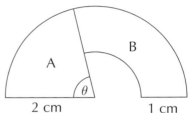

2. Small Angle Approximations

When θ (measured in radians) is very small, you can approximate the value of $\sin \theta$, $\cos \theta$ and $\tan \theta$ using the **small angle approximations**:

$$\sin \theta \approx \theta \qquad \cos \theta \approx 1 - \frac{1}{2}\theta^2 \qquad \tan \theta \approx \theta$$

Tip: These approximations only work when $\theta < 1$.

Example Give an approximation for cos 0.2.

Use the small angle approximation for cos and set $\theta = 0.2$: $\cos \theta \approx 1 - \frac{1}{2}\theta^2$

$$\cos 0.2 \approx 1 - \frac{1}{2}(0.2)^2$$
$$= 1 - 0.02 = \mathbf{0.98}$$

Tip: The actual value of cos 0.2 is 0.980067 (to 6 d.p.), so the approximation is pretty accurate.

These approximations can be used to approximate more **complicated functions**, which could involve sin, cos and tan of **multiples** of θ (when θ is small, you can assume that multiples of θ are also small). Make sure that you apply the approximation to **everything** inside the trig function — for example:

$$\tan 4\theta \approx 4\theta \qquad \sin \frac{1}{2}\theta \approx \frac{1}{2}\theta \qquad \cos 3\theta \approx 1 - \frac{1}{2}(3\theta)^2$$

Example **Find an approximation for f(θ) = 4 cos θ tan 3θ when θ is small.**

Replace cos and tan with the small angle approximations:

$$f(\theta) \approx 4 \times (1 - \tfrac{1}{2}\theta^2) \times 3\theta = (4 - 2\theta^2) \times 3\theta = \mathbf{12\theta - 6\theta^3} \text{ (or } \mathbf{6\theta(2 - \theta^2))}$$

$\approx$ cos θ $\approx$ tan 3θ

Exercise 2.1

Q1 Use the small angle approximations to estimate the following values, then calculate the actual values:
   a) sin 0.23   b) sin 0.12   c) cos 0.01   d) cos 0.24   e) tan 0.18

Q2 For the values of θ below, use the small angle approximations to estimate the value of f(θ) = sin θ + cos θ, then use a calculator to find the actual answer:
   a) $\theta = 0.3$ b) $\theta = 0.5$ c) $\theta = 0.25$ d) $\theta = 0.01$ e) $\theta = 0.03$

Q3 Find an approximation for the following if θ is small:
   a) sin θ cos θ
   b) θ tan 5θ sin θ
   c) $\dfrac{\sin 4\theta \cos 3\theta}{2\theta}$
   d) 3 tan θ + cos 2θ
   e) sin $\tfrac{1}{2}\theta$ − cos θ
   f) $\dfrac{\cos\theta - \cos 2\theta}{1 - (\cos 3\theta + 3\sin\theta\tan\theta)}$

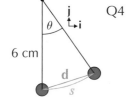

6 cm

Q4 A pendulum of length 6 cm follows the arc of a circle.
   Its straight-line displacement as a vector is given by: **d** = 6 sin θ **i** + 6(1 − cos θ)**j**.
   a) Show that the magnitude of the displacement is $6\sqrt{2(1-\cos\theta)}$.
   b) Show that, when θ is small, the magnitude of the displacement can be approximated by the arc length s.

MODELLING

3. Inverse Trig Functions

The inverse trig functions **reverse** the effect of sin, cos and tan. **Arcsin** is the inverse of **sin**, **arccos** is the inverse of **cos** and **arctan** is the inverse of **tan**. You might see them written as arcsine or sin^{-1} etc.

The functions sine, cosine and tangent **aren't one-to-one** mappings (see p.240). For the inverses to be **functions**, you have to **restrict the domains** of the trigonometric functions to make them **one-to-one**.

Tip: The graphs of the inverse functions are the **reflections** of the sin, cos and tan graphs in the line y = x.

Arcsin

- For arcsin, limit the **domain** of sin x to $-\dfrac{\pi}{2} \leq x \leq \dfrac{\pi}{2}$
  (the range of sin x is still −**1 ≤ sin x ≤ 1**).

- So the **domain** of arcsin x is −**1 ≤ x ≤ 1**.

- The **range** of arcsin x is $-\dfrac{\pi}{2} \leq$ **arcsin x** $\leq \dfrac{\pi}{2}$.

- The graph of **y = arcsin x** goes through the **origin**.

- The coordinates of its **endpoints** are $\left(-1, -\dfrac{\pi}{2}\right)$ and $\left(1, \dfrac{\pi}{2}\right)$.

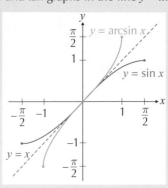

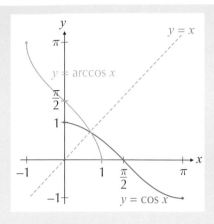

Arccos

- For arccos, limit the **domain** of cos x to $\mathbf{0 \leq x \leq \pi}$ (the range of cos x is still $-1 \leq \cos x \leq 1$).

- So the **domain** of arccos x is $\mathbf{-1 \leq x \leq 1}$.

- The **range** of arccos x is $\mathbf{0 \leq arccos\ x \leq \pi}$.

- The graph of $y = $ arccos x crosses the **y-axis** at $\left(0, \frac{\pi}{2}\right)$.

- The coordinates of its **endpoints** are $(-1, \pi)$ and $(1, 0)$.

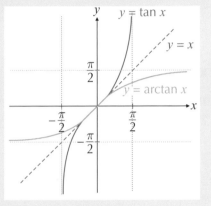

Arctan

- For arctan, limit the **domain** of tan x to $-\frac{\pi}{2} < x < \frac{\pi}{2}$ (this **doesn't limit** the range of tan x).

- This means that the **domain** of arctan x **isn't** limited (it's $x \in \mathbb{R}$).

- The **range** of arctan x is $-\frac{\pi}{2} < arctan\ x < \frac{\pi}{2}$.

- The graph of $y = $ arctan x goes through the **origin**.

- It has **asymptotes** at $y = \frac{\pi}{2}$ and $y = -\frac{\pi}{2}$.

This table shows the trig values of common angles, both in **degrees** and **radians**: →

For an angle, a, such than $\sin a = x$, $\arcsin x = a$.

When you use a **calculator** to evaluate arcsin or arctan, you'll get an angle, a, in the interval $-\frac{\pi}{2} \leq a \leq \frac{\pi}{2}$ (or $-90° \leq a \leq 90°$).

When you evaluate arccos, the angle will be in the interval $0 \leq a \leq \pi$ (or $0° \leq a \leq 180°$).

$x°$	0	30	45	60	90	180
x (rad)	0	$\frac{\pi}{6}$	$\frac{\pi}{4}$	$\frac{\pi}{3}$	$\frac{\pi}{2}$	π
$\sin x$	0	$\frac{1}{2}$	$\frac{1}{\sqrt{2}}$	$\frac{\sqrt{3}}{2}$	1	0
$\cos x$	1	$\frac{\sqrt{3}}{2}$	$\frac{1}{\sqrt{2}}$	$\frac{1}{2}$	0	−1
$\tan x$	0	$\frac{1}{\sqrt{3}}$	1	$\sqrt{3}$	—	0

Examples

a) **Evaluate, without using a calculator, arccos 0.5. Give your answer in degrees.**

Work out the angle a for which cos $a = 0.5$. Since you're expected to do this without a calculator, it will be a common angle (see table above): arccos $0.5 = \mathbf{60°}$

Tip: 60° lies within the domain for cos ($0° \leq a \leq 180°$) so the answer is correct.

b) **Evaluate, without using a calculator, arctan −1. Give your answer in radians.**

From the table, you know that tan $\frac{\pi}{4} = 1$, so use the symmetry of the tan graph (see p.71) to find the value for which tan $a = -1$, over $-\frac{\pi}{2} < a < \frac{\pi}{2}$: arctan $1 = -\frac{\pi}{4}$

Example Evaluate arcsin $-\dfrac{1}{\sqrt{2}}$ without using your calculator.

Give your answer in radians.

1. From the table, $\sin \dfrac{\pi}{4} = \dfrac{1}{\sqrt{2}}$

2. Use the symmetry of the sin graph to find the angle a such that $\sin a = -\dfrac{1}{\sqrt{2}}$.
   The only solution within the appropriate domain is $-\dfrac{\pi}{4}$, so: arcsin $-\dfrac{1}{\sqrt{2}} = -\dfrac{\pi}{4}$

Tip: You could also use a CAST diagram to find the solutions — you'd end up with $a = \dfrac{5\pi}{4}$ and $a = -\dfrac{\pi}{4}$, then choose the answer that's in the given domain.

Exercise 3.1

Answer the questions in this exercise without using a calculator.

Q1　Evaluate the following, giving your answer in radians.

a) arccos 1　　b) arcsin $\dfrac{\sqrt{3}}{2}$　　c) arctan $\sqrt{3}$　　d) arccos $\dfrac{1}{\sqrt{2}}$　　e) arcsin 0

Q2　a) Sketch the graph of $y = 2 \arccos x$ for $-1 \le x \le 1$.

b) Sketch the graph of $y = \dfrac{1}{2} \arctan x$ and state the range.

Q3　By drawing the graphs of $y = \dfrac{x}{2}$ and $y = \cos^{-1} x$,
determine the number of real roots of the equation $\cos^{-1} x = \dfrac{x}{2}$.

Q4　Evaluate the following, giving your answers in radians:

a) $\sin^{-1}(-1)$　　b) $\cos^{-1}\left(-\dfrac{\sqrt{3}}{2}\right)$　　c) $\tan^{-1}\left(-\dfrac{1}{\sqrt{3}}\right)$　　d) $\sin^{-1}\left(-\dfrac{1}{2}\right)$

Q5　Evaluate the following:　　a) $\tan\left(\arcsin\dfrac{1}{2}\right)$　　b) $\cos^{-1}\left(\cos\dfrac{2\pi}{3}\right)$　　c) $\cos\left(\arcsin\dfrac{1}{2}\right)$

Q6　$f(x) = 1 + \sin 2x$. Find an expression for $f^{-1}(x)$.

4. Cosec, Sec and Cot

When you take the **reciprocal** of the three main trig functions, sin, cos and tan, you get three new trig functions — **cosecant** (or **cosec**), **secant** (or **sec**) and **cotangent** (or **cot**).

$$\operatorname{cosec} \theta \equiv \dfrac{1}{\sin\theta} \qquad \sec\theta \equiv \dfrac{1}{\cos\theta} \qquad \cot\theta \equiv \dfrac{1}{\tan\theta}$$

Tip: Since $\tan\theta \equiv \dfrac{\sin\theta}{\cos\theta}$, you can also think of **cot θ** as being $\dfrac{\cos\theta}{\sin\theta}$.

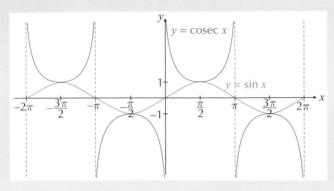

y = cosec x

- Since $\operatorname{cosec} x = \dfrac{1}{\sin x}$, $y = \operatorname{cosec} x$ is **undefined** at any point where $\sin x = 0$.

- So $y = \operatorname{cosec} x$ has **vertical asymptotes** at $x = n\pi$ (where n is any integer).

- The graph $y = \operatorname{cosec} x$ has **minimum** points at $x = ..., -\dfrac{3\pi}{2}, \dfrac{\pi}{2}, \dfrac{5\pi}{2}, ...$ (wherever the graph $y = \sin x$ has a **maximum**). At these points, $y = 1$.

- It has **maximum** points at $x = ..., -\dfrac{\pi}{2}, \dfrac{3\pi}{2}, \dfrac{7\pi}{2}, ...$ (wherever the graph $y = \sin x$ has a **minimum**). At these points, $y = -1$.

y = sec x

- As $\sec x = \dfrac{1}{\cos x}$, $y = \sec x$ is **undefined** at any point where $\cos x = 0$.

- So $y = \sec x$ has **vertical asymptotes** at $x = \left(n\pi + \dfrac{\pi}{2}\right)$ (where n is any integer).

- The graph of $y = \sec x$ has **minimum** points at $x = 0, \pm 2\pi, \pm 4\pi, ...$ (wherever the graph of $y = \cos x$ has a **maximum**). At these points, $y = 1$.

- It has **maximum** points at $x = \pm\pi, \pm 3\pi, ...$ (wherever the graph of $y = \cos x$ has a **minimum**). At these points, $y = -1$.

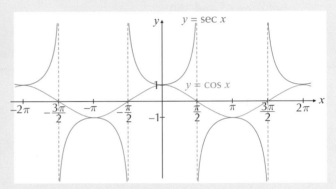

Tip: Just like the graphs of $\sin x$ and $\cos x$, the graphs of $\operatorname{cosec} x$ and $\sec x$ have a **period** of 2π radians — this just means they repeat themselves every 2π (or 360°).

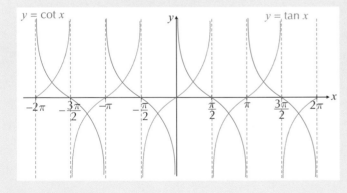

y = cot x

- Since $\cot x = \dfrac{1}{\tan x}$, $y = \cot x$ is **undefined** at any point where $\tan x = 0$.

- So $y = \cot x$ has **vertical asymptotes** at $x = n\pi$ (where n is any integer).

- $y = \cot x$ **crosses the x-axis** at every place where the graph of $\tan x$ has an asymptote. This is any point with the coordinates $\left(\left(n\pi + \dfrac{\pi}{2}\right), 0\right)$.

The graphs of the cosec, sec and cot functions can be transformed in the same way as other functions.

Examples   a)   **Sketch the graph of $y = \cot 2x$ over the interval $-\pi \le x \le \pi$.**

If $f(x) = \cot x$, then $y = f(2x)$. This transformation is a horizontal stretch by a factor of $\dfrac{1}{2}$ (i.e. the graph is squashed up in the x-direction by a factor of 2). The period of the graph is also halved: $y = \cot 2x$ repeats itself every $\dfrac{\pi}{2}$ radians. See next page for the graph of $y = \cot 2x$.

The x-intercepts for $y = \cot 2x$ are half of those for $y = \cot x$.

$y = \cot 2x$

$y = \cot x$

The x-coordinates of the asymptotes for $y = \cot 2x$ are half of those for $y = \cot x$.

$-\pi \quad -\dfrac{3\pi}{4} \quad -\dfrac{\pi}{2} \quad -\dfrac{\pi}{4} \qquad \dfrac{\pi}{4} \quad \dfrac{\pi}{2} \quad \dfrac{3\pi}{4} \quad \pi$

b) Give the coordinates of the maximum point on the graph of $y = \sec(x - 30°) + 1$, between 0° and 360°.

- The graph of $f(x) = \sec x$ has a maximum point at $(180°, -1)$.

- $y = f(x - 30°) + 1$. This is a horizontal translation right by 30°, followed by a vertical translation up by 1. The x-coordinate of the maximum point will be increased by 30° and the y-coordinate will be increased by 1.

- So the coordinates of the maximum point on the transformed graph will be: **(210°, 0)**

Exercise 4.1

Q1   a) Sketch the graph of $y = \sec x$ for $-2\pi \leq x \leq 2\pi$.

      b) Give the coordinates of the maximum and minimum points within this interval.

      c) State the range of $y = \sec x$.

Q2   a) Sketch the graph of $y = \operatorname{cosec} x$ for $0 < x < 2\pi$.

      b) Give the coordinates of any maximum and minimum points within this interval.

      c) State the domain and range of $y = \operatorname{cosec} x$.

Q3   Describe the transformation that maps $y = \sec x$ onto $y = \operatorname{cosec} x$.

Q4   a) Describe the transformation that maps $y = \cot x$ onto $y = \cot \frac{x}{4}$.

      b) What is the period, in degrees, of the graph $y = \cot \frac{x}{4}$?

      c) Sketch the graph of $y = \cot \frac{x}{4}$ for $0 < x \leq 360°$.

Q5   a) Sketch the graph of $y = 2 + \sec x$ for $-2\pi \leq x \leq 2\pi$ and state its domain and range.

      b) Give the coordinates of any maximum and minimum points within this interval.

Q6   a) Sketch the graph of $y = 2 \operatorname{cosec} 2x$ for $0° \leq x \leq 360°$.

      b) Give the coordinates of the maximum and minimum points within this interval.

      c) For what values of x in this interval is $y = 2 \operatorname{cosec} 2x$ undefined?

Q7   a) Describe the position of the asymptotes on the graph of $y = 2 + 3 \operatorname{cosec} x$.

      b) What is the period, in degrees, of the graph $y = 2 + 3 \operatorname{cosec} x$?

      c) Sketch the graph of $y = 2 + 3 \operatorname{cosec} x$ for $-180° < x < 180°$ and state its range.

Evaluating cosec, sec and cot

To **evaluate** cosec, sec or cot of a number, evaluate sin, cos or tan then work out the **reciprocal**.

Examples   **a) Evaluate 2 sec(–20°) + 5, giving your answer to 3 significant figures.**

1. First write out the expression in terms of sin, cos or tan:

$$\sec x = \frac{1}{\cos x}, \text{ so } 2\sec(-20°) + 5 = \frac{2}{\cos(-20°)} + 5$$

2. Now evaluate using a calculator: $\dfrac{2}{\cos(-20°)} + 5 = \dfrac{2}{0.93969...} + 5 = \textbf{7.13 to 3 s.f.}$

b) Find the exact value of $\cot\left(-\dfrac{\pi}{6}\right)$.

1. $\cot x = \dfrac{1}{\tan x}$, so $\cot\left(-\dfrac{\pi}{6}\right) = \dfrac{1}{\tan\left(-\dfrac{\pi}{6}\right)}$.

2. From the table on p.263, $\tan\dfrac{\pi}{6} = \dfrac{1}{\sqrt{3}}$.

   From the symmetry of the graph, if $\tan\dfrac{\pi}{6} = \dfrac{1}{\sqrt{3}}$ then $\tan\left(-\dfrac{\pi}{6}\right) = -\dfrac{1}{\sqrt{3}}$.

3. So: $\cot\left(-\dfrac{\pi}{6}\right) = \dfrac{1}{\left(-\dfrac{1}{\sqrt{3}}\right)} = -\sqrt{3}$

c) Find cosec 300° without using a calculator.

1. $\operatorname{cosec}300° = \dfrac{1}{\sin 300°} = \dfrac{1}{\sin(360° - 60°)}$. Using a CAST diagram shows that sin 300° is the same size as sin 60°, but it lies in a quadrant where sin is negative.

2. So $\sin 300° = -\sin 60° = -\dfrac{\sqrt{3}}{2}$, which means: $\operatorname{cosec}300° = \dfrac{1}{\left(-\dfrac{\sqrt{3}}{2}\right)} = -\dfrac{2}{\sqrt{3}} = -\dfrac{2\sqrt{3}}{3}$

Exercise 4.2

Q1 Evaluate the following, giving your answers to 2 decimal places:

a) cosec 80°   b) sec 75°   c) cot 30°   d) cosec –15°

e) sec (–70°)   f) 3 – cot 250°   g) 2 cosec 25°   h) 4 sec 200°

Q2 Evaluate the following, giving your answers to 3 significant figures:

a) sec 3   b) cot 0.6   c) cosec 1.8   d) sec (–1)

e) $\operatorname{cosec}\dfrac{\pi}{8}$ f) $8 + \cot\dfrac{\pi}{8}$ g) $\dfrac{1}{1 + \sec\dfrac{\pi}{10}}$ h) $\dfrac{1}{6 + \cot\dfrac{\pi}{5}}$

Q3 Using the table of common angles on p.263, find the exact values of:

a) sec 60°   b) cosec 30°   c) cot 45°   d) $\operatorname{cosec}\dfrac{\pi}{3}$

e) sec (–180°)   f) cosec 135°   g) cot 330°   h) $\sec\dfrac{5\pi}{4}$

i) $\operatorname{cosec}\dfrac{5\pi}{3}$ j) $\operatorname{cosec}\dfrac{2\pi}{3}$ k) $3 - \cot\dfrac{3\pi}{4}$ l) $\dfrac{\sqrt{3}}{\cot\dfrac{\pi}{6}}$

Q4 Find, without a calculator, the exact values of:

a) $\dfrac{1}{1 + \sec 60°}$ b) $\dfrac{2}{6 + \cot 315°}$ c) $\dfrac{1}{\sqrt{3} - \sec 30°}$ d) $1 + \cot 420°$ e) $\dfrac{2}{7 + \sqrt{3}\cot 150°}$

Simplifying expressions and solving equations

Examples

a) Simplify $\cot^2 x \tan x$.

$\cot x = \dfrac{1}{\tan x}$, so: $\cot^2 x \tan x = \left(\dfrac{1}{\tan^2 x}\right)\tan x = \dfrac{1}{\tan x} = \mathbf{\cot x}$

b) Show that $\dfrac{\cot x \sec x}{\cosec^2 x} \equiv \sin x$.

$\cot x = \dfrac{\cos x}{\sin x}$, so: $\dfrac{\cot x \sec x}{\cosec^2 x} = \dfrac{\left(\dfrac{\cos x}{\sin x}\right)\left(\dfrac{1}{\cos x}\right)}{\left(\dfrac{1}{\sin^2 x}\right)} = \dfrac{\left(\dfrac{1}{\sin x}\right)}{\left(\dfrac{1}{\sin^2 x}\right)} = \mathbf{\sin x}$ as required

c) Write the expression $(\cosec x + 1)(\sin x - 1)$ as a single fraction in terms of $\sin x$ only.

1. First expand the brackets: $(\cosec x + 1)(\sin x - 1) = \cosec x \sin x + \sin x - \cosec x - 1$

2. $\cosec x \sin x = \left(\dfrac{1}{\sin x}\right)\sin x = 1$, so: $1 + \sin x - \cosec x - 1 = \sin x - \cosec x$

3. Using $\cosec x = \dfrac{1}{\sin x}$ the expression becomes: $= \sin x - \dfrac{1}{\sin x} = \dfrac{\sin^2 x - 1}{\sin x}$

Examples

a) Solve $\sec x = \sqrt{2}$ in the interval $0 \le x \le 2\pi$.

1. Write in terms of $\cos x$ by giving the reciprocal: $\sec x = \sqrt{2}$, so $\cos x = \dfrac{1}{\sqrt{2}}$

2. From the table on p.263, one solution to $\cos x = \dfrac{1}{\sqrt{2}}$ is: $x = \dfrac{\pi}{4}$

3. Using a CAST diagram (see p.74), the other positive solution will be in the 'C' quadrant, so:
$$x = 2\pi - \dfrac{\pi}{4} = \dfrac{7\pi}{4}$$

4. So the two solutions in the interval $0 \le x \le 2\pi$ are: $x = \dfrac{\pi}{4}$ and $x = \dfrac{7\pi}{4}$

b) Solve $\cosec^2 x - 3\cosec x + 2 = 0$ in the interval $-180° \le x \le 180°$.

1. This is a quadratic equation in $\cosec x$, so factorise:
$$\cosec^2 x - 3\cosec x + 2 = 0 \Rightarrow (\cosec x - 1)(\cosec x - 2) = 0$$

2. This gives two equations to solve:

$\cosec x - 1 = 0$	$\cosec x - 2 = 0$
$\cosec x = 1$	$\cosec x = 2$
$\sin x = 1 \Rightarrow x = 90°$	$\sin x = \dfrac{1}{2} \Rightarrow x = 30°, 150°$

3. So the three solutions are: $\mathbf{x = 30°,\ x = 90°}$ **and** $\mathbf{x = 150°}$

Tip: Once you've found the solutions at $x = 90°$ and $x = 30°$, use the graph of $y = \sin x$ to find the other solutions in the given interval. $\sin x = 1$ only has one solution between $-180°$ and $180°$, but there's another solution to $\sin x = 0.5$ at $180° - 30° = 150°$.

Exercise 4.3

Q1 Simplify the following expressions:

a) $\sec x + \dfrac{1}{\cos x}$

b) $(\text{cosec}^2\, x)(\sin^2 x)$

c) $2 \cot x + \dfrac{1}{\tan x}$

d) $\dfrac{\sec x}{\text{cosec}\, x}$

e) $(\cos x)(\text{cosec}\, x)$

f) $\dfrac{\text{cosec}^2 x}{\cot x}$

g) $5 \cot x - \dfrac{\text{cosec}\, x}{\sec x}$

h) $\dfrac{1}{\sec^2 x} + \dfrac{1}{\text{cosec}^2 x}$

Q2 Show that:

a) $\sin x \cot x \equiv \cos x$

b) $\sec x - \cos x \equiv \tan x \sin x$

c) $\dfrac{\sec x}{\cot x} \equiv \sin x \sec^2 x$

d) $\tan x \,\text{cosec}\, x \equiv \sec x$

e) $\dfrac{(\tan^2 x)(\text{cosec}\, x)}{\sin x} \equiv \sec^2 x$

f) $\text{cosec}\, x\,(\sin x + \cos x) \equiv 1 + \cot x$

Q3 Solve these equations for $0° \le x \le 360°$. Give your answers in degrees to one decimal place.

a) $\sec x = 1.9$

b) $\cot x = 2.4$

c) $\text{cosec}\, x = -2$

d) $\sec x = -1.3$

e) $\cot x = -2.4$

f) $\frac{1}{2} \text{cosec}\, x = 0.7$

g) $4 \sec 2x = -7$

h) $5 \cot 3x = 4$

Q4 Solve these equations for $0 \le x \le 2\pi$, giving your answers in radians in terms of π.

a) $\sec x = 2$

b) $\text{cosec}\, x = -2$

c) $\cot 2x = 1$

d) $\sec 5x = -1$

Q5 Solve the equation $\cot 2x - 4 = -5$ in the interval $0 \le x \le 2\pi$. Give your answers in terms of π.

Q6 Solve for $0° \le x \le 360°$: $2 \,\text{cosec}\, 2x = 3$. Give your answers to 1 decimal place.

Q7 Find, for $0 \le x \le 2\pi$, all the solutions of the equation $-2 \sec x = 4$. Give your answers in terms of π.

Q8 Solve $\sqrt{3}\,\text{cosec}\, 3x = 2$ for $0 \le x \le 2\pi$. Give your answers in terms of π.

Q9 Solve the following for $0° \le x \le 180°$, giving your answers to 1 d.p. where appropriate:

a) $\sec^2 x - 2\sqrt{2} \sec x + 2 = 0$

b) $2 \cot^2 x + 3 \cot x - 2 = 0$

Q10 Solve the equation $(\text{cosec}\, x - 3)(2 \tan x + 1) = 0$ for $0° \le x \le 360°$. Give your answers to 1 decimal place.

5. Identities Involving Cosec, Sec and Cot

You should be familiar with the **trig identities** $\cos^2 \theta + \sin^2 \theta \equiv 1$ and $\tan \theta \equiv \dfrac{\sin \theta}{\cos \theta}$ from p.69.

You can use these to produce two more identities involving **cosec**, **sec** and **cot**:

$$\sec^2 \theta \equiv 1 + \tan^2 \theta \qquad\qquad \text{cosec}^2 \theta \equiv 1 + \cot^2 \theta$$

Example Solve the equation $\cot^2 x + 5 = 4 \,\text{cosec}\, x$ in the interval $0° \le x \le 360°$.

1. Use the identity $\text{cosec}^2 \theta \equiv 1 + \cot^2 \theta$ to swap $\cot^2 x$ for $\text{cosec}^2 x - 1$:

$\text{cosec}^2 x - 1 + 5 = 4 \,\text{cosec}\, x$

$\text{cosec}^2 x + 4 = 4 \,\text{cosec}\, x$

$\text{cosec}^2 x - 4 \,\text{cosec}\, x + 4 = 0$

2. This leaves a quadratic in $\text{cosec}\, x$ which will factorise:

$(\text{cosec}\, x - 2)(\text{cosec}\, x - 2) = 0$

3. Both the brackets are the same, so there's only one equation to solve:
$(\operatorname{cosec} x - 2) = 0 \implies \operatorname{cosec} x = 2$

4. Convert this into sin x, and solve it: $\sin x = \dfrac{1}{2} \implies x = 30°$

5. From the graph of $y = \sin x$, you can see that $\sin x$ takes the value of $\dfrac{1}{2}$ twice in the given interval, so the solutions are: $x = \mathbf{30°}$ and $x = 180 - 30 = \mathbf{150°}$

Exercise 5.1

Q1 Use the identities $\sin^2 \theta + \cos^2 \theta \equiv 1$ and $\tan \theta \equiv \dfrac{\sin \theta}{\cos \theta}$ to prove the following identities:

a) $\sec^2 \theta \equiv 1 + \tan^2 \theta$ b) $\operatorname{cosec}^2 \theta \equiv 1 + \cot^2 \theta$

Q2 Express $\operatorname{cosec}^2 x + 2 \cot^2 x$ in terms of $\operatorname{cosec} x$ only.

Q3 Simplify the following expression: $\tan^2 x - \dfrac{1}{\cos^2 x}$.

Q4 Given that $x = \sec \theta + \tan \theta$, show that $x + \dfrac{1}{x} = 2 \sec \theta$.

Q5 a) Show that the equation $\tan^2 x = 2 \sec x + 2$ can be written as $\sec^2 x - 2 \sec x - 3 = 0$.

b) Hence solve $\tan^2 x = 2 \sec x + 2$ over the interval $0° \le x \le 360°$, giving your answers in degrees to 1 decimal place.

Q6 a) Show that the equation $2 \operatorname{cosec}^2 x = 5 - 5 \cot x$ can be written as $2 \cot^2 x + 5 \cot x - 3 = 0$.

b) Hence solve $2 \operatorname{cosec}^2 x = 5 - 5 \cot x$ over the interval $-\pi \le x \le \pi$, giving your answers in radians to 2 decimal places.

Q7 a) Show that the equation $2 \cot^2 A + 5 \operatorname{cosec} A = 10$ can be written as $2 \operatorname{cosec}^2 A + 5 \operatorname{cosec} A - 12 = 0$.

b) Hence solve $2 \cot^2 A + 5 \operatorname{cosec} A = 10$ over the interval $0° \le x \le 360°$, giving your answers in degrees to 1 decimal place.

Q8 Solve the equation $\sec^2 x + \tan x = 1$ for $0 \le x \le 2\pi$, giving exact answers.

Q9 a) Given that $\operatorname{cosec}^2 \theta + 2 \cot^2 \theta = 2$, find the possible values of $\sin \theta$.

b) Hence solve the equation $\operatorname{cosec}^2 \theta + 2 \cot^2 \theta = 2$ in the interval $0° \le \theta \le 180°$.

Q10 Solve the equation $\sec^2 x = 3 + \tan x$ in the interval $0° \le x \le 360°$, giving your answers to 1 decimal place.

Q11 Solve the equation $\cot^2 x + \operatorname{cosec}^2 x = 7$, giving all the solutions in the interval $0 \le x \le 2\pi$ in terms of π.

Q12 Solve the equation $\tan^2 x + 5 \sec x + 7 = 0$, giving all the solutions in the interval $0 \le x \le 2\pi$ to 2 decimal places.

Q13 a) Given that $\tan \theta = \dfrac{60}{11}$, and $180° \le \theta \le 270°$, find the exact value of:

(i) $\sin \theta$ (ii) $\sec \theta$ (iii) $\operatorname{cosec} \theta$

b) Given that $\operatorname{cosec} \theta = -\dfrac{17}{15}$, and $180° \le \theta \le 270°$, find the exact value of:

(i) $\cos \theta$ (ii) $\sec \theta$ (iii) $\cot \theta$

Q14 Given that $\cos x = \dfrac{1}{6}$, use the identity $\sec^2 \theta = 1 + \tan^2 \theta$ to find the two possible exact values of $\tan x$.

Proving other identities

You can also use identities to prove that two trig expressions are the same.
You just need to take one side of the identity and rearrange it until you get what's on the other side.

 a) Show that $\dfrac{\tan^2 x}{\sec x} \equiv \sec x - \cos x$.

Replace $\tan^2 x$ with $\sec^2 x - 1$ on the left-hand side of the identity:

$$\frac{\tan^2 x}{\sec x} \equiv \frac{\sec^2 x - 1}{\sec x} \equiv \frac{\sec^2 x}{\sec x} - \frac{1}{\sec x} \equiv \sec x - \cos x$$

b) Prove the identity $\dfrac{\tan^2 x}{\sec x + 1} \equiv \sec x - \cos^2 x - \sin^2 x$.

As before, replace $\tan^2 x$ with $\sec^2 x - 1$:

$$\frac{\tan^2 x}{\sec x + 1} \equiv \frac{\sec^2 x - 1}{\sec x + 1}$$

Factorise the $\sec^2 x - 1$ as it's the difference of two squares.

$$\equiv \frac{(\sec x + 1)(\sec x - 1)}{\sec x + 1}$$

$$\equiv \sec x - 1$$

Use $\cos^2 x + \sin^2 x \equiv 1$ to replace the '1' here.

$$\equiv \sec x - (\cos^2 x + \sin^2 x)$$

$$\equiv \sec x - \cos^2 x - \sin^2 x$$

Exercise 5.2

Q1 Prove the identity $\tan^2 \theta \equiv (\sec \theta + 1)(\sec \theta - 1)$.

Q2 a) Show that $\sec^2 \theta - \operatorname{cosec}^2 \theta \equiv \tan^2 \theta - \cot^2 \theta$.
   b) Hence prove that $(\sec \theta + \operatorname{cosec} \theta)(\sec \theta - \operatorname{cosec} \theta) \equiv (\tan \theta + \cot \theta)(\tan \theta - \cot \theta)$.

Q3 Prove the identity $(\tan x + \cot x)^2 \equiv \sec^2 x + \operatorname{cosec}^2 x$.

Q4 Prove the identity $\sec^2 \theta \operatorname{cosec}^2 \theta \equiv 2 + \cot^2 \theta + \tan^2 \theta$.

Q5 Prove the identity $\cot^2 x + \sin^2 x \equiv (\operatorname{cosec} x + \cos x)(\operatorname{cosec} x - \cos x)$.

Q6 Prove the identity $\dfrac{1 - \cot^4 x}{\operatorname{cosec}^2 x} \equiv 2 - \operatorname{cosec}^2 x$.

Q7 Prove the identity $\dfrac{(\sec x - \tan x)(\tan x + \sec x)}{\operatorname{cosec} x - \cot x} \equiv \cot x + \operatorname{cosec} x$.

Q8 Prove that $\dfrac{\cot x}{1 + \operatorname{cosec} x} + \dfrac{1 + \operatorname{cosec} x}{\cot x} \equiv 2 \sec x$.

Q9 Prove the identity $\dfrac{\operatorname{cosec} x + 1}{\operatorname{cosec} x - 1} \equiv 2 \sec^2 x + 2 \tan x \sec x - 1$.

6. The Addition Formulas

The identities shown below are known as the **addition formulas**. You can use the addition formulas to find the **sin**, **cos** or **tan** of the **sum** or **difference** of two angles, and to 'expand the brackets' in expressions such as $\sin (x + 60°)$ or $\cos \left(n - \frac{\pi}{2}\right)$.

$$\sin (A \pm B) \equiv \sin A \cos B \pm \cos A \sin B$$

$$\cos (A \pm B) \equiv \cos A \cos B \mp \sin A \sin B$$

$$\tan (A \pm B) \equiv \frac{\tan A \pm \tan B}{1 \mp \tan A \tan B}$$

Tip: Watch out for the $\pm$ and $\mp$ signs in the formulas — especially for cos and tan. If you use the sign on the **top** on the **left-hand side** of the identity, you have to use the sign on the **top** on the **right-hand side** too. So $\cos (A + B) = \cos A \cos B - \sin A \sin B$.

Examples

a) **Find the exact value of $\sin 18° \cos 12° + \cos 18° \sin 12°$.**

A is 18° and B is 12°.

Using the sin addition formula: $\sin A \cos B + \cos A \sin B \equiv \sin (A + B)$.

$$\sin 18° \cos 12° + \cos 18° \sin 12° = \sin (18° + 12°)$$
$$= \sin 30° = \frac{1}{2}$$

b) **Write $\dfrac{\tan 5x - \tan 2x}{1 + \tan 5x \tan 2x}$ as a single trigonometric ratio.**

Use the tan addition formula, with $A = 5x$ and $B = 2x$:

$$\frac{\tan 5x - \tan 2x}{1 + \tan 5x \tan 2x} = \tan (5x - 2x)$$
$$= \tan 3x$$

c) **Find $\cos (x + y)$ if $\sin x = \dfrac{4}{5}$ and $\sin y = \dfrac{15}{17}$. Both x and y are acute. Give an exact answer.**

First find $\cos x$ and $\cos y$. x and y are acute, so use SOH CAH TOA and Pythagoras:

$$\cos x = \frac{\text{adj}}{\text{hyp}} = \frac{3}{5} \longrightarrow$$

$$\longleftarrow \cos y = \frac{\text{adj}}{\text{hyp}} = \frac{8}{17}$$

So $\cos (x + y) = \cos x \cos y - \sin x \sin y = \left(\frac{3}{5} \times \frac{8}{17}\right) - \left(\frac{4}{5} \times \frac{15}{17}\right) = -\dfrac{36}{85}$

d) **Using the addition formula for tangent, show that $\tan 15° = 2 - \sqrt{3}$.**

1. Pick two angles that add or subtract to give 15°, and put them into the tan addition formula:

   It's easiest to use tan 60° and tan 45° here, since neither of them are fractions.

   $$\tan 15° = \tan (60° - 45°) = \frac{\tan 60° - \tan 45°}{1 + \tan 60° \tan 45°}$$

2. Substitute the values for tan 60° ($= \sqrt{3}$) and tan 45° ($= 1$) into the equation:

   $$= \frac{\sqrt{3} - 1}{1 + (\sqrt{3} \times 1)} = \frac{\sqrt{3} - 1}{\sqrt{3} + 1}$$

3. Now rationalise the denominator:

   $$= \frac{(\sqrt{3} - 1)(\sqrt{3} - 1)}{(\sqrt{3} + 1)(\sqrt{3} - 1)} = \frac{3 - 2\sqrt{3} + 1}{3 - 1}$$

4. And simplify the expression:

   $$= \frac{4 - 2\sqrt{3}}{2} = 2 - \sqrt{3}$$

Exercise 6.1

Q1 Use the addition formulas to find the exact values of the following:

a) $\cos 72° \cos 12° + \sin 72° \sin 12°$ b) $\cos 13° \cos 17° - \sin 13° \sin 17°$

c) $\dfrac{\tan 12° + \tan 18°}{1 - \tan 12° \tan 18°}$ d) $\dfrac{\tan 500° - \tan 140°}{1 + \tan 500° \tan 140°}$

e) $\sin 35° \cos 10° + \cos 35° \sin 10°$ f) $\sin 69° \cos 9° - \cos 69° \sin 9°$

Q2 Use the addition formulas to find the exact values of the following:

a) $\sin \dfrac{2\pi}{3} \cos \dfrac{\pi}{2} - \cos \dfrac{2\pi}{3} \sin \dfrac{\pi}{2}$ b) $\cos 4\pi \cos 3\pi + \sin 4\pi \sin 3\pi$ c) $\dfrac{\tan \dfrac{5\pi}{12} + \tan \dfrac{5\pi}{4}}{1 - \tan \dfrac{5\pi}{12} \tan \dfrac{5\pi}{4}}$

Q3 Write the following expressions as a single trigonometric ratio:

a) $\sin 5x \cos 2x - \cos 5x \sin 2x$ b) $\cos 4x \cos 6x - \sin 4x \sin 6x$ c) $\dfrac{\tan 7x + \tan 3x}{1 - \tan 7x \tan 3x}$

d) $5 \sin 2x \cos 3x + 5 \cos 2x \sin 3x$ e) $8 \cos 7x \cos 5x + 8 \sin 7x \sin 5x$ f) $\dfrac{\tan 8x - \tan 5x}{1 + \tan 8x \tan 5x}$

Q4 $\sin x = \dfrac{5}{13}$ and $\cos y = \dfrac{24}{25}$, where x and y are both acute angles. Calculate the exact value of:

a) $\sin (x - y)$ b) $\cos (x + y)$ c) $\cos (x - y)$ d) $\tan (x + y)$

Q5 $\sin x = \dfrac{3}{4}$ and $\cos y = \dfrac{3}{\sqrt{10}}$, where x and y are both acute angles. Calculate the exact value of:

a) $\sin (x + y)$ b) $\cos (x - y)$ c) $\operatorname{cosec} (x + y)$ d) $\sec (x - y)$

Q6 Using the addition formula for cos, show that $\cos \dfrac{\pi}{12} = \dfrac{\sqrt{6} + \sqrt{2}}{4}$.

Q7 Using the addition formula for sin, show that $\sin 75° = \dfrac{\sqrt{6} + \sqrt{2}}{4}$.

Q8 Using the addition formula for tan, show that $\tan 75° = \dfrac{\sqrt{3} + 1}{\sqrt{3} - 1}$.

Simplifying, solving equations and proving identities

You can use the addition formulas to **prove an identity**. All you need to do is put the numbers and variables from the left-hand side into the addition formulas and simplify.

Example   **Prove that cos $(a + 60°)$ + sin $(a + 30°) \equiv$ cos a.**

1. Put the numbers from the question into the addition formulas:

$$\cos(a + 60°) + \sin(a + 30°)$$
$$\equiv (\cos a \cos 60° - \sin a \sin 60°) + (\sin a \cos 30° + \cos a \sin 30°)$$

2. Now substitute in any sin and cos values that you know:

$$= \frac{1}{2} \cos a - \frac{\sqrt{3}}{2} \sin a + \frac{\sqrt{3}}{2} \sin a + \frac{1}{2} \cos a$$

$$\cos 60° \quad \sin 60° \quad \cos 30° \quad \sin 30°$$

3. And simplify:

$$= \frac{1}{2} \cos a + \frac{1}{2} \cos a = \textbf{cos } \textbf{\textit{a}} \text{ as required}$$

You can also use the addition formulas to **solve** complicated trig equations.

Example Solve $\sin\left(x + \frac{\pi}{2}\right) = \sin x$ in the interval $0 \le x \le 2\pi$.

1. First replace $\sin\left(x + \frac{\pi}{2}\right)$ using the sin addition formula:

$$\sin x \cos \frac{\pi}{2} + \cos x \sin \frac{\pi}{2} = \sin x \implies 0 + \cos x = \sin x$$

$$\cos \frac{\pi}{2} = 0 \text{ and } \sin \frac{\pi}{2} = 1.$$

2. Divide through by $\cos x$: $\quad \dfrac{\cos x}{\cos x} = \dfrac{\sin x}{\cos x}$

3. Replace $\dfrac{\sin x}{\cos x}$ with $\tan x$: $\quad \dfrac{\cos x}{\cos x} = \tan x \implies \tan x = 1$

4. Solve for $0 \le x \le 2\pi$: $\qquad x = \dfrac{\pi}{4} \text{ and } x = \dfrac{5\pi}{4}$

Exercise 6.2

Q1 Use the sine and cosine addition formulas to prove that $\tan(A - B) \equiv \dfrac{\tan A - \tan B}{1 + \tan A \tan B}$.

Q2 Prove the following identities:

a) $\dfrac{\cos(A - B) - \cos(A + B)}{\cos A \sin B} \equiv 2 \tan A$

b) $\frac{1}{2}[\cos(A - B) - \cos(A + B)] \equiv \sin A \sin B$

c) $\sin(x + 90°) \equiv \cos x$

d) $\cos(x + 180°) \equiv -\cos x$

Q3 Solve $4 \sin\left(x - \frac{\pi}{3}\right) = \cos x$ in the interval $-\pi \le x \le \pi$. Give your answers in radians to 2 d.p.

Q4 a) Show that $\tan\left(-\frac{\pi}{12}\right) = \sqrt{3} - 2$.

b) Use your answer to a) to solve the equation $\cos x = \cos\left(x + \frac{\pi}{6}\right)$ in the interval $0 \le x \le \pi$. Give your answer in terms of π.

Q5 Show that $2 \sin(x + 30°) \equiv \sqrt{3} \sin x + \cos x$.

Q6 Write an expression for $\tan\left(\frac{\pi}{3} - x\right)$ in terms of $\tan x$ only.

Q7 a) $\tan A = \frac{3}{8}$ and $\tan(A + B) = \frac{1}{4}$. Find the exact value of $\tan B$.

b) Hence find the exact value of $\tan(A - B)$.

Q8 a) Given that $\sin(x + y) = 4 \cos(x - y)$, write an expression for $\tan x$ in terms of $\tan y$.

b) Use your answer to a) to solve $\sin\left(x + \frac{\pi}{4}\right) = 4 \cos\left(x - \frac{\pi}{4}\right)$ in the interval $0 \le x \le 2\pi$.

Q9 Solve the following equations in the given interval. Give your answers to 2 decimal places.

a) $\sqrt{2} \sin(\theta + 45°) = 3 \cos\theta,$ $\qquad 0° \le \theta \le 360°$

b) $2 \cos\left(\theta - \frac{2\pi}{3}\right) - 5 \sin\theta = 0,$ $\qquad 0 \le \theta \le 2\pi$

c) $\sin(\theta - 30°) - \cos(\theta + 60°) = 0,$ $\qquad 0° \le \theta \le 360°$

Q10 Use the sin addition formula to show that $\sin\left(x + \frac{\pi}{6}\right) \approx \frac{1}{2} + \frac{\sqrt{3}}{2}x - \frac{1}{4}x^2$ when x is small.

7. The Double Angle Formulas

Double angle formulas are a special case of the addition formulas, using $(A + A)$ instead of $(A + B)$. They take an expression with a $2x$ term (a double angle) inside a trig function, and change it into an expression with only single x's inside the trig functions. Here are the formulas for sin, cos and tan:

$$\sin 2A \equiv 2\sin A \cos A$$

$$\cos 2A \equiv \cos^2 A - \sin^2 A$$

$$\tan 2A \equiv \frac{2\tan A}{1 - \tan^2 A}$$

Use the identity $\cos^2\theta + \sin^2\theta \equiv 1$ to rearrange the cos double angle formula:

$$\cos 2A \equiv 2\cos^2 A - 1$$

$$\cos 2A \equiv 1 - 2\sin^2 A$$

Examples   a) $\sin x = \frac{2}{3}$, where x is acute. **Find the exact value of $\cos 2x$ and $\sin 2x$.**

1. For $\cos 2x$, use the cos double angle formula in terms of sin: $\cos 2A \equiv 1 - 2\sin^2 A$

$$\Rightarrow \cos 2x = 1 - 2\left(\frac{2}{3}\right)^2 = \frac{1}{9}$$

2. For $\sin 2x$, use the sin double angle formula: $\sin 2A \equiv 2\sin A \cos A$

3. To use this, first work out $\cos x$ from $\sin x$ using the triangle method:

$$\cos x = \frac{\text{adj}}{\text{hyp}} = \frac{\sqrt{5}}{3}$$

4. Now put the values into the sin double angle formula: $\sin 2x = 2\sin x \cos x$

$$= 2 \times \frac{2}{3} \times \frac{\sqrt{5}}{3} = \frac{4\sqrt{5}}{9}$$

b) **Write $1 - 2\sin^2\left(\frac{3x}{2}\right)$ as a single trigonometric ratio.**

1. Use an identity that contains a 'sin²' term (the cos double angle formula in terms of sin):
$$\cos 2A \equiv 1 - 2\sin^2 A$$

2. Comparing the expression with the right-hand side of the identity: $A = \frac{3x}{2}$, so $2A = 3x$

3. Putting this into the identity gives: $1 - 2\sin^2\frac{3x}{2} \equiv \cos 3x$

Exercise 7.1

Q1 Use the double angle formulas to write down the exact values of:

a) $4\sin\frac{\pi}{12}\cos\frac{\pi}{12}$ b) $\cos\frac{2\pi}{3}$ c) $\frac{\sin 120°}{2}$ d) $\frac{\tan 15°}{2 - 2\tan^2 15°}$ e) $2\sin^2 15° - 1$

Q2 An acute angle x has $\sin x = \frac{1}{6}$. Find the exact values of:

a) $\cos 2x$ b) $\sin 2x$ c) $\tan 2x$ d) $\sec 2x$ e) $\operatorname{cosec} 2x$ f) $\cot 2x$

Q3 Angle x has $\sin x = -\frac{1}{4}$, and $\pi \le x \le \frac{3\pi}{2}$. Find the exact values of:

a) $\cos 2x$ b) $\sin 2x$ c) $\tan 2x$ d) $\sec 2x$ e) $\operatorname{cosec} 2x$ f) $\cot 2x$

Q4 Write the following expressions as a single trigonometric ratio:

a) $\frac{\sin 3\theta \cos 3\theta}{3}$ b) $\sin^2\left(\frac{2y}{3}\right) - \cos^2\left(\frac{2y}{3}\right)$ c) $\frac{1 - \tan^2\left(\frac{x}{2}\right)}{2\tan\left(\frac{x}{2}\right)}$

Solving equations and proving identities

Examples   a) **Solve the equation $\cos 2x - 5 \cos x = 2$ in the interval $0 \leq x \leq 2\pi$.**

1. First use the cos double angle formula to get rid of $\cos 2x$:
$$\cos 2A \equiv 2\cos^2 A - 1 \implies 2\cos^2 x - 1 - 5\cos x = 2$$

2. Simplify so you have zero on one side: $2\cos^2 x - 5\cos x - 3 = 0$

3. Then factorise and solve the quadratic: $(2\cos x + 1)(\cos x - 3) = 0$
$$\implies (2\cos x + 1) = 0 \text{ or } (\cos x - 3) = 0$$

4. The second bracket gives $\cos x = 3$, which has no solutions since $-1 \leq \cos x \leq 1$.

5. Solve the first bracket to find x: $2\cos x + 1 = 0 \implies \cos x = -\dfrac{1}{2}$

6. $\cos x = \dfrac{1}{2}$ for $x = \dfrac{\pi}{3}$ so using the symmetry of the graph $y = \cos x$ gives: $\boldsymbol{x = \dfrac{2\pi}{3}}$ **or** $\boldsymbol{x = \dfrac{4\pi}{3}}$

b) **Prove that $2 \cot \dfrac{x}{2}\left(1 - \cos^2 \dfrac{x}{2}\right) \equiv \sin x$.**

1. Use the identity $\sin^2 \theta \equiv 1 - \cos^2 \theta$ to replace the $1 - \cos^2 \dfrac{x}{2}$ on the left-hand side:

   Left-hand side: $2 \cot \dfrac{x}{2} \sin^2 \dfrac{x}{2}$

2. Now write $\cot \theta$ as $\dfrac{\cos \theta}{\sin \theta}$: $\dfrac{2 \cos \dfrac{x}{2} \sin^2 \dfrac{x}{2}}{\sin \dfrac{x}{2}} \equiv 2 \cos \dfrac{x}{2} \sin \dfrac{x}{2}$

3. Now use the sin double angle formula, using $A = \dfrac{x}{2}$: $2 \cos \dfrac{x}{2} \sin \dfrac{x}{2} \equiv \boldsymbol{\sin x}$ as required

The half angle formulas

The double angle formulas for cos can be **rearranged** to give another three useful identities known as the **half angle formulas**:

$$\cos^2\left(\frac{\theta}{2}\right) \equiv \frac{1}{2}(1 + \cos \theta) \qquad \sin^2\left(\frac{\theta}{2}\right) \equiv \frac{1}{2}(1 - \cos \theta) \qquad \tan^2\left(\frac{\theta}{2}\right) \equiv \frac{1 - \cos \theta}{1 + \cos \theta}$$

Example   **Show that $\cos^2\left(\dfrac{\theta}{2}\right) \equiv \dfrac{1}{2}(1 + \cos \theta)$.**

1. Start with the double angle formula for cos: $\cos 2A \equiv 2\cos^2 A - 1$

2. Replace A with $\dfrac{\theta}{2}$: $\cos \theta \equiv 2\cos^2\left(\dfrac{\theta}{2}\right) - 1$

3. Rearrange to get the half angle formula for cos: $\cos^2\left(\dfrac{\theta}{2}\right) \equiv \dfrac{1}{2}\boldsymbol{(1 + \cos \theta)}$ as required

Tip: Use a similar method for the sin half angle formula. To derive the tan half angle formula, use the half angle formulas for sin and cos and the identity $\tan \theta \equiv \dfrac{\sin \theta}{\cos \theta}$.

Exercise 7.2

Q1 Solve the equations below in the interval $0 \leq x \leq 360°$. Give your answers to 1 decimal place.

a) $4 \cos 2x = 14 \sin x$

b) $5 \cos 2x + 9 \cos x = -7$

c) $4 \cot 2x + \cot x = 5$

d) $\tan x - 5 \sin 2x = 0$

Q2 Solve the equations below in the interval $0 \leq x \leq 2\pi$. Give your answers to 3 s.f.

a) $4 \cos 2x - 10 \cos x + 1 = 0$

b) $\dfrac{\cos 2x - 3}{2 \sin^2 x - 1} = 3$

c) $2 \sin x \cos x = 4 \cos^2 x - 4 \sin^2 x$

Q3 Solve the equations below in the interval $0 \leq x \leq 2\pi$. Give your answers in terms of π.

a) $\cos 2x + 7 \cos x = -4$

b) $\sin x + \cos \dfrac{x}{2} = 0$

c) $\sin x - \cos 2x = 0$

Q4 Use the double angle formulas to prove each of the identities below.

a) $\sin 2x \sec^2 x \equiv 2 \tan x$

b) $\dfrac{2}{1 + \cos 2x} \equiv \sec^2 x$

c) $\cot x - 2 \cot 2x \equiv \tan x$

d) $\tan 2x + \cot 2x \equiv 2 \csc 4x$

Q5 a) Show that $\dfrac{1 + \cos 2x}{\sin 2x} \equiv \cot x$.

b) Use your answer to a) to solve $\dfrac{1 + \cos 4\theta}{\sin 4\theta} = 7$ in the interval $0 \leq \theta \leq 360°$. Give your answers to 1 d.p.

Q6 a) Show that $\csc x - \cot \dfrac{x}{2} \equiv -\cot x$.

b) Use your answer to a) to solve $\csc y = \cot \dfrac{y}{2} - 2$ in the interval $-\pi \leq y \leq \pi$. Give your answers to 3 s.f.

Q7 a) Given that $\sin \theta = \dfrac{5}{13}$, and that θ is acute, find: (i) $\cos \left(\dfrac{\theta}{2}\right)$ (ii) $\sin \left(\dfrac{\theta}{2}\right)$

b) Hence find $\tan \left(\dfrac{\theta}{2}\right)$.

8. The R Addition Formulas

The **R formulas** allow you to rewrite an equation that contains **both** $\sin \theta$ and $\cos \theta$ terms (e.g. $3 \sin \theta + 4 \cos \theta = 1$), in terms of only **one** trig function. There's one set for sin and one set for cos:

$$a \sin \theta \pm b \cos \theta \equiv R \sin (\theta \pm \alpha)$$

where a, b and R are **positive**, and α is **acute**.

$$a \cos \theta \pm b \sin \theta \equiv R \cos (\theta \mp \alpha)$$

Tip: Be careful with the + and − signs in the cosine formula. If you have $a \cos \theta + b \sin \theta$ then use $R \cos (\theta - \alpha)$.

- You'll start with an identity like $2 \sin x + 5 \cos x \equiv R \sin (x + \alpha)$, where R and α need to be found.

- First, **expand** the right-hand side using the **addition formulas** (see p.272):
$2 \sin x + 5 \cos x \equiv R \sin x \cos \alpha + R \cos x \sin \alpha$.

- **Equate the coefficients** of $\sin x$ and $\cos x$.
You'll get two equations: ①$R \cos \alpha = 2$ and ②$R \sin \alpha = 5$

- To find α, **divide** equation ② by equation ①,
(because $\dfrac{R \sin \alpha}{R \cos \alpha} = \tan \alpha$) then take **tan⁻¹** of the result.

- To find R, **square** equations ① and ②, **add** them together, then take the **square root** of the answer.

Examples   a) **Express 4 cos x + 5 sin x in the form R cos (x ± α).**

1. Choose the formula to use: $4 \cos x + 5 \sin x \equiv R \cos (x - \alpha)$

2. Now expand the right-hand side using the cos addition formula:
$$4 \cos x + 5 \sin x \equiv R \cos x \cos \alpha + R \sin x \sin \alpha$$

3. Equating the coefficients of cos x gives: ① $R \cos \alpha = 4$
and equating the coefficients of sin x gives: ② $R \sin \alpha = 5$

4. Dividing ② by ① gives: $\tan \alpha = \dfrac{5}{4} \Rightarrow \alpha = 51.3°$ (1 d.p.)

5. Squaring ① and ② gives: ①²: $R^2 \cos^2 \alpha = 16$
                                ②²: $R^2 \sin^2 \alpha = 25$

6. ①² + ②²: $R^2 \cos^2 \alpha + R^2 \sin^2 \alpha = 16 + 25 \Rightarrow R^2 (\cos^2 \alpha + \sin^2 \alpha) = 41$
                                                  $\Rightarrow R^2 = 41$ $\nwarrow$ $\sin^2 \alpha + \cos^2 \alpha \equiv 1$
                                                  $\Rightarrow R = \sqrt{41}$

7. Finally, put the values for α and R back into the identity to give:
$$4 \cos x + 5 \sin x \equiv \sqrt{41} \ \cos (x - 51.3°)$$

b) **Show that** $5 \sin x - 5\sqrt{3} \cos x \equiv 10 \sin \left(x - \dfrac{\pi}{3}\right)$.

1. This time, use the sin addition formula: $5 \sin x - 5\sqrt{3} \cos x \equiv R \sin (x - \alpha)$
                                                          $\equiv R \sin x \cos \alpha - R \cos x \sin \alpha$

2. Equate coefficients of sin x and cos x to get: ① $R \cos \alpha = 5$ and ② $R \sin \alpha = 5\sqrt{3}$

3. Then: ② ÷ ①: $\dfrac{R \sin \alpha}{R \cos \alpha} = \tan \alpha = \dfrac{5\sqrt{3}}{5} = \sqrt{3} \Rightarrow \alpha = \dfrac{\pi}{3}$
           ①² + ②²: $R^2 \cos^2 \alpha + R^2 \sin^2 \alpha = 5^2 + (5\sqrt{3})^2 \Rightarrow R^2(1) = 100 \Rightarrow R = 10$

4. So: $5 \sin x - 5\sqrt{3} \cos x \equiv \mathbf{10 \sin} \left(x - \dfrac{\pi}{3}\right)$ as required

Exercise 8.1

Q1   Express $3 \sin x - 2 \cos x$ in the form $R \sin (x - \alpha)$. Give R in surd form and α in degrees to 1 d.p.

Q2   Express $6 \cos x - 5 \sin x$ in the form $R \cos (x + \alpha)$. Give R in surd form and α in degrees to 1 d.p.

Q3   Express $\sin x + \sqrt{7} \cos x$ in the form $R \sin (x + \alpha)$. Give R in the form $m\sqrt{2}$ and α in radians to 3 s.f.

Q4   Show that $\sqrt{2} \sin x - \cos x \equiv \sqrt{3} \sin (x - \alpha)$, where $\tan \alpha = \dfrac{1}{\sqrt{2}}$.

Q5   Show that $3 \cos 2x + 5 \sin 2x \equiv \sqrt{34} \cos (2x - \alpha)$, where $\tan \alpha = \dfrac{5}{3}$.

Q6   a) Express $\sqrt{3} \sin x + \cos x$ in the form $R \sin (x + \alpha)$.
       Give R and α as exact answers and α in radians in terms of π.
    b) Hence sketch the graph of $y = \sqrt{3} \sin x + \cos x$ in the interval $-\pi \le x \le \pi$.
    c) State the coordinates of any maximum and minimum points
       and intersections with the axes of the graph in b).

Applying the R addition formulas

To **solve** an equation of the form $a \sin \theta + b \cos \theta = c$, first rewrite it using one of the R formulas, then solve the resulting equation.

Examples a) **Solve $2 \sin x - 3 \cos x = 1$ in the interval $0° \leq x \leq 360°$.**

1. First, rewrite the equation $2 \sin x - 3 \cos x$ in the form $R \sin (x - \alpha)$:
$$2 \sin x - 3 \cos x \equiv R \sin (x - \alpha)$$
$$2 \sin x - 3 \cos x \equiv R \sin x \cos \alpha - R \cos x \sin \alpha$$

2. Equating coefficients gives the equations: $R \cos \alpha = 2$ and $R \sin \alpha = 3$

3. Solving for α: $\dfrac{R \sin \alpha}{R \cos \alpha} = \tan \alpha = \dfrac{3}{2} \Rightarrow \alpha = \tan^{-1} 1.5 = 56.31°$ (2 d.p.)

4. Solving for R: $R^2 \cos^2 \alpha + R^2 \sin^2 \alpha = 2^2 + 3^2 \Rightarrow R^2 = 13 \Rightarrow R = \sqrt{13}$

5. So: $2 \sin x - 3 \cos x = \sqrt{13} \sin (x - 56.31°)$

6. Now solve the equation. If $2 \sin x - 3 \cos x = 1$, then: $\sqrt{13} \sin (x - 56.31°) = 1$
$$\Rightarrow \sin (x - 56.31°) = \dfrac{1}{\sqrt{13}}$$

7. Since, $0° \leq x \leq 360°$, you should be looking for solutions in the interval
$-56.31° \leq (x - 56.31°) \leq 303.69°$ (just take 56.31 away from the original interval — see p.77).

8. Solve the equation: $x - 56.31° = \sin^{-1}\left(\dfrac{1}{\sqrt{13}}\right) = 16.10°$, or $180 - 16.10 = 163.90°$ (2 d.p.)

9. There are no solutions in the range $-56.31° \leq (x - 56.31°) \leq 0°$
since $\sin x$ is negative in the range $-90° \leq x \leq 0°$.

10. So: $x = 16.10 + 56.31 = $ **72.4° (1 d.p.)** or $x = 163.90 + 56.31 = $ **220.2° (1 d.p.)**

b) **What are the maximum and minimum values of $2 \sin x - 3 \cos x$?**

- The maximum and minimum values of the sin (and cos) function are ± 1,
so the maximum and minimum values of $R \sin (x - \alpha)$ are $\pm R$.

- As $2 \sin x - 3 \cos x = \sqrt{13} \sin (x - 56.31°)$, $R = \sqrt{13}$,
so the maximum and minimum values are $\pm\sqrt{13}$.

Tip: You can use this to help you sketch the graph.

Exercise 8.2

Q1 a) Express $5 \cos \theta - 12 \sin \theta$ in the form $R \cos (\theta + \alpha)$, where $R > 0$ and α is an acute angle (in degrees, to 1 decimal place).

b) Hence solve $5 \cos \theta - 12 \sin \theta = 4$ in the interval $0 \leq \theta \leq 360°$.

c) State the maximum and minimum values of $5 \cos \theta - 12 \sin \theta$.

Q2 a) Express $2 \sin 2\theta + 3 \cos 2\theta$ in the form $R \sin (2\theta + \alpha)$, where $R > 0$ (given in surd form) and $0 < \alpha < \dfrac{\pi}{2}$ (to 3 significant figures).

b) Hence solve $2 \sin 2\theta + 3 \cos 2\theta = 1$ in the interval $0 \leq \theta \leq 2\pi$.

Q3 a) Express $3 \sin \theta - 2\sqrt{5} \cos \theta$ in the form $R \sin (\theta - \alpha)$.
   Give R in surd form and α in degrees to 1 decimal place.

   b) Hence solve $3 \sin \theta - 2\sqrt{5} \cos \theta = 5$ in the interval $0 \le \theta \le 360°$.

   c) Find the maximum value of $f(x) = 3 \sin x - 2\sqrt{5} \cos x$ and the smallest positive value of x at which it occurs.

Q4 $f(x) = 3 \sin x + \cos x$.

   a) Express $f(x)$ in the form $R \sin (x + \alpha)$ where $R > 0$ (given in surd form) and $0 < \alpha < 90°$ (to 1 d.p.).

   b) Hence solve the equation $f(x) = 2$ in the interval $0 \le x \le 360°$.

   c) State the maximum and minimum values of $f(x)$.

Q5 a) Express $4 \sin x + \cos x$ in the form $R \sin (x + \alpha)$, where $R > 0$
   (given in surd form) and $0 < \alpha < \frac{\pi}{2}$ (to 3 significant figures).

   b) Hence find the greatest value of $(4 \sin x + \cos x)^4$.

   c) Solve the equation $4 \sin x + \cos x = 1$ for values of x in the interval $0 \le x \le \pi$.

Q6 $f(x) = 8 \cos x + 15 \sin x$.

   a) Write $f(x)$ in the form $R \cos(x - \alpha)$, where $R > 0$ and $0 < \alpha < \frac{\pi}{2}$.

   b) Solve the equation $f(x) = 5$ in the interval $0 \le x \le 2\pi$.

   c) Find the minimum value of $g(x) = (8 \cos x + 15 \sin x)^2$
   and the smallest positive value of x at which it occurs.

Q7 The function g is given by $g(x) = 2 \cos x + \sin x$, $x \in \mathbb{R}$.
   $g(x)$ can be written as $R \cos (x - \alpha)$, where $R > 0$ and $0 < \alpha < 90°$.

   a) Show that $R = \sqrt{5}$, and find the value of α (to 3 s.f.).

   b) Hence state the range of $g(x)$.

Q8 Express $3 \sin \theta - \frac{3}{2} \cos \theta$ in the form $R \sin (\theta - \alpha)$, where $R > 0$ and $0 < \alpha < \frac{\pi}{2}$, and hence solve
   the equation $3 \sin \theta - \frac{3}{2} \cos \theta = 3$ for values of θ in the interval $0 \le \theta \le 2\pi$.

Q9 Solve the equation $4 \sin 2\theta + 3 \cos 2\theta = 2$ for values of θ in the interval $0 \le \theta \le \pi$.

9. Modelling with Trig Functions

Example The height of an object bouncing on a spring is modelled by the equation
$h = 5 + 2 \sin \left(5t + \frac{\pi}{3}\right)$, where t is the time in seconds and h is the height in cm.
Find the first time at which $h = 4$ cm.

1. Solve the equation $5 + 2 \sin \left(5t + \frac{\pi}{3}\right) = 4$:　　$2 \sin \left(5t + \frac{\pi}{3}\right) = -1 \Rightarrow \sin \left(5t + \frac{\pi}{3}\right) = -\frac{1}{2}$

   $\left(5t + \frac{\pi}{3}\right) = \sin^{-1} \left(-\frac{1}{2}\right) = -\frac{\pi}{6}, \frac{7\pi}{6}, \frac{11\pi}{6}, \dots$ etc.

2. Time can't be negative, which means that:　　$t \ge 0 \Rightarrow 5t + \frac{\pi}{3} \ge \frac{\pi}{3}$

3. The first solution that satisfies this inequality is $\frac{7\pi}{6}$:　　$5t + \frac{\pi}{3} = \frac{7\pi}{6} \Rightarrow 5t = \frac{5\pi}{6} \Rightarrow t = \frac{\pi}{6}$

4. So the first time it has a height of 4 cm is when:　　$t = \frac{\pi}{6} = $ **0.524 s (3 s.f.)**

Two sound waves are modelled by the functions f(θ) and g(θ),
where f(θ) = 12 sin θ and g(θ) = $4\sqrt{3}$ cos θ.
The two waves combine to produce a new wave given by h(θ) = f(θ) + g(θ).

a) **Write the equation for this new wave in the form $R \sin(\theta + \alpha)$, where α is measured in radians, giving your answers as exact values.**

1. Find the equation for h(θ): h(θ) = 12 sin θ + $4\sqrt{3}$ cos θ = $R \sin(\theta + \alpha)$

2. Expand $R \sin(\theta + \alpha)$ using the sin addition formula and equate coefficients:
$R \sin(\theta + \alpha) = R \sin \theta \cos \alpha + R \cos \theta \sin \alpha \Rightarrow R \cos \alpha = 12$ and $R \sin \alpha = 4\sqrt{3}$

3. Now solve for R and α: $R = \sqrt{12^2 + (4\sqrt{3})^2} = \sqrt{144 + 48} = \sqrt{192} = 8\sqrt{3}$

$\tan \alpha = \dfrac{4\sqrt{3}}{12} = \dfrac{\sqrt{3}}{3} = \dfrac{1}{\sqrt{3}} \Rightarrow \alpha = \dfrac{\pi}{6}$. So **h($\theta$) = $8\sqrt{3}$ sin $\left(\theta + \dfrac{\pi}{6}\right)$**

b) **The amplitude, a, of a sound wave is equivalent to half the distance between the maximum and minimum values of the wave. Find the amplitude of h(θ).**

1. sin θ has a maximum of 1 and a minimum of –1, so its amplitude is $\dfrac{1}{2}(1 - (-1)) = 1$.

2. The maximum and minimum values of h(θ) are $\pm R$ — i.e. $8\sqrt{3}$ and $-8\sqrt{3}$, so its amplitude is: $\dfrac{1}{2}(8\sqrt{3} - (-8\sqrt{3})) = \mathbf{8\sqrt{3}}$

Exercise 9.1

MODELLING

Q1 A circular plot of land with a radius of 20 m is separated into three gardens.
Each garden is a sector of the circle, with angles of 120°, 144° and 96° respectively.
Calculate the area and perimeter of each garden (to 3 s.f.).

Q2 Adam wants to form a function to model the hours of daylight in his town throughout the year.
He knows that the function should be of the form f(t) = $A + B$ cos t, where A and B are positive constants and the time, t, is in radians.
   a) The daylight hours vary from / to 17. Find the values of A and B.
   b) He now wants to adjust the model so that t is measured in months.
   He rewrites his function as g(t) = $A + B$ cos $(Ct + D)$. Find the values of C and D, such that the longest day of the year occurs at $t = 0$ and the shortest day of the year occurs at $t = 6$.

Q3 The height of a buoy floating in a harbour, measured in metres, is modelled by the function
h(t) = 14 + 5 (sin t + cos t), where t is time in hours. By writing h(t) in the form
14 + R cos $(t - \alpha)$, find the maximum and minimum height of the buoy (to 1 d.p.).

Q4 Antonia goes on a fairground ride. She is strapped into a small spinning disc, which is attached to a large rotating wheel.
   a) The height, in metres, of the centre of the disc above the ground
   after t seconds is given by: $H = 10 + \dfrac{7}{2}(\sin t - \sqrt{3} \cos t)$.
   Write this in the form $H = 10 + R \sin(t - \alpha)$, where $R > 0$ and $0 < \alpha \le \dfrac{\pi}{2}$.
   b) Antonia's height above the ground, h, is given by $h = H - \cos 2(t - \alpha)$.
   Use the double angle formulas to show that $h = A + R \sin(t - \alpha) + B \sin^2(t - \alpha)$, and give the values of A and B.
   c) Hence find the first time when Antonia is 13 m above the ground.

Q1 a) Convert these angles into radians, giving your answers in terms of π:

(i) $15°$ (ii) $50°$ (iii) $330°$ (iv) $225°$

b) Convert these angles into degrees:

(i) $\dfrac{7\pi}{12}$ (ii) $\dfrac{7\pi}{6}$ (iii) $\dfrac{5\pi}{3}$ (iv) $\dfrac{13\pi}{12}$

Q2 The diagram on the right shows a sector ABC of a circle, with centre A and a radius of 10 cm. The angle BAC is 0.7 radians. Find the arc length BC and area of this sector.

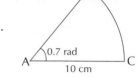

Q3 The sector ABC on the left is part of a circle, where the angle BAC is $50°$. Given that the area of the sector is 20π cm², find the arc length BC. Give your answer in terms of π.

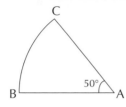

Q4 Use the small angle approximations to estimate:

a) (i) $\sin 0.42$ (ii) $\cos 0.17$ (iii) $\tan 0.22$

b) $\tan\theta - \cos\theta$ for: (i) $\theta = 0.13$ (ii) $\theta = 0.07$ (iii) $\theta = 0.26$

Q5 When θ is small, find an approximation for the expressions below:

a) $\sin 3\theta \tan 4\theta$ b) $\cos 4\theta + \cos 8\theta$ c) $\dfrac{2\theta^3}{\sin 2\theta \cos\theta}$

Q6 Using trig values for common angles, evaluate the following in radians, between 0 and $\dfrac{\pi}{2}$:

a) $\sin^{-1}\dfrac{1}{\sqrt{2}}$ b) $\cos^{-1}(0)$ c) $\tan^{-1}\sqrt{3}$

Q7 Sketch the graphs of arcsin, arccos and arctan showing their domains and ranges.

Q8 The diagram on the right shows the curve $y = \dfrac{1}{1+\cos x}$ for $0 \le x \le \dfrac{\pi}{2}$:

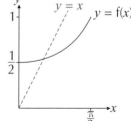

a) If $y = f(x)$, show that $f^{-1}(x) = \arccos\left(\dfrac{1}{x} - 1\right)$.

b) State the domain and range of this inverse function.

c) Sketch $y = f^{-1}(x)$ on the same axes as $y = f(x)$.

Q9 Given that $f(x) = \sin^{-1} x + \cos^{-1} x + \tan^{-1} x$, find the value, in radians, of:

a) $f(1)$ b) $f(-1)$

Q10 For $\theta = 30°$, find the exact values of:

a) $\operatorname{cosec}\theta$ b) $\sec\theta$ c) $\cot\theta$

Q11 Sketch the graphs of cosecant, secant and cotangent for $-2\pi \le x \le 2\pi$.

Q12 a) Describe the transformation that maps $y = \sec x$ onto $y = \sec 4x$.

b) What is the period, in radians, of the graph $y = \sec 4x$?

c) Sketch the graph of $y = \sec 4x$ for $0 \le x \le \pi$.

d) For what values of x in this interval is $\sec 4x$ undefined?

Q13 Use the trig identities to show that $\cot^2\theta + \sin^2\theta \equiv \cosec^2\theta - \cos^2\theta$.

Q14 Given that $x = \cosec\theta$ and $y = \cot^2\theta$, show that $y = x^2 - 1$.

Q15 If $x = \sec\theta$ and $y = 2\tan\theta$, express y in terms of x only.

Q16 a) Show that the equation $\cosec^2 x = \dfrac{3\cot x + 4}{2}$ can be written as: $2\cot^2 x - 3\cot x - 2 = 0$.

b) Hence solve the equation $\cosec^2 x = \dfrac{3\cot x + 4}{2}$.
Give all the values of x in the interval $0 \le x \le 2\pi$ in radians to 2 decimal places.

Q17 Given that θ is acute and $\cos\theta = \dfrac{1}{2}$:
a) Give the exact value of $\sec\theta$.
b) Use Pythagoras' Theorem to find the value of $\tan\theta$.
c) Use the identity $\sec^2\theta \equiv 1 + \tan^2\theta$ to find the value of $\tan\theta$ and confirm that it is the same as in part b).
d) Give the exact value of $\cot\theta$.
e) Using the identity $\cosec^2\theta \equiv 1 + \cot^2\theta$, give the exact value of $\sin\theta$.

Q18 Express the following as a single trig function:
a) $\sin 2x \cos 9x + \cos 2x \sin 9x$ 　　　　b) $3\cos 5x \cos 7x - 3\sin 5x \sin 7x$

c) $\dfrac{\tan 12x - \tan 8x}{1 + \tan 12x \tan 8x}$ 　　　　d) $12\sin\dfrac{7x}{2}\cos\dfrac{3x}{2} - 12\cos\dfrac{7x}{2}\sin\dfrac{3x}{2}$

Q19 Using the addition formula for cos, find the exact value of $\cos\dfrac{\pi}{12}$.

Q20 Find $\sin(A + B)$, given that $\sin A = \dfrac{4}{5}$ and $\sin B = \dfrac{7}{25}$ and that both A and B are acute angles.
You might find these triangles useful:

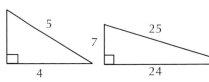

Q21 Use the double angle formula to solve the equation:
$\sin 2\theta = -\sqrt{3}\sin\theta$, $0° \le \theta \le 360°$.

Q22 Solve the equations below in the interval $0 \le x \le 2\pi$.
Give your answers in radians to 3 significant figures.
a) $4\sin x = \sin\dfrac{x}{2}$ 　　　　b) $\tan\dfrac{x}{2}\tan x = 2$

Q23 Solve the equations below in the interval $0 \le x \le 2\pi$.
Give your answers in radians in terms of π.
a) $2\tan 2x = \tan x$ 　　　　b) $\sin 6x - \cos 3x = 0$

Q24 Show that $\dfrac{\cos\theta}{\sin\theta} + \dfrac{\sin\theta}{\cos\theta} \equiv 2\cosec 2\theta$.

Q25 Write $5\sin\theta - 6\cos\theta$ in the form $R\sin(\theta - \alpha)$, where $R > 0$ and $0 \le \alpha \le 90°$.

Q26 a) Write $3\cos\theta - 8\sin\theta$ in the form $R\cos(\theta + \alpha)$, where $R > 0$ and $0 \le \alpha \le 90°$.

b) Hence solve $3\cos\theta - 8\sin\theta = 1.2$ in the interval $0° \le \theta \le 360°$.

Q27 The height, h m, of a rider on a pirate ship at a theme park is modelled by the function:
$h = 5\sin t + 3\cos t + 2$, where t is the time in seconds. Find the maximum height above the ground that the rider reaches. Give your answer to 2 decimal places.

Chapter 19 — Parametric Equations

Parametric equations are ones where you have x and y in separate equations, both defined in terms of another variable. It sounds complicated, but it can often make things a lot easier, as you'll see in this chapter.

1. Parametric Equations of Curves

Finding coordinates from parametric equations

- Normally, graphs in the (x, y) plane are described using a **Cartesian equation** — a single equation linking x and y. Sometimes, it's easier to have two linked equations, called **parametric equations**.

- In parametric equations, x and y are each defined separately in terms of a **third variable**, called a **parameter**. The parameter is usually either t or θ.

 A flying disc is thrown from the point (0, 0). After t seconds, it has travelled x m horizontally and y m vertically, modelled by the parametric equations $x = t^2 + 2t$ and $y = 6t - t^2$ ($0 \leq t \leq 6$).

a) **Find the x- and y- values of the position of the disc after 2.5 seconds.**

Substitute $t = 2.5$ into the equations for x and y:

$x = 2.5^2 + 2 \times 2.5 = 6.25 + 5 = \mathbf{11.25}$

$y = 6 \times 2.5 - 2.5^2 = 15 - 6.25 = \mathbf{8.75}$

b) **After how many seconds does the disc reach a height of 5 metres?**

You want the value of t when $y = 5$:　$5 = 6t - t^2$　$\Rightarrow t^2 - 6t + 5 = 0$

$\Rightarrow (t - 1)(t - 5) = 0$

$\Rightarrow \mathbf{t = 1\ s}$ **and** $\mathbf{t = 5\ s}$

c) **What is the value of y when the disc reaches the point $x = 24$ m?**

- Use the equation for x to find t first:　$24 = t^2 + 2t \Rightarrow t^2 + 2t - 24 = 0$

$\Rightarrow (t + 6)(t - 4) = 0$

$\Rightarrow t = -6$ or $t = 4$

- ...but t is restricted to $0 \leq t \leq 6$, so:　　　　　　　$t = 4\ s$
- Then use it in the other equation to find y:　$y = 6 \times 4 - 4^2 = 24 - 16 = \mathbf{8}$

 Sketch the graph given by $x = \cos \theta$ and $y = \sin \theta + 1$.

- Make a table with values for θ over a suitable interval (such as $0 \leq \theta \leq 2\pi$):

- Plot the points — they lie on a circle with centre $(0, 1)$ and radius 1:

θ	0	$\dfrac{\pi}{2}$	π	$\dfrac{3\pi}{2}$	2π
x	1	0	–1	0	1
y	1	2	1	0	1

Tip: $x = a + r \cos \theta$, $y = b + r \sin \theta$ are the general parametric equations for a circle with centre (a, b). If r takes different values in the x and y equations, the curve is an ellipse.

Exercise 1.1

Q1 A curve is defined by the parametric equations $x = 3t$, $y = t^2$.

a) Find the coordinates of the point where $t = 5$.

b) Find the value of t at the point where $x = 18$.

c) Find the possible values of x at the point where $y = 36$.

Q2 A curve is defined by the parametric equations $x = 2t - 1$, $y = 4 - t^2$.

a) Find the coordinates of the point where $t = 7$.

b) Find the value of t at the point where $x = 15$.

c) Find the possible values of x at the point where $y = -5$.

Q3 A curve has parametric equations $x = 2 + \sin\theta$, $y = -3 + \cos\theta$.

a) Find the coordinates of the point where $\theta = \frac{\pi}{4}$.

b) Find the acute value of θ at the point where $x = \dfrac{4 + \sqrt{3}}{2}$.

c) Find the obtuse value of θ at the point where $y = -\dfrac{7}{2}$.

Q4 For the curve defined by the parametric equations $x = t^2 + 5t$, $y = 6 + 3t^2$:

a) Find the possible values of t when $y = 33$.

b) Find the possible values of y when $x = 6$.

Q5 Complete the table on the right, and hence sketch the curve represented by $x = 5t$, $y = \frac{2}{t}$, for $t \neq 0$.

t	−5	−4	−3	−2	−1	1	2	3	4	5
x										
y										

Q6 Sketch the curve represented by the parametric equations $x = 1 + \sin\theta$, $y = 2 + \cos\theta$ for $0 \leq \theta \leq 2\pi$. Use the table on the right to help you.

θ	0	$\frac{\pi}{4}$	$\frac{\pi}{3}$	$\frac{\pi}{2}$	$\frac{2\pi}{3}$	$\frac{3\pi}{4}$	π	$\frac{4\pi}{3}$	$\frac{3\pi}{2}$	$\frac{5\pi}{3}$	2π
x											
y											

Q7 The curve C is defined by the parametric equations $y = 10 - t^2$, $x = 2t^2 - 7t$.

a) Find the value of a if $(a, 1)$ is a point on the curve and $a > 1$.

b) Show that the point $(-6, 4)$ does not lie on curve C.

Q8 The orbit of a comet around the Sun is modelled by the parametric equations $x = 3\sin\theta$, $y = 7 + 9\cos\theta$, for $0 \leq \theta \leq 2\pi$, where the point $(0, 0)$ represents the Sun, and where 1 unit on the x- and y-axes represents 1 astronomical unit (AU, 1 AU ≈ 150 million km).

How far, in AU, is the comet from the Sun when: a) $\theta = 0$, b) $\theta = \frac{\pi}{2}$?

Q9 The path of a toy plane thrown from a tower is modelled by the parametric equations $x = t^2 + 4t$, $y = 25 - t^2$ for $0 \leq t \leq 5$, where t is the time taken in seconds, and x and y are the horizontal and vertical distances in metres to the plane from the point at ground level at the foot of the tower.

a) How far does the plane travel in the horizontal direction in the first 2 seconds?

b) Sonia is standing 21 m from the base of the tower, in line with the path of the plane. At what height above the ground does the toy plane pass over Sonia's head?

Finding intersections

To find the coordinates of the **points of intersection** of a parametric curve with a straight line or with another curve:

- Use the information in the question to solve for **t** at the intersection point(s).
- Then **substitute the value(s) of t** into the parametric equations to work out the **x and y values** (i.e. the **coordinates**) at the intersection point(s).

 The curve shown has the parametric equations $y = t^3 - t$ **and** $x = 4t^2 - 1$. **Find the coordinates of the points where the graph crosses:**
  a) **the x-axis,**   b) **the line** $8y = 3x + 3$.

a)
- On the x-axis, $y = 0$. Use the parametric equation for y to find the values of t where the graph crosses the x-axis. Factorise and solve the cubic:

  $$0 = t^3 - t \implies t(t^2 - 1) = 0 \implies t(t + 1)(t - 1) = 0 \implies t = 0, t = -1, t = 1$$

- Now use those values of t to find the x-coordinates:

When $t = 0$:	When $t = -1$:	When $t = 1$:
$x = 4(0)^2 - 1 = -1$	$x = 4(-1)^2 - 1 = 3$	$x = 4(1)^2 - 1 = 3$

  Note that $t = -1$ and $t = 1$ give the same coordinates — that's where the curve crosses over itself.

- So the graph crosses the x-axis at the points: **(–1, 0) and (3, 0)**

b)
- First, substitute the parametric equations into $8y = 3x + 3$:

  $$8y = 3x + 3 \implies 8(t^3 - t) = 3(4t^2 - 1) + 3$$

- Rearrange and factorise to find the values of t you need:

  $$8t^3 - 8t = 12t^2 \implies 8t^3 - 12t^2 - 8t = 0 \implies t(2t + 1)(t - 2) = 0 \implies t = 0, t = -\frac{1}{2}, t = 2$$

- Go back to the parametric equations to find the x- and y-coordinates:

  When $t = 0$: $x = -1, y = 0$

  When $t = -\frac{1}{2}$: $x = 4\left(\frac{1}{4}\right) - 1 = 0, y = \left(-\frac{1}{2}\right)^3 + \frac{1}{2} = \frac{3}{8}$

  When $t = 2$: $x = 4(4) - 1 = 15, y = 2^3 - 2 = 6$

- So the graph crosses the line $8y = 3x + 3$ at the points: **(–1, 0),** $\left(0, \frac{3}{8}\right)$**, (15, 6)**

Exercise 1.2

Q1 The curve with parametric equations $x = 3 + t$, $y = -2 + t$ meets the x-axis at the point A and the y-axis at the point B. Find the coordinates of A and B.

Q2 The curve C has parametric equations $x = 2t^2 - 50$, $y = 3t^3 - 24$.
  a) Find the value of t where the curve meets the x-axis.
  b) Find the values of t where the curve meets the y-axis.

Q3 The curve with parametric equations $x = 64 - t^3$, $y = \frac{1}{t}$, for $t \neq 0$, meets the y-axis at the point P. Find the coordinates of the point P.

Q4 Find the coordinates of the point of intersection, P, of the line $y = x - 3$ and the curve with parametric equations $x = 2t + 1$, $y = 4t$.

Q5 Find the coordinates of the point(s) of intersection of the curve $y = x^2 + 32$ and the curve with parametric equations $x = 2t$, $y = 6t^2$.

Q6 Find the points of intersection of the circle $x^2 + y^2 = 32$ and the curve with parametric equations $x = t^2$, $y = 2t$.

Q7 The curve with parametric equations $x = a(t - 2)$, $y = 2at^2 + 3$ (where $a \neq 0$), meets the y-axis at the point $(0, 4)$.
a) Find the value of the constant a.
b) Hence determine whether the curve meets the x-axis.

Q8 A curve has parametric equations $x = \dfrac{2}{t}$, $y = t^2 - 9$, for $t \neq 0$.
a) Find the point(s) at which the curve crosses the x-axis.
b) Does the curve meet the y-axis? Explain your answer.
c) Find the coordinates of the point(s) at which this curve meets the curve $y = \dfrac{10}{x} - 3$.

Q9 A curve has parametric equations $x = 3 \sin t$, $y = 5 \cos t$ and is defined for the domain $0 \leq t \leq 2\pi$.
a) Determine the coordinates at which this curve meets the x- and y-axes.
b) Find the points where the curve meets the line $y = \left(\dfrac{5\sqrt{3}}{9} \right)x$.

Q10 A simulation models the paths of two ships using parametric equations. The ships are modelled as points, with no width or length. The path taken by the first ship is given by $x_1 = 24 - t$, $y_1 = 10 + 3t$. The path taken by the second ship is given by $x_2 = t + 10$, $y_2 = 12 + 2t - 0.1t^2$. For both sets of equations, $0 \leq t \leq 30$, where t is the time in hours since the start of the simulation, and x and y are measured in miles East and North respectively. According to the simulation, will the two ships collide?

2. Parametric and Cartesian Equations

Some parametric equations can be **converted** into **Cartesian equations**. There are two main ways to do this:

> - **Rearrange** one of the equations to make the **parameter** the subject, then **substitute** the result into the **other** equation.

> - If your equations involve **trig functions**, use **trig identities** to **eliminate** the parameter.

Tip: See Chapters 6 and 18 if you need to refresh your memory on the trig identities you've seen so far in this book.

Example
Give the Cartesian equation, in the form $y = f(x)$, of the curve represented by the parametric equations $y = t^3 - 1$ and $x = t + 1$.

1. Rearrange the equation for x to make t the subject: $\quad x = t + 1 \implies t = x - 1$

2. Eliminate t from the equation for y: $\quad y = t^3 - 1 \implies y = (x - 1)^3 - 1 = (x - 1)(x^2 - 2x + 1) - 1$
$$\implies y = x^3 - 2x^2 + x - x^2 + 2x - 1 - 1$$
$$\implies y = x^3 - 3x^2 + 3x - 2$$

So the Cartesian equation is $y = x^3 - 3x^2 + 3x - 2$.

A curve has parametric equations $x = 1 + \sin \theta$, $y = 1 - \cos 2\theta$.
Give the Cartesian equation of the curve in the form $y = f(x)$.

1. Find a way to get both x and y in terms of the same trig function.
   Use the identity $\cos 2\theta \equiv 1 - 2 \sin^2 \theta$ in the equation for y:
   $$y = 1 - \cos 2\theta = 1 - (1 - 2 \sin^2 \theta) = 2 \sin^2 \theta$$

2. Rearranging the equation for x gives: $\sin \theta = x - 1$

3. Replace '$\sin \theta$' in the equation for y
   with '$x - 1$' to get y in terms of x: $y = 2 \sin^2 \theta \implies y = 2(x - 1)^2 = 2x^2 - 4x + 2$

   So the Cartesian equation is **$y = 2x^2 - 4x + 2$**.

Exercise 2.1

Q1 For each of the following parametrically-defined curves,
find the Cartesian equation of the curve in an appropriate form.

a) $x = t + 3$, $y = t^2$

b) $x = 3t$, $y = \dfrac{6}{t}$, $t \neq 0$

c) $x = 2t^3$, $y = t^2$

d) $x = t + 7$, $y = 12 - 2t$

e) $x = t + 4$, $y = t^2 - 9$

f) $x = \dfrac{t + 2}{3}$, $y = t^2 - t$

g) $x = t^2 - \dfrac{t}{2}$, $y = 5 - 8t$

h) $x = \sin \theta$, $y = \cos \theta$

i) $x = 1 + \sin \theta$, $y = 2 + \cos \theta$

j) $x = \sin \theta$, $y = \cos 2\theta$

k) $x = \cos \theta$, $y = \cos 2\theta$

l) $x = \cos \theta - 5$, $y = \cos 2\theta$

Q2 By eliminating the parameter θ, express the curve defined by the parametric equations $x = \tan \theta$, $y = \sec \theta$ in the form $y^2 = f(x)$.

Q3 Write the curve $x = 2 \cot \theta$, $y = 3 \operatorname{cosec} \theta$ in the form $y^2 = f(x)$.

Q4 A circle is defined by the parametric equations $x = 5 + \sin \theta$, $y = -3 + \cos \theta$.
a) Find the coordinates of the centre of the circle, and the radius of the circle.
b) Write the equation of the curve in Cartesian form.

Q5 A curve has parametric equations $x = \dfrac{1 + 2t}{t}$, $y = \dfrac{3 + t}{t^2}$, $t \neq 0$.
a) Express t in terms of x.
b) Hence show that the Cartesian equation of the curve is: $y = (3x - 5)(x - 2)$.
c) Sketch the curve.

Q6 Express $x = \dfrac{2 - 3t}{1 + t}$, $y = \dfrac{5 - t}{4t + 1}$ ($t \neq -1$, $t \neq -0.25$), in Cartesian form.

Q7 Find the Cartesian equation of the curve defined by the parametric equations $x = 5 \sin^2 \theta$, $y = \cos \theta$.
Express your answer in the form $y^2 = f(x)$.

Q8 a) Express $x = a \sin \theta$, $y = b \cos \theta$ in Cartesian form.
b) Use your answer to a) to sketch the curve.
c) What type of curve has the form $x = a \sin \theta$, $y = b \cos \theta$?

Q9 A curve has parametric equations $x = 3t^2$, $y = 2t - 1$.
a) Show that the Cartesian equation of the curve is $x = \dfrac{3}{4}(y + 1)^2$.
b) Hence find the point(s) of intersection of this curve with the line $y = 4x - 3$.

Q10 Find the Cartesian equation of the curve $x = 7t + 2$, $y = \dfrac{5}{t}$, $t \neq 0$, in the form $y = f(x)$ and hence sketch the curve, labelling any asymptotes and points of intersection with the axes clearly.

Q1 A curve is defined by the parametric equations $x = \frac{1}{t}$, $y = \frac{2}{t^2}$ ($t \neq 0$).

a) Find the value of t when $x = \frac{1}{4}$ and hence find the corresponding y-coordinate.

b) Find the possible values of t when $y = \frac{1}{50}$.

Q2 A curve is defined by the parametric equations $x = t^3 + t^2 - 6t$, $y = 4t - 5$.
Find the coordinates of the points where this curve crosses the y-axis.

Q3 A curve is defined by the parametric equations $y = 2t^2 + t + 4$ and $x = \frac{6-t}{2}$.

a) Find the values of x and y when $t = 0$, 1, 2 and 3.

b) What are the values of t when: (i) $x = -7$ (ii) $y = 19$?

c) Find the Cartesian equation of the curve, in the form $y = f(x)$.

Q4 Find the coordinates of the points where the line $y = 10x - 8$ crosses
the curve defined by the parametric equations $x = \frac{t+3}{5}$ and $y = t^2 - t$.

Q5 The parametric equations of a curve are $x = 2\sin\theta$ and $y = \cos^2\theta + 4$, $-\frac{\pi}{2} \leq \theta \leq \frac{\pi}{2}$.

a) What are the coordinates of the points where: (i) $\theta = \frac{\pi}{4}$ (ii) $\theta = \frac{\pi}{6}$?

b) What is the Cartesian equation of the curve?

c) What restrictions are there on the values of x for this curve?

Q6 The curve C is defined by the parametric equations $x = \frac{\sin\theta}{3}$ and $y = 3 + 2\cos 2\theta$.
Find the Cartesian equation of C.

Q7 A curve has parametric equations $y = 4 + \frac{3}{t}$ and $x = t^2 - 1$ ($t \neq 0$).
What are the coordinates of the points where this curve crosses:

a) the y-axis,   b) the line $x + 2y = 14$?

Q8 The parametric equations describing curve K are $x = 4 - \cos 2\theta$, $y = \sin^4\theta - \frac{1}{2}$, $0 \leq \theta \leq \pi$.

a) Find the coordinates of the point on curve K where $\theta = \frac{\pi}{3}$.

b) Explain why curve K does not cross the y-axis.

c) Find the Cartesian equation of curve K, in the form $y = f(x)$.

Q9 The movement of a particle is modelled by the parametric
equations $x = -e^t \sin 2t$, $y = e^t \cos 2t$, for $0 \leq t \leq 2\pi$.

a) Find the exact value of x at each point where $y = 0$.

b) If d is the distance of the particle from the origin $(0, 0)$:

(i)   Find an equation for d in terms of t.

(ii)   Find the exact coordinates of the point where $d = e^{\frac{\pi}{8}}$.

Chapter 20 — Sequences and Series

A sequence is a list of numbers that follow a certain pattern. If you add all the terms in a sequence together, you get a series. There are two main types of sequences/series in this course — arithmetic and geometric.

1. Sequences

u_n just means the nth **term** of the sequence — e.g. u_4 is the 4th term, and u_{n+1} is the term after u_n.
A formula for the nth term of a sequence allows you to generate any term from its **position**, n.

Example

A sequence has the nth term $an^2 + b$, where a and b are constants.

a) If the 3rd term is 7 and the 5th term is 23, find the nth term formula.

1. Form equations using the information given in the question:
   For the 3rd term $n = 3$: $a(3^2) + b = 9a + b = 7$,
   for the 5th term $n = 5$: $a(5^2) + b = 25a + b = 23$

2. Solve the equations simultaneously to find the values of a and b:

$$25a + b = 23$$
$$- (9a + b = 7)$$
$$\overline{16a \quad\;\; = 16}$$
$$a = 1 \qquad a = 1 \Rightarrow 9(1) + b = 7 \Rightarrow b = -2$$

3. So the nth term formula is: $\mathbf{n^2 - 2}$

b) Is 35 a term in the sequence?

Form and solve an equation in n and see if you get a positive whole number:

$$n^2 - 2 = 35 \Rightarrow n^2 = 37 \Rightarrow n = \sqrt{37}$$

$\sqrt{37}$ is not an integer, so 35 is **not** in the sequence.

Increasing, decreasing and periodic sequences

There are a few types of sequence that you need to know:

- In an **increasing sequence**, each term is larger than the previous term,
  so $u_{k+1} > u_k$ for all terms — e.g. the square numbers 1, 4, 9, 16, 25, ...

- In a **decreasing sequence**, each term is smaller than the previous term,
  so $u_{k+1} < u_k$ for all terms — e.g. the sequence 16, 13, 10, 7, 4, ...

- In a **periodic sequence**, the terms **repeat** in a cycle. The number of repeated terms is known as the **order**. For example, the sequence 1, 0, 1, 0, 1, 0... is periodic with order 2.

Tip: A **finite** sequence is one that has a 'last term' (see p.293), while an **infinite** sequence keeps on going forever.

Example

A sequence has the nth term $7n - 16$. **Show that the sequence is increasing.**

1. Use the nth term formula to find u_k and u_{k+1}:

   $u_k = 7k - 16$
   $u_{k+1} = 7(k + 1) - 16 = 7k - 9$

2. Show that $u_{k+1} > u_k$ for all k:

   $7k - 9 > 7k - 16 \Rightarrow -9 > -16$
   This is true so it is an **increasing** sequence.

Exercise 1.1

Q1 A sequence has n^{th} term $u_n = 3n - 5$.   a) Find the value of: (i) u_{20} (ii) u_9 (iii) u_{50}
      b) Is this sequence increasing or decreasing?

Q2 Find the 4th term of the sequence with n^{th} term $n(n + 2)$.

Q3 Find the first 5 terms of the sequence with n^{th} term $(n - 1)(n + 1)$.

Q4 The kth term of a sequence is 29. The nth term of this sequence is $4n - 3$. Find the value of k.

Q5 A sequence has the nth term $13 - 6n$. Show that the sequence is decreasing.

Q6 A sequence has n^{th} term $= an^2 + b$, where a and b are constants.
      If the 2nd term is 15, and the 5th term is 99, find a and b.

Q7 A sequence starts 9, 20, 37, ... Its nth term is given by $en^2 + fn + g$, (PROBLEM SOLVING)
      where e, f and g are constants. Find the values of e, f and g.

Q8 The nth term of the sequence is given by $(n - 1)^2$. A term in the sequence is 49.
      Find the position of this term.

Q9 a) How many terms of the sequence with n^{th} term $15 - 2n$ are positive?
      b) Is this sequence increasing or decreasing?

Recurrence relations

A **recurrence relation** is another way to describe a sequence.
Recurrence relations tell you how to work out a term in a sequence from the previous term.
So a recurrence relation describes how to work out u_{k+1} from u_k.

- For example, if each term in the sequence is **2 more** than the previous term: $u_{k+1} = u_k + 2$.
  This recurrence relation will be true for lots of sequences, such as 1, 3, 5, 7..., and 4, 6, 8, 10...

- So to describe a **particular sequence** you also have to give one term.
  The sequence 1, 3, 5, 7... is described by: $u_{k+1} = u_k + 2$, $u_1 = 1$.

[Examples]   a) **Find the recurrence relation of the sequence 5, 8, 11, 14, 17, ...**

1. Each term in this sequence equals the one before it, plus 3,
   so the recurrence relation is written like this: $u_{k+1} = u_k + 3$

2. The description needs to be more specific, so give one term
   in the sequence, as well as the recurrence relation: $u_{k+1} = u_k + 3$, $u_1 = 5$

b) **A sequence is generated by the recurrence relation: $u_{n+1} = 3u_n + c$, $u_1 = 2$.**
   Given that $u_4 = 28$, find c.

1. First, find an expression for u_4 in terms of c. You're given the first term, u_1, so use this to
   generate the second term, u_2, then repeat this step to generate the third and fourth terms:
   $$u_{n+1} = 3u_n + c \Rightarrow u_2 = 3u_1 + c = 3(2) + c = 6 + c$$
   $$\Rightarrow u_3 = 3u_2 + c = 3(6 + c) + c = 18 + 4c$$
   $$\Rightarrow u_4 = 3u_3 + c = 3(18 + 4c) + c = 54 + 13c$$

2. Using the information from the question, form an equation and solve to find c:
   $$28 = 54 + 13c \Rightarrow 13c = -26 \Rightarrow c = -2$$

Exercise 1.2

Q1   A sequence is defined for $n \geq 1$ by $u_{n+1} = 3u_n$ and $u_1 = 10$. Find the first 5 terms of the sequence.

Q2   Find the first 4 terms of the sequence in which $u_1 = 2$ and $u_{n+1} = u_n^2$ for $n \geq 1$.

Q3   Write down a recurrence relation which produces the sequence 3, 6, 12, 24, 48, ...

Q4   a) Write down a recurrence relation which produces the sequence 12, 16, 20, 24, 28, ...
      b) The sequence is finite and ends at 100. Find the number of terms.

Q5   Find a recurrence relation which generates the sequence 7, 4, 7, 4, 7, ...

Q6   In a sequence $u_1 = 4$ and $u_{n+1} = 3u_n - 1$ for $n \geq 1$. Find the value of k if $u_k = 95$.

Q7   In a sequence $x_1 = 9$ and $x_{n+1} = (x_n + 1) \div 2$ for $n \geq 1$. Find the value of r if $x_r = \dfrac{5}{4}$.

Q8   Find the first 5 terms of the sequence in which $u_1 = 7$ and $u_{n+1} = u_n + n$ for $n \geq 1$.

Q9   In a sequence $u_1 = 6$, $u_2 = 7$ and $u_3 = 8.5$. If the recurrence relation is of the form $u_{n+1} = au_n + b$, find the values of the constants a and b.

Q10   A sequence is generated by $u_1 = 8$ and $u_{n+1} = \dfrac{1}{2}u_n$ for $n \geq 1$.
      Find the first 5 terms and a formula for u_n in terms of n.

2. Arithmetic Sequences

When the terms of a sequence progress by **adding a fixed amount** each time (e.g. 5, 7, 9, 11... where you add 2 each time), this is called an **arithmetic sequence** or **arithmetic progression**. The formula for the nth term of an arithmetic sequence is:

$$u_n = a + (n - 1)d$$

where a is the **first term**, d is the amount you add each time (the **common difference**) and n is the **position** of any term.

Examples   a) **For the arithmetic sequence 2, 5, 8, 11, ... find u_{20} and the formula for u_n.**

- For this sequence, $a = 2$ and $d = 3$, so plug the numbers into the nth term formula:
  $$u_n = a + (n - 1)d \implies u_{20} = 2 + (20 - 1) \times 3 = 2 + 19 \times 3 = \mathbf{59}$$

- u_n is the general term, i.e. $a + (n - 1)d$. So substitute in the a and d values and simplify:
  $$u_n = 2 + (n - 1)3 = \mathbf{3n - 1}$$

Tip: You can check your n^{th} term formula by sticking in some values for n and seeing if it produces the terms of the sequence. So here, $n = 1$ gives $3(1) - 1 = 2$ and $n = 2$ gives $3(2) - 1 = 5$ as expected.

b) **The 2nd term of an arithmetic sequence is 21, and the 9th term is –7. Find the 23rd term.**

1. Set up equations for the known terms: 2nd term = 21, so $a + (2 - 1)d = 21 \implies a + d = 21$
                                             9th term = –7, so $a + (9 - 1)d = -7 \implies a + 8d = -7$

2. Solve these simultaneous equations to find a and d: $d = -4$ and $a = 25$

3. Find the nth term formula and use it to find the 23rd term: n^{th} term $= a + (n - 1)d$
   $$= 25 + (n - 1) \times -4 = 29 - 4n$$
   $$23^{rd} \text{ term} = 29 - 4 \times 23 = \mathbf{-63}$$

Exercise 2.1

Q1 An arithmetic progression has first term 7 and common difference 5. Find its 10th term.

Q2 Find the nth term for each of the following sequences:
   a) 6, 9, 12, 15, ...
   b) 4, 9, 14, 19, ...
   c) 12, 8, 4, 0, ...
   d) 1.5, 3.5, 5.5, 7.5, ...
   e) 77, 69, 61, 53, ...
   f) −2, −2.5, −3, −3.5, ...

Q3 In an arithmetic sequence, the fourth term is 19 and the tenth term is 43.
Find the first term and common difference.

Q4 In an arithmetic progression, $u_1 = -5$ and $u_5 = 19$. Find u_{10}.

Q5 In an arithmetic sequence, $u_7 = 8$ and $u_{11} = 10$. Find u_3.

Q6 In an arithmetic sequence, $u_3 = 15$ and $u_7 = 27$. Find the value of k if $u_k = 66$.

Q7 In an arithmetic sequence the first three terms are $\ln(x)$, $\ln(x + 8)$, $\ln(x + 48)$.
Find the value of x and the next term in the sequence.

3. Arithmetic Series

Sequences become **series** when you **add up** their terms to find **sums**. There are two **formulas** you can use to find the sum of the first n terms (written S_n) of an **arithmetic series**:

$$S_n = \frac{1}{2} n[2a + (n-1)d]$$ or $$S_n = \frac{1}{2} n(a + l)$$

a, d and n are the same as on the previous page.
l is the last term.

Example

a) Is 67 a term in the sequence –5, –2, 1, 4, 7…? If it is, give its position.

1. First, find the formula for the nth term of the sequence: n^{th} term $= a + (n - 1)d$
         $a = -5$ and $d = 3$, so n^{th} term $= -5 + (n - 1)3 = 3n - 8$

2. Put 67 into the formula and see if this gives a whole number for n: $67 = 3n - 8$
                                $3n = 75 \implies n = 25$

3. So: 67 **is** a term in the sequence. It's the **25th** term.

b) Find the sum of the first 20 terms.

$a = -5$, $d = 3$ and $n = 20$, so plug these values into the formula $S_n = \frac{n}{2}[2a + (n-1)d]$:

$$S_{20} = \frac{20}{2}[2(-5) + (20 - 1)3] = 10[-10 + 19 \times 3] = \textbf{470}$$

Sigma notation

In the formulas above, the letter S was used for the sum.
The Greek capital letter **sigma** (written Σ) can also be used for the sum of a series.
For example, the following means the sum of the series with n^{th} term $2n + 3$.

Starting with $n = 1$...
$$\sum_{n=1}^{15} (2n + 3)$$
...and ending with $n = 15$.

Example Find $\sum_{n=1}^{15}(2n+3)$.

- The first term ($n = 1$) is 5, the second term ($n = 2$) is 7, the third is 9, ... and the last term ($n = 15$) is 33. So you need to find $5 + 7 + 9 + ... + 33$. This gives $a = 5$, $d = 2$, $n = 15$ and $l = 33$.

- You know all of a, d, n and l, so you can use either formula (using $S_n = \frac{1}{2}n(a+l)$ here):

$$S_n = \frac{1}{2}n(a+l)$$

$$S_{15} = \frac{1}{2} \times 15(5+33)$$

$$S_{15} = \frac{1}{2} \times 15 \times 38$$

$$S_{15} = \mathbf{285}$$

Exercise 3.1

Q1 An arithmetic series has first term 8 and common difference 3. Find the 10th term and the sum of the first 10 terms.

Q2 An arithmetic progression has n[th] term $8n - 6$. Find the sum of the first 20 terms.

Q3 In an arithmetic series $u_2 = 16$ and $u_5 = 10$. Find a, d and S_8.

Q4 An arithmetic series has first term –6 and the sum of the first 10 terms is 345. Find the common difference.

Q5 In an arithmetic series $a = 12$ and $d = 6$. Find u_{100} and S_{100}.

Q6 Find the sum of the arithmetic series with first term 7, last term 79 and common difference 6.

Q7 Find $\sum_{n=1}^{12}(5n-2)$.

Q8 Find $\sum_{n=1}^{9}(20-2n)$.

Q9 In an arithmetic series $a = 3$ and $d = 2$. Find n if $S_n = 960$.

Q10 Given that $\sum_{n=1}^{k}(5n+2) = 553$, show that the value of k is 14.

Q11 An arithmetic sequence begins $x + 11$, $4x + 4$, $9x + 5$, ... Find the sum of the first 11 terms. (PROBLEM SOLVING)

Q12 An arithmetic progression begins 36, 32, 28, 24, ... Find the possible values of n if $S_n = 176$. (PROBLEM SOLVING)

Sum of the first n natural numbers

The **natural numbers** are the positive whole numbers, i.e. 1, 2, 3, 4... They form a simple arithmetic progression with $a = 1$ and $d = 1$.

The sum of the first n natural numbers is:

$$S_n = \frac{1}{2}n(n+1)$$

a) **Find the sum of the first 100 natural numbers.** $S_n = \frac{1}{2}n(n+1)$

$$S_{100} = \frac{1}{2} \times 100 \times 101 = \textbf{5050}$$

b) **The sum of the first k natural numbers is 861. Find the value of k.**

1. Form an equation in k: $\qquad\qquad\qquad$ $\frac{1}{2}k(k+1) = 861$

2. Expand the brackets and rearrange: $\quad$ $k^2 + k = 1722 \Rightarrow k^2 + k - 1722 = 0$

3. Factorise and solve the quadratic in k: $(k+42)(k-41) = 0$ $\quad$ **Tip:** It looks tricky to factorise, but
$\qquad\qquad\qquad\qquad\qquad\qquad\qquad$ $k = -42$ or $k = 41$ $\qquad\qquad$ notice that $b = 1$, so you need
$\qquad\qquad\qquad\qquad\qquad\qquad\qquad\qquad\qquad\qquad\qquad\qquad\qquad\qquad\qquad\qquad$ two numbers that are 1 apart
4. Ignore the negative solution, so: $\qquad$ **$k = 41$** $\qquad\qquad\qquad\qquad\qquad\qquad$ and multiply to 1722.

Exercise 3.2

Q1 **a)** Find the sum of the first: (i) 15, $\qquad$ (ii) 25, $\qquad$ (iii) 2000 natural numbers. $\qquad\qquad$ **b)** Find $\displaystyle\sum_{n=1}^{32} n$.

Q2 Find $\displaystyle\sum_{n=1}^{10} n$ and $\displaystyle\sum_{n=1}^{20} n$. Hence find $\displaystyle\sum_{n=11}^{20} n$.

Q3 **a)** The sum of the first n natural numbers is 66. Find n. $\qquad$ **b)** Find k if $\displaystyle\sum_{n=1}^{k} n = 120$.

Q4 Find the sum of the series $16 + 17 + 18 + \ldots + 35$.

Q5 What is the first natural number k for which $\displaystyle\sum_{n=1}^{k} n$ is greater than 1 000 000?

4. Geometric Sequences and Series

- In a **geometric sequence** (also called a **geometric progression**), you get from one term to the next by **multiplying** by a **constant** called the **common ratio** (r) — e.g. 1, 2, 4, 8, ... has common ratio 2.

- If r is **negative**, the signs of the sequence will **alternate** (e.g. for 2, –6, 18, –54, ..., $r = -3$).

- If r is between **0 and 1**, the terms will get **smaller** (e.g. for 16, 12, 9, $\frac{27}{4}$, $\frac{81}{16}$, ..., $r = \frac{3}{4}$).

- The **formula** that describes the nth term in a geometric sequence is:

$$\boxed{u_n = ar^{(n-1)}}$$ where a is the **first term** and r is the **common ratio**.

a) **Find the 5th term in the geometric sequence 1, 3, 9, ...**

1. First find the common ratio r. Each term is the previous term multiplied by r, so find the common ratio by dividing consecutive terms:

$$\text{second term} = \text{first term} \times r \Rightarrow r = \frac{\text{second term}}{\text{first term}} = \frac{3}{1} = 3$$

2. Then find the 5th term. The 3rd term is 9, so: $\quad$ 4th term = 3rd term $\times r = 9 \times 3 = 27$
$\qquad\qquad\qquad\qquad\qquad\qquad\qquad\qquad\qquad\qquad\qquad$ 5th term = 4th term $\times r = 27 \times 3 = \textbf{81}$

b) The 8ᵗʰ term of a geometric sequence is 4374 and the common ratio is 3. What is the first term?

- The common ratio $r = 3$, so the nᵗʰ term is: $u_n = ar^{n-1} = a(3)^{n-1}$

- Then the 8th term is: $4374 = a(3)^7 = 2187a \Rightarrow a = \dfrac{4374}{2187} = \mathbf{2}$

Exercise 4.1

Q1 Find the seventh term in the geometric progression 2, 3, 4.5, 6.75 ...

Q2 The sixth and seventh terms of a geometric sequence are 2187 and 6561 respectively.
a) What is the first term? b) What is the tenth term?

Q3 A geometric sequence is 24, 12, 6, ... What is the 9ᵗʰ term?

Q4 The 14ᵗʰ term of a geometric progression is 9216. The first term is 1.125. Calculate the common ratio.

Q5 The first and second terms of a geometric progression are 1 and 1.1 respectively.
How many terms in this sequence are less than 4?

Q6 A geometric progression has a common ratio of 0.6. If the first term is 5, what is the difference between the 10ᵗʰ term and the 15ᵗʰ term? Give your answer to 5 d.p.

Q7 A geometric sequence has a first term of 25 000 and a common ratio of 0.8.
Which term is the first to be below 1000?

Q8 A geometric sequence is 5, –5, 5, –5, 5, ... Give the common ratio.

Q9 The first three terms of a geometric progression are $\dfrac{1}{4}$, $\dfrac{3}{16}$ and $\dfrac{9}{64}$.
a) Calculate the common ratio. b) Find the 8ᵗʰ term. Give your answer as a fraction.

Q10 The 7ᵗʰ term of a geometric sequence is 196.608 and the common ratio is 0.8. What is the first term?

Q11 3, –2.4, 1.92, ... is a geometric progression.
a) What is the common ratio?
b) How many terms are there in the sequence before you reach a term with modulus less than 1?

Geometric series

The **sum** of the first n terms of a **geometric series** is:

$$S_n = \frac{a(1-r^n)}{1-r} \quad \text{or} \quad \sum_{k=0}^{n-1} ar^k = \frac{a(1-r^n)}{1-r}$$

 A geometric series has first term 3.5 and common ratio 5. Find the sum of the first 6 terms.

$a = 3.5$ and $r = 5$, and you're looking for the sum of the first 6 terms, so use the formula for S_6:

$$S_6 = \frac{a(1-r^6)}{1-r} = \frac{3.5\,(1-5^6)}{1-5} = \mathbf{13\ 671}$$

Examples

a) **The first two terms in a geometric series are 20, 22. To 2 decimal places, the sum of the first k terms of the series is 271.59. Find k.**

$a = 20$, $r = \dfrac{\text{second term}}{\text{first term}} = \dfrac{22}{20} = 1.1$, so: $S_k = \dfrac{a(1-r^k)}{1-r} = \dfrac{20(1-(1.1)^k)}{1-1.1} = -200(1-(1.1)^k)$

So $271.59 = -200(1-(1.1)^k)$

$\Rightarrow -\dfrac{271.59}{200} - 1 = -(1.1)^k \Rightarrow 2.35795 = 1.1^k$

$\Rightarrow \log(2.35795) = k\log(1.1) \Rightarrow k = \dfrac{\log(2.35795)}{\log(1.1)} = \mathbf{9}$

b) **$a + ar + ar^2 + \ldots$ is a geometric series, and $\displaystyle\sum_{k=0}^{4} ar^k = 85.2672$. Given that $r = -1.8$, find the first term a.**

1. You have the sum of the first 5 terms: $85.2672 = \displaystyle\sum_{k=0}^{4} ar^k = S_5 = \dfrac{a(1-r^5)}{1-r}$

2. So plug the value of r into the formula:

$85.2672 = \dfrac{a(1-r^5)}{1-r} = \dfrac{a(1-(-1.8)^5)}{1-(-1.8)} = a\dfrac{19.89568}{2.8} = 7.1056a \Rightarrow a = \dfrac{85.2672}{7.1056} = \mathbf{12}$

Exercise 4.2

Q1 The first term of a geometric sequence is 8 and the common ratio is 1.2. Find the sum of the first 15 terms.

Q2 A geometric series has first term $a = 25$ and common ratio $r = 0.7$. Find $\displaystyle\sum_{k=0}^{9} 25(0.7)^k$.

Q3 The sum of the first n terms of a geometric series is 196 605.
The common ratio of the series is 2 and the first term is 3. Find n.

Q4 A geometric progression starts with 4, 5, 6.25.
The first x terms add up to 103.2 to 4 significant figures. Find x.

Q5 The 3rd term of a geometric series is 6 and the 8th term is 192. Find:
a) the common ratio
b) the first term
c) the sum of the first 15 terms

Q6 $m + 10$, m, $2m - 21$, ... is a geometric progression, m is a positive constant.
a) Show that $m^2 - m - 210 = 0$.
b) Hence show that $m = 15$.
c) Find the common ratio of this series.
d) Find the sum of the first 10 terms.

Q7 The first three terms of a geometric series are 1, x, x^2.
The sum of these terms is 3 and each term has a different value.
a) Find x.
b) Calculate the sum of the first 7 terms.

Q8 a, ar, ar^2, ar^3, ... is a geometric progression. Given that $a = 7.2$ and $r = 0.38$, find $\displaystyle\sum_{k=0}^{9} ar^k$.

Q9 The sum of the first eight terms of a geometric series is 1.2.
Find the first term of the series, given that the common ratio is $-\dfrac{1}{3}$.

Q10 a, $-2a$, $4a$, $-8a$, ... is a geometric sequence. Given that $\displaystyle\sum_{k=0}^{12} a(-2)^k = -5735.1$, find a.

Convergent geometric series

- Some geometric sequences **tend towards zero** — in other words, they get closer and closer to zero (but they never actually reach it). Sequences like this are called **convergent sequences**.

- When you **sum** a geometric sequence that tends to zero you get a **convergent series**. The **series converges** to a **limit** (a value the sum gets closer and closer to, but never actually reaches).

- If a sequence or series **doesn't** converge, it is called a **divergent** sequence or series.

- A geometric sequence or series **converges** when the value of r is between -1 and $+1$ (i.e. $|r| < 1$), and **diverges** if $|r| \geq 1$. For example, the sequence 1, 2, 4, 8, 16, ... has $r = 2$ (> 1), so it is **divergent**, but the sequence 81, -27, 9, -3, 1, ... has $r = -\frac{1}{3}$. $|r| < 1$ so the sequence **converges**.

- When a series is **convergent** you can find its **sum to infinity** (S_∞) — it's the **limit** of S_n as $n \to \infty$. Use the following formula to find the sum to infinity: $\boxed{S_\infty = \dfrac{a}{1-r}}$

Examples   a) If $a = 2$ and $r = \frac{1}{2}$, find the sum to infinity of the geometric series.

$|r| = \left|\frac{1}{2}\right| = \frac{1}{2} < 1$, so the series converges.
Find its sum to infinity using the formula: $S_\infty = \dfrac{a}{1-r} = \dfrac{2}{1-\frac{1}{2}} = \dfrac{2}{\frac{1}{2}} = \mathbf{4}$

b) **Find the sum to infinity of the geometric series $8 + 2 + 0.5 + 0.125 + \ldots$**

- First find a and r: $a = 8$, $r = \dfrac{2^{nd}\ \text{term}}{1^{st}\ \text{term}} = \dfrac{2}{8} = 0.25$. $|r| < 1$, so the series converges.

- Now find the sum to infinity: $S_\infty = \dfrac{a}{1-r} = \dfrac{8}{1-0.25} = \dfrac{32}{3} = \mathbf{10\frac{2}{3}}$

Exercise 4.3

Q1   State which of these sequences will converge and which will not.

a) 1, 1.1, 1.21, 1.331, ...

b) 0.8, 0.8^2, 0.8^3, ...

c) 1, $\frac{1}{4}$, $\frac{1}{16}$, $\frac{1}{64}$, ...

d) 3, $\frac{9}{2}$, $\frac{27}{4}$, ...

e) 1, $-\frac{1}{2}$, $\frac{1}{4}$, $-\frac{1}{8}$, $\frac{1}{16}$, ...

f) 5, 5, 5, 5, 5, ...

Q2   A geometric series is $9 + 8.1 + 7.29 + \ldots$ Calculate the sum to infinity.

Q3 a, ar, ar^2, ... is a geometric sequence. Given that $S_\infty = 2a$, find r.

Q4   The sum to infinity of a geometric progression is 13.5 and the first 3 terms add up to 13.
a) Find the common ratio r b) Find the first term a.

Q5 $a + ar + ar^2 + \ldots$ is a geometric series. $ra = 3$ and $S_\infty = 12$. Find r and a.

Q6   The sum to infinity of a geometric series is 10 and the first term is 6.
a) Find the common ratio.   b) What is the 5th term?

Q7   The 2nd term of a geometric progression is -48 and the 5th term is 0.75. Find:
a) the common ratio   b) the first term   c) the sum to infinity

Q8   The sum of the terms after the 10th term of a convergent geometric series is less than 1% of the sum to infinity. The first term is positive. Show that the common ratio $|r| < 0.631$.

Q9   In a convergent geometric series $S_\infty = \frac{9}{8} \times S_4$. Find the value of r, given that r is positive and real.

5. Modelling Problems

Modelling problems might not say the words sequence, series, arithmetic or geometric in the question — you have to decide what you're dealing with. Look for questions that have a **time period** (e.g. each year) and describe how values **increase** or **decrease** over that time period.

 Mo is training for a 10 km running race. On the first day he runs 2 km.
He schedules his training to increase by 0.5 km each day, so that he runs
2.5 km on the second day and 3 km on the third day and so on. This continues
until he reaches the maximum distance of 10 km on the seventeenth day.
The distance he runs each day then remains at 10 km until the race. There are
20 days before the race. What is the total distance Mo will run in training?

- The question describes the arithmetic sequence 2, 2.5, 3, ..., 10
  which has common difference 0.5.

- You're asked for the total distance, so use the series formula: $\qquad S_n = \frac{n}{2}(2a + (n-1)d)$

- The series contains 17 terms and you know that $a = 2$ and $d = 0.5$, so
$$S_{17} = \frac{17}{2}(2 \times 2 + (17-1) \times 0.5) = \frac{17}{2}(4 + 8) = 102 \text{ km}$$

- There are also 3 extra days where he will run 10 km: $\qquad\qquad 3 \times 10 = 30 \text{ km}$

- So the total distance Mo will run is: $\qquad\qquad\qquad\qquad 102 + 30 = \textbf{132 km}$

 When a baby is born, £3000 is invested in an account
with a fixed interest rate of 4% per year.

a) What will the account be worth at the start of the seventh year?

- Start by working out the first few terms: The first term is: $u_1 = a = 3000$ $\qquad$ This is the interest.

    The second term is: $u_2 = 3000 + (4\% \text{ of } 3000)$
    $$= 3000 \times 1.04$$
    The third term is: $u_3 = u_2 \times 1.04 = (3000 \times 1.04) \times 1.04$
    $$= 3000 \times (1.04)^2$$

    And so on — this is a geometric sequence with $r = 1.04$

- So the nth term of the sequence is: $\qquad\qquad u_n = ar^{n-1} = 3000 \times (1.04)^{n-1}$

- The value of the account at the start of the first year is the 1st term,
  so the value of the account at the start of the seventh year is the 7th term:
  $$u_7 = ar^6 = 3000 \times (1.04)^6 = 3795.957... = \textbf{£3795.96 (to the nearest penny)}$$

b) After how many full years will the account have doubled in value?

- You need to know when $u_n > 3000 \times 2 = 6000$. From part a) you know $u_n = 3000 \times (1.04)^{n-1}$

    So $3000 \times (1.04)^{n-1} > 6000 \Rightarrow (1.04)^{n-1} > 2$

- To complete this you need to use logs: $\qquad \Rightarrow \log(1.04)^{n-1} > \log 2 \Rightarrow (n-1)\log(1.04) > \log 2$

    $$\Rightarrow n - 1 > \frac{\log 2}{\log 1.04} \Rightarrow n - 1 > 17.67$$

    $$\Rightarrow n > 18.67 \text{ (to 2 d.p.)}$$

- So $u_n > 6000$ when $n > 18.67$. Then u_{19} (the amount at the start of the 19th year) will be more than double the original amount. After **18 years**, the account will have doubled in value.

Exercise 5.1

Q1 Morag starts a new job. In the first week she is paid £60, but this rises by £3 per week, so she earns £63 in the second week and £66 in the third week. How much does she earn in her 12th week?

Q2 A collector has 8 china dolls that fit inside each other. The smallest doll is 3 cm high and each doll is 25% taller than the previous one. If he lines them up from shortest to tallest, how tall is the 8th doll?

Q3 Mario opens a sandwich shop. On the first day he sells 40 sandwiches. As people hear about the shop, sales increase and on the second day he sells 45 sandwiches. Daily sales rise in an arithmetic sequence. On which day will he sell 80 sandwiches?

Q4 A retro cassette player is launched into the market. In the first month after launch, the product takes £300 000 of revenue. It takes £270 000 in the second month and £240 000 in the third. If this pattern continues, when would you expect monthly sales to fall below £50 000?

Q5 A car depreciates by 15% each year. The value of the car after each year forms a geometric sequence. After 10 years from new the car is valued at £2362. How much was the car when new?

Q6 A fishing licence cost £120 in 2011. The cost rose 3% each year for the next 5 years.
a) How much was a fishing licence in 2012?
b) Nikhil bought a fishing licence every year between 2011 and 2016 (including 2011 and 2016). How much in total did he spend?

Q7 "Cornflake Collector" magazine sells 6000 copies in its first month of publication, 8000 in its second month and 10 000 in its third month. If this pattern continues, how many copies will it sell in the first year of publication?

Q8 Ravi is growing his prize leeks for the Village Show. The bag of compost he's using on his leeks says it will increase their height by 15% every 2 days. After 4 weeks the leeks' height has increased from 5 cm to 25 cm. Has the compost done what it claimed?

Q9 It's predicted that garden gnome value will go up by 2% each year, forming a geometric progression. Jean-Claude has a garden gnome currently valued at £80 000. If the rate of inflation is correct:
a) What will Jean-Claude's gnome be worth after 1 year?
b) What is the common ratio of the geometric progression?
c) What will Jean-Claude's gnome be worth after 10 years?
d) It will take k years for the value of Jean-Claude's gnome to exceed £120 000. Find k.

Q10 Frazer draws one dot in the first square of his calendar for July, two dots in the second square, and so on up to 31 dots in the last day of the month. How many dots does he draw in total?

Q11 The thickness of a piece of paper is 0.01 cm. The Moon is 384 000 km from the Earth. The piece of paper is on the Earth. Assuming you can fold the piece of paper as many times as you like, how many times would you have to fold it for it to reach the Moon?

Q12 An athlete is preparing for an important event and sets herself a target of running 3% more each day. On day 1 she runs 12 miles.
a) How far does she run on day 10?
b) Her training schedule lasts for 20 days. To the nearest mile, how far does she run altogether?

Q13 Laura puts 1p in her jar on the first day, 2p in on the second day, 3p in on the third day, etc. How many days will it take her to collect over £10?

Q14 Chardonnay wants to invest her savings for the next 10 years. She wants her investment to double during this time. If interest is added annually, what interest rate does she need?

Q1 Find the nth term for each of the following sequences:
    a) 2, 6, 10, 14, ...   b) 0.2, 0.7, 1.2, 1.7, ...   c) 21, 18, 15, 12, ...
    d) 76, 70, 64, 58, ...   e) 4.9, 4.6, 4.3, 4.0, ...   f) −19, −16.5, −14, −11.5, ...

Q2 a) Find the 10th term of the sequence with n^{th} term $(n − 1) \div (n + 2)$.
    b) Is this sequence increasing or decreasing?

Q3 Find the 8th term of the sequence $x_n = n^2 − 3$. Is this sequence increasing or decreasing?

Q4 The rth term of the sequence $u_n = n^3$ is 64. Find the value of r.

Q5 In the sequence $u_n = n^2 + 3n + 4$, $u_k = 44$. Find the value of k.

Q6 Find the first 5 terms of the sequence $u_n = (−1)^n n$.

Q7 A sequence has the form $u_n = an^2 + bn$, where a and b are constants.
If the 3rd term is 18, and the 7th term is 70, find the values of a and b.

Q8 Describe the sequence 32, 37, 42, 47, ... using a recurrence relation.

Q9 Find the first 5 terms of the sequence in which:
    a) $x_1 = 7$ and $x_{n+1} = x_n + 3$ for $n \geq 1$.   b) $u_1 = 2$ and $u_{n+1} = 6 \div u_n$ for $n \geq 1$.

Q10 Find a recurrence relation which generates the sequence:
    a) 65 536, 256, 16, 4, 2, ...   b) 40, 38, 34, 28, 20, ...   c) 1, 1, 2, 3, 5, 8, ...

Q11 In a sequence $u_1 = 5$, $u_2 = 7$ and $u_{n+2} = u_{n+1} − u_n$ for $n \geq 1$.
Find the first 10 terms and describe the behaviour of the sequence.

Q12 In a sequence $u_1 = 2$, $u_2 = 8$ and $u_3 = 26$. If the recurrence relation is of
the form $u_{n+1} = au_n + b$, find the values of the constants a and b.

Q13 A sequence is generated by a recurrence relation of the form $u_{n+1} = ku_n + 3$,
where k is a constant. If $u_1 = 4$ and $u_2 = 11$, find the values of k, u_3 and u_4.

Q14 A sequence is generated by $u_1 = 8$ and $u_{n+1} = 18 − u_n$ for $n \geq 1$. Find the first 5 terms and a
formula for u_n in terms of n. State whether the sequence is increasing, decreasing or periodic.

Q15 Find the common difference in a sequence that starts with −2, ends with 19 and has 29 terms.

Q16 In an arithmetic series, $u_7 = 8$ and $u_{11} = 10$. Find u_3.

Q17 In an arithmetic series, $u_4 = 8$ and $u_9 = −7$. Find the value of k if $u_k = −52$.

Q18 An arithmetic series has seventh term 36 and tenth term 30.
Find the nth term and the sum of the first five terms.

Q19 Find $\displaystyle\sum_{n=1}^{20}(3n − 1)$.

Q20 a) Find the sum of the first 24 natural numbers.   b) Find $\displaystyle\sum_{n=13}^{24} n$.

Q21 Find k if $\displaystyle\sum_{n=1}^{k} n = 630$.

Q22 Find the common ratio of the geometric progression 3125, 1875, 1125, 675, 405, ...

Q23 Write an expression for the nth term of the geometric sequence 3, –9, 27, –81, 243, ...

Q24 For the geometric progression 2, –6, 18, ..., find:
a) the 10th term,
b) the sum of the first 10 terms.

Q25 Find the sum of the first 12 terms of the following geometric series:
a) 2 + 8 + 32 + ...
b) 30 + 15 + 7.5 + ...
c) 0.5 + 1.5 + 4.5 + ...

Q26 A geometric series has first term $a = 7$ and common ratio $r = 0.6$. Find $\sum_{k=0}^{5} 7(0.6)^k$ to 2 d.p.

Q27 A geometric progression begins 2, 6, ... Which term of the geometric progression equals 1458?

Q28 Show that the sum of the first n terms of a geometric sequence with first term a and common ratio r is: $S_n = \dfrac{a(1-r^n)}{1-r}$.

Q29 Find the common ratio for the following geometric series. State which ones are convergent and which are divergent.
a) 1 + 2 + 4 + ...
b) 81 + 27 + 9 + ...
c) $1 + \dfrac{1}{3} + \dfrac{1}{9} + ...$
d) $4 + 1 + \dfrac{1}{4} + ...$
e) 2 + 5 + 12.5 + ...
f) 10 000 + 1000 + 100 + ...

Q30 For the geometric progression 24, 12, 6, ..., find:
a) the common ratio,
b) the seventh term,
c) the sum of the first 10 terms,
d) the sum to infinity.

Q31 A geometric series has first term $a = 33$, common ratio $r = 0.25$. Find $\sum_{k=0}^{\infty} ar^k$ for this series.

Q32 In the first week of release, "Extreme Excitement 7" takes £3 million at the box office. In the second week it only takes £2.8 million, and in the third week it takes £2.6 million. If this pattern continues, how much will it make in the 10th week of release?

Q33 A new shop takes £300 on its first day of business, £315 on its second day and £330 on its third day. If this pattern continues, on which day will the shop first take over £500?

Q34 Paula is following a 12 week training plan to prepare for a half marathon. She does a 30 minute run in the first week and a 40 minute run in the second. If the run lengths increase by 10 minutes each week, how much will she have to do in the last week of training? How many hours will she have run in total at the end of the training?

Q35 Hussain puts one stone on the wall on his way to school on the first day of term, two stones on the wall on the second day of term and three on the third day of term. The term has 13 weeks of 5 days each. If he continues like this, how many stones will he have put on the wall in total by the holiday?

Q36 A charity received £20 000 of donations from the public one year (Year 1). The charity predict that the public donations will increase by 8% each year, forming a geometric sequence.
a) Show that their predicted donations from the public the following year are £21 600.
b) Write down the common ratio of the geometric sequence.
c) Write down an expression for the predicted public donations in Year n.
d) Find the total amount of public donations the charity will get (if their prediction is correct) in the ten years from Year 1 to Year 10.

Chapter 21 — The Binomial Expansion 2

In this chapter, you'll see how to use a binomial expansion when the power is negative or a fraction, and how you can use partial fractions to help solve more complicated problems.

1. The Binomial Expansion

Expansions where n is negative or a fraction

In Chapter 5, you saw the formula for expanding an expression of the form $(1 + x)^n$ (see p.59):

$$(1+x)^n = 1 + nx + \frac{n(n-1)}{1 \times 2}x^2 + ... + \frac{n(n-1)...(n-r+1)}{1 \times 2 \times ... \times r}x^r + ...$$

The formula also works when n is **negative** or a **fraction**, but the expansion will have an **infinite** number of terms — you can just write down the first few terms, but this will only be an **approximation**. Expansions like these are **not valid** for all values of x — to find the valid range, use the following rule:

If n is negative or a fraction, the expansion of $(p + qx)^n$ is **valid** when $\left|\frac{qx}{p}\right| < 1 \Rightarrow |x| < \left|\frac{p}{q}\right|$

Example

a) Find the binomial expansion of $\frac{1}{(1+x)^2}$ up to and including the term in x^3.

$\frac{1}{(1+x)^2} = (1+x)^{-2}$ i.e. $n = -2$:

$$(1+x)^{-2} = 1 + (-2)x + \frac{(-2) \times (-3)}{1 \times 2}x^2 + \frac{(-2) \times (-3) \times (-4)}{1 \times 2 \times 3}x^3 + ...$$

$$= 1 + (-2)x + \frac{3}{1}x^2 + \frac{(-4)}{1}x^3 + ... = \mathbf{1 - 2x + 3x^2 - 4x^3 + ...}$$

b) State the range for which this expansion is valid.

$p = 1$ and $q = 1$, so the expansion is valid for: $|x| < \left|\frac{1}{1}\right| \rightarrow |x| < 1$

Example

a) Find the binomial expansion of $\sqrt[3]{1 + 2x}$, up to and including the term in x^3.

$\sqrt[3]{1+2x} = (1+2x)^{\frac{1}{3}}$ i.e. $n = \frac{1}{3}$ (and replace x in the formula with $2x$):

$$(1+2x)^{\frac{1}{3}} = 1 + \frac{1}{3}(2x) + \frac{\frac{1}{3} \times \left(-\frac{2}{3}\right)}{1 \times 2}(2x)^2 + \frac{\frac{1}{3} \times \left(-\frac{2}{3}\right) \times \left(-\frac{5}{3}\right)}{1 \times 2 \times 3}(2x)^3 + ...$$

$$= 1 + \frac{2}{3}x + \frac{\left(-\frac{2}{9}\right)}{2}(4x^2) + \frac{\left(\frac{10}{27}\right)}{6}(8x^3) + ...$$

$$= 1 + \frac{2}{3}x + \left(-\frac{1}{9}\right)(4x^2) + \left(\frac{5}{81}\right)(8x^3) + ... = \mathbf{1 + \frac{2}{3}x - \frac{4}{9}x^2 + \frac{40}{81}x^3 - ...}$$

b) State the range for which this expansion is valid.

$p = 1$ and $q = 2$, so the expansion is valid for: $|x| < \left|\frac{1}{2}\right| \Rightarrow |x| < \frac{1}{2}$

Exercise 1.1

Q1 Find the first four terms in each expansion, stating the range of x for which it is valid:

a) $(1 + x)^{-4}$ b) $(1 - 6x)^{-3}$ c) $(1 + 4x)^{\frac{1}{3}}$ d) $(1 + 4x)^{-\frac{1}{2}}$ e) $(1 - 3x)^{\frac{2}{3}}$

f) $\dfrac{1}{(1 - 4x)^2}$ g) $\sqrt{1 + 6x}$ h) $\dfrac{1}{\sqrt{1 - 3x}}$ i) $\sqrt[3]{1 + \dfrac{x}{2}}$ j) $\sqrt[3]{\dfrac{1}{(1 - x)^2}}$

Q2 a) Find the coefficient of the x^3 term in the expansion of $\dfrac{1}{(1 + 7x)^4}$.

b) For what range of x is this expansion valid?

Q3 a) What is the coefficient of x^5 in the expansion of $\sqrt[4]{1 - 4x}$?

b) For what values of x is the binomial expansion of $\sqrt[4]{1 - 4x}$ valid?

When you have two brackets multiplied together, expand them separately, then multiply the expressions together at the end. For the combined expression to be valid, x must be in the valid range for **both** expansions i.e. where they **overlap**.

[Example] **Write down the first three terms in the expansion of $\dfrac{(1 + 2x)^3}{(1 - x)^2}$.**
State the range of x for which the expansion is valid.

1. $\dfrac{(1 + 2x)^3}{(1 - x)^2} = (1 + 2x)^3 (1 - x)^{-2}$, so expand these separately:

$(1 + 2x)^3 = 1 + 3(2x) + \dfrac{3 \times 2}{1 \times 2}(2x)^2 + \dfrac{3 \times 2 \times 1}{1 \times 2 \times 3}(2x)^3 = 1 + 6x + 3(4x^2) + 8x^3$

$= 1 + 6x + 12x^2 + 8x^3$

$(1 - x)^{-2} = 1 + (-2)(-x) + \dfrac{(-2) \times (-3)}{1 \times 2}(-x)^2 + \dfrac{(-2) \times (-3) \times (-4)}{1 \times 2 \times 3}(-x)^3 + ...$

$= 1 + 2x + 3x^2 + 4x^3 + ...$

2. Multiply the two expansions together, ignoring any terms with higher powers of x than x^2.

$(1 + 2x)^3(1 - x)^{-2} = (1 + 6x + 12x^2 + 8x^3)(1 + 2x + 3x^2 + 4x^3 + ...)$

$= 1(1 + 2x + 3x^2) + 6x(1 + 2x) + 12x^2(1) + ... = \mathbf{1 + 8x + 27x^2 + ...}$

3. Find the validity of each expansion:

$(1 + 2x)^3$ is valid for all x $(1 - x)^{-2}$ is valid if $|x| < \left| \dfrac{1}{-1} \right| \Rightarrow |x| < 1$

4. So the combined expression is valid for: $\mathbf{|x| < 1}$

Exercise 1.2

Q1 a) Find the first three terms of the expansion of $(1 - 5x)^{\frac{1}{6}}$.

b) Hence find the binomial expansion of $(1 + 4x)^4(1 - 5x)^{\frac{1}{6}}$, up to and including the term in x^2.

c) State the validity of the expansion in b).

Q2 Expand, up to and including the term in x^2, giving the range for which the expansion is valid:

a) $(1 + x)^2(1 - 2x)^{-2}$ b) $(1 + 2x)^2(1 + 3x)^{-3}$ c) $(1 - 7x)(1 + 2x)^{\frac{1}{7}}$ d) $(1 - x)^2(1 + 4x)^{\frac{1}{3}}$

Q3 Find the first three terms of the binomial expansion of $\dfrac{(1 + 3x)^4}{(1 + x)^3}$, and the range of x for which it is valid.

Q4 a) Write out the expansion of: (i) $(1 + ax)^4$ (all terms)   (ii) $(1 - bx)^{-3}$, up to the term in x^2

b) Hence expand $\dfrac{(1 + ax)^4}{(1 - bx)^3}$, up to and including the term in x^2.

c) Find the two possible pairs of values of a and b if the start of this expansion is $1 + x + 24x^2...$

Expanding $(p + qx)^n$

In order to use the formula to expand a bracket of the form $(p + qx)^n$, you need to factorise so that the constant term is 1.
This means that you have to rewrite the expression as shown: ⟶

$$(p + qx)^n = p^n\left(1 + \frac{qx}{p}\right)^n$$

Example

Give the first 3 terms in the binomial expansion of $(3x + 4)^{\frac{3}{2}}$, stating the range of x for which the expansion is valid.

1. Factorise before using the formula:

$$(3x + 4)^{\frac{3}{2}} = \left[4\left(1 + \frac{3}{4}x\right)\right]^{\frac{3}{2}} = 4^{\frac{3}{2}}\left(1 + \frac{3}{4}x\right)^{\frac{3}{2}} = 8\left(1 + \frac{3}{4}x\right)^{\frac{3}{2}}$$

2. Use the $(1 + x)^n$ formula with $n = \frac{3}{2}$, and $\frac{3}{4}x$ instead of x:

$$\left(1 + \frac{3}{4}x\right)^{\frac{3}{2}} = 1 + \frac{3}{2}\left(\frac{3}{4}x\right) + \frac{\frac{3}{2}\times\left(\frac{3}{2}-1\right)}{1\times 2}\left(\frac{3}{4}x\right)^2 + \dots = 1 + \frac{9}{8}x + \frac{\frac{3}{2}\times\frac{1}{2}}{2}\left(\frac{9}{16}x^2\right) + \dots$$

$$= 1 + \frac{9x}{8} + \frac{27x^2}{128} + \dots$$

3. Put this back into the original expression:

$$(3x + 4)^{\frac{3}{2}} = 8\left(1 + \frac{3}{4}x\right)^{\frac{3}{2}} = 8\left(1 + \frac{9x}{8} + \frac{27x^2}{128} + \dots\right) = \mathbf{8 + 9x + \frac{27x^2}{16} + \dots}$$

4. Give the valid range: Valid when $|x| < \frac{4}{3}$

Exercise 1.3

Q1 Find the binomial expansion of the following functions, up to and including the term in x^3:

a) $(2 + 4x)^3$ b) $(3 + 4x)^5$ c) $(4 + x)^{\frac{1}{2}}$ d) $(8 + 2x)^{-\frac{1}{3}}$ e) $(3 - 2x)^{-4}$ f) $(9 + x)^{0.5}$

Q2 If the x^2 coefficient of the binomial expansion of $(a + 5x)^5$ is 2000, what is the value of a?

Q3 a) Find the binomial expansion of $(2 - 5x)^7$ up to and including the term in x^2.

b) Hence, or otherwise, find the expansion of $(1 + 6x)^3(2 - 5x)^7$, up to and including the term in x^2.

Q4 a) Find the binomial expansion of $\left(1 + \frac{6}{5}x\right)^{-\frac{1}{2}}$, up to and including the term in x^3, stating the range of x for which it is valid.

b) Hence, or otherwise, express $\sqrt{\dfrac{20}{5 + 6x}}$ in the form $a + bx + cx^2 + dx^3 + \dots$ (PROBLEM SOLVING)

Q5 a) Find the binomial expansion of $\dfrac{1}{\sqrt{5 - 2x}}$, up to and including the term in x^2.

b) Hence show that $\dfrac{3 + x}{\sqrt{5 - 2x}} \approx \dfrac{3}{\sqrt{5}} + \dfrac{8x}{5\sqrt{5}} + \dfrac{19x^2}{50\sqrt{5}}$.

Q6 a) Find the binomial expansion of $(9 + 4x)^{-\frac{1}{2}}$, up to and including the term in x^2.

b) Hence, or otherwise, find the binomial expansion of $\dfrac{(1 + 6x)^4}{\sqrt{9 + 4x}}$, up to and including the term in x^2.

Q7 Expand, up to and including the term in x^2, giving the range for which the expansion is valid:

a) $\dfrac{(1 - 5x)}{(1 + 3x)^{\frac{1}{3}}}$ b) $\dfrac{(4 + x)^{\frac{1}{2}}}{(1 + 3x)^2}$ c) $\dfrac{(8 + 3x)^{\frac{1}{3}}}{(4 - x)^{\frac{1}{2}}}$ d) $\dfrac{(3 + 4x)^3}{(4 - 3x)^4}$

2. Binomial Expansions as Approximations

Binomial expansions with negative and fractional powers can also be used to **approximate** values, as long as x is within the valid range of the expansion.

Example

The binomial expansion of $(1 + 3x)^{-1}$ up to the term in x^3 is:

$(1 + 3x)^{-1} \approx 1 - 3x + 9x^2 - 27x^3$. The expansion is valid for $|x| < \frac{1}{3}$.

Use this expansion to approximate $\frac{100}{103}$. Give your answer to 4 d.p.

1. Find the value of x you need:

$$\frac{100}{103} = \frac{1}{1.03} = \frac{1}{1 + 0.03} = (1 + 0.03)^{-1} \Rightarrow x = 0.01$$

2. Check that it is in the valid range:

$0.01 < \frac{1}{3}$, so the expansion is valid

3. Substitute this into the expansion:

$(1 + 3(0.01))^{-1} \approx 1 - 3(0.01) + 9(0.01^2) - 27(0.01^3)$

$\frac{100}{103} = 0.97087...$ so this is a pretty good approximation.

$= 1 - 0.03 + 0.0009 - 0.000027$

$= 1.0009 - 0.030027 = 0.970873$

$= \mathbf{0.9709}$ (4 d.p.)

Example

The binomial expansion of $(1 - 5x)^{\frac{1}{2}}$ up to the term in x^2 is

$(1 - 5x)^{\frac{1}{2}} \approx 1 - \frac{5x}{2} - \frac{25x^2}{8}$. The expansion is valid for $|x| < \frac{1}{5}$.

a) Use $x = \frac{1}{50}$ in this expansion to show that $\sqrt{10} \approx \frac{800}{253}$.

1. Substitute $x = \frac{1}{50}$ into both sides of the given expansion:

$$\sqrt{\left(1 - 5\left(\frac{1}{50}\right)\right)} \approx 1 - \frac{5}{2}\left(\frac{1}{50}\right) - \frac{25}{8}\left(\frac{1}{50}\right)^2$$

$$\sqrt{\left(1 - \frac{1}{10}\right)} \approx 1 - \frac{1}{20} - \frac{1}{800}$$

$$\sqrt{\frac{9}{10}} \approx \frac{759}{800}$$

$$\frac{3}{\sqrt{10}} \approx \frac{759}{800}$$

2. Rearrange to find an estimate for $\sqrt{10}$:

$$\frac{3}{\sqrt{10}} \approx \frac{759}{800}$$

$$3 \times 800 \approx 759\sqrt{10}$$

$$\sqrt{10} \approx \frac{3 \times 800}{759} = \frac{800}{253} \text{ as required}$$

b) Find the percentage error in your approximation, to 2 s.f.

Use the percentage error formula: $\left|\dfrac{\text{real value} - \text{estimate}}{\text{real value}}\right| \times 100\% = \left|\dfrac{\sqrt{10} - \frac{800}{253}}{\sqrt{10}}\right| \times 100\%$

The % error is really small, which means the approximation is very close to the real answer.

$= \mathbf{0.0070}\%$ (2 s.f.)

Exercise 2.1

Q1 a) Find the binomial expansion of $(1 + 6x)^{-1}$, up to and including the term in x^2.
  b) What is the validity of the expansion in part a)?
  c) Use an appropriate substitution to find an approximation for the following values:
   (i) $\dfrac{100}{106}$ (ii) $\dfrac{100}{112}$ (iii) $\dfrac{100}{94}$ (iv) $\dfrac{5}{8}$

Q2 a) Use the binomial theorem to expand $(1 + 3x)^{\frac{1}{4}}$, up to and including the term in x^3.
  b) For what values of x is this expansion valid?
  c) Use this expansion to find an approximate value of $\sqrt[4]{1.9}$ correct to 4 decimal places.
  d) Find the percentage error of this approximation, correct to 3 significant figures.

Q3 a) Find the first four terms in the binomial expansion of $(1 - 2x)^{-\frac{1}{2}}$.
  b) For what range of x is this expansion valid?
  c) Use $x = \dfrac{1}{10}$ in this expansion to find an approximate value of $\sqrt{5}$.
  d) Find the percentage error of this approximation, correct to 2 significant figures.

Q4 a) Expand $(2 - 5x)^6$ up to and including the x^2 term.
  b) By substituting an appropriate value of x into this expansion, find an approximate value for 1.95^6.
  c) What is the percentage error of this approximation? Give your answer to 2 significant figures.

Q5 a) Find the first three terms in the binomial expansion of $\sqrt{3 - 4x}$.
  b) For what values of x is this expansion valid?
  c) Use $x = \dfrac{3}{40}$ in this expansion to estimate the value of $\dfrac{3}{\sqrt{10}}$. Leave your answer as a fraction.
  d) Find the percentage error of this approximation, correct to 1 significant figure.

3. Binomial Expansion and Partial Fractions

You can find the binomial expansion of some expressions by splitting them into **partial fractions** (p.254).

Example The function $f(x) = \dfrac{x-1}{(3+x)(1-5x)}$ can be expressed
as partial fractions in the form: $\dfrac{A}{(3+x)} + \dfrac{B}{(1-5x)}$.

a) **Find the values of A and B, and hence express f(x) as partial fractions.**

   1. Write this as an identity:
   $$\dfrac{x-1}{(3+x)(1-5x)} \equiv \dfrac{A}{(3+x)} + \dfrac{B}{(1-5x)}$$
   $$\Rightarrow x - 1 \equiv A(1 - 5x) + B(3 + x)$$

   2. Using the substitution method:
   $x = -3 \quad \Rightarrow \quad -3 - 1 = A(1 - (-15)) + B(0)$
   $$\Rightarrow \quad -4 = 16A \quad \Rightarrow \quad A = -\dfrac{1}{4}$$
   $x = \dfrac{1}{5} \quad \Rightarrow \quad \dfrac{1}{5} - 1 = A(0) + B\left(3 + \dfrac{1}{5}\right)$
   $$\Rightarrow \quad -\dfrac{4}{5} = \dfrac{16}{5}B \quad \Rightarrow \quad B = -\dfrac{1}{4}$$

   3. So f(x) can be written:
   $$f(x) = -\dfrac{1}{4(3+x)} - \dfrac{1}{4(1-5x)}$$

b) **Use your answer to part a) to find the binomial expansion of f(x), up to and including the term in x^2.**

    1. Rewrite each term of f(x) in $(p + qx)^n$ form:

$$f(x) = -\frac{1}{4}(3 + x)^{-1} - \frac{1}{4}(1 - 5x)^{-1}$$

    2. Expand these separately:

$$(3 + x)^{-1} = \left(3\left(1 + \frac{1}{3}x\right)\right)^{-1} = \frac{1}{3}\left(1 + \frac{1}{3}x\right)^{-1}$$

$$= \frac{1}{3}\left(1 + (-1)\left(\frac{1}{3}x\right) + \frac{(-1)(-2)}{2}\left(\frac{1}{3}x\right)^2 + ...\right)$$

$$= \frac{1}{3}\left(1 - \frac{1}{3}x + \frac{1}{9}x^2 - ...\right) = \frac{1}{3} - \frac{1}{9}x + \frac{1}{27}x^2 - ...$$

$$(1 - 5x)^{-1} = 1 + (-1)(-5x) + \frac{(-1)(-2)}{2}(-5x)^2 + ...$$

$$= 1 + 5x + 25x^2 + ...$$

    3. Substitute these back into f(x):

$$f(x) = -\frac{1}{4}(3 + x)^{-1} - \frac{1}{4}(1 - 5x)^{-1}$$

$$\approx -\frac{1}{4}\left(\frac{1}{3} - \frac{1}{9}x + \frac{1}{27}x^2\right) - \frac{1}{4}(1 + 5x + 25x^2)$$

$$= -\frac{1}{12} + \frac{x}{36} - \frac{x^2}{108} - \frac{1}{4} - \frac{5x}{4} - \frac{25x^2}{4}$$

$$= -\frac{1}{3} - \frac{11x}{9} - \frac{169x^2}{27}$$

c) **Find the range of values of x for which your answer to part b) is valid.**

    1. Find the valid range for each expansion: $(3 + x)^{-1}$ is valid when $|x| < \left|\frac{3}{1}\right| \Rightarrow |x| < 3$

$$(1 - 5x)^{-1} \text{ is valid when } |x| < \left|\frac{1}{-5}\right| \Rightarrow |x| < \frac{1}{5}$$

    2. So the valid range for the combined expression is where these overlap:

The expansion of f(x) is valid for $|x| < \frac{1}{5}$

Exercise 3.1

Q1   a) $\dfrac{5 - 12x}{(1 + 6x)(4 + 3x)} \equiv \dfrac{A}{(1 + 6x)} + \dfrac{B}{(4 + 3x)}$. Find A and B.

     b) Find the binomial expansions of $(1 + 6x)^{-1}$ and $(4 + 3x)^{-1}$, up to and including the term in x^2.

     c) Hence find the binomial expansion of $\dfrac{5 - 12x}{(1 + 6x)(4 + 3x)}$, up to and including the term in x^2.

     d) For what values of x is this expansion valid?

Q2   a) Show that $f(x) = \dfrac{6}{(1 - x)(1 + x)(1 + 2x)}$ can be expressed as: $\dfrac{1}{(1 - x)} - \dfrac{3}{(1 + x)} + \dfrac{8}{(1 + 2x)}$

     b) Give the binomial expansion of f(x) in ascending powers of x, up to and including the term in x^2.

     c) Find the percentage error, to 2 significant figures, when you use this expansion to estimate f(0.01).

Q3   a) Factorise fully $2x^3 + 5x^2 - 3x$, and hence express $\dfrac{5x - 6}{2x^3 + 5x^2 - 3x}$ as partial fractions.

     b) Find the binomial expansion of $\dfrac{5x - 6}{2x^3 + 5x^2 - 3x}$, up to and including the term in x^2.

     c) For what values of x is this expansion valid?

Q4   a) Express $f(x) = \dfrac{55x + 7}{(2x - 5)(3x + 1)^2}$ in the form $\dfrac{A}{(2x - 5)} + \dfrac{B}{(3x + 1)} + \dfrac{C}{(3x + 1)^2}$ (A, B, C are integers).

     b) Hence, or otherwise, use the binomial formula to expand f(x), up to and including the term in x^2.

Q1 Give the binomial expansion of:

a) $(1 + 2x)^3$ b) $(1 - x)^5$ c) $(1 - 4x)^4$ d) $\left(1 - \frac{2}{3}x\right)^4$

Q2 For what values of n does the binomial expansion of $(1 + x)^n$ result in a finite expression?

Q3 a) If the x^2 coefficient of the binomial expansion of $(1 + ax)^{-2}$ is 48 and a is a positive integer, what is the value of a?

b) If the x^4 coefficient of the binomial expansion of $(1 - ax)^{\frac{1}{3}}$ is $-\frac{10}{3}$, and a is positive, what is the value of a?

Q4 If the full binomial expansion of $(c + dx)^n$ is an infinite series, what values of x is the expansion valid for?

Q5 Find the binomial expansion of each of the following, up to and including the term in x^3, stating the range of x for which the expansions are valid.

a) $\dfrac{1}{(1 + x)^5}$ b) $\dfrac{1}{(1 - 3x)^3}$ c) $\sqrt{1 - 5x}$ d) $\dfrac{1}{\sqrt[3]{1 + 2x}}$

Q6 a) Give the binomial expansions of the following, up to and including the term in x^2. State the range of x for which each expansion is valid.

(i) $\dfrac{1}{(3 + 2x)^2}$ (ii) $\sqrt[3]{8 - x}$

b) Use your answers to a) to give the binomial expansion of $\dfrac{\sqrt[3]{8 - x}}{(3 + 2x)^2}$, up to and including the term in x^2. State the range of x for which this expansion is valid.

c) (i) Use the expansion in a)(ii) to find an approximate value of $\sqrt[3]{7}$, leaving your answer as a fraction.

(ii) Find the percentage error of this approximation, correct to 2 significant figures.

Q7 a) Show that $\dfrac{5 - 10x}{(1 + 2x)(2 - x)}$ can be expressed as: $\dfrac{4}{(1 + 2x)} - \dfrac{3}{(2 - x)}$.

b) Give the binomial expansion of the expression in a), up to and including the term in x^2.

c) Find the percentage error when you use $x = 0.1$ in this expansion to estimate $\dfrac{4}{1.2 \times 1.9}$, giving your answer to 2 significant figures.

Q8 $f(x) = \dfrac{1}{(a - 2x)^2}$

a) Find the binomial expansion of $f(x)$, up to and including the term in x^2, in terms of a.

b) Give the range for which this expansion is valid in terms of a.

$g(x) = \dfrac{1}{\sqrt{4 - ax}}$

c) Find the binomial expansion of $g(x)$, up to and including the term in x^2, in terms of a.

d) Give the range for which this expansion is valid in terms of a.

e) Hence find the binomial expansion of $f(x) \times g(x)$, up to and including the term in x.

f) Write down the coefficient of x in the combined expansion of $f(x) \times g(x)$, given that $a = 2$.

Chapter 22 — Differentiation 2

You'll have done quite a bit of differentiation back in Chapter 8. Make sure you're familiar with first and second order derivatives, maximum and minimum points and equations of tangents and normals.

1. Points of Inflection

Convex and concave curves

Continuous curves of the form $y = f(x)$ can be described as **convex** or **concave**.

- **Convex curves** are u-shaped. A straight line joining any two points on a convex curve lies **above** the curve between those points. **Convex curves** have an **increasing gradient**, so a curve $y = f(x)$ is **convex** if $f''(x) > 0$ for all values of x.

- **Concave curves** are n-shaped. A straight line joining any two points on a concave curve lies **below** the curve between those points. **Concave curves** have a **decreasing gradient**, so curve $y = f(x)$ is **concave** if $f''(x) < 0$ for all values of x.

Tip: Most curves aren't **entirely** convex or concave — but you can divide a curve into concave and convex **sections**.

 Example   The graph of $y = x^3 + x^2 - x$ has concave and convex sections. Find the range of values of x where the graph of $y = x^3 + x^2 - x$ is convex.

1. Find the second derivative: $\dfrac{dy}{dx} = 3x^2 + 2x - 1 \implies \dfrac{d^2y}{dx^2} = 6x + 2$

2. The graph is convex when the second derivative is positive:

$$\frac{d^2y}{dx^2} > 0 \implies 6x + 2 > 0 \implies 6x > -2 \implies x > -\frac{1}{3}$$

Exercise 1.1

Q1 Find the values of x for which the following graphs are concave:

    a) $y = \dfrac{1}{3}x^3 - x^2 - 15x$ b) $y = \dfrac{1}{6}x^3 - \dfrac{5}{2}x^2 + \dfrac{1}{4}x + \dfrac{1}{9}$ c) $y = 4x^2 - x^4$

Q2 Find the values of x for which the following graphs are convex:

    a) $y = 4x^2 - 12x + 15$ b) $y = x^3 + 9x^2 - 21x$ c) $y = 2x^4 - 24x^2$

Q3 If $f(x) = \dfrac{1}{16}x^4 + \dfrac{3}{4}x^3 - \dfrac{21}{8}x^2 - 6x + 20$, identify the ranges of values of x for which the graph of $y = f(x)$ is concave and convex.

Points of inflection

A point where the curve **changes** between concave and convex (i.e. where $f''(x)$ changes between positive and negative) is called a **point of inflection**.

At a point of inflection, $f''(x) = 0$, but not all points where $f''(x) = 0$ are points of inflection. You need to look what's happening on **either side** of the point to see if the sign of $f''(x)$ is changing — if the sign of $f''(x)$ **doesn't** change either side of the point, it's **not** a point of inflection.

Tip: 'Point of inflection' can be used as the name for 'the other type' of stationary point (i.e. not a maximum or a minimum). These are more properly called **stationary points of inflection** — see next page.

> **Example** Find the coordinates of the points of inflection
> of the graph of $y = 2x^4 + 4x^3 - 72x^2$.
>
> 1. Find the second derivative of $y = 2x^4 + 4x^3 - 72x^2$: $\frac{dy}{dx} = 8x^3 + 12x^2 - 144x$
>
> $$\Rightarrow \frac{d^2y}{dx^2} = 24x^2 + 24x - 144$$
>
> 2. Now find the points where $\frac{d^2y}{dx^2} = 0$. These could be points of inflection:
>
> $\frac{d^2y}{dx^2} = 0 \Rightarrow 24x^2 + 24x - 144 = 0 \Rightarrow x^2 + x - 6 = 0$
> $\Rightarrow (x + 3)(x - 2) = 0 \Rightarrow x = -3$ and $x = 2$
>
>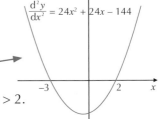
>
> 3. So there could be points of inflection at $x = -3$ and $x = 2$.
>
> Think about what happens to $\frac{d^2y}{dx^2}$ either side of these points.
> $\frac{d^2y}{dx^2}$ is a quadratic, so you can do this easily with a sketch:
>
> $\frac{d^2y}{dx^2} > 0$ for $x < -3$, $\frac{d^2y}{dx^2} < 0$ for $-3 < x < 2$, and $\frac{d^2y}{dx^2} > 0$ for $x > 2$.
>
> 4. So $\frac{d^2y}{dx^2}$ changes sign at $x = -3$ and $x = 2$, so both are points of inflection.
>
> 5. The question asks for the coordinates of the points of inflection, so find the y-values:
> At $x = -3$, $y = 2(-3)^4 + 4(-3)^3 - 72(-3)^2 = -594$
> At $x = 2$, $y = 2(2)^4 + 4(2)^3 - 72(2)^2 = -224$
>
> 6. So the points of inflection are: **(−3, −594)** and **(2, −224)**

Exercise 1.2

Q1 The graph of $y = \frac{3}{2}x^4 - x^2 - 3x$ has two points of inflection. Find the x-coordinates of these two points.

Q2 Show that the graph of $y = x^2 - \frac{1}{x}$ has a point of inflection at $(1, 0)$.

Q3 Find the coordinates of the point of inflection of the graph of $y = 3 + 3x + 3x^2 + x^3$.

Q4 Show that the graph of $y = x^5 - 6x^4 - \frac{16}{3}x^3 + 4$ has a point of inflection at $(0, 4)$.

Stationary points of inflection

Stationary points are points where **f'(x) = 0**. A stationary point can be a **maximum** point, a **minimum** point or a **stationary point of inflection**. The value of f''(x) can help you work out which type of stationary point it is. As you saw in Chapter 8:

- If f'(x) = 0 and **f''(x) > 0**, it's a **minimum**.
- If f'(x) = 0 and **f''(x) < 0**, it's a **maximum**.

BUT

- If f'(x) = 0 and **f''(x) = 0**, it could be **any one** of the three types
  — so you have to look at f''(x) on either side of the stationary point.

For $f(x) = x^5 - 60x^3$, find the value of x at each stationary point of the graph of $y = f(x)$, and determine the nature of each one.

1. Find the first derivative to locate the stationary points (i.e. where $f'(x) = 0$):
$f(x) = x^5 - 60x^3 \Rightarrow f'(x) = 5x^4 - 180x^2 = 5x^2(x^2 - 36) = 5x^2(x + 6)(x - 6)$
So $f'(x) = 0$ when $x = 0$, $x = -6$ and $x = 6$.

2. Find the second derivative and use it to work out the nature of the three stationary points:
$f'(x) = 5x^4 - 180x^2 \Rightarrow f''(x) = 20x^3 - 360x$
$f''(-6) = 20(-6)^3 - 360(-6) = -2160 < 0$, so the stationary point at $x = -6$ is a **maximum**.
$f''(6) = 20(6)^3 - 360(6) = 2160 > 0$, so the stationary point at $x = 6$ is a **minimum**.
$f''(0) = 20(0)^3 - 360(0) = 0$, so the stationary point at $x = 0$ could be a maximum, a minimum or a point of inflection.

3. Look at the values of $f''(x)$ close to $x = 0$: $\quad$ $f''(x) = 20x^3 - 360x = 20x(x^2 - 18)$
When x is small and negative, $20x$ is negative and $x^2 - 18$ is negative, so $f''(x)$ is positive.
When x is small and positive, $20x$ is positive and $x^2 - 18$ is negative, so $f''(x)$ is negative.
The sign of $f''(x)$ changes at $x = 0$, so $x = 0$ is a **point of inflection**.

Exercise 1.3

Q1   For $f(x) = x^3 + 2x^2 + 3x + 3$, show that:

    a) the graph of $y = f(x)$ has one point of inflection,

    b) the point of inflection is not a stationary point.

Q2   Find the coordinates of the stationary points of the graph of $y = x^4 - 2x^3 + 1$ and determine their nature.

Q3   Find the coordinates of the stationary points of the graph of $y = \frac{1}{10}x^5 - \frac{1}{3}x^3 + \frac{1}{2}x + 4$ and determine their nature.

Q4   Find the coordinates of the stationary points of the graph of $y = x^7 - 140x^5$ and determine their nature.

2. Chain Rule

The **chain rule** helps you **differentiate** complicated functions by **splitting them up** into functions that are easier to differentiate.

Once you've worked out how to split up the function, you can differentiate it using this **formula**:

If $y = f(u)$ and $u = g(x)$ then: $\dfrac{dy}{dx} = \dfrac{dy}{du} \times \dfrac{du}{dx}$

To differentiate a function using the chain rule, just follow these steps:

1. Pick a suitable function of x for 'u' and rewrite y in terms of u.

2. Differentiate u (with respect to x) to get $\dfrac{du}{dx}$...

3. ...and differentiate y (with respect to u) to get $\dfrac{dy}{du}$.

4. Stick it all in the formula and write everything in terms of x.

Examples   a) Find $\dfrac{dy}{dx}$ if $y = (6x - 3)^5$.

1. Decide which part of the function to replace with u.
   The bit inside the brackets is easy to differentiate, so that's u:
   $y = (6x - 3)^5$, so let $y = u^5$ where $u = 6x - 3$

2. Differentiate the two parts separately: $\dfrac{dy}{du} = 5u^4$ and $\dfrac{du}{dx} = 6$

3. Finally, put everything back into the chain rule formula:
   $\dfrac{dy}{dx} = \dfrac{dy}{du} \times \dfrac{du}{dx} = 5u^4 \times 6 = 30u^4 = \mathbf{30(6x - 3)^4}$

b) **Find the equation of the tangent to the curve** $y = \dfrac{1}{\sqrt{x^2 + 3x}}$ **at** $(1, \tfrac{1}{2})$.

1. First rewrite the function in terms of powers: $y = \dfrac{1}{\sqrt{x^2 + 3x}} = (x^2 + 3x)^{-\frac{1}{2}}$

2. Then identify which part to turn into u.
   $y = (x^2 + 3x)^{-\frac{1}{2}}$, so let $y = u^{-\frac{1}{2}}$ where $u = (x^2 + 3x)$

3. Differentiate y and u:
   $y = u^{-\frac{1}{2}} \Rightarrow \dfrac{dy}{du} = \left(-\dfrac{1}{2}\right)u^{-\frac{3}{2}} = -\dfrac{1}{2(\sqrt{x^2 + 3x})^3}$ and $u = x^2 + 3x \Rightarrow \dfrac{du}{dx} = 2x + 3$

4. Put it all back into the chain rule formula:
   $\dfrac{dy}{dx} = \dfrac{dy}{du} \times \dfrac{du}{dx} = \left(-\dfrac{1}{2(\sqrt{x^2 + 3x})^3}\right) \times (2x + 3) = -\dfrac{2x + 3}{2(\sqrt{x^2 + 3x})^3}$

5. To find the equation of the tangent, you first need to know the gradient at the point $(1, \tfrac{1}{2})$,
   so put the x-value into your equation for $\dfrac{dy}{dx}$:
   $\dfrac{dy}{dx} = -\dfrac{(2 \times 1) + 3}{2(\sqrt{1^2 + (3 \times 1)})^3} = -\dfrac{5}{16}$

6. Then use your gradient and the values you're given to find c:
   $y = mx + c \Rightarrow \dfrac{1}{2} = (-\dfrac{5}{16} \times 1) + c \Rightarrow c = \dfrac{13}{16}$

7. So the equation of the tangent at $(1, \tfrac{1}{2})$ is: $\mathbf{y = -\dfrac{5}{16}x + \dfrac{13}{16}}$

Exercise 2.1

Q1   Differentiate with respect to x:
   a) $y = (x + 7)^2$ b) $y = (2x - 1)^5$ c) $y = 3(4 - x)^8$ d) $y = (3 - 2x)^7$
   e) $y = (x^2 + 3)^5$ f) $y = (5x^2 + 3)^2$ g) $y = 3(x^2 - 1)^3$ h) $y = 2(4x^2 + 5)^6$

Q2   Find $f'(x)$ for the following:
   a) $f(x) = (4x^3 - 9)^8$ b) $f(x) = (6 - 7x^2)^4$ c) $f(x) = (x^2 + 5x + 7)^6$ d) $f(x) = (x + 4)^{-3}$
   e) $f(x) = (5 - 3x)^{-2}$ f) $f(x) = \dfrac{1}{(5 - 3x)^4}$ g) $f(x) = (3x^2 + 4)^{\frac{3}{2}}$ h) $f(x) = \dfrac{1}{\sqrt{5 - 3x}}$

Q3   Find the exact value of $\dfrac{dy}{dx}$ when $x = 1$ for: a) $y = \dfrac{1}{\sqrt{5x - 3x^2}}$ b) $y = \dfrac{12}{\sqrt[3]{x + 6}}$

Q4 Differentiate $\left(\sqrt{x} + \dfrac{1}{\sqrt{x}}\right)^2$ with respect to x by:

    a) Multiplying the brackets out and differentiating term by term.   b) Using the chain rule.

Q5 Find the equation of the tangent to the curve $y = (x - 3)^5$ at $(1, -32)$.

Q6 Find the equation of the normal to the curve $y = \dfrac{1}{4}(x - 7)^4$ when $x = 6$.

Q7 Find the value of $\dfrac{dy}{dx}$ when $x = 1$ for $y = (7x^2 - 3)^{-4}$.

Q8 Find f$'(x)$ if f$(x) = \dfrac{7}{\sqrt[3]{3 - 2x}}$.

Q9 Find the equation of the tangent to the curve $y = \sqrt{5x - 1}$
when $x = 2$, in the form $ax + by + c = 0$, $a, b, c \in \mathbb{Z}$.

Q10 Find the equation of the normal to the curve $y = \sqrt[3]{3x - 7}$ when $x = 5$.

Q11 Find the equation of the tangent to the curve $y = (x^4 + x^3 + x^2)^2$ when $x = -1$.

Q12 Show that the curve $y = (2x - 3)^7$ has one point of inflection, and find the coordinates of that point.

Q13 Find the ranges of values of x for which the curve $y = \left(\dfrac{x}{4} - 2\right)^3$ is convex and concave.

Finding $\dfrac{dy}{dx}$ when $x = f(y)$

When x **is given in terms of** y (i.e. $x = f(y)$), use the following rule:

$$\boxed{\dfrac{dy}{dx} = \dfrac{1}{\left(\dfrac{dx}{dy}\right)}}$$

Example   A curve has the equation $x = y^3 + 2y - 7$. Find $\dfrac{dy}{dx}$ at the point $(-4, 1)$.

1. Forget that the x's and y's are in the 'wrong' place and differentiate as usual:

$$x = y^3 + 2y - 7 \implies \dfrac{dx}{dy} = 3y^2 + 2$$

2. Use $\dfrac{dy}{dx} = \dfrac{1}{\left(\dfrac{dx}{dy}\right)}$ to find $\dfrac{dy}{dx}$: $\dfrac{dy}{dx} = \dfrac{1}{3y^2 + 2}$

3. $y = 1$ at the point $(-4, 1)$, so put this in the equation:

$$\dfrac{dy}{dx} = \dfrac{1}{3(1)^2 + 2} = \dfrac{1}{5} = 0.2, \text{ so } \dfrac{dy}{dx} = \mathbf{0.2} \text{ at the point } (-4, 1).$$

Exercise 2.2

Q1 Find $\dfrac{dy}{dx}$ for each of the following functions at the given point.

    a) $x = 3y^2 + 5y + 7$ at $(5, -1)$ b) $x = y^3 - 2y$ at $(-4, -2)$ c) $x = (2y + 1)(y - 2)$ at $(3, -1)$

    d) $x = \dfrac{4 + y^2}{y}$ at $(5, 4)$ e) $x = y^5 + 4y^4$ at $(3, -1)$ f) $x = \dfrac{2}{y^2}$ at $(0.5, 2)$

Q2 Find $\dfrac{dy}{dx}$ in terms of y if $x = (2y^3 - 5)^3$.

Q3 Given that $x = \sqrt{4 + y}$, find $\dfrac{dy}{dx}$ in terms of x by: a) finding $\dfrac{dx}{dy}$ first,

                                                    b) rearranging into the form $y = f(x)$.

3. Differentiation of e^x, $\ln x$ and a^x

Differentiating e^x

Remember from Chapter 7 that 'e' is just a number for which the **gradient of e^x is e^x**, which makes it easy to **differentiate**. The **chain rule** gives another useful formula for differentiating $e^{f(x)}$:

$$y = e^x \implies \frac{dy}{dx} = e^x$$

$$y = e^{f(x)} \implies \frac{dy}{dx} = f'(x)e^{f(x)}$$

Examples   a) If $f(x) = e^{x^2} + 2e^x$, find $f'(x)$ when $x = 0$.

1. The function is in two parts, so differentiate each part separately.

2. The second bit's easy: If $y = 2e^x$ then $\frac{dy}{dx} = 2e^x$ too.

3. For the first bit, just use the formula above:
$$y = e^{x^2}, \text{ so let } y = e^{g(x)} \text{ where } g(x) = x^2$$
$$g'(x) = 2x, \text{ so } \frac{dy}{dx} = 2xe^{x^2}$$

4. Now put the bits back together: $f'(x) = 2xe^{x^2} + 2e^x$

5. And finally, work out the value of $f'(x)$ at $x = 0$: $f'(0) = (2 \times 0 \times e^{0^2}) + 2e^0 = 0 + 2 = \mathbf{2}$

b) The graph of $y = e^{2x} - 6x^2$ has one point of inflection. Find the exact coordinates of this point.

1. To find the point of inflection, you need to find where $\frac{d^2y}{dx^2} = 0$.

2. Start by finding $\frac{dy}{dx}$. Split the function up into two parts and differentiate the parts separately.

3. The second bit's easy: $y = -6x^2 \implies \frac{dy}{dx} = -12x$

4. For the first bit, use the formula given above. $y = e^{2x} = e^{f(x)}$
$$f(x) - 2x \text{ so } f'(x) = 2 \implies \frac{dy}{dx} = f'(x)e^{f(x)} = 2e^{2x}$$

5. Now just put the two parts back together: $\frac{dy}{dx} = 2e^{2x} - 12x$

6. Now differentiate again to find $\frac{d^2y}{dx^2}$:
$$\frac{dy}{dx} = 2e^{2x} - 12x = 2e^{f(x)} - 12x \implies \frac{d^2y}{dx^2} = 2f'(x)e^{f(x)} - 12 = 2(2 \times e^{2x}) - 12 = 4e^{2x} - 12$$

7. Now to find the point of inflection, set $\frac{d^2y}{dx^2} = 0$:   Take logs of both sides to solve for x: $\ln(e^x) = x$
$$4e^{2x} - 12 = 0 \implies e^{2x} = 3 \implies 2x = \ln 3 \implies x = \frac{1}{2}\ln 3 = \ln 3^{\frac{1}{2}} = \ln \sqrt{3}$$

8. Substitute $x = \ln \sqrt{3}$ into $y = e^{2x} - 6x^2$ to find the y-coordinate:
$$y = e^{2\ln\sqrt{3}} - 6(\ln \sqrt{3})^2 \implies y = e^{\ln 3} - 6(\ln \sqrt{3})^2 \implies y = 3 - 6(\ln \sqrt{3})^2$$

9. So the point of inflection is at: $(\ln \sqrt{3}, 3 - 6(\ln \sqrt{3})^2)$

Tip: There's only one point where $\frac{d^2y}{dx^2} = 0$, and the question tells you there's one point of inflection, so that must be the point you're looking for here — there's no need to prove it's a point of inflection.

Exercise 3.1

Q1 Differentiate with respect to x:

a) $y = e^{3x}$ b) $y = e^{2x-5}$ c) $y = e^{x+7}$ d) $y = e^{3x+9}$ e) $y = e^{7-2x}$ f) $y = e^{x^3}$

Q2 Find $f'(x)$ if:

a) $f(x) = e^{x^3+3x}$ b) $f(x) = e^{x^3-3x-5}$ c) $f(x) = e^{x(2x+1)}$ d) $f(x) = e^{x^4-x^2}$

Q3 Find $f'(x)$ if:

a) $f(x) = \frac{1}{2}(e^x - e^{-x})$ b) $f(x) = e^{(x+3)(x+4)}$ c) $f(x) = e^{x^4+3x^2} + 2e^{2x}$ d) $f(x) = 3e^{8x} - e^{2x^5}$

Q4 Find the equation of the tangent to the curve $y = e^{2x}$ at the point $(0, 1)$.

Q5 Find the exact value of the x-coordinate of the point of the inflection on the curve $y = \frac{1}{2}x^2 - e^{2x-6}$.

Q6 Find the equation of the tangent to the curve $y = e^{2x^2}$ when $x = 1$.
Leave the numbers in your answer in exact form.

Q7 Show that the curve $y = e^{2x-4} - x$ is convex for all values of x.

Q8 Find the equation of the normal to the curve $y = e^{3x} + 3$ where it cuts the y-axis.

Q9 Find the exact coordinates of any points of inflection on the curve $y = 2e^{2x} - \frac{1}{2}e^{3-4x}$.

Q10 Show that the curve $y = e^{x^3-3x-5}$ has stationary points at $x = \pm 1$.

Q11 Find the x-coordinate of the stationary point for the curve $y = e^{3x} - 6x$ and
determine the nature of this point. Leave the numbers in your answer in exact form.

Differentiating ln x

The **natural logarithm** of a function is the logarithm with **base e**, written as **ln x** (see p.84).
Here are the **formulas** for differentiating ln x and ln f(x):

$$y = \ln x \implies \frac{dy}{dx} = \frac{1}{x}$$

$$y = \ln f(x) \implies \frac{dy}{dx} = \frac{f'(x)}{f(x)}$$

Example   Find $f'(x)$ if $f(x) = \ln(x^3 - 4x)$.

1. $f(x)$ is in the form $\ln(g(x))$, so use the formula above:

$$f'(x) = \frac{g'(x)}{g(x)}$$

$$g(x) = x^3 - 4x \implies g'(x) = 3x^2 - 4$$

2. Put this into the formula:

$$f(x) = \ln(x^3 - 4x) \implies f'(x) = \frac{g'(x)}{g(x)} = \frac{3x^2 - 4}{x^3 - 4x}$$

Exercise 3.2

Q1 Differentiate with respect to x:
   a) $y = \ln (3x)$
   b) $y = \ln (1 + x)$
   c) $y = \ln (1 + 5x)$
   d) $y = 4 \ln (4x - 2)$

Q2 Differentiate with respect to x:
   a) $y = \ln (1 + x^2)$
   b) $y = \ln (2 + x)^2$
   c) $y = 3 \ln x^3$
   d) $y = \ln (x^3 + x^2)$

Q3 Find $f'(x)$ if:
   a) $f(x) = \ln \dfrac{1}{x}$
   b) $f(x) = \ln \sqrt{x}$
   c) $f(x) = \ln \dfrac{1}{\sqrt{x}}$

Q4 Find $f'(x)$ if $f(x) = \ln (x - \sqrt{x - 4})$.

Q5 Find the equation of the tangent to the curve $y = \ln (3x)^2$:   a) when $x = -2$ b) when $x = 2$

Q6 Find the equation of the normal to the curve $y = \ln (x + 6)^2$:   a) when $x = -3$ b) when $x = 0$

Q7 Find any stationary points for the curve $y = \ln (x^3 - 3x^2 + 3x)$.

Differentiating a^x

For any constant a:

$$\frac{d}{dx}(a^x) = a^x \ln a$$

Use the **chain rule** (see p.312) to differentiate functions of the form $a^{f(x)}$, by differentiating $y = a^u$ and $u = f(x)$ separately, then using the chain rule formula.

> **Examples** **Differentiate the following:**
>
> $\ln \left(\frac{1}{2}\right) = -\ln 2$
>
> **a)** $y = 2^x$ $\dfrac{dy}{dx} = 2^x \ln 2$
>
> **b)** $y = \left(\dfrac{1}{2}\right)^x$ $\dfrac{dy}{dx} = \left(\dfrac{1}{2}\right)^x \ln \left(\dfrac{1}{2}\right) = -2^{-x} \ln 2$
>
> $\left(\dfrac{1}{2}\right)^x = 2^{-x}$
>
> **c) Find the equation of the tangent to the curve $y = 3^{-2x}$ at the point $\left(\frac{1}{2}, \frac{1}{3}\right)$.**
>
> 1. Use the chain rule to find $\dfrac{dy}{dx}$: Let $u = -2x$ and $y = 3^u$.
>
>   Then $\dfrac{du}{dx} = -2$ and $\dfrac{dy}{du} = 3^u \ln 3$
>
>   So $\dfrac{dy}{dx} = \dfrac{dy}{du} \times \dfrac{du}{dx} = 3^u \ln 3 \times -2 = -2(3^{-2x} \ln 3)$
>
> 2. Now find the gradient of the tangent: at $\left(\frac{1}{2}, \frac{1}{3}\right)$, $\dfrac{dy}{dx} = -2(3^{-1} \ln 3) = -\dfrac{2}{3} \ln 3$
>
> 3. So if the equation of the tangent at $\left(\frac{1}{2}, \frac{1}{3}\right)$ has the form $y = mx + c$, then
>
> $\dfrac{1}{3} = (-\dfrac{2}{3} \ln 3)\dfrac{1}{2} + c \Rightarrow c = \dfrac{1}{3} + \dfrac{1}{3} \ln 3$
>
> 4. So the equation of the tangent to $y = 3^{-2x}$ at $\left(\frac{1}{2}, \frac{1}{3}\right)$ is: $y = -\dfrac{2x}{3} \ln 3 + \dfrac{1}{3} + \dfrac{1}{3} \ln 3$
>
>   or $3y = (1 - 2x)\ln 3 + 1$

Exercise 3.3

Q1 Differentiate the following:

a) $y = 5^x$ b) $y = 7^x$ c) $y = 3^{2x}$ d) $y = 10^{-x}$ e) $y = p^{qx}$

Q2 A curve has the equation $y = 2^{4x}$.

a) Show that the gradient of the curve is $\frac{dy}{dx} = 4(2^{4x} \ln 2)$.

b) Find the equation of the tangent to the curve when $x = 2$.

Q3 A curve $y = 2^{px}$ passes through the point $(1, 32)$.

a) Find p.   b) Hence find the gradient of the curve at this point.

Q4 A curve has the equation $y = p^{x^3}$.

a) Show that the gradient of the curve is $\frac{dy}{dx} = 3x^2(p^{x^3} \ln p)$.

b) If the curve passes through the point $(2, 6561)$, find p.

c) Hence find the equation of the tangent to the curve when $x = 1$.

Q5 The curve $y = 4^{\sqrt{x}}$ passes through the point $(25, a)$. Show that the equation of the tangent to the curve at $(25, a)$ is $y = 142x - 2520$ (to 3 s.f.).   (PROBLEM SOLVING)

Q6 A curve C has the equation $y = 2^{-3x}$. It passes through the point $(2, b)$.

a) Find the gradient $\frac{dy}{dx}$ of the curve.   b) Find b and the gradient of the curve at $(2, b)$.

c) Hence show that the equation of the tangent to the curve at $(2, b)$ is $64y = 1 + 6 \ln 2 - (3 \ln 2)x$.

---

4. Differentiating Trig Functions

For **trigonometric functions** where the angle is measured in **radians** the following rules apply:

$y = \sin x$	$y = \cos x$	$y = \tan x$
$\frac{dy}{dx} = \cos x$	$\frac{dy}{dx} = -\sin x$	$\frac{dy}{dx} = \sec^2 x$

Tip: Remember, $\sec x = \frac{1}{\cos x}$ — see p.264.

If you have a **multiple** of x inside the trig function (e.g. $\sin kx$), just **multiply** the **derivative** by k (so for $\sin kx$, $\cos kx$ and $\tan kx$, the derivatives would be $k \cos kx$, $-k \sin kx$ and $k \sec^2 kx$).
These rules can be combined with the **chain rule** to differentiate **more complicated** functions.

Examples   a) Find $\frac{dy}{dx}$ when $y = \cos (2x)$.

Use the rule above for $y = \cos kx$, where $k = 2$: $y = \cos 2x$, so $\frac{dy}{dx} = -2 \sin (2x)$

b) Find $\frac{dy}{dx}$ when $x = \tan (3y)$.

1. First find $\frac{dx}{dy}$ with the rule above: $x = \tan 3y$, so $\frac{dx}{dy} = 3 \sec^2 (3y)$

2. Then use $\frac{dy}{dx} = \frac{1}{\left(\frac{dx}{dy}\right)}$ (see p.314) to get the final answer: $\frac{dy}{dx} = \frac{1}{3 \sec^2 (3y)} = \frac{1}{3} \cos^2 (3y)$

Example Find $\dfrac{dy}{dx}$ if $y = \sin^3 x$.

1. Start off by rewriting the function as: $y = (\sin x)^3$

2. Now you have a function of a function so use the chain rule as before:
   $y = (\sin x)^3$, so let $y = u^3$ where $u = \sin x$

3. Differentiate y and u:
   $$y = u^3 \implies \dfrac{dy}{du} = 3u^2 = 3 \sin^2 x \text{ and } \dfrac{du}{dx} = \cos x$$

4. Then put it all into the chain rule formula:
   $$\dfrac{dy}{dx} = \dfrac{dy}{du} \times \dfrac{du}{dx} = 3 \sin^2 x \cos x$$

Exercise 4.1

Q1 Differentiate with respect to x:

a) $y = \sin (3x)$

b) $y = \cos (-2x)$

c) $y = \cos \dfrac{x}{2}$

d) $y = \sin \left(x + \dfrac{\pi}{4} \right)$

e) $y = 6 \tan \dfrac{x}{2}$

f) $y = 3 \tan (5x)$

Q2 Find $f'(x)$ when:

a) $f(x) = 3 \tan (2x - 1)$

b) $f(x) = 3 \tan x + \tan (3x)$

c) $f(x) = \sin \left(x^2 + \dfrac{\pi}{3} \right)$

d) $f(x) = \sin^2 x$

e) $f'(x)$ if $f(x) = 2 \sin^3 x$

f) $f(x) = \cos^4 x + \tan 2x$

Q3 a) Find $f'(x)$ if $f(x) = 3 \sin x + 2 \cos x$.   b) Find the value of x for which $f'(x) = 0$ and $0 \leq x \leq \dfrac{\pi}{2}$.

Q4 Find $\dfrac{dy}{dx}$ if $y = \dfrac{1}{\cos x}$.

Q5 a) Use differentiation from first principles and the sin addition formula to show that $\dfrac{d}{dx}(\sin x) = \cos x$.

b) Use differentiation from first principles to show that $\dfrac{dy}{dx} = -\sin x$ when $y = \cos x$.

Q6 Differentiate $y = \cos^2 x$ by:

a) Using the chain rule directly.   b) Expressing y in terms of $\cos (2x)$ and differentiating the result.

Q7 For $y = 6 \cos^2 x - 2 \sin (2x)$ show that $\dfrac{dy}{dx} = -6 \sin (2x) - 4 \cos (2x)$.

Q8 Find the gradient of the curve $y = \sin x$ when $x = \dfrac{\pi}{4}$.

Q9 Find the equation of the normal to the curve $y = \cos (2x)$ when $x = \dfrac{\pi}{4}$.

Q10 For the curve $x = \sin (2y)$:

a) Find the equation of the tangent at the point $\left(\dfrac{\sqrt{3}}{2}, \dfrac{\pi}{6} \right)$.

b) Find the equation of the normal at the point $\left(\dfrac{\sqrt{3}}{2}, \dfrac{\pi}{6} \right)$.

Q11 a) If $y = 2 \sin (2x) \cos x$, express y as a difference of two expressions involving $\sin x$ and $\sin^3 x$.

b) Hence find $\dfrac{dy}{dx}$.

Differentiating by using the chain rule twice

Use the chain rule **twice** when you have a function of a function of a function, like $\sin^3 (x^2)$.

> **Example** Find $\dfrac{dy}{dx}$ if $y = \sin^2 (2x + 1)$
>
> 1. Set up the first stage of differentiation with the chain rule:
> $$y = \sin^2 (2x + 1) = [\sin (2x + 1)]^2 \Rightarrow y = u^2, u = \sin (2x + 1)$$
>
> 2. Find $\dfrac{dy}{du}$: $\qquad \dfrac{dy}{du} = 2u = 2 \sin (2x + 1)$
>
> 3. To find $\dfrac{du}{dx}$ you're going to need the chain rule again, so set it up with u in terms of v
>   instead of y in terms of u: $\qquad u = \sin (2x + 1)$ so let $u = \sin v$ where $v = 2x + 1$
>
> 4. Then go through the usual stages: $\qquad u = \sin v \Rightarrow \dfrac{du}{dv} = \cos v = \cos (2x + 1)$
> $$v = 2x + 1 \Rightarrow \dfrac{dv}{dx} = 2$$
> $$\dfrac{du}{dx} = \dfrac{du}{dv} \times \dfrac{dv}{dx} = 2 \cos (2x + 1)$$
>
> 5. You now have $\dfrac{dy}{du}$ and $\dfrac{du}{dx}$ so you can find $\dfrac{dy}{dx}$:
> $$\dfrac{dy}{dx} = \dfrac{dy}{du} \times \dfrac{du}{dx} = [2 \sin (2x + 1)] \times [2 \cos (2x + 1)] = \textbf{4 sin (2x + 1) cos (2x + 1)}$$

Exercise 4.2

Q1 Find $\dfrac{dy}{dx}$ if: a) $y = \sin (\cos (2x))$ b) $y = 2 \ln (\cos (3x))$ c) $y = \ln (\tan^2 (x))$ d) $y = e^{\tan (2x)}$

Q2 Differentiate the following functions with respect to x:

a) $y = \sin^4 (x^2)$ b) $y = e^{\sin^2 x}$ c) $y = \tan^2 (3x) + \sin x$ d) $y = e^{2 \cos (2x)} + \cos^2 (2x)$

5. Product Rule

To differentiate two functions multiplied together, use the **product rule**:

$$\text{If } y = uv, \quad \dfrac{dy}{dx} = u\dfrac{dv}{dx} + v\dfrac{du}{dx}$$

Where u and v are functions of x, i.e. $u(x)$ and $v(x)$.

> **Example** Differentiate $x^3 \tan x$ with respect to x.
>
> 1. Start by identifying 'u' and 'v': $\qquad u = x^3$ and $v = \tan x$
>
> 2. Now differentiate these two separately, with respect to x: $\qquad \dfrac{du}{dx} = 3x^2$ and $\dfrac{dv}{dx} = \sec^2 x$
>
> 3. Put all the bits into the formula: $\qquad \dfrac{dy}{dx} = u\dfrac{dv}{dx} + v\dfrac{du}{dx} = (x^3 \times \sec^2 x) + (\tan x \times 3x^2)$
>
> 4. Finally, rearrange to make it look nicer: $\qquad \dfrac{dy}{dx} = x^3 \sec^2 x + 3x^2 \tan x$

You might have to differentiate functions using a mixture of the **product rule** and the **chain rule** (as well as the rules for e, ln and trig functions).

Examples   a) **Differentiate $e^{2x}\sqrt{2x-3}$ with respect to x.**

1. It's a product of two functions,
   so start by identifying 'u' and 'v': $u = e^{2x}$ and $v = \sqrt{2x-3} = (2x-3)^{\frac{1}{2}}$

2. Each of these requires the chain rule: $\dfrac{du}{dx} = 2e^{2x}$ and $\dfrac{dv}{dx} = 2\left(\dfrac{1}{2}(2x-3)^{-\frac{1}{2}}\right) = \dfrac{1}{\sqrt{2x-3}}$

3. Put it all into the product rule formula: $\dfrac{dy}{dx} = u\dfrac{dv}{dx} + v\dfrac{du}{dx} = \left(e^{2x} \times \dfrac{1}{\sqrt{2x-3}}\right) + (\sqrt{2x-3} \times 2e^{2x})$

4. Rearrange and then simplify:

$$\frac{dy}{dx} = e^{2x}\left(\frac{1}{\sqrt{2x-3}} + 2(\sqrt{2x-3})\right) = e^{2x}\left(\frac{1 + 2(2x-3)}{\sqrt{2x-3}}\right) = \frac{e^{2x}(4x-5)}{\sqrt{2x-3}}$$

b) **The graph of $y = x^3 \ln x$, for $x > 0$, has one point of inflection.**
   Find the x-coordinate of this point, leaving your answer as an exact value.

1. There'll be a point of inflection when $\dfrac{d^2y}{dx^2} = 0$.

2. Start by finding $\dfrac{dy}{dx}$ — identify u and v and use the product rule:
   $u = x^3$ and $v = \ln x \Rightarrow \dfrac{du}{dx} = 3x^2$ and $\dfrac{dv}{dx} = \dfrac{1}{x}$

   So $\dfrac{dy}{dx} = u\dfrac{dv}{dx} + v\dfrac{du}{dx} = \left(x^3 \times \dfrac{1}{x}\right) + (\ln x \times 3x^2) = x^2 + 3x^2 \ln x$

3. Now differentiate again to find $\dfrac{d^2y}{dx^2}$:
   First part: $\dfrac{d}{dx}(x^2) = 2x$

   Second part: $\dfrac{d}{dx}(3x^2 \ln x)$ — use the product rule again.
   $u = 3x^2$ and $v = \ln x \Rightarrow \dfrac{du}{dx} = 6x$ and $\dfrac{dv}{dx} = \dfrac{1}{x}$
   $u\dfrac{dv}{dx} + v\dfrac{du}{dx} = \left(3x^2 \times \dfrac{1}{x}\right) + (\ln x \times 6x) = 3x + 6x \ln x$

   Putting these together: $\dfrac{d^2y}{dx^2} = 2x + 3x + 6x \ln x = x(5 + 6 \ln x)$

4. For $x > 0$, $\dfrac{d^2y}{dx^2} = 0$ when: $5 + 6 \ln x = 0 \Rightarrow 6 \ln x = -5 \Rightarrow \ln x = -\dfrac{5}{6} \Rightarrow x = e^{-\frac{5}{6}}$

Tip: You're told that there is one point of inflection, so this x-coordinate must be the answer.

Exercise 5.1

Q1   Differentiate $y = x(x + 2)$ with respect to x by:
   a) Multiplying the brackets out and differentiating directly.
   b) Using the product rule.

Q2   Differentiate with respect to x:
   a) $y = x^2(x + 6)^3$ b) $y = x^3(5x + 2)^4$ c) $y = x^3e^x$ d) $y = xe^{4x}$
   e) $y = xe^{x^2}$ f) $y = e^{2x}\sin x$ g) $y = x^4\cos x$ h) $y = x^2\ln x$

Q3　Find $f'(x)$ if:

a)　$f(x) = x^3(x + 3)^{\frac{1}{2}}$　　b)　$f(x) = \dfrac{x^2}{\sqrt{x-7}}$　　　　c)　$f(x) = x^4 \ln x$　　　　d)　$f(x) = 4x \ln x^2$

e)　$f(x) = 2x^3 \cos x$　　f)　$f(x) = x^2 \cos(2x)$　　　g)　$f(x) = \sin x \cos x$　　h)　$f(x) = \sqrt{x}\,\tan x$

Q4　For parts a) and b), multiply out the brackets in your answer and simplify:

a)　Differentiate $y = (x + 1)^2(x^2 - 1)$.　　　b)　Differentiate $y = (x + 1)^3(x - 1)$.

c)　Show by rearranging that the expressions for y in parts a) and b) are the same.

Q5　Find the range of values of x for which the curve $y = xe^x$ is concave.

Q6　Find the equation of the tangent to the curve $y = (\sqrt{x + 2})(\sqrt{x + 7})$ at the point $(2, 6)$.
　　Write your answer in the form $ax + by + c = 0$, where a, b and c are integers.

Q7　For the curve $y = \dfrac{\sqrt{x - 1}}{\sqrt{x + 4}}$

a)　Find the equation of the tangent to the curve when $x = 5$
　　in the form $ax + by + c = 0$ where a, b and c are integers.

b)　Find the equation of the normal to the curve when $x = 5$
　　in the form $ax + by + c = 0$ where a, b and c are integers.

Q8　Differentiate $y = e^{x^2\sqrt{x+3}}$.

Q9　Find $f'(x)$ if $f(x) = \ln\left((2x + 1)^2\sqrt{x - 4}\right)$.

Q10　Find any stationary points for the curve $y = xe^{x - x^2}$.

Q11　a)　Find any stationary points of the curve $y = (x - 2)^2(x + 4)^3$.

b)　By writing the first derivative of $y = (x - 2)^2(x + 4)^3$ in the form $\dfrac{dy}{dx} = (Ax^2 + Bx + C)(x + D)^n$, find $\dfrac{d^2y}{dx^2}$
　　and hence identify the nature of the stationary points of the curve.

6. Quotient Rule

To differentiate one function divided by another, use the **quotient rule**:

$$\text{If } y = \frac{u}{v}, \quad \frac{dy}{dx} = \frac{v\dfrac{du}{dx} - u\dfrac{dv}{dx}}{v^2}$$

Where u and v are functions of x, i.e. $u(x)$ and $v(x)$.

Example　Find $\dfrac{dy}{dx}$ if $y = \dfrac{\sin x}{2x + 1}$.

1.　y is a quotient in the form of $\dfrac{u}{v}$. First identify u and v and differentiate them separately:

　　$u = \sin x \implies \dfrac{du}{dx} = \cos x$　　and　　$v = 2x + 1 \implies \dfrac{dv}{dx} = 2$

2.　Then put the correct bits into the quotient rule:

　　$\dfrac{dy}{dx} = \dfrac{v\dfrac{du}{dx} - u\dfrac{dv}{dx}}{v^2} = \dfrac{(2x + 1)(\cos x) - (\sin x)(2)}{(2x + 1)^2}$

3.　Now just neaten it up:　$\dfrac{dy}{dx} = \dfrac{(2x + 1)\cos x - 2\sin x}{(2x + 1)^2}$

Examples   **a) Determine the nature of the stationary point of the curve $y = \dfrac{\ln x}{x^2}$ $(x > 0)$.**

1. First use the quotient rule to find $\dfrac{dy}{dx}$:

$$u = \ln x \implies \frac{du}{dx} = \frac{1}{x} \quad \text{and} \quad v = x^2 \implies \frac{dv}{dx} = 2x$$

So $\dfrac{dy}{dx} = \dfrac{(x^2)\left(\frac{1}{x}\right) - (\ln x)(2x)}{x^4} = \dfrac{x - 2x\ln x}{x^4} = \dfrac{1 - 2\ln x}{x^3}$

2. The stationary point occurs where $\dfrac{dy}{dx} = 0$ (i.e. zero gradient), so this is when:

$$\frac{1 - 2\ln x}{x^3} = 0 \implies \ln x = \frac{1}{2} \implies x = e^{\frac{1}{2}}$$

3. To find out whether it's a maximum or minimum (see p.103), differentiate $\dfrac{1 - 2\ln x}{x^3}$ using the quotient rule to find $\dfrac{d^2 y}{dx^2}$:

$$u = 1 - 2\ln x \implies \frac{du}{dx} = -\frac{2}{x} \quad \text{and} \quad v = x^3 \implies \frac{dv}{dx} = 3x^2.$$

So $\dfrac{d^2 y}{dx^2} = \dfrac{(x^3)\left(-\frac{2}{x}\right) - (1 - 2\ln x)(3x^2)}{x^6} = \dfrac{6x^2 \ln x - 5x^2}{x^6} = \dfrac{6\ln x - 5}{x^4}$

4. Now put in the x-value of your stationary point:

$$\frac{d^2 y}{dx^2} = \frac{6\ln e^{\frac{1}{2}} - 5}{(e^{\frac{1}{2}})^4} = \frac{3 - 5}{e^2} = -0.27\ldots$$

$\dfrac{d^2 y}{dx^2}$ is negative, so it's a **maximum stationary point**.

b) Prove that the derivative of tan x with respect to x is sec^2 x.

PROBLEM SOLVING

1. First write tan x out as a quotient and set up u and v for the quotient rule:

$$\tan x = \frac{\sin x}{\cos x} = \frac{u}{v}, \text{ so } u = \sin x, \frac{du}{dx} = \cos x \quad \text{and} \quad v = \cos x, \frac{dv}{dx} = -\sin x$$

2. Then just put all the right bits into the quotient rule:

 $\cos^2 x + \sin^2 x \equiv 1$

$$\frac{d}{dx}(\tan x) = \frac{v\frac{du}{dx} - u\frac{dv}{dx}}{v^2} = \frac{\cos x \cos x - \sin x(-\sin x)}{\cos^2 x} = \frac{\cos^2 x + \sin^2 x}{\cos^2 x}$$

$$= \frac{1}{\cos^2 x} = \textbf{sec}^2 \textbf{\textit{x}} \text{ as required}$$

Exercise 6.1

Q1   Differentiate with respect to x:

a) $y = \dfrac{x + 5}{x - 3}$ b) $y = \dfrac{(x - 7)^4}{(5 - x)^3}$ c) $y = \dfrac{e^x}{x^2}$ d) $y = \dfrac{3x}{(x - 1)^2}$

Q2   Find $f'(x)$ for each of the following functions:

a) $f(x) = \dfrac{x^3}{(x + 3)^3}$ b) $f(x) = \dfrac{x^2}{\sqrt{x - 7}}$ c) $f(x) = \dfrac{e^{2x}}{e^{2x} + e^{-2x}}$

d) $f(x) = \dfrac{x}{\sin x}$ e) $f(x) = \dfrac{\sin x}{x}$ f) $f(x) = \dfrac{\ln x}{x^3}$

Q3   Find $f'(x)$ if $f(x) = \dfrac{x^2}{\tan x}$, giving your answer in terms of cot x and cosec x.

Q4 The graph of $y = \frac{5x-4}{2x^2}$ has one stationary point.
Find the coordinates of this point, and show that it is a maximum.

Q5 Use the quotient rule to find the coordinates of any points of inflection of the graph $y = \frac{x}{e^x}$.

Q6 a) Differentiate $y = \frac{x}{\cos(2x)}$ with respect to x.

b) Show that $\frac{dy}{dx} = 0$ when $x = -\frac{1}{2}\cot(2x)$ (you do not need to solve this equation).

Q7 For the curve $y = \frac{1}{1+4\cos x}$:

a) Find the equation of the tangent to the curve when $x = \frac{\pi}{2}$.

b) Find the equation of the normal to the curve when $x = \frac{\pi}{2}$.

Q8 For the curve $y = \frac{2x}{\cos x}$, find the exact value of $\frac{dy}{dx}$ when $x = \frac{\pi}{3}$.

Q9 Show that if $y = \frac{x-\sin x}{1+\cos x}$ then $\frac{dy}{dx} = \frac{x\sin x}{(1+\cos x)^2}$.

Q10 Find $f'(x)$ if $f(x) = \ln\left(\frac{(3x+1)^2}{\sqrt{2x+1}}\right)$.

Q11 Find any turning points on the curve $y = \frac{\cos x}{4-3\cos x}$ in the range $0 \le x \le 2\pi$.

Q12 Differentiate $y = e^{\frac{1+x}{1-x}}$ with respect to x. (PROBLEM SOLVING)

Q13 Find the set of values of x for which $\frac{2+3x^2}{3x-1}$ is increasing.

7. More Trig Differentiation

Since **cosec**, **sec** and **cot** are just **reciprocals** of **sin**, **cos** and **tan** (see p.264), the quotient rule can be used to differentiate them. Using the quotient rule gives the following results:

$y = \operatorname{cosec} x$	$y = \sec x$	$y = \cot x$
$\dfrac{dy}{dx} = -\operatorname{cosec} x \cot x$	$\dfrac{dy}{dx} = \sec x \tan x$	$\dfrac{dy}{dx} = -\operatorname{cosec}^2 x$

As with other rules covered in this chapter, the rules for $\sec x$, $\operatorname{cosec} x$ and $\cot x$ can be used with the **chain**, **product** and **quotient rules** and in combination with all the other functions you've seen so far.

> **Example** Find $\frac{dy}{dx}$ if $y = \cot\frac{x}{2}$.
>
> 1. This is a function (cot) of a function ($\frac{x}{2}$), so you need the chain rule.
>
> 2. You know that $\cot x$ differentiates to give $-\operatorname{cosec}^2 x$ so go straight to identifying u to use in the chain rule:
>
> $$y = \cot u \implies \frac{dy}{du} = -\operatorname{cosec}^2 u = -\operatorname{cosec}^2\frac{x}{2} \quad \text{and} \quad u = \frac{x}{2} \implies \frac{du}{dx} = \frac{1}{2}$$
>
> So $\frac{dy}{dx} = \frac{dy}{du} \times \frac{du}{dx} = -\frac{1}{2}\operatorname{cosec}^2\frac{x}{2}$

Examples   a)   Find $\dfrac{dy}{dx}$ if $y = \sec (2x^2)$.

This is another function of a function, so use the chain rule again:

$$y = \sec u \quad \text{and} \quad u = 2x^2$$

$$\frac{dy}{du} = \sec u \tan u = \sec (2x^2) \tan (2x^2) \quad \text{and} \quad \frac{du}{dx} = 4x$$

So $\dfrac{dy}{dx} = \dfrac{dy}{du} \times \dfrac{du}{dx} = \mathbf{4x \sec (2x^2) \tan (2x^2)}$

b)   Find $\dfrac{dy}{dx}$ if $y = e^x \cot x.$

This is a product of two functions, so use the product rule (see p.320):

$$u = e^x \quad \text{and} \quad v = \cot x \;\Rightarrow\; \frac{du}{dx} = e^x \text{ and } \frac{dv}{dx} = -\text{cosec}^2\, x$$

So $\dfrac{dy}{dx} = u\dfrac{dv}{dx} + v\dfrac{du}{dx} = (e^x \times -\text{cosec}^2\, x) + (\cot x \times e^x) = \mathbf{e^x(\cot x - \text{cosec}^2\, x)}$

Exercise 7.1

Q1   a)   Use the quotient rule to differentiate $y = \dfrac{\cos x}{\sin x}$ and hence show that for $y = \cot x$, $\dfrac{dy}{dx} = -\text{cosec}^2\, x.$

    b)   Show that $\dfrac{d}{dx} \text{cosec}\, x = -\text{cosec}\, x \cot x.$

    c)   Show that $\dfrac{d}{dx} \sec x = \sec x \tan x.$

Q2   Differentiate with respect to x:

    a) $y = \text{cosec}\, (2x)$ b) $y = \text{cosec}^2\, x$ c) $y = \cot (7x)$

    d) $y = \cot^7 x$ e) $y = x^4 \cot x$ f) $y = (x + \sec x)^2$

    g) $y = \text{cosec}\, (x^2 + 5)$ h) $y = e^{3x} \sec x$ i) $y = (2x + \cot x)^3$

Q3   Find $f'(x)$ if:

    a) $f(x) = \dfrac{\sec x}{x + 3}$ b) $f(x) = \sec \dfrac{1}{x}$ c) $f(x) = \sec \sqrt{x}$

Q4   Find $f'(x)$ if:

    a) $f(x) = (\sec x + \text{cosec}\, x)^2$ b) $f(x) = \dfrac{1}{x \cot x}$ c) $(x) = e^x \text{cosec}\, x$

    d) $f(x) = e^{3x} \sec x$ e) $f(x) = e^{3x} \cot (4x)$ f) $f(x) = e^{-2x} \text{cosec}\, (4x)$

    g) $f(x) = \ln (x) \text{cosec}\, x$ h) $f(x) = \sqrt{\sec x}$ i) $f(x) = e^{\sec x}$

Q5   a)   Find $f'(x)$ if $f(x) = \ln (\text{cosec}\, x).$

    b)   Show that the function in part a) can be written as $-\ln (\sin x)$ and differentiate it — you should get the same answer as in part a).

Q6   Find $f'(x)$ if $f(x) = \ln (x + \sec x).$

Q7   Differentiate $y = \sec (\sqrt{x^2 + 5}).$

8. Connected Rates of Change

- Some situations have a number of **linked variables**, like length, surface area and volume or distance, speed and acceleration.

- If you know the **rate of change** of one of these linked variables, and the equations that connect the variables, you can use the **chain rule** to help you find the rate of change of the other variables.

- An equation connecting variables with their rates of change (i.e. with a derivative term) is called a **differential equation** (see p.361-365 for more on differential equations).

Tip: When something changes over time, the derivative is $\frac{d}{dt}$ of that variable.

Example   If $y = 3e^{5x}$ and $\frac{dx}{dt} = 2$, work out $\frac{dy}{dt}$ when $x = -1$.

1. Start by differentiating the expression for y, with respect to x: $\quad\quad y = 3e^{5x} \Rightarrow \frac{dy}{dx} = 15e^{5x}$

2. Write out the chain rule for $\frac{dy}{dt}$, using the information available: $\quad\quad \frac{dy}{dt} = \frac{dy}{dx} \times \frac{dx}{dt}$

3. Put in all the things you know to work out $\frac{dy}{dt}$: $\quad\quad\quad\quad\quad\quad \frac{dy}{dt} = 15e^{5x} \times 2 = 30e^{5x}$

4. Now find the value of $\frac{dy}{dt}$ at $x = -1$: $\quad\quad\quad\quad\quad\quad\quad x = -1 \Rightarrow \frac{dy}{dt} = \mathbf{30e^{-5}}$

In the example below, you have to spot that there's a hidden derivative described in words.

You also need to remember the rule $\frac{dy}{dx} = \frac{1}{\left(\frac{dx}{dy}\right)}$ (see p.314).

Example   **The surface area of a cube is decreasing at a constant rate of 0.027 m² s⁻¹.**
If the side length of the cube after t seconds is x m,
find $\frac{dx}{dt}$ at the point when $x = 15$ m.

1. Start with what you know:

   The cube has side length x m.

   So the surface area of the cube is: $\quad A = 6x^2 \Rightarrow \frac{dA}{dx} = 12x$

   A decreases at a constant rate of 0.027 m² s⁻¹.

   We can write this as $\frac{dA}{dt} = -0.027$. $\longleftarrow$ This value is negative because A is decreasing.

2. Now use the chain rule to find $\frac{dx}{dt}$:

$$\frac{dx}{dt} = \frac{dx}{dA} \times \frac{dA}{dt} = \frac{1}{\left(\frac{dA}{dx}\right)} \times \frac{dA}{dt} = \frac{1}{12x} \times -0.027 = -\frac{0.00225}{x}$$

3. So when $x = 15$: $\quad \frac{dx}{dt} = -\frac{0.00225}{x} = -\frac{0.00225}{15} = \mathbf{-0.00015 \ m \ s^{-1}}$

Exercise 8.1

Q1 A cube with sides x cm is cooling and the sides are shrinking by 0.1 cm min^{-1}.
Find an expression for $\dfrac{dV}{dt}$, the rate of change of volume with respect to time.

Q2 A cuboid block of sides $2x$ cm by $3x$ cm by $5x$ cm expands when heated such that x increases at a rate of 0.15 cm °C^{-1}. If the volume of the cuboid at temperature θ °C is V cm^3, find $\dfrac{dV}{d\theta}$ when $x = 3$.

Q3 A snowball of radius r cm is melting. Its radius decreases by 1.6 cm h^{-1}. If the surface area of the snowball at time t hours is A cm^2, find $\dfrac{dA}{dt}$ when $r = 5.5$ cm. Give your answer to 2 d.p.

Q4 A spherical satellite, radius r m, expands as it enters the atmosphere. The radius grows by 2×10^{-2} mm for every 1 °C rise in temperature. Find an expression $\dfrac{dV}{d\theta}$ for the rate of change of volume with respect to temperature.

Q5 Heat, H, is lost from a closed cylindrical tank of radius r cm and height $3r$ cm at a rate of 2 J cm^{-2} of surface area, A. Find $\dfrac{dH}{dr}$ when $r = 12.3$. Give your answer to 2 d.p.

Q6 A cylindrical polishing block of radius r cm and length H cm is worn down at one circular end at a rate of 0.5 mm h^{-1}. Find an expression for the rate of change of the volume of the block with respect to time.

Q7 A crystal of a salt is shaped like a prism. Its cross section is an equilateral triangle with sides x mm and the height of the crystal is 20 mm. New material is deposited only on the rectangular faces of the prism (i.e. the height does not change), so that x increases at a rate of 0.6 mm per day.

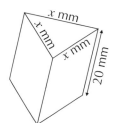

a) Find an expression for the area of the end of the prism in terms of x.

b) Find an expression for the rate of change of the volume of the crystal with respect to time.

c) Find the rate of change of the volume of the crystal with respect to time when $x = 0.5$.

Q8 The growth of a population of bacteria in a sample dish is modelled by the equation: $D = 1 + 2^{\lambda t}$ where D is the diameter of the colony in mm, t is time in days, and λ is a constant. The number of bacteria in the colony, n, is directly proportional to the diameter. A biologist counts the bacteria in the colony when its diameter is 2 mm and estimates that there are approximately 208 bacteria.

a) Find an expression for the rate of change of n with respect to time.

b) Find the rate of increase in number of bacteria after 1 day if $\lambda = 5$.

Q9 Water is dripping from a hole in the base of a cylinder of radius r cm, where the water height is h cm, at a rate of 0.3 cm^3 s^{-1}.

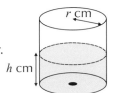

a) Find an expression for $\dfrac{dh}{dt}$, the rate at which the water level falls in the cylinder.

b) Hence find the rate of change in the water level, per minute, in a cylinder of radius 6 cm when the height of water is 4 cm.

Q10 The volume, V, of a hemisphere of radius r cm, varies with its temperature, θ, at a rate of k cm^3 °C^{-1}, where k is a constant that depends on the material of which the hemisphere is made.

a) Find an expression for the rate of change of radius with respect to temperature.

b) Hence find $\dfrac{dr}{d\theta}$ for a material with $k = 1.5$, when $V = 4$ cm^3.

9. Differentiation with Parametric Equations

- In **parametric equations** (see Chapter 19), x and y are defined separately in terms of a third variable.
- A curve can be defined by **two parametric equations**, often with the parameter t:

$$y = f(t) \text{ and } x = g(t)$$

- To find the gradient, $\frac{dy}{dx}$, you could convert the equations into **Cartesian** form (see p.287), but this isn't always possible or convenient.

- By rearranging the **chain rule**, you can get a formula that allows you to differentiate parametric equations without needing to convert to Cartesian form. It looks like this:

$$\frac{dy}{dx} = \frac{dy}{dt} \div \frac{dx}{dt}$$

- So to find $\frac{dy}{dx}$ from parametric equations, **differentiate** each equation with respect to the parameter t, then put the two expressions you get into the formula.

Example The curve C is defined by the parametric equations
$x = t^2 - 1$ and $y = t^3 - 3t + 4$.

a) Find $\frac{dy}{dx}$ in terms of t.

1. Start by differentiating the two parametric equations with respect to t:

$$x = t^2 - 1 \implies \frac{dx}{dt} = 2t$$

$$y = t^3 - 3t + 4 \implies \frac{dy}{dt} = 3t^2 - 3 = 3(t^2 - 1)$$

2. Now use the chain rule to combine them: $\dfrac{dy}{dx} = \dfrac{dy}{dt} \div \dfrac{dx}{dt} = \dfrac{3(t^2 - 1)}{2t}$

b) Find the gradient of C when $t = -2$.

Use the answer to a) to find the gradient for a specific value of t.
So, when $t = -2$:

$$\frac{dy}{dx} = \frac{3((-2)^2 - 1)}{2(-2)} = \frac{3(3)}{-4} = -\frac{9}{4}$$

c) Find the coordinates of the turning points.

1. The turning points occur when $\frac{dy}{dx} = 0$, so solve to find the values of t at the turning points:
$$\frac{dy}{dx} = \frac{3(t^2 - 1)}{2t} = 0 \implies 3(t^2 - 1) = 0 \implies t^2 = 1 \implies t = \pm 1$$

2. Now put these values for t into the original parametric equations to find the Cartesian coordinates of the turning points:
   When $t = 1$ $\quad x = (1)^2 - 1 = 0$
   $\qquad\qquad\quad y = (1)^3 - 3(1) + 4 = 2$. So there's a turning point at **(0, 2)**
   When $t = -1$ $\quad x = (-1)^2 - 1 = 0$
   $\qquad\qquad\quad y = (-1)^3 - 3(-1) + 4 = 6$. So there's another turning point at **(0, 6)**

Exercise 9.1

Q1 For each curve C, defined by the parametric equations given below, find $\frac{dy}{dx}$ in terms of t.

a) $x = t^2$, $y = t^3 - t$
b) $x = t^3 + t$, $y = 2t^2 + 1$
c) $x = t^4$, $y = t^3 - t^2$

d) $x = \cos t$, $y = 4t - t^2$
e) $x = \sin t$, $y = \cos t$
f) $x = e^t$, $y = t^2 - 4t$

Q2 The curve C is defined by the parametric equations $x = t^2$, $y = e^{2t}$.

a) Find $\frac{dy}{dx}$ in terms of t.
b) Find the gradient of C when $t = 1$.

Q3 The curve C is defined by the parametric equations $x = e^{3t}$, $y = 4t^3 - 2t^2$.

a) Find $\frac{dy}{dx}$ in terms of t.
b) Find the gradient of C when $t = 0$.

Q4 The curve C is defined by the parametric equations $x = t^3$, $y = t^2 \cos t$.

a) Find $\frac{dy}{dx}$ in terms of t.
b) Find the gradient of C when $t = \pi$.

Q5 The curve C is defined by the parametric equations $x = t^2 \sin t$, $y = t^3 \sin t + \cos t$.

a) Find $\frac{dy}{dx}$ in terms of t.
b) Find the gradient of C when $t = \pi$.

Q6 The curve C is defined by the parametric equations $x = \ln t$, $y = 3t^2 - t^3$.

a) Find $\frac{dy}{dx}$ in terms of t.
b) Evaluate $\frac{dy}{dx}$ when $t = -1$.

c) Find the exact coordinates of the turning point of the curve C.

Finding tangents and normals

Once you've found the **gradient** of a parametric curve at a particular point, you can use this to find the **equation** of the **tangent** or **normal** to the curve at that point (see p.99 for a reminder of the method).

Example The curve C is defined by the following parametric equations:
$x = \sin t$, $y = 2t \cos t$.

a) **Find the gradient of the curve, and the (x, y) coordinates, when $t = \pi$.**

$\frac{dx}{dt} = \cos t$, $\frac{dy}{dt} = 2\cos t - 2t \sin t$ $\Rightarrow$ $\frac{dy}{dx} = \frac{2\cos t - 2t \sin t}{\cos t} = 2 - 2t \tan t$

When $t = \pi$, $\frac{dy}{dx} = 2 - 2\pi(0) = \mathbf{2}$

When $t = \pi$, $x = 0$, and $y = -2\pi$, so the coordinates are $\mathbf{(0, -2\pi)}$.

b) **Find the equation of the normal to C when $t = \pi$.**

1. The gradient of the normal at $t = \pi$ is: $-1 \div 2 = -\frac{1}{2}$

2. So substitute $m = -\frac{1}{2}$, $x = 0$ and $y = -2\pi$ into $y = mx + c$, to find c:
$$y = mx + c$$
$$-2\pi = -\frac{1}{2}(0) + c \Rightarrow c = -2\pi$$

3. Putting c back into the equation gives: $\mathbf{y = -\frac{1}{2}x - 2\pi}$ or $\mathbf{x + 2y + 4\pi = 0}$

Exercise 9.2

Q1 A curve is defined by the parametric equations $x = t^2$, $y = t^3 - 6t$.
Find the equation of the tangent to the curve at $t = 3$, giving your answer in the form $ax + by + c = 0$.

Q2 A curve C is defined parametrically by $x = t^3 - 2t^2$, $y = t^3 - t^2 + 5t$.
Find the equation of the tangent at the point $t = -1$.

Q3 A curve C is defined by the parametric equations $x = \sin 2t$, $y = t \cos t + 2 \sin t$.
Find the equation of the normal to the curve at $t = \pi$.

Q4 The parametric representation of a curve is given by $x = t \ln t$, $y = t^3 - t^2 + 3$.
Find the equation of the tangent to the curve at $t = 1$.

Q5 The path of a particle is given parametrically by $x = \theta \sin 2\theta$, $y = \theta^2 + \theta \cos \theta$.
Find the equation of the normal to the particle's path at $\theta = \dfrac{\pi}{2}$.

Q6 The motion of a particle is modelled by the parametric equations $x = t^2 - t$, $y = 3t - t^3$.
a) Find the equation of the tangent to the path of the particle when $t = 2$, giving your answer in a suitable form.
b) Find the Cartesian coordinates of the point at which the normal to the path at $t = 2$ cuts the x-axis.

Q7 A particle moves along a path modelled by the parametric equations $x = \sin 2\theta + 2 \cos \theta$, $y = \theta \sin \theta$.
a) Find the gradient $\dfrac{dy}{dx}$ of the particle's path in terms of θ.
b) Evaluate $\dfrac{dy}{dx}$ at $\theta = \dfrac{\pi}{2}$. Hence obtain equations of the tangent and normal to the path at this point.

Q8 A particle moves along a path given parametrically by $x = s^3 \ln s$, $y = s^3 - s^2 \ln s$.
a) Give the value(s) of s at which the path cuts the y-axis.
b) Hence show that the equation of a tangent to the curve when $x = 0$ is $y = 2x + 1$.

Q9 A curve is given parametrically by $x = \theta^2 \sin \theta$, $y = \dfrac{\cos \theta}{\theta^3}$.
a) Show that the gradient of the curve when $\theta = \pi$ is $-\dfrac{3}{\pi^6}$.
b) Hence find the equation of the normal to the curve at this point.

10. Implicit Differentiation

An **'implicit relation'** is the mathematical name for any equation in x and y that's written in the form $f(x, y) = g(x, y)$ instead of $y = f(x)$. For example, $y^2 = xy + x + 2$ is implicit.

Some implicit relations are either awkward or impossible to rewrite in the form $y = f(x)$.
This can make implicit relations tricky to differentiate — the solution is **implicit differentiation**:

- **Step 1:** Differentiate terms in x only (and **constant** terms) with respect to x, as normal.

- **Step 2:** Use the **chain rule** to differentiate terms in y only: $\dfrac{d}{dx}f(y) = \dfrac{d}{dy}f(y)\dfrac{dy}{dx}$

  Tip: In practice, this means 'differentiate with respect to y, and put a $\dfrac{dy}{dx}$ at the end'.

- **Step 3:** Use the **product rule** to differentiate terms in **both x and y**:
  $$\frac{d}{dx}u(x)v(y) = u(x)\frac{d}{dx}v(y) + v(y)\frac{d}{dx}u(x)$$

- **Step 4:** **Rearrange** the resulting equation in x, y and $\dfrac{dy}{dx}$ to make $\dfrac{dy}{dx}$ the subject.

Example a) Use implicit differentiation to find $\dfrac{dy}{dx}$ for $2x^2y + y^3 = 6x^2 - 15$.

1. Start by putting '$\dfrac{d}{dx}$' in front of each term: $\qquad \dfrac{d}{dx}2x^2y + \dfrac{d}{dx}y^3 = \dfrac{d}{dx}6x^2 - \dfrac{d}{dx}15$

2. First, deal with the terms in x and constant terms — the two terms on the right-hand side:
$$\dfrac{d}{dx}2x^2y + \dfrac{d}{dx}y^3 = 12x - 0$$

3. Now use the chain rule on the term in y: $\qquad \dfrac{d}{dx}2x^2y + 3y^2\dfrac{dy}{dx} = 12x - 0$

4. Use the product rule on the term in x and y, where $u(x) = 2x^2$ and $v(y) = y$:
$$2x^2\dfrac{d}{dx}(y) + y\dfrac{d}{dx}(2x^2) + 3y^2\dfrac{dy}{dx} = 12x + 0 \;\Rightarrow\; 2x^2\dfrac{dy}{dx} + y4x + 3y^2\dfrac{dy}{dx} = 12x + 0$$

5. Finally, rearrange to make $\dfrac{dy}{dx}$ the subject: $\qquad \dfrac{dy}{dx}(2x^2 + 3y^2) = 12x - 4xy \;\Rightarrow\; \dfrac{dy}{dx} = \dfrac{12x - 4xy}{2x^2 + 3y^2}$

b) **Find the gradient of the curve $2x^2y + y^3 = 6x^2 - 15$ at the point (2, 1).**

Just put the values for x and y into $\dfrac{dy}{dx}$: $\qquad \dfrac{dy}{dx} = \dfrac{12(2) - 4(2)(1)}{2(2)^2 + 3(1)^2} = \dfrac{16}{11}$

Exercise 10.1

Q1 Use implicit differentiation to find $\dfrac{dy}{dx}$ for each of these curves:

a) $y + y^3 = x^2 + 4$

b) $x^2 + y^2 = 2x + 2y$

c) $\tan y - \sin x = 3x^2$

d) $3x^3 - 4y = y^2 + x$

e) $5x - y^2 = x^5 - 6y$

f) $\cos x + \sin y = x^2 + y^3$

g) $x^3y^2 + \cos x = 4xy$

h) $e^x + e^y = x^3 - y$

i) $3xy^2 + 2x^2y = x^3 + 4x$

Q2 Find the gradient, $\dfrac{dy}{dx}$, for each of these curves given below:

a) $x^3 + 2xy = y^4$

b) $x^2y + y^2 = x^3$

c) $y^3x + y = \sin x$

d) $y\cos x + x\sin y = xy$

e) $e^x + e^y = xy$

f) $\ln x + x^2 = y^3 + y$

g) $e^{2x} + e^{3y} = 3x^2y^2$

h) $x\ln x + y\ln x = x^5 + y^3$

Q3 a) Show that the curve C, defined implicitly by $e^x + 2\ln y = y^3$, passes through (0, 1).

b) Find the gradient of the curve at this point.

Q4 A curve is defined implicitly by $x^3 + y^2 - 2xy = 0$.

a) Find $\dfrac{dy}{dx}$ for this curve.

b) Show that $y = -2 \pm 2\sqrt{3}$ when $x = -2$.

c) Evaluate the gradient at $(-2, -2 + 2\sqrt{3})$, leaving your answer in surd form.

Q5 The curve $x^3 - xy = 2y^2$ passes through the points $(1, -1)$ and $(1, a)$.

a) Find the value of a.

b) Evaluate the gradient of the curve at each of these points.

Q6 A curve is defined implicitly by $x^2y + y^2x = xy + 4$.

a) At which two values of y does the line $x = 1$ cut the curve?

b) By finding $\dfrac{dy}{dx}$, evaluate the gradient at each of these points.

Applications of implicit differentiation

For some equations of the form $y = f(x)$, the easiest way to differentiate them is to **rearrange** them and use implicit differentiation. This method of rearranging and using implicit differentiation is also used to differentiate the **inverse trig functions** (see p.262-263 for more on the inverse trig functions).

Example Find $\dfrac{dy}{dx}$ if $y = \arcsin x$ for $-1 \le x \le 1$.

1. Rearrange the equation to get rid of the arcsin by taking sin of both sides:
$$\sin y = \sin(\arcsin x) \Rightarrow \sin y = x$$

Differentiate the x-term

2. Now use implicit differentiation:
$$\frac{d}{dx}(\sin y) = \frac{d}{dx}(x) \Rightarrow \cos y \, \frac{dy}{dx} = 1$$

3. Rearrange to give an equation for $\dfrac{dy}{dx}$: $\quad \dfrac{dy}{dx} = \dfrac{1}{\cos y}$

Use the chain rule on the y-term

4. To get $\dfrac{1}{\cos y}$ in terms of x, use the identity $\cos^2 x + \sin^2 x \equiv 1$ to write $\cos y$ in terms of $\sin y$:
$$\frac{dy}{dx} = \frac{1}{\sqrt{\cos^2 y}} \Rightarrow \frac{dy}{dx} = \frac{1}{\sqrt{1 - \sin^2 y}}$$

5. Now use the equation $\sin y = x$ to get $\dfrac{dy}{dx}$ in terms of x: $\quad \dfrac{dy}{dx} = \dfrac{1}{\sqrt{1 - x^2}}$

You can use a similar method to differentiate the other inverse trig functions as well — the derivatives are:

$y = \arcsin x$	$y = \arccos x$	$y = \arctan x$
$\dfrac{dy}{dx} = \dfrac{1}{\sqrt{1 - x^2}}$	$\dfrac{dy}{dx} = -\dfrac{1}{\sqrt{1 - x^2}}$	$\dfrac{dy}{dx} = \dfrac{1}{1 + x^2}$

Example A curve defined implicitly by $\sin x - y \cos x = y^2$ passes through two points (π, a) and (π, b), where $a < b$.

a) **Find the values of a and b.**

Put $x = \pi$ into the equation and solve for y:
$$\sin \pi - y \cos \pi = y^2 \Rightarrow 0 + y = y^2$$
$$\Rightarrow y^2 - y = 0 \Rightarrow y(y - 1) = 0$$
$$\Rightarrow y = 0 \text{ and } y = 1, \text{ so } \mathbf{a = 0} \text{ and } \mathbf{b = 1}$$

b) **Find the equations of the tangents to the curve at each of these points.**

1. First find $\dfrac{dy}{dx}$ using implicit differentiation as usual:
$$\cos x + y \sin x - \cos x \, \frac{dy}{dx} = 2y \, \frac{dy}{dx}$$
$$\Rightarrow \frac{dy}{dx} = \frac{\cos x + y \sin x}{2y + \cos x}$$

2. Now put in $x = \pi$ and $y = 0$ to find the gradient at $(\pi, 0)$:
$$\frac{dy}{dx} = \frac{\cos \pi + 0 \sin \pi}{2(0) + \cos \pi} = 1$$

3. So the gradient of the tangent at $(\pi, 0)$ is 1. Putting these values into $y = mx + c$ gives:
$0 = \pi + c \Rightarrow c = -\pi$. So the equation of the tangent at $(\pi, 0)$ is $\mathbf{y = x - \pi}$.

4. Do the same to find the equation of the tangent at $(\pi, 1)$:
$$\frac{dy}{dx} = \frac{\cos \pi + \sin \pi}{2(1) + \cos \pi} = -1$$
$1 = -\pi + c \Rightarrow c = 1 + \pi$. So the equation of the tangent at $(\pi, 1)$ is $\mathbf{y = 1 + \pi - x}$.

Exercise 10.2

Q1 A curve is defined implicitly by $x^2 + 2x + 3y - y^2 = 0$.

a) Find the coordinates of the stationary points (to 2 decimal places).

b) Show that the curve intersects the y-axis when $y = 0$ and $y = 3$.
Hence find the equation of the tangent at each of these points.

Q2 A curve is defined implicitly by $x^3 + x^2 + y = y^2$.

a) Find the coordinates of the stationary points (to 2 decimal places).

b) Show that the curve intersects the line $x = 2$ when $y = 4$ and $y = -3$.
Hence find the equation of the tangent at each of these points.

Q3 A curve is defined implicitly by $x^2y + y^3 = x + 7$.

a) Calculate the x-coordinates of the points on the curve where $y = 1$
and hence find the equations of the normals at these points.

b) Find the coordinates of the point where the normals intersect.

Q4 $e^x + y^2 - xy = 5 - 3y$ is a curve passing through two points $(0, a)$ and $(0, b)$, where $a < b$.

a) Find the values of a and b and show that one of these points is a stationary point of the curve.

b) Find the equations of the tangent and normal to the curve at the other point.

Q5 Differentiate arccos x with respect to x.

Q6 If $y = \arctan x$, show that $\dfrac{dy}{dx} = \dfrac{1}{1+x^2}$.

Q7 The curve C is defined by $\ln x + y^2 = x^2y + 6$.

a) Show that C passes through $(1, 3)$ and $(1, -2)$.

b) Find the equations of the normals to the curve at each of these points
and explain why these normals cannot intersect.

Q8 A curve is defined implicitly by $e^y + x^2 = y^3 + 4x$. Find the equations of the tangents
that touch the curve at $(a, 0)$ and $(b, 0)$. Leave your answer in surd form.

Q9 Show that any point on the curve $y \ln x + x^2 = y^2 - y + 1$ which satisfies $y + 2x^2 = 0$ is a stationary point.

Q10 If $f(x) = \arccos(x^2)$ for $-1 \le x \le 1$, find the equation of the tangent to the graph of $y = f(x)$ when
$x = \dfrac{1}{\sqrt{2}}$ and $0 \le y \le \pi$. Give your answer in the form $y = mx + c$, using exact values for m and c.

Q11 A curve is defined by $e^{2y} + e^x - e^4 = 2xy + 1$.

a) Find the equation of the tangent to the curve when $y = 0$.

b) Find the equation of the normal to the curve when $y = 0$.

c) Show that these two lines intersect when $x = \dfrac{4e^8 + 144}{e^8 + 36}$.

Q12 $y^2x + 2xy - 3x^3 = x^2 + 2$ passes through two points where $x = 2$. Find the equations
of the tangents to the curve at these points, and hence show that they intersect at $\left(-\dfrac{14}{25}, -1\right)$.

Q13 The curve C is defined implicitly by $\cos y \cos x + \cos y \sin x = \dfrac{1}{2}$.

a) Find y when $x = \dfrac{\pi}{2}$ and when $x = \pi$, $0 \le y \le \pi$.

b) Find the equations of the tangents at these points.

Q14 Find the coordinates of the stationary points of the graph $\dfrac{1}{3}y^2 = 6x^3 - 2xy$.

Q1 A curve C has the equation $y = 2x^3 - 12x^2 + 18x + 2$.

    a) Find the values of x for which the curve is: (i) concave,   (ii) convex.

    b) (i) Find the coordinates of the point of inflection.

        (ii) Is this a stationary point of inflection? Explain your answer.

Q2 Differentiate with respect to x:

    a) $y = \sqrt{x^3 + 2x^2}$ b) $y = \dfrac{1}{\sqrt{x^3 + 2x^2}}$ c) $y = e^{5x^2}$ d) $y = \ln(6 - x^2)$

Q3 A curve C has the equation $y = (x^2 - 1)^3$

    a) Differentiate y with respect to x.

    b) Hence find the equation of the normal to the curve C when $x = 2$ in the form $ax + by + c = 0$, where a, b, and c are integers.

Q4 Differentiate the following with respect to x.

    a) $\sqrt{(e^x + e^{2x})}$ b) $3e^{2x+1} - \ln(1 - x^2) + 2x^3$ c) $16^x + e^{\sqrt{x}} + \ln(\cos x)$

Q5 a) Find $\dfrac{dy}{dx}$ as a function of x when: (i) $x = 2e^{2y}$ (ii) $x = \ln(2y + 3)$

    b) Find $\dfrac{dy}{dx}$ as a function of y when $x = \tan y$.

Q6 Find $f'(x)$ for the following functions:

    a) $f(x) = \sin^2(x + 2)$ b) $f(x) = 2\cos(3x)$ c) $f(x) = \sqrt{\tan x}$

Q7 Find $f'(x)$ if $f(x) = e^{\cos(3x)}$.

Q8 Find $f'(x)$ if $f(x) = \sin(4x)\tan x^3$.

Q9 Find the value of the gradient for:

    a) $y = e^{2x}(x^2 - 3)$ when $x = 0$ b) $y = (\ln x)(\sin x)$ when $x = 1$

Q10 Find $\dfrac{dy}{dx}$ when $x = 1$ if $y = e^{x^2}\sqrt{x+1}$.

Q11 Find $\dfrac{dy}{dx}$ if $y = \dfrac{\sqrt{x^2 + 3}}{\cos 3x}$. (PROBLEM SOLVING)

Q12 Differentiate with respect to x:

    a) $y = \cos x \ln x^2$ b) $y = \dfrac{e^{x^2 - x}}{(x + 2)^4}$

Q13 Find the coordinates of the stationary point on the curve $y = \dfrac{e^x}{\sqrt{x}}$.

Q14 Find $f'(x)$ if $f(x) = \dfrac{\cos x^2}{\ln(2x)}$.

Q15 Find the equation of the tangent to the curve $y = \dfrac{6x^2 + 3}{4x^2 - 1}$ at the point (1, 3).

Q16 Find the equation of the normal to the curve for $y = 3\csc\dfrac{x}{4}$ when $x = \pi$ (x is in radians).

Q17 Find $\dfrac{dy}{dx}$ when $x = 0$ for $y = \csc(3x - 2)$.

Q18 Differentiate with respect to x:

    a) $y = \sqrt{\operatorname{cosec} x}$ b) $y = \cot(x^2 + 5)$ c) $y = \dfrac{\sec x}{x^2}$ d) $y = e^{2x}\operatorname{cosec}(5x)$

Q19 A cuboid has length x cm, width $2x$ cm and height $3x$ cm. The cuboid is expanding, because it is being heated. If A is the surface area of the cuboid and V is its volume, find $\dfrac{dA}{dx}$ and $\dfrac{dV}{dx}$, and use them to show that if $\dfrac{dV}{dt} = 3$, then $\dfrac{dA}{dt} = \dfrac{22}{3x}$.

Q20 At the end of its life in the main sequence, a small star like our Sun first expands to a Red Giant and then shrinks to a White Dwarf.

    a) When the star becomes a Red Giant, it expands and cools. The rate of change of radius with respect to temperature is approximately −2500 km K⁻¹. Find an expression for the rate of change of volume (V) with temperature (θ). Model the star as a sphere.

    b) When the star collapses to a White Dwarf, density (ρ) and temperature both increase as the diameter decreases. The rate of change of diameter with respect to temperature, $\dfrac{dD}{d\theta}$, is approximately −215 km K⁻¹. Using the expression $V = kD^3$ for the volume of the star, find an expression for the rate of change of density $\dfrac{d\rho}{d\theta}$, if the mass of the star is m kg ($m = \rho V$).

Q21 A curve is defined by the parametric equations $x = t^2$, $y = 3t^3 - 4t$.

    a) Find $\dfrac{dy}{dx}$ for this curve.

    b) Find the coordinates of the stationary points of the curve.

Q22 The curve C is defined by the parametric equations $x = t \ln t$, $y = 2t^3 - t^2$.

    a) Find $\dfrac{dy}{dx}$ in terms of t.

    b) Find the gradient of C when $t = 1$.

    c) Explain why you cannot evaluate $\dfrac{dy}{dx}$ when $t = 0$.

Q23 The path of a particle is described parametrically by $x = t^2 - 6t$, $y = 2t^3 - 6t^2 - 18t$.

    a) Find $\dfrac{dy}{dx}$ in terms of t.

    b) Hence find any stationary points on the path of the particle.

Q24 A curve C defined by $x = t^3 - t^2$, $y = t^3 + 3t^2 - 9t$ has turning points at (a, b) and (c, d).

    a) Find the coordinates (a, b) and (c, d).

    b) Find the values of t at the points where C cuts the x-axis and hence show that C passes through the origin. Leave your answers in surd form if necessary.

    c) Find the equation of the tangent to C when $t = 2$.

Q25 A curve is given parametrically by $x = 3se^s$, $y = e^{2s} + se^{2s}$

    a) Find the equations of the tangents to the curve at $s = 0$ and $s = 2$.

    b) Hence find the coordinates of the point of intersection of these tangents, leaving your answer in terms of e.

Q26 Use implicit differentiation to prove that $\dfrac{d}{dx}a^x = a^x \ln a$, where a is a constant.

Q27 Curve C is given by $x = \dfrac{\sin\theta}{\theta^2}$, $y = \theta\cos 2\theta$.

    a) Find the gradient of C when $\theta = \dfrac{\pi}{2}$.

    b) Hence find the equation of the tangent to the curve at this point.

    c) Find the values of θ where the curve cuts the x-axis ($\theta \geq 0$), and hence find the coordinates of the point with $0 \leq \theta \leq \dfrac{\pi}{2}$ where the curve cuts the x-axis.

Q28 The trajectory of a particle is given by the parametric equations $x = t^3 + t^2$, $y = \dfrac{1}{2}t^2 - 6t$.

    a) Find the gradient $\dfrac{dy}{dx}$ of the trajectory in terms of t.

    b) Hence find the turning point of the trajectory.

    c) Find the equations of the tangents to the trajectory when $y = 0$.

Q29 Use implicit differentiation to find $\dfrac{dy}{dx}$ for each of the following equations:

    a) $4x^2 - 2y^2 = 7x^2 y$ b) $3x^4 - 2xy^2 = y$ c) $\cos x \sin y = xy$

Q30 Using your answers to Q29 above, find:

    a) the gradient of the tangent to the graph of $4x^2 - 2y^2 = 7x^2 y$ at $(1, -4)$,

    b) the gradient of the normal to the graph of $3x^4 - 2xy^2 = y$ at $(1, 1)$.

Q31 The curve $x^2 y + y^2 = x^2 + 1$ passes through the points $(1, -2)$ and $(1, a)$.

    a) Find a.

    b) Find the gradient of the curve at $(1, -2)$.

    c) Show that $(1, a)$ is a turning point of the curve.

Q32 A curve is defined implicitly by $y\cos x - y^2 = x\sin x$.

    a) Show that $x = 0$, $y = 1$ is a solution to the equation.

    b) Show that $(0, 1)$ is a turning point of the curve.

Q33 A curve is defined implicitly by $x\cos x + y\sin x = y^3$.

    a) Find the gradient $\dfrac{dy}{dx}$ of the curve.

    b) Show that at the stationary points of the curve, $y = x\tan x - 1$.

    c) Show that there are three points on the curve with coordinates $\left(\dfrac{\pi}{2}, a\right)$.

    d) Find the equations of the tangents at each of these points and hence show that two of these tangents will never intersect.

Q34 The curve $4y + x^2 y^2 = 4x$ passes through the two points $(2, a)$ and $(2, b)$, where $a > b$.

By finding a and b and the gradient $\dfrac{dy}{dx}$ of the curve, show that the tangents to the curve at $(2, a)$ and $(2, b)$ intersect at $(5, 1)$.

Q35 The curve $x\ln x + x^2 y = y^2 x - 6x$ passes through two points $(1, a)$ and $(1, b)$, where $a > b$.

    a) Find a and b.

    b) Use implicit differentiation to find the gradient of the curve at each of these points and hence the equations of the normals passing through the points.

    c) Find the coordinates of the point where the normals intersect.

Chapter 23 — Integration 2

You've already seen how to integrate functions of the form x^n in Chapter 9. In this chapter, you'll learn some new methods that will help you to integrate much more complicated functions.

1. Integration of $(ax + b)^n$

Differentiating $(ax + b)^{n+1}$ using the chain rule gives $a(n + 1)(ax + b)^n$ (see p.312 for the chain rule). You can use this result to get the following rule for **integrating** $(ax + b)^n$:

$$\int (ax + b)^n \, dx = \frac{1}{a(n+1)}(ax + b)^{n+1} + C$$

Tip: This rule only works for $n \neq -1$. See p.339 to find out how to integrate x^{-1} and $(ax + b)^{-1}$.

Examples

a) Find $\int (3 - 4x)^2 \, dx$, using the general expression for $\int (ax + b)^n \, dx$.

Write down the values of a, b and n and then substitute them into the formula.
Here $a = -4$, $b = 3$ and $n = 2$.

$$\int (3 - 4x)^2 \, dx = \frac{1}{-4 \times 3}(3 - 4x)^3 + C = -\frac{1}{12}(3 - 4x)^3 + C$$

Don't forget the constant of integration.

$a = -4$ $n + 1 = 3$

b) **Work out the area enclosed by the curve $y = (x - 2)^3$, the x-axis and the lines $x = 2$ and $x = 3$.**

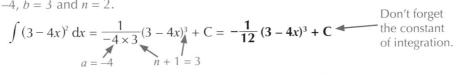

$y = (x - 2)^3$

1. You need to evaluate the integral $\int_2^3 (x - 2)^3 \, dx$, so use the formula with $a = 1$, $b = -2$ and $n = 3$:

$$\int_2^3 (x - 2)^3 \, dx = \frac{1}{4}[(x - 2)^4]_2^3$$

2. Substitute in the limits of integration to find the area.

$$= \frac{1}{4}[(3 - 2)^4] - \frac{1}{4}[(2 - 2)^4] = \frac{1}{4}[1^4] - \frac{1}{4}[0^4] = \frac{1}{4} - 0 = \frac{1}{4}$$

Exercise 1.1

Q1 Integrate with respect to x:

a) $(x + 10)^{10}$ b) $(5x)^7$ c) $(5x + 2)^4$ d) $(3 - 5x)^{-2}$ e) $(3x - 4)^{-\frac{4}{3}}$

Q2 a) By using the general expression for $\int (ax + b)^n \, dx$,

show that the integral $A = \int 8(2x - 4)^4 \, dx = \frac{4(2x - 4)^5}{5} + C$.

b) Hence evaluate A between the values $x = \frac{3}{2}$ and $x = \frac{5}{2}$.

Q3 Evaluate: a) $\int_0^1 (6x + 1)^{-3} \, dx$ b) $\int_1^{1.5} (3 - 2x)^3 \, dx$ c) $\int_2^{2.5} (4x - 7)^{-2} \, dx$

Q4 The curve $y = f(x)$ goes through the point $\left(1, \frac{3}{35}\right)$ and $f'(x) = (8 - 7x)^4$. Find $f(x)$.

2. Integration of e^x and $\dfrac{1}{x}$

Integrating e^x and e^{ax+b}

e^x differentiates to give e^x, so it makes sense that e^x **integrates** to give $e^x + C$:

$$\int e^x dx = e^x + C$$

Example **Integrate the function $6x^2 - 4x + 3e^x$ with respect to x.**

Integrate each term separately:

$$\int 3e^x \, dx = 3 \int e^x \, dx = 3e^x + c$$

$$\int 6x^2 - 4x + 3e^x \, dx = 2x^3 - 2x^2 + 3e^x + C$$

Differentiating e^{ax+b} using the chain rule gives ae^{ax+b}.
You can use this result to get the following rule for **integrating** e^{ax+b}:

$$\int e^{ax+b} dx = \frac{1}{a} e^{ax+b} + C \qquad \text{for } a \neq 0$$

This means you just need to **divide** by the **coefficient of x** and add a constant of integration — the e^{ax+b} bit **doesn't change**.

Examples **Integrate the following:**

a) e^{7x}

$$\int e^{7x} \, dx = \frac{1}{7} e^{7x} + C$$

b) $e^{\frac{x}{2}}$

$$\int e^{\frac{x}{2}} \, dx = \int e^{\frac{1}{2}x} \, dx = 2e^{\frac{x}{2}} + C$$

c) $2e^{4-3x}$

$$\int 2e^{4-3x} \, dx = -\frac{2}{3} e^{4-3x} + C$$

Multiplying by 2 doesn't change the integration — the coefficient of x is -3, so divide by -3 and you're done.

Exercise 2.1

Q1 Find the following indefinite integrals:

a) $\displaystyle\int 2e^x \, dx$

b) $\displaystyle\int 4x + 7e^x \, dx$

c) $\displaystyle\int e^{10x} \, dx$

d) $\displaystyle\int e^{-3x} + x \, dx$

e) $\displaystyle\int e^{\frac{7}{2}x} \, dx$

f) $\displaystyle\int e^{4x-2} \, dx$

g) $\displaystyle\int \frac{1}{2} e^{2-\frac{3}{2}x} \, dx$

h) $\displaystyle\int e^{4\left(\frac{x}{3}+1\right)} \, dx$

Q2 Find the equation of the curve that has the derivative $\dfrac{dy}{dx} = 10e^{-5x-1}$ and passes through the origin.

Q3 Integrate the function e^{8y+5} with respect to y.

Q4 Evaluate the following definite integrals, giving exact answers:

a) $\displaystyle\int_2^3 e^{2x} \, dx$

b) $\displaystyle\int_{-1}^0 12e^{12x+12} \, dx$

c) $\displaystyle\int_{-\frac{\pi}{2}}^{\frac{\pi}{2}} e^{\pi-2x} \, dx$

d) $\displaystyle\int_3^6 \sqrt[6]{e^x} + \frac{1}{\sqrt[3]{e^x}} \, dx$

Integrating $\frac{1}{x}$ and $\frac{1}{ax + b}$

The method for integrating x^n (see p.113) and $(ax + b)^n$ (see p.337) doesn't work for $n = -1$.

For these functions you need to consider the fact that $\frac{d}{dx}(\ln x) = \frac{1}{x}$, which you should

remember from Chapter 22. This gives a general result for integrating $\frac{1}{x}$:

$$\int \frac{1}{x}\,dx = \ln|x| + C$$

Tip: Notice that this result uses $|x|$ instead of just x.
This is because the function $\ln x$ is **not defined** for **negative values** of x.
Using the modulus means you'll never end up taking $\ln$ of a negative value.

Example Find $\int_3^9 \frac{1}{3x}\,dx$.

1. Take the coefficient $\left(\frac{1}{3}\right)$ outside the integral and integrate using the result above:
$$\int_3^9 \frac{1}{3x}\,dx = \frac{1}{3}\int_3^9 \frac{1}{x}\,dx = \frac{1}{3}[\ln|x|]_3^9$$

2. Put in the limits and use log laws (see p.86) to simplify: $= \frac{1}{3}(\ln|9| - \ln|3|) = \frac{1}{3}(\ln(\frac{9}{3})) = \frac{1}{3}\ln 3$

$$\ln a - \ln b = \ln \frac{a}{b}$$

The **general result** for integrating functions of the form $\frac{1}{ax + b}$ is:

$$\int \frac{1}{ax + b}\,dx = \frac{1}{a}\ln|ax + b| + C$$

Example Find $\int \frac{1}{2x + 5}\,dx$.

Using the general rule, $a = 2$ and $b = 5$ so the integral is: $\int \frac{1}{2x + 5}\,dx = \frac{1}{2}\ln|2x + 5| + C$

Exercise 2.2

Q1 Find the following:

a) $\int \frac{19}{x}\,dx$ b) $\int \frac{1}{7x}\,dx$ c) $\int \frac{1}{7x + 2}\,dx$ d) $\int \frac{4}{1 - 3x}\,dx$ e) $\int \frac{-2}{3 - 8x}\,dx$

Q2 Integrate $y = \frac{1}{8x} - \frac{20}{x}$ with respect to x.

Q3 a) Show that $\int \frac{6}{x} - \frac{3}{x}\,dx = \ln|x^3| + C$. b) Evaluate $\int_4^5 \frac{6}{x} - \frac{3}{x}\,dx$, giving an exact answer.

Q4 Show that $\int_b^a 15(5 + 3x)^{-1}\,dx = \ln\left|\frac{5 + 3a}{5 + 3b}\right|^5$.

Q5 The graph of the curve $y = f(x)$ passes through the point $(1, 2)$.
The derivative of $f(x)$ is given by $f'(x) = \frac{4}{10 - 9x}$. Find $f(x)$.

Q6 a) Express the area bounded by the curve $y = \frac{-7}{16 - 2x}$, the x-axis, the y-axis, and the line $x = -3$
as an integral with respect to x.

b) Show that the area is equal to $\ln\left[\left(\frac{8}{11}\right)^{\frac{7}{2}}\right]$.

Q7 Given that $\int_1^A \frac{4}{6x - 5}\,dx = 10$ and $A \geq 1$, find A in terms of e.

3. Integration of Trigonometric Functions

Integration of $\sin x$ and $\cos x$

Remember from Chapter 22 that $\sin x$ differentiates to $\cos x$, and $\cos x$ differentiates to $-\sin x$. Working backwards from this, we get:

$$\int \sin x \, dx = -\cos x + C \qquad\qquad \int \cos x \, dx = \sin x + C$$

Example Find $\int_0^\pi \dfrac{\sin x}{2} + \dfrac{1}{\pi} \, dx$.

1. Integrate each term separately: $\int_0^\pi \dfrac{\sin x}{2} + \dfrac{1}{\pi} \, dx = \left[\dfrac{1}{2}(-\cos x) + \dfrac{1}{\pi}x\right]_0^\pi = \left[-\dfrac{1}{2}\cos x + \dfrac{1}{\pi}x\right]_0^\pi$

2. Put in the limits: $\left[-\dfrac{1}{2}\cos x + \dfrac{1}{\pi}x\right]_0^\pi = \left[-\dfrac{1}{2}\cos\pi + \left(\dfrac{1}{\pi} \times \pi\right)\right] - \left[-\dfrac{1}{2}\cos 0 + \left(\dfrac{1}{\pi} \times 0\right)\right]$

$$= \left[-\dfrac{1}{2}(-1) + 1\right] - \left[-\dfrac{1}{2}(1) + 0\right] = \left[\dfrac{1}{2} + 1\right] - \left[-\dfrac{1}{2} + 0\right] = \mathbf{2}$$

To integrate trig functions of the form $\sin(ax + b)$ and $\cos(ax + b)$, use the following results:

$$\int \sin(ax + b) \, dx = -\dfrac{1}{a}\cos(ax + b) + C \qquad\qquad \int \cos(ax + b) \, dx = \dfrac{1}{a}\sin(ax + b) + C$$

Example Find $\int \sin(1 - 6x) \, dx$.

Using the general formula with $a = -6$ and $b = 1$ gives: $\int \sin(1 - 6x) \, dx = \dfrac{1}{-6} \times -\cos(1 - 6x) + C$

$$= \dfrac{1}{6}\cos(1 - 6x) + C$$

Exercise 3.1

Q1 Integrate the following functions with respect to x.

a) $\dfrac{1}{7}\cos x$ b) $-3\sin x$ c) $-3\cos x - 3\sin x$ d) $\sin 5x$ e) $\cos\left(\dfrac{x}{7}\right)$

f) $2\sin(-3x)$ g) $5\cos\left(3x + \dfrac{\pi}{5}\right)$ h) $-4\sin\left(4x - \dfrac{\pi}{3}\right)$ i) $\cos(4x + 3) + \sin(3 - 4x)$

Q2 Integrate $\dfrac{1}{2}\cos 3\theta - \sin\theta$ with respect to θ.

Q3 Evaluate the following definite integrals:

a) $\displaystyle\int_0^{\frac{\pi}{2}} \sin x \, dx$ b) $\displaystyle\int_0^{\frac{\pi}{2}} 2\cos x \, dx$ c) $\displaystyle\int_{\frac{\pi}{6}}^{\frac{\pi}{3}} \sin 3x \, dx$ d) $\displaystyle\int_{-1}^{2} 3\sin(\pi x + \pi) \, dx$

Q4 a) Integrate the function $y = 2\pi\cos\left(\dfrac{\pi x}{2}\right)$ with respect to x between the limits $x = 1$ and $x = 2$.

b) Given that the function doesn't cross the x-axis between these limits, state whether the area between the curve and the x-axis for $1 \leq x \leq 2$ lies above or below the x-axis, justifying your answer.

Q5 Show that $\displaystyle\int_{\frac{\pi}{3}}^{\frac{\pi}{2}} \sin(-x) + \cos(-x) \, dx = \dfrac{1 - \sqrt{3}}{2}$.

Q6 Show that the integral of the function $y = 5\cos\left(\dfrac{x}{6}\right)$ between $x = -2\pi$ and $x = \pi$ is $15(1 + \sqrt{3})$.

Integration of sec² x

Use the following results to integrate $\sec^2 x$ and $\sec^2(ax + b)$:

$$\int \sec^2 x \, dx = \tan x + C \qquad \qquad \int \sec^2(ax + b) \, dx = \frac{1}{a}\tan(ax + b) + C$$

Example Find $\int \cos 4x - 2\sin 2x + \sec^2\left(\frac{1}{2}x\right) dx.$

Integrate each term separately using the results from above and the previous page:

$$\int \cos 4x - 2\sin 2x + \sec^2\left(\frac{1}{2}x\right) dx = \frac{1}{4}\sin 4x + \cos 2x + 2\tan\left(\frac{1}{2}x\right) + C$$

Exercise 3.2

Q1 Find the following integrals:

a) $\int 2\sec^2 x + 1 \, dx$

b) $\int \sec^2 9x \, dx$

c) $\int 20\sec^2 3y \, dy$

d) $\int \sec^2 \frac{x}{7} \, dx$

e) $\int_0^{\frac{\pi}{3}} -\frac{1}{\cos^2\theta} \, d\theta$

f) $\int_0^{\frac{\pi}{4}} 3\sec^2(3x) \, dx$

Q2 Find the value of the integral of the function $y = \sec^2 x$ between the limits $x = \frac{2}{3}\pi$ and $x = \pi$.

Q3 Integrate $\sec^2(x + \alpha) + \sec^2(3x + \beta)$ with respect to x, where α and β are constants.

Q4 For a constant A, integrate $5A\sec^2\left(\frac{\pi}{3} - 2\theta\right)$ with respect to θ between the limits of $\theta = \frac{\pi}{12}$ and $\theta = \frac{\pi}{6}$.

Integration of other trigonometric functions

The $ax + b$ bit has to be the same in each trig function.

Use the results below to integrate more complicated trig functions:

$$\int \text{cosec}\,x \cot x \, dx = -\text{cosec}\,x + C$$
$$\int \sec x \tan x \, dx = \sec x + C$$
$$\int \text{cosec}^2 x \, dx = -\cot x + C$$

$$\int \text{cosec}(ax + b)\cot(ax + b) \, dx = -\frac{1}{a}\text{cosec}(ax + b) + C$$
$$\int \sec(ax + b)\tan(ax + b) \, dx = \frac{1}{a}\sec(ax + b) + C$$
$$\int \text{cosec}^2(ax + b) \, dx = -\frac{1}{a}\cot(ax + b) + C$$

Example Find $\int_0^{\pi} \text{cosec}^2\left(\frac{x}{2} - \frac{\pi}{4}\right) dx.$

This is a definite integral, so you need to evaluate between the limits.

$$\int_0^{\pi} \text{cosec}^2\left(\frac{x}{2} - \frac{\pi}{4}\right) dx = \left[-\frac{1}{\left(\frac{1}{2}\right)}\cot\left(\frac{x}{2} - \frac{\pi}{4}\right)\right]_0^{\pi} = -2\left[\cot\left(\frac{x}{2} - \frac{\pi}{4}\right)\right]_0^{\pi} = -2\left[\frac{1}{\tan\left(\frac{x}{2} - \frac{\pi}{4}\right)}\right]_0^{\pi}$$

$$= -2\left(\frac{1}{\tan\left(\frac{\pi}{2} - \frac{\pi}{4}\right)} - \frac{1}{\tan\left(0 - \frac{\pi}{4}\right)}\right) = -2\left(\frac{1}{\tan\left(\frac{\pi}{4}\right)} - \frac{1}{\tan\left(-\frac{\pi}{4}\right)}\right) = -2\left(\frac{1}{1} - \frac{1}{(-1)}\right) = -4$$

Example Find $\int 10\sec 5x \tan 5x + \frac{1}{2}\operatorname{cosec} 3x \cot 3x - \operatorname{cosec}^2(6x+1)\,dx$.

Integrate each bit in turn and add the constant:

$\int 10\sec 5x \tan 5x + \frac{1}{2}\operatorname{cosec} 3x \cot 3x - \operatorname{cosec}^2(6x+1)\,dx$

$= 10\left(\frac{1}{5}\sec 5x\right) + \frac{1}{2}\left(-\frac{1}{3}\operatorname{cosec} 3x\right) - \left(-\frac{1}{6}\cot(6x+1)\right) = \mathbf{2\sec 5x - \frac{1}{6}\operatorname{cosec} 3x + \frac{1}{6}\cot(6x+1) + C}$

Exercise 3.3

Q1 Find the following integrals:

a) $\int \operatorname{cosec}^2 11x\,dx$

b) $\int 5\sec 10\theta \tan 10\theta\,d\theta$

c) $\int -\operatorname{cosec}(x+17)\cot(x+17)\,dx$

d) $\int -3\operatorname{cosec} 3x \cot 3x\,dx$

e) $\int 13\sec\left(\frac{\pi}{4}-x\right)\tan\left(\frac{\pi}{4}-x\right)dx$

Q2 Find $\int 10\operatorname{cosec}^2\left(\alpha - \frac{x}{2}\right) - 60\sec(\alpha - 6x)\tan(\alpha - 6x)\,dx$ where α is a constant.

Q3 Integrate the function $6\sec 2x \tan 2x + 6\operatorname{cosec} 2x \cot 2x$ with respect to x between the limits of $x = \frac{\pi}{12}$ and $x = \frac{\pi}{8}$.

Q4 Find the area of the region bounded by $y = \operatorname{cosec}^2(3x)$, the x-axis and the lines $x = \frac{\pi}{12}$ and $x = \frac{\pi}{6}$.

4. Integration of $\dfrac{f'(x)}{f(x)}$

If you have a fraction where the **numerator** is the **derivative** of the **denominator**, e.g. $\frac{3x^2}{x^3+1}$, it integrates to give **ln** of the denominator:

$$\int \frac{f'(x)}{f(x)}\,dx = \ln|f(x)| + C$$

Examples **a)** Integrate $\dfrac{x(3x-4)}{x^3 - 2x^2 - 1}$ with respect to x.

1. Differentiate the denominator: $\frac{d}{dx}(x^3 - 2x^2 - 1) = 3x^2 - 4x = x(3x-4)$

2. The numerator is the derivative of the denominator, so use the formula:

$$\int \frac{x(3x-4)}{x^3 - 2x^2 - 1}\,dx = \ln|x^3 - 2x^2 - 1| + C$$

b) Find $\int \dfrac{8x^3 - 4}{x^4 - 2x}\,dx$.

1. Differentiating: $\frac{d}{dx}(x^4 - 2x) = 4x^3 - 2$ and $8x^3 - 4 = 2(4x^3 - 2)$

2. The numerator is $2 \times$ the derivative of the denominator, so

$$\int \frac{8x^3 - 4}{x^4 - 2x}\,dx = 2\int \frac{4x^3 - 2}{x^4 - 2x}\,dx = \mathbf{2\ln|x^4 - 2x| + C}$$

Example Find $\int \dfrac{3\sin 3x}{\cos 3x + 2}\, dx$.

1. Differentiating: $\dfrac{d}{dx}(\cos 3x + 2) = -3\sin 3x$

2. The numerator is $-1 \times$ the derivative of the denominator, so
$$\int \frac{3\sin 3x}{\cos 3x + 2}\, dx = -\int \frac{-3\sin 3x}{\cos 3x + 2}\, dx = -(\ln|\cos 3x + 2| + C)$$

3. You can combine the answer into one logarithm by writing C as $\ln k$ and using log laws:
$$= -(\ln|\cos 3x + 2| + \ln k) = -\ln|k(\cos 3x + 2)|$$

Exercise 4.1

Q1 Find the following integrals:

a) $\int \dfrac{4x^3}{x^4 - 1}\, dx$

b) $\int \dfrac{2x - 1}{x^2 - x}\, dx$

c) $\int \dfrac{x^4}{3x^5 + 6}\, dx$

d) $\int \dfrac{12x^3 + 18x^2 - 3}{x^4 + 2x^3 - x}\, dx$

Q2 Find the indefinite integrals below:

a) $\int \dfrac{e^x}{e^x + 6}\, dx$

b) $\int \dfrac{2(e^{2x} + 3e^x)}{e^{2x} + 6e^x}\, dx$

c) $\int \dfrac{e^x}{3(e^x + 3)}\, dx$

d) $\int \dfrac{18e^{3x+4}}{2e^{3x+4} + 8}\, dx$

Q3 Find the following integrals:

a) $\int \dfrac{2\cos 2x}{1 + \sin 2x}\, dx$

b) $\int \dfrac{\sin 3x}{\cos 3x - 1}\, dx$

c) $\int \dfrac{3\,\text{cosec}\, x\cot x + 6x}{\text{cosec}\, x - x^2 + 4}\, dx$

d) $\int \dfrac{\sec^2 x}{\tan x}\, dx$

e) $\int \dfrac{\sec x\tan x}{\sec x + 5}\, dx$

f) $\int \dfrac{-5\,\text{cosec}^2 5x}{\cot 5x}\, dx$

Q4 Show that $\int \dfrac{4\cos(2x + 7)}{\sin(2x + 7)}\, dx = 2\ln|k\sin(2x + 7)|$.

You can use this method to integrate **trig functions** by writing them as fractions.

You can work out the integral of **tan x** using this method: $\tan x = \dfrac{\sin x}{\cos x}$, and $\dfrac{d}{dx}(\cos x) = -\sin x$

The numerator is **$-1 \times$** the **derivative** of the **denominator**, so $\int \tan x\, dx = \int \dfrac{\sin x}{\cos x}\, dx = -\ln|\cos x| + C$

You might see this result written in the following form:

Tip: The integral of tan, $-\ln|\cos x|$, is the same as $\ln|\sec x|$ by the laws of logs.

$$\int \tan kx\, dx = \frac{1}{k}\ln|\sec kx| + C$$

There are some other **trig functions** that you can integrate in the same way:

$$\int \text{cosec}\, x\, dx = -\ln|\text{cosec}\, x + \cot x| + C$$
$$\int \sec x\, dx = \ln|\sec x + \tan x| + C$$
$$\int \cot x\, dx = \ln|\sin x| + C$$

Example Find $\int \dfrac{\cot x}{5}\, dx$.　　$\dfrac{\cot x}{5} = \dfrac{1}{5}\cot x$ so there is a constant of $\dfrac{1}{5}$.

Use the result for $\cot x$ above: $\int \dfrac{\cot x}{5}\, dx = \dfrac{1}{5}\ln|\sin x| + C$

> **Example** Find $\int \frac{1}{2} \operatorname{cosec} 2x \, dx.$ Divide by 2 when you integrate.
>
> Use the result for cosec x: $\int \frac{1}{2} \operatorname{cosec} 2x \, dx = -\frac{1}{4} \ln|\operatorname{cosec} 2x + \cot 2x| + C$

Exercise 4.2

Q1 Find the following integrals:

a) $\int 2 \tan x \, dx$ b) $\int \tan 2x \, dx$ c) $\int 4 \operatorname{cosec} x \, dx$

d) $\int \cot 3x \, dx$ e) $\int \frac{1}{2} \sec 2x \, dx$ f) $\int 3 \operatorname{cosec} 6x \, dx$

Q2 Find $\int \frac{\sec^2 x}{2 \tan x} - 4 \sec 2x \tan 2x + \frac{\operatorname{cosec} 2x \cot 2x - 1}{\operatorname{cosec} 2x + 2x} \, dx.$

Q3 a) If $f(x) = \sec x + \tan x$, show that $\frac{f'(x)}{f(x)} = \sec x.$

   b) Hence prove that $\int \sec x \, dx = \ln|\sec x + \tan x| + C.$

5. Integrating $\frac{du}{dx} f'(u)$

Integrating using the reverse of the chain rule

In Chapter 22, you used the chain rule to differentiate a **function of a function**.
Using the chain rule **in reverse** gives you the following result:

$$\int \frac{du}{dx} f'(u) \, dx = f(u) + C$$

Tip: If you're integrating an expression which contains a **function of a function**, f(u), try differentiating the function u. If the **derivative** of u is also part of the expression, you might be able to use this formula.

> **Examples** Find the following integrals:
>
> a) $\int 6x^5 e^{x^6} \, dx$
>
> 1. Here, $u = x^6$ — it appears once differentiated $(6x^5)$ and once within a function (e^{x^6}).
>
> 2. Split the integral into $\frac{du}{dx}$ and f'(u): $\int \underbrace{6x^5}_{\frac{du}{dx}} \underbrace{e^{x^6}}_{f'(u)} \, dx$ $f(u) = e^u$
>
> 3. Now use the formula $\int \frac{du}{dx} f'(u) \, dx = f(u) + C$ to write down the result: $\int 6x^5 e^{x^6} \, dx = e^{x^6} + C$
>
> b) $\int x^4 \sin(x^5) \, dx$
>
> 1. Here, $u = x^5$. You'll need to take out a constant to get the integral you want:
> $$\int x^4 \sin(x^5) \, dx = \frac{1}{5} \int 5x^4 \sin(x^5) \, dx$$
>
> 2. Now split up the integral: $\frac{du}{dx} = 5x^4$ and $f'(u) = \sin(x^5)$ $f(u) = -\cos u$
>
> 3. Use the formula: $\frac{1}{5} \int 5x^4 \sin(x^5) \, dx = \frac{1}{5}(-\cos(x^5) + c) = -\frac{1}{5} \cos(x^5) + C$

Exercise 5.1

Q1 Find the following integrals:

a) $\int 2xe^{x^2} \, dx$

b) $\int 6x^2 e^{2x^3} \, dx$

c) $\int \frac{1}{2\sqrt{x}} e^{\sqrt{x}} \, dx$

d) $\int x^3 e^{x^4} \, dx$

e) $\int (4x-1)e^{(x^2 - \frac{1}{2}x)} \, dx$

f) $\int 2x \sin(x^2 + 1) \, dx$

g) $\int x^3 \cos(x^4) \, dx$

h) $\int x \sec^2(x^2) \, dx$

i) $\int e^{\cos x} \sin x \, dx$

j) $\int \cos 2x \, e^{\sin 2x} \, dx$

k) $\int \sec^2 x \, e^{\tan x} \, dx$

l) $\int \sec x \tan x \, e^{\sec x} \, dx$

Integrating f'(x) × [f(x)]ⁿ

Some expressions are made up of a **function** and its **derivative**:

If part of a product is the **derivative** of the other part of it (which is raised to a **power**), you can integrate it using this rule (which is a special case of the 'reverse chain rule' on p.344):

This bracket is the **derivative**...

e.g. $3(3x^2 + 4)(x^3 + 4x)^2$

...of this bracket.

This function is the **derivative**...

$$\int (n + 1)f'(x)[f(x)]^n \, dx = [f(x)]^{n + 1} + C$$

...of this function.

Exercise 5.2

Q1 Find the following indefinite integrals:

a) $\int 6x(x^2 + 5)^2 \, dx$

b) $\int (2x + 7)(x^2 + 7x)^4 \, dx$

c) $\int (x^3 + 2x)(x^4 + 4x^2)^3 \, dx$

d) $\int \dfrac{2x}{(x^2 - 1)^3} \, dx$

e) $\int \dfrac{6e^{3x}}{(e^{3x} - 5)^2} \, dx$

f) $\int \sin x \cos^5 x \, dx$

g) $\int 2 \sec^2 x \tan^3 x \, dx$

h) $\int 3e^x(e^x + 4)^2 \, dx$

i) $\int 32(2e^{4x} - 3x)(e^{4x} - 3x^2)^7 \, dx$

j) $\int \dfrac{\cos x}{(2 + \sin x)^4} \, dx$

k) $\int 5 \operatorname{cosec} x \cot x \operatorname{cosec}^4 x \, dx$

l) $\int 2 \operatorname{cosec}^2 x \cot^3 x \, dx$

Q2 Find the following integrals:

a) $\int 6 \tan x \sec^6 x \, dx$

b) $\int \cot x \operatorname{cosec}^3 x \, dx$

c) $\int 30 \operatorname{cosec}^2 x \cot^5 x \, dx$

Q3 Integrate the following functions with respect to x:

a) $4 \cos x \, e^{\sin x}(e^{\sin x} - 5)^3$

b) $(\sin x \, e^{\cos x} - 4)(e^{\cos x} + 4x)^6$

c) $5 \sec^2 x \, e^{\tan x}(e^{\tan x} + 3)^4$

Q4 Integrate:

a) $\int \dfrac{\sin x}{\cos^5 x} \, dx$

b) $\int \dfrac{\sec^2 x}{\tan^4 x} \, dx$

c) $\int \cot x \operatorname{cosec} x \sqrt{\operatorname{cosec} x} \, dx$

6. Using Trigonometric Identities in Integration

If you're given a tricky **trig function** to integrate (e.g. things like **cos² x**, **sin² x** and **sin x cos x**), you might be able to simplify it using one of the **double angle formulas** (see p.275):

$$\sin 2A \equiv 2 \sin A \cos A$$

$$\cos 2A \equiv \cos^2 A - \sin^2 A$$

$$\tan 2A \equiv \dfrac{2 \tan A}{1 - \tan^2 A}$$

Tip: Remember, you can rearrange the cos double angle formula into two different forms:
$\cos 2A \equiv 2\cos^2 A - 1$ and $\cos 2A \equiv 1 - 2\sin^2 A$.

Examples Find the following: a) $\int \cos^2 5x \, dx$

1. Rearrange the cos double angle formula: $\cos 2x \equiv 2 \cos^2 x - 1 \Rightarrow \cos^2 x \equiv \dfrac{1}{2}(\cos 2x + 1)$

2. Rewrite the integration:

$$\int \cos^2 5x \, dx = \int \dfrac{1}{2}(\cos 10x + 1) \, dx = \dfrac{1}{2}\left(\dfrac{1}{10}\sin 10x + x\right) + C = \dfrac{1}{20}\sin 10x + \dfrac{1}{2}x + C$$

Don't forget to double the x coefficient and to divide by 10 when you integrate.

b) $\int \dfrac{4 \tan \frac{x}{2}}{1 - \tan^2 \frac{x}{2}} \, dx$

1. Rearrange using the tan double angle formula:

$$\dfrac{4 \tan \frac{x}{2}}{1 - \tan^2 \frac{x}{2}} = 2\left(\dfrac{2 \tan \frac{x}{2}}{1 - \tan^2 \frac{x}{2}}\right) = 2\left(\tan\left(2 \times \dfrac{x}{2}\right)\right) = 2 \tan x$$

2. Rewrite the integration: $\int \dfrac{4 \tan \frac{x}{2}}{1 - \tan^2 \frac{x}{2}} \, dx = \int 2 \tan x \, dx = -2 \ln|\cos x| + C$

Example Evaluate $\int_0^{\frac{\pi}{4}} \sin 2x \cos 2x \, dx$.

1. Rearrange the sin double angle formula with x replaced with $2x$:

$$\sin 4x \equiv 2 \sin 2x \cos 2x \Rightarrow \sin 2x \cos 2x \equiv \frac{1}{2} \sin 4x$$

2. Rewrite the integration and put in the limits:

$$\int_0^{\frac{\pi}{4}} \sin 2x \cos 2x \, dx = \int_0^{\frac{\pi}{4}} \frac{1}{2} \sin 4x \, dx = \left[\frac{1}{2} \left(-\frac{1}{4} \cos 4x \right) \right]_0^{\frac{\pi}{4}} = -\frac{1}{8} \left[\cos 4x \right]_0^{\frac{\pi}{4}}$$

$$= -\frac{1}{8} \left(\left[\cos \frac{4\pi}{4} \right] - [\cos 0] \right) = \frac{1}{8} (\cos 0 - \cos \pi)$$

$$= \frac{1}{8}(1-(-1)) = \frac{2}{8} = \frac{1}{4}$$

Exercise 6.1

Q1 Find the following indefinite integrals:

a) $\int \cos^2 x \, dx$

b) $\int 6 \sin x \cos x \, dx$

c) $\int \sin^2 6x \, dx$

d) $\int \frac{2 \tan 2x}{1 - \tan^2 2x} \, dx$

e) $\int 2 \sin 4x \cos 4x \, dx$

f) $\int 2 \cos^2 4x \, dx$

g) $\int \cos x \sin x \, dx$

h) $\int \sin 3x \cos 3x \, dx$

i) $\int \frac{6 \tan 3x}{1 - \tan^2 3x} \, dx$

j) $\int 5 \sin 2x \cos 2x \, dx$

k) $\int (\sin x + \cos x)^2 \, dx$

l) $\int 4 \sin x \cos x \cos 2x \, dx$

Q2 Find the following: a) $\int (\cos x + \sin x)(\cos x - \sin x) \, dx$

b) $\int \sin^2 x \cot x \, dx$

Q3 Evaluate the following definite integrals, giving exact answers:

a) $\int_0^{\frac{\pi}{4}} \sin^2 x \, dx$

b) $\int_0^{\pi} \cos^2 2x \, dx$

c) $\int_0^{\pi} \sin \frac{x}{2} \cos \frac{x}{2} \, dx$

d) $\int_{\frac{\pi}{4}}^{\frac{\pi}{2}} \sin^2 2x \, dx$

e) $\int_0^{\frac{\pi}{4}} \cos 2x \sin 2x \, dx$

f) $\int_{\frac{\pi}{4}}^{\frac{\pi}{2}} \sin^2 x - \cos^2 x \, dx$

If you have to integrate **tan² x** or **cot² x**, you can use the identities from p.269:

$\boxed{\sec^2 x \equiv 1 + \tan^2 x}$ $\boxed{\operatorname{cosec}^2 x \equiv 1 + \cot^2 x}$ **Tip:** You know from p.343 how to integrate $\sec^2 x$ and $\operatorname{cosec}^2 x$.

Example Find $\int \cot^2 3x \, dx$.

$\operatorname{cosec}^2 x \equiv 1 + \cot^2 x$

1. Get the function in terms of $\operatorname{cosec}^2 x$: $\cot^2 3x = \operatorname{cosec}^2 3x - 1$

2. Then integrate: $\int \cot^2 3x \, dx = \int \operatorname{cosec}^2 3x - 1 \, dx = -\frac{1}{3} \cot 3x - x + C$

Example Evaluate $\int_0^{\frac{\pi}{3}} 6 \sin 3x \cos 3x + \tan^2 \frac{1}{2}x + 1 \, dx.$

1. Using the sin double angle formula: $\quad 6 \sin 3x \cos 3x \equiv 3 \sin 6x$
   and using the identity for $\tan^2 x$: $\quad \tan^2 \frac{1}{2}x + 1 \equiv \sec^2 \frac{1}{2}x$

2. Now integrate and put in the limits:

$$\int_0^{\frac{\pi}{3}} 6 \sin 3x \cos 3x + \tan^2 \frac{1}{2}x + 1 \, dx$$

$$= \int_0^{\frac{\pi}{3}} 3 \sin 6x + \sec^2 \frac{1}{2}x \, dx = \left[-\frac{3}{6} \cos 6x + 2 \tan \frac{1}{2}x \right]_0^{\frac{\pi}{3}}$$

$$= \left[-\frac{1}{2} \cos(2\pi) + 2 \tan\left(\frac{\pi}{6}\right) \right] - \left[-\frac{1}{2} \cos(0) + 2 \tan(0) \right]$$

$$= \left[-\frac{1}{2}(1) + 2\left(\frac{1}{\sqrt{3}}\right) \right] - \left[-\frac{1}{2}(1) + 2(0) \right] = -\frac{1}{2} + \frac{2}{\sqrt{3}} + \frac{1}{2} = \frac{2}{\sqrt{3}} = \frac{2\sqrt{3}}{3}$$

Exercise 6.2

Q1 Find the following integrals:

a) $\int \cot^2 x - 4 \, dx$

b) $\int \tan^2 x \, dx$

c) $\int 3 \cot^2 x \, dx$

d) $\int \tan^2 4x \, dx$

Q2 Find the exact value of $\int_0^{\frac{\pi}{4}} \tan^2 x + \cos^2 x - \sin^2 x \, dx.$

Q3 Find the following integrals:

a) $\int (\sec x + \tan x)^2 \, dx$

b) $\int (\cot x + \operatorname{cosec} x)^2 \, dx$

c) $\int 4 + \cot^2 3x \, dx$

d) $\int \cos^2 4x + \cot^2 4x \, dx$

Q4 Integrate the following functions with respect to x:

a) $\tan^3 x + \tan^5 x$

b) $\cot^5 x + \cot^3 x$

c) $\sin^3 x$

Q5 Use the identity $\sin A + \sin B \equiv 2 \sin\left(\frac{A+B}{2}\right) \cos\left(\frac{A-B}{2}\right)$ to find $\int 2 \sin 4x \cos x \, dx.$

7. Finding Area Using Integration

To find the area between a curve, a line and the x-axis, you'll either have to **add** or **subtract** integrals to find the area you're after — it's always best to **draw a diagram** of the area.

Example **Find the area enclosed by the curve $y = x^2$, the line $y = 2 - x$ and the x-axis.**

1. Draw a diagram of the curve and the line. You have to find area A — but you'll need to split it into two smaller bits.

2. Find out where the curve and line meet by solving $x^2 = 2 - x$. They meet at $x = 1$ (they also meet at $x = -2$, but this isn't in A).

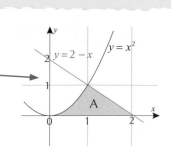

348 Chapter 23 Integration 2

3. The area A is the area under the black curve between 0 and 1 added to the area under the blue line between 1 and 2.

4. A_1 is the area under the curve $y = x^2$ between 0 and 1, so integrate between these limits to find the area:

$$\int_0^1 x^2 \, dx = \left[\frac{x^3}{3}\right]_0^1 = \frac{1}{3} - 0 = \frac{1}{3}$$

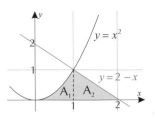

5. A_2 is the area of the triangle with base $2 - 1 = 1$ and height 1:

$$\text{Area} = \frac{1}{2} \times \text{base} \times \text{height} = \frac{1}{2} \times 1 \times 1 = \frac{1}{2}$$

You could find area A_2 by doing the integration of the line $y = 2 - x$ between 1 and 2.

6. Add the areas together to find the area A: $A = A_1 + A_2 = \frac{1}{3} + \frac{1}{2} = \frac{5}{6}$

Exercise 7.1

Q1 Find the shaded area in the following diagrams:

PROBLEM SOLVING

a) $y = 3x^2 + 4$

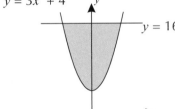

b) $y = x^3 + 4$

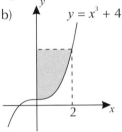

c) $y = \frac{1}{x^2}$

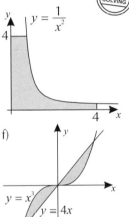

d)

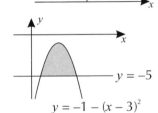

$y = -5$

$y = -1 - (x - 3)^2$

e) $y = x^2$

$y = 2x$

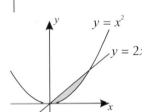

f)

$y = x^3$

$y = 4x$

Q2 For each part, find the area enclosed by the curve and line:

a) $y = x^2 + 4$ and $y = x + 4$

b) $y = 3x^2 + 11x + 6$ and $y = 9x + 6$

Example The diagram below shows the curves $y = \sin x + 1$ and $y = \cos x + 1$. Find the area of the shaded grey region.

PROBLEM SOLVING

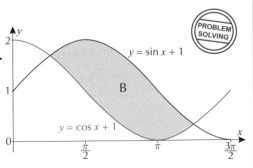

1. Find out where the graphs meet by solving $\sin x + 1 = \cos x + 1$

$$\Rightarrow \sin x = \cos x \Rightarrow \frac{\sin x}{\cos x} = 1 \Rightarrow \tan x = 1$$

$$\Rightarrow x = \tan^{-1}(1) = \frac{\pi}{4}, \frac{5\pi}{4}$$

They meet at $x = \frac{\pi}{4}$ and $x = \frac{5\pi}{4}$

2. You need to find two different integrals to work out the area of B:

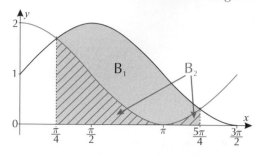

3. The area B is the area under the black curve between $\frac{\pi}{4}$ and $\frac{5\pi}{4}$ (B$_1$) minus the area under the blue curve between $\frac{\pi}{4}$ and $\frac{5\pi}{4}$ (B$_2$).

$$B_1 = \int_{\frac{\pi}{4}}^{\frac{5\pi}{4}} \sin x + 1\, dx = [-\cos x + x]_{\frac{\pi}{4}}^{\frac{5\pi}{4}}$$

$$= \left(-\cos\left(\frac{5\pi}{4}\right) + \frac{5\pi}{4}\right) - \left(-\cos\left(\frac{\pi}{4}\right) + \frac{\pi}{4}\right)$$

$$= \left(-\left(-\frac{\sqrt{2}}{2}\right) + \frac{5\pi}{4}\right) - \left(-\frac{\sqrt{2}}{2} + \frac{\pi}{4}\right) = \sqrt{2} + \pi$$

$$B_2 = \int_{\frac{\pi}{4}}^{\frac{5\pi}{4}} \cos x + 1\, dx = [\sin x + x]_{\frac{\pi}{4}}^{\frac{5\pi}{4}} = \left(\sin\left(\frac{5\pi}{4}\right) + \frac{5\pi}{4}\right) - \left(\sin\left(\frac{\pi}{4}\right) + \frac{\pi}{4}\right)$$

$$= \left(-\frac{\sqrt{2}}{2} + \frac{5\pi}{4}\right) - \left(\frac{\sqrt{2}}{2} + \frac{\pi}{4}\right) = -\sqrt{2} + \pi$$

You could find the area as one integral — i.e. $\int (\sin x + 1) - (\cos x + 1)\, dx$

4. So the area is: $B = B_1 - B_2 = (\sqrt{2} + \pi) - (-\sqrt{2} + \pi) = \mathbf{2\sqrt{2}}$

Exercise 7.2

Q1 Find the areas enclosed by the following curves:

a) $y = x^2 - 6x + 9$ and $y = 9 - x^2$

b) $y = x^3 + 3x^2 + 1$ and $y = x^2 + 1$

Q2 Find the exact area enclosed by the curves $y = 3\cos x$ and $y = 3\sin x$ between the y-axis and the smallest positive value of x where the two curves meet.

Q3 A company has designed a logo based on multiples of the sine curve, shown on the right. Calculate the total area of the grey sections of the logo.

PROBLEM SOLVING

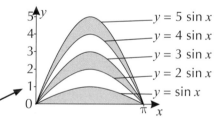

Example Find the area enclosed by the curve $y = x^2 - 2x$ and the line $y = 2x$.

1. Draw a diagram of the curve and the line.

2. You have to find area C — so split it up into areas which you can find by integration.

3. Find out where the graphs meet by solving $x^2 - 2x = 2x$:
$$x^2 - 2x = 2x \Rightarrow x^2 - 4x = 0$$
$$\Rightarrow x(x - 4) = 0$$
$$\Rightarrow x = 0 \text{ or } x = 4$$
They meet at $x = 0$ and $x = 4$

Tip: The curve $y = x^2 - 2x$ crosses the x-axis at $x = 0$ and $x = 2$.

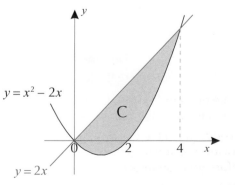

4. Split up the area C:

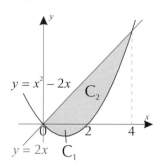

5. The area C_1 is the integral of $y = x^2 - 2x$ between 0 and 2:

$$\int_0^2 (x^2 - 2x)\,dx = \left[\frac{x^3}{3} - x^2\right]_0^2$$
$$= \left(\frac{2^3}{3} - 2^2\right) - \left(\frac{0^3}{3} - 0^2\right) = \frac{8}{3} - 4 = -\frac{4}{3}$$

Area is positive so the area C_1 is $\frac{4}{3}$

6. To find C_2, you'll have to subtract integrals (it can't be found by a single integration). C_2 is the area under the blue line between 0 and 4 minus the area under the black curve between 2 and 4.

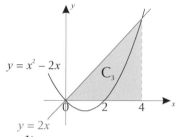

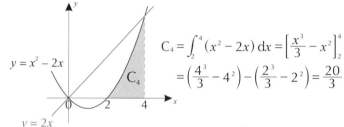

$$C_4 = \int_2^4 (x^2 - 2x)\,dx = \left[\frac{x^3}{3} - x^2\right]_2^4$$
$$= \left(\frac{4^3}{3} - 4^2\right) - \left(\frac{2^3}{3} - 2^2\right) = \frac{20}{3}$$

$$C_3 = \int_0^4 2x\,dx = \left[x^2\right]_0^4 = 4^2 - 0^2 = 16$$

So the area $C_2 = C_3 - C_4 = 16 - \frac{20}{3} = \frac{28}{3}$

7. Now the total area is given by adding the two areas: $\quad C = C_1 + C_2 = \frac{4}{3} + \frac{28}{3} = \mathbf{\frac{32}{3}}$

Exercise 7.3

Q1 Find the area enclosed by the curve $y = x^2 + 2x - 3$ and the line $y = 4x$.

Q2 Find the area enclosed by the curve $y = 4 - x^2$ and the line $y = 2x - 4$.

Q3 Find the shaded area shown to the right:

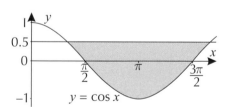

Q4 The area between the graphs of $y = x^2$ and $y = ax$ is 36, where a is a constant and $a > 0$. Find a.

Integrating with respect to y

In the previous examples, you've had to find the area between a curve and the x-axis. If you're asked to find the area between a curve and the **y-axis**, you have to integrate **with respect to y**.

If you're given the curve written as a function of y (i.e. $x = f(y)$, just integrate between the y-limits given. However, if you're given the function in the form $y = f(x)$, you'll have to **rearrange** to make y the subject **before** you can integrate. You do this in the same way you find the **inverse function**, $f^{-1}(x)$ (see p.246). For example, if $y = x^3$, then $x = \sqrt[3]{y}$.

> **Example** Find the area enclosed by the curve $y = \sqrt{x}$, the y-axis and the lines $y = 1$ and $y = 2$.

1. Draw a sketch of the area you're trying to find:
   The area is bounded by the lines $y = 1$ and $y = 2$,
   so you're integrating with respect to y.

2. Rewrite the function as a function of y:
   $$y = \sqrt{x} \implies x = y^2$$

3. Now integrate this function with respect to y
   between the limits $y = 1$ and $y = 2$:
   $$\int_1^2 y^2 \, dy = \left[\frac{y^3}{3}\right]_1^2 = \left(\frac{2^3}{3}\right) - \left(\frac{1^3}{3}\right) = \frac{8}{3} - \frac{1}{3} = \frac{7}{3}$$

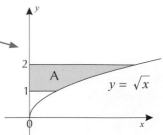

Exercise 7.4

Q1 Evaluate the following integrals:

a) $\displaystyle\int_0^2 3y^5 + 10y^4 - 2y^3 \, dy$

b) $\displaystyle\int_1^2 \frac{6y^2 + 2}{y^3 + y} \, dy$

c) $\displaystyle\int_0^{\frac{\pi}{2}} 8 \sin 2y \, dy$

d) $\displaystyle\int_0^1 2ye^{y^2} \, dy$

Q2 Find the areas enclosed by the following:

a) The curve $y = x^3$, the y-axis and the lines $y = 1$ and $y = 8$.

b) The curve $y = \ln x$, the y-axis and the lines $y = 0$ and $y = 3$.

c) The curve $y = \arcsin x$, the y-axis and the lines $y = 0$ and $y = \frac{\pi}{2}$.

d) The curve $y = \frac{1}{x}$, the y-axis and the lines $y = 1$ and $y = 2$.

Q3 Find the area enclosed by the curve $y = \frac{1}{\sqrt{x}}$, the y-axis
and the lines $y = 0.5$ and $y = 1$, as shown on the graph on the right:

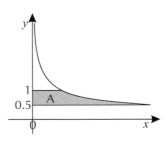

8. Parametric Integration

- Normally, to find the **area** under a graph, you can do a **simple integration**. But if you've got **parametric equations**, things are more difficult — you can't find $\int y \, dx$ if y isn't written in terms of x.

- To get around this, use the following equation (for parameter t):
  This comes from the chain rule (see p.312).

- Both y and $\frac{dx}{dt}$ are written **in terms of** t, so you can **multiply** them together to get an expression you can **integrate with respect to** t.

$$\int y \, dx = \int y \frac{dx}{dt} \, dt$$

> **Example** A curve is defined by the parametric equations $y = t^2 + 2t + 3$ and $x = t^3 + 3$.
> Show that $\int y \, dx = \int 3t^4 + 6t^3 + 9t^2 \, dt$.

$\frac{dx}{dt} = 3t^2$, so using the formula above:

$$\int y \, dx = \int y \frac{dx}{dt} \, dt = \int (t^2 + 2t + 3)(3t^2) \, dt = \int 3t^4 + 6t^3 + 9t^2 \, dt$$

With a **definite integral**, you need to **alter the limits** as well (see p.356 for more on altering limits). So if you have x-values as limits, work out the corresponding values of t before you integrate.

Example

The shaded region marked A on the sketch below is bounded by the x-axis, the line $x = 2$, and by the curve with parametric equations
$x = t^2 - 2$ and $y = t^2 - 9t + 20$, $t \geq 0$, which crosses the x-axis at $x = 14$.
Find the area of A.

1. The area of A is $\int_2^{14} y \, dx$.

2. You need to use $\int y \, dx = \int y \frac{dx}{dt} \, dt$ to integrate, so first find $\frac{dx}{dt}$:
$$\frac{dx}{dt} = \frac{d}{dt}(t^2 - 2) = 2t$$

3. Now sort out the limits. 14 and 2 are the limits for integrating with respect to x. You need to find the corresponding values of t:
$$x = 2 \implies t^2 - 2 = 2 \implies t^2 = 4 \implies t = 2$$
$$x = 14 \implies t^2 - 2 = 14 \implies t^2 = 16 \implies t = 4$$

Tip: $t \geq 0$ so ignore the negative square roots.

4. Now integrate to find the area of A:
$$A = \int_2^{14} y \, dx = \int_2^4 y \frac{dx}{dt} \, dt$$
$$= \int_2^4 (t^2 - 9t + 20)(2t) \, dt = \int_2^4 2t^3 - 18t^2 + 40t \, dt = \left[\frac{1}{2}t^4 - 6t^3 + 20t^2 \right]_2^4$$
$$= \left(\frac{1}{2}(4)^4 - 6(4)^3 + 20(4)^2 \right) - \left(\frac{1}{2}(2)^4 - 6(2)^3 + 20(2)^2 \right) = 64 - 40 = \mathbf{24}$$

Exercise 8.1

Q1 For each of the following curves, find an expression in parametric form that is equivalent to the indefinite integral $\int y \, dx$. You do not need to carry out the integration.

a) $x = \dfrac{3}{t}$, $y = 4t^2$

b) $x = \sqrt{t}$, $y = 3t^2 - 4$

c) $x = 3t + 2$, $y = t^3$

d) $x = \sin^2 \theta$, $y = \cos \theta$

e) $x = \tan 5\theta$, $y = \sec^2 5\theta$

f) $x = e^{2t}$, $y = 5t^4$

Q2 For each of the following curves, find an expression equivalent to $\int y \, dx$ and integrate it.

a) $x = t - 2$, $y = 4t + 3$

b) $x = 3t^2$, $y = 5t - 1$

c) $x = \dfrac{2}{t}$, $y = 8t^3$

d) $x = (4t - 5)^2$, $y = t^2 - 3t$

e) $x = t^2 + 3$, $y = 4t - 1$

f) $x = t^3 - 5$, $y = 5t^2 + 1$

Q3 A curve has parametric equations $x = \cos 3\theta + 4$, $y = 2 \cos 3\theta$. Show that $\int y \, dx$ is equivalent to $\dfrac{1}{2} \cos 6\theta + C$.

Q4 A curve has parametric equations $x = 3t + 6$, $y = 2t - 8$.
Find an expression for $y \dfrac{dx}{dt}$, and hence evaluate $\int_{-2}^{2} y \dfrac{dx}{dt} \, dt$.

Q5 A curve has parametric equations $x = 3t^2$, $y = \dfrac{5}{t}$, where $t > 0$.

Find an expression for $y\,\dfrac{dx}{dt}$, and hence evaluate $\displaystyle\int_3^{75} y\,dx$.

Q6 The curve shown here has parametric equations $x = 4t(t + 1)$, $y = 3t^3$.

a) Find the values t_1 and t_2 that correspond to $x = 8$ and $x = 120$, given that $t > 0$.

b) Hence find a parametric integral corresponding to $\displaystyle\int_8^{120} y\,dx$, and evaluate this to find the area A.

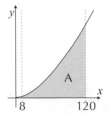

9. Integration by Substitution

Integration by substitution is a way of integrating a **function of a function** by simplifying the integral. Like differentiating with the chain rule, to integrate by substitution you have to write part of the function in terms of u, where u is some **function** of x.

Here's the method:

- You'll be given an integral that's made up of **two functions of x**.

- **Substitute** u for one of the functions of x to give a function that's **easier to integrate**.

- Next, find $\dfrac{du}{dx}$, and **rewrite** it so that dx is on its own.

- **Rewrite** the original integral in terms of u and du.

- You should now be left with something that's **easier** to integrate — just **integrate** as normal, then at the last step **replace** u with the **original substitution**.

Example   Use the substitution $u = x^2 - 2$ to find $\displaystyle\int 4x(x^2 - 2)^4\,dx$.

1. Start by differentiating u with respect to x: $u = x^2 - 2 \;\Rightarrow\; \dfrac{du}{dx} = 2x$

2. Now rearrange the equation for $\dfrac{du}{dx}$ to get dx on its own:

   $\dfrac{du}{dx}$ isn't really a fraction, but you can treat it like one for this bit. $\longrightarrow$ $\dfrac{du}{dx} = 2x \;\Rightarrow\; du = 2x\,dx \;\Rightarrow\; dx = \dfrac{1}{2x}\,du$

3. Substitute what you've got so far back into the original expression:

   $$\int 4x(x^2 - 2)^4\,dx = \int 4xu^4\frac{1}{2x}\,du = \int 2u^4\,du$$

4. Now you've got a much simpler expression to integrate with respect to u:

   $$\int 2u^4\,du = \frac{2}{5}u^5 + C$$

5. And finally, substitute $u = x^2 - 2$ back in: $= \dfrac{2}{5}(x^2 - 2)^5 + C$

This example worked out nicely, because the x's **cancelled out** when you substituted in the expressions for u and dx. It isn't always quite so straightforward — sometimes you need to get rid of some x's by **rearranging** the equation to get x in terms of u (like in the example on the next page).

> **Example** Find $\int x(3x + 2)^3\ dx$, using the substitution $u = 3x + 2$.

1. Start by finding $\dfrac{du}{dx}$ and then rearrange to get dx on its own:
$$u = 3x + 2 \implies \frac{du}{dx} = 3 \implies dx = \frac{1}{3}\ du$$

2. If you substitute for u and dx, you end up with an x still in the integral:
$$\int x(3x + 2)^3\ dx = \int xu^3\ \frac{1}{3}\ du$$

3. To get rid of that x, you have to rearrange the equation for u:
$$u = 3x + 2 \implies x = \frac{u - 2}{3}$$

4. So:
$$\int x(3x + 2)^3\ dx = \int \left(\frac{u - 2}{3}\right)u^3\ \frac{1}{3}\ du$$
$$= \int \frac{u^4 - 2u^3}{9}\ du$$
$$= \frac{1}{9}\left(\frac{u^5}{5} - \frac{u^4}{2}\right) + C$$

Don't forget to rewrite your answer in terms of x again at the end.
$$- \frac{u^5}{45} - \frac{u^4}{18} + C$$
$$= \frac{(3x + 2)^5}{45} - \frac{(3x + 2)^4}{18} + C$$

Exercise 9.1

Q1 Find the following integrals using the given substitutions:

a) $\int 12(x + 3)^5\ dx,\ \ u = x + 3$

b) $\int (11 - x)^4\ dx,\ \ u = 11 - x$

c) $\int 24x(x^2 + 4)^3\ dx,\ \ u = x^2 + 4$

d) $\int \sin^5 x \cos x\ dx,\ \ u = \sin x$

e) $\int x(x - 1)^5\ dx,\ \ u = x - 1$

f) $\int 5 \tan^4 x \sec^2 x\ dx,\ \ u = \tan x$

Q2 Use an appropriate substitution to find:

a) $\int 21(x + 2)^6\ dx$

b) $\int (5x + 4)^3\ dx$

c) $\int x(2x + 3)^3\ dx$

d) $\int 24x(x^2 - 5)^7\ dx$

Q3 a) Find $\int 6x\sqrt{x + 1}\ dx$ using the substitution $u = \sqrt{x + 1}$.

b) Find $\int \dfrac{x}{\sqrt{4 - x}}\ dx$ using the substitution $u = \sqrt{4 - x}$.

c) Find $\int \dfrac{15(\ln x)^4}{x}\ dx$ using the substitution $u = \ln x$.

Q4 Find the following integrals by substitution:

a) $\int \dfrac{4x}{\sqrt{(2x - 1)}}\ dx$

b) $\int \dfrac{1}{4 - \sqrt{x}}\ dx$

c) $\int \dfrac{e^{2x}}{1 + e^x}\ dx$

d) $\int 6x\sqrt{x^2 + 5}\ dx$

Q5 Use integration by substitution to prove that $\int (n + 1)f'(x)[f(x)]^n\ dx = [f(x)]^{n + 1} + C$.

Definite integrals

To find a **definite integral** using a substitution, you have to **change the limits** to u-limits.
To do this, put the x-limits into the equation for u to find the corresponding values of u.

Doing it this way means you **don't** have to **put x back in** at the last step
— just put the values of u into the integration for u.

Example — Use a suitable substitution to find $\int_2^{\frac{7}{2}} x\sqrt{2x-3}\ dx$.

1. The square root is the most awkward part of the integral, so use the substitution $u = \sqrt{2x-3}$.

2. Differentiate the substitution, and rearrange to get dx on its own:
$$u = \sqrt{2x-3} \implies \frac{du}{dx} = \frac{1}{\sqrt{2x-3}} = \frac{1}{u} \implies dx = u\ du$$

3. Rearrange the substitution to get an expression for x: $\quad u = \sqrt{2x-3} \implies x = \frac{u^2+3}{2}$

4. Convert the limits from x-values to u-values:
$$x = 2 \implies u = \sqrt{2(2)-3} = \sqrt{1} = 1$$
$$x = \frac{7}{2} \implies u = \sqrt{2\left(\frac{7}{2}\right)-3} = \sqrt{4} = 2$$

5. Substituting everything back into the original integral gives:
$$\int_2^{\frac{7}{2}} x\sqrt{2x-3}\ dx = \int_1^2 \frac{u^2+3}{2} \times u \times u\ du$$
$$= \frac{1}{2}\int_1^2 u^4 + 3u^2\ du = \frac{1}{2}\left[\frac{u^5}{5} + u^3\right]_1^2$$
$$= \left[\frac{2^5}{10} + \frac{2^3}{2}\right] - \left[\frac{1^5}{10} + \frac{1^3}{2}\right] = \frac{36}{5} - \frac{3}{5} = \frac{33}{5}$$

Sometimes when you convert the limits of a definite integral, the **upper limit** converts to a **lower number** than the **lower limit** does. You can either keep the converted limits in the **same places** as the corresponding original limits and carry on as normal or **swap them** so the higher value is the upper limit and stick a **minus sign** in front of the whole integral.

Exercise 9.2

Q1 Find the exact values of the following using the given substitutions:

a) $\int_{\frac{2}{3}}^1 (3x-2)^4\ dx,\ u = 3x - 2$

b) $\int_{-2}^1 2x(x+3)^4\ dx,\ u = x + 3$

c) $\int_0^{\frac{\pi}{6}} 8\sin^3 x\cos x\ dx,\ u = \sin x$

d) $\int_0^3 x\sqrt{x+1}\ dx,\ u = \sqrt{x+1}$

Q2 Use an appropriate substitution to find the exact value of each of the following:

a) $\int_2^{\sqrt{5}} x(x^2-3)^4\ dx$

b) $\int_1^2 x(3x-4)^3\ dx$

c) $\int_2^{10} \frac{x}{\sqrt{x-1}}\ dx$

Q3 Integrate the function $y = \dfrac{1}{3-\sqrt{x}}$ between $x = 1$ and $x = 4$, using a suitable substitution.
Give your answer in the form $a + b\ln 2$, where a and b are integers.

Q4 Find $\int_0^1 2e^x(1+e^x)^3\ dx$, using the substitution $u = 1 + e^x$. Give your answer to 1 decimal place.

Q5 Use integration by substitution to find the integral of the function $y = \dfrac{x}{\sqrt{3x+1}}$ between the limits $x = 1$ and $x = 5$.

Trig identities

The **trig identities** from p.69 can also be used in integration by substitution. They can often be used as a substitution in integrals that **don't** appear to contain a trig function — so watch out for these cases.

Example Calculate $\int_{\frac{1}{2}}^{\frac{\sqrt{3}}{2}} \frac{4}{\sqrt{1-x^2}}\, dx$, using the substitution $x = \sin\theta$, where $-\frac{\pi}{2} \le \theta \le \frac{\pi}{2}$.

1. Start by differentiating x with respect to θ, and use the result to find dx:
$$x = \sin\theta \ \Rightarrow\ \frac{dx}{d\theta} = \cos\theta \ \Rightarrow\ dx = \cos\theta\, d\theta$$

2. Use the substitution to convert the limits from x to θ: $\quad x = \sin\theta \ \Rightarrow\ \theta = \sin^{-1}x$
$$\text{So } x = \frac{\sqrt{3}}{2} \ \Rightarrow\ \theta = \frac{\pi}{3} \ \text{ and } \ x = \frac{1}{2} \ \Rightarrow\ \theta = \frac{\pi}{6}$$

3. Now solve the integral:
$$\int_{\frac{1}{2}}^{\frac{\sqrt{3}}{2}} \frac{4}{\sqrt{1-x^2}}\, dx = \int_{\frac{\pi}{6}}^{\frac{\pi}{3}} \frac{4}{\sqrt{1-\sin^2\theta}} \cos\theta\, d\theta = \int_{\frac{\pi}{6}}^{\frac{\pi}{3}} \frac{4\cos\theta}{\sqrt{\cos^2\theta}}\, d\theta$$
$$= \int_{\frac{\pi}{6}}^{\frac{\pi}{3}} 4\, d\theta = [4\theta]_{\frac{\pi}{6}}^{\frac{\pi}{3}} = \frac{4\pi}{3} - \frac{2\pi}{3} = \frac{2\pi}{3}$$

Use the identity $\sin^2\theta + \cos^2\theta \equiv 1$.

Exercise 9.3

Q1 Find the exact value of $\int_0^1 \frac{1}{1+x^2}\, dx$ using the substitution $x = \tan\theta$ where $-\frac{\pi}{2} < \theta < \frac{\pi}{2}$.

Q2 Find the exact value of $\int_0^{\frac{\pi}{6}} 3\sin x \sin 2x\, dx$ using the substitution $u = \sin x$.

Q3 Use the substitution $x = 2\sin\theta$, where $-\frac{\pi}{2} \le \theta \le \frac{\pi}{2}$, to find the exact value of $\int_1^{\sqrt{3}} \frac{1}{(4-x^2)^{\frac{3}{2}}}\, dx$.

Q4 Find the exact value of $\int_{\frac{1}{2}}^1 \frac{1}{x^2\sqrt{1-x^2}}\, dx$. Use the substitution $x = \cos\theta$ where $0 \le \theta \le \pi$.

Q5 Find $\int 2\tan^3 x\, dx$ using the substitution $u = \sec^2 x$.

10. Integration by Parts

- If you have a **product** to integrate but you can't use any of the methods you've learnt so far, you might be able to use **integration by parts**. The **formula** for integrating by parts is:

$$\int u\frac{dv}{dx}\, dx = uv - \int v\frac{du}{dx}\, dx$$

where u and v are both functions of x.

Tip: The integration by parts formula is sometimes written $\int uv'\, dx = uv - \int vu'\, dx$.

- The hardest thing about integration by parts is **deciding** which bit of the product should be u and which bit should be $\frac{dv}{dx}$.

- There's no set rule for this — you just have to look at both parts, see which one **differentiates** to give something **nice**, then set that one as u.

- For example, if you have a product that has a **single x** as one part of it, choose this to be u. It differentiates to **1**, which makes **integrating** $v\frac{du}{dx}$ very easy.

Example Find $\int 2x e^x \, dx$.

1. Start by working out what should be u and what should be $\dfrac{dv}{dx}$ — choose them so that $v\dfrac{du}{dx}$ is easier to integrate than $2x e^x$.

2. The two factors are $2x$ and e^x, so try them both ways round:

   If $u = 2x$ and $\dfrac{dv}{dx} = e^x$, then $v\dfrac{du}{dx} = 2e^x$

   If $u = e^x$ and $\dfrac{dv}{dx} = 2x$, then $v\dfrac{du}{dx} = x^2 e^x$

   So let $u = 2x$ and $\dfrac{dv}{dx} = e^x$

   You don't have to try them both ways round if you can spot which one will make the integration easier straight away.

3. Put u, v, $\dfrac{du}{dx}$ and $\dfrac{dv}{dx}$ into the integration by parts formula:

   $u = 2x \implies \dfrac{du}{dx} = 2, \quad \dfrac{dv}{dx} = e^x \implies v = e^x$

   $\int 2x e^x \, dx = \int u \dfrac{dv}{dx} \, dx = uv - \int v \dfrac{du}{dx} \, dx = 2x e^x - \int 2e^x \, dx = \mathbf{2x e^x - 2e^x + C}$

Until now, you haven't been able to integrate **ln x**, but **integration by parts** gives you a way to get around this. The trick is to write $\ln x$ as $(1 \times \ln x)$.

- You can write $\ln x$ as $(\ln x \times 1)$. So let $u = \ln x$ and let $\dfrac{dv}{dx} = 1$.

  Then $u = \ln x \implies \dfrac{du}{dx} = \dfrac{1}{x}, \dfrac{dv}{dx} = 1 \implies v = x$

- Putting these into the formula gives:

  $\int \ln x \, dx = \int (\ln x \times 1) \, dx = \ln x \times x - \int x \dfrac{1}{x} \, dx = x \ln x - \int 1 \, dx = \mathbf{x \ln x - x + C}$

Exercise 10.1

Q1 Use integration by parts to find:

a) $\int x e^x \, dx$ b) $\int x e^{-x} \, dx$ c) $\int x e^{-\frac{x}{3}} \, dx$ d) $\int x(e^x + 1) \, dx$

Q2 Use integration by parts to find: a) $\int 2x \cos x \, dx$ b) $\int 3x \cos\left(\frac{1}{2}x\right) dx$

Q3 Use integration by parts to find:

a) $\int 2 \ln x \, dx$ b) $\int x^4 \ln x \, dx$ c) $\int \ln 4x \, dx$ d) $\int \ln x^3 \, dx$

Q4 Find: a) $\int \dfrac{x}{e^{2x}} \, dx$ b) $\int (x + 1)\sqrt{x + 2} \, dx$ c) $\int \ln(x + 1) \, dx$

Definite integrals

You can use **integration by parts** on definite integrals too. The only change from the method for indefinite integrals is that you have to **apply the limits** of the integral to the uv bit.

The integration by parts formula for definite integrals can be written like this:

$$\int_a^b u \dfrac{dv}{dx} \, dx = [uv]_a^b - \int_a^b v \dfrac{du}{dx} \, dx$$

1. Choose u and $\frac{dv}{dx}$. $\sin\left(\frac{x}{2}\right)$ will give a cos function whether you integrate or differentiate it, so the only way to get a simpler $\int v\frac{du}{dx}\,dx$ is to make $u = 4x$.

So let $u = 4x$ and $\frac{dv}{dx} = \sin\left(\frac{x}{2}\right)$

$u = 4x \implies \frac{du}{dx} = 4, \quad \frac{dv}{dx} = \sin\left(\frac{x}{2}\right) \implies v = -2\cos\left(\frac{x}{2}\right)$

2. Substitute everything into the formula and complete the integration:

$\int_0^{\frac{\pi}{2}} 4x\sin\left(\frac{x}{2}\right)\,dx = \left[-8x\cos\left(\frac{x}{2}\right)\right]_0^{\frac{\pi}{2}} - \int_0^{\frac{\pi}{2}} -8\cos\left(\frac{x}{2}\right)\,dx$

$= -8\left[x\cos\left(\frac{x}{2}\right)\right]_0^{\frac{\pi}{2}} + 16\left[\sin\left(\frac{x}{2}\right)\right]_0^{\frac{\pi}{2}}$

$= -8\left[\frac{\pi}{2}\cos\left(\frac{\pi}{4}\right) - 0\cos(0)\right] + 16\left[\sin\left(\frac{\pi}{4}\right) - \sin(0)\right]$

$= -8\left[\frac{\pi}{2}\frac{1}{\sqrt{2}}\right] + 16\left[\frac{1}{\sqrt{2}}\right] = -\frac{4\pi}{\sqrt{2}} + \frac{16}{\sqrt{2}} = 8\sqrt{2} - 2\pi\sqrt{2}$

Exercise 10.2

Q1 Use integration by parts to find:

a) $\int_0^{\pi} x\sin x\,dx$ 　　b) $\int_{-\frac{\pi}{2}}^{\frac{\pi}{2}} 2x(1-\sin x)\,dx$ 　　c) $\int_{-1}^{1} 20x(x+1)^3$ 　　d) $\int_0^{1.5} 30x\sqrt{2x+1}\,dx$

Q2 Use integration by parts to find the exact values of the following:

a) $\int_0^1 12x\,e^{2x}\,dx$ 　　b) $\int_0^{\frac{\pi}{3}} 18x\sin 3x\,dx$ 　　c) $\int_1^2 \frac{1}{x^2}\ln x\,dx$ 　　d) $\int_0^{\frac{\pi}{12}} 6x\cos 2x\,dx$

Repeated use of integration by parts

Sometimes **integration by parts** leaves you with a function for $v\frac{du}{dx}$ which is **simpler** than the function you started with, but still **tricky to integrate**.

You might have to carry out integration by parts **again** to find $\int v\frac{du}{dx}\,dx$.

Example Use integration by parts to find $\int_2^3 x^2(x-1)^{-4}\,dx$.

1. Use integration by parts: Let $u = x^2$ and let $\frac{dv}{dx} = (x-1)^{-4}$. Then $\frac{du}{dx} = 2x$ and $v = -\frac{1}{3}(x-1)^{-3}$.

2. Putting these into the formula gives:

$\int_2^3 x^2(x-1)^{-4}\,dx = \left[-\frac{x^2}{3}(x-1)^{-3}\right]_2^3 - \int_2^3 -\frac{2x}{3}(x-1)^{-3}\,dx$

$= \left[-\frac{x^2}{3}(x-1)^{-3}\right]_2^3 + \frac{2}{3}\int_2^3 x(x-1)^{-3}\,dx$

See p.337 if you can't remember how to integrate $(ax + b)^n$.

3. $\int_2^3 x(x-1)^{-3}\,dx$ is still tricky to integrate. Use integration by parts again:

Let $u_1 = x$ and let $\frac{dv_1}{dx} = (x-1)^{-3}$. Then $\frac{du_1}{dx} = 1$ and $v_1 = -\frac{1}{2}(x-1)^{-2}$.

4. Put these into the formula:

$$\int_2^3 x(x-1)^{-3}\,dx = \left[-\frac{x}{2}(x-1)^{-2}\right]_2^3 - \int_2^3 -\frac{1}{2}(x-1)^{-2}\,dx$$

$$= \left[-\frac{x}{2}(x-1)^{-2}\right]_2^3 - \frac{1}{2}\left[(x-1)^{-1}\right]_2^3$$

$$= \left[-\frac{3}{2}(2)^{-2}+\frac{2}{2}(1)^{-2}\right] - \frac{1}{2}[2^{-1}-1^{-1}] = \left[-\frac{3}{8}+1\right] - \frac{1}{2}\left[\frac{1}{2}-1\right]$$

$$= \frac{5}{8}+\frac{1}{4} = \frac{7}{8}$$

5. Now you can evaluate the original integral:

$$\int_2^3 x^2(x-1)^{-4}\,dx = \left[-\frac{x^2}{3}(x-1)^{-3}\right]_2^3 + \frac{2}{3}\int_2^3 x(x-1)^{-3}\,dx$$

$$= \left[-\frac{x^2}{3}(x-1)^{-3}\right]_2^3 + \frac{2}{3}\left(\frac{7}{8}\right) = \left[\left(-\frac{9}{3}(2)^{-3}\right)-\left(-\frac{4}{3}(1)^{-3}\right)\right] + \frac{7}{12}$$

$$= \left[-\frac{9}{24}+\frac{4}{3}\right] + \frac{7}{12} = \frac{23}{24}+\frac{7}{12} = \frac{37}{24}$$

Exercise 10.3

Q1 Use integration by parts twice to find:

a) $\int x^2 e^x\,dx$ b) $\int x^2\cos x\,dx$ c) $\int 4x^2\sin 2x\,dx$ d) $\int 40x^2(2x-1)^4\,dx$

Q2 Find $\int_{-1}^0 x^2(x+1)^4\,dx$ using integration by parts.

Q3 Use integration by parts to find the area enclosed by the curve $y = x^2 e^{-2x}$, the x-axis and the lines $x = 0$ and $x = 1$.

11. Integration Using Partial Fractions

You can integrate algebraic fractions where the denominator can be written as a product of **linear factors** by splitting them up into **partial fractions** (see p.254). Each fraction can then be **integrated separately** using the method on p.339.

Example   **Find the exact value of $\int_3^4 \frac{2}{x(x-2)}\,dx$, writing it as a single logarithm.**

1. Start by writing $\frac{2}{x(x-2)}$ as partial fractions.

2. Write as an identity with partial fractions:

$$\frac{2}{x(x-2)} \equiv \frac{A}{x}+\frac{B}{x-2} \equiv \frac{A(x-2)+Bx}{x(x-2)} \quad\Rightarrow\quad 2 \equiv A(x-2)+Bx$$

3. Use the equating coefficients method to find A and B:

       Equating constant terms: $2 = -2A \Rightarrow A = -1$

       Equating x coefficients: $0 = A + B \Rightarrow 0 = -1 + B \Rightarrow B = 1$

4. Replace A and B in the original identity:

$$\frac{2}{x(x-2)} \equiv \frac{-1}{x}+\frac{1}{x-2} \equiv \frac{1}{x-2}-\frac{1}{x}$$

5. So:
$$\int_3^4 \frac{2}{x(x-2)}\,dx = \int_3^4 \frac{1}{(x-2)} - \frac{1}{x}\,dx$$

6. Integrate each term separately:
$$= \left[\ln|x-2| - \ln|x|\right]_3^4$$

$$\log a - \log b = \log\left(\frac{a}{b}\right) \longrightarrow = \left[\ln\left|\frac{x-2}{x}\right|\right]_3^4 = \ln\left|\frac{4-2}{4}\right| - \ln\left|\frac{3-2}{3}\right|$$

$$= \ln\left(\frac{1}{2}\right) - \ln\left(\frac{1}{3}\right) = \mathbf{ln}\left(\frac{\mathbf{3}}{\mathbf{2}}\right)$$

Exercise 11.1

Q1 Integrate the following functions by writing them as partial fractions:

a) $\displaystyle\int \frac{3}{(x+1)(x+2)}\,dx$

b) $\displaystyle\int \frac{24(x-1)}{9-4x^2}\,dx$

c) $\displaystyle\int \frac{21x-82}{(x-2)(x-3)(x-4)}\,dx$

Q2 Find $\displaystyle\int_0^1 \frac{x}{(x-2)(x-3)}\,dx$ by expressing as partial fractions. Give your answer as a single logarithm.

Q3 a) Express $\dfrac{6}{2x^2-5x+2}$ in partial fractions.

b) Hence find $\displaystyle\int \frac{6}{2x^2-5x+2}\,dx$ where $x > 2$.

c) Evaluate $\displaystyle\int_3^5 \frac{6}{2x^2-5x+2}\,dx$, expressing your answer as a single logarithm.

Q4 Given that f$(x) = 3x + 5$ and g$(x) = x(x + 10)$, find $\displaystyle\int_1^2 \frac{f(x)}{g(x)}\,dx$ to 3 d.p. by expressing $\dfrac{f(x)}{g(x)}$ as partial fractions.

Q5 Show that $\displaystyle\int_0^{\frac{2}{3}} \frac{-(t+3)}{(3t+2)(t+1)}\,dt = 2\ln\frac{5}{3} - \frac{7}{3}\ln 2$.

Q6 Use the substitution $u = \sqrt{x}$ to find the exact value of $\displaystyle\int_9^{16} \frac{4}{\sqrt{x}(9x-4)}\,dx$. (PROBLEM SOLVING)

12. Differential Equations

- A **differential equation** is an equation that includes a **derivative term** such as $\dfrac{dy}{dx}$ (or $\dfrac{dP}{dt}$, $\dfrac{ds}{dt}$, $\dfrac{dV}{dr}$, etc, depending on the variables), as well as **other variables** (like x **and** y).

- Before **solving** them, you have to be able to **set up** ('**formulate**') differential equations.

- Differential equations tend to involve a **rate of change** (giving a derivative term) and a **proportion relation**, where the rate of change will be directly or inversely proportional to some function of the variables.

- It helps to think about what the derivative **actually means**. $\dfrac{dy}{dx}$ is defined as 'the **rate of change** of y with respect to x'. In other words, it tells you how y changes as x changes.

a) **The number of bacteria, b, in a petri dish is increasing over time, t, at a rate directly proportional to the number of bacteria. Formulate a differential equation that shows this information.**

- Work out the derivative term of the differential equation first. The number of bacteria (b) increases as time (t) increases — so that's the rate of change of b with respect to t, or $\dfrac{db}{dt}$.

- The rate of change, $\dfrac{db}{dt}$, is proportional to b, so : $\dfrac{db}{dt} \propto b$

- Rewrite it as an equation, not a proportion relation: $\dfrac{db}{dt} = kb$ **for some constant k, $k > 0$**

b) **The volume of interdimensional space jelly, V, in a container is decreasing over time, t, at a rate inversely proportional to the square of its volume. Show this as a differential equation.**

- This time the question tells you how V decreases as t increases
  — the derivative term is the rate of change of V with respect to t, or $\dfrac{dV}{dt}$.

- $\dfrac{dV}{dt}$ is inversely proportional to the square of V, so: $\dfrac{dV}{dt} \propto \dfrac{1}{V^2}$

- The equation needs a minus sign, because V is decreasing as t increases:

$$\dfrac{dV}{dt} = -\dfrac{k}{V^2} \text{ for some constant } k,\ k > 0$$

Exercise 12.1

Q1 The number of fleas (N) on a cat is increasing over time, t, at a rate directly proportional to the number of fleas. Show this as a differential equation.

Q2 The value, x, of a house is increasing over time, t, at a rate inversely proportional to the square of x. Formulate a differential equation to show this.

Q3 The rate of depreciation of the amount (£A) a car is worth is directly proportional to the square root of A. Show this as a differential equation.

Q4 The rate of decrease of a population, y, with respect to time is directly proportional to the difference between y and λ where λ is a constant and $y \geq \lambda$. Formulate a differential equation to show this.

Q5 The volume of water which is being poured into a container is directly proportional to the volume of water (V) in the container. The container has a hole in it from which water flows out at a rate of $20 \text{ cm}^3\text{s}^{-1}$. Show this as a differential equation.

Solving differential equations

- **Solving** a differential equation means using it to find an **equation** in terms of the two variables, **without** a derivative term. To do this, you need to use **integration**.

- The only differential equations containing x and y terms that you'll have to solve in A-level Maths are ones with **separable variables** — where x and y can be separated into functions $f(x)$ and $g(y)$.

- The **method** for solving a differential equation is given on the next page.

Step 1: Write the differential equation in the form $\dfrac{dy}{dx} = f(x)g(y)$.

Step 2: **Rearrange** the equation into the form: $\dfrac{1}{g(y)}dy = f(x)\,dx$.

　　　To do this, get all the terms containing y on the **left-hand side**,
　　　and all the terms containing x on the **right-hand side** and split up the $\dfrac{dy}{dx}$.

Step 3: Now **integrate both sides**: $\displaystyle\int \dfrac{1}{g(y)}\,dy = \int f(x)\,dx$.

　　　Don't forget the **constant of integration** (you only need one — not one on each side).

　　　Tip: It might be useful to write the constant as **ln k** rather than **C**.

Step 4: **Rearrange** your answer to get it in a **nice form** — e.g. get it in the form $y = h(x)$.

Step 5: If you're asked for a **general solution**, leave C (or k) in your answer. If you're asked
　　　for a **particular solution**, you'll be given the x and y values for a certain point.
　　　All you do is put these values into your equation and use them to **find C** (or k).

⟦Examples⟧　　**a) Find the particular solution of $\dfrac{dy}{dx} = 2y(1+x)^2$ when $x = -1$ and $y = 4$.**

1. Identify $f(x)$ and $g(y)$:　　$f(x) = 2(1+x)^2$ and $g(y) = y$

2. Separate the variables:　$\dfrac{1}{y}\,dy = 2(1+x)^2\,dx$

3. And integrate:　　　　$\displaystyle\int \dfrac{1}{y}\,dy = \int 2(1+x)^2\,dx \;\Rightarrow\; \ln|y| = \tfrac{2}{3}(1+x)^3 + C$

4. Now to find the particular solution, work out the value of C for the given values of x and y:

$$\ln 4 = \tfrac{2}{3}(1+(-1))^3 + C \;\Rightarrow\; \ln 4 = C, \text{ so } \mathbf{\ln|y| = \tfrac{2}{3}(1+x)^3 + \ln 4}$$

b) Find the general solution of $(x-2)(2x+3)\dfrac{dy}{dx} = xy + 5y$, where $x > 2$.
Give your answer in the form $y = f(x)$.

1. First, separate the variables:　$\dfrac{dy}{dx} = \dfrac{x+5}{(x-2)(2x+3)} \times y \;\Rightarrow\; \dfrac{1}{y}\,dy = \dfrac{x+5}{(x-2)(2x+3)}\,dx$

2. To make the right-hand side easier to integrate, write it as partial fractions (see p.254):

$$\dfrac{x+5}{(x-2)(2x+3)} \equiv \dfrac{A}{x-2} + \dfrac{B}{2x+3} \;\Rightarrow\; x+5 \equiv A(2x+3) + B(x-2)$$

Solving for A and B gives $A = 1$, $B = -1$, so $\dfrac{1}{y}\,dy = \dfrac{1}{x-2} - \dfrac{1}{2x+3}\,dx$.

3. Now you can integrate:　　$\displaystyle\int \dfrac{1}{y}\,dy = \int \dfrac{1}{x-2} - \dfrac{1}{2x+3}\,dx$

$$\Rightarrow \ln|y| = \ln|x-2| - \tfrac{1}{2}\ln|2x+3| + \ln k$$

$$\Rightarrow \ln|y| = \ln\left|\dfrac{k(x-2)}{\sqrt{2x+3}}\right| \;\Rightarrow\; \mathbf{y = \dfrac{k(x-2)}{\sqrt{2x+3}}}$$

Exercise 12.2

Q1　Find the general solutions of the following differential equations where $x \geq 0$.
　　Give your answers in the form $y = f(x)$.

a) $\dfrac{dy}{dx} = 8x^3$

b) $\dfrac{dy}{dx} = 5y$

c) $\dfrac{dy}{dx} = 6x^2y$

d) $\dfrac{dy}{dx} = \dfrac{y}{x}$

e) $\dfrac{dy}{dx} - \cos x = y\cos x$

f) $\dfrac{dy}{dx} = \dfrac{3xy - 6y}{(x-4)(2x-5)}$

Q2 Find the particular solutions of the following differential equations at the given conditions:

a) $\dfrac{dA}{dt} = 6\sqrt{A}$, $t = 5$, $A = 400$

b) $\dfrac{dy}{dx} = -\dfrac{x}{y}$, $x = 0$, $y = 2$

c) $\dfrac{dx}{dt} = \dfrac{2}{\sqrt{x}}$, $t = 5$, $x = 9$

d) $\dfrac{dV}{dt} = 3(V - 1)$, $t = 0$, $V = 5$

e) $\dfrac{dy}{dx} = \dfrac{\tan y}{x}$, $x = 2$, $y = \dfrac{\pi}{2}$

f) $\dfrac{dx}{dt} = 10x(x + 1)$, $t = 0$, $x = 1$

Q3 The rate of increase of the variable V at time t satisfies the differential equation $\dfrac{dV}{dt} = a - bV$, where a and b are positive constants.

a) Show that $V = \dfrac{a}{b} - Ae^{-bt}$, where A is a positive constant.

b) Given that $V = \dfrac{a}{4b}$ when $t = 0$, find A in terms of a and b.

c) Find the value V approaches as t gets very large.

Applying differential equations to real-life problems

Some questions involve taking **real-life problems** and using differential equations to **model** them.

- **Population** questions come up quite often — the population might be **increasing** or **decreasing** over time, t, and you have to find and solve differential equations to show it.

- You might be given a **starting condition** — e.g. the **initial population**. The important thing to remember is that the starting condition occurs when $t = 0$.

- Once you've solved the differential equation you can use it to **answer questions** about the model — e.g. finding a **population** after a certain number of years, or the **number of years** it takes to reach a certain population. Don't forget to relate the answer back to the situation given in the question.

You may also have to identify **limitations** of the model, as well as suggest possible **changes** that would **improve** it. Common things that you should think about are:

- Is there any information **missing** from the model?
- What happens to the model when the variables get really **big/small**?
- Is the model appropriate? Is a **continuous** function used for a **discrete** variable? Does the function allow **negative** values that don't make sense?
- Are there **other factors** that have not been accounted for in the model? E.g. **natural immunity** to a disease, **immigration/emigration** of a population or **seasonal variation** in weather.

 Example | The population of rabbits in a park is decreasing as winter approaches. The rate of decrease is directly proportional to the current number of rabbits (P).

a) **Explain why this situation can be modelled by the differential equation** $\dfrac{dP}{dt} = -kP$, **where t is the time in days and k is a positive constant.** (MODELLING)

The model states that the rate of decrease in the rabbit population (i.e. $\dfrac{dP}{dt}$) is proportional to P. This means $\dfrac{dP}{dt} \propto P$. By introducing a constant of proportionality, the model becomes: $\dfrac{dP}{dt} = -kP$. The minus sign shows that the population is decreasing.

b) **If the initial population is P_0, solve your differential equation to find P in terms of P_0, k and t.**

1. First, solve the differential equation to find the general solution:

$$\dfrac{dP}{dt} = -kP \implies \dfrac{1}{P}\,dP = -k\,dt \implies \int \dfrac{1}{P}dP = \int -k\,dt \implies \ln P = -kt + C$$

2. At $t = 0$, $P = P_0$. Putting these values into the equation gives: $\ln P_0 = -k(0) + C \implies \ln P_0 = C$

3. So the equation becomes: $\ln P = -kt + \ln P_0 \implies P = e^{(-kt + \ln P_0)} = e^{-kt}e^{\ln P_0} \implies \boldsymbol{P = P_0 e^{-kt}}$

c) Given that $k = 0.1$, find the time at which the population of rabbits will have halved, to the nearest day.

When the population of rabbits has halved, $P = \frac{1}{2}P_0$. You've been told that $k = 0.1$, so substitute these values into the equation above and solve for t:

$$\frac{1}{2}P_0 = P_0 e^{-0.1t} \Rightarrow \frac{1}{2} = e^{-0.1t} \Rightarrow \ln\frac{1}{2} = -0.1t \Rightarrow -0.6931 = -0.1t \Rightarrow t = 6.931$$

So to the nearest day, $t = 7$. This means that it will take **7 days** for the population to halve.

d) Give a limitation of the model and suggest a possible improvement that could be made.

E.g. The situation being modelled is the approach of winter — the model could give a limit on t to show at which point the model stops being appropriate.

Exercise 12.3

MODELLING

Q1 A virus spreads so that t hours after infection, the rate of increase of the number of germs (N) in the body of an infected person is directly proportional to the number of germs in the body.

a) Given that this can be represented by the differential equation $\frac{dN}{dt} = kN$, show that the general solution of this equation is $N = Ae^{kt}$, where A and k are positive constants.

b) Given that a person catching the virus will initially be infected with 200 germs and that this will double to 400 germs in 8 hours, find the number of germs an infected person has after 24 hours.

c) Give one possible limitation of this model.

Q2 The rate of depreciation of the value (V) of a car at time t after it is first purchased is directly proportional to V.

a) If the initial value of the car is V_0, show that $V = V_0 e^{-kt}$, where k is a positive constant.

b) If the car drops to one half of its initial value in the first year after purchase, how long (to the nearest month) will it take to be worth 5% of its initial value?

Q3 A cube has side length x. At time t seconds, the side length is increasing at a rate of $\frac{1}{x^2(t+1)}$ cm s^{-1}.

a) Show that the volume (V) is increasing at a rate which satisfies the differential equation $\frac{dV}{dt} = \frac{3}{t+1}$.

b) Given that the volume of the cube is initially 15 cm³, find the length of time, to 3 s.f., for it to reach a volume of 18 cm³.

Q4 A local activist is trying to get lots of signatures on his petition, and has just launched a new online campaign. The rate of increase of the number of signatures (y) he's gathered can be represented by the differential equation $\frac{dy}{dt} = k(p - y)$, where p is the population of his town, t is the time in days since the new campaign was launched and k is a positive constant.

a) Find the general solution of this equation.

b) Given that the population of his town is 30 000, he initially has 10 000 signatures on his petition and it takes 5 days for him to reach 12 000 signatures, how long, to the nearest day, will it take for him to reach 25 000 signatures?

c) Draw a graph to show this particular solution.

d) The activist wants 28 000 signatures within 92 days of launching his new campaign. According to the model, will he achieve this?

e) What is a likely limitation of this model and how could it be addressed?

Q1 a) Find $\int \dfrac{1}{\sqrt[3]{(2-11x)}}\,dx$

b) Show that the area under the curve $y = \dfrac{1}{\sqrt[3]{(2-11x)}}$ between $x = -\dfrac{123}{11}$ and $x = -\dfrac{62}{11}$ is $\dfrac{27}{22}$.

Q2 Find the equation of the curve that has the derivative $\dfrac{dy}{dx} = (1-7x)^{\frac{1}{2}}$ and goes through the point $(0, 1)$.

Q3 Find the following integrals, giving your answers in terms of e or ln.

a) $\int 4e^{2x}\,dx$ b) $\int e^{3x-5}\,dx$ c) $\int \dfrac{2}{3x}\,dx$ d) $\int \dfrac{2}{2x+1}\,dx$

Q4 If $\int \dfrac{8}{2-x} - \dfrac{8}{x}\,dx = \ln P + C$, where P is an expression in terms of x and C is a constant, find P.

Q5 Find the following integrals (A and B are constants):

a) $\int \cos(x+A)\,dx$ b) $\int \sin(A-x)\,dx$ c) $\int \text{cosec}^2((A+B)t + A + B)\,dt$

Q6 Find the following integrals:

a) $\int \cos 4x - \sec^2 7x\,dx$ b) $\int 6\sec 3x \tan 3x - \text{cosec}^2\dfrac{x}{5}\,dx$

Q7 Find the following integrals:

a) $\int \dfrac{\cos x}{\sin x}\,dx$ b) $\int \dfrac{20x^4 + 12x^2 - 12}{x^5 + x^3 - 3x}\,dx$ c) $\int \dfrac{10e^{4x} + 5}{5e^{4x} + 10x}\,dx$

Q8 Find the following integrals:

a) $\int 3x^2 e^{x^3}\,dx$ b) $\int 2x\cos(x^2)e^{\sin(x^2)}\,dx$ c) $\int \sec 4x \tan 4x\, e^{\sec 4x}\,dx$

Q9 Use an appropriate trig identity to find $\int \dfrac{2\tan 3x}{1 - \tan^2 3x}\,dx$.

Q10 Find the following integrals:

a) $\int 2\sin^2 x\,dx$ b) $\int \sin 2x \cos 2x\,dx$ c) $\int \tan^2 x + 1\,dx$

Q11 Find the exact shaded area in each of these graphs:

a)   b)   c)

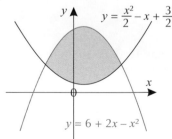

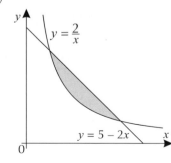

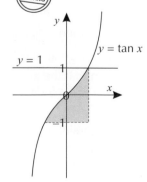

Q12 Find the areas enclosed by the following:

a) The curve $y = \sqrt[4]{x}$, the y-axis and the lines $y = 2$ and $y = 3$.

b) The curve $y = \arctan x$, the y-axis and the lines $y = \frac{\pi}{6}$ and $y = \frac{\pi}{4}$.

c) The curve $y = \frac{1}{x^2}$, the y-axis and the lines $y = 4$ and $y = 16$.

Q13 The curve on the right has the parametric equations $x = t^2 + 3$, $y = 4t - 1$.

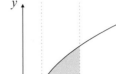

a) Given that $t > 0$, find the values of t when $x = 4$ and $x = 12$.

b) Hence find the shaded area.

Q14 The curve below has parametric equations $x = 2t^3$, $y = \frac{2}{t}$ $(t \neq 0)$.

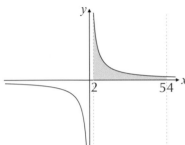

Show that the shaded area between the curve, the lines $x = 2$ and $x = 54$ and the x-axis is 48.

Q15 Find the following integrals, using the given substitution in each case. Where appropriate, give your answers as exact values.

a) $\int 16x(5 - x^2)^5 \, dx$, using $u = 5 - x^2$

b) $\int e^x(e^x + 1)(e^x - 1)^2 \, dx$, using $u = e^x - 1$

c) $\int_{\frac{\pi}{4}}^{\frac{\pi}{3}} \sec^4 x \tan x \, dx$, using $u = \sec x$

d) $\int_3^{11} \frac{2x}{\sqrt{3x - 8}} \, dx$, using $u = \sqrt{3x - 8}$

Q16 Find the following integrals, giving exact answers where appropriate:

a) $\int_2^4 x(x^2 - 4)^3 \, dx$, using $u = x^2 - 4$

b) $\int 3 \sin\theta \cos^4\theta \, d\theta$, using $u = \cos\theta$

Q17 Find: a) $\int_0^{\frac{\pi}{2}} \frac{1}{4} \cos x \sin 2x \, dx$, using the substitution $u = \cos x$

b) $\int_1^{\sqrt{3}} \frac{4x}{\sqrt{1 + x^2}} \, dx$, using the substitution $x = \cot\theta$, $-\frac{\pi}{2} \leq \theta \leq \frac{\pi}{2}$

Q18 Use integration by parts to solve:

a) $\int 3x^2 \ln x \, dx$

b) $\int 4x \cos 4x \, dx$

c) $\int_0^4 e^{\frac{x}{2}} x^2 \, dx$

Q19 Use integration by parts twice to find $\int 10x^2 e^{5x} \, dx$.

Q20 Given that $\frac{3x + 10}{(2x + 3)(x - 4)} \equiv \frac{A}{2x + 3} + \frac{B}{x - 4}$, find $\int \frac{3x + 10}{(2x + 3)(x - 4)} \, dx$.

Q21 Given that $f(x) = \frac{13x - 18}{(x - 3)^2(2x + 1)} \equiv \frac{A}{(x - 3)^2} + \frac{B}{(x - 3)} + \frac{C}{(2x + 1)}$, find $\int_4^9 f(x) \, dx$.

Q22 Formulate differential equations to represent the following:

    a) The rate of increase of x as y increases is directly proportional to the square of x.

    b) The volume (V) of water in a container is decreasing with time (t) at a rate inversely proportional to the square root of V.

    c) The speed, s, of a moving object is decreasing with time at a rate directly proportional to the difference between s and the object's initial speed, s_0.

Q23 Find the general solution to the differential equation $\dfrac{dy}{dx} = \dfrac{1}{y}\cos x$.
Give your answer in the form $y^2 = f(x)$.

Q24 Given that $x = 0$ when $t = 1$ and $x = -3$ when $t = 0$, find the particular solution
of the differential equation $\dfrac{dx}{dt} = kte^t$, where k is a constant.

Q25 a) Find the general solution of the equation $\dfrac{dx}{d\theta} = \cos^2 x \cot \theta$.

    b) Given that $x = \dfrac{\pi}{4}$ when $\theta = \dfrac{\pi}{2}$, find a particular solution.

    c) Hence find the value of x when $\theta = \dfrac{\pi}{6}$, for $0 < x < \dfrac{\pi}{2}$.

Q26 The population of squirrels is increasing suspiciously quickly.
The rate of increase is directly proportional to the number of squirrels, S.

    a) Formulate a differential equation to model the rate of increase in terms of S, t (time in weeks) and k, a positive constant.

    b) The squirrels need a population of 150 to successfully take over the forest.
If, initially, $S = 30$ and $\dfrac{dS}{dt} = 6$, how long (to the nearest week) will it take
before they can overthrow the evil hedgehogs?

Q27 The rate of decrease of temperature ($T\,°C$) of a cup of tea with time (t minutes)
satisfies the differential equation $\dfrac{dT}{dt} = -k(T - 21)$, where k is a positive constant.

    a) Given that the initial temperature of the tea is 90 °C, and it cools to 80 °C in 5 minutes, find a particular solution for T.

    b) Use this solution to find: (i) the temperature of the tea after 15 minutes,

                                     (ii) the time it takes to drop to 40 °C.

    c) Sketch the graph of T against t.

Q28 It is thought that the rate of increase of the number of field mice (N)
in a given area is directly proportional to N.

    a) Formulate a differential equation for N.

    b) Given that in 4 weeks the number of mice in a particular field has risen from 20 to 30, find the length of time, to the nearest week, before the field is over-run with 1000 mice.

    A biologist believes that the rate of increase of the number of field mice is actually directly proportional to the square root of N when natural factors such as predators and disease are taken into account.

    c) Repeat parts a) and b) using this new model.

    d) Suggest another refinement that could be made to improve this model.

Chapter 24 — Numerical Methods

Sometimes finding the solutions of an equation algebraically is quite difficult. In these situations, there are a number of methods you can use to approximate these roots, although they're not always guaranteed to work.

1. Location of Roots

Locating roots by changes of sign

- 'Solving' or 'finding the roots of' an equation (where $f(x) = 0$) is the same as finding the values of x where the graph crosses the x-axis.

- For a **continuous** function $f(x)$ (i.e. one with no **breaks** or **asymptotes** in its graph), if $f(x)$ changes sign between two values of x, $f(x) = 0$ has a root within that interval. You can use this fact to find a root to a given number of decimal places.

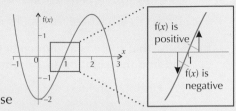

f(x) is positive / f(x) is negative

> **[Example]** Show that one root of the equation $x^3 - x^2 - 9 = 0$ is 2.472, correct to 3 d.p.
>
> 1. If the root is 2.472 to 3 d.p., the exact value must lie between the upper and lower bounds of this value: $2.4715 \leq x < 2.4725$
>
> 2. The function is continuous, so if there is a root in this interval, the function will change sign: $f(2.4715) = -0.0116...$
> $f(2.4725) = 0.0017...$
>
> 3. So there is a root within this interval. Any value within the interval rounds to 2.472 to 3 d.p. so: $x = 2.472$ **(3 d.p.)**

Tip: This method might fail to find a particular root — for example, if you take too large of an interval to start with, or if the function touches the x-axis but doesn't cross it. An accurate sketch of the graph will help to avoid this.

Exercise 1.1

Q1 Show that the following equations have a solution within the given interval:
   a) $x^3 - 5x + 1 = 0$, $2 < x < 3$
   b) $\sin 2x - x = 0$ (x in radians), $0.9 < x < 1.0$
   c) $x^3 + \ln x - 2 = 0$, $[1.2, 1.3]$
   d) $4x - 2x^3 = 15$, $-2.3 < x < -2.2$
   e) $\ln(x + 3) = 5x$, $[0.23, 0.24]$
   f) $e^{3x}\sin x = 5$ (x in radians), $(0, 1)$

Q2 A bird is observed diving into the sea. Its height above the water after x seconds is modelled by the equation $f(x) = 2x^2 - 8x + 7$, where $f(x)$ is the height in metres. Show that the bird hits the water in the interval $1.2 < x < 1.3$ seconds.

Q3 Show that there are 2 solutions, α and β, to the equation $3x - x^4 + 3 = 0$, such that $1.6 < \alpha < 1.7$ and $-1 < \beta < 0$.

Q4 Show that there are 2 solutions, α and β, to the equation $e^{x-2} - \sqrt{x} = 0$, such that $0.01 < \alpha < 0.02$ and $2.4 < \beta < 2.5$.

Q5 Show that $x = 2.8$ is a solution to the equation $x^3 - 7x - 2 = 0$ to 1 d.p.

Q6 a) Show that $x = 0.7$ is a solution to the equation $2x - \dfrac{1}{x} = 0$ to 1 d.p.
   b) Explain why a change of sign in the interval $[-0.1, 0.1]$ does not mean there is a root in this interval.

Q7 $f(x) = e^x - x^3 - 5x$. Verify that a root of the equation $f(x) = 0$ is $x = 0.25$ correct to 2 d.p.

Sketching graphs to find approximate roots

Sometimes it's easier to find the number of roots and roughly where they are if you **sketch** the graphs first. Draw the graphs of f(x) and g(x) on the same axes — the values of x where they **intersect** will be the solutions of the equation f(x) = g(x), or f(x) − g(x) = 0.

Examples   The diagram shows the graphs of $y = \ln x$ and $y = (x - 3)^2$.

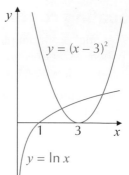

a)   **Write down the number of roots of the equation $\ln x - (x - 3)^2 = 0$.**

The roots are where the graphs cross, so: There are **two** roots.

b)   **Show that there is a solution between 2 and 3, and find this solution to 1 decimal place.**

1.   Find f(2) and f(3):   f(2) = ln 2 − (2 − 3)² = −0.306...
                               f(3) = ln 3 − (3 − 3)² = 1.098...

2.   So there is a root within this interval. Keep trying values in the function until you find the solution to 1 d.p.:
    f(2.2) = ln 2.2 − (2.2 − 3)² = 0.148... ⇒ 2 < x < 2.2
    f(2.1) = ln 2.1 − (2.1 − 3)² = −0.068... ⇒ 2.1 < x < 2.2
    f(2.15) = ln 2.15 − (2.15 − 3)² = 0.0429... ⇒ 2.1 < x < 2.15

3.   All the values in the interval 2.1 < x < 2.15 round to 2.1, so: **x = 2.1** (1 d.p.)

Exercise 1.2

Sketch all graphs in this exercise for $-5 < x < 5$ unless otherwise stated.

Q1   a) On the same axes, sketch the graphs of $y = \dfrac{1}{x}$ and $y = x - 2$.

   b) Using your graph from part a), write down the number of solutions of $\dfrac{1}{x} = x - 2$ in this interval.

   c) Show that one solution of the equation $\dfrac{1}{x} = x - 2$ lies in the interval $2.4 < x < 2.5$.

Q2   a) On the same axes, sketch the graphs of $y = 2x^3 - 7x$ and $y = x^2$.

   b) Using your graph from part a), write down the number of solutions of $2x^3 - x^2 - 7x = 0$ in this interval.

   c) Show that the equation $2x^3 - x^2 - 7x = 0$ has a root between $x = -2$ and $x = -1$.

Q3   a) Sketch the graphs of $y = 2^x - 3$ and $y = \ln x$ on the same axes.

   b) f(x) = ln $x - 2^x + 3$. Using your graph, write down the number of roots of the equation f(x) = 0.

   c) Show that the equation f(x) = 0 has a root between 1.8 and 2.2 and find this root to 1 decimal place.

Q4   a) Sketch the graphs of $y = \sqrt{x + 1}$ and $y = 2x$ on the same axes.

   b) Write down the number of solutions of the equation $\sqrt{x + 1} = 2x$.

   c) Show that the equation $\sqrt{x + 1} = 2x$ has a solution in the interval (0.6, 0.7).

   d) By rearranging the equation $\sqrt{x + 1} = 2x$, use the quadratic formula to find the solution of the equation from part c) to 3 s.f.

Q5   a) Sketch the graphs of $y = e^{2x}$ and $y = 3 - x^2$ on the same axes.

   b) Using your graph from part a), explain how you know that $e^{2x} + x^2 = 3$ has two solutions.

   c) Show that the negative solution of $e^{2x} + x^2 = 3$ lies between $x = -2$ and $x = -1$, and find it to 1 d.p.

2. Iterative Methods

- **Iteration** is a numerical method for **solving equations**, like **trial and improvement**.

- You put an approximate value of a root x into an iteration formula, and it gives you a **slightly more accurate** value. You then put the new value into the iteration formula, and keep going until your answers are the same when rounded to the level of accuracy needed.

Tip: Use the ANS button on your calculator to speed things up and avoid rounding errors.

Example   Use the iteration formula $x_{n+1} = \sqrt[3]{x_n + 4}$ to solve $x^3 - 4 - x = 0$, to 2 d.p.
Start with $x_0 = 2$.

1. Use the iteration formula to find x_1: $x_0 = 2$, so $x_1 = \sqrt[3]{x_0 + 4} = \sqrt[3]{2 + 4} = 1.8171...$

2. Put this value back into the formula: $x_2 = \sqrt[3]{x_1 + 4} = \sqrt[3]{1.8171... + 4} = 1.7984...$

   $x_3 = \sqrt[3]{x_2 + 4} = \sqrt[3]{1.7984... + 4} = 1.7965...$

3. x_2 and x_3 (and all further iterations) are the same when rounded to 2 d.p., so the root is:

$$x = 1.80 \text{ (2 d.p.)}$$

- Sometimes an iteration formula will **not find a root**. In these cases, no matter how close to the root you have x_0, the iteration sequence **diverges** — the numbers get further and further apart.

- The iteration might also **stop working** — for example, if you have to take the square root of a negative number.

Example   The equation $x^3 - x^2 - 9 = 0$ has a root close to $x = 2.5$.
What is the result of using $x_{n+1} = \sqrt{x_n^3 - 9}$ with $x_0 = 2.5$ to find this root?

1. Find the first few iterations: $x_0 = 2.5$, $x_1 = \sqrt{2.5^3 - 9} = 2.5739...$, $x_2 = 2.8376...$,
   $x_3 = 3.7214...$, $x_4 = 6.5221...$

2. The results are getting further apart with each iteration, so: The sequence **diverges**.

Exercise 2.1

Q1   a) Show that the equation $x^3 + 3x^2 - 7 = 0$ has a root in the interval $(1, 2)$.

   b) Use the iterative formula $x_{n+1} = \sqrt{\dfrac{7 - x_n^3}{3}}$ with $x_0 = 1$
   to find values for x_1, x_2, x_3 and x_4 to 3 decimal places.

Q2   An intersection of the curves $y = \ln x$ and $y = x - 2$ is at the point $x = \alpha$, where α is 3.1 to 1 d.p.

   a) Starting with $x_0 = 3.1$, use the iterative formula $x_{n+1} = 2 + \ln x_n$ to find the first 5 iterations, giving your answers to 4 decimal places.

   b) Write down an estimate of the value of α to 3 decimal places.

Q3   a) Show that the equation $x^4 - 5x + 3 = 0$ has a root between $x = 1.4$ and $x = 1.5$.

   b) Use the iterative formula $x_{n+1} = \sqrt[3]{5 - \dfrac{3}{x_n}}$ and $x_0 = 1.4$ to find iterations x_1 to x_6 to 3 decimal places.

   c) Hence write down an approximation of the root from part a) to 2 decimal places.

Q4 a) Show that the function $f(x) = x^2 - 5x - 2$ has a root that lies between $x = 5$ and $x = 6$.

b) The root in part a) can be estimated using the iterative formula $x_{n+1} = \dfrac{2}{x_n} + 5$. Using a starting value of $x_0 = 5$, find the values of x_1, x_2, x_3 and x_4, giving your answers to 4 significant figures.

Q5 Use the iterative formula $x_{n+1} = 2 - \ln x_n$, $x_0 = 1.5$ to find the root of the equation $\ln x = 2 - x$ to 2 d.p.

Q6 a) Show that the equation $e^x - 10x = 0$ has a root in the interval $(3, 4)$.

b) Using the iterative formula $x_{n+1} = \ln(10x_n)$ with $x_0 = 3$, find values for x_1, x_2, x_3 and x_4 to 3 d.p.

c) Verify that the value of the root from part a) is $x = 3.577$ to 3 d.p.

d) Describe what happens when you use the alternative formula $x_{n+1} = \dfrac{e^{x_n}}{10}$ with $x_0 = 3$.

Q7 The formula $x_{n+1} = \dfrac{x_n^2 - 3x_n}{2} - 5$ is used to try and find approximations to a root of $f(x) = x^2 - 5x - 10$.

a) Find the values of x_1, x_2, x_3 and x_4, starting with $x_0 = -1$, and describe what happens to the sequence $x_1, x_2, x_3, x_4\ldots$

b) Using the alternative iterative formula $x_{n+1} = \sqrt{5x_n + 10}$ with starting value $x_0 = 6$, find a root of the equation $f(x) = 0$ to 3 significant figures. Verify your answer is correct to this level of accuracy.

Finding iteration formulas

The **iteration formula** is just a **rearrangement** of the equation, leaving a single 'x' on one side. There are lots of **different ways** to rearrange any given equation, so you'll often have to 'show that' it can be rearranged in a certain way (which will avoid formulas that lead to **divergent** iterations).

 Example

Show that $x^3 - x^2 - 9 = 0$ can be rearranged into $x = \sqrt{\dfrac{9}{x-1}}$.

Use this to make an iteration formula and find the value of a root to 2 d.p. with starting value $x_0 = 2.5$.

1. Rearrange the equation:
$$x^3 - x^2 - 9 = 0 \implies x^3 - x^2 = 9$$
$$\implies x^2(x - 1) = 9 \implies x^2 = \frac{9}{x - 1}$$
$$\implies x = \sqrt{\frac{9}{x - 1}} \text{ as required}$$

2. You can now use the iteration formula $x_{n+1} = \sqrt{\dfrac{9}{x_n - 1}}$ to find approximations of the root:

$x_0 = 2.5$, $x_1 = \sqrt{\dfrac{9}{2.5 - 1}} = 2.449\ldots$, $x_2 = \sqrt{\dfrac{9}{2.449 - 1}} = 2.491\ldots$, $x_3 = 2.456\ldots$,

$\ldots x_{13} = 2.469\ldots$, $x_{14} = 2.474\ldots$, $x_{15} = 2.470\ldots$

3. So the value of the root is: $x = 2.47$ (2 d.p.)

Exercise 2.2

Q1 Show that the equation $x^4 + 7x - 3 = 0$ can be written in the form:

a) $x = \sqrt[4]{3 - 7x}$

b) $x = \dfrac{3 - 5x - x^4}{2}$

c) $x = \dfrac{\sqrt{3 - 7x}}{x}$

Q2 a) Show that the equation $x^3 - 2x^2 - 5 = 0$ can be rewritten as $x = 2 + \dfrac{5}{x^2}$.

b) Use the iterative formula $x_{n+1} = 2 + \dfrac{5}{x_n^2}$ with starting value $x_0 = 2$ to find x_5 to 1 decimal place.

c) Verify that the value found in part b) is a root of the equation $x^3 - 2x^2 - 5 = 0$ to 1 decimal place.

Q3 a) Rearrange the equation $x^2 + 3x - 8 = 0$ into the form $x = \dfrac{a}{x} + b$ where a and b are values to be found.

b) Verify that a root of the equation $x^2 + 3x - 8 = 0$ lies in the interval $(-5, -4)$.

c) Use the iterative formula $x_{n+1} = \dfrac{a}{x_n} + b$ with $x_0 = -5$ to find the values for x_1 to x_6, giving your answers to 3 d.p. Hence find a value of the root of the equation $x^2 + 3x - 8 = 0$ to 2 d.p.

Q4 a) Show that the equation $2^{x-1} = 4\sqrt{x}$ can be written as $x = 2^{2x-6}$.

b) Use the iterative formula $x_{n+1} = 2^{2x_n - 6}$, with $x_0 = 1$, to find the values of x_1, x_2, x_3 and x_4 to 4 d.p.

c) Verify that the value for x_4 is a correct approximation to 4 d.p. for the root of $2^{x-1} = 4\sqrt{x}$.

Q5 a) Given that $f(x) = \ln 2x + x^3$, show that $f(x) = 0$ has a solution in the interval $0.4 < x < 0.5$.

b) Show that the equation $f(x) = 0$ can be rewritten in the form $x = \dfrac{e^{-x^3}}{2}$.

c) Using an iterative formula based on part b) and an appropriate value for x_0, find an approximation of the root of the equation $f(x) = 0$ to 3 decimal places.

Q6 $f(x) = x^2 - 9x - 20$

a) Find an iterative formula for $f(x) = 0$ in the form $x_{n+1} = \sqrt{px_n + q}$, where p and q are constants.

b) By using the formula in part a) and a starting value of $x_0 = 10$, find an approximation to a root of the equation $f(x) = 0$. Give your answer to 3 significant figures.

c) Show that an alternative iterative formula is $x_{n+1} = \dfrac{x_n^2 - 4x_n}{5} - 4$.

d) By using the iterative formula in part c) with starting value $x_0 = 1$, find the value of $x_1, x_2 ... x_8$.

e) Describe the behaviour of this sequence.

3. Sketching Iterations

Cobweb and staircase diagrams

- **Iteration diagrams** are a way of showing the iteration process **graphically**.

- You start by drawing the graphs of $y = x$ and $y = f(x)$ on the same axes (where $f(x)$ is the iteration formula). The point where the graphs **cross** is the root you're aiming for.

- Depending on $f(x)$ and x_0, you'll end up with either a **cobweb diagram** or a **staircase diagram**.

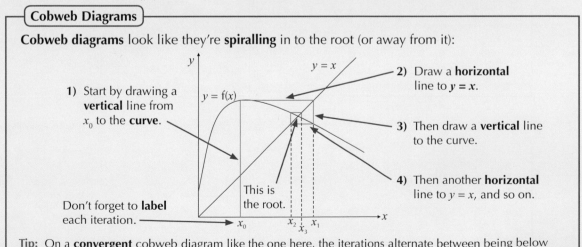

Cobweb Diagrams

Cobweb diagrams look like they're **spiralling** in to the root (or away from it):

1) Start by drawing a **vertical** line from x_0 to the **curve**.

Don't forget to **label** each iteration.

This is the root.

2) Draw a **horizontal** line to $y = x$.

3) Then draw a **vertical** line to the curve.

4) Then another **horizontal** line to $y = x$, and so on.

Tip: On a **convergent** cobweb diagram like the one here, the iterations alternate between being below and above the root, but are getting closer each time. A **divergent** cobweb diagram would have a similar shape, but each iteration would **spiral away from the root** rather than towards it.

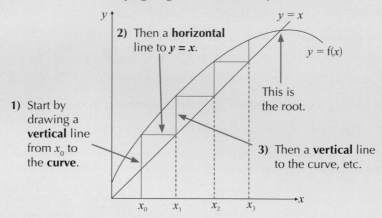

Staircase Diagrams

Staircase diagrams form a set of **steps** going towards (or away from) the root.

2) Then a **horizontal** line to $y = x$.

1) Start by drawing a **vertical** line from x_0 to the **curve**.

This is the root.

3) Then a **vertical** line to the curve, etc.

Tip: On a **convergent** staircase diagram, each iteration gets **closer** to the root.
On a **divergent** staircase diagram, the steps would lead away from the root, not towards it.

These methods will only find a root $x = a$ (for a suitable starting point x_0) if the graph **isn't too steep** at the root — the iterations will converge if the gradient $f'(a)$ is **between –1 and 1** (i.e. $|f'(a)| < 1$).

Exercise 3.1

Q1 For each graph below, draw a diagram to show the convergence or divergence of the iterative sequence for the given value of x_0, and say whether it is a convergent or divergent staircase or cobweb diagram. Label x_0, x_1 and x_2 on each diagram where possible.

a) $x_0 = 3.5$

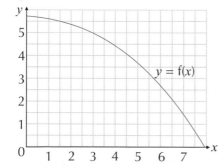

b) $x_0 = 3$

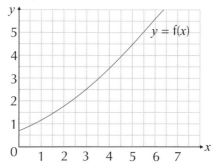

c) $x_0 = 1.75$

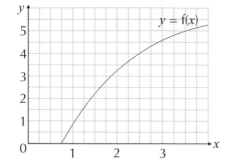

d) $x_0 = 4$

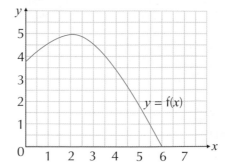

4. The Newton-Raphson Method

The **Newton-Raphson method** is another iterative method that works by using **differentiation** to find the **tangent** to a function at a point x_0, and using its **x-intercept** for the next iteration, x_1. The iterative formula is:

$$x_{n+1} = x_n - \frac{f(x_n)}{f'(x_n)}$$

Example

Use the Newton-Raphson method with a starting point of $x_0 = -2$ to find a root of $f(x) = x^3 - 3x + 5$ correct to 5 decimal places.

1. Differentiate $f(x)$: $\qquad f'(x) = 3x^2 - 3$

2. So the iteration formula is: $\qquad x_{n+1} = x_n - \dfrac{x_n^3 - 3x_n + 5}{3x_n^2 - 3} \quad \leftarrow f(x_n) \\ \leftarrow f'(x_n)$

3. Find the iterations: $\qquad x_0 = -2, \; x_1 = -2 - \dfrac{(-2)^3 - 3(-2) + 5}{3(-2)^2 - 3} = -\dfrac{7}{3} = -2.333333...$

   $$x_2 = -\frac{7}{3} - \frac{\left(-\frac{7}{3}\right)^3 - 3\left(-\frac{7}{3}\right) + 5}{3\left(-\frac{7}{3}\right)^2 - 3} = -2.280555...$$

   $x_3 = -2.279020..., \quad x_4 = -2.279018..., \quad x_5 = -2.279018...$

4. So the root is: $\qquad \mathbf{x = -2.27902}$ (5 d.p.)

There are times when the Newton-Raphson method can't be used to find a root.

- If the function $f(x)$ cannot be differentiated, you won't be able to form an iteration formula to use.

- Like other iterative methods, if you choose a starting point x_0 too far away from the root, the sequence might diverge.

- If the tangent to $f(x)$ is **horizontal** at the point x_n (i.e. if $f(x)$ has a **stationary point** at x_n), the method will fail, as shown:

- Similarly, if the gradient at x_n is too **shallow**, the tangent might meet the x-axis **far** from the root, causing the iterations to diverge.

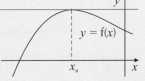

Exercise 4.1

Q1 Using the Newton-Raphson method, give an iteration formula for finding the roots of each of these functions:

   a) $f(x) = 5x^2 - 6$ $\qquad$ b) $g(x) = e^{3x} - 4x^2 - 1$ $\qquad$ c) $h(x) = \sin x + x^3 - 1$

Q2 Use the Newton-Raphson method to find a root of $x^4 - 2x^3 - 5 = 0$ to 5 s.f., starting with $x_0 = 2.5$.

Q3 Use the Newton-Raphson method to find the negative root of $f(x) = x^2 - 5x - 12$ to 5 s.f. Use $x_0 = -1$ as your start value.

Q4 Use the Newton-Raphson method to find a root to the equation $x^2 \ln x = 5$ to 5 s.f., using $x_0 = 2$.

Q5 Show that the Newton-Raphson method will fail to find a root of the equation $2x^3 - 15x^2 + 109 = 0$ if $x_0 = 1$ is used as the starting value. (PROBLEM SOLVING)

Q6 A scientist is analysing the speed at which a rocket uses fuel. She determines that the volume of fuel (in cm³) left in the rocket after t minutes is modelled by the function $f(t) = 3e^{-t} + 2t - \frac{1}{2}t^2$. (MODELLING)
Use the Newton-Raphson method with $t_0 = 10$ to find when the rocket will run out of fuel (to 3 s.f.).

5. The Trapezium Rule

The trapezium rule is a method for approximating the **area under a curve** (i.e. an **integral**) by splitting the area up into lots of **trapeziums** and **adding** the areas together.

The **trapezium rule** for approximating $\int_a^b f(x)\,dx$ works like this:

- n is the **number** of strips i.e. trapeziums.
- h is the **width** of each strip — so $h = \dfrac{(b-a)}{n}$.
- The **x-values** go up in steps of h, starting with $x_0 = a$.
- The **y-values** are found by putting the x-values into the equation of the curve — so $y_1 = f(x_1)$. They give the **heights** of the sides of the trapeziums.
- The **area** of each trapezium is $A = \dfrac{h}{2}(y_r + y_{r+1})$.

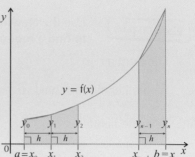

Then an **approximation** for $\int_a^b f(x)\,dx$ is found by **adding** the **areas** of all the trapeziums:

$$\int_a^b f(x)\,dx \approx \frac{h}{2}(y_0 + y_1) + \frac{h}{2}(y_1 + y_2) + \dots + \frac{h}{2}(y_{n-1} + y_n) \approx \boxed{\frac{h}{2}\left[y_0 + 2(y_1 + y_2 + \dots + y_{n-1}) + y_n\right]}$$

Examples   Use the trapezium rule to approximate $\int_0^4 \dfrac{6x^2}{x^3+2}\,dx$ to 3 d.p. using:

a) $n = 2$

1. Find h and the x-values: $n = 2$, so $h = \dfrac{4-0}{2} = 2$. The x-values are 0, 2 and 4.

2. Calculate the corresponding y-values:

3. Put these values into the formula:

x	$x_0 = 0$	$x_1 = 2$	$x_2 = 4$
$y = \dfrac{6x^2}{x^3+2}$	$y_0 = 0$	$y_1 = 2.4$	$y_2 = 1.4545\dots$

$$\int_0^4 \frac{6x^2}{x^3+2}\,dx \approx \frac{h}{2}[y_0 + 2y_1 + y_2]$$
$$= \frac{2}{2}[0 + 2(2.4) + 1.4545\dots] = \mathbf{6.255} \text{ (3 d.p.)}$$

b) $n = 4$

1. Find h and the x-values: $n = 4$, so $h = \dfrac{4-0}{4} = 1$. The x-values are 0, 1, 2, 3 and 4.

2. Calculate the corresponding y-values:

x	$x_0 = 0$	$x_1 = 1$	$x_2 = 2$	$x_3 = 3$	$x_4 = 4$
$y = \dfrac{6x^2}{x^3+2}$	$y_0 = 0$	$y_1 = 2$	$y_2 = 2.4$	$y_3 = 1.8620\dots$	$y_4 = 1.4545\dots$

3. Put these values into the formula:

$$\int_0^4 \frac{6x^2}{x^3+2}\,dx \approx \frac{h}{2}[y_0 + 2(y_1 + y_2 + y_3) + y_4] = \frac{1}{2}[0 + 2(2 + 2.4 + 1.8620\dots) + 1.4545\dots]$$
$$= \frac{1}{2}[13.9787] = \mathbf{6.989} \text{ (3 d.p.)}$$

Upper and lower bounds

The **approximation** that the trapezium rule gives will either be an **overestimate** (too big) or an **underestimate** (too small). This will depend on the **shape** of the graph — sketching the graph can show whether the tops of the trapeziums lie **above** the curve or stay **below** it.

The estimate is **more** than the real area.

The estimate is **less** than the real area.

Using **more strips** (i.e. **increasing** n) gives you a **more accurate** approximation.

You can calculate an **upper** and **lower bound** for the area under a curve using these simplified formulas:

$$\int_a^b f(x)\, dx \approx h[y_0 + y_1 + y_2 + ... + y_{n-1}]$$

$$\int_a^b f(x)\, dx \approx h[y_1 + y_2 + ... + y_{n-1} + y_n]$$

When you approximate the area under a curve using the **trapezium rule**, the approximation will be **between** these two bounds. Which one is the upper and which is the lower bound will depend on f(x).

If you can find the **exact value** of the area by integrating, you can find the **percentage error** in your approximation (the difference between your estimate and the actual value — see p.306).

Exercise 5.1

Q1 Use the trapezium rule to find approximations of each of the following integrals. Use the given number of intervals in each case. Give your answers to 3 significant figures.

a) $\int_1^3 2(\ln x)^2\, dx$, 4 intervals

b) $\int_{-\frac{\pi}{4}}^{\frac{\pi}{4}} 4x\tan x\, dx$, 4 intervals

c) $\int_0^{0.3} \sqrt{e^x + 1}\, dx$, 6 intervals

d) $\int_0^{\pi} \ln(2 + \sin x)\, dx$, 6 intervals

e) $\int_{-2}^{2} \frac{1}{(x^2 + 2)(2^x - x)}\, dx$, 4 intervals

f) $\int_0^{2\pi} (\sin^2 x + 1)\sqrt{5\cos^2 x + 4}\, dx$, 8 intervals

Q2 Use the trapezium rule with 3 intervals to find an estimate to $\int_0^{\frac{\pi}{2}} \sin^3 \theta\, d\theta$. Give your answer to 3 d.p.

Q3 The shape of an aeroplane's wing is modelled by the curve $y = \sqrt{\ln x}$, where x and y are measured in metres. Use the trapezium rule with 5 intervals to estimate the area of a cross-section of the wing enclosed by the curve $y = \sqrt{\ln x}$, the x-axis and the lines $x = 2$ and $x = 7$. Give your answer to 3 d.p.

Q4 a) Complete the table of values for $y = e^{\sin x}$, giving values to 3 d.p.

x	0	$\frac{\pi}{8}$	$\frac{\pi}{4}$	$\frac{3\pi}{8}$	$\frac{\pi}{2}$
y	1	1.466			2.718

b) Use the trapezium rule to estimate $\int_0^{\frac{\pi}{2}} e^{\sin x}\, dx$ to 2 d.p. using: (i) 2 intervals   (ii) 4 intervals

c) Which is the better estimate? Explain your answer.

Q5 For the integrals: a) $\int_0^2 \sqrt{x + 2}\, dx$ and   b) $\int_0^{0.4} xe^{x^2}\, dx$, find:

(i) an approximation to 3 s.f. using the trapezium rule with 2 intervals,
(ii) an upper and lower bound for the area beneath the curve, to 4 s.f.
(iii) the percentage error to 3 s.f. for each approximation.

Q6 a) Using the trapezium rule with $h = \frac{\pi}{6}$, show that $\int_{-\frac{\pi}{2}}^{\frac{\pi}{2}} \cos x\, dx \approx \frac{\pi(2 + \sqrt{3})}{6}$.

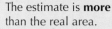

b) Without further calculation, explain whether this approximation is an under- or overestimate.

c) Calculate the percentage error for the approximation in part a). Give your answer to 3 s.f.

Review Exercise — Chapter 24

Q1 Show that there is a root in the interval:

a) $3 < x < 4$ for $\sin(2x) = 0$ (x in radians)　　　b) $2.1 < x < 2.2$ for $\ln(x - 2) + 2 = 0$

c) $4.3 < x < 4.5$ for $x^3 - 4x^2 = 7$

Q2 The graph shows the function $f(x) = e^x - x^3$ for $0 \leq x \leq 5$. How many roots does the equation $e^x - x^3 = 0$ have in the interval $0 \leq x \leq 5$?

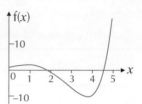

Q3 By selecting an appropriate interval, show that, to 1 d.p, $x = 1.2$ is a root of the equation $x^3 + x - 3 = 0$.

Q4 Explain why change of sign methods cannot be used to identify a solution of the equation $f(x) = 0$, where $f(x) = x^2 + 4x + 4$.

Q5 a) On the same axes sketch the graphs of $y = \ln x$ and $y = \dfrac{2}{x}$. Hence find the number of roots of the equation $\ln x - \dfrac{2}{x} = 0$.

b) Show that there is a root of the equation $\ln x - \dfrac{2}{x} = 0$ between $x = 2$ and $x = 3$.

Q6 a) Sketch the graphs of $y = \dfrac{1}{x+1}$ and $y = x - 2$ on the same axes.

b) $f(x) = \dfrac{1}{x+1} - x + 2$. Show that a root of the equation $f(x) = 0$ lies between $x = -1.4$ and -1.3.

c) Show that the equation $f(x) = 0$ can be written in the form $x^2 - x - 3 = 0$.

Q7 Use the formula $x_{n+1} = -\dfrac{1}{2}\cos x_n$, with $x_0 = -1$, to find a root of $\cos x + 2x = 0$ to 2 d.p.

Q8 Use the formula $x_{n+1} = \sqrt{\ln x_n + 4}$, with $x_0 = 2$, to find a root of $x^2 - \ln x - 4 = 0$ to 3 d.p.

Q9 a) Show that the equation $2x^2 - x^3 + 1 = 0$ can be written in the form:

(i) $x = \sqrt{\dfrac{1}{x-2}}$　　　(ii) $x = \sqrt[3]{2x^2 + 1}$　　　(iii) $x = \sqrt{\dfrac{x^3 - 1}{2}}$

b) Use iteration formulas based on each of the above rearrangements with $x_0 = 2.3$ to find a root of $2x^2 - x^3 + 1 = 0$ to 2 d.p. Which of the three formulas converge to a root?

Q10 a) Show that the equation $x^x = 3$ has a root between $x = 1.5$ and $x = 2$

b) Using the iterative formula $x_{n+1} = 3^{\frac{1}{x_n}}$, with an appropriate value for x_0, find an approximation for the root of the equation $x^x = 3$ to 1 decimal place.

c) An alternative iterative formula is $x_{n+1} = 3x_n^{1-x_n}$. Using a starting value of $x_0 = 1.5$, find x_n values up to and including x_5. What happens if you use this formula?

Q11 a) Show that a solution to the equation $2x - 5\cos x = 0$ (x in radians) lies in the interval $(1.1, 1.2)$.

b) Show that the equation in part a) can be written as $x = p\cos x$, stating the value of p.

c) Using an iterative formula based on part b) and a starting value of $x_0 = 1.1$, find the values up to and including x_8, giving your answers to 4 decimal places. Comment on your findings.

Q12 Use the Newton-Raphson method with $x_0 = 1$ to find a root, to 3 d.p., of the following functions:

a) $f(x) = x^3 + 3x^2 + 5x + 7$　　　　b) $f(x) = \sin x - x + 1$ (x in radians)

c) $f(x) = e^x - x^4$　　　　d) $f(x) = e^{-x} - 2\cos\dfrac{1}{2}x$ (x in radians)

Q13 Using the position of x_0 as given on the graph on the right, draw a staircase or cobweb diagram showing how the sequence converges. Label x_1 and x_2 on the diagram.

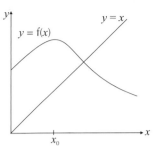

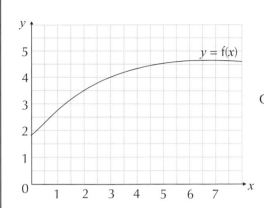

Q14 Using f(x) as shown on the graph on the left with $x_0 = 2$, draw a staircase or cobweb diagram to show how the sequence converges. Label x_1 and x_2 on the diagram.

Q15 Let $f(x) = x^4 + 2x^3 - 4x^2 - 7x + 2$ and $g(x) = x^3 - 4x + 1$

a) Show that $f(x) = (x + 2)g(x)$. Hence give an integer root of f(x).

b) Show that a root of g(x), α, lies between 1 and 2.

c) Show that $g(x) = 0$ can be rearranged into the formula $x = \sqrt[3]{4x - 1}$.

d) Use the iteration formula $x_{n+1} = \sqrt[3]{4x_n - 1}$ with $x_0 = 2$ to find α to 3 s.f.

e) Use the Newton-Raphson method with $x_0 = -2$ to find another root of g(x), β, to 4 s.f.

f) Explain why the Newton-Raphson method for g(x) fails when $x_n = \dfrac{2\sqrt{3}}{3}$.

Q16 a) Use the trapezium rule with 3 intervals to find an approximate value of $\int_1^7 \dfrac{5}{x}\,dx$. Give your answers to 3 significant figures.

b) Calculate the exact value of $\int_1^7 \dfrac{5}{x}\,dx$. Hence find the percentage error in your estimate.

Q17 a) Complete the following table of values to 3 d.p. for $y = \ln(x^3 + 4)$.

x	1	1.1	1.2	1.3	1.4	1.5
y	1.609	1.674	1.745		1.909	

b) Use the trapezium rule and all the values in the table to estimate $\int_1^{1.5} \ln(x^3 + 4)\,dx$ to 2 d.p.

Q18 Use the trapezium rule with n intervals to estimate the following to 3 s.f. Give y values to 5 d.p. where appropriate:

a) $\int_0^3 (9 - x^2)^{\frac{1}{2}}\,dx,\ n = 3$ 　　b) $\int_{0.2}^{1.2} x^{x^2}\,dx,\ n = 5$ 　　c) $\int_1^3 2^{x^2}\,dx,\ n = 4$ 　　d) $\int_1^3 2^{x^2}\,dx,\ n = 5$

Q19 Use the trapezium rule to estimate the value of $\int_0^6 (6x - 12)(x^2 - 4x + 3)^2\,dx$, first using 4 strips and then again with 6 strips. Calculate the percentage error for each answer.

Q20 The diagram on the right shows part of the curve $y = \dfrac{3}{\ln x}$.

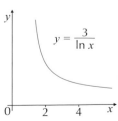

a) Using the trapezium rule with $n = 4$, find an estimate to 2 d.p. for $\int_2^4 \dfrac{3}{\ln x}\,dx$.

b) Without further calculation, state whether your answer to part a) is an overestimate or underestimate of the true area. Explain your answer.

Chapter 25 — Vectors 2

In Chapter 10 you learnt how to represent, calculate with, and model situations using vectors in two dimensions. Now you're going to find out how to do all of that in three dimensions.

1. Vectors in Three Dimensions

Three-dimensional position vectors

Three-dimensional vectors have components in the direction of the x-, y- and z-axes. The points in three dimensions are given (x, y, z) coordinates.

The **unit vector** in the direction of the z-axis is **k**, so three-dimensional vectors can be written like this: $\quad x\mathbf{i} + y\mathbf{j} + z\mathbf{k}$ or $\begin{pmatrix} x \\ y \\ z \end{pmatrix}$

Calculating with 3D vectors is just the same as with 2D vectors, as the next example shows.

> **Example**   The diagram shows the position of the points P and Q.
>
>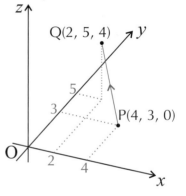
>
> a) **Write the position vectors $\overrightarrow{OP}$ and $\overrightarrow{OQ}$ as column vectors.**
>
> $$\overrightarrow{OP} = 4\mathbf{i} + 3\mathbf{j} + 0\mathbf{k} = \begin{pmatrix} 4 \\ 3 \\ 0 \end{pmatrix} \qquad \overrightarrow{OQ} = 2\mathbf{i} + 5\mathbf{j} + 4\mathbf{k} = \begin{pmatrix} 2 \\ 5 \\ 4 \end{pmatrix}$$
>
> b) **Hence find $\overrightarrow{PQ}$ as a column vector.**
>
> $$\overrightarrow{PQ} = -\overrightarrow{OP} + \overrightarrow{OQ} = -\begin{pmatrix} 4 \\ 3 \\ 0 \end{pmatrix} + \begin{pmatrix} 2 \\ 5 \\ 4 \end{pmatrix} = \begin{pmatrix} 2-4 \\ 5-3 \\ 4-0 \end{pmatrix} = \begin{pmatrix} -2 \\ 2 \\ 4 \end{pmatrix}$$
>
> The point R lies on the line PQ such that PR : RQ = 3 : 1.
>
> c) **Find the position vector of point R, in unit vector form.**
>
> 1. The ratio tells you that point R is $\frac{3}{4}$ of the way along PQ from point P: $\qquad \overrightarrow{PR} = \frac{3}{4}\overrightarrow{PQ} \quad \Rightarrow \quad \overrightarrow{PR} = \frac{3}{4} \times \begin{pmatrix} -2 \\ 2 \\ 4 \end{pmatrix} = \begin{pmatrix} -1.5 \\ 1.5 \\ 3 \end{pmatrix}$
>
> 2. Now find position vector $\overrightarrow{OR}$:
>
> $$\overrightarrow{OR} = \overrightarrow{OP} + \overrightarrow{PR} = \begin{pmatrix} 4 \\ 3 \\ 0 \end{pmatrix} + \begin{pmatrix} -1.5 \\ 1.5 \\ 3 \end{pmatrix} = \begin{pmatrix} 4-1.5 \\ 3+1.5 \\ 0+3 \end{pmatrix} = \begin{pmatrix} 2.5 \\ 4.5 \\ 3 \end{pmatrix} = 2.5\mathbf{i} + 4.5\mathbf{j} + 3\mathbf{k}$$

Exercise 1.1

Q1   R is the point (4, –5, 1) and S is the point (–3, 0, –1).
Write down the position vectors of R and S, giving your answers:
a) as column vectors   b) in unit vector form.

Q2   Triangle JKL has vertices at points J (4, 0, –3), K (–1, 3, 0) and L (2, 2, 7). Find the vectors $\overrightarrow{JK}$, $\overrightarrow{KL}$ and $\overrightarrow{LJ}$.

Q3 Give $\overrightarrow{GH}$ and $\overrightarrow{HG}$ as column vectors, where $\overrightarrow{OG} = \begin{pmatrix} 2 \\ -3 \\ 4 \end{pmatrix}$ and $\overrightarrow{OH} = \begin{pmatrix} -1 \\ 4 \\ 9 \end{pmatrix}$.

Q4 M is a point on the line CD, where C has coordinates (–1, 3, –5), 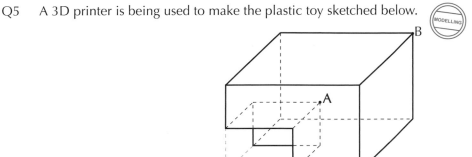(PROBLEM SOLVING)

M has coordinates (1, 1, –2) and $\overrightarrow{CD} = \begin{pmatrix} 4 \\ -4 \\ 6 \end{pmatrix}$. Show that M is the midpoint of CD.

Q5 A 3D printer is being used to make the plastic toy sketched below. (MODELLING)

The toy can be modelled as a large cuboid with a smaller cuboid section missing. The large cuboid section is an enlargement of the smaller, 'missing' cuboid, by a scale factor of 2, centred at point O.

a) Prove that $\overrightarrow{AB} = \overrightarrow{OA}$.　　　b) Find the position vector of point B, if $\overrightarrow{OA} = 3\mathbf{i} + \mathbf{j} + 2\mathbf{k}$.

As with two-dimensional vectors, **parallel** vectors in three dimensions are **scalar multiples** of each other.

If two vectors are **parallel**, and also have a **point in common**, then they must lie on the same straight line — their points are **collinear**.

Example Show that points A, B and C are collinear, if $\overrightarrow{OA} = 2\mathbf{i} - \mathbf{j} + \mathbf{k}$, $\overrightarrow{OB} = \mathbf{i} + 2\mathbf{j} + 3\mathbf{k}$ and $\overrightarrow{OC} = -\mathbf{i} + 8\mathbf{j} + 7\mathbf{k}$.

First, find vectors $\overrightarrow{AB}$ and $\overrightarrow{BC}$:

$\overrightarrow{AB} = -\overrightarrow{OA} + \overrightarrow{OB} = (-2 + 1)\mathbf{i} + (1 + 2)\mathbf{j} + (-1 + 3)\mathbf{k} = -\mathbf{i} + 3\mathbf{j} + 2\mathbf{k}$

$\overrightarrow{BC} = -\overrightarrow{OB} + \overrightarrow{OC} = (-1 - 1)\mathbf{i} + (-2 + 8)\mathbf{j} + (-3 + 7)\mathbf{k} = -2\mathbf{i} + 6\mathbf{j} + 4\mathbf{k}$

Show that $\overrightarrow{AB}$ and $\overrightarrow{BC}$ are parallel by finding a **scalar multiple**:

$\overrightarrow{BC} = -2\mathbf{i} + 6\mathbf{j} + 4\mathbf{k} = 2(-\mathbf{i} + 3\mathbf{j} + 2\mathbf{k}) = 2\overrightarrow{AB}$

$\overrightarrow{BC}$ is a scalar multiple of $\overrightarrow{AB}$, so they are parallel, and also have a point in common (B).

So A, B and C must all lie on the same line — they are **collinear**.

Exercise 1.2

Q1 Show that vectors $\mathbf{a} = \frac{3}{4}\mathbf{i} + \frac{1}{3}\mathbf{j} - 2\mathbf{k}$ and $\mathbf{b} = \frac{1}{4}\mathbf{i} + \mathbf{j} - \frac{2}{3}\mathbf{k}$ are <u>not</u> parallel. (PROBLEM SOLVING)

Q2 In a 3D board game, players take turns to position counters at points inside a cuboid grid. Players score by forming a straight line with three of their counters, (MODELLING) unblocked by their opponent.

Show that counters placed at coordinates (1, 0, 3), (3, 1, 2) and (7, 3, 0) lie on a straight line.

2. Calculating with Vectors

You calculate the length, or **magnitude**, of a vector in 3D the same as you would a 2D vector, by using Pythagoras:

$$|\mathbf{v}| = |a\mathbf{i} + b\mathbf{j} + c\mathbf{k}| = \sqrt{a^2 + b^2 + c^2}$$

- The **distance** between any two points $P(x_1, y_1, z_1)$ and $Q(x_2, y_2, z_2)$ is the magnitude of the vector $\overrightarrow{PQ}$.

- The **unit vector** in the direction of **v** is $\dfrac{\mathbf{v}}{|\mathbf{v}|}$, as it is for 2D vectors.

Tip: Go back to p.124 for more about unit vectors in 2D.

Example   The diagram below shows the position of point Q.

a) Find $|\overrightarrow{OQ}|$, giving your answer in reduced surd form.

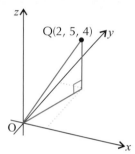

$$\overrightarrow{OQ} = 2\mathbf{i} + 5\mathbf{j} + 4\mathbf{k}$$

Plug the coordinates, which are the i, j and k coefficients in $\overrightarrow{OQ}$, into the formula:

$$|\overrightarrow{OQ}| = \sqrt{x^2 + y^2 + z^2} = \sqrt{2^2 + 5^2 + 4^2} = \sqrt{45} = \mathbf{3\sqrt{5}}$$

b) Find the unit vector in the direction of $\overrightarrow{OQ}$.

To find a unit vector, divide the vector by its magnitude:

$$\frac{\overrightarrow{OQ}}{|\overrightarrow{OQ}|} = \frac{1}{3\sqrt{5}}(2\mathbf{i} + 5\mathbf{j} + 4\mathbf{k}) = \frac{2}{3\sqrt{5}}\mathbf{i} + \frac{5}{3\sqrt{5}}\mathbf{j} + \frac{4}{3\sqrt{5}}\mathbf{k} = \frac{2\sqrt{5}}{15}\mathbf{i} + \frac{\sqrt{5}}{3}\mathbf{j} + \frac{4\sqrt{5}}{15}\mathbf{k}$$

Example   The position vector of point A is 3i + 2j + 4k, and the position vector of point B is 2i + 6j – 5k. Find $|\overrightarrow{AB}|$ to 1 decimal place.

$$\overrightarrow{AB} = \overrightarrow{OB} - \overrightarrow{OA} = (2 - 3)\mathbf{i} + (6 - 2)\mathbf{j} + (-5 - 4)\mathbf{k}$$

$$|\overrightarrow{AB}| = \sqrt{(2-3)^2 + (6-2)^2 + (-5-4)^2} = \sqrt{1 + 16 + 81} = \sqrt{98} = \mathbf{9.9} \text{ (1 d.p.)}$$

Exercise 2.1

Unless specified, give each answer in this exercise as an integer or as a simplified surd.

Q1 Find the magnitude of each of the following vectors:

a) $\mathbf{i} + 4\mathbf{j} + 8\mathbf{k}$
     b) $\begin{pmatrix} 4 \\ 2 \\ 4 \end{pmatrix}$
     c) $\begin{pmatrix} -4 \\ -5 \\ 20 \end{pmatrix}$
     d) $7\mathbf{i} + \mathbf{j} - 7\mathbf{k}$
     e) $\begin{pmatrix} -2 \\ 4 \\ -6 \end{pmatrix}$

Q2 Find the magnitude of the resultant of each pair of vectors.

a) $\mathbf{i} + \mathbf{j} + 2\mathbf{k}$ and $\mathbf{i} + 2\mathbf{j} + 4\mathbf{k}$
     b) $2\mathbf{i} + 11\mathbf{j} + 25\mathbf{k}$ and $3\mathbf{j} - 2\mathbf{k}$
     c) $\begin{pmatrix} 4 \\ 2 \\ 8 \end{pmatrix}$ and $\begin{pmatrix} -2 \\ 4 \\ 1 \end{pmatrix}$

d) $\begin{pmatrix} 3 \\ 0 \\ 10 \end{pmatrix}$ and $\begin{pmatrix} -1 \\ 5 \\ 4 \end{pmatrix}$
     e) $\begin{pmatrix} 8 \\ 4 \\ 10 \end{pmatrix}$ and $\begin{pmatrix} 2 \\ -2 \\ 4 \end{pmatrix}$
     f) $3\mathbf{i} - \mathbf{j} + 5\mathbf{k}$ and $\mathbf{i} + 3\mathbf{j} - 4\mathbf{k}$

Q3 Find the distance between the points represented by each of these pairs of position vectors:

a) $\overrightarrow{OA} = 3\mathbf{i} + 4\mathbf{j} + 5\mathbf{k}$, $\overrightarrow{OB} = 5\mathbf{i} + 6\mathbf{j} + 6\mathbf{k}$

b) $\overrightarrow{OC} = 7\mathbf{i} + 2\mathbf{j} + 9\mathbf{k}$, $\overrightarrow{OD} = -11\mathbf{i} + \mathbf{j} + 15\mathbf{k}$

c) $\overrightarrow{OE} = 10\mathbf{i} - 2\mathbf{j} - \mathbf{k}$, $\overrightarrow{OF} = 6\mathbf{i} + 10\mathbf{j} - 4\mathbf{k}$

d) $\overrightarrow{OG} = -4\mathbf{j} + 10\mathbf{k}$, $\overrightarrow{OH} = 7\mathbf{i} + 14\mathbf{k}$

e) $\overrightarrow{OI} = -4\mathbf{i} + 7\mathbf{j} + 10\mathbf{k}$, $\overrightarrow{OJ} = 2\mathbf{i} + 4\mathbf{j} - 12\mathbf{k}$

f) $\overrightarrow{OK} = 7\mathbf{i} - \mathbf{j} + 4\mathbf{k}$, $\overrightarrow{OL} = 30\mathbf{i} + 9\mathbf{j} - 6\mathbf{k}$

Q4 The flight path of a toy aeroplane is modelled by the vector $2\mathbf{m} - \mathbf{n}$,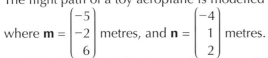

where $\mathbf{m} = \begin{pmatrix} -5 \\ -2 \\ 6 \end{pmatrix}$ metres, and $\mathbf{n} = \begin{pmatrix} -4 \\ 1 \\ 2 \end{pmatrix}$ metres.

Find the distance of the plane's destination from its starting position.
Give your answer in metres to 1 decimal place.

Q5 $\overrightarrow{OA} = \mathbf{i} - 4\mathbf{j} + 3\mathbf{k}$ and $\overrightarrow{OB} = -\mathbf{i} - 3\mathbf{j} + 5\mathbf{k}$. Find $|\overrightarrow{AO}|$, $|\overrightarrow{BO}|$ and $|\overrightarrow{BA}|$.
Show that triangle AOB is right-angled.

Q6 Find the unit vector in the direction of the following vectors:

a) $\mathbf{t} = 4\mathbf{i} - 4\mathbf{j} - 7\mathbf{k}$.

b) $\mathbf{u} = -\mathbf{i} + 2\mathbf{j} - 2\mathbf{k}$

c) $\mathbf{v} = 2\mathbf{i} + 3\mathbf{j} - \mathbf{k}$

Q7 P is the point $(2, -1, 4)$ and Q is the point $(q - 2, 5, 2q + 1)$.
Given that the length of the line PQ is 11, find the possible coordinates of the point Q.

To find the angle between two vectors:

- Create a **triangle** with the vectors as two sides, and angle θ between them.
- Find the **magnitude** of each side of the triangle.
- Use the **cosine rule** to find the angle θ from these lengths.

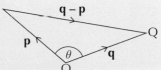

Example Two aeroplanes A and B taking off from the same runway fly straight line paths to position vectors $\mathbf{a} = 5\mathbf{i} - 2\mathbf{j} + \mathbf{k}$, and $\mathbf{b} = -3\mathbf{i} + 3\mathbf{j} + \mathbf{k}$ respectively. Find the angle between the two flight paths, in degrees, to 1 d.p.

1. $\mathbf{a}$ and $\mathbf{b}$ form two sides of the triangle AOB. Find the lengths of its sides:

$$|\mathbf{a}| = \sqrt{5^2 + (-2)^2 + 1^2} = \sqrt{30} \qquad |\mathbf{b}| = \sqrt{(-3)^2 + 3^2 + 1^2} = \sqrt{19}$$

$$\overrightarrow{AB} = \mathbf{b} - \mathbf{a} = -8\mathbf{i} + 5\mathbf{j} + 0\mathbf{k} \qquad |\overrightarrow{AB}| = \sqrt{(-8)^2 + 5^2 + 0^2} = \sqrt{89}$$

2. Using the cosine rule:

$$\cos\theta = \frac{(\sqrt{30})^2 + (\sqrt{19})^2 - (\sqrt{89})^2}{2 \times \sqrt{30} \times \sqrt{19}} = \frac{-40}{2\sqrt{570}} \Rightarrow \theta = \cos^{-1}\left(\frac{-40}{2\sqrt{570}}\right) = \mathbf{146.9°}\ (1\ \text{d.p.})$$

Exercise 2.2

Q1 Find the angle, in degrees to 1 d.p., that the vector $\begin{pmatrix} 1 \\ 3 \\ 2 \end{pmatrix}$ makes with:

a) vector $\begin{pmatrix} 3 \\ 2 \\ 1 \end{pmatrix}$,

b) the unit vector $\mathbf{j}$.

c) vector $\begin{pmatrix} -3 \\ 1 \\ -2 \end{pmatrix}$

d) vector $\begin{pmatrix} 2 \\ 2 \\ 2 \end{pmatrix}$

Q2 Find the angle between the vectors $\mathbf{a} = \mathbf{i} - 2\mathbf{j} + \mathbf{k}$ and $\mathbf{b} = 2\mathbf{i} + \mathbf{j} - 3\mathbf{k}$ to the nearest degree.

Q3 A toy rocket is launched at an angle of $60°$ to the unit vector in the $\mathbf{i}$ direction, with a velocity $\mathbf{v} = (\mathbf{i} + a\mathbf{j} + \mathbf{k})$ ms^{-1}. Find the possible values of a, in surd form, and hence the launch speed of the rocket.

Q1 Give, in unit vector form, the position vector of point P, which has the coordinates (2, –4, 5).

Q2 X is the point (6, –1, 0) and Y is the point (4, –4, 7).
Write the vectors $\overrightarrow{XO}$ and $\overrightarrow{YO}$ in unit vector form and in column vector form.

Q3 Give two vectors that are parallel to each of the following:

a) $2\mathbf{a}$

b) $3\mathbf{i} + 4\mathbf{j} - 2\mathbf{k}$

c) $\begin{pmatrix} 1 \\ 2 \\ -1 \end{pmatrix}$

Q4 Given that $\mathbf{a} = 2\mathbf{i} - 3\mathbf{j} + \mathbf{k}$, $\mathbf{b} = -\mathbf{i} + 4\mathbf{j} - 7\mathbf{k}$ and $\mathbf{c} = -6\mathbf{i} + 4\mathbf{j} + 10\mathbf{k}$, show that $2\mathbf{a} + \mathbf{b}$ is parallel to $\mathbf{c}$.

Q5 Show that points A, B and C are collinear, given that $\overrightarrow{OA} = \begin{pmatrix} 2 \\ 1 \\ 3 \end{pmatrix}$, $\overrightarrow{OB} = \begin{pmatrix} 1 \\ 5 \\ 7 \end{pmatrix}$ and $\overrightarrow{OC} = \begin{pmatrix} -2 \\ 17 \\ 19 \end{pmatrix}$.

Q6 Find the magnitudes of these vectors:

a) $3\mathbf{i} + 4\mathbf{j} - 2\mathbf{k}$

b) $\begin{pmatrix} 1 \\ 2 \\ -1 \end{pmatrix}$

Q7 If A is (1, 2, 3) and B is (3, –1, –2), find:

a) $|\overrightarrow{OA}|$

b) $|\overrightarrow{OB}|$

c) $|\overrightarrow{AB}|$

Q8 Find the unit vectors in the direction of each of these vectors:

a) $\mathbf{i} - 3\mathbf{k}$

b) $-2\mathbf{i} + 2\mathbf{j} + 5\mathbf{k}$

c) $\begin{pmatrix} -1 \\ -3 \\ 3 \end{pmatrix}$

d) $\begin{pmatrix} 7 \\ -1 \\ 12 \end{pmatrix}$

Q9 Find the exact distance between points P and Q given by position vectors $\overrightarrow{OP} = -\mathbf{i} + 2\mathbf{j} + 3\mathbf{k}$ and $\overrightarrow{OQ} = 2\mathbf{i} - 2\mathbf{j} + 4\mathbf{k}$.

Q10 X is the point (–2, 1, 0).

The distance between X and Y is 6. The unit vector in the direction $\overrightarrow{XY}$ is $\begin{pmatrix} \frac{2}{3} \\ \frac{2}{3} \\ -\frac{1}{3} \end{pmatrix}$. **PROBLEM SOLVING**

Find the coordinates of Y.

Q11 Given that $\overrightarrow{OA} = \begin{pmatrix} 4 \\ 3 \\ -3 \end{pmatrix}$, $\overrightarrow{OB} = \begin{pmatrix} -1 \\ 2 \\ -4 \end{pmatrix}$, find the angle between $\overrightarrow{AB}$ and $\overrightarrow{OB}$ to one decimal place.

Q12 A simple mathematical model of the motion of two asteroids following a collision is given in terms of vectors.
The velocity of asteroid R is given by $\mathbf{r} = 5\mathbf{i} + 3\mathbf{j} - \mathbf{k}$ ms^{-1}.
The velocity of asteroid S is given by $\mathbf{s} = -2\mathbf{i} - 2\mathbf{j} + 7\mathbf{k}$ ms^{-1}.

a) Calculate the exact speed of each asteroid.

b) After 5 seconds, how much further has S travelled than R?
Give your answer to the nearest metre.

c) Calculate the angle between the two asteroids' paths to the nearest degree.

d) Comment on the suitability of this model.

Chapter 26 — Correlation and Regression

You came across correlation and regression back in Chapter 11. In this Chapter, you'll look at how to measure the strength of correlation between two variables, and carry out hypothesis testing on the result.

1. Regression

- **Correlation** measures how closely two variables are **linked**. Correlation can be **positive** or **negative** (you can draw a **line of best fit** on the scatter diagram) — or there may be **no correlation**. Be careful though — correlation does **not** mean that one variable **causes** the other to change.

- The **explanatory variable** (or **independent variable**) is the variable you can directly control, or the one that you think is **affecting** the other. The **response variable** (or **dependent variable**) is the variable you think is **being affected**.

- **Linear regression** is a method for finding the equation of a line of best fit on a scatter diagram. The formula below shows you the form of the **regression line of *y* on *x*:**

$$y = a + bx$$ where a = *y*-intercept and b = gradient

Tip: The '...**of *y* on *x***' part means that *x* is the explanatory variable, and *y* is the response variable.
A **positive** value of b means **positive correlation**, and a **negative** value of b means **negative correlation**.

- You can use the **statistical functions** on your **calculator** to find the values of a and b.

 Example   The data below shows the amount of exercise done per week, *x* (in hours), and the body fat, *y* (as a percentage of total weight), of a group of men.

x	1.3	1.5	2.2	2.4	4.1	4.3	5.4	6.9	8.7	9.8
y	24.2	23.1	22.4	22.7	20.2	20.1	19	18.8	17.3	15.2

Find the equation of the regression line of *y* on *x*.

1. Go into the statistical functions on your calculator and input the data. Then find the values of a and b the calculator produces. For this example you should find that:
   a = 24.60905... = 24.6 (3 s.f.) and b = −0.92468... = −0.925 (3 s.f.).

2. This means that the regression line of *y* on *x* is: **y = 24.6 − 0.925x**

- You can use a regression line to predict values of your **response variable**. **Interpolation** is where you use *x*-values from **within** your data range (and is fairly **reliable**) and **extrapolation** uses *x*-values **outside** your data range (and can be **unreliable**).

Exercise 1.1

Q1 The data below shows the number of shots, *x*, and the number of goals scored, *y*, by a football team over a number of matches.

Number of shots, *x*	15	18	19	7	18	12	12	21	16	13
Number of goals, *y*	2	3	3	0	2	1	2	3	2	2

a) Identify the explanatory variable and the response variable.

b) Calculate the equation of the regression line of *y* on *x*.

c) Describe the type of correlation shown.

d) In the next match the team has 5 shots. Use your regression equation to estimate the number of goals scored by the team.

e) Explain why this estimate is unreliable.

Linear regression with coded data

Coded data has been transformed by some mathematical function to make the data **easier** to work with. You can find a **regression line** for coded data, then transform it into a regression line for the **original data**.

 The annual heating bill (*h*, in £) for 8 office buildings is shown below, along with the total floor area (*f*, in m²) of each building.

f	600	1000	1500	1800	2400	3400	4400	4900
h	1500	2600	3100	3400	3900	5500	5900	6100

These results were coded in the following way: $u = \dfrac{f - 2500}{100}$, $v = \dfrac{h - 4000}{100}$

a) Find the equation of the regression line of *v* on *u*.

1. First make a table of the coded data.

u	−19	−15	−10	−7	−1	9	19	24
v	−25	−14	−9	−6	−1	15	19	21

2. Find a and b to write the regression line in the form $v = a + bu$. Go into the statistical functions on your calculator and input the data. Then find the values of a and b the calculator produces. a = 0 and b = 1.036488... = 1.036 (4 s.f.).

3. So the regression line of *v* on *u* is: **$v = 1.036u$**

b) Hence find the equation of the regression line of *h* on *f*.

1. Substitute the expressions defining *u* and *v* into your regression equation.

$$v = 1.036u$$
$$\frac{h - 4000}{100} = 1.036 \times \frac{f - 2500}{100}$$

2. Then rearrange into the form $h = c + df$.

$$h - 4000 = 1.036f - (1.036 \times 2500)$$
$$\text{So } \boldsymbol{h = 1410 + 1.036f}$$

If the variables *x* and *y* are linked by a **non-linear** equation in the form of either $y = ax^n$ or $y = kb^x$, you can turn it into a linear equation by **taking logs** of both sides (see p.87-88).

$y = ax^n \Rightarrow \log y = \log ax^n$
$\Rightarrow \log y = \log a + \log x^n$
$\Rightarrow \boxed{\log y = n\log x + \log a}$

$y = kb^x \Rightarrow \log y = \log kb^x$
$\Rightarrow \log y = \log k + \log b^x$
$\Rightarrow \boxed{\log y = x\log b + \log k}$

 A student records the height of five plants (*h* cm) and the amount of fertilizer each plant was given (*f* ml). The relationship can be modelled by the equation $h = af^b$.

Use the data on the right to find the values of a and b to 3 d.p.

Fertilizer (*f* ml)	12.3	13.1	6.4	2.5	7.2
Height (*h* cm)	20.5	20.4	18.9	15.7	19.2

1. Rearrange $h = af^b$ into linear form. $\log h = b\log f + \log a$

2. Make a table of the values of log *f* and log *h*, using *f* and *h* given above.

log *f*	1.089...	1.117...	0.806...	0.397...	0.857...
log *h*	1.311...	1.309...	1.276...	1.195...	1.283...

3. Go into the statistical functions on your calculator and input the data. Comparing the values from your calculator to $\log h = b\log f + \log a$ gives:
$\log a = 1.138... \Rightarrow a = 10^{1.138...} \Rightarrow$ **a = 13.752 (3 d.p.) and b = 0.161 (3 d.p.)**

So $h = 13.752f^{0.161}$

Exercise 1.2

Q1 A set of bivariate data (x, y) has been coded using $p = x - 7$ and $q = y - 50$. The regression line of q on p is given by $q = 40 + 2p$. Find the equation of the regression line of y on x.

Q2 The time (t, in hours) that seedlings could survive in water containing different concentrations of salt (s, in mg per litre) was recorded. The results were coded such that $x = \frac{s}{10}$ and $y = t - 29$. The coded data is in the table below.

x	1	2	3	5	7	10
y	19	11	9	-1	-14	-24

a) Find the equation of the regression line of y on x.

b) Hence find the equation of the regression line of t on s.

Q3 The population (p, to the nearest thousand) of a town is measured over time (t, years). This can be modelled by the equation $p = ab^t$.

Number of years (t)	7	14	22	29	42
Population (p, in thousands)	3	5	16	20	38

Using the data above, find the values of a and b to 3 d.p.

2. The Product Moment Correlation Coefficient

The **product moment correlation coefficient** (r) measures the **strength** of the linear correlation between two variables. It basically tells you how close to a straight line the points on a scatter diagram lie.

To calculate the PMCC you need to use the **statistical functions** on your calculator.

The PMCC is always between +1 and –1.

- If all the points lie **exactly on a straight line** with a **positive** gradient (perfect positive correlation), $r = +1$.

- If all the points lie **exactly on a straight line** with a **negative** gradient (perfect negative correlation), $r = -1$.

> The closer the value of r to +1 or –1, the stronger the correlation between the two variables.

- If $r = 0$ (or more likely, pretty close to 0), that would mean the variables **aren't correlated**.

 The following data show the score (x) of 10 students in a reading test, and the time in seconds (y) it took them to run 40 metres.

x	3.5	5.5	6.1	4.2	2.7	1.9	5.5	3.8	5.1	3.7
y	9.8	4.7	8.4	8.4	5.8	8.4	7.6	8.2	8.9	5.4

Illustrate the data with a scatter diagram, and find the product moment correlation coefficient (r) between the variables x and y.

- First, plot the points on the scatter diagram. ────→

- The points on the scatter diagram look randomly scattered — so you'd expect a correlation coefficient fairly close to zero.

- Go into the statistical functions on your calculator and input the data. This gives: $r = -0.044$ **(to 3 d.p.)**

Exercise 2.1

Q1 The table below shows the heights and weights of 8 teenage boys.

Height in cm, x	180	171	182	184	166	180	173	167
Weight in kg, y	70	67	66	59	61	75	65	56

Find the value of the product moment correlation coefficient (r) for x and y. Interpret your value of r.

Q2 For the data shown in this table:

p	13	9	15	10	8	11	12	14
q	5	7	2	4	3	8	1	2

Find the value of the product moment correlation coefficient (r) for p and q. Interpret your value of r.

Q3 A nurse at a health centre did a memory test on some patients of different ages. Her results are shown below.

Age in years, a	57	65	94	88	71	62	79	82	52
Test score, s	8.9	4.8	5.4	2.8	7.1	7.5	3.1	6.2	8.4

Calculate the correlation coefficient r and interpret your result.

PMCC hypothesis testing

To test whether your value of r is likely to mean that the two variables are actually correlated, you need to do a **hypothesis test**. The method used is very similar to the hypothesis testing you did in Chapter 14.

- A **test statistic** is a statistic calculated from the sample data — here it's r.

- A **parameter** describes a characteristic of a population — here it's ρ, the PMCC of the population.

- The **null hypothesis** (H_0) is a statement about the value of the population parameter, ρ. The null hypothesis here is always that ρ is **zero** (H_0: $\rho = 0$) — i.e. that there's **no correlation**.

- The **alternative hypothesis** (H_1) is what you're going to conclude if you **reject** the null hypothesis. A **one-tailed** alternative hypothesis specifies whether the parameter you're investigating is **greater than** or **less than** the value you used in H_0 (i.e. H_1: $\rho > 0$ or $\rho < 0$). A **two-tailed** alternative hypothesis says that the parameter you're investigating is **not equal** to the value in H_0 (i.e. H_1: $\rho \neq 0$).

- The **significance level** of a test (α) determines **how unlikely** your data needs to be under the null hypothesis before you reject H_0. Common values are $\alpha = 0.1$ (10%), $\alpha = 0.05$ (5%) and $\alpha = 0.01$ (1%).

On p.473 there's a table of critical values. For a given sample size and significance level you can find the **critical value** — the point at which your test statistic r would be **significant**.

Example A teacher thinks that test scores are related to the number of hours spent revising. She samples 10 students and finds that the PMCC is 0.76. Carry out a hypothesis test at the 5% significance level to investigate whether the evidence suggests that test scores and hours spent revising are positively correlated.

1. Write down the test statistic for the sample. $r = 0.76$

2. The null hypothesis is that there is no correlation. H_0: $\rho = 0$

3. This is a one-tailed test, so formulate the alternative hypothesis. H_1: $\rho > 0$

4. Write down the significance level of the test. $\alpha = 0.05$

---

5. Find the critical value using $\alpha = 0.05$ and sample size 10. If $r \geq$ critical value, the result is significant.

Using the table the critical value is 0.5494.

Since $0.76 > 0.5494$ the result is significant.

n	0.10	0.05	0.025	0.01	0.005
3	0.9511	0.9877	0.9969	0.9995	0.9999
–	–	–	–	–	–
10	0.4428	0.5494	0.6319	0.7155	0.7646
11	0.4187	0.5214	0.6021	0.6851	0.7348

Tip: If your alternative hypothesis was $\rho < 0$, you'd make the critical value from the table negative — i.e. use -0.5494 not 0.5494.

6. Write your conclusion.

There is evidence at the 5% level of significance to reject H_0 and to support the alternative hypothesis that test scores and hours spent revising are positively correlated.

The **critical region** is the set of **all** values of the test statistic that would cause you to **reject H_0**. You can carry out a hypothesis test by finding the critical region, then checking if your **test statistic** lies in the critical region or not.

 Jo records the number of hours of sleep 7 people get one night and their score in a spelling test the next day. She claims that there is correlation between the two variables.

a) Find the critical region for a test of Jo's claim at the 5% level.

- This is a two-tailed test — Jo thinks there is correlation, i.e. the PMCC is not zero. So write down the hypotheses.

H_0: $\rho = 0$ and H_1: $\rho \neq 0$

- Find the critical value for significance level 0.025 and sample size 7.
The critical region is $r \geq$ critical value or $r \leq$ –critical value.

$\alpha = 0.05$, so $\frac{\alpha}{2} = 0.025$

Using the table, the critical value is 0.7545

So the critical region is $r \geq 0.7545$ or $r \leq -0.7545$

b) The PMCC of the data is 0.7282. Is there evidence to support Jo's claim at the 5% level?

$r = 0.7282$ is outside the critical region so, at the 5% level, there is insufficient evidence to reject H_0 and to support Jo's claim that there is correlation between the number of hours of sleep people get and their score in a spelling test the next day.

Exercise 2.2

Q1 For each situation below, test the hypothesis that the PMCC for the population, ρ, is greater than zero, at the 2.5% significance level.

a) The ages and weights of 12 baby elephants are measured. The PMCC is $r = 0.5749$.

b) The amounts spent on food and petrol in 15 households are recorded. The PMCC is $r = 0.5152$.

Q2 A doctor checked the kidney function (k, percentage efficiency) of some of her patients to see if it was related to their weight (w, kg). She thinks kidney function and weight are correlated. The table below shows the results from a sample of her patients.

Weight in kg, w	66	74	96	83	79	54	64	71	88
Kidney function, k	79	82	23	71	48	91	84	68	37

a) Find the product moment correlation coefficient, r.

b) Find the critical region for a test of the doctor's claim at the 1% significance level.

c) Say whether these results provide sufficient evidence to back the doctor's claim.

3. Rank Correlation

- When your data is a set of **ranks** (the **positions** of the values when you put them **in an order** — e.g. from biggest to smallest, or from best to worst, etc.), you can calculate a **rank correlation coefficient**, which measures the correlation between these ranks. Rank correlation coefficients can also be useful when the relationship between two variables is **not linear** (so you can't use the PMCC), but when they are clearly **linked** in some way.

- A rank correlation coefficient shows how two variables are **associated** — positive association (values close to **+1**), **negative association** (values close to **–1**), or **no association** (values close to **0**).

- You can carry out **hypothesis testing** on the rank correlation coefficient, just like for the PMCC. A common rank correlation coefficient is **Spearman's rank correlation coefficient** (**SRCC**, or r_s). A table of critical values for Spearman's coefficient is given on p.473.

 Example At a dog show, two judges each rank the dogs in order. For a sample of 8 of the dogs, the Spearman's rank correlation coefficient between the two judges' scores was calculated to be 0.9048 (to 4 s.f.).

a) **Interpret this value of the rank correlation coefficient.**

The value is positive and quite close to 1, so there is strong positive association between the two judges' scores.

b) **An adjudicator claims that there is some association between the judges' scores across the whole competition. Use the data above to test this claim at the 5% significance level.**

1. Write down the test statistic.
   There's no handy letter like ρ for the SRCC, so you have to write out the hypotheses in words. $r_s = 0.9048$

2. Formulate the null hypothesis.
   H_0: No association

3. This is a two-tailed test, so write the alternative hypothesis.
   H_1: Some association

4. Write down the significance level of the test.
   $\alpha = 0.05$, so $\frac{\alpha}{2} = 0.025$

5. Find the critical value for significance level 0.025 and sample size 8.   Critical value = 0.7381

6. Compare r_s to the critical value, and write your conclusion.
   r_s is greater than the critical value, so there is significant evidence at the 5% level to reject H_0 in favour of H_1 — there is some association between the judges' scores.

Exercise 3.1

Q1 For each situation below, test the hypothesis that there is negative association between the two variables at the 1% significance level.

    a) Athletes are timed running 100 m and 1500 m and their results recorded. A group of 10 athletes are sampled, and the SRCC for their times is $r_s = -0.7504$.

    b) The ages of some pensioners are recorded. The pensioners are then tested to find the minimum volume of sound (dB) they can hear from 15 m away. The SRCC for a sample of 20 is $r_s = -0.5213$.

Q2 At a gymnastics competition, two different judges rank the gymnasts based on different criteria. Beth claims that there is positive association between the judges' ranks. She takes a sample of one class of the competition, which contains 15 gymnasts.

    a) Find the critical value for a SRCC to test Beth's claim at the 5% significance level.

    b) Spearman's rank correlation coefficient for the sample is calculated to be 0.4750. Does this provide significant evidence to support Beth's claim at the 5% level?

    c) Does this value of r_s provide significant evidence at the 1% level?

Review Exercise — Chapter 26

Q1 The table below shows the hours spent designing the cover of a book, h, and the number of books sold in the first year, b.

Number of hours, h	5	10	8	12	4	7	15	2	9
Sales in the first year, b	5000	6500	3500	7000	1200	5200	7800	3000	4100

a) Identify the explanatory variable and the response variable.

b) Calculate the equation of the regression line of b on h.

c) Use your regression line to predict the first year sales of a book which had 6 hours spent on its cover. Is your estimate reliable?

Q2 The number of fans at a venue's concerts, n, and the average cost of a ticket, c, are recorded. The data is coded as follows: $x = c - 150$, $y = \frac{n}{2000}$. The regression line of y on x is $y = 1.8x + 50$. Find the regression line of n on c.

Q3 The data in the table can be modelled by the equation $y = kb^x$. Find the values of k and b.

x	8.2	7.1	7.9	6.4	6.8
y	15	12	14	10	11

Q4 Find the value of the product moment correlation coefficient, r, for x and y, shown in the table below. Interpret your value of r.

x	0.6	0.4	1.2	0.8	1.1	0.5	1.2	0.7
y	62	65	52	62	50	52	51	60

Q5 The ages of 12 paintings in years and their values in £ are recorded. The PMCC for the data is calculated to be $r = 0.7126$. Is there evidence at the 1% significance level to support the hypothesis that there is some correlation between a painting's age and its value?

Q6 The lengths and widths (in cm) of 8 leaves from a tree were measured. The results are shown below.

Length, l	4.6	7.2	5.1	8.3	2.4	6.4	5.7	3.3
Width, w	3.1	5.2	3.6	5.6	1.7	4.7	4.0	2.5

a) Find the product moment correlation coefficient, r.

b) Test the hypothesis that the PMCC for the population, ρ, is greater than zero, at the 2.5% significance level.

Q7 For the situations below, explain whether the value of the rank correlation coefficient (r_s) between variables x and y shows positive association, negative association or no association.

a) $r_s = 0.8924$ 　　　　　b) $r_s = 0.0185$ 　　　　　c) $r_s = -0.7983$

Q8 At a baking competition, one judge ranks the entries based on appearance, and a second judge ranks them based on taste. Mel claims that there is some association between the ranks, and samples a class which has 12 entries to test her claim.

a) Find the critical region for a test of Mel's claim at the 5% significance level.

b) Spearman's rank correlation coefficient for Mel's sample is calculated to be -0.5438. Does this provide significant evidence to support Mel's claim at the 5% level?

c) Does this value of r_s provide significant evidence at the 10% level?

Chapter 27 — Probability 2

You've seen a lot of the probability in this chapter before, just using different notation. What's new here is conditional probability, which is the probability of an event happening, given that another event happens.

1. Conditional Probability

Set notation

The laws of probability you saw in Chapter 12 can be written using **set notation**.
In set notation, ∪ means the **union** of two sets (everything that is in **either** set),
and ∩ means the **intersection** (only the things that are in **both**).

In this notation, the **addition law** is:	$P(A \cup B) = P(A) + P(B) - P(A \cap B)$
You should also know that:	$P(A') = 1 - P(A)$
	$P(A) = P(A \cap B) + P(A \cap B')$
For **mutually exclusive** events:	$P(A \cap B) = 0 \Rightarrow P(A \cup B) = P(A) + P(B)$
And for **independent** events:	$P(A \cap B) = P(A) \times P(B)$

Tip: See p.174 if you need a reminder about mutually exclusive events, and p.175 for independent events.

> **Example**
>
> **For two independent events A and B, P(A) = 0.5 and P(A ∪ B) = 0.6. Find P(B) and P(A ∩ B).**
>
> 1. Use the addition law:
>
> $P(A \cup B) = P(A) + P(B) - P(A \cap B) \Rightarrow 0.6 = 0.5 + P(B) - P(A \cap B) \Rightarrow 0.1 = P(B) - P(A \cap B)$
>
> 2. The events are independent, so $P(A \cap B) = P(A)P(B)$.
>
> $0.1 = P(B) - P(A)P(B) \Rightarrow 0.1 = P(B) - 0.5P(B) \Rightarrow 0.1 = 0.5P(B) \Rightarrow$ **P(B) = 0.2**
>
> 3. Use the formula for independent events to find $P(A \cap B)$:
>
> $P(A \cap B) = P(A)P(B) = 0.5 \times 0.2 =$ **0.1**

Conditional probability

A probability is **conditional** if it **depends** on what has already happened.
The probability that an event B happens, **given** that an event A has already happened, is called the **conditional probability** of 'B given A', written **P(B | A)**:

$$P(B \mid A) = \frac{P(A \cap B)}{P(A)}$$

If you rearrange this you get a formula called the **product law**: $P(A \cap B) = P(A)P(B \mid A)$

> **Examples**
>
> **For events A and B: P(A) = 0.6, P(B) = 0.5, P(A ∩ B) = 0.3, P(B' | A) = 0.5.**
>
> a) **Find P(A | B).**   Using the conditional probability formula: $P(A|B) = \dfrac{P(A \cap B)}{P(B)} = \dfrac{0.3}{0.5} =$ **0.6**
>
> b) **Find P(A ∩ B').**   Using the product law: $P(A \cap B') = P(A)P(B'|A) = 0.6 \times 0.5 =$ **0.3**

Examples

Vikram either walks or runs to the bus stop. The probability that
he walks is 0.4. The probability that he catches the bus is 0.54.
If he walks to the bus stop, the probability that he catches the bus is 0.3.

 MODELLING

a) Draw a Venn diagram representing the events W,
'Vikram walks to the bus stop', and C, 'Vikram catches the bus'.

1. Write down the probabilities you know:
P(W) = 0.4, P(C) = 0.54 and P(C|W) = 0.3

2. To draw the Venn diagram, you need to
find P(C ∩ W). Use the product law:
P(C ∩ W) = P(W)P(C|W) = 0.4 × 0.3 = 0.12

3. Now draw the Venn diagram:

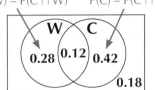

P(W) – P(C ∩ W)   P(C) – P(C ∩ W)

b) Find the probability that Vikram catches the bus, given that he runs to the bus stop.

This is the probability P(C|W'). Using the formula for conditional probability:

$$P(C|W') = \frac{P(C \cap W')}{P(W')}$$

He either walks or runs to the bus stop, so P(runs) = P(W').

P(C ∩ W') = 0.42 and P(W') = 1 – 0.4 = 0.6, so $P(C|W') = \frac{P(C \cap W')}{P(W')} = \frac{0.42}{0.6} = 0.7$

So P(Vikram catches the bus, given that he runs to the bus stop) = **0.7**

Exercise 1.1

Q1 Given that P(A) = 0.3, P(B) = 0.5 and P(A ∪ B) = 0.7, find: a) P(A')   b) P(A ∩ B)   c) P(A ∩ B')

Q2 The events X and Y are independent, where P(X) = 0.8 and P(Y) = 0.15.
Find the probability that neither X nor Y occurs.

Q3 If P(G) = 0.7, P(H) = 0.63 and P(G ∩ H) = 0.24, find: a) P(G|H)   b) P(H|G)

Q4 P(A) = 0.68, P(B') = 0.44, P(C) = 0.44, P(A ∩ B) = 0.34, P(A ∩ C) = 0.16 and P(B ∩ C') = 0.49.
Find: a) P(B|A)   b) P(A|C)   c) P(C'|B)

Q5 For events J and K, P(J) = 0.4, P(J|K) = 0.64 and P(K|J) = 0.2.   a) Find P(J ∪ K).   b) Find P(J' ∩ K').

Q6 In a group of eleven footballers, five are over 6 feet tall. Two of the three players who can play in goal
are over 6 feet tall. One of the players is selected at random.
a) If the player is over 6 feet tall, what is the probability that they can play in goal?
b) If the player can play in goal, what is the probability that they are over 6 feet tall?

Q7 The Venn diagram on the right shows the numbers of students studying Maths, English
and Art, from a group of 100 students. One of the students is selected at random.
a) If the student is studying Art, what is the probability they are also studying Maths?
b) If the student is studying English and Maths,
what is the probability that they are also studying Art?
c) If the student is not studying Maths, what is the probability that they are studying English?
d) Find P(A|E').   e) Find P(M|A ∩ E).

Q8 Given that $P(X) = 0.44$, $P(Y') = 0.72$, $P(Z) = 0.61$, $P(X|Y) = 0.75$,
$P(Z|X) = 0.25$, $P(Y \cap Z') = 0.2$ and $P(X \cap Y \mid Z) = \frac{7}{61}$, find:
a) $P(Y)$ b) $P(X \cap Y)$ c) $P(X \cap Z)$ d) $P(Y|Z')$ e) $P(X \cap Y \cap Z)$

Using conditional probability

Independent events

If A and B are **independent**, then P(B) is the same, whether A happens or not.

- This means: $P(B|A) = P(B|A') = P(B)$ and $P(A|B) = P(A|B') = P(A)$
- The **conditional probability** formula becomes: $P(B|A) = P(B) = \dfrac{P(A \cap B)}{P(A)}$
- The **product law** becomes: $P(A \cap B) = P(A)P(B|A) = P(A)P(B)$

To show that events A and B are independent, you just need to show that **one** of the following is true:
$$P(B|A) = P(B) \ [\text{or } P(A|B) = P(A)] \quad \text{or} \quad P(A) \times P(B) = P(A \cap B)$$

Examples   For events A and B, $P(A) = 0.25$, $P(B|A) = 0.8$ and $P(A' \cap B) = 0.4$.

a) **Find:** (i) $P(A \cap B)$, (ii) $P(A')$, (iii) $P(B'|A)$, (iv) $(B|A')$, (v) $P(B)$, (vi) $P(A|B)$.

(i)   Using the product law: $P(A \cap B) = P(A)P(B|A) = 0.25 \times 0.8 = \mathbf{0.2}$

(ii) $P(A') = 1 - P(A) = 1 - 0.25 = \mathbf{0.75}$

At this stage, it'll help a lot to draw a Venn diagram.
From the question, $P(A) = 0.25$, $P(B|A) = 0.8$ and $P(A' \cap B) = 0.4$
And you've found $P(A \cap B) = 0.2$ and $P(A') = 0.75$

(iii) Using the conditional probability formula:
$$P(B'|A) = \frac{P(B' \cap A)}{P(A)} = \frac{0.05}{0.25} = \mathbf{0.2}$$

(iv) Using the conditional probability formula: $P(B|A') = \dfrac{P(B \cap A')}{P(A')} = \dfrac{0.4}{0.75} = \dfrac{40}{75} = \mathbf{\dfrac{8}{15}}$

(v) You can see from the Venn diagram that: $P(B) = P(B \cap A) + P(B \cap A') = 0.2 + 0.4 = \mathbf{0.6}$

(vi) $P(A|B) = \dfrac{P(A \cap B)}{P(B)} = \dfrac{0.2}{0.6} = \mathbf{\dfrac{1}{3}}$

b) **Say whether or not A and B are independent.**

There are different ways you can do this. For example:
$P(B|A) = 0.8 \ne P(B) = 0.6$, so A and B are **not independent**.

Exercise 1.2

Q1   For events A and B, $P(A) = 0.75$, $P(B|A') = 0.4$, $P(A \cap B') = 0.45$. Are A and B independent?

Q2   The Venn diagram on the right shows the probabilities for events R, S and T:
a) Which events are: (i) mutually exclusive?   (ii) independent?
b) Find: (i) $P(R|S)$ (ii) $P(R|(S \cap T'))$

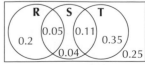

Q3   X, Y and Z are independent events. $P(X) = 0.84$, $P(Y) = 0.68$ and $P(Z) = 0.48$.
Find: a) $P(X \cap Y)$ b) $P(Y' \cap Z')$ c) $P(Y|Z)$ d) $P(Z'|Y')$ e) $P(Y|X')$

Q4   Amena sometimes goes to the park, depending on the weather. If it's a sunny
      day, the probability that she goes to the park is 0.6. If it isn't sunny, she goes to
      the park with probability 0.2. The probability that it is sunny is 0.45.

      a) Draw a Venn diagram to show the event 'it is sunny' (S) and the event 'she goes to the park' (P).

      b) What is the probability that it's sunny, given that she goes to the park?

Tree diagrams

You may not have realised it when you saw them
on p.177, but **tree diagrams** are actually all about
conditional probability. You can label the branches of
a tree diagram using **set notation** like this:

Tree diagrams are really useful for seeing how the
result of one trial **affects** the probability of another
event happening.

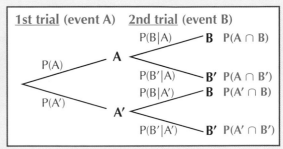

{Examples}   For events M and N: $P(M) = 0.2$, $P(N \mid M) = 0.4$ and $P(N' \mid M') = 0.7$.

a)   **Draw a tree diagram representing events M and N.**

  ▪ You need two sets of branches — one for event M and one
    for event N. Since you're told the probability of M, but not
    that of N, show M on the first set and N on the second set.

  ▪ Each pair of branches will show either M and its
    complement M', or N and its complement N'.

  ▪ You can find the probabilities of the remaining branches
    by doing (1 – the probability on the other branch).

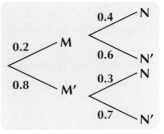

b)   **Find P(N).** $P(N) = P(M \cap N) + P(M' \cap N) = P(M)P(N|M) + P(M')P(N|M')$

                            $= (0.2 \times 0.4) + (0.8 \times 0.3) = \textbf{0.32}$

c)   **Find P(M' | N').**

  ▪ If N' is conditional on M', then M' is conditional on N'.
    Using the conditional probability formula: $P(M'|N') = \dfrac{P(M' \cap N')}{P(N')}$

  ▪ Using the probabilities you found above: $P(N') = 1 - P(N) = 0.68$

                            $P(M' \cap N') = P(M')P(N'|M') = 0.8 \times 0.7 = 0.56$

                            So, $P(M'|N') = \dfrac{P(M' \cap N')}{P(N')} = \dfrac{0.56}{0.68} = \dfrac{56}{68} = \dfrac{\textbf{14}}{\textbf{17}}$

Exercise 1.3

Q1   A group of people were asked about their mobile phones. 62% of them own a smartphone.
      Of those with a smartphone, 29% have a contract costing £25 a month or less. 68% of those without
      a smartphone have a contract costing £25 a month or less. Use a tree diagram to find the probability
      that a person from the group owns a smartphone, given that their contract costs over £25 a month.

Q2   A bag contains red, white and blue counters. There are 10 red counters, 15 white counters and 11 blue
      counters. One counter is drawn at random. It is not replaced. A second counter is then drawn.
      Draw a tree diagram to represent this situation, and use it to find the probability that the second
      counter is blue, given that the first counter is not red.

Two-way tables

Probabilities can also be shown in **two-way tables**, like this:

Two-way tables can make finding conditional probabilities easy — if you're trying to find a probability "given A", look in the A column (or row) of the table. **Divide** the **relevant entry** by the **total** for that column or row to get the conditional probability.

	A	A′	Total
B	P(A ∩ B)	P(A′ ∩ B)	P(B)
B′	P(A ∩ B′)	P(A′ ∩ B′)	P(B′)
Total	P(A)	P(A′)	1

[Examples] 22 children are at a Halloween party. The two-way table below shows the costumes that they are wearing. A child is picked at random.

	Werewolf	Zombie	Ghost	Total
Boys	4	3	3	10
Girls	2	4	6	12
Total	6	7	9	22

a) **Given that the child is a girl, what is the probability that they're dressed as a zombie?**

- The child is a girl, so look at the Girls row of the table — there are 12 girls in total.

- The Zombie entry in this row is 4, so: $\qquad$ P(Zombie|Girl) = $\frac{4}{12}$ = $\frac{1}{3}$

b) **Two girls dressed as ghosts go home. Draw an updated two-way table showing the probabilities of selecting a child from each category.**

To find the probabilities, divide every entry by the new total of 20. Don't forget to change the Ghost ∩ Girls entry to 6 − 2 = 4 and update the Girl, Ghost and overall totals before dividing.

2 ÷ 20 = 0.1   3 ÷ 20 = 0.15

	Werewolf	Zombie	Ghost	Total
Boys	0.2	0.15	0.15	0.5
Girls	0.1	0.2	0.2	0.5
Total	0.3	0.35	0.35	1

7 ÷ 20 = 0.35   20 ÷ 20 = 1

c) **Another child is picked at random.**
Given that the child is dressed as a werewolf, what is the probability that they're a boy?

The child is dressed as a werewolf, so look in the Werewolf column — the Boys entry is 0.2, and the total is 0.3, so: $\qquad$ P(Boy|Werewolf) = $\frac{0.2}{0.3}$ = $\frac{2}{3}$

Exercise 1.4

Q1 A dance competition has three age categories, 11-13 years, 14-16 years and 17-18 years. The two-way table shows the number of male and female competitors in each age category in this year's contest.

a) Use the table to calculate the probability that a randomly selected competitor is:

(i) Female, given that they are 11-13 years old.

(ii) 17-18 years old, given that they are male.

(iii) Male, given that they are under 17 years old.

(iv) Not in the 14-16 age group, given that they are female.

b) There is a probability of 0.2 that a girl will be 11 years old given that she is chosen at random from the 11-13 age group. How many 11-year-old girls are there in the competition?

	Male	Female	Total
11-13 years	10	15	25
14-16 years	14	16	30
17-18 years	8	12	20
Total	32	43	75

Q2   Joe records the ages of people going to a cinema on a Sunday evening. He obtains the following data:
26 of the 40 people were under 20 years old. 18 people went to see a comedy film.
Of the people who watched an action film, 6 of them were 20 years old or above.

a) Copy the two-way table and fill it in using Joe's data.

b) One of the cinema-goers is picked at random.
Given that they saw a comedy film, what is the
probability that they are under 20?

	Action	Comedy	Total
Under 20			
20 and over			
Total			

2. Modelling with Probability

Modelling assumptions and probability

In most models, the probability of an event is based on some **assumptions**.
Evaluating and **criticising** the assumptions being made is an important part of the modelling process.

Some common issues to think about are:

- Have you assumed that two (or more) events are **equally likely**?
  Is this true? Could the probabilities be **biased** in some way?

- Is the probability based on **past data**? Is the data **appropriate**?
  How **reliable** is the data? How was the data **sampled**?

- Is the experiment itself **truly random**? Is there anything about the way
  that the experiment is being **carried out** that could affect the outcome?

    Sanaa wants to know the probability that it will rain tomorrow. She looks
up the weather data for the previous 30 days, and finds that it has rained on
12 of them. She concludes that the probability that it will rain is $\frac{12}{30}$ = 0.4.
Give a reason why this model might be inaccurate.

There are lots of answers you could give. For example:

- She has only taken data from the past 30 days, which might not be a large enough sample
  to give an accurate estimate, or might not take seasonal variations into account.

- She has assumed that the probability that it rains on one day is not affected by whether or
  not it rained the day before (i.e. that they are independent events) but this might not be true.

Exercise 2.1

For the following models, give an assumption that has been made and explain how it may lead to inaccuracy.

Q1   Ella throws a wooden cuboid in the air. She says, "The probability that it lands on any given face is $\frac{1}{6}$."

Q2   Harriet shows a selection of 10 playing cards to a volunteer. The volunteer chooses one, replaces it
and chooses another. Harriet says, "The probability of a particular card being chosen twice is 0.01."

Q3   In a class of primary school children, 56% walked to school one day. Their teacher says,
"The probability that a child from any primary school walks to school on a given day is 0.56."

Review Exercise — Chapter 27

Q1 For two events, C and D, P(C) = 0.4, P(D) = 0.24, P(C ∩ D) = 0.15. Find P(C|D) and P(D|C).

Q2 The Venn diagram on the right shows the number of outcomes matching two events, A and B. Find:

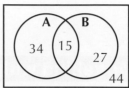

  a) P(A ∩ B)   b) P(A ∪ B')   c) P(A|B)   d) P(B|A')

Q3 Cliff is planting flower bulbs in his garden.
The bulbs produce flowers that are either red or yellow, and either short or tall.
Each bulb produces one flower. If Cliff chooses a bulb at random, the probability it produces a red flower is 0.35 and the probability that it produces a tall flower is 0.46.
If one of the yellow flowers is chosen at random, the probability that it is short is 0.4.

  a) Find the probability that a randomly chosen bulb produces a short yellow flower.

  b) Find the probability that a flower is short, given that it is red.

Q4 Asmaa either catches the bus to school or rides her bike to school. She either arrives at school on time or late. The probability that she catches the bus is 0.6. If she catches the bus, the probability that she's late is 0.1. The probability that she arrives on time is 0.92. Draw a tree diagram to represent this information, and hence find the probability Asmaa is late, given that she rides her bike.

Q5 Georgie owns a coffee kiosk at a railway station. The kiosk is open seven days a week. Georgie chooses a day's sales figures at random from the last ten weeks. The probability that she sold more than 150 cups of coffee on that day, given it was on a weekend, is $\frac{3}{10}$.
The probability it was not on a weekend and she did not sell more than 150 cups of coffee is $\frac{1}{2}$.
Show that the probability that Georgie sold more than 150 cups of coffee on a particular day is independent of whether or not it was a weekend.

Q6 On a Monday morning, each student in a particular group has either a French lesson or a Spanish lesson, followed by one of biology, chemistry and physics. Use the following information to complete a two-way table showing the probabilities of a randomly chosen student having each combination of lessons.
Let F = French, S = Spanish, B = biology, C = chemistry and P = physics.
Then: P(F ∩ P) = 0.08, P(F) = 0.37, P(B) = 0.25, P(S|B) = $\frac{2}{5}$, P(F|C) = $\frac{1}{3}$

Q7 For each of the following models, state one assumption that may have been made and explain why it might not be valid.

  a) Baz sets three maths puzzles, numbered 1-3, on his website and offers a prize for the first correct answer he receives for each puzzle.
     He predicts that each puzzle has a probability of $\frac{1}{3}$ of being the first to be solved.

  b) Ariel calculates that the a probability that she will see her neighbour's cat in her back garden is 0.8 on sunny days and 0.1 on rainy days.
     Without looking at the weather forecast, she predicts that the probability she will see the cat in her back garden tomorrow is 0.5 × 0.8 + 0.5 × 0.1 = 0.45.

Chapter 28 — The Normal Distribution

In this chapter you'll be introduced to the normal distribution and use it to find different probabilities. Many variables can be modelled by normal distributions, which can be very useful in real-life situations.

1. The Normal Distribution

In real-life situations, the distribution of a set of data often follows a **particular pattern** — with most of the data values falling **somewhere in the middle**, and only a small proportion taking much higher or lower values. A quantity like this can often be modelled by a **normal distribution**.

If X is a **continuous random variable** that follows a **normal** distribution, you can describe the probability distribution of X using just two measures — its **mean**, μ and **variance**, σ^2.

Whatever the values of μ and σ^2, the **graph** of a normal distribution always looks like the **curve** below.

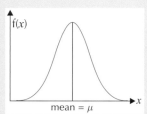

- The curve is '**bell-shaped**'.

- There's a **peak** at the **mean**, μ.

- It's **symmetrical** about the mean — so values the same distance above and below the mean are equally likely.

The **area** under a normal curve shows **probabilities**.

- The **total area** under the curve represents the **total probability** of the random variable taking one of its possible values. And since the total probability is 1, the **total area under the curve** must also be **1**.

- The **probability** of the variable taking a value **between two limits** is the **area under the curve** between those limits.

- Values of the **cumulative distribution function** (cdf) are the **areas** under the curve to the **left of x** (the **probability** that $X \leq x$) for different values of x.

- Since X is a **continuous** random variable, $P(X = x) = 0$, which means that $P(X \leq x)$ and $P(X < x)$ are the **same thing**. So you can **interchange** the $\leq$ and $<$ signs.

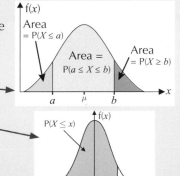

If a continuous random variable X is **normally** distributed with mean μ and variance σ^2, it is written like this: $\longrightarrow$ $X \sim N(\mu,\ \sigma^2)$

'**N**' stands for '**normal**' and '~' is short for '**is distributed**'.

Examples Find the probabilities for the normal distributions given below to 4 s.f.

a) If $X \sim N(100, 16)$, find $P(X \leq 105)$ to 4 s.f.

   1. Draw a sketch showing the area you need to find.

   2. Input the upper bound $x = 105$, a lower bound (e.g. −9999), $\mu = 100$, and $\sigma = \sqrt{16} = 4$ into the normal cdf function on your calculator.

      So $P(X \leq 105) = 0.894350... = \mathbf{0.8944}$ **to 4 s.f.**

Tip: For a question with $P(X > x)$ or $P(X \geq x)$, use a large number (e.g. 9999) for the upper bound on your calculator — or you can use the fact that $P(X > x) = 1 - P(X \leq x)$.

b) If $X \sim N(102, 144)$, find $P(84 \leq X \leq 106)$ to 4 s.f.

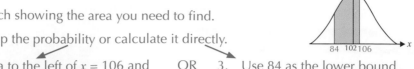

1. Draw a sketch showing the area you need to find.

2. Either split up the probability or calculate it directly.

3. Find the area to the left of $x = 106$ and subtract the area to the left of $x = 84$.

   $P(84 \leq X \leq 106) = P(X \leq 106) - P(X < 84)$

   $= 0.630558... - 0.066807...$

   $= \mathbf{0.5638}$ **to 4 s.f.**

OR   3. Use 84 as the lower bound and 106 as the upper bound in the normal cdf function.

   $P(84 \leq X \leq 106) = 0.563751...$

   $= \mathbf{0.5638}$ **to 4 s.f.**

Exercise 1.1

Give all answers in this exercise to 4 decimal places.

Q1 If $X \sim N(40, 25)$, find:　　a) $P(X < 50)$　　b) $P(X \leq 43)$　　c) $P(X < 38)$

Q2 If $X \sim N(24, 6)$, find:　　a) $P(X \geq 28)$　　b) $P(X > 25)$　　c) $P(X \geq 21)$

Q3 If $X \sim N(120, 40)$, find:　　a) $P(X > 107)$　　b) $P(X > 115)$　　c) $P(X \geq 135)$

Q4 If $X \sim N(17, 3^2)$, find:　　a) $P(X \leq 15)$　　b) $P(X < 12)$　　c) $P(X > 21)$

Q5 If $X \sim N(50, 5^2)$, find:　　a) $P(52 < X < 63)$　　b) $P(57 \leq X < 66)$

Q6 If $X \sim N(0.6, 0.04)$, find:　a) $P(0.45 \leq X \leq 0.55)$　b) $P(0.53 < X < 0.58)$

Q7 If $X \sim N(260, 15^2)$, find:　a) $P(240 < X \leq 280)$　b) $P(232 < X < 288)$

The standard normal distribution, Z

The **standard normal distribution**, Z, is a normal distribution that has mean $\boldsymbol{\mu = 0}$ and variance $\boldsymbol{\sigma^2 = 1}$, so $Z \sim N(0, 1)$.

Values of the **cumulative distribution function** (cdf) are usually written $\Phi(z)$ — i.e. $\Phi(z) = P(Z \leq z)$.

Tip: Since $P(Z = z) = 0$, you can **interchange** the $\leq$ and $<$ signs — i.e. $\Phi(z) = P(X < z)$ as well.

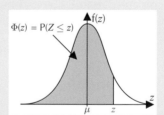

Examples　　Given that $Z \sim N(0, 1)$, find the following probabilities to 4 s.f.

a) $P(Z > -0.42)$

1. Draw a sketch of the area you need to find.

2. On a calculator, input lower bound -0.42, an upper bound (e.g. 9999), $\sigma = 1$ and $\mu = 0$ into the normal cdf.

   $P(Z > -0.42) = 0.662757... = \mathbf{0.6628}$ **to 4 s.f.**

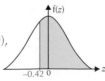

b) **P(0.12 < Z ≤ 0.82)**

1. Draw a sketch of the area you need to find.
2. On a calculator, input lower bound 0.12, upper bound 0.82, $\sigma = 1$ and $\mu = 0$ into the normal cdf.
   P(0.12 < Z ≤ 0.82) = 0.246133... = **0.2461 to 4 s.f.**

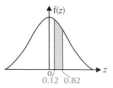

Exercise 1.2

Use a calculator to find the following probabilities to 4 s.f.

Q1 a) $P(Z \le 1.87)$ b) $P(Z < 0.99)$ c) $P(Z > 2.48)$ d) $P(Z \ge 0.14)$

   e) $P(Z > -0.24)$ f) $P(Z > -1.21)$ g) $P(Z < -0.62)$ h) $P(Z \le -2.06)$

   i) $P(Z \ge 1.23)$ j) $P(Z < 0.75)$ k) $P(Z > 0.62)$ l) $P(Z \ge -1.76)$

Q2 a) $P(1.34 < Z < 2.18)$ b) $P(0.76 \le Z < 1.92)$ c) $P(-1.45 \le Z \le 0.17)$

   d) $P(-2.14 < Z < 1.65)$ e) $P(-1.66 < Z \le 1.66)$ f) $P(-0.34 \le Z < 0.34)$

   g) $P(-3.25 \le Z \le -2.48)$ h) $P(-1.11 < Z < -0.17)$ i) $P(-0.27 \le Z \le -0.05)$

Converting to the Z distribution

Any continuous random variable, X, where $X \sim N(\mu, \sigma^2)$, can be **transformed** to the **standard normal variable**, Z, by **subtracting the mean (μ)**, and then **dividing by the standard deviation (σ)**.

$$\text{If } X \sim N(\mu, \sigma^2), \text{ then } \frac{X - \mu}{\sigma} = Z, \text{ where } Z \sim N(0, 1)$$

 If $X \sim N(5, 16)$, find the probabilities below by transforming X to the standard normal variable, Z. Give your answers to 4 d.p.

a) **P(X < 7)**

1. Transform X to Z by subtracting $\mu = 5$ and dividing by $\sigma = \sqrt{16} = 4$.

   $$P(X < 7) = P\left(Z < \frac{7-5}{4}\right) = P(Z < 0.5)$$

2. Draw a sketch showing the area you need to find.
3. Using a calculator: P(Z < 0.5) = **0.6915 to 4 d.p.**

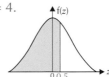

b) **P(5 < X < 11)**

1. Transform X to Z.

   $$P(5 < X < 11) = P\left(\frac{5-5}{4} < Z < \frac{11-5}{4}\right) = P(0 < Z < 1.5)$$

2. Draw a sketch showing the area you need to find.
3. Using a calculator: P(0 < Z < 1.5) = **0.4332 to 4 d.p.**

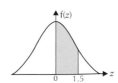

Exercise 1.3

Q1 If $X \sim N(106, 100)$, transform X to the standard normal variable to find: a) $P(X \leq 100)$ b) $P(X > 122)$

Q2 If $X \sim N(11, 2^2)$, transform X to the standard normal variable to find: a) $P(X \geq 9)$ b) $P(10 \leq X \leq 12)$

Q3 If $X \sim N(260, 15^2)$, transform X to the standard normal variable to find:
   a) $P(240 < X < 280)$ b) $P(232 < X < 288)$ c) $P(245 \leq X \leq 255)$ d) $P(260 < X \leq 277)$

Finding *x*-values

You might be given a **probability**, p, and be asked to find a specific **range of *x*-values** where the probability of X falling in this range is equal to p.

For any probability involving **less than** or **less than or equal to** (e.g. find x where $P(X \leq x) = p$), these questions can be done **directly** on your calculator. To do this, choose the **inverse normal** function on your calculator. Then input the **probability**, **mean** and **standard deviation**.

Example $X \sim N(85, 25)$. If $P(X < a) = 0.9192$, find the value of a to 2 s.f.

1. Draw a sketch of the area you're given.

2. Input probability = 0.9192, $\mu = 85$ and $\sigma = \sqrt{25} = 5$ into the inverse normal function on your calculator.
    $P(X < x) = 0.9192$ for $x = 91.998...$, so $a = \textbf{92 to 2 s.f.}$

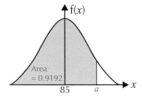

More complicated probabilities involving two *x*-values need to be split up using this formula:

$$P(a \leq X \leq b) = P(X \leq b) - P(X < a)$$

Example $X \sim N(24, 9)$. If $P(x < X < 24) = 0.2$, find the value of x to 3 s.f.

1. Draw a sketch of the area you're given.

2. Split up the probability. $P(x < X < 24) = P(X < 24) - P(X \leq x) = 0.2$
    So $P(X \leq x) = P(X < 24) - 0.2$

3. Since the mean is 24, $P(X < 24) = 0.5$. $P(X \leq x) = 0.5 - 0.2 = 0.3$

4. Use the inverse normal function. $P(X \leq x) = 0.3$ for $x = 22.426...$, so $x = \textbf{22.4 to 3 s.f.}$

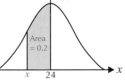

To work out values for **greater than** (or **greater than or equal to**) probabilities, you can find $1 - P(X > x)$ to get $P(X \leq x)$, then you can use the inverse normal function on your **calculator**.

Example $Z \sim N(0, 1)$. If $P(Z > z) = 0.15$, find the value of z.

1. Draw a sketch of the area you're given.

2. Subtract 0.15 from 1 to get the area to the left of z. $1 - 0.15 = 0.85$

3. Use a calculator to find the value of z. $P(Z \leq z) = 0.85$ for $z = \textbf{1.0364 to 4 d.p.}$

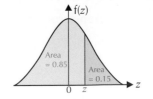

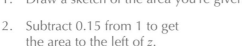

Exercise 1.4

Q1 If $X \sim N(12, 0.64)$, find the value of x such that:
    a) $P(X < x) = 0.8944$ b) $P(X \leq x) = 0.0304$ c) $P(X \geq x) = 0.2660$ d) $P(X > x) = 0.7917$

Q2 For the standard normal distribution, find the value of z to 2 d.p. that gives the following probabilities:
    a) $P(Z < z) = 0.004$ b) $P(Z > z) = 0.0951$ c) $P(Z \geq z) = 0.6884$
    d) $P(-z < Z < z) = 0.9426$ e) $P(z < Z < -1.25) = 0.0949$ f) $P(-0.48 \leq Z \leq z) = 0.1327$

Q3 If $X \sim N(48, 5^2)$, find the value of x such that:
    a) $P(53 < X < x) = 0.05$ b) $P(x < X < 49) = 0.4312$ c) $P(x \leq X \leq 45) = 0.2515$

You can also use the **percentage points** table to work out values for some probabilities. The table on p.472 gives the value of z for some probabilities, p, where $p = P(Z > z)$. E.g. in the previous example, to find z where $P(Z > z) = 0.15$, you can just look up $p = 0.15$ in the percentage points table.

Exercise 1.5

Q1 Use the percentage points table to find the value of z such that:
    a) $P(Z > z) = 0.005$ b) $P(Z > z) = 0.2$ c) $P(Z < z) = 0.7$ d) $P(Z < z) = 0.999$

Q2 If $X \sim N(25, 4^2)$, use the percentage points table to find the value of x such that:
    a) $P(X > x) = 0.4$ b) $P(X < x) = 0.975$

Finding the mean and standard deviation of a normal distribution

$X \sim N(\mu, \sigma^2)$ can be **transformed** to the standard normal variable, Z, by using $Z = \dfrac{X - \mu}{\sigma}$ (see p.401).

You can use this to find the **mean** and **standard deviation** of a distribution when they're **unknown** but you know some **probabilities** for the distribution.

 If the random variable $X \sim N(\mu, 4)$ and $P(X < 23) = 0.9015$, find μ.

1. Transform the probability for X into a probability for Z.
Draw a sketch to show the information.

$$P(X < 23) = P\left(Z < \frac{23 - \mu}{2}\right) = 0.9015$$

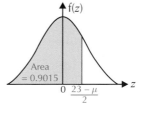

2. Find z for which $\Phi(z) = 0.9015$.

$\Phi(z) = 0.9015$ for $z = 1.29$ to 2 d.p.

3. Form an equation in μ and solve it.

$$\frac{23 - \mu}{2} = 1.29 \implies 23 - \mu = 2.58 \implies \mu = 20.42$$

Exercise 1.6

Q1 For each of the following, use the information to find μ.
    a) $X \sim N(\mu, 6^2)$ and $P(X < 23) = 0.9332$ b) $X \sim N(\mu, 8^2)$ and $P(X < 57) = 0.9970$
    c) $X \sim N(\mu, 100^2)$ and $P(X > 528) = 0.1292$ d) $X \sim N(\mu, 0.4^2)$ and $P(X < 11.06) = 0.0322$
    e) $X \sim N(\mu, 0.02^2)$ and $P(X > 1.52) = 0.9938$ f) $X \sim N(\mu, 9)$ and $P(X \geq 15) = 0.8413$

Q2 $X \sim N(\mu, 3.5^2)$. If the middle 95% of the distribution lies between 6.45 and 20.17, find the value of μ.

You can find an unknown **standard deviation** (s.d.) in exactly the same way.

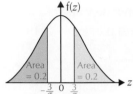 **If the random variable $X \sim N(53, \sigma^2)$ and $P(X < 50) = 0.2$, find σ.**

1. Transform the probability from X to Z.

$$P(X < 50) = P\left(Z < \frac{50-53}{\sigma}\right) = P\left(Z < -\frac{3}{\sigma}\right) = 0.2$$

2. Draw a sketch to show the information.

3. Use symmetry and the percentage points table.

$$P\left(Z > \frac{3}{\sigma}\right) = 0.2 \text{ and } P(Z > z) = 0.2 \text{ for } z = 0.8416$$

4. Form an equation in σ and solve it.

$$\frac{3}{\sigma} = 0.8416 \Rightarrow \sigma = 3 \div 0.8416 \Rightarrow \boldsymbol{\sigma = 3.56 \text{ to 3 s.f.}}$$

Exercise 1.7

Q1   For each of the following, use the information to find σ.

a) $X \sim N(48, \sigma^2)$ and $P(X < 53) = 0.8944$ b) $X \sim N(510, \sigma^2)$ and $P(X < 528) = 0.7734$

c) $X \sim N(17, \sigma^2)$ and $P(X > 24) = 0.0367$ d) $X \sim N(0.98, \sigma^2)$ and $P(X < 0.95) = 0.3085$

e) $X \sim N(5.6, \sigma^2)$ and $P(X > 4.85) = 0.8365$ f) $X \sim N(3.3, \sigma^2)$ and $P(X \geq 3.8) = 0.1902$

Q2 $X \sim N(68, \sigma^2)$. If the middle 70% of the distribution lies between 61 and 75, find the value of σ.

If you have to find the mean **and** the standard deviation, you'll be given two probabilities. You'll end up with two **simultaneous equations**, which you **solve** to find μ and σ.

 The random variable $X \sim N(\mu, \sigma^2)$. If $P(X < 9) = 0.5596$ and $P(X > 14) = 0.0322$, find μ and σ.

1. Transform the first probability from X to Z. $P(X < 9) = P\left(Z < \frac{9-\mu}{\sigma}\right) = 0.5596$

2. Draw a sketch to show the information.

3. Find z for which $\Phi(z) = 0.5596$ $\Phi(z) = 0.5596$ for $z = 0.15$ to 2 d.p.
    and form an equation in μ and σ. $\frac{9-\mu}{\sigma} = 0.15 \Rightarrow 9 - \mu = 0.15\sigma$

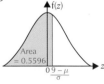

4. Transform the second probability. $P(X > 14) = P\left(Z > \frac{14-\mu}{\sigma}\right) = 0.0322$

5. Draw a sketch to show the information.

6. Use the graph. $P\left(Z \leq \frac{14-\mu}{\sigma}\right) = 1 - P\left(Z > \frac{14-\mu}{\sigma}\right) = 1 - 0.0322 = 0.9678$

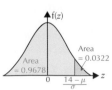

7. Find z for which $\Phi(z) = 0.9678$ $\Phi(z) = 0.9678$ for $z = 1.85$ to 2 d.p.
    and form an equation in μ and σ. $\frac{14-\mu}{\sigma} = 1.85 \Rightarrow 14 - \mu = 1.85\sigma$

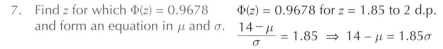

8. Label the simultaneous equations.

$9 - \mu = 0.15\sigma$ ① $14 - \mu = 1.85\sigma$ ②

9. Subtract the equations to get rid of μ, and solve the resulting equation for σ.

② – ①: $14 - 9 - \mu - (-\mu) = 1.85\sigma - 0.15\sigma$
$\Rightarrow 5 = 1.7\sigma \Rightarrow \sigma = 2.9411...$
$\Rightarrow \sigma = \textbf{2.94 to 3 s.f.}$

10. Find μ by substituting $\sigma = 2.94...$ back into one of the equations.

①: $9 - \mu = 0.15\sigma$
$\Rightarrow \mu = 9 - 0.15 \times 2.9411...$
$\Rightarrow \mu = 8.5588... = \textbf{8.56 to 3 s.f.}$

Exercise 1.8

Q1   If $X \sim N(\mu, \sigma^2)$, find μ and σ for each of the following pairs of probabilities.

a) P($X < 30$) = 0.9192 and P($X < 36$) = 0.9953   b) P($X < 4$) = 0.9332 and P($X < 4.3$) = 0.9987

c) P($X < 20$) = 0.7881 and P($X < 14$) = 0.0548   d) P($X < 696$) = 0.9713 and P($X < 592$) = 0.2420

e) P($X > 33$) = 0.1056 and P($X > 21$) = 0.9599   f) P($X > 66$) = 0.3632 and P($X < 48$) = 0.3446

The normal distribution in real-life situations

When the normal distribution is applied to a real-life context, start by **defining** a **normally-distributed random variable** to represent the information you're given. Then use it to find what you need to know.

 A machine which fills boxes of cereal is set so that the mass of cereal going into the boxes follows a normal distribution with mean 766 g and standard deviation 8 g.

a) **Find the probability that a randomly selected box of cereal contains less than 780 g of cereal.**

1. Define a random variable.

If X represents the mass of cereal in g, then $X \sim N(766, 64)$.

2. Turn the question into a probability for X.

Find P($X < 780$).

3. Sketch the area you need to find.

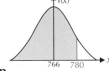

4. Use a calculator to find the probability.   P($X < 780$) = **0.9599 to 4 d.p.**

b) **The machine fills 2138 boxes of cereal in an hour. Find the number of boxes that you would expect to contain less than 780 g.**

Multiply the total number of boxes by the probability calculated in a). $2138 \times$ P($X < 780$) = $2138 \times 0.9599 \approx$ **2052 boxes**

c) **Find the probability that a randomly selected box of cereal contains between 780 g and 790 g of cereal.**

1. Turn the question into a probability for X.   Find P($780 < X < 790$).

2. Sketch the area you need to find.

3. Use a calculator to find the probability.   P($780 < X < 790$) = **0.0387 to 4 d.p.**

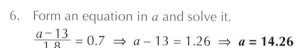

The forces needed to snap lengths of a certain type of elastic are normally distributed with $\mu = 13$ N and $\sigma = 1.8$ N.

a) **The probability that a randomly selected length of elastic is snapped by a force of less than a N is 0.7580. Find the value of a.**

1. Define a random variable.   If F represents the force needed in N, then $F \sim N(13, 1.8^2)$.

2. Turn the question into a probability for F. $P(F < a) = 0.7580$.

3. Transform F to Z. $P(F < a) = P\left(Z < \dfrac{a-13}{1.8}\right) = 0.7580$

4. Draw a sketch.

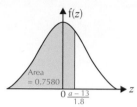

5. Find z for which $\Phi(z) = 0.7580$.

   $\Phi(z) = 0.7580$ for $z = 0.70$

6. Form an equation in a and solve it.

   $\dfrac{a-13}{1.8} = 0.7 \Rightarrow a - 13 = 1.26 \Rightarrow \mathbf{a = 14.26}$

b) **Find the range of values that includes the middle 80% of forces needed to snap the length of elastic.**

1. Sketch the distribution of F.

2. Write probability statements for a and b.

   $P(F < a) = 0.1$ $P(F > b) = 0.1$

3. Transform F to Z.

   $P(F < a) = P\left(Z < \dfrac{a-13}{1.8}\right) = 0.1$ $P(F > b) = P\left(Z > \dfrac{b-13}{1.8}\right) = 0.1$

4. Sketch the distribution of Z.

5. Find b with the percentage points table.

   $p = 0.1$ for $z = 1.2816$ $\dfrac{b-13}{1.8} = 1.2816 \Rightarrow b = 15.31$ to 2 d.p.

6. Use symmetry to find a.

   $\dfrac{a-13}{1.8} = -1.2816 \Rightarrow a = 10.69$ to 2 d.p.

   So the range of values is **10.69 N to 15.31 N**

Tip: On some calculators you can find the values of a and b directly, using the inverse normal function, without having to convert to Z.

Exercise 1.9

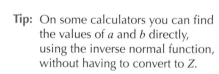

Q1   The lengths of time taken by a group of 56 blood donors to replace their red blood cells are modelled by a normal distribution with a mean of 36 days and a standard deviation of 6 days.

a) It takes Edward 28 days to replace his red blood cells. Find the probability that a randomly selected donor from the group takes less time than Edward to replace their red blood cells.

b) Find the number of blood donors that this model would predict to take less time than Edward to replace their blood cells.

c) 6.3% of the group take longer than Bella to replace their red blood cells.
   How long does it take Bella?

Q2   The personal best times taken by athletes at a sports club to run 400 m are known to follow
a normal distribution with a mean of 51 seconds and a standard deviation of 2.1 seconds.

a) Gary's personal best time is 49.3 seconds.
What percentage of the athletes have a slower personal best time than Gary?

b) The athletes with personal bests in the top 20% of times are selected for a special training
programme. What time do they have to beat to be selected for the programme?

Q3   The volume of vinegar contained in bottles is modelled by a normal distribution with a
standard deviation of 5 ml. It is found that 71.9% of bottles contain less than 506 ml of vinegar.

a) Find the mean volume of vinegar contained in the bottles.

b) The label on each bottle says it contains 500 ml of vinegar.
Find the probability that a random bottle contains less than 500 ml.

c) A shop's store room has 1303 bottles of vinegar.
Find the number of bottles that this model would predict to contain at least 500 ml.

Q4   A particular type of toy car uses two identical batteries. The lifetimes of individual batteries can be
modelled by a normal distribution with a mean of 300 hours and a standard deviation of 50 hours.

a) Find the probability that a battery lasts less than 200 hours.

b) Find the probability that a battery lasts at least 380 hours.

c) Stating any assumptions you make, find the probability that both of the batteries in a car
last at least 380 hours.

d) The probability that a randomly selected battery lasts more than 160 hours,
but less than h hours, is 0.9746. Find the value of h.

Q5   The heights of a population of 17-year-old boys are assumed to follow a normal distribution
with a mean of 175 cm. 80% of this population of 17-year-old boys are taller than 170 cm.

a) Find the standard deviation of the heights of the 17-year-old boys in this population.

b) One 17-year-old boy is selected from the population at random.
Find the probability that his height is within 4 cm of the mean height.

Q6   The masses of the eggs laid by the hens on farmer Elizabeth's farm are assumed to follow
a normal distribution with mean 60 g and standard deviation 3 g.

a) The probability that a randomly selected egg has a mass of at least $60 - m$ grams is 0.9525.
Find the value of m to the nearest gram.

b) Farmer Elizabeth keeps the lightest 10% of eggs for herself and uses them to make sponge cakes.
Find the maximum mass of an egg that could end up in one of farmer Elizabeth's sponge cakes.

Q7   In a particularly wet village, it rains almost continuously.
The daily rainfall, in cm, is modelled by a normal distribution.
The daily rainfall is less than 4 cm on only 10.2% of days,
and it's greater than 7 cm on 64.8% of days.

Find the mean and standard deviation of the daily rainfall.

2. Normal Approximation to a Binomial Distribution

Continuity corrections

The binomial distribution (see p.187) is **discrete**, so if $X \sim B(n, p)$, you can find $P(X = 0)$, $P(X = 1)$, etc.
The normal distribution can be used to approximate a binomial distribution in particular circumstances.
But the normal distribution is **continuous**, so if $Y \sim N(\mu, \sigma^2)$ then $P(Y = 0) = P(Y = 1) = 0$ (see p.399).

To allow for this when approximating, you might have to use a **continuity correction**.

- You assume that the discrete value $X = 1$ is 'spread out' over the interval $0.5 < Y < 1.5$.

- Then to approximate the discrete probability $P(X = 1)$, you find the continuous probability $P(0.5 < Y < 1.5)$.

- The interval you need to use with the normal distribution depends on the discrete probability you're trying to find.

- The general idea is always the same — each discrete value $X = b$ covers the continuous interval $b - \frac{1}{2} < Y < b + \frac{1}{2}$.

Discrete	Normal
$P(X = b)$	$P(b - \frac{1}{2} < Y < b + \frac{1}{2})$
$P(X \leq b)$	$P(Y < b + \frac{1}{2})$
$P(X < b)$	$P(Y < b - \frac{1}{2})$
$P(X \geq b)$	$P(Y > b - \frac{1}{2})$
$P(X > b)$	$P(Y > b + \frac{1}{2})$

Exercise 2.1

Q1 A discrete random variable X has possible values 0, 1, 2, 3... X is to be approximated by the normal variable Y. What interval for Y would you use to approximate:
   a) $P(X = 5)$?   b) $P(12 \leq X \leq 15)$?   c) $P(X \leq 10)$?   d) $P(6 < X < 9)$?

Q2 The random variable X follows a binomial distribution. The normal random variable Y is to be used to approximate probabilities for X. Write down the probability for Y that would approximate:
   a) $P(X = 50)$ b) $P(X < 300)$ c) $P(X \geq 99)$ d) $P(144 \leq X < 169)$

Q3 An unfair coin is to be tossed 1000 times and the number of heads (X) recorded. A random variable Y following a normal distribution is to be used to approximate the probabilities below. Write down the probability for Y that would approximate the probability of getting:
   a) exactly 200 heads
   c) less than 300 heads
   e) between 250 and 750 heads (inclusive)

   b) at least 650 heads
   d) exactly 499, 500 or 501 heads
   f) at least 100 heads but less than 900 heads

Normal approximation to a binomial distribution

Certain binomial distributions can be **approximated** by a normal distribution.

Suppose $X \sim B(n, p)$. If (i) $p \approx \frac{1}{2}$, and (ii) n is large,

then X can be approximated by the normal random variable $Y \sim N(np, np(1 - p))$.

Tip: $1 - p$ is sometimes written as q. So $Y \sim N(np, npq)$.

Even if p isn't that close to 0.5, this approximation works well if np and $n(1 - p)$ are both **bigger than 5**.

Examples   The random variable $X \sim B(80, 0.4)$ is to be approximated using the normally distributed random variable $Y \sim N(\mu, \sigma^2)$.

a) **Verify that a normal approximation is appropriate, and specify the distribution of Y.**

   1. Check the conditions. n is fairly large, and p is not far from $\frac{1}{2}$, so a normal approximation is appropriate.

   2. Calculate np and $np(1 - p)$. $\mu = np = 80 \times 0.4 = 32$
      $\sigma^2 = np(1 - p) = 80 \times 0.4 \times 0.6 = 19.2$
      So use the approximation $Y \sim N(32, 19.2)$.

b) **Apply a continuity correction to the probability P(32 < X ≤ 35).**
P(32 < X ≤ 35) means the probability that X is either 33, 34 or 35.
Write down the probability for Y that corresponds to this probability for X.
Using a continuity correction, this corresponds to **P(32.5 < Y < 35.5)**.

c) **Find an approximate value for P(32 < X ≤ 35).**
1. Apply a continuity correction.   P(32 < X ≤ 35) ≈ P(32.5 < Y < 35.5)
2. Use the normal cdf on your calculator: **= 0.2424 to 4 d.p.**

d) **Find an approximate value for P(X < 45).**
1. Apply a continuity correction.   P(X < 45) ≈ P(Y < 44.5)
2. Use the normal cdf on your calculator: **= 0.9978 to 4 d.p.**

Exercise 2.2

Q1 Which of the binomial distributions described below would a normal approximation be suitable for?
Give reasons for your answers.
   a) $X \sim B(600, 0.51)$ b) $X \sim B(100, 0.98)$ c) $X \sim B(100, 0.85)$
   d) $X \sim B(6, 0.5)$ e) $X \sim B(37, 0.7)$ f) $X \sim B(8, 0.62)$

Q2 The normal random variable $Y \sim N(\mu, \sigma^2)$ is to be used to approximate these binomial distributions.
Find μ and σ^2 in each case.
   a) $X \sim B(350, 0.45)$ b) $X \sim B(250, 0.35)$ c) $X \sim B(70, 0.501)$ d) $X \sim B(20, 0.625)$

Q3 The random variable $X \sim B(200, 0.6)$.
Use the normal approximation to the binomial distribution to find:
   a) $P(X < 105)$ b) $P(X = 122)$ c) $P(110 < X < 130)$ d) $P(115 \leq X < 130)$

Normal distributions can be really useful to approximate binomial distributions in **real-life** situations.

 Only 23% of robin chicks survive to adulthood.
A sample of 80 robin chicks are randomly selected.

a) **Using a normal approximation, find the probability that**
at least 30% of the selected chicks survive to adulthood.

1. Define a random variable. If X represents the number of survivors, then $X \sim B(80, 0.23)$.

2. p isn't particularly close to 0.5, so see if $np = 80 \times 0.23 = 18.4$
   np and $n(1 - p)$ are both larger than 5. $n(1 - p) = 80 \times (1 - 0.23) = 61.6$
                                              So a normal approximation is OK.

3. Approximate X with the random $\mu = np = 18.4$
   variable Y using $\mu = np$ $\sigma^2 = np(1 - p) = 18.4 \times (1 - 0.23) = 14.168$
   and $\sigma^2 = np(1 - p)$.   So $Y \sim N(18.4, 14.168)$.

4. Apply a continuity correction.   30% of 80 = 24, so work out $P(X \geq 24)$.
                                    $P(X \geq 24) \approx P(Y > 23.5)$.

5. Use the normal cdf on your calculator. $P(Y > 23.5) = $ **0.0877 to 4 d.p.**

b) **If the survival rate was 18%, use a normal approximation to find the probability that more than three-quarters of the 80 chicks would die.**

1. The distribution of X has changed, so check that a normal approximation is still reasonable.

$np = 80 \times 0.18 = 14.4$
$n(1 - p) = 80 \times (1 - 0.18) = 65.6$.
$np > 5$ and $n(1 - p) > 5$,
so a normal approximation is reasonable.

2. Approximate X with the random variable Y using $\mu = np$ and $\sigma^2 = np(1 - p)$.

$\mu = np = 14.4$
$\sigma^2 = np(1 - p) = 14.4 \times (1 - 0.18) = 11.808$
So $Y \sim N(14.4, 11.808)$.

3. Apply a continuity correction.

The probability that more than three-quarters of the chicks do not survive is $P(X < 20)$.
$P(X < 20) \approx P(Y < 19.5)$.

4. Use the normal cdf on your calculator.

$P(Y < 19.5) = \textbf{0.9311 to 4 d.p.}$

Exercise 2.3

MODELLING

Q1 In a certain village, the probability that a person drives to work is estimated to be 0.8. An environmental group surveys a sample of 80 people from the village to find out if they drive to work. If X represents the number of people in the sample who drive to work:

a) Calculate $P(X = 70)$ using the binomial distribution. Give your answer to four decimal places.

b) Calculate $P(X = 70)$ using a normal approximation. Give your answer to four decimal places.

Q2 It is estimated that 5% of people are carriers of a certain disease. A health authority tests a sample of 1000 people to see if they carry the disease. If more than 75 people test positive they will offer a vaccination to the whole population.

a) Explain why the normal distribution would be a suitable approximation for this distribution.

b) Estimate the probability that the whole population will be offered a vaccination.

3. Choosing Probability Distributions

You might have to **choose** a suitable probability distribution or **explain** why one is appropriate.

Normal Distribution: $X \sim N(\mu, \sigma^2)$

- Conditions: the data must be **continuous** and **symmetrically distributed**, with a **peak** in the **middle** representing the **mean** of the data.

- In this case, the data can be modelled by a **normal distribution** and you can define the **continuous** random variable $X \sim N(\mu, \sigma^2)$, with **mean** μ and **standard deviation** σ. The mean of X (μ) will correspond to the mean of your data.

- The graph of X has **points of inflection** at $x = \mu - \sigma$ and $x = \mu + \sigma$. These points are where the curve changes between concave and convex (see p.310).

- **68%** of the area under the graph of X is between $x = \mu + \sigma$ and $x = \mu - \sigma$. This means that roughly 68% of your data should fall between $x = \mu \pm \sigma$. Similarly, about **95%** of your data should fall between $x = \mu \pm 2\sigma$ and **nearly all** of your data (99.7%) should fall between $x = \mu \pm 3\sigma$.

- You can estimate the **probability** that a data value will fall within a range by using the normal distribution functions on your **calculator**.

Binomial distribution: $X \sim B(n, p)$

- Conditions — the data represents the **number of 'successes'** in a **fixed number** (n) of trials, where each trial involves either '**success**' or '**failure**'.
  — trials are **independent**, and the probability of 'success' (p) is **constant**.

- In this case, the data can be modelled by a **binomial distribution** and you can define the **discrete** random variable $X \sim B(n, p)$.

- The **binomial probability function** is $P(X = x) = \binom{n}{x} \times p^x \times (1 - p)^{n-x}$, for $x = 0, 1, ..., n$.

- Probabilities can be found using **binomial tables** for certain values of n and p (see p.468) or the binomial distribution functions on your **calculator**.

- If n is large and $p \approx \frac{1}{2}$, then your data can also be approximately modelled using a **normal distribution**, $N(np, np(1 - p))$. In this case, you might have to use a **continuity correction**.

 The times taken by runners to finish a 10 km race are normally distributed. Use the diagram to estimate the mean and standard deviation of the times.

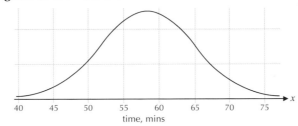

Use the facts about the normal distribution.

1. The mean is in the middle of the data. $\mu \approx \textbf{58 minutes}$

2. Find the point of inflection — where the line changes from concave to convex.   There is a point of inflection at $x = \mu + \sigma$. This is approximately at $x = 65$.

3. Use your values for x and μ to find σ. $65 = 58 + \sigma \implies \sigma = \textbf{7 minutes}$

 A restaurant has several vegetarian meal options on its menu. The probability of any person ordering a vegetarian meal is 0.15. One lunch time, 20 people order a meal.

a) Suggest a suitable model to describe the number of people ordering a vegetarian meal and give the values of any parameters.

There are a fixed number of trials (20 meals), with probability of success (= vegetarian meal) = 0.15. If X is the number of people ordering a vegetarian meal, then $X \sim \textbf{B(20, 0.15)}$.

b) Explain why it wouldn't be suitable to use a normal approximation here.

$n = 20$ is not particularly large and $p = 0.15$ is far away from 0.5 (so $np = 20 \times 0.15 = 3 < 5$).

c) Find the probability that at least 5 people order a vegetarian meal.

1. You need to get a probability in the form $P(X \leq x)$. $P(X \geq 5) = 1 - P(X < 5)$
                                                $= 1 - P(X \leq 4)$

2. Use the binomial table (for $n = 20$ and $p = 0.15$) or your calculator to find $P(X \leq 4)$. $= 1 - 0.8298$
                                                $= \textbf{0.1702}$

Exercise 3.1

Q1 Estimate the mean and standard deviation of the normal distribution shown below.

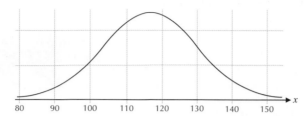

Q2 The speeds of 100 randomly selected cars on a stretch of road are recorded by a speed camera. The table below shows the results.

Speed s, mph	$s < 35$	$35 \leq s < 40$	$40 \leq s < 45$	$45 \leq s < 50$	$50 \leq s < 55$	$55 \leq s < 60$	$s \geq 60$
Frequency	0	3	28	40	27	2	0

a) Explain why it would be reasonable to use a normal distribution to model the cars' speeds.

b) The distribution of cars' speeds on a different stretch of road is shown in the diagram below. Estimate the standard deviation of the speeds.

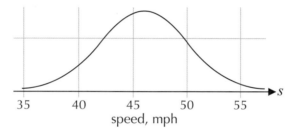

speed, mph

Q3 A tennis player successfully completes a first-serve 65% of the time. Give a suitable distribution to model the number of successful first-serves in each of the situations below. State any parameters.

a) The number of successful first-serves in one game, given that the player attempts 10 first-serves.

b) The number of successful first-serves in one match, given that the player attempts 100 first-serves.

Q4 The masses of 1000 pumpkins are measured and the mean mass is calculated to be 6.5 kg. The distribution of the pumpkins' masses is symmetrical about the mean, with the lightest pumpkin having a mass of 2.0 kg and the heaviest having a mass of 10.9 kg. The standard deviation of the pumpkins' masses is 1.5 kg.

a) Explain why the distribution of the pumpkins' masses could be modelled by a normal distribution.

b) Pumpkins with a mass between 3.0 kg and 9.0 kg (inclusive) are sold to Safeco Supermarkets. Estimate the number of pumpkins from this sample that will be sold to Safeco.

Q5 At a particular test centre, 41% of people pass their driving test on the first attempt. On a random day at the test centre, 11 people are taking their driving test for the first time.

a) Suggest a suitable model to describe the number of people who pass their test first time on the chosen day and give the values of any parameters.

b) Find the probability that between 3 and 6 people (inclusive) pass their driving test at the first attempt on the chosen day.

4. Hypothesis Tests of the Mean of a Population

In Chapter 14 you saw the general theory of **hypothesis testing** and tests for a proportion in a binomial distribution. This section will cover tests of the mean of a population.

You can carry out hypothesis tests of the **mean** of a normal distribution, based on a **random sample** of *n* observations from the population. For a population that is **normally distributed** with **known variance** (i.e. $X \sim N(\mu, \sigma^2)$), here's what you have to do:

1. Identify the **population parameter** you're testing — this will always be the mean, μ.

2. Write down the **null** hypothesis — $\boxed{H_0: \mu = a}$ for some constant *a*.

3. Write down the **alternative** hypothesis, H_1 — this depends on the type of test.

   One-tailed test $\boxed{H_1: \mu < a}$ or $\boxed{H_1: \mu > a}$ Two-tailed test $\boxed{H_1: \mu \neq a}$

4. State the **significance level, α** — you'll usually be given this.

5. Find the value of the **test statistic**, Z:
   — Calculate the **sample mean**, $\bar{x}$.
   — If $X \sim N(\mu, \sigma^2)$, then $\bar{X} \sim N(\mu, \frac{\sigma^2}{n})$, so $Z = \dfrac{\bar{X} - \mu}{\sigma / \sqrt{n}} \sim N(0, 1)$.

   — The value of your **test statistic** will be: $\boxed{z = \dfrac{\bar{x} - \mu}{\sigma / \sqrt{n}}}$

6. Use a **calculator** to test for significance, either by:
   — finding the *p*-value: the **probability** of your test statistic taking a value **at least as extreme** as your observed value, and comparing it to the significance level α.
   — finding the **critical value(s)** of the test statistic and seeing if your observed value lies in the **critical region**.

Tip: Remember, $\bar{X}$ is a random variable representing the mean of any sample. $\bar{x}$ is the mean for a particular sample.

   The times, in minutes, taken by the athletes in a running club to complete a certain run have been found to follow an N(12, 4) distribution.
The coach increases the number of training sessions per week, and a random sample of 20 times run since the increase has a mean of 11.2 minutes.
Assuming that the variance has remained unchanged, test at the 5% level whether there is evidence that the mean time has decreased.

1. Identify the population parameter.

   Let μ = mean time (in minutes) since the increase in training sessions.

2. Write down the hypotheses (this is a one-tailed test).

   $H_0: \mu = 12$ and $H_1: \mu < 12$

3. State the significance level.

   $\alpha = 0.05$

4. Find the value of your test statistic.

   $\bar{x} = 11.2$, so $z = \dfrac{\bar{x} - \mu}{\sigma / \sqrt{n}} = \dfrac{11.2 - 12}{2 / \sqrt{20}} = -1.7888...$

5. Test for significance by finding the *p*-value or finding the critical region.

Method 1: Finding the *p*-value

This is a one-tailed test and values more likely to occur under H$_1$ are at the lower end of the distribution. So the *p*-value is P($Z \leq -1.7888...$).

P($Z \leq -1.7888...$) = 0.0368 < 0.05 (= α), so the result is significant.

Method 2: Finding the critical region

- This is a one-tailed test and the critical region will be at the lower end of the distribution.

  The critical value is z such that P($Z < z$) = 0.05.

- Use your calculator to find z. $z = -1.6449$ (4 d.p.), so the critical region is $Z < -1.6449$.

  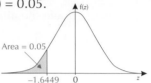
  Area = 0.05
  −1.6449   0

  Since $z = -1.7888... < -1.6449$, the observed value of the test statistic lies in the critical region. So the result is significant.

---

6. Write your conclusion.   **There is evidence at the 5% level of significance to reject H$_0$ and to suggest that the mean time has decreased.**

Example

The volume (in ml) of a cleaning fluid dispensed in each operation by a machine is normally distributed with mean μ and standard deviation 3. Out of a random sample of 20 measured volumes, the mean volume dispensed was 30.9 ml. Does this data provide evidence at the 1% level of significance that the machine is dispensing a mean volume that is different from 30 ml?

1. Identify the population parameter.

   Let μ = mean volume (in ml) dispensed in all possible operations of the machine.

2. Write down the hypotheses (this is a two-tailed test).

   H$_0$: $\mu = 30$ and H$_1$: $\mu \neq 30$

3. State the significance level.

   $\alpha = 0.01$

4. Find the value of your test statistic.

   $\bar{x} = 30.9$, so $z = \dfrac{\bar{x} - \mu}{\sigma / \sqrt{n}} = \dfrac{30.9 - 30}{3 / \sqrt{20}} = 1.3416...$

5. Test for significance by checking whether the *p*-value is less than $\frac{\alpha}{2} = 0.005$.

   P($Z \geq 1.3416...$) = 0.0899 > $\frac{\alpha}{2}$.

   So the result is not significant at the 1% level.

6. Write your conclusion.   **There is no evidence at the 1% level to support the claim that the machine is dispensing a mean volume different from 30 ml.**

If the population variance, σ^2, is **unknown**, you can still do a hypothesis test on the mean. You can use the **sample variance**, s^2 (see p.157), to estimate the **population variance**, σ^2. The sample size has to be **large** ($n > 30$), so that the **sample variance** is close to the population variance.

Most of the method is similar, but you need to replace σ with s in the **test statistic**, Z:

$$Z = \frac{\bar{X} - \mu}{s / \sqrt{n}}$$

Example

The weights of oranges sold in a shop are normally distributed. The mean weight is claimed to be 250 g. Greg wants to test whether the mean weight is different. He measures the weights, X, of a random sample of 40 oranges from the shop. He calculates that the sample mean is 245 g and the sample variance is 100 g. Carry out Greg's test at the 5% level of significance.

1. Identify the population parameter.

Let μ = mean weight (in g) of oranges from the shop.

2. Write down the hypotheses (this is a two-tailed test).

H_0: $\mu = 250$ and H_1: $\mu \neq 250$

3. State the significance level.

$\alpha = 0.05$

4. Find the value of your test statistic.

$\bar{x} = 245$ and $s = \sqrt{100} = 10$,

so $z = \dfrac{\bar{x} - \mu}{s/\sqrt{n}} = \dfrac{245 - 250}{10/\sqrt{40}} = -3.1622...$

5. Test for significance by looking up $p = 0.025$ in the percentage points table.

Critical values are z such that $P(Z > z) = 0.025$ and $-z$ such that $P(Z < -z) = 0.025$. From the percentage points table, $P(Z > 1.96) = 0.025$, so the critical region is $Z < -1.96$ or $Z > 1.96$. $z = -3.1622... < -1.96$, so the result is significant.

6. Write your conclusion.

There is evidence at the 5% level of significance to reject H_0 and to suggest that the mean weight is not 250 g.

Exercise 4.1

MODELLING

Q1 The weight of plums (in grams) from a tree follows the distribution N(42, 16). It is suggested that the weight of plums has increased. A random sample of 25 plums gives a mean weight of 43.5 grams. Assuming the variance has remained unchanged, test this claim at:
a) the 5% significance level   b) the 1% significance level

Q2 Bree plays cards with her friends, and the amount of money she wins each week is normally distributed with a mean, μ, of £24 and standard deviation, σ, of £2. A new friend has joined the game and Bree thinks this will change the amount she wins. In a random sample of 12 weeks the sample mean, $\bar{x}$, was found to be £22.50. Test Bree's claim at the 1% level.

Q3 The marks obtained in a language test by students in a school have followed a normal distribution with mean 70 and variance 64. A teacher suspects that this year the mean score is lower. A sample of 40 students is taken and the mean score is 67.7. Assuming the variance remains unchanged, test the teacher's claim at the 5% level of significance.

Q4 The weights (in grams) of pigeons in a city centre are normally distributed with mean 300 and standard deviation 45. The council claims that this year the city's pigeons are, on average, heavier. A random sample of 25 pigeons gives a mean of 314 g.
a) State the null hypothesis and the alternative hypothesis.
b) State whether it is a one- or two-tailed test.
c) Assuming the variance remains unchanged, use a 1% level of significance to test the hypothesis.

Q5 The waiting times (in minutes) of people queuing for a roller coaster are normally distributed. The mean waiting time is stated to be 18 minutes, but the manager claims that it is actually shorter. Over a week, the waiting times, X, of 100 randomly selected people in the queue are recorded. The sample mean is calculated to be 17.5 minutes and the sample variance is 9 minutes. Test the manager's claim at the 5% level of significance.

Review Exercise — Chapter 28

Q1 If $X \sim N(50, 16)$ find: a) $P(X < 55)$ b) $P(X < 42)$ c) $P(X > 56)$ d) $P(47 < X < 57)$

Q2 If $X \sim N(5, 7^2)$ find: a) $P(X < 0)$ b) $P(X < 1)$ c) $P(X > 7)$ d) $P(2 < X < 4)$

Q3 If $X \sim N(26, 4)$ find: a) $P(X \leq 20)$ b) $P(X \geq 23)$ c) $P(X > 27)$ d) $P(26 < X < 28)$

Q4 Find the probability that:
a) $Z < 0.84$ b) $Z < 2.95$ c) $Z > 0.68$ d) $Z \geq 1.55$
e) $Z < -2.10$ f) $Z \leq -0.01$ g) $Z > 0.10$ h) $Z \leq 0.64$
i) $Z > 0.23$ j) $0.10 < Z \leq 0.50$ k) $-0.62 \leq Z < 1.10$ l) $-0.99 < Z \leq -0.74$

Q5 If $X \sim N(21, 6.25)$, transform X to the standard normal variable to find:
a) $P(X \leq 18)$ b) $P(X > 20)$ c) $P(19 < X < 22)$ d) $P(23 \leq X \leq 25)$

Q6 If $X \sim N(64, 6^2)$ find, to the nearest whole number, the value of x such that:
a) $P(X \leq x) = 0.5$ b) $P(X \geq x) = 0.2525$ c) $P(X > x) = 0.9332$
d) $P(58 < X < x) = 0.4075$ e) $P(51 \leq X \leq x) = 0.0761$ f) $P(x \leq X < 75) = 0.6581$

Q7 $X \sim N(80, 15)$.
a) If $P(X < a) = 0.99$, find a.   b) If $P(|X - 80| < b) = 0.8$, find b.

Q8 Find the value of z if:
a) $P(Z < z) = 0.9131$ b) $P(Z < z) = 0.5871$ c) $P(Z > z) = 0.0359$
d) $P(Z > z) = 0.01$ e) $P(Z \leq z) = 0.4013$ f) $P(Z \geq z) = 0.995$
g) $P(-z < Z < z) = 0.5034$ h) $P(0.25 < Z < z) = 0.3917$ i) $P(z \leq Z \leq 0.5) = 0.2902$

Q9 $X \sim N(\mu, 10)$ and $P(X < 8) = 0.8925$. Find μ.

Q10 $X \sim N(\mu, 8^2)$ and $P(X > 221) = 0.3085$. Find μ.

Q11 $X \sim N(11, \sigma^2)$ and $P(X < 13) = 0.6$. Find σ.

Q12 $X \sim N(108, \sigma^2)$ and $P(X \leq 110) = 0.9678$. Find σ.

Q13 The random variable $X \sim N(\mu, \sigma^2)$.
If $P(X < 15.2) = 0.9783$ and $P(X > 14.8) = 0.1056$, then find μ and σ.

Q14 The masses of items made by a factory are normally distributed with a mean of 55 g and a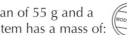
standard deviation of 4.4 g. Find the probability that a randomly chosen item has a mass of:
a) less than 55 g   b) less than 50 g   c) more than 60 g

Q15 The masses of eggs laid by an ostrich are normally distributed with a mean of 1.4 kg
and a standard deviation of 300 g. If 88.3% of the eggs laid by this ostrich have
a mass of less than a kg, find the value of a.

Q16 The weights of apples (in grams) at a greengrocers are modelled by a normal distribution.
The probability that an apple weighs less than 120 g is 0.1147 and the probability that
an apple weighs more than 140 g is 0.1587. Find the mean and standard deviation
of the apples' weights.

Q17 A biased dice is rolled 200 times and the number of sixes, X, is recorded. A random variable Y following a normal distribution is to be used to approximate the probabilities below. Write down the probability for Y that would approximate the probability of getting:

a) $P(X > 100)$ b) $P(X = 110)$ c) $P(90 \leq X \leq 105)$ d) $P(113 \leq X < 119)$

Q18 The random variable X follows a binomial distribution: $X \sim B(100, 0.45)$. Using a normal approximation and continuity corrections, find:

a) $P(X = 50)$ b) $P(X > 50)$ c) $P(X \leq 45)$ d) $P(40 < X \leq 47)$

Q19 The probability that an applicant is accepted into a particular university is 0.28. The university randomly samples 120 applicants to see if they are accepted or not. X is the number of applicants that are successful from the sample:

a) Calculate $P(X = 34)$ using a binomial distribution.

b) Calculate $P(X = 34)$ using a normal approximation.

c) Comment on the accuracy of the normal approximation.

Q20 At a nature reserve, it is estimated that 10% of toads are rare natterjack toads. A random sample of 80 toads is to be collected from the nature reserve.

a) Explain why the normal distribution would be a suitable approximation for this distribution.

b) Use a normal approximation to find the probability that exactly 8 of the toads are natterjacks.

c) Use a normal approximation to find the probability that fewer than 5 of the toads are natterjacks.

Q21 Estimate the mean and standard deviation of the normal distribution represented by this graph:

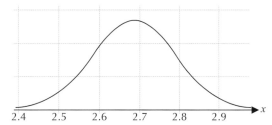

Q22 On a fairground game, a player wins a prize 33% of the time. In an hour, 14 games are played, each by a different random passer-by.

a) Suggest a suitable model to describe the number of prizes won in the hour and give the values of any parameters.

b) Find that probability that between 5 and 10 prizes are won (inclusive).

Q23 Carry out the following test of the mean, μ, of a normal distribution with variance $\sigma^2 = 9$. A random sample of 16 observations from the distribution was taken and the sample mean ($\bar{x}$) calculated.

Test $H_0: \mu = 45$ against $H_1: \mu < 45$, at the 5% significance level, using $\bar{x} = 42$.

Q24 The number of hours that Kyle spends studying each week follows a normal distribution with mean 32 and standard deviation 5. Kyle believes that the mean amount of time he spends studying each week has increased. In a random sample of 20 weeks over the past year, the mean number of hours he spent studying was recorded as 34. Use a 5% and a 1% level to test Kyle's belief. Comment on your answers.

Q25 A random sample of 10 observations is taken from a normal distribution with unknown mean μ and unknown variance σ^2. The sample mean is calculated to be 19.78 and the sample variance is calculated to be 0.811. Test at the 5% level of significance the claim that $\mu < 20$.

Chapter 29 — Kinematics 2

A projectile is an object which has been projected (e.g. thrown or fired) through the air. When you're doing projectile questions, you'll have to consider the motion of the projectile in two dimensions. That means you'll have to split the projectile's velocity into its horizontal and vertical components, then use the constant acceleration equations to find out more information about the projectile's motion.

1. Projectiles

The two components of velocity

When you project a body through the air with **initial speed u**, at an **angle of θ** to the horizontal, it will move along a **curved path**:

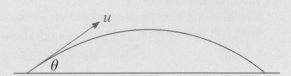

You can use **trigonometry** to resolve the body's initial velocity into its **horizontal** and **vertical components**:

Horizontal component (x):

$\cos \theta = \dfrac{\text{adj}}{\text{hyp}} = \dfrac{x}{u}$, so $x = u \cos \theta$

Vertical component (y):

$\sin \theta = \dfrac{\text{opp}}{\text{hyp}} = \dfrac{y}{u}$, so $y = u \sin \theta$

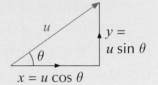

Given the horizontal and vertical components of a projectile's velocity, you can find:

- its **speed** using **Pythagoras' theorem**.
- its **direction of motion** using **trigonometry**.

a) **A ball is thrown with initial speed 9 ms⁻¹ at an angle of 40° above the horizontal. Find the horizontal and vertical components of the ball's initial velocity.**

1. Draw a diagram:

2. Resolving horizontally: Horizontal component = 9 cos 40° = **6.89 ms⁻¹** (3 s.f.)

3. Resolving vertically: Vertical component = 9 sin 40° = **5.79 ms⁻¹** (3 s.f.)

b) **At a particular point on its trajectory, a particle has velocity v, with horizontal component 12 ms⁻¹ and vertical component –5 ms⁻¹. Find the particle's speed, v, and direction of motion at this point.**

Draw a diagram to show the particle's motion.

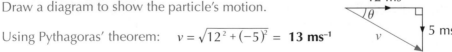

Using Pythagoras' theorem: $v = \sqrt{12^2 + (-5)^2}$ = **13 ms⁻¹**

Using trigonometry: $\theta = \tan^{-1}\left(\dfrac{5}{12}\right)$ = **22.6° (3 s.f.) below the horizontal**
(or 337.4° measured anticlockwise)

Exercise 1.1

Q1 Each of the following diagrams shows the speed of a projectile and the angle its velocity makes with the horizontal. In each case, find the horizontal and vertical components of the projectile's velocity.

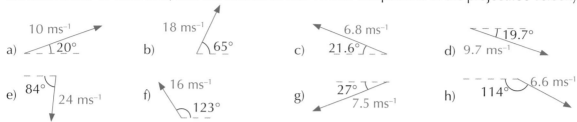

a) 10 ms⁻¹ 20°

b) 18 ms⁻¹ 65°

c) 6.8 ms⁻¹ 21.6°

d) 19.7° 9.7 ms⁻¹

e) 84° 24 ms⁻¹

f) 16 ms⁻¹ 123°

g) 27° 7.5 ms⁻¹

h) 114° 6.6 ms⁻¹

Q2 A particle is moving with speed 8 ms⁻¹ at an angle of 35° above the horizontal. Find the horizontal and vertical components of its velocity.

Q3 A rocket is fired vertically upwards with speed 45 ms⁻¹. Find the horizontal and vertical components of its initial velocity.

Q4 A body is fired at an angle α above the horizontal with speed 22 kmh⁻¹. Find the horizontal and vertical components of its initial velocity, giving your answer in metres per second.

Q5 A ball is thrown with velocity **v**, with horizontal component 6 ms⁻¹ and vertical component 8 ms⁻¹. Find the speed and direction of projection of the ball.

Q6 A particle moves with velocity **u**. The horizontal component of **u** is 17 ms⁻¹ and the vertical component is –2.5 ms⁻¹. Find the magnitude and direction of **u**.

The constant acceleration equations

To solve problems involving projectile motion, you will need to make certain **modelling assumptions**:

- The projectile is moving only under the influence of **gravity** (i.e. there'll be **no external forces** acting on it).
- The projectile is a **particle** — i.e. its weight acts from a single point, so its dimensions don't matter.
- The projectile moves in a **two-dimensional vertical plane** — i.e. it doesn't swerve from side to side.

Because the projectile is modelled as moving only under the influence of gravity, the only acceleration the projectile will experience will be **acceleration due to gravity** (usually **g = 9.8 ms⁻²**, although you might be given other values of **g**).

Acceleration due to gravity acts **vertically downwards**, so it only affects the **vertical component** of the projectile's velocity. The **horizontal component** of the velocity will remain **constant** throughout the motion.

> When **modelling real situations**, consider which of these assumptions would not be **valid**.
>
> For example, a falling parachutist would encounter significant **air resistance**, so the model should ideally allow for this.

To answer a projectiles question, split the vector quantities you know into their **horizontal** and **vertical components**. Then you can deal with the components **separately** using the *suvat* equations (see p.211).

a) **A particle is projected with initial speed 18 ms⁻¹ from a point on horizontal ground, at an angle of 40° above the horizontal. Find the distance of the particle from its point of projection 1.8 seconds after it is projected.**

Consider the horizontal and vertical motion separately.
Remember, there is no horizontal acceleration.

Resolving horizontally, taking right as positive (→):

$s = s_x$, $u = 18 \cos 40°$, $a = 0$, $t = 1.8$

Using $s = ut + \frac{1}{2}at^2$:

$s_x = (18 \cos 40° \times 1.8) + 0 = 24.8198...$

Resolving vertically, taking up as positive (↑):

$s = s_y$, $u = 18 \sin 40°$, $a = -9.8$, $t = 1.8$

Using $s = ut + \frac{1}{2}at^2$:

$s_y = (18 \sin 40° \times 1.8) + (\frac{1}{2} \times -9.8 \times 1.8^2) = 4.9503...$

So the particle's horizontal displacement from its starting point is 24.8198... metres and its vertical displacement is 4.9503... metres. Use Pythagoras' theorem to find its distance from the starting point:

distance $= \sqrt{(24.8198...)^2 + (4.9503...)^2} = \mathbf{25.3\ m}$ (3 s.f.)

b) **A ball is kicked from a point on horizontal ground. The initial velocity of the ball is 23 ms⁻¹, at an angle α to the horizontal. The ball reaches a maximum vertical height above the ground of 4.8 m.**

Find the value of α.

Resolving vertically, taking up as positive (↑):

$s = 4.8$, $u = 23 \sin \alpha$, $v = 0$, $a = -9.8$

When the ball reaches its maximum height, the vertical component of its velocity will momentarily be zero.

Using $v^2 = u^2 + 2as$:

$0 = (23 \sin \alpha)^2 + (2 \times -9.8 \times 4.8)$

$0 = 529 \sin^2 \alpha - 94.08$

$\sin^2 \alpha = 94.08 \div 529 = 0.1778...$

$\sin \alpha = 0.4217... \Rightarrow \alpha = \mathbf{24.9°}$ (3 s.f.)

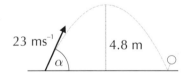

Exercise 1.2

Q1 A projectile is launched from a point on horizontal ground with speed 15 ms⁻¹ at an angle of 50° above the horizontal. Find:

a) the time taken for the projectile to reach its maximum height,

b) the maximum height the projectile reaches above the ground.

Q2 A stone is catapulted with speed 12 ms⁻¹ at an angle of 37° above the horizontal. It hits a target 0.5 seconds after being fired. Find:

a) the stone's horizontal displacement 0.5 seconds after being fired,

b) the stone's vertical displacement 0.5 seconds after being fired,

c) the straight-line distance from the stone's point of projection to the target.

Q3 A ball is kicked from a point on a flat, horizontal field.
It has initial speed 8 ms⁻¹ and leaves the ground at an angle of 59°. Find:
a) the ball's time of flight,   b) the horizontal range of the ball before it hits the ground.

Q4 A particle is projected at an angle θ above the horizontal with speed 18 ms⁻¹.
Given that $\tan \theta = \sqrt{3}$, find:
a) the particle's speed 2 seconds after being projected,
b) the direction of motion of the particle at this time.

Q5
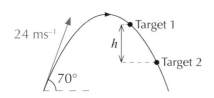

A ball is fired from a machine with speed 24 ms⁻¹ at an angle of 70° above the horizontal.
The ball passes through a target 3 seconds after being fired, and then passes through a second
target 4 seconds after being fired. Find h, the difference in height between the two targets.

Q6 A ball is hit by a bat from a point on flat, horizontal ground. The ball leaves the
ground with speed V ms⁻¹, at an angle of θ above the horizontal, where $\tan \theta = \frac{3}{4}$.
The ball lands a horizontal distance of 50 m away. Find the value of V.

Q7 A golf ball is struck by a golf club from a point on flat, horizontal ground.
It leaves the ground at an angle of 40° to the horizontal. 2 seconds after being struck,
the ball is travelling upwards at an angle of 10° to the horizontal. Find:
a) the ball's speed of projection,
b) the height of the ball above the ground 2 seconds after being struck by the golf club.

Projection problems may involve a particle being **projected horizontally** from a
height above the ground. Here, remember that the initial vertical velocity is 0.

   **A stone is thrown horizontally
with speed 10 ms⁻¹ from a height
of 2 m above horizontal ground.**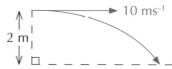

a) **Find the speed and direction of motion of the stone after 0.5 seconds.**

1. Consider the vertical and
   horizontal motion separately.

   Resolving vertically, taking
   down as positive ($\downarrow$):
   $u = 0, \quad v_y = ?, \quad a = 9.8, \quad t = 0.5$
   Using $v = u + at$: $v_y = 9.8 \times 0.5 = 4.9$ ms⁻¹

2. The horizontal component of velocity is constant,
   as there is no acceleration horizontally:

   $v_x = u_x = 10$ ms⁻¹.

3. You can now find the speed and direction of
   motion of the stone at this time.

   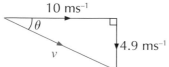

   $v = \sqrt{10^2 + (-4.9)^2} = \textbf{11.1 ms}^{-1}$ (3 s.f.)
   $\tan \theta = \frac{4.9}{10}$
   $\Rightarrow \theta = \textbf{26.1°}$ (3 s.f.)
   below the horizontal

b) Find the stone's horizontal displacement when it lands on the ground.

1. First, you need to find
   the length of time that the
   stone is in the air before it lands.

   Resolving vertically, taking down ($\downarrow$) as positive:
   $s = 2$, $u = 0$, $a = 9.8$, $t = ?$
   Using $s = ut + \frac{1}{2}at^2$:
   $2 = \frac{1}{2} \times 9.8 \times t^2 \Rightarrow t^2 = 0.4081... \Rightarrow t = 0.6388...$ s

2. Now you know how long the stone
   is in the air, you can find its
   horizontal displacement in this time.

   Resolving horizontally, taking right ($\rightarrow$) as positive:
   $s = ?$, $u = 10$, $a = 0$, $t = 0.6388...$
   Using $s = ut + \frac{1}{2}at^2$:
   $s = 10 \times 0.6388... = \textbf{6.39 m}$ (3 s.f.)

Exercise 1.3

Q1   A bullet is fired horizontally at a speed of 80 ms⁻¹ from the edge
     of a vertical cliff 40 m above sea level, as shown.

     a) How long after being fired does the bullet hit the sea?

     b) Find the horizontal distance from the bottom of the cliff
        to the point that the bullet hits the sea.

     c) Suggest how the model used to calculate the bullet's motion in air
        should be refined to calculate its motion in the water.

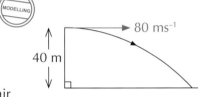

Q2   A rifle fires a bullet horizontally at 145 ms⁻¹. The bullet hits a target
     a horizontal distance of 100 m from the rifle. Find the vertical
     distance, d, between the rifle and where the bullet hits the target.

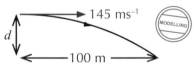

Q3   A man throws a cabbage horizontally from the top of a cliff. The cliff is 215 m high.
     The cabbage strikes the sea 179 m from the base of the cliff. Ignoring air resistance, calculate
     the speed at which the cabbage is thrown. Give your answer to three significant figures.

In trickier problems, the particle is projected **at an angle** from an **initial height** above the ground.
In these cases you must be careful selecting a value for s when resolving vertically.

   A particle is used to model a ball thrown at a velocity of 30 ms⁻¹ at an angle
of 25° above the horizontal, from a height of 1.5 m above horizontal ground.

a)   Calculate how long the ball is in the air before it hits the ground.

1. The ground is 1.5 m below
   where the ball is projected
   from, so let $s = 1.5$ m.

   Resolving vertically, taking down as positive ($\downarrow$):
   $s = 1.5$ m, $u = -30\sin 25$, $a = 9.8$, $t = ?$

   Using $s = ut + \frac{1}{2}at^2$:
   $1.5 = -(30\sin 25)t + 4.9t^2$
   $\Rightarrow 4.9t^2 - (30\sin 25)t - 1.5 = 0.$

   Using the quadratic formula:
   $$t = \frac{12.67... \pm \sqrt{(-12.67...)^2 - 4 \times 4.9 \times (-1.5)}}{2 \times (4.9)}$$
   $\Rightarrow t = -0.113...$ or $2.700...$

2. Ignore the negative value of t.

   The ball is in the air for **2.7 s** (1 d.p.).

b) Find the length of time the ball is at least 5 m above the ground.

1. Find when the ball is exactly 5 m above the ground by setting $s = 3.5$m

Resolving vertically, taking up ($\uparrow$) as positive:
$s = 3.5$, $u = 30 \sin 25°$, $a = -9.8$, $t = ?$

Using $s = ut + \frac{1}{2}at^2$:

$$3.5 = (30 \sin 25° \times t) + (\tfrac{1}{2} \times -9.8 \times t^2)$$

This gives a quadratic in t to solve. $\longrightarrow$ $\Rightarrow 4.9t^2 - (12.67...)t + 3.5 = 0$

Using the quadratic formula:

$$t = \frac{12.67... \pm \sqrt{(-12.67...)^2 - (4 \times 4.9 \times 3.5)}}{9.8}$$

$\Rightarrow$ $t = 0.314...$ or $t = 2.273...$

2. So the ball is exactly 5 m above the ground 0.314... seconds after being thrown, and again 2.273... seconds after being thrown:

0.314... s   2.273... s
5 m   5 m

3. So the length of time that the ball is at least 5 m above the ground is:

$2.273... - 0.314... = \mathbf{1.96\ s}$ (3 s.f.)

c) Calculate the particle's horizontal range.

Use the value of t calculated in part a) to find the particle's horizontal displacement when it hits the ground.

Resolving horizontally , taking right as positive ($\rightarrow$):
$s = ?$, $u = 30\cos 25°$, $a = 0$, $t = 2.700...$ s

Using $s = ut + \frac{1}{2}at^2$:
$s = 30\cos 25° \times 2.700...$ $\Rightarrow$ $s = \mathbf{73.4\ m}$ (1 d.p.)

Exercise 1.4

Q1

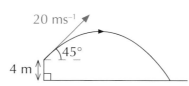

20 ms⁻¹

45°

4 m

An object is fired from a point 4 m directly above flat, horizontal ground. It has initial speed 20 ms⁻¹ at an angle of 45° above the horizontal. For how long is it higher than 11 m above the ground?

Q2   A particle is projected from a point 0.6 m above flat, horizontal ground. The particle's initial speed is 7.5 ms⁻¹ at an angle of α above the horizontal. It reaches a maximum height of 2.8 m above the ground. Find the horizontal distance travelled by the particle in the first 1.2 seconds of its motion.

Q2 A particle is projected from a point on flat, horizontal ground with speed V ms^{-1} at an angle of α above the horizontal. Using a suitable trigonometrical identity, show that the horizontal range $x = V^2 \dfrac{\sin 2\alpha}{9.8}$.

Q3 A projectile is moving relative to the x- and y-coordinate axes. The projectile is fired from the origin with speed 3 ms^{-1}, at an angle α above the x-axis. The projectile moves freely under gravity and passes through the point (3, 1) m. Show that:

$$1 = 3 \tan \alpha - \frac{g}{2 \cos^2 \alpha}$$

Q4 The flight of a golf ball is modelled as a particle projected with initial speed u ms^{-1} at an angle α. When the ball has horizontal displacement x, its vertical displacement is y.

a) Show that $x = (u\cos \alpha)t$ and $y = (u\sin \alpha)t - \dfrac{g}{2}t^2$

b) Hence, show that the equation of the path of the projectile is $y = x\tan \alpha - \dfrac{gx^2}{2u^2 \cos^2 \alpha}$.

c) The golf ball is struck with an angle of 60°, and passes through the point (4, 2). What was the initial speed of the ball?

i and j vectors

You can describe projectile motion in terms of the **unit vectors i** and **j** — the **i**-component of the vector describes the **horizontal** motion of the projectile, and the **j**-component of the vector describes the **vertical** motion of the projectile.

When you're using **i** and **j** vectors you can either consider horizontal and vertical motion **separately**, as before, or you can deal with both components in one go using the *suvat* equations in **vector form**:

$\mathbf{v} = \mathbf{u} + \mathbf{a}t$	$\mathbf{s} = \mathbf{u}t + \frac{1}{2}\mathbf{a}t^2$
$\mathbf{s} = \frac{1}{2}(\mathbf{u} + \mathbf{v})t$	$\mathbf{s} = \mathbf{v}t - \frac{1}{2}\mathbf{a}t^2$

If you're using the *suvat* equations in vector form, then acceleration due to gravity will be $\mathbf{a} = -g\mathbf{j}$ ($= -9.8\mathbf{j}$ ms^{-2}).

Tip: $v^2 = u^2 + 2as$ doesn't have a vector equivalent, as you can't really square a vector.

Example

A particle is projected from the point 5**j** m, relative to a fixed origin *O*. The particle's initial velocity is (7**i** + 3**j**) ms^{-1}, and it moves freely under gravity.

a) Find the position vector of the particle 0.8 seconds after it is projected.

1. Write down the *suvat* values:　　$\mathbf{s} = ?,$　　$\mathbf{u} = (7\mathbf{i} + 3\mathbf{j}),$　　$\mathbf{a} = -9.8\mathbf{j},$　　$t = 0.8$

Using $\mathbf{s} = \mathbf{u}t + \frac{1}{2}\mathbf{a}t^2$:

$\mathbf{s} = 0.8(7\mathbf{i} + 3\mathbf{j}) - \dfrac{1}{2} \times (9.8\mathbf{j}) \times 0.8^2$

$= 5.6\mathbf{i} + 2.4\mathbf{j} - 3.136\mathbf{j} = (5.6\mathbf{i} - 0.736\mathbf{j})$ m

2. This is the particle's displacement from the point of projection 0.8 seconds after it is projected. Add this to its initial position vector to find its new position vector:

Position vector after 0.8 s is: $5\mathbf{j} + 5.6\mathbf{i} - 0.736\mathbf{j} = (5.6\mathbf{i} + 4.264\mathbf{j})$ m

b) Find the velocity of the particle at this time.

Using $\mathbf{v} = \mathbf{u} + \mathbf{a}t$:　　　　$\mathbf{v} = (7\mathbf{i} + 3\mathbf{j}) + 0.8(-9.8\mathbf{j})$

$= 7\mathbf{i} + 3\mathbf{j} - 7.84\mathbf{j} = (7\mathbf{i} - 4.84\mathbf{j})$ ms^{-1}

Example A stone is launched from a point 1.2 metres vertically above the point O, which is on flat, horizontal ground.

The stone is launched with velocity $\begin{pmatrix} 2q \\ q \end{pmatrix}$ ms⁻¹, where q is a constant.

It travels freely under gravity for 4 seconds, before landing on the ground.

a) **Find the value of q and hence the initial speed of the stone.**

1. First, find the initial velocity.

The distance from the stone's starting point to the ground is 1.2 m.

$\begin{pmatrix} 2q \\ q \end{pmatrix}$

1.2 m ⟶ O

O

Resolving vertically, taking up as positive (↑):
$$s = -1.2, \quad u = q, \quad a = -9.8, \quad t = 4$$
Using $s = ut + \frac{1}{2}at^2$:
$$-1.2 = 4q + (-4.9 \times 4^2) \implies 4q = 77.2$$
$$\implies q = 19.3$$

So the stone's initial velocity is $\begin{pmatrix} 38.6 \\ 19.3 \end{pmatrix}$ ms⁻¹.

2. Now you can find its initial speed using Pythagoras' theorem:

$$\text{Speed} = \sqrt{38.6^2 + 19.3^2}$$
$$= \textbf{43.2 ms}^{-1} \text{ (3 s.f.)}$$

b) **Find the horizontal range of the stone.**

Use the initial velocity from part a):

Resolving horizontally, taking right as positive (→):
$$s = ?, \quad u = 38.6, \quad a = 0, \quad t = 4$$
Using $s = ut + \frac{1}{2}at^2$:
$$s = 38.6 \times 4 = \textbf{154.4 m}$$

c) **Find the position vector of the stone relative to O when it is at its highest point.**

First consider only the vertical motion to find the time taken for the stone to reach its maximum height.

Resolving vertically, taking up as positive (↑):
$$u = 19.3, \quad v = 0, \quad a = -9.8, \quad t = ?$$
Using $v = u + at$:
$$0 = 19.3 - 9.8t \implies \textbf{\textit{t} = 1.969... seconds}$$

Use the *suvat* equations in column vector form to find **s** at the highest point.

$$\mathbf{s} = ?, \quad \mathbf{u} = \begin{pmatrix} 38.6 \\ 19.3 \end{pmatrix}, \quad \mathbf{a} = \begin{pmatrix} 0 \\ -9.8 \end{pmatrix}, \quad t = 1.969...$$

Using $\mathbf{s} = \mathbf{u}t + \frac{1}{2}\mathbf{a}t^2$:

$$\mathbf{s} = (1.969...) \times \begin{pmatrix} 38.6 \\ 19.3 \end{pmatrix} + \frac{1}{2} \times (1.969...^2) \times \begin{pmatrix} 0 \\ -9.8 \end{pmatrix}$$

$$\mathbf{s} = \begin{pmatrix} 76.01... \\ 38.00... \end{pmatrix} + \begin{pmatrix} 0 \\ -19.00... \end{pmatrix} = \begin{pmatrix} 76.01... \\ 19.00... \end{pmatrix} \text{ m}$$

This is the stone's displacement from its starting point at its highest point. Add it to the stone's initial position vector to find the new position vector.

So the position vector relative to O is:

$$\begin{pmatrix} 0 \\ 1.2 \end{pmatrix} + \begin{pmatrix} 76.01... \\ 19.00... \end{pmatrix} = \begin{pmatrix} 76.01... \\ 20.20... \end{pmatrix} = \begin{pmatrix} \textbf{76.0} \\ \textbf{20.2} \end{pmatrix} \text{ m (3 s.f.)}$$

Exercise 1.6

Q1 A particle is projected from a point on flat, horizontal ground with velocity $(12\mathbf{i} + 16\mathbf{j})$ ms^{-1}.
Find the particle's velocity:

a) 2 seconds after projection,   b) when it reaches its maximum height,   c) when it hits the ground.

Q2 A projectile is fired from a height of 5 m directly above a fixed point O, which is on flat,

horizontal ground. The particle's initial velocity is $\begin{pmatrix} 17 \\ 10 \end{pmatrix}$ ms^{-1}. Find:

a) the particle's maximum height above the ground,

b) the speed of the particle as it hits the ground,

c) the direction of motion of the particle when it hits the ground.

Q3 A stone is thrown with velocity $(6\mathbf{i} + 9\mathbf{j})$ ms^{-1} from a window 2.5 m vertically above flat, horizontal ground. It is thrown towards a target on the ground, a horizontal distance of 20 m from the window.

a) Find the length of time that the stone is at least 6 m above the ground.

b) Find the distance by which the stone falls short of the target.

Q4 A golf ball is hit off the edge of a 40 m high vertical cliff with velocity $(a\mathbf{i} + b\mathbf{j})$ ms^{-1}, where a and b are constants. It takes 5 seconds to land on the ground below, level with the foot of the cliff, a horizontal distance of 200 m away. Find:

a) the values of a and b,

b) the velocity of the golf ball when it hits the ground.

Q5 A football is kicked from a point on flat, horizontal ground towards a vertical wall, a horizontal distance of 15 m away. The ball's initial velocity is $\mathbf{u}$ ms^{-1}. The ball hits the wall 6 m above the ground, 3 seconds after being kicked.

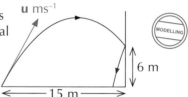

Find, as vectors in $\mathbf{i} + \mathbf{j}$ notation:

a) the initial velocity of the ball,   b) the velocity of the ball as it hits the wall.

The ball rebounds from the wall and lands on the ground. As a result of the impact with the wall, the horizontal component of the ball's velocity is reversed and halved in magnitude. The vertical component of its velocity is unaffected by the impact.

c) Find the horizontal distance between the wall and the point on the ground where the ball lands.

d) Suggest how the model you have used could be improved.

Q6 A submarine is moving underwater at a constant depth, with an initial velocity at time $t = 0$ of $(-0.6\mathbf{i} + 3\mathbf{j})$ ms^{-1}, where the $\mathbf{i}$ direction is due east and the $\mathbf{j}$ direction due north. The submarine is modelled as a particle moving with constant acceleration of $(0.1\mathbf{i} + 0.5\mathbf{j})$ ms^{-2}.

a) At what value of t will the submarine be moving due north?

b) Find the approximate bearing on which the submarine is moving at $t = 2.5$ s.

c) Find the distance of the submarine from its starting point after 1 minute.

d) Suggest two adaptations that would allow the model to better represent the movement of an object underwater.

Q7 A particle moves across a horizontal surface with a constant, non-zero acceleration of $(p\mathbf{i} + q\mathbf{j})$ ms^{-2}, where the $\mathbf{i}$ direction is due east and the $\mathbf{j}$ direction due north. At $t = 0$, the particle is moving north-west with a speed of 5 ms^{-1}. After 10 seconds, it is moving due south with a speed of $\sqrt{2}$ ms^{-1}.

Find p and q, in simplified surd form.

2. Non-Uniform Acceleration in 2 Dimensions

Using vectors

You've just seen how to use the *suvat* equations in vector form on page 426, but if the body is moving with **variable acceleration**, you'll have to use **calculus** instead.

The relationships between **displacement** (or **position**), **velocity** and **acceleration** are shown to the right.

To differentiate or integrate vectors written in **i** and **j** notation, just differentiate or integrate each component **separately**:

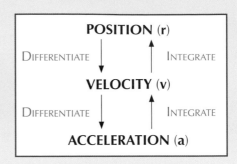

POSITION (r)

DIFFERENTIATE ↓   INTEGRATE ↑

VELOCITY (v)

DIFFERENTIATE ↓   INTEGRATE ↑

ACCELERATION (a)

For position vector: $\mathbf{r} = x\mathbf{i} + y\mathbf{j}$

Velocity $\mathbf{v} = \dfrac{d\mathbf{r}}{dt} = \dfrac{dx}{dt}\mathbf{i} + \dfrac{dy}{dt}\mathbf{j}$

Acceleration, $\mathbf{a} = \dfrac{d\mathbf{v}}{dt} = \dfrac{d^2\mathbf{r}}{dt^2} = \dfrac{d^2x}{dt^2}\mathbf{i} + \dfrac{d^2y}{dt^2}\mathbf{j}$

For acceleration $\mathbf{a} = p\mathbf{i} + q\mathbf{j}$:

$\mathbf{v} = \displaystyle\int \mathbf{a}\,dt = \int (p\mathbf{i} + q\mathbf{j})\,dt = \left(\int p\,dt\right)\mathbf{i} + \left(\int q\,dt\right)\mathbf{j}$

For velocity $\mathbf{v} = w\mathbf{i} + z\mathbf{j}$:

$\mathbf{r} = \displaystyle\int \mathbf{v}\,dt = \int (w\mathbf{i} + z\mathbf{j})\,dt = \left(\int w\,dt\right)\mathbf{i} + \left(\int z\,dt\right)\mathbf{j}$

Tip: The shorthand for $\dfrac{d\mathbf{r}}{dt}$ is $\dot{\mathbf{r}}$ (the single dot means differentiate **r** once with respect to time).

The shorthand for $\dfrac{d^2\mathbf{r}}{dt^2}$ is $\ddot{\mathbf{r}}$ (the double dots mean differentiate **r** twice with respect to time).

Example
A particle is moving in a plane. At time *t* seconds, its position in the plane is given by r = [(t^2 – 1)i + (2 + 5*t*)j] m relative to a fixed origin *O*.

Find the particle's speed and direction of motion at time *t* = 7.5 seconds.

1. Differentiate the expression for the particle's position vector to find its velocity. Remember to treat the **i** and **j** components separately.

   $\mathbf{v} = \dfrac{d\mathbf{r}}{dt} = \left[\dfrac{d}{dt}(t^2 - 1)\right]\mathbf{i} + \left[\dfrac{d}{dt}(2 + 5t)\right]\mathbf{j}$

   $= [2t\mathbf{i} + 5\mathbf{j}] \text{ ms}^{-1}$

2. Substitute *t* = 7.5 into this expression.

   $t = 7.5 \Rightarrow \mathbf{v} = 2(7.5)\mathbf{i} + 5\mathbf{j} = (15\mathbf{i} + 5\mathbf{j})$ m

3. Use the **i** and **j** components to draw a right-angled triangle.

   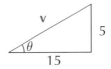

4. Now use Pythagoras' theorem to find the particle's speed, and trigonometry to find its direction of motion.

   Speed $= |\mathbf{v}| = \sqrt{15^2 + 5^2} = 15.8 \text{ ms}^{-1}$ (3 s.f.)

   $\theta = \tan^{-1}\left(\dfrac{5}{15}\right)$

   $= \mathbf{18.4°}$ (3 s.f.)

   anticlockwise from the **i**-direction

Exercise 2.1

Q1 A particle is moving in a plane. At time t seconds, the particle's position relative to a fixed origin O is given by $\mathbf{r} = [(t^3 - 3t)\mathbf{i} + (t^2 + 2)\mathbf{j}]$ m. Find:

a) (i) an expression for the particle's velocity in terms of t,

   (ii) the particle's speed and direction of motion at time $t = 3$ s,

b) (i) an expression for the particle's acceleration in terms of t,

   (ii) the magnitude of the particle's acceleration at time $t = 4$ s.

Q2 A particle is moving in a vertical plane so that at time t seconds it has velocity $\mathbf{v}$ ms^{-1}, where $\mathbf{v} = (2 + 4t^2)\mathbf{i} + (t - 3)\mathbf{j}$. Find the acceleration of the particle at time $t = 8$ s.

Q3 A car is modelled as a particle travelling in a plane. Its velocity at time t seconds is given by the expression $\mathbf{v} = [(\frac{1}{3}t^3 + 2t^2 - 12t)\mathbf{i} + 14\mathbf{j}]$ ms^{-1}, where $0 \leq t \leq 4$. At a certain time, the car reaches its maximum velocity when the acceleration falls to zero. Find the car's velocity at this time.

When **integrating** (to find velocity from acceleration, or displacement from velocity) remember to include the **constant of integration**. You'll normally be given **initial conditions** that will allow you to find its value.

A particle is moving in a vertical plane so that at time t seconds it has velocity v ms^{-1}, where $v = (8 + 2t)\mathbf{i} + (t^3 - 6t)\mathbf{j}$. When $t = 2$, the particle has position vector $(10\mathbf{i} + 3\mathbf{j})$ m with respect to a fixed origin O.

a) **Find the acceleration of the particle at time t.**

Differentiate the expression for velocity with respect to time.

$$\mathbf{a} = \frac{d\mathbf{v}}{dt} = \left[\frac{d}{dt}(8 + 2t)\right]\mathbf{i} + \left[\frac{d}{dt}(t^3 - 6t)\right]\mathbf{j}$$
$$= [2\mathbf{i} + (3t^2 - 6)\mathbf{j}] \text{ ms}^{-2}$$

b) **Show that the position vector of the particle when $t = 4$ is $\mathbf{r} = (38\mathbf{i} + 27\mathbf{j})$ m.**

1. Integrate the expression for velocity with respect to time:

$$\mathbf{r} = \int \mathbf{v}\, dt = \left(\int (8 + 2t)dt\right)\mathbf{i} + \left(\int (t^3 - 6t)dt\right)\mathbf{j}$$
$$= (8t + t^2)\mathbf{i} + \left(\frac{t^4}{4} - 3t^2\right)\mathbf{j} + \mathbf{C}$$

2. When $t = 2$, $\mathbf{r} = (10\mathbf{i} + 3\mathbf{j})$. Use these values to find $\mathbf{C}$:

$$10\mathbf{i} + 3\mathbf{j} = (8(2) + 2^2)\mathbf{i} + \left(\frac{2^4}{4} - 3(2)^2\right)\mathbf{j} + \mathbf{C}$$
$$10\mathbf{i} + 3\mathbf{j} = 20\mathbf{i} - 8\mathbf{j} + \mathbf{C}$$
$$\Rightarrow \mathbf{C} = (10 - 20)\mathbf{i} + (3 - -8)\mathbf{j} = -10\mathbf{i} + 11\mathbf{j}$$
$$\Rightarrow \mathbf{r} = \left[(8t + t^2 - 10)\mathbf{i} + \left(\frac{t^4}{4} - 3t^2 + 11\right)\mathbf{j}\right] \text{ m}$$

3. Substitute $t = 4$ into the equation:

$$t = 4 \Rightarrow \mathbf{r} = (8(4) + 4^2 - 10)\mathbf{i} + \left(\frac{4^4}{4} - 3(4)^2 + 11\right)\mathbf{j}$$
$$= (32 + 16 - 10)\mathbf{i} + (64 - 48 + 11)\mathbf{j}$$
$$= (38\mathbf{i} + 27\mathbf{j}) \text{ m} \quad \text{— as required.}$$

c) Find the value of *t* for which the particle is directly above *O*.

1. When the particle is directly above *O*, the
   i-component of its position vector is zero: $8t + t^2 - 10 = 0$

2. Solve for *t* using the quadratic formula:

$$t = \frac{-8 \pm \sqrt{8^2 - (4 \times 1 \times -10)}}{2}$$

$$\Rightarrow t = 1.099\ldots \quad \text{or} \quad t = -9.099\ldots \text{ (ignore)}$$

3. Check that the **j**-component of **r** is
   greater than zero for $t = 1.099\ldots$

$$\frac{(1.099\ldots)^4}{4} - 3(1.099\ldots)^2 + 11 = 7.741\ldots > 0$$

So the particle is directly
above *O* when **t = 1.10 s** (3 s.f.).

Exercise 2.2

Q1 A particle is moving in a vertical plane so that at time *t* seconds it has velocity **v** ms⁻¹,
where $\mathbf{v} = (3 - 6t)\mathbf{i} + (t^2 + 2t)\mathbf{j}$. When $t = 2$, the particle has position vector $(-2\mathbf{i} + 7\mathbf{j})$ m
with respect to a fixed origin *O*.

a) Find the acceleration of the particle at time $t = 5$ s.

b) Find the value of *t* for which the particle is directly above *O*.

Q2 A particle is moving in a plane. At time *t* seconds, the particle's acceleration is given by
$\mathbf{a} = [(2t - 1)\mathbf{i} + (t^2 + t)\mathbf{j}]$ ms⁻². When $t = 3$ s, the particle has velocity $7(\mathbf{i} + 2\mathbf{j})$ ms⁻¹. Find:

a) an expression for the particle's velocity in terms of *t*,

b) the particle's speed and direction of motion at time $t = 5$ s.

Q3 The velocity of a particle at time *t* seconds ($t \geq 0$) is given by $\mathbf{v} = [(t^2 - 6t)\mathbf{i} + (4t + 5)\mathbf{j}]$ ms⁻¹.
The particle is moving in a plane, and at time $t = 0$ the particle passes through the origin, *O*.
The particle passes through the point with position vector $(b\mathbf{i} + 12\mathbf{j})$ m, where *b* is a constant.
Find the value of *b*.

Q4 The velocity of a particle at time *t* seconds ($t \geq 0$) is given by $\mathbf{v} = -\mathbf{i} + (8t + 2)\mathbf{j}$ ms⁻¹.
The particle's displacement at $t = 1$ s is $\mathbf{r} = (4\mathbf{i} + 12\mathbf{j})$ m.

a) Find the particle's displacement **r** at time *t*.

b) Show that the Cartesian equation representing the particle's path is $y = 4x^2 - 42x + 116$.

Q5 Particle *A* is moving in a vertical plane. At time *t* seconds, the particle's position relative to a fixed
origin *O* is given by $\mathbf{r}_A = [(t^3 - t^2 - 4t + 3)\mathbf{i} + (t^3 - 2t^2 + 3t - 7)\mathbf{j}]$ m. Find:

a) the value of *t* for which the particle's velocity is $(-3\mathbf{i} + 2\mathbf{j})$ ms⁻¹,

b) the value of *t* for which the direction of motion of the particle is 45° above **i**.

A second particle, *B*, is moving in the same plane as particle *A*. At time *t* seconds,
the acceleration of *B* is given by $\mathbf{a}_B = (6t\mathbf{i} + 6t\mathbf{j})$ ms⁻². At time $t = 1$ second,
B passes the point $(2\mathbf{i} + 3\mathbf{j})$ m relative to *O*, with velocity $(4\mathbf{i} - \mathbf{j})$ ms⁻¹. Find:

c) an expression for the position vector of particle *B* relative to *O* in terms of *t*,

d) an expression for the position vector of particle *B* relative to particle *A* in terms of *t*,

e) the distance between particles *A* and *B* at time $t = 4$ seconds.

Some of the functions of t might be more complicated, like exponentials or trig functions.

Example A boat is modelled as a particle moving across a horizontal surface with acceleration a = ($e^{0.2t}$ i + sin t j) ms^{-2} at time t seconds (for $0 \leq t \leq 5$). At time $t = 0$, the boat is at 2j m from the origin, moving in the positive j direction at a speed of 10 ms^{-1}. Find an expression for the boat's position vector, r, at time t. (MODELLING)

1. Integrate with respect to time to find an expression for velocity:

$$\mathbf{v} = \int \mathbf{a}\, dt = \left(\int e^{0.2t} dt\right)\mathbf{i} + \left(\int \sin t\, dt\right)\mathbf{j}$$
$$= \left(\frac{e^{0.2t}}{0.2}\right)\mathbf{i} - (\cos t)\mathbf{j} + \mathbf{C} = 5e^{0.2t}\,\mathbf{i} - (\cos t)\mathbf{j} + \mathbf{C}$$

2. When $t = 0$, v = 0i + 10j. Use this information to find C, and hence v:

$$0\mathbf{i} + 10\mathbf{j} = 5e^0\,\mathbf{i} - (\cos 0)\mathbf{j} + \mathbf{C}$$
$$\Rightarrow 0\mathbf{i} + 10\mathbf{j} = 5\mathbf{i} - 1\mathbf{j} + \mathbf{C} \Rightarrow \mathbf{C} = -5\mathbf{i} + 11\mathbf{j}$$
So, v = $(5e^{0.2t} - 5)\mathbf{i} + (-\cos t + 11)\mathbf{j}$
$= 5(e^{0.2t} - 1)\mathbf{i} + (11 - \cos t)\mathbf{j}$

3. Integrate again to find an expression for the position vector r at time t:

$$\mathbf{r} = \int \mathbf{v}\, dt = \left(\int 5(e^{0.2t} - 1)dt\right)\mathbf{i} + \left(\int (11 - \cos t)dt\right)\mathbf{j}$$
$$= 5\left(\frac{e^{0.2t}}{0.2} - t\right)\mathbf{i} + (11t - \sin t)\mathbf{j} + \mathbf{D}$$
$$= 5(5e^{0.2t} - t)\mathbf{i} + (11t - \sin t)\mathbf{j} + \mathbf{D}$$

4. When $t = 0$, the boat is at r = 2j. Use this information to find D, and hence r:

$0\mathbf{i} + 2\mathbf{j} = 5(5e^0 - 0)\mathbf{i} + (0 - \sin 0)\mathbf{j} + \mathbf{D}$
$0\mathbf{i} + 2\mathbf{j} = 25\mathbf{i} + 0\mathbf{j} + \mathbf{D} \Rightarrow \mathbf{D} = -25\mathbf{i} + 2\mathbf{j}$
$\Rightarrow \mathbf{r} = (5(5e^{0.2t} - t) - 25)\mathbf{i} + (11t - \sin t + 2)\mathbf{j}$
$= 5(5e^{0.2t} - t - 5)\mathbf{i} + (2 + 11t - \sin t)\mathbf{j}$

Exercise 2.3

Q1 A body is moving in a plane. At time t seconds, the body's acceleration is given by $\mathbf{a} = \begin{pmatrix} 3e^{3t} \\ 6 \\ \sqrt{t} \end{pmatrix}$ ms^{-2}.

At $t = 0$, the body has position vector $\mathbf{r} = \begin{pmatrix} 2 \\ -9 \end{pmatrix}$ m relative to a fixed origin O, and is travelling at $\begin{pmatrix} 4 \\ 6 \end{pmatrix}$ ms^{-1}. Find:

a) a column vector expression for the body's velocity in terms of t,

b) the body's position vector, as a column vector, in terms of t.

Q2 An object is travelling in a plane with non-uniform acceleration. At time t seconds, the object's position relative to a fixed origin O is given by $\mathbf{r} = [(\sin t)\mathbf{i} + (\cos t)\mathbf{j}]$ m. i and j are the unit vectors directed due east and due north respectively. Angles in this question are in radians.

a) What is the first non-zero value of t for which the object is moving in an easterly direction?

b) Describe the object's position and distance from O at this time.

Q3 A particle moves so that it traces a curve C, as defined by the parametric equations $y = \ln t$ and $x = \frac{1}{t^3}$. x and y represent the particle's displacement from the origin in the i and j directions respectively, at time t seconds.

a) Find the gradient of C, $\frac{dy}{dx}$, when $t = \frac{1}{2}$. (PROBLEM SOLVING)

b) Show that the acceleration of the particle at this time is 384i – 4j.

Q4 Angles in this question are in radians. The velocity of a particle at time t seconds is given by (PROBLEM SOLVING)
$\mathbf{v} = [(2 \sin^2 t)\mathbf{i} + (4 \sin 2t \cos 2t)\mathbf{j}]$ ms^{-1}. At time $t = \frac{\pi}{4}$, the particle has position vector $\mathbf{r} = \left[\frac{\pi}{4}\mathbf{i} + \mathbf{j}\right]$ m, relative to the origin. What was the particle's initial distance from the origin at time $t = 0$?

Review Exercise — Chapter 29

Q1 A particle is projected with initial velocity u ms^{-1} at an angle α to the horizontal. Write down the horizontal and vertical components of the particle's initial velocity.

Q2 A golf ball is hit with a golf club from a point on flat, horizontal ground. The ball lands 4 seconds after it is hit. Given that the ball leaves the club with a speed of 22 ms^{-1}, at an angle of α to the horizontal, find α.

Q3

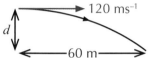

A rifle fires a bullet horizontally at 120 ms^{-1}. The bullet hits a target a horizontal distance of 60 m from the end of the rifle. Find the vertical distance, d, between the target and the rifle.

Q4 A projectile is fired from a point 0.3 m above flat, horizontal ground. The projectile's initial speed is 6.5 ms^{-1}, at an angle of 29° above the horizontal. Find:
a) the horizontal range of the projectile,   b) the speed of the projectile when it lands.

Q5 A javelin is thrown from a height of 1.5 m above flat horizontal ground at an angle of 38° to the horizontal. It reaches a maximum height of 12.5 m.
a) Calculate the javelin's initial velocity in ms^{-1} to 1 d.p.
b) Calculate the horizontal distance travelled by the javelin to the nearest metre.

Q6 A body is projected from a point on flat, horizontal ground with velocity $(2\mathbf{i} + 11\mathbf{j})$ ms^{-1}. Find:
a) the velocity of the body 0.8 seconds after projection,
b) the time of flight of the body,   c) the maximum height reached by the body.

Q7

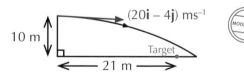

A ball is projected from the top of a building of height 10 m with velocity $(20\mathbf{i} - 4\mathbf{j})$ ms^{-1}. The ball is aimed towards a target on flat, horizontal ground, 21 m from the foot of the building. The ball overshoots, and lands beyond the target. Find:
a) the time taken for the ball to land on the ground,
b) the horizontal distance by which the ball overshoots the target,
c) the speed of the ball when it is vertically above the target.

Q8 A particle sets off from the origin at $t = 0$ and moves along the x-axis with velocity $v = (8t^2 - 2t)$ ms^{-1}. Find an expression for:
a) the acceleration of the particle at time t seconds,
b) the displacement of the particle at time t seconds.

Q9   A particle moves in a straight line along the x-axis.
      At time t seconds, the particle's velocity is v ms^{-1}, where v is given by:

$$v = \begin{cases} t^2 - 3t & 0 \le t \le 2 \\ 2 - t^2 & t > 2 \end{cases}$$

      When $t = 0$, the particle is at the origin. Find:
      a) the particle's maximum speed in the time interval $0 \le t \le 2$,
      b) the particle's displacement from the origin when $t = 2$,
      c) the particle's displacement from the origin when $t = 4$.

Q10   At time $t = 0$, a particle sets off from rest at the origin, O, and moves in a
      plane with velocity $\mathbf{v} = (4t\mathbf{i} + t^2\mathbf{j})$ ms^{-1}, where t is the time in seconds. Find:
      a) the particle's acceleration at time t,   b) the particle's position vector at time t.

Q11   A buggy is modelled as a particle moving across a horizontal surface with
      acceleration a = (e$^{0.75t}$ **i** + cos t **j**) ms^{-2} at time t seconds (for $0 \le t \le 5$).
      At time $t = 0$, the buggy is moving in the positive **i** direction at a speed of 17 ms^{-1}.

      Find an expression for the buggy's velocity vector **v** at time t.

Q12   A particle moves in a vertical plane. At time t seconds, the particle's position vector
      relative to a fixed origin, O, is given by $\mathbf{r} = [(t^2 - 3t + 2)\mathbf{i} + (t^2 - 5)\mathbf{j}]$ m. Find:
      a) the particle's initial position,
      b) the values of t for which the particle is directly below O,
      c) the velocity of the particle when $t = 4$.

Q13   A body is moving in a plane with acceleration $\mathbf{a} = -10\mathbf{j}$ ms^{-2} relative to a fixed origin, O.
      The body's initial velocity is $(15\mathbf{i} + 12\mathbf{j})$ ms^{-1}. At time $t = 1$ second, the body passes through
      the point with position vector $(15\mathbf{i} + 16\mathbf{j})$ m. Given that **i** and **j** are unit vectors directed
      due east and due north respectively, find:
      a) an expression for the body's velocity at time t seconds,
      b) an expression for the body's position vector at time t seconds,
      c) the body's velocity when it is due east of O.

Q14   A particle is moving with a velocity of $\mathbf{v} = [m\mathbf{i} + n\mathbf{j}]$ ms^{-1}. It has a constant acceleration
      of 0.1 ms^{-2} in the **i** direction, and a variable acceleration in the **j** direction, such that
      $\dfrac{\mathrm{d}n}{\mathrm{d}t} = (kn - 10)$ ms^{-2} and $\dfrac{\mathrm{d}n}{\mathrm{d}t} < 0$ (k is a constant).

      The particle is stationary at $t = 0$, and when its acceleration is -2 ms^{-2} in the **j** direction,
      its velocity in the **j** direction is -4 ms^{-1}.
      a) Show that $n + 5 > 0$.
      b) Hence show that the velocity of the particle can expressed as $\mathbf{v} = \left[0.1t\mathbf{i} + 5(e^{-2t} - 1)\mathbf{j}\right]$ ms^{-1}.

Chapter 30 — Dynamics

You've seen problems with more than one force acting on an object before, but things get more complicated when these forces are acting at different angles. You'll often need to use trigonometry to resolve the forces into their horizontal and vertical components.

1. Resolving Forces

Components of forces

Here's a quick recap about resolving forces (you've already resolved vectors on p.418):

- A **component of a force** is the **magnitude** of the force in a **particular direction**.

- You can use **trigonometry** to **resolve** forces into their **horizontal** and **vertical** components:

Horizontal component, F_x:

$$\cos \theta = \frac{\text{adj}}{\text{hyp}} = \frac{F_x}{F}, \text{ so } F_x = F \cos \theta$$

Vertical component, F_y:

$$\sin \theta = \frac{\text{opp}}{\text{hyp}} = \frac{F_y}{F}, \text{ so } F_y = F \sin \theta$$

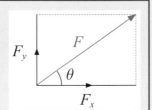

Example

A particle is acted on by a force of 15 N at 30° above the positive horizontal. Find the horizontal and vertical components of the force.

1. Draw a vector triangle.

2. Use trigonometry to calculate the horizontal and vertical components.

$F_x = 15 \cos 30°$ $F_y = 15 \sin 30°$
     $= \textbf{13.0 N (to 3 s.f.) to the right}$ $= \textbf{7.5 N upwards}$

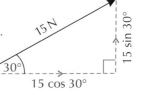

Tip: If you're resolving in a direction which is perpendicular to the line of action of a force, then the component of the force in that direction will be zero — e.g. a force acting horizontally has a vertical component of zero.

Exercise 1.1

Q1   Find the horizontal and vertical components of each of the forces shown:

a)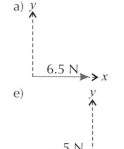

b)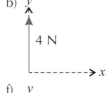

c)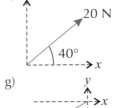

d)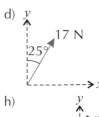

e)

f)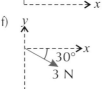

g)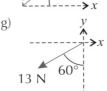

h)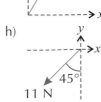

Forces can be described using **i** and **j** notation (see p.124). When resolving forces, arrows can be used to show which direction you're taking as positive.

Example **Find the i and j components of the force shown.**

1. Resolve in the **i**-direction (→). $-4.8 \cos 28° = \mathbf{-4.24\ N\ (to\ 3\ s.f.)}$

2. Resolve in the **j**-direction (↑). $4.8 \sin 28° = \mathbf{2.25\ N\ (to\ 3\ s.f.)}$

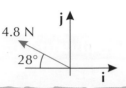

You can resolve forces in **any two perpendicular directions**, not just horizontally and vertically.

Example **The diagram shows a particle at rest on a smooth inclined plane. A force of magnitude 4 N acts on the particle at an angle of 10° to the horizontal. Find the components of the force that act parallel and perpendicular to the plane.**

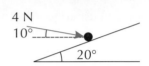

1. Use the alternate angles theorem to find the angle between the force and the slope. This is shown on the diagrams.

2. Resolve parallel to the plane (↗). $F_{parallel} = 4 \cos 30°$
   $= \mathbf{3.46\ N\ (to\ 3\ s.f.)}$

3. Resolve perpendicular to the plane (↖). $F_{perpendicular} = -4 \sin 30°$
   $= \mathbf{-2\ N}$

Exercise 1.2

Q1 Each of the following diagrams shows a force and the angle it makes with the horizontal. Write each force in the form $(a\mathbf{i} + b\mathbf{j})$ N.

a)

b)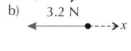

c)

d)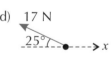

Q2 The force $(c\mathbf{i} + 7\mathbf{j})$ N acts at 25° to **i**, where c is a positive constant.
a) Find the value of c.
b) Find the magnitude of this force.

Q3

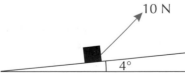

The diagram shows a force of magnitude 10 N acting on an object on an inclined plane. The component of the force in the direction parallel to the plane is 7.1 N.

a) Find the angle between the direction of the force and the incline of the plane.

b) Find the horizontal component of the force.

Resultant forces and equilibrium

The **resultant force** is the sum of all the forces acting on an object.
You can calculate the resultant force by **adding the corresponding components** of the forces.

If the resultant force on an object is **zero**, then the object is in **equilibrium**.

 Three forces of magnitude 9 N, 12 N and 13 N act on a particle P in the directions shown in the diagram. Find the magnitude and direction of the resultant of the three forces.

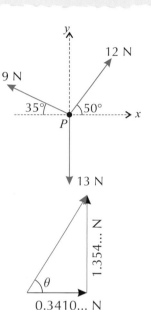

1. Resolve in the y-direction ($\uparrow$). $9 \sin 35° + 12 \sin 50° - 13$
    $= 1.354... = 1.35$ N (to 3 s.f.)

2. Resolve in the x-direction ($\rightarrow$). $12 \cos 50° - 9 \cos 35°$
    $= 0.3410... = 0.341$ N (to 3 s.f.)

3. Use the components to form a right-angled triangle.
    The resultant is shown by the hypotenuse of the triangle.

4. Use Pythagoras' theorem to find the magnitude.
    $\sqrt{1.354...^2 + 0.3410...^2} = \mathbf{1.40}$ **N (to 3 s.f.)**

5. Use trigonometry to find the required direction.

    $\theta = \tan^{-1}\left(\dfrac{1.354...}{0.3410...}\right) = \mathbf{75.9°}$ **(to 3 s.f.)**

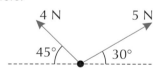

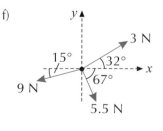

Exercise 1.3

Q1   Each of the diagrams below shows the forces acting on a particle.
Find the magnitude and direction of the resultant force on each particle.

a)

8.2 N

39°   7 N

b)

6 N

49°

4.8 N

c)

4 N   5 N

45°   30°

d) 11 N y

75°

80°

10 N

12 N

e)

8 N y 6.5 N

61°   69°

47°

10 N

f)

y 3 N

15°   32°

9 N   67°

5.5 N

Q2   A force of magnitude 18 N acts on a particle at 60° above the positive horizontal.
A force of magnitude 16 N also acts vertically upwards on the particle.

a) Draw a diagram to illustrate the forces acting on the particle.

b) Find the magnitude and direction of the resultant of the two forces.

Q3 Forces of magnitude 1 N and 2 N act at angles of 10° and 35° above **i** respectively.
A third force of magnitude 3 N acts at an angle of θ above **i**, where $180° \leq \theta \leq 360°$.
The resultant of the three forces has no horizontal component.

a) Find θ.

b) Calculate the magnitude of the resultant of the three forces.

Q4 A particle is acted on by a force of magnitude 9 N in the positive horizontal direction
and a force of magnitude 10 N at 30° above the positive horizontal. A third force of
magnitude P N acts on the particle at 60° above the positive horizontal. Find P, given
that the resultant of the three forces acts at 45° above the positive horizontal.

If an object is in equilibrium, you can use the fact that the resultant force is **zero** to find a missing force.

 Example

**The diagram shows all the forces acting on a particle.
Given that the particle is in equilibrium,
find the magnitudes of the missing forces P and Q.**

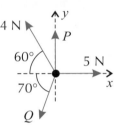

1. Resolve to find two perpendicular components of the resultant force,
   then make each component equal to zero.

2. Resolving in the x-direction ($\rightarrow$).　　$5 - Q \cos 70° - 4 \cos 60° = 0$

   $Q \cos 70° = 3$

   $\Rightarrow Q = \dfrac{3}{\cos 70°} = \textbf{8.77 N (to 3 s.f.)}$

3. Resolving in the y-direction ($\uparrow$).　　$P + 4 \sin 60° - Q \sin 70° = 0$

   $P = \dfrac{3}{\cos 70°} \sin 70° - 4 \sin 60°$

   $\Rightarrow P = \textbf{4.78 N (to 3 s.f.)}$

Tip: You might see a closed figure used to show the addition of the forces on an object
in equilibrium. This example's closed figure diagram is shown on the right.

Exercise 1.4

Q1 The diagrams below show all the forces acting on a particle in equilibrium.
Find the magnitude of the missing forces, acting on each particle.

a) 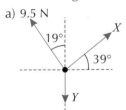　　b) 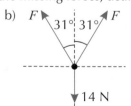　　c) 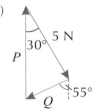　　d)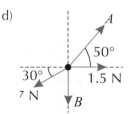

Q2 Forces of magnitude P N and $2P$ N act on a particle vertically upwards
and horizontally, as shown in the diagram. A third force of 20 N acts at
an angle θ to the downward vertical. No other forces act on the particle.
Given that the particle is in equilibrium, find the values of P and θ.

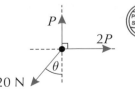

(PROBLEM SOLVING)

Harder equilibrium problems

Objects hanging from **strings** and objects on **inclined planes** are some examples of **real-life situations** where you might see forces in equilibrium.

 Example

The diagram shows a body of mass 8 kg held in equilibrium by two light, inextensible strings. One string is horizontal, and the other string makes an angle of 30° with the vertical.

Find the magnitude of the tension in each string.

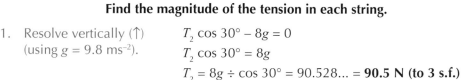

1. Resolve vertically (↑) (using $g = 9.8$ ms^{-2}).

$T_2 \cos 30° - 8g = 0$
$T_2 \cos 30° = 8g$
$T_2 = 8g \div \cos 30° = 90.528... = \mathbf{90.5 \text{ N (to 3 s.f.)}}$

2. Resolve horizontally (→). $T_1 - T_2 \sin 30° = 0$
$T_1 = T_2 \sin 30° = 90.528... \sin 30° = 45.264... = \mathbf{45.3 \text{ N (to 3 s.f.)}}$

Exercise 1.5

Q1 Each of the following diagrams shows a particle held in equilibrium by two light, inextensible strings. In each case, find the magnitude of the missing tension, T, and the mass of the particle, m.

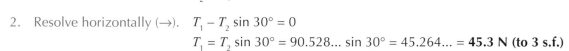

a) b) c) d)

Q2 The diagram shows a particle suspended from two light, inextensible strings. The particle is in equilibrium. Find the weight of the particle, W, and the angle x.

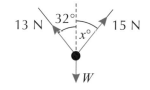

Remember, when resolving forces for an object on an **inclined plane**, it's usually best to resolve **parallel** and **perpendicular to the plane**.

You'll need to use the **components of weight** parallel and perpendicular to the plane:

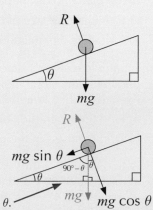

- Component of weight **parallel** to the plane: $\mathbf{\mathit{mg} \sin \theta}$

- Component of weight **perpendicular** to the plane: $\mathbf{\mathit{mg} \cos \theta}$

Where mg is the object's weight and θ is the plane's incline.

Tip: The angle between the object's weight and its component perpendicular to the plane is equal to θ.

Example A stone of mass 0.1 kg rests on a smooth plane inclined at 20° to the horizontal. It is held in equilibrium by a force, F, acting parallel to the plane, as shown.

Find the magnitude of force F and the normal reaction, R, of the plane on the stone.

1. Resolve parallel to the plane $(\nearrow)$. $F - 0.1g \sin 20° = 0$
$$F = 0.98 \sin 20° = \textbf{0.335 N (to 3 s.f.)}$$

2. Resolve perpendicular to the plane $(\nwarrow)$. $R - 0.1g \cos 20° = 0$
$$R = 0.98 \cos 20° = \textbf{0.921 N (to 3 s.f.)}$$

Examples A rock of mass 9 kg rests on a smooth plane inclined at 35° to the horizontal. The rock is held in equilibrium by a horizontal force of magnitude 10 N directed towards the plane and the tension in a string parallel to the plane.

a) **Find the normal reaction force, R, between the plane and rock.**

1. Draw a diagram showing all the forces acting on the rock.

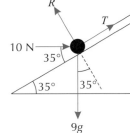

2. Resolve perpendicular to the plane $(\nwarrow)$.
$R - 10 \sin 35° - 9g \cos 35° = 0$
$R = 10 \sin 35° + 9g \cos 35° = \textbf{78.0 N (to 3 s.f.)}$

b) **Find the magnitude of the tension in the string.**
Resolve parallel to the plane $(\nearrow)$. $T + 10 \cos 35° - 9g \sin 35° = 0$
$$T = 9g \sin 35° - 10 \cos 35° = \textbf{42.4 N (to 3 s.f.)}$$

Exercise 1.6

Q1 A particle of weight 10 N rests on a smooth inclined plane. The plane is inclined at an angle $x°$ to the horizontal. A force of magnitude 8 N acting along the line of greatest slope of the plane holds the particle in equilibrium.

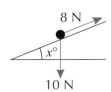

a) Calculate the size of the angle x.

b) Calculate the magnitude of the normal reaction force exerted by the plane on the particle.

Q2 A particle rests on a smooth plane inclined at 45° to the horizontal. A force acting up the plane, parallel to the slope, holds the particle in equilibrium. The magnitude of the normal reaction force exerted by the plane on the particle is 25 N.

a) Find the magnitude of the force which holds the particle at rest.

b) Find the mass of the particle.

Q3 A smooth wire is threaded through a bead of mass m kg and inclined at an angle of 60° to the horizontal. The bead is held at rest by a force of magnitude 4.2 N acting parallel to the wire.

a) Find the mass of the bead.

b) Find the magnitude of the normal reaction from the wire on the bead.

Q4 The diagram shows a 2 kg block held at rest on a smooth inclined plane by a horizontal force of 14.7 N. The plane is inclined at an angle of θ to the horizontal. Show that $\tan \theta = 0.75$.

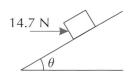

Things get trickier if **two** different angles are involved — make sure you use the correct one when resolving the different forces.

  A block of mass 30 kg is at rest on a smooth plane inclined at an angle α to the horizontal. The block is held in equilibrium by a force of 147 N, pushing on the block at an angle of 60° to the plane.

a) **Show that $\sin \alpha = 0.25$.**
  1. Draw a diagram showing all the forces acting on the block.
  2. Resolve parallel to the plane ($\nearrow$).
      $147 \cos 60° - 30g \sin \alpha = 0$
      $(30 \times 9.8) \sin \alpha = 147 \times 0.5 \Rightarrow \sin \alpha = 73.5 \div 294 = \mathbf{0.25}$

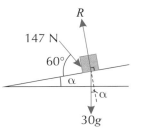

b) **Find the normal reaction, R, of the plane on the block.**
  1. Find the value of α. $\alpha = \sin^{-1}(0.25) = 14.4775...°$
  2. Resolve perpendicular to the plane ($\nwarrow$).
      $R - 147 \sin 60° - 30g \cos \alpha = 0$
      $R = 147 \sin 60° + 30g \cos(14.4775...°) = \mathbf{412\ N\ (to\ 3\ s.f.)}$

Exercise 1.7

Q1 A particle with a mass of 5 kg rests on a smooth plane inclined at 10° to the horizontal, as shown. The particle is held in place by a light, inextensible string inclined at an angle of 30° to the plane.

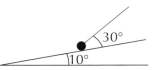

  a) Calculate the magnitude of the tension in the string.
  b) Calculate the magnitude of the normal reaction of the plane on the particle.

Q2 A particle of mass m is held at rest on a smooth plane inclined at 12° to the horizontal by a light, inextensible string. The string is inclined at 45° to the horizontal. The magnitude of the normal reaction force from the plane on the particle is 15 N. Find:
  a) the magnitude of the tension, T, in the string,
  b) the mass, m, of the particle in kg.

Q3 A brick of mass 2 kg is at rest on a smooth plane inclined at an angle θ to the horizontal. The brick is held in equilibrium by a force of 18 N, acting at an angle of 30° to the plane, as shown. Find:
  a) the size of the angle θ.
  b) the magnitude of the normal reaction, R, from the plane on the brick.

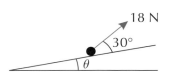

Q4 A particle is held in equilibrium on a smooth plane by a light, inextensible string. The plane is inclined at 50° to the horizontal and the string is inclined at 70° to the horizontal. The tension in the string has magnitude 5 N. A force, F, also acts on the particle, down the plane, parallel to the slope. Given that the magnitude of the normal reaction of the plane on the particle is four times the magnitude of F, find the weight of the particle.

2. Friction

- If an object is in contact with a **rough** surface, then **friction** acts in the **opposite direction to motion** (or potential motion) to **oppose it**.

- The magnitude of the frictional force can take a **range of possible values**. As the magnitude of the force trying to move the object **increases**, the magnitude of the frictional force will **also increase**. Eventually, the frictional force reaches its **maximum possible value** and the object will start to move.

- The maximum possible magnitude of the frictional force depends on the **coefficient of friction**, μ, between the surface and the object.

- The frictional force, F, acting on a **stationary** object obeys the inequality: $\boxed{F \leq \mu R}$

- When the object starts to **move**, or is on the point of moving, friction is said to be **limiting** and takes its **maximum value**: $\boxed{F_{max} = \mu R}$ — R is the normal reaction of the surface on the object.

A horizontal force of 30 N acts on a 4 kg block which is at rest on a rough horizontal plane. The block is on the point of moving.
Find the coefficient of friction between the block and the plane.

1. Draw a diagram showing all the forces acting on the block.

2. Resolve horizontally ($\rightarrow$). $F = 30$ N

3. Resolve vertically ($\uparrow$). $R = 4g$

4. Friction is limiting, so use $F = \mu R$. $F = \mu R \Rightarrow 30 = \mu \times 4g$

$\Rightarrow \mu = 30 \div 4g = \textbf{0.77 (to 2 d.p.)}$

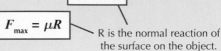

Exercise 2.1

Q1 A particle of weight W rests on a rough horizontal surface with coefficient of friction μ between them. A horizontal force is applied to the particle such that the particle is on the point of slipping. Find the magnitude of the frictional force, F, on the particle if:

a) $W = 5$ N, $\mu = 0.25$ b) $W = 8$ N, $\mu = 0.3$ c) $W = 15$ N, $\mu = 0.75$

d) $W = 6$ N, $\mu = 0$ e) $W = 17$ N, $\mu = 0.82$ f) $W = 0.5$ N, $\mu = 0.95$

Q2 A particle of weight W is at rest on a rough horizontal surface. A horizontal force P acts on the particle. Given that the particle is on the point of moving, calculate the coefficient of friction if:

a) $W = 20$ N, $P = 5$ N b) $W = 15$ N, $P = 8$ N

c) $W = 28$ N, $P = 3.5$ N d) $W = 13$ N, $P = 6$ N

Q3 A horizontal force, P, acts on a particle of mass 12 kg, which is at rest on a rough horizontal plane. Find the range of values that the frictional force, F, can take, given that the coefficient of friction between the particle and the plane is 0.4

Q4 A particle of mass 12 kg is placed on a rough horizontal surface. A horizontal force of magnitude 50 N is applied to the particle. The coefficient of friction between the particle and the surface is 0.5.

a) Will the 50 N force cause the particle to move?

b) What is the maximum possible magnitude of force that can be applied horizontally to the particle, such that the particle will remain in equilibrium?

Example

A force Q acts on a box at an angle of $10°$ above the horizontal. The box has mass 10 kg and is on the point of slipping across a rough horizontal plane. Given that the coefficient of friction between the box and the plane is 0.7, find the magnitude of the normal reaction, R, from the plane and the magnitude of Q.

1. Draw a diagram showing all the forces acting on the box.

2. Resolve vertically ($\uparrow$). $R + Q \sin 10° = 10g$

    $Q \sin 10° = 10g - R$ — equation ①

3. Resolve horizontally ($\rightarrow$). $Q \cos 10° = F \Rightarrow Q \cos 10° = \mu R$

    $Q \cos 10° = 0.7R$ — equation ②

4. Divide equation ① by equation ②. $\dfrac{Q \sin 10°}{Q \cos 10°} = \dfrac{10g - R}{0.7R}$

    $\tan 10° = \dfrac{10g - R}{0.7R} \Rightarrow 0.7R \tan 10° = 10g - R$

    $R = \dfrac{10g}{(1 + 0.7 \tan 10°)} = 87.232... = \textbf{87.2 N (to 3 s.f.)}$

5. Substitute R into equation ②. $Q \cos 10° = 0.7 \times 87.232...$

    $Q = 61.063... \div \cos 10° = \textbf{62.0 N (to 3 s.f.)}$

Exercise 2.2

(MODELLING)

Q1

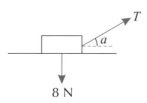

A pull-along toy of weight 8 N rests on a rough horizontal surface with coefficient of friction $\mu = 0.61$ between the toy and the surface. A light, inextensible string is attached to the toy, at an angle of α to the horizontal, as shown. Find the maximum possible tension in the string given that the toy remains stationary when:

a) $\alpha = 0°$ b) $\alpha = 35°$

Q2

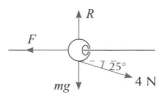

A horizontal wire is threaded through a bead of mass m kg. A force of magnitude 4 N is applied to the bead, at an angle of $25°$ to the horizontal, as shown. The bead is on the point of sliding along the wire. Given that the coefficient of friction between the wire and the bead is 0.15, find:

a) the magnitude of R, the normal reaction of the wire on the bead,

b) the value of m.

You've seen problems involving objects on smooth inclined planes on pages 439-441.
For **rough** inclined planes, a frictional force will act **parallel** to the slope to **oppose** potential motion.

 A box of mass 10 kg is at rest on a rough slope inclined at 33° to the horizontal. A force of magnitude 18 N acts on the box at an angle of 20° above the slope. Calculate the coefficient of friction, μ, given that the force of magnitude 18 N is just large enough to stop the box sliding down the slope.

1. Draw a diagram showing all the forces acting on the box.

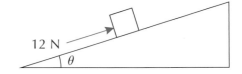

2. Resolve parallel to the plane ($\nearrow$).
$$F + 18 \cos 20° = 10g \sin 33°$$
$$\Rightarrow F = 36.460...$$

3. Resolve perpendicular to the plane ($\nwarrow$).
$$R + 18 \sin 20° = 10g \cos 33°$$
$$\Rightarrow R = 76.033...$$

4. Friction is limiting, so use $F = \mu R$.
$$F = \mu R \Rightarrow \mu = \frac{36.460...}{76.033...} = \mathbf{0.48 \text{ (to 2 d.p.)}}$$

Exercise 2.3

Q1 A box of mass 2 kg is at rest on a rough plane inclined at an angle of θ to the horizontal. A force of 12 N acts up the plane on the box, which is on the point of moving up the slope. Given that $\cos \theta = \frac{4}{5}$, find the coefficient of friction between the box and the plane.

Q2 An object is placed on a rough plane inclined at an angle α to the horizontal. The coefficient of friction between the object and the plane is μ. Show that the object will be at rest on the plane if $\tan \alpha \leq \mu$.

Q3 A block of mass 7 kg is at rest on a rough plane inclined at an angle of 45° to the horizontal. A force of 30 N acts up the plane on the block, which is on the point of moving down the slope. Find the coefficient of friction between the block and the plane.

Q4 A sledge of mass 20 kg is at rest on a rough slope inclined at 29° to the horizontal. The coefficient of friction between the slope and the sledge is 0.1. A force, T, acts on the sledge at an angle of 15° to the slope, as shown.

Calculate the magnitude of T, given that this force is only just large enough to stop the sledge sliding down the slope.

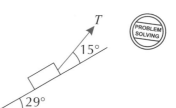

Q5 A wire is threaded through a bead of mass 0.5 kg and inclined at an angle of 10° to the horizontal. The coefficient of friction between the wire and the bead is 0.25. A force of P N is applied to the bead, at an angle of 45° to the wire, as shown.

Calculate the magnitude of the normal reaction to the bead, R, given that P is only just large enough to stop the bead sliding down the slope.

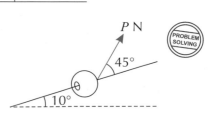

Q6 A block of mass 5 kg is at rest on a rough plane inclined at 35° to the horizontal. The coefficient of friction between the block and the plane is 0.4. The block is being held in equilibrium by a force D acting parallel to the plane. Find the range of possible values of the magnitude of D.

3. Newton's Laws of Motion

Newton's Laws of Motion

You've already been introduced to Newton's laws on p.225. Now they will be combined with what you've seen so far in this chapter. Here's a quick reminder of the laws:

> **Newton's first law:**
> A body will stay at **rest** or maintain a **constant velocity** unless a **resultant force** acts on the body.

> **Newton's second law:**
> The **overall resultant force** (F_{net}) acting on a body is equal to the **mass** of the body multiplied by the body's **acceleration**.
>
> i.e. $F_{net} = ma$

> **Newton's third law:**
> For **two bodies**, A and B, **in contact** with each other, the force exerted by A on B is **equal in magnitude** but **opposite in direction** to the force exerted by B on A.

Newton's second law finds **acceleration**, which you can then use in one of the **constant acceleration equations** (see p.211) to find the variable you're asked for (e.g. displacement or velocity).

Example

A particle of weight 18 N is being pulled along a smooth horizontal surface by a force of 7 N acting at an angle of 25° to the horizontal, as shown. Find the speed of the particle after 3 seconds, given that it starts from rest.

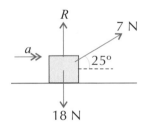

1. Resolve horizontally (→). $F_{net} = 7 \cos 25°$

2. Use Newton's second law to find the acceleration.

   $F_{net} = ma \Rightarrow 7 \cos 25° = \dfrac{18}{g}a$

   $6.344... = 1.836... \times a \Rightarrow a = 3.454...$ ms^{-2}

3. List the variables and use the '$suvat$' equations.

   $u = 0, \quad v = ?, \quad a = 3.454..., \quad t = 3$

   $v = u + at = 0 + 3.454... \times 3 = \mathbf{10.4}$ ms^{-1} **(to 3 s.f.)**

Exercise 3.1

Q1 A particle of mass 4 kg is accelerated from rest across a smooth, horizontal plane by a horizontal force of 20 N. Find the distance travelled by the particle after 2.5 seconds.

Q2 A particle of mass 3 kg is accelerated from rest across a smooth, horizontal plane by a force of 10 N acting at an angle of 45° to the horizontal. Find:

a) the acceleration of the particle,

b) the distance travelled when the particle reaches 8 ms^{-1},

c) the magnitude of the normal reaction with the plane.

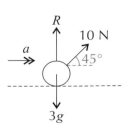

Q3   A particle of weight 49 N initially at rest on a smooth horizontal plane is acted on by a constant horizontal resistive force of 7 N and a force of 16 N acting at an angle of 20° to the horizontal, as shown. Find:

a) the acceleration of the particle,

b) the speed of the particle after 7 seconds,

c) the magnitude of the normal reaction with the plane.

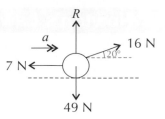

Forces might be described as **vectors** with **i** and **j** notation.

> **Two forces acting in a horizontal plane are given by the vectors $(12\mathbf{i} - 4\mathbf{j})$ N and $(-3\mathbf{i} + 16\mathbf{j})$ N. They act on a particle of mass 3 kg, causing it to accelerate from rest.**
>
> **a)   Find the acceleration of the particle as a vector.**
>
> 1.   Find the resultant force on the particle.
>
> $$\mathbf{F}_{net} = (12\mathbf{i} - 4\mathbf{j}) + (-3\mathbf{i} + 16\mathbf{j}) = 9\mathbf{i} + 12\mathbf{j}$$
>
> 2.   Use Newton's second law (with vectors).
>
> $$\mathbf{F}_{net} = m\mathbf{a} \Rightarrow 9\mathbf{i} + 12\mathbf{j} = 3\mathbf{a}$$
> $$\mathbf{a} = (3\mathbf{i} + 4\mathbf{j}) \text{ ms}^{-2}$$
>
> **b)   Find the velocity vector of the particle after 7 seconds.**
>
> List the variables and use the 'suvat' equations.
>
> $$\mathbf{u} = 0 \quad \mathbf{v} = ? \quad \mathbf{a} = 3\mathbf{i} + 4\mathbf{j} \quad t = 7$$
> $$\mathbf{v} = \mathbf{u} + \mathbf{a}t \Rightarrow \mathbf{v} = 0 + (3\mathbf{i} + 4\mathbf{j}) \times 7 = (21\mathbf{i} + 28\mathbf{j}) \text{ ms}^{-1}$$
>
> **c)   How far does the particle travel in the first 4 seconds?**
>
> 1.   Find the magnitude of the acceleration. $|\mathbf{a}| = \sqrt{3^2 + 4^2} = 5 \text{ ms}^{-2}$
>
> 2.   List the variables and use the '*suvat*' equations.
>
> $$s = ? \quad u = 0 \quad a = 5 \quad t = 4$$
> $$s = ut + \frac{1}{2}at^2 = (0 \times 4) + \frac{1}{2} \times 5 \times 4^2 = \mathbf{40 \text{ m}}$$
>
> **d)   A third force K is applied to the particle, which now moves with acceleration $(7\mathbf{i} - 2\mathbf{j})$ ms^{-2}. Find the force K in terms of i and j.**
>
> 1.   Use Newton's second law to find the new resultant force.
>
> $$\mathbf{F}_{net} = m\mathbf{a} = 3(7\mathbf{i} - 2\mathbf{j}) = 21\mathbf{i} - 6\mathbf{j}$$
>
> 2. $\mathbf{F}_{net}$ is the sum of the three forces acting on the particle.
>
> $$(12\mathbf{i} - 4\mathbf{j}) + (-3\mathbf{i} + 16\mathbf{j}) + \mathbf{K} = (21\mathbf{i} - 6\mathbf{j})$$
> $$\mathbf{K} = (21\mathbf{i} - 6\mathbf{j}) - (12\mathbf{i} - 4\mathbf{j}) - (-3\mathbf{i} + 16\mathbf{j}) = \mathbf{(12\mathbf{i} - 18\mathbf{j}) \text{ N}}$$

Exercise 3.2

Q1   A particle of mass 5 kg is acted on by two forces, $(6\mathbf{i} - 10\mathbf{j})$ N and $(4\mathbf{i} + 5\mathbf{j})$ N.

a) Find the magnitude of the acceleration of the particle.

b) A third force, of $(-6\mathbf{i} + 2\mathbf{j})$ N, begins to act on the particle.
   Describe the effect this has on the magnitude of the acceleration of the particle.

Q2   Three forces are acting on a particle of mass 10 kg.

a) Two of the forces are given by $(6\mathbf{i} - 2\mathbf{j})$ N and $(5\mathbf{i} + 5\mathbf{j})$ N and the resultant force is $(7\mathbf{i} + \mathbf{j})$ N.
   Find the third force in vector form.

b) Find the particle's velocity vector 8 seconds after it begins accelerating from rest.

c) A fourth force, of $(-7\mathbf{i} - \mathbf{j})$ N, begins to act on the particle.
   Describe the effect this has on the particle's motion.

Moving objects on inclined planes

For objects on an inclined plane, remember to resolve forces **parallel** and **perpendicular** to the plane and that weight ($W = mg$) always acts **vertically downwards**.

 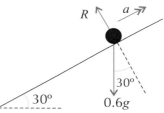

A particle of mass 600 g is propelled up the line of greatest slope of a smooth plane inclined at 30° to the horizontal. Immediately after the propelling force has stopped, the particle has speed 3 ms⁻¹. Find:

a)   **the distance the particle travels before coming to rest.**

   1.   Resolve parallel to the plane ($\nearrow$): $F_{net} = ma$

$$-0.6g \sin 30° = 0.6a \Rightarrow a = -4.9 \text{ ms}^{-2}$$

   2.   Use the 'suvat' equations. $v^2 = u^2 + 2as, \quad s = ? \quad u = 3 \quad v = 0 \quad a = -4.9$

$$0 = 3^2 + 2(-4.9)s \Rightarrow s = \textbf{0.918 m (3 s.f.)}$$

b)   **the magnitude of the normal reaction from the plane.**

   Resolve perpendicular to the plane ($\nwarrow$) $F_{net} = ma$
   ($a = 0$ as the particle is moving parallel to the plane). $R - 0.6g \cos 30° = 0.6 \times 0$
      $\Rightarrow R = \textbf{5.09 N (3 s.f.)}$

Exercise 3.3

Q1   A particle of mass 300 g is propelled up the line of greatest slope of a smooth plane inclined at 17° to the horizontal. Immediately after the propelling force has stopped, the particle has speed 7 ms⁻¹. Find:

   a) the distance the particle travels before coming to rest.

   b) the magnitude of the normal reaction from the plane.

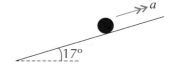

Q2   A wooden block of mass 1.5 kg is placed on a smooth plane which is inclined at 25° to the horizontal, as shown in the diagram. The block is released from rest and begins to accelerate down the slope.

   a) What is the magnitude of the block's acceleration?

   b) Assuming that the block's acceleration is constant, find the speed of the block 3 seconds after it is released.

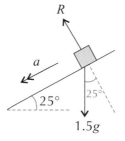

Moving objects on rough surfaces

- When a **moving** object is acted on by a **frictional force**, friction is **limiting**, and takes its maximum value, $F = \mu R$ (where μ is the coefficient of friction and R is the normal reaction between the object and the surface).

- Friction **opposes** motion, so it will always act in the **opposite direction** to the object's motion.

- You'll need to use Newton's laws and $F = \mu R$ to solve problems involving objects which are accelerating and being acted on by friction.

A small body of weight 20 N is released from rest on a rough plane angled at 15° to the horizontal.

Given that the body accelerates down the plane at a rate of 0.44 ms⁻², find the coefficient of friction between the body and the plane.

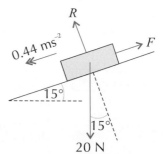

1. Resolve parallel to the plane (↙). $F_{net} = ma$

    $$20 \sin 15° - F = \frac{20}{g} \times 0.44$$

    $$F = 4.278... \text{ N}$$

2. Resolve perpendicular to the plane (↖). $F_{net} = ma$

    $$R - 20 \cos 15° = \frac{20}{g} \times 0$$

    $$\Rightarrow R = 20 \cos 15° = 19.318... \text{ N}$$

3. Friction is limiting. $F = \mu R \Rightarrow 4.278... = \mu \times 19.318... \Rightarrow \mu = \textbf{0.22 (to 2 d.p.)}$

Exercise 3.4

Q1   A horizontal force of magnitude 26 N is acting on a box of mass 4 kg, causing the box to accelerate across a rough, horizontal plane at a rate of 1.2 ms⁻².

a) Draw a labelled diagram to show the forces acting on the box.

b) Calculate the normal reaction, R, of the plane on the box.

c) Use Newton's second law to find the magnitude of the frictional force acting on the box.

d) Find the coefficient of friction, μ, between the box and the plane.

Q2   A taut rope is pulling a block up a rough inclined plane angled at 40° to the horizontal. The rope is parallel to the plane. The coefficient of friction between the block and the surface is 0.35 and the tension in the rope is 70 N.

a) Draw a diagram to show the forces acting on the block.

b) Given that the block is accelerating at a rate of 3.2 ms⁻², find the mass of the block.

Q3   A block of mass 1 kg is sliding down a rough plane of length 2 m, which is inclined at an angle of 50° to the horizontal. The coefficient of friction between the block and the surface is 0.4.

a) Draw a diagram to show the forces acting on the block.

b) If the block is released from rest at the top of the plane, find how long it will take to reach the bottom of the plane.

Q4   A rock weighing 5000 N is being pulled up a rough inclined plane which is at an angle of 10° to the horizontal, as shown. The coefficient of friction between the rock and the plane is 0.1. The rock is accelerating up the plane at a rate of 0.35 ms⁻².

Find T, the tension in the rope pulling the rock.

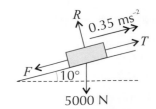

Connected particles, pegs and pulleys

Connected particles (see p.227) may be joined by a **taut**, **inextensible string** or a **rigid rod**. Connecting strings exert an **equal tension** force on both particles, and connecting rods exert an **equal thrust** or **tension** force. The particles will also have the same **magnitude** of **acceleration**.

To approach these problems you may need to resolve forces on each particle **separately** and form a pair of **simultaneous equations**, or you may be able to treat the **whole system** as **one object**.

Example

Two particles, A and B, of mass 6 kg and 8 kg respectively, are connected by a light, inextensible string. The particles are accelerating up a rough slope which is inclined at an angle of 20° to the horizontal. The force causing the acceleration has magnitude 200 N and acts on A in a direction parallel to the slope. The coefficient of friction between each particle and the slope is 0.6. Find the magnitude of the acceleration.

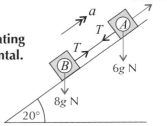

1. Treat them as one combined particle with mass 14 kg, experiencing reaction R and friction F. Resolve perpendicular to the plane ($\nwarrow$).

    $F_{net} = ma \Rightarrow R - 14g \cos 20° = 0$
    $R = 14g \cos 20°$ N

2. Find the total frictional force acting on the two particles.

    Friction, $F = \mu R = 0.6 \times 14g \cos 20°$
    $\qquad\qquad = 8.4g \cos 20°$

3. Resolve parallel to the plane ($\nearrow$).

    $F_{net} = ma$
    $\Rightarrow 200 - 14g \sin 20° - F = 14a$
    $\Rightarrow 200 - 14g \sin 20° - 8.4g \cos 20° = 14a$
    $\Rightarrow a = \textbf{5.41 ms}^{-2}$ **(3 s.f.)**

Example

A block of mass 3 kg is held in equilibrium on a rough plane inclined at 30° to the horizontal. It is attached via a light, inextensible string to a mass of M kg hanging vertically beneath a fixed smooth pulley, as shown. The coefficient of friction between A and the plane is 0.4.

Find M, given that A is on the point of sliding up the plane.

1. Resolve perpendicular to the plane for A ($\nwarrow$).

    $R - 3g \cos 30° = 3 \times 0 \Rightarrow R = 3g \cos 30°$

2. Friction is limiting.

    $F = \mu R = 0.4 \times 3g \cos 30° = 10.184...$ N

3. Resolve vertically for B ($\downarrow$).

    $Mg - T = M \times 0 \Rightarrow T = Mg$

4. Resolve parallel to the plane for A ($\nearrow$).

    $T - F - 3g \sin 30° = 3 \times 0$
    $Mg - 10.184... - 3g \sin 30° = 0$
    $M = \textbf{2.54 kg}$ **(to 3 s.f.)**

Exercise 3.5

Q1 A light, inextensible string passing
over a smooth pulley connects
boxes *A* and *B*, of mass 10 kg
and 8 kg respectively, as shown
in the diagram. The system is released
from rest and the boxes begin to accelerate
at a rate of 0.5 ms⁻². Find:

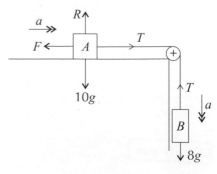

a) the tension in the connecting string, *T*.

b) the coefficient of friction between *A* and the surface.

Q2 Two identical objects, *A* and *B*, are connected by a rigid rod.
The objects are being pushed up a rough slope
inclined at an angle θ to the horizontal, by a force
of 20 N acting parallel to the slope.
Calculate the thrust force in the rod.

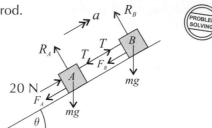

Problems may require use of the *'suvat'* equations — e.g. when a system is released from rest.

   **Particles *A* and *B*, of mass 4 kg and 10 kg
respectively, are connected by a light
inextensible string which passes over
a fixed smooth pulley. A force of 15 N
acts on *A* at an angle of 25° to a rough
horizontal plane, as shown. The coefficient
of friction between *A* and the plane is 0.7.
B is released from rest and falls *d* m vertically
to the ground in 2 seconds. Find *d*.**

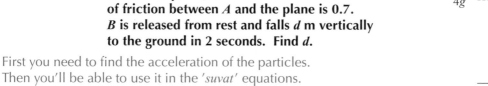

First you need to find the acceleration of the particles.
Then you'll be able to use it in the *'suvat'* equations.

1. Resolve vertically for *A* (↑).

$R + 15 \sin 25° - 4g = 0 \Rightarrow R = 32.860...$ N

2. Find the maximum frictional force.

$F = \mu R = 0.7 \times 32.860... = 23.002...$ N

3. Resolve horizontally for *A* (→).

$T - 23.002... - 15 \cos 25° = 4a$
$T = 4a + 36.597...$ — equation ①

4. Resolve vertically for *B* (↓).

$10g - T = 10a \Rightarrow T = 98 - 10a$ — equation ②

5. Substitute equation ① into equation ②.

$4a + 36.597... = 98 - 10a \Rightarrow a = 4.385...$ ms⁻²

6. Now list the variables and use
the *'suvat'* equations to find *d*.

$s = d, \quad u = 0, \quad t = 2, \quad a = 4.385...$
$d = ut + \frac{1}{2}at^2$
$= (0 \times 2) + \frac{1}{2}(4.385... \times 2^2) =$ **8.77 m (to 3 s.f.)**

Exercise 3.6

Q1

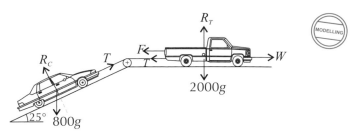

A truck of mass 2 tonnes is moving along a rough, horizontal plane ($\mu = 0.8$), and towing a car of mass 0.8 tonnes up a smooth plane, angled at 25° to the horizontal, as shown in the diagram above. The chain between the truck and the car is modelled as a light, inextensible string passing over a fixed, smooth pulley. The car is initially 25 m from the pulley and is towed 10 m towards the pulley in the first 30 seconds after starting from rest. The truck and the car move with constant acceleration.

Assume that the frictional force between the truck and the horizontal plane takes its maximum value.

a) Find the tension in the chain.

b) Calculate W, the driving force of the truck.

c) The chain connecting the truck to the car snaps. Assuming that all other forces remain constant, calculate the instantaneous acceleration of the truck.

Q2 A light, inextensible string attaches a block P of mass 60 kg to a block Q of mass 20 kg over a fixed, smooth pulley. P lies on a rough plane ($\mu = 0.1$) inclined at an angle of 50° to the horizontal, and Q hangs vertically below the pulley, as shown. The system is held in limiting equilibrium with P on the point of sliding down the plane by a second light, inextensible string attached to Q at one end and the horizontal ground at the other.

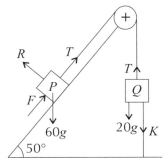

a) Find the tension in the second string, K.

b) The string fixing Q to the ground is cut. Given that Q does not hit the pulley, find the speed of P 5 seconds after it starts moving.

Q3 Particles A and B, of mass 8 kg and 9 kg respectively, are connected by a light, inextensible string which passes over a fixed, smooth pulley. A force of 60 N acts on A at an angle of 40° to the rough, horizontal plane that A rests on, away from the pulley. Particle A is held 20 cm from the pulley and, when released from rest, accelerates towards the pulley at a rate of 0.4 ms⁻².

a) Draw a diagram of the system, showing all the forces acting on the particles.

b) Find μ, the coefficient of friction between A and the plane.

c) Find the speed of A when it hits the pulley.

d) When A hits the pulley, the string breaks and B falls freely. Given that B was initially released from a position 60 cm above the horizontal ground, find the speed of B when it hits the ground.

Q4 Particles A and B, of mass 0.2 kg and 0.9 kg respectively, are connected by a light inextensible string. The string passes over a smooth pulley fixed to the apex of a wedge, as shown. A rests on a rough plane ($\mu_A = 0.7$) inclined at an angle of 40° to the horizontal and B rests on a different rough plane ($\mu_B = 0.05$) inclined at an angle of 20° to the horizontal. The particles are held at rest with A 35 cm from the pulley.

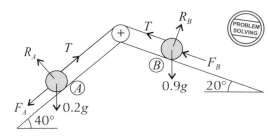

a) Given that A begins to accelerate up the slope when the particles are released from rest, find the tension in the string.

b) Find the speed of A when it reaches the pulley.

Q1 Each of the following diagrams shows a force and the angle it makes with the horizontal or vertical. Write each force in the form $(a\mathbf{i} + b\mathbf{j})$ N.

a)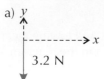

b)

c)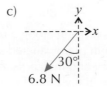

d)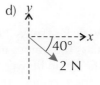

Q2 The diagram shows a force of magnitude 8 N acting on an object on an inclined plane. The component of the force in the direction parallel to the plane is 6.5 N.

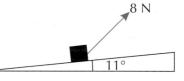

a) Find the angle between the direction of the force and the incline of the plane.

b) Find the horizontal component of the force.

Q3 The diagrams below show all the forces acting on a particle in equilibrium. Find the magnitudes of the missing forces acting on each particle.

a)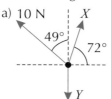

b)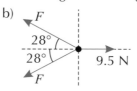

c)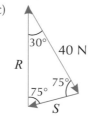

d)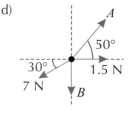

Q4 A particle, Q, of mass m kg, rests on a smooth plane which makes an angle of 60° to the vertical.
It is held in equilibrium by a light, inextensible string angled at 10° to the plane, as shown.
The magnitude of the tension in the string is 70 N.

Find the mass of Q and the normal reaction of the plane on Q.

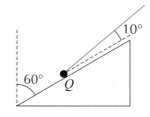

Q5 The diagrams below show a particle on the point of slipping on a rough surface. Calculate the coefficient of friction, μ, between each particle and the surface shown.

a)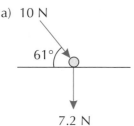

b)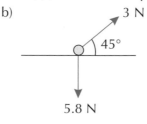

c)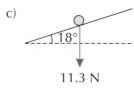

Q6 A brick lies at rest on a rough plane, inclined at an angle of θ to the horizontal. The brick is on the point of sliding. Given that $\mu = 0.3$, find the value of θ.

Q7 A stone of mass 8 kg is at rest on a rough slope inclined at 23° to the horizontal. A force of magnitude 9 N acts on the box at an angle of 10° to the slope. Calculate the coefficient of friction, μ, given that the force of 9 N is only just large enough to stop the stone sliding down the slope.

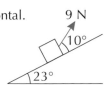

Q8 A horizontal force P, acting on a 2 kg mass, generates an acceleration of 0.3 ms^{-2}.

a) Given that the mass is in contact with a rough horizontal plane which resists motion with a force of 1 N, find P.

b) Find the coefficient of friction, μ, to 2 d.p.

Q9 Three forces are acting on a particle of mass 2.5 kg.

a) Two of the forces are given by $(4\mathbf{i} - 7\mathbf{j})$ N and $(6\mathbf{i} + 4\mathbf{j})$ N and the resultant force is $(5\mathbf{i} + \mathbf{j})$ N. Find the third force in vector form.

b) Find the distance travelled by the particle, 4 seconds after it begins accelerating from rest.

Q10 A brick of mass 1.2 kg is sliding down a rough plane which is inclined at 25° to the horizontal.

a) Given that the brick's acceleration is 0.3 ms^{-2}, find the coefficient of friction between the brick and the plane.

b) What assumptions have you made?

Q11 A mass of 3 kg is being pulled up a plane inclined at 20° to the horizontal by a rope parallel to the surface. Given that the mass is accelerating at 0.6 ms^{-2} and the coefficient of friction between the mass and the plane is 0.4, find T, the tension in the rope.

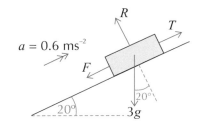

Q12 An army recruit of weight 600 N steps off a tower and accelerates down a "death slide" wire as shown. The recruit hangs from a light rope held between her hands and looped over the wire. The coefficient of friction between the rope and wire is 0.5. Given that the wire is 20 m long and makes an angle of 30° to the horizontal throughout its length, find how fast the recruit is travelling when she reaches the end of the wire.

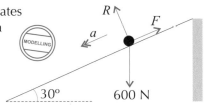

Q13 Two particles of mass 3 kg and 4 kg are connected by a light, inextensible string passing over a fixed, smooth pulley as shown. The 3 kg mass is on a smooth slope angled at 40° to the horizontal and the 4 kg mass hangs vertically below the pulley. Find:

a) the acceleration of the particles immediately after being released from rest,

b) the tension in the string,

c) the magnitude of force acting on the 3 kg mass in a direction parallel to the plane which would hold the particles in equilibrium.

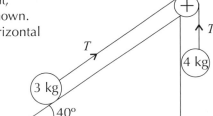

Chapter 31 — Moments

So far you've seen that a force applied to a particle can cause the particle to accelerate in a straight line. A force can also have a turning effect, called a moment — usually when a body is pivoted at a point.

1. Moments

A **moment** is the **turning effect** a force has **around a point**. The **larger the magnitude** of the force, and the **greater the distance** between the force and the **pivot point**, the **greater the moment**. Moments are either **clockwise** or **anticlockwise**.

You can use the following formula to find the moment of a force about a pivot point:

$$\text{Moment} = \begin{array}{c}\text{Magnitude}\\\text{of Force}\end{array} \times \begin{array}{c}\text{Perpendicular Distance}\\\text{from the line of action}\\\text{of the force to the pivot}\end{array}$$

Tip: The 'line of action' of the force is just the direction that the force acts in.

Or, more concisely: **Moment = Fd**. If the force F is measured in newtons and the distance d is measured in metres, then the moment is measured in newton-metres, **Nm**.

Examples   **Find the moment about the point O for the following light rods:**

a)

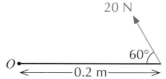

Method 1
1. Find the **component** of the force that **acts perpendicular** to the rod: $\quad F = 20 \sin 60°$
2. Using the formula:

$$\text{Moment} = 20 \sin 60° \times 0.2$$
$$= \textbf{3.46 Nm anticlockwise } (3 \text{ s.f.})$$

b)

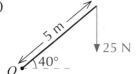

Method 2
1. Find the **perpendicular distance** from the pivot point to the force: $\quad d = 5 \cos 40°$
2. Using the formula:

$$\text{Moment} = 25 \times 5 \cos 40°$$
$$= \textbf{95.8 Nm clockwise } (3 \text{ s.f.})$$

Tip: These are two different methods for finding the moment when the force acts at an angle to the rod, but they will both give the same answer — use whichever makes the most sense to you.

Exercise 1.1

Q1   For each of the following light rods, find the moment of the force about A.

a)

b)
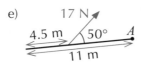

c)
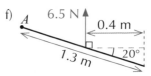

d)

e)

f)

Finding the sum of moments about a point

If there are **two or more** forces acting on a rod or beam, then you can find the **sum of the moments** about a particular point. If the sum of the moments about a pivot point is **not zero**, the rod will **turn** clockwise or anticlockwise about **that point**.

The diagram shows the light rod AB. A force of magnitude 5 N acts vertically downwards at point C. A force of magnitude 4 N acts at point B, making an angle of 30° with the rod, as shown:

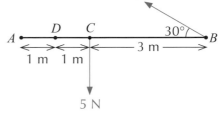

a) **The rod is pivoted at point A. Show that there is no overall turning effect about this point.**

Taking moments about A (with clockwise being the positive direction), and finding their sum:

$$\text{Sum of moments} = (5 \times 2) - (4 \sin 30° \times 5)$$
$$= 10 - 10 = 0 \text{ Nm}$$

Total moment is zero, so there is **no overall turning effect** about A.

b) **The rod is now pivoted at point D. Given that the forces acting at B and C are the same as in part a), will the rod rotate clockwise or anticlockwise about this point?**

Taking moments about D (with clockwise being the positive direction), and finding their sum:

$$\text{Sum of moments} = (5 \times 1) - (4 \sin 30° \times 4) = 5 - 8 = -3 \text{ Nm}$$

The sum of moments is negative, so the rod will **rotate anticlockwise**.

Exercise 1.2

Q1 A light rod, AB, has length 4 m. A force of magnitude 5 N is applied to A at an angle of 40° above the rod, as shown. A second force of magnitude 3 N is applied vertically upwards at the rod's midpoint. Find the sum of the moments of the forces acting on the rod about B.

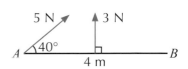

Q2 For each of the following light rods, find the sum of the moments about X.

a)
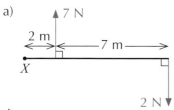

b)
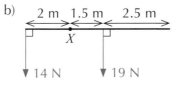

c)
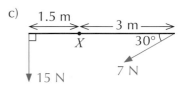

d)
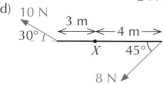

e)
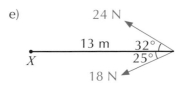

f)
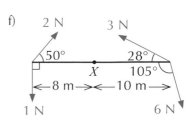

Q3 Two children sit on a light horizontal see-saw of length 3 m, pivoted at its centre. One child, of mass 30 kg, sits on one end, and the other child, whose mass is 25 kg, sits on the other end. Find the overall turning effect about the centre of the see-saw.

Q4 The diagram shows the light rod AB.

Find the range of possible values for X, given that AB rotates clockwise about the point O.

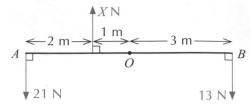

Q5 The diagram shows the light rod PQ.

Find the range of possible values for d which will cause PQ to rotate anticlockwise about the point O.

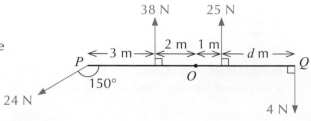

Moments in equilibrium

A rigid body which is in **static equilibrium** will **not move**. This means that there is **no resultant force** in **any direction** — any forces acting on the body will cancel each other out. It also means that the **sum of the moments** on the body **about any point** is **zero**. So, for a body in equilibrium:

> Total Clockwise Moment = Total Anticlockwise Moment

Example

The diagram below shows a light rod AB, of length 10 m. Particles of mass M_A kg and M_B kg are placed at A and B respectively. The rod is supported in equilibrium by two vertical reaction forces of magnitude 145 N and 90 N, as shown below:

Find the values of M_A and M_B.

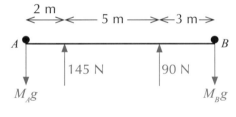

1. The rod is in equilibrium, so
   clockwise moments = anticlockwise moments

   Taking moments about A:
   $$M_B g \times 10 = (145 \times 2) + (90 \times 7)$$
   $$\Rightarrow M_B = 920 \div 98 = 9.387... = \textbf{9.39 kg} \text{ (3 s.f.)}$$

2. There is no resultant force acting on the rod. Resolving forces vertically ($\uparrow$):
   $$145 + 90 - M_A g - M_B g = 0 \Rightarrow M_A + M_B = 235 \div 9.8 = 23.979...$$
   $$\Rightarrow M_A = 23.979... - 9.387... = \textbf{14.6 kg} \text{ (3 s.f.)}$$

Exercise 1.3

Q1 Given that the light rod AB is in equilibrium, find the values of x and y in each diagram:

a)
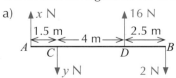

b)
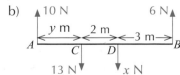

Q2 A light rod, AB, of length 4 m, supports an object of weight 4 N at its midpoint. It rests in equilibrium in a horizontal position on vertical supports at C and D, where $AC = 1$ m and $AD = 3.5$ m. Find:

a) the magnitude of the reaction force at C,   b) the magnitude of the reaction force at D.

Q3 A light rod, AB, has an object of mass 11 kg attached to it, 13 m from A. The rod is held in equilibrium by two light, inextensible strings. The strings are attached to the rod at A and B, making angles with the horizontal of $38°$ and α respectively, as shown. Find:

a) the length of the rod,   b) the value of α,

c) the magnitude of T, the tension in the string attached at B.

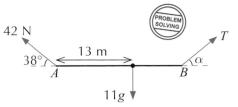

Centres of mass

The **centre of mass (COM)** of an object is the point where the object's **weight** can be considered to act. The mass of a **uniform beam** is spread evenly along the length of the beam, and so the centre of mass is at its **midpoint**. The centre of mass of a **non-uniform beam** could be at **any point** along the beam. When you're **taking moments** and **resolving forces** for a heavy (i.e. not light) beam, you need to remember to include the **weight** of the beam in your calculations.

 A 6 m long uniform beam AB of weight 40 N is supported at A by a vertical reaction R. AB is held horizontally by a vertical wire attached 1 m from the other end. A particle of weight of 30 N is placed 2 m from the support R.

Find the tension T in the wire and the force R.

- The beam is uniform, so its weight acts at its centre (i.e. 3 m from A). Taking moments about A:

  Clockwise moments = Anticlockwise moments
  $(30 \times 2) + (40 \times 3) = 5T$
  $\Rightarrow T = 180 \div 5 \Rightarrow \mathbf{T = 36\ N}$

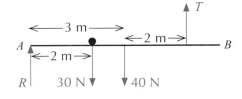

- Resolving vertically ($\uparrow$):
  $T + R - 30 - 40 = 0 \Rightarrow R = 70 - T = 70 - 36 \Rightarrow \mathbf{R = 34\ N}$

The point of tilting

If a rod is '**about to tilt**' about a point, then any **normal reactions** acting at any other supports along the rod will be **zero**. The **tension** in any strings supporting the rod at any other points will also be **zero**.

 A non-uniform wooden plank of mass M kg rests horizontally on supports at A and B, as shown. When a bucket of water of mass 18 kg is placed at point C, the plank is in equilibrium, and is on the point of tilting about B.

Find the value of M and the magnitude of the reaction at B.

- The plank is on the point of tilting about B, so $R_A = 0$. Taking moments about B:
  $(18g \times 1.2) + (R_A \times d) = Mg \times 0.8$
  $(18g \times 1.2) + 0 = Mg \times 0.8 \Rightarrow \mathbf{M = 27\ kg}$

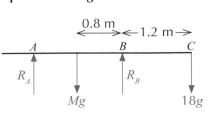

- Resolving vertically ($\uparrow$):
  $R_A + R_B - Mg - 18g = 0 \Rightarrow 0 + R_B = 27g + 18g \Rightarrow \mathbf{R_B = 441\ N}$

Exercise 1.4

Q1 A non-uniform beam, AB, of mass 3 kg and length 1.6 m, rests horizontally in equilibrium on vertical supports at A and B. The normal reaction at A is 12 N. Find:

a) the magnitude of the normal reaction at B,

b) the distance of the centre of mass of the beam from A.

Q2 A uniform rod, AB, of mass 8 kg and length 14 m, rests horizontally in equilibrium on vertical supports at C and D. Given that C is 2.5 m from A and D is 1.5 m from B, find the magnitudes of the reaction forces at C and D.

Q3 A uniform rod, AB, of length 5 m and mass M kg, rests horizontally in equilibrium on supports at C and D, as shown. If the magnitude of the normal reaction at C is 49 N, find:

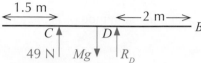

a) the magnitude of the normal reaction at D, b) the mass, M, of the rod.

Q4 A non-uniform rod, AB, has length 4.8 m and mass 500 g. It rests horizontally in equilibrium on vertical supports at C and D, where $AC = 1.6$ m and $AD = 4.2$ m, and is held by a light, inextensible, vertical string attached at A. The normal reaction at D is twice that at C, and the tension in the string is 1 N.

a) Find the magnitudes of the normal reactions at C and D.

b) Find the distance of the centre of mass of the rod from A.

Q5 A non-uniform rod, AB, of length 6 m, is held horizontally in equilibrium by two light, inextensible strings, as shown. The centre of mass of the rod is 2.7 m from A. Find:

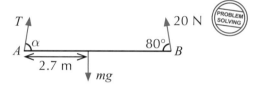

a) the mass of the rod, b) the value of α,

c) the magnitude of the tension in the string at A.

Q6 A non-uniform rod, AB, of mass 2 kg and length 2.4 m, is held horizontally in equilibrium by two light, inextensible strings, as shown in the diagram. Find:

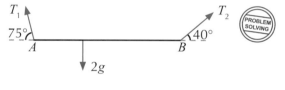

a) the tension in each string,

b) the distance of the centre of mass of the rod from A.

Q7 A uniform rod, AB, of mass 9 kg, is held in equilibrium by a fixed vertical wire at C and a support at D, as shown. When an object of mass 3 kg is placed at B, the rod is still horizontal and in equilibrium, but is on the point of tilting clockwise about D. Find the length of the rod.

Q8 A uniform beam, AB, has length 5 m and mass 8 kg. It is held horizontally in equilibrium by vertical ropes at B and the point C, 1 m from A.

a) Find the tension in each rope.

b) When a particle of mass 16 kg is placed on the beam, the beam remains horizontal and in equilibrium, but is on the point of tilting about C. Find the distance of the particle from A.

Q9 A painter of mass 80 kg stands on a horizontal non-uniform 4 m plank, AB, of mass 20 kg. The plank rests on supports 1 m from each end, at C and D. The painter places paint pots, of mass 2.5 kg, 0.2 m from each end of the plank.

a) He stands at the centre of mass of the plank and finds that the reaction forces at C and D are in the ratio 4:1. Find the distance of the centre of mass of the plank from A.

b) He uses up all the paint in the pot near A, and discards the pot. He then stands on the plank at a point between D and B, and the plank is on the point of tilting about D. How far is he from B?

Laminas

A **lamina** is a flat 2D object (its thickness can be ignored). The centre of mass of a **uniform rectangular** lamina is at the symmetrical centre of the rectangle.

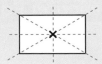

 A uniform lamina, *ABCD*, of weight 8 N, is pivoted at point *A*. The lamina is held in equilibrium by a vertical force *F* acting at point *C* as shown.

a) **Find the horizontal and vertical distances of the centre of mass of the lamina from *A*.**

The centre of mass is at the centre of the lamina, so:

The horizontal distance is $3 \div 2 = $ **1.5 m** and the vertical distance is $1 \div 2 = $ **0.5 m**

b) **Find the magnitude of the force *F*.**

Both the lamina's weight and *F* act vertically, so the perpendicular distance from each force to the pivot is just the horizontal distance.

Taking moments about *A*: $8 \times 1.5 = F \times 3 \Rightarrow F = 12 \div 3 = $ **4 N**

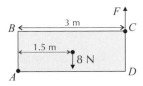

If there are forces acting **at angles** to the lamina, it's usually easier to resolve them **perpendicular** and **parallel** to the lamina's base. Remember that **both components** will have a separate turning effect.

 A uniform rectangular lamina of mass 12 kg is pivoted at one corner at *A*. A light, inextensible string attached at the opposite corner applies a tension force *T* to the lamina as shown.

Given that the string holds the lamina in equilibrium at an angle of 20° to the horizontal, find the tension in the string.

1. Here, the lamina's **weight** acts at an angle to its base. Find the components of its weight parallel and perpendicular to the base of the lamina.

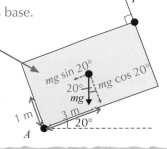

2. Taking moments about *A*:
$(mg \cos 20° \times 3) = (mg \sin 20° \times 1) + (T \times 6)$
$\Rightarrow 6T = mg(3 \cos 20° - \sin 20°)$
$\Rightarrow T = 19.6(2.4770...) = $ **48.6 N** (3 s.f.)

Tip: You could do the above example **without** breaking the weight into components — instead, you'd find the horizontal distance from *A* to the COM, which is the **perpendicular distance** from *A* to the **weight force**.

Exercise 1.5

Q1 A uniform rectangular lamina *ABCD* of weight 6 N is pivoted at point *A* and acted on by a force *F* at point *C*. *F* has magnitude 10 N, and acts at an angle of θ to the horizontal, as shown. Find the sum of the moments about *A* if:

a) $x = 10$, $y = 6$, $\theta = 90°$ b) $x = 1$, $y = 5$, $\theta = 0°$ c) $x = 4$, $y = 8$, $\theta = 270°$
d) $x = 7$, $y = 6$, $\theta = 180°$ e) $x = 5$, $y = 5$, $\theta = 30°$ f) $x = 1$, $y = 11$, $\theta = 120°$

Q2 A uniform rectangular lamina of mass *m* has corners at the following coordinates: *A* (0, 0), *B* (−2, 8), *C* (2, 9), *D* (4, 1). The lamina is pivoted at *A*. A horizontal force of 8 N acts on the lamina in the negative *x*-direction at *D*, and a vertical force of 11 N pulls upwards on the lamina at *C*.

a) Draw a diagram to show this information, given that gravity acts in the negative *y*-direction.

b) Given that the system is in equilibrium, find *m*.

2. Reaction Forces and Friction in Moments

If a **rigid body** is fixed to a **surface** by a **hinge** or **pivot**, you can deal with the reaction force on the body from the hinge by **splitting it up** into two **components**, **parallel** and **perpendicular** to the **surface**.

Example

A uniform rod, *AB*, of mass 2 kg and length 1.2 m, is freely hinged on a vertical wall. The rod is held horizontally in equilibrium by a light, inextensible string attached at *C*, 0.4 m from *B*, which makes an angle of 45° with the rod, as shown. Find the tension in the string and the magnitude of the reaction force, *R*, on the rod at *A*.

1. Taking moments about *A*:
   $T \sin 45° \times (1.2 - 0.4) = 2g \times 0.6$
   $T \sin 45° = 14.7 \Rightarrow T = 20.788... = \textbf{20.8 N}$ (3 s.f.)

2. Split *R* into horizontal and vertical components, R_H and R_V.

3. Resolving horizontally (→):
   $R_H - T \cos 45° = 0 \Rightarrow R_H = (20.788...) \cos 45° = 14.7$ N

4. Resolving vertically (↑): $R_V + T \sin 45° - 2g = 0 \Rightarrow R_V = 2g - (20.788...) \sin 45° = 4.9$ N

5. Use Pythagoras' theorem to find the magnitude of *R*:
   $|R| = \sqrt{R_H^2 + R_V^2} = \sqrt{14.7^2 + 4.9^2} = \textbf{15.5 N}$ (3 s.f.)

Example

A non-uniform rod, *AB*, of length 6 m and mass 0.1 kg, is freely hinged on a vertical wall. The rod is supported by a light strut at an angle of 70° to the wall, as shown. The strut exerts a thrust of 16 N at the midpoint of the rod. A particle of weight 2 N rests at *B*, and the rod is in horizontal equilibrium.

Find the distance of the centre of mass of the rod from *A*, and the magnitude and direction of the reaction force on the rod at *A*.

1. Let *x* be the distance of the centre of mass of the rod from *A*. Taking moments about *A*:
   $(0.1g \times x) + (2 \times 6) = 16 \cos 70° \times 3 \Rightarrow 0.1gx = 4.416... \Rightarrow x = \textbf{4.51 m}$ (3 s.f.)

2. Resolving horizontally (→): $16 \sin 70° + R_H = 0 \Rightarrow R_H = -15.035...$ N (so R_H acts ←)

3. Resolving vertically (↑): $16 \cos 70° + R_V - 0.1g - 2 = 0 \Rightarrow R_V = -2.492...$ N (so R_V acts ↓)

4. Use Pythagoras' theorem to find the magnitude:
   $|R| = \sqrt{R_H^2 + R_V^2} = \sqrt{(15.035...)^2 + (2.492...)^2} = \textbf{15.2 N}$ (3 s.f.)

5. Use trigonometry to find the direction:

   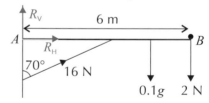

   $\theta = \tan^{-1}\left(\dfrac{2.492...}{15.035...}\right) = 9.41...°$
   So direction = $180° + 9.41...° = \textbf{189°}$ (3 s.f.)

Tip: You may be able to work out the correct direction of the reaction force components from the question. But it doesn't matter if you pick the wrong directions (as we did above), you'll just get negative values for them.

Exercise 2.1

Q1 A uniform rod, *AB*, of mass 3 kg and length 4 m, is freely hinged to a vertical wall at *A*. The rod is held horizontal in equilibrium by a light vertical wire attached to the rod 1 m from *A*, as shown. The reaction force, *R*, at the hinge, acts vertically downwards.

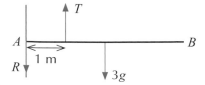

a) Find the magnitude of the tension in the wire.

b) Find the magnitude of the reaction force, *R*, acting on the rod at *A*.

Q2 A uniform rod, *AB*, of mass 0.6 kg and length 0.8 m, is freely hinged to a vertical wall at *A*. The rod is held horizontally and in equilibrium by a light wire attached to the rod 0.6 m from *A*. The wire makes an angle of 60° with the rod, as shown. Find:

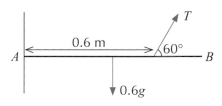

a) the magnitude of the tension in the wire.

b) the magnitude and direction of the reaction force acting on the rod at *A*.

Q3 A non-uniform beam, *AB*, of mass 1.5 kg and length 2.4 m, is freely hinged to a vertical wall at *A*. The centre of mass of the beam is 0.6 m from *A*. One end of a light, inextensible string is attached to *B*, and the other end is fixed to the wall, directly above *A*, as shown. The string makes an angle of 20° with the beam. A body of mass 0.5 kg is placed at the beam's midpoint. The beam is horizontal and in equilibrium. Find:

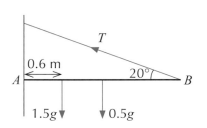

a) the tension in the string.

b) the magnitude and direction of the reaction force acting on the beam at *A*.

Q4 A non-uniform rod, *AB*, of mass 1.8 kg and length 7 m, is freely hinged to a vertical wall at *A*. A light strut, fixed to the wall, supports the rod at its midpoint, so the rod is kept horizontal and in equilibrium. The strut makes an angle of 71° with the wall, and the thrust in the strut has magnitude 95 N. A force of magnitude 3.5 N is applied to the rod at *B*, at an angle of 80° to the rod, as shown.

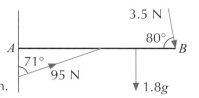

a) Find the distance of the centre of mass of the rod from *A*.

b) Find the magnitude and direction of the reaction force acting on the rod at *A*.

Q5 A uniform plank, *AB*, of mass 1.75 kg and length 8 m, is freely hinged to a vertical wall at *A*. An object of mass 2.25 kg is placed on the plank at *B*. The plank is kept horizontal and in equilibrium by a light wire fixed at its midpoint, at an angle of 30° above the plank, and a light strut fixed at *C*, 2 m along the plank from *A*, at an angle of 30° to the wall, as shown. The thrust in the strut has magnitude 110 N.

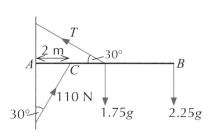

a) Find *T*, the magnitude of the tension in the wire.

b) Calculate the magnitude and direction of the reaction force acting on the plank at *A*.

Q6 A pub sign is suspended from a uniform rod of mass 2 kg and length 1 m by a pair of light, inextensible strings attached 20 cm from each end. The rod is held in equilibrium by a light wire attached at *B*, which makes an angle of 25° with the horizontal. Given that the tension in each string has a magnitude of 8 N, find the magnitude of the tension in the wire, T_W, and the magnitude and direction of the reaction force on the rod at *A*.

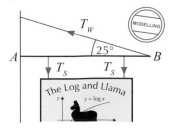

Friction

You saw in Chapter 30 that if a body is in contact with a **rough** surface, then a **frictional force** will act between the body and the surface to oppose motion. The frictional force can take a range of values, and will reach its maximum ($F = \mu R$) when the body is **on the point of moving**, or in 'limiting equilibrium'. If you have a rigid body resting on a rough surface, you will have a **normal reaction** force acting **perpendicular** to the surface, and a **frictional force** acting **parallel** to it, in the **opposite** direction to any potential motion.

 A non-uniform rod, AB, rests against a rough vertical wall at A. The rod is held in limiting equilibrium perpendicular to the wall by a light, inextensible string attached at B at an angle of 22° above the rod. The tension in the string is 42 N, the length of the rod is 5.5 m and the centre of mass of the rod is 1.7 m from A.

Find the mass of the rod, m, and the coefficient of friction, μ, between the wall and the rod.

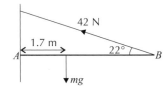

1. Taking moments about A:

   $mg \times 1.7 = 42 \sin 22° \times 5.5$

   $\Rightarrow m = 86.534... \div 16.66 = 5.194... = \mathbf{5.19\ kg}$ (3 s.f.)

2. There will be two forces acting at A — the normal reaction, R, acting horizontally, and friction, F, acting vertically. Resolving horizontally ($\rightarrow$):

   $R - 42 \cos 22° = 0 \Rightarrow R = 38.941...\ N$

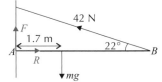

3. Resolving vertically ($\uparrow$): $\quad F + 42 \sin 22° - mg = 0$

   $\Rightarrow F = 50.902... - 15.733... = 35.168...\ N$

4. The rod is in limiting equilibrium, so friction is at its maximum:

   $F = \mu R \Rightarrow 35.168... = \mu \times 38.941... \Rightarrow \mathbf{\mu = 0.90}$ (2 d.p.)

Exercise 2.2

Q1 A uniform rod, AB, of mass 12 kg and length 16 m, rests against a rough, vertical wall at A. The rod is held horizontally in limiting equilibrium by a light wire attached at B, at an angle of 20° to the rod.

a) Find the magnitude of the tension in the wire.

b) Find the coefficient of friction between the wall and the rod.

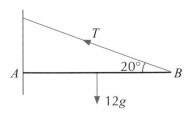

Q2 A non-uniform plank, AB, of mass 5.4 kg and length 11 m, rests with A against a rough, vertical wall. A wire with tension of magnitude 86 N is fixed to B, at an angle of 10° to the plank, keeping the plank horizontal. A particle of mass M kg rests on the plank at B, as shown. The plank is in limiting equilibrium. Given that the coefficient of friction between the wall and the plank is 0.55, find:

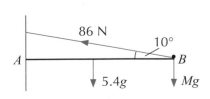

a) the value of M,   b) the distance of the centre of mass of the plank from A.

Q3   Eliza is holding a nail in place against a rough wall. The nail is modelled
     as a uniform rod with length 5 cm and mass 2 grams. Eliza applies
     a force D with her finger, acting at an angle of $\theta°$ to the horizontal,
     such that the nail is horizontal and in equilibrium, and is on the point
     of slipping down the wall. Given that the coefficient of friction
     between the nail and the wall is $\mu = 0.7$, calculate the magnitude of the force D and the angle θ.

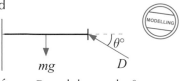

Q4   A uniform rod, AB, of mass 20 kg and length 2 m, is held horizontally
     in equilibrium against a rough wall by a light wire fixed to the wall
     at point C, which is 1 m above point A. The other end of the wire
     is attached at B. Given that the rod is on the point of slipping down
     the wall, find the tension in the wire and the coefficient of friction
     between the rod and the wall.

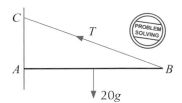

'Ladder' questions

When a rigid body rests at an angle against the ground and a wall (a simple example of a situation like
this is a **ladder**), it will experience a **normal reaction** force from the **ground**, a **normal reaction** force
from the **wall**, and possibly **frictional forces** between the body and either of the surfaces, depending on
whether they are **rough** or **smooth**.

There are four possible combinations in these situations:

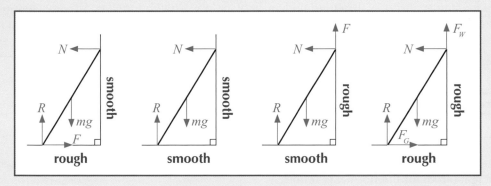

A ladder rests against a smooth vertical wall at an angle of 65° to rough
horizontal ground. The ladder has mass 4.5 kg and length $5x$ m.
A cat of mass 1.3 kg sits on the ladder at C, $4x$ m from the base.
The ladder is in limiting equilibrium.

**Modelling the ladder as a uniform rod and the cat as a particle,
find the coefficient of friction between the ground and the ladder.**

1.   Taking moments about the base of the ladder:

     $N \sin 65° \times 5x = (4.5g \cos 65° \times 2.5x) + (1.3g \cos 65° \times 4x)$
     $(4.531...)xN = (46.593..)x + (21.536...)x$
     $\Rightarrow N = (68.130...)x \div (4.531...)x = 15.034...$ N

2.   Resolving vertically: $R = 1.3g + 4.5g = 56.84$ N

3.   Resolving horizontally: $F = N$

4.   The ladder is in limiting equilibrium, so $F = \mu R$:

     $F = \mu R \Rightarrow N = \mu R \Rightarrow 15.034... = \mu \times 56.84 \Rightarrow \mu = 15.034... \div 56.84 = \mathbf{0.26}$ (2 d.p.)

Example A uniform ladder of mass 11 kg and length 4 m rests against a smooth vertical wall, at an angle of 58° to rough horizontal ground. The coefficient of friction between the ladder and the ground is 0.45. A bucket of water is hung 3 m from the base of the ladder.

What is the maximum possible mass of the bucket for which the ladder remains in equilibrium?

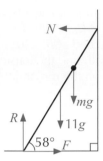

1. Resolving vertically: $R = 11g + mg = g(11 + m)$

2. Resolving horizontally: $F = N$

3. The ladder is in limiting equilibrium, so $F = \mu R$:
$$F = \mu R \implies N = 0.45R = 0.45g(11 + m)$$

4. Taking moments about the base of the ladder:
$$N \sin 58° \times 4 = (11g \cos 58° \times 2) + (mg \cos 58° \times 3)$$
$$1.8g(11 + m) \sin 58° = 22g \cos 58° + 3mg \cos 58°$$
$$19.8 \sin 58° - 22 \cos 58° = m(3 \cos 58° - 1.8 \sin 58°)$$
$$\implies m = 5.133... \div 0.06327... = \textbf{81.1 kg} \text{ (3 s.f.)}$$

Bodies supported along their lengths

Rather than leaning against a wall, a rigid body may be held in equilibrium by resting on **supports** at points along its length. You can solve problems like this just as before, by **resolving forces** and **taking moments**. You need to know whether the **ground** and **supports** are **rough** or **smooth**, and you should also remember that the **normal reaction** at a **support** will always act **perpendicular** to the body.

Example A uniform rod, AB, of length 3.3 m and weight 10 N, rests with A on rough horizontal ground. The rod is supported by a smooth peg at C, where $AC = 2.4$ m, in such a way that the rod makes an angle of 28° with the ground. A particle of weight 25 N is placed at B.

Given that the rod is in limiting equilibrium, find the magnitude of the normal reaction, N, at the peg and the magnitude of the frictional force, F, between the rod and the ground.

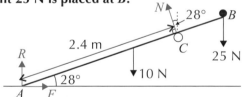

1. Taking moments about A:
$$2.4N = (25 \cos 28° \times 3.3) + (10 \cos 28° \times (3.3 \div 2))$$
$$\implies N = 36.421... = \textbf{36.4 N} \text{ (3 s.f.)}$$

The rod is uniform so its weight acts at its midpoint

2. Resolving horizontally:
$$F = N \sin 28° = (36.421...) \sin 28° \implies F = \textbf{17.1 N} \text{ (3 s.f.)}$$

Exercise 2.3

Q1   A uniform ladder of mass 11 kg and length 7 m rests against a rough vertical wall, at an angle of 60° to smooth, horizontal ground, as shown. A horizontal force of magnitude 35 N is applied to the base of the ladder, keeping it in limiting equilibrium, with the ladder on the point of sliding up the wall. Find:

a) the magnitude of the normal reaction of the wall on the ladder,

b) the frictional force between the wall and the ladder,

c) the coefficient of friction between the wall and the ladder.

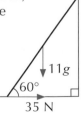

464   Chapter 31 Moments

Q2 A uniform beam, *AB*, of mass 1.6 kg and length 1.5 m, rests with *A* on rough, horizontal ground. The beam is supported by a smooth peg at *C*, where *AC* = 1.1 m, so that it makes an angle of 20° with the horizontal, as shown. The beam is on the point of slipping. Find:

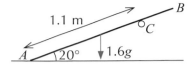

a) the magnitude of the normal reaction of the peg on the beam,

b) the magnitude of the normal reaction of the ground on the beam,

c) the magnitude of the frictional force between the ground and the beam,

d) the coefficient of friction between the ground and the beam.

Q3 A uniform ladder of mass 10 kg and length 6 m rests with one end on rough, horizontal ground and the other end against a smooth, vertical wall. The coefficient of friction between the ground and the ladder is 0.3, and the ladder makes an angle of 65° with the ground. A girl of mass 50 kg begins to climb the ladder. How far up the ladder can she climb before the ladder slips?

Q4 A uniform ladder of length 4 m and weight 80 N rests against a smooth, vertical wall on rough horizontal ground. The ladder makes an angle of 50° with the horizontal, and the coefficient of friction between the ground and the ladder is 0.75. A horizontal force, *D*, is exerted on the ladder, 3 m from its base. Given that the ladder is on the point of slipping down the wall, find the magnitude of *D*, stating whether the force acts towards or away from the wall.

Q5 A uniform ladder of mass 9 kg and length 4.8 m rests in limiting equilibrium with one end on rough, horizontal ground and the other end against a rough, vertical wall. The normal reactions at the wall and the ground have magnitude 22 N and 75 N respectively. Find:

a) the angle that the ladder makes with the ground,

b) the coefficient of friction between the wall and the ladder,

c) the coefficient of friction between the ground and the ladder.

Q6 A uniform beam, *AB*, of weight *W* N rests in limiting equilibrium at an angle of 30° to the horizontal on a rough peg at *A* and a smooth peg at *C*, where *AC* = 0.75*AB*. The reaction forces at *A* and *C* are both perpendicular to the beam.

Find the coefficient of friction between the peg and the beam at *A*.

Q7 A uniform beam *AB* of weight 12 N and length 5 m rests on a smooth surface at *A* and a rough peg at *C*, 4 m from *A*. The beam makes an angle of 40° with the horizontal, as shown. Given that the beam is in equilibrium, find the range of possible values of the coefficient of friction between the beam and the peg.

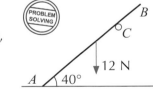

Q8 A uniform beam, AB, of weight 50 N and length 2 m, rests with A on rough, horizontal ground, as shown. The beam is supported at an angle of 35° to the ground by a smooth peg at *C*, where *AC* = 1.4 m. A horizontal force of magnitude 10 N is applied to the beam at B.

Find the range of values of the coefficient of friction between the ground and the beam for which the beam will remain in equilibrium.

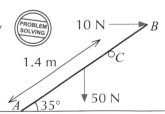

Q9 Robert holds an 8 m uniform ladder in place against a smooth vertical wall by applying a horizontal force of *K* N to it, 1 m from the base of the ladder. The ladder weighs 100 N, and makes an angle of 75° with the rough horizontal floor, where μ = 0.1. Given that the ladder remains at rest, find the range of possible values for the magnitude of the force *K*.

Q1 For each of the following light rods, find the moment of the force about A.

a)
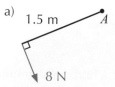

b)
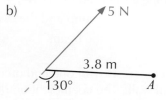

c)
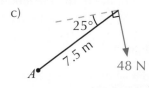

Q2 A horizontal uniform rod AB of length 12 m and mass 1.6 kg is acted on by an upward vertical force of magnitude 23 N at B. Find the sum of the moments about A.

Q3 A uniform rod, AB, has mass 4.7 kg and length 6.8 m. The rod is pivoted at A and a particle of mass 0.75 kg is placed on the rod 1.1 m from B. Find the sum of the moments about A of the forces acting on the rod when the rod is horizontal.

Q4 The diagram shows a light rod held horizontally in equilibrium by two vertical strings. Find the magnitudes of the forces P and Q.

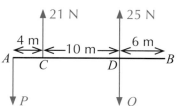

Q5 The diagram shows a light rod held horizontally in equilibrium by two vertical strings. Find U and l, giving your answers in N and m respectively.

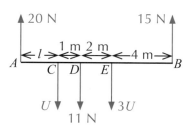

Q6 A 60 kg uniform beam, AE, of length 14 m, is horizontal and in equilibrium, supported by two vertical ropes attached to B and D, as shown. Find the tension in the two ropes.

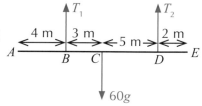

Q7 A uniform rod of mass 3.5 kg is pivoted about one of its ends. When the rod is horizontal, there is a moment of 205.8 Nm about the pivot. Assuming that the only forces acting on the rod are its weight and the reaction at the pivot, find the rod's length.

Q8 A non-uniform rod of mass 1.5 kg rests horizontally in equilibrium on supports at A and B, as shown. When a downwards force of magnitude F N is applied to the rod at C, the rod remains horizontal and in equilibrium, but is on the point of tilting about B, where the normal reaction has magnitude 44 N. Given that the distance between B and the centre of mass of the rod is 2.5 m, find:

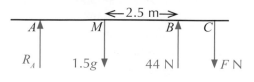

a) the value of F,

b) the distance between the points B and C.

Q9 A uniform beam, *AB*, of mass 2 kg and length 1.6 m, is freely hinged to a vertical wall at *A*. The beam is held horizontally in equilibrium by a force of magnitude 30 N applied at *B*, at an angle α to the horizontal, as shown.

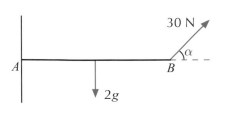

a) Find the value of α.

b) Find the magnitude and direction of the reaction force in the hinge at *A*.

Q10 A non-uniform beam, *AB*, of mass 5 kg and length *b* m, is freely hinged to a vertical wall at *A*. The beam is held in equilibrium at an angle of 30° to the horizontal by a force of magnitude 40 N, applied horizontally at *B*, as shown.

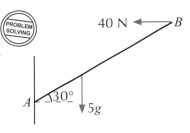

Find the distance of the centre of mass of the beam from *A*. Give your answer in terms of *b*.

Q11 A uniform rod, *AB*, of mass 3 kg and length 1.2 m, rests horizontally in equilibrium with *A* against a rough, vertical wall. A wire is attached to the rod at *B*. The other end of the wire is attached to the wall, 0.9 m directly above *A*. A particle of mass 5 kg rests on the rod, *x* m from *A*, as shown, and the tension in the wire has magnitude 85 N. Find:

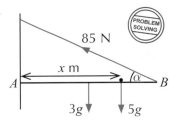

a) the value of *x*,

b) the range of possible values for the coefficient of friction between the wall and the rod at *A*.

Q12 A uniform ladder of mass 20 kg rests with one end on rough, horizontal ground, and the other end against a smooth, vertical wall. The ladder makes an angle of 60° with the horizontal, and is on the point of slipping.

a) Show that the coefficient of friction between the ladder and the ground is $\frac{\sqrt{3}}{6}$.

b) A person of mass 60 kg stands three-quarters of the way up the ladder. Find the magnitude of the minimum horizontal force which must be applied to the base of the ladder to keep it in limiting equilibrium.

Q13 A uniform ladder of mass 25 kg and length 9 m rests with one end on rough, horizontal ground and the other end against a smooth, vertical wall. The ladder makes an angle of 68° with the horizontal, as shown. A window cleaner of mass 76 kg stands two-thirds of the way up the ladder, and the ladder is in equilibrium.

Find the range of possible values of the coefficient of friction between the ground and the ladder.

Q14 A uniform beam, *AB*, of mass 14 kg and length 15 m, rests with *A* on rough, horizontal ground. The beam is supported by a smooth peg at *C*, where *AC* = 13 m, so that it makes an angle of 18° with the horizontal, as shown. The beam is on the point of slipping.

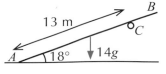

Find the coefficient of friction between the ground and the beam at *A*.

Statistical Tables

The binomial cumulative distribution function

The values below show $P(X \leq x)$, where $X \sim B(n, p)$.

			0.05	0.10	0.15	0.20	0.25	0.30	0.35	0.40	0.45	0.50
$p =$												
$n = 5$	$x =$	0	0.7738	0.5905	0.4437	0.3277	0.2373	0.1681	0.1160	0.0778	0.0503	0.0313
		1	0.9774	0.9185	0.8352	0.7373	0.6328	0.5282	0.4284	0.3370	0.2562	0.1875
		2	0.9988	0.9914	0.9734	0.9421	0.8965	0.8369	0.7648	0.6826	0.5931	0.5000
		3	1.0000	0.9995	0.9978	0.9933	0.9844	0.9692	0.9460	0.9130	0.8688	0.8125
		4	1.0000	1.0000	0.9999	0.9997	0.9990	0.9976	0.9947	0.9898	0.9815	0.9688
$n = 6$	$x =$	0	0.7351	0.5314	0.3771	0.2621	0.1780	0.1176	0.0754	0.0467	0.0277	0.0156
		1	0.9672	0.8857	0.7765	0.6554	0.5339	0.4202	0.3191	0.2333	0.1636	0.1094
		2	0.9978	0.9842	0.9527	0.9011	0.8306	0.7443	0.6471	0.5443	0.4415	0.3438
		3	0.9999	0.9987	0.9941	0.9830	0.9624	0.9295	0.8826	0.8208	0.7447	0.6563
		4	1.0000	0.9999	0.9996	0.9984	0.9954	0.9891	0.9777	0.9590	0.9308	0.8906
		5	1.0000	1.0000	1.0000	0.9999	0.9998	0.9993	0.9982	0.9959	0.9917	0.9844
$n = 7$	$x =$	0	0.6983	0.4783	0.3206	0.2097	0.1335	0.0824	0.0490	0.0280	0.0152	0.0078
		1	0.9556	0.8503	0.7166	0.5767	0.4449	0.3294	0.2338	0.1586	0.1024	0.0625
		2	0.9962	0.9743	0.9262	0.8520	0.7564	0.6471	0.5323	0.4199	0.3164	0.2266
		3	0.9998	0.9973	0.9879	0.9667	0.9294	0.8740	0.8002	0.7102	0.6083	0.5000
		4	1.0000	0.9998	0.9988	0.9953	0.9871	0.9712	0.9444	0.9037	0.8471	0.7734
		5	1.0000	1.0000	0.9999	0.9996	0.9987	0.9962	0.9910	0.9812	0.9643	0.9375
		6	1.0000	1.0000	1.0000	1.0000	0.9999	0.9998	0.9994	0.9984	0.9963	0.9922
$n = 8$	$x =$	0	0.6634	0.4305	0.2725	0.1678	0.1001	0.0576	0.0319	0.0168	0.0084	0.0039
		1	0.9428	0.8131	0.6572	0.5033	0.3671	0.2553	0.1691	0.1064	0.0632	0.0352
		2	0.9942	0.9619	0.8948	0.7969	0.6785	0.5518	0.4278	0.3154	0.2201	0.1445
		3	0.9996	0.9950	0.9786	0.9437	0.8862	0.8059	0.7064	0.5941	0.4770	0.3633
		4	1.0000	0.9996	0.9971	0.9896	0.9727	0.9420	0.8939	0.8263	0.7396	0.6367
		5	1.0000	1.0000	0.9998	0.9988	0.9958	0.9887	0.9747	0.9502	0.9115	0.8555
		6	1.0000	1.0000	1.0000	0.9999	0.9996	0.9987	0.9964	0.9915	0.9819	0.9648
		7	1.0000	1.0000	1.0000	1.0000	1.0000	0.9999	0.9998	0.9993	0.9983	0.9961
$n = 9$	$x =$	0	0.6302	0.3874	0.2316	0.1342	0.0751	0.0404	0.0207	0.0101	0.0046	0.0020
		1	0.9288	0.7748	0.5995	0.4362	0.3003	0.1960	0.1211	0.0705	0.0385	0.0195
		2	0.9916	0.9470	0.8591	0.7382	0.6007	0.4628	0.3373	0.2318	0.1495	0.0898
		3	0.9994	0.9917	0.9661	0.9144	0.8343	0.7297	0.6089	0.4826	0.3614	0.2539
		4	1.0000	0.9991	0.9944	0.9804	0.9511	0.9012	0.8283	0.7334	0.6214	0.5000
		5	1.0000	0.9999	0.9994	0.9969	0.9900	0.9747	0.9464	0.9006	0.8342	0.7461
		6	1.0000	1.0000	1.0000	0.9997	0.9987	0.9957	0.9888	0.9750	0.9502	0.9102
		7	1.0000	1.0000	1.0000	1.0000	0.9999	0.9996	0.9986	0.9962	0.9909	0.9805
		8	1.0000	1.0000	1.0000	1.0000	1.0000	1.0000	0.9999	0.9997	0.9992	0.9980
$n = 10$	$x =$	0	0.5987	0.3487	0.1969	0.1074	0.0563	0.0282	0.0135	0.0060	0.0025	0.0010
		1	0.9139	0.7361	0.5443	0.3758	0.2440	0.1493	0.0860	0.0464	0.0233	0.0107
		2	0.9885	0.9298	0.8202	0.6778	0.5256	0.3828	0.2616	0.1673	0.0996	0.0547
		3	0.9990	0.9872	0.9500	0.8791	0.7759	0.6496	0.5138	0.3823	0.2660	0.1719
		4	0.9999	0.9984	0.9901	0.9672	0.9219	0.8497	0.7515	0.6331	0.5044	0.3770
		5	1.0000	0.9999	0.9986	0.9936	0.9803	0.9527	0.9051	0.8338	0.7384	0.6230
		6	1.0000	1.0000	0.9999	0.9991	0.9965	0.9894	0.9740	0.9452	0.8980	0.8281
		7	1.0000	1.0000	1.0000	0.9999	0.9996	0.9984	0.9952	0.9877	0.9726	0.9453
		8	1.0000	1.0000	1.0000	1.0000	1.0000	0.9999	0.9995	0.9983	0.9955	0.9893
		9	1.0000	1.0000	1.0000	1.0000	1.0000	1.0000	1.0000	0.9999	0.9997	0.9990

The binomial cumulative distribution function (continued)

$p =$		0.05	0.10	0.15	0.20	0.25	0.30	0.35	0.40	0.45	0.50
$n = 12$ $x =$	0	0.5404	0.2824	0.1422	0.0687	0.0317	0.0138	0.0057	0.0022	0.0008	0.0002
	1	0.8816	0.6590	0.4435	0.2749	0.1584	0.0850	0.0424	0.0196	0.0083	0.0032
	2	0.9804	0.8891	0.7358	0.5583	0.3907	0.2528	0.1513	0.0834	0.0421	0.0193
	3	0.9978	0.9744	0.9078	0.7946	0.6488	0.4925	0.3467	0.2253	0.1345	0.0730
	4	0.9998	0.9957	0.9761	0.9274	0.8424	0.7237	0.5833	0.4382	0.3044	0.1938
	5	1.0000	0.9995	0.9954	0.9806	0.9456	0.8822	0.7873	0.6652	0.5269	0.3872
	6	1.0000	0.9999	0.9993	0.9961	0.9857	0.9614	0.9154	0.8418	0.7393	0.6128
	7	1.0000	1.0000	0.9999	0.9994	0.9972	0.9905	0.9745	0.9427	0.8883	0.8062
	8	1.0000	1.0000	1.0000	0.9999	0.9996	0.9983	0.9944	0.9847	0.9644	0.9270
	9	1.0000	1.0000	1.0000	1.0000	1.0000	0.9998	0.9992	0.9972	0.9921	0.9807
	10	1.0000	1.0000	1.0000	1.0000	1.0000	1.0000	0.9999	0.9997	0.9989	0.9968
	11	1.0000	1.0000	1.0000	1.0000	1.0000	1.0000	1.0000	1.0000	0.9999	0.9998
$n = 15$ $x =$	0	0.4633	0.2059	0.0874	0.0352	0.0134	0.0047	0.0016	0.0005	0.0001	0.0000
	1	0.8290	0.5490	0.3186	0.1671	0.0802	0.0353	0.0142	0.0052	0.0017	0.0005
	2	0.9638	0.8159	0.6042	0.3980	0.2361	0.1268	0.0617	0.0271	0.0107	0.0037
	3	0.9945	0.9444	0.8227	0.6482	0.4613	0.2969	0.1727	0.0905	0.0424	0.0176
	4	0.9994	0.9873	0.9383	0.8358	0.6865	0.5155	0.3519	0.2173	0.1204	0.0592
	5	0.9999	0.9978	0.9832	0.9389	0.8516	0.7216	0.5643	0.4032	0.2608	0.1509
	6	1.0000	0.9997	0.9964	0.9819	0.9434	0.8689	0.7548	0.6098	0.4522	0.3036
	7	1.0000	1.0000	0.9994	0.9958	0.9827	0.9500	0.8868	0.7869	0.6535	0.5000
	8	1.0000	1.0000	0.9999	0.9992	0.9958	0.9848	0.9578	0.9050	0.8182	0.6964
	9	1.0000	1.0000	1.0000	0.9999	0.9992	0.9963	0.9876	0.9662	0.9231	0.8491
	10	1.0000	1.0000	1.0000	1.0000	0.9999	0.9993	0.9972	0.9907	0.9745	0.9408
	11	1.0000	1.0000	1.0000	1.0000	1.0000	0.9999	0.9995	0.9981	0.9937	0.9824
	12	1.0000	1.0000	1.0000	1.0000	1.0000	1.0000	0.9999	0.9997	0.9989	0.9963
	13	1.0000	1.0000	1.0000	1.0000	1.0000	1.0000	1.0000	1.0000	0.9999	0.9995
	14	1.0000	1.0000	1.0000	1.0000	1.0000	1.0000	1.0000	1.0000	1.0000	1.0000
$n = 20$ $x =$	0	0.3585	0.1216	0.0388	0.0115	0.0032	0.0008	0.0002	0.0000	0.0000	0.0000
	1	0.7358	0.3917	0.1756	0.0692	0.0243	0.0076	0.0021	0.0005	0.0001	0.0000
	2	0.9245	0.6769	0.4049	0.2061	0.0913	0.0355	0.0121	0.0036	0.0009	0.0002
	3	0.9841	0.8670	0.6477	0.4114	0.2252	0.1071	0.0444	0.0160	0.0049	0.0013
	4	0.9974	0.9568	0.8298	0.6296	0.4148	0.2375	0.1182	0.0510	0.0189	0.0059
	5	0.9997	0.9887	0.9327	0.8042	0.6172	0.4164	0.2454	0.1256	0.0553	0.0207
	6	1.0000	0.9976	0.9781	0.9133	0.7858	0.6080	0.4166	0.2500	0.1299	0.0577
	7	1.0000	0.9996	0.9941	0.9679	0.8982	0.7723	0.6010	0.4159	0.2520	0.1316
	8	1.0000	0.9999	0.9987	0.9900	0.9591	0.8867	0.7624	0.5956	0.4143	0.2517
	9	1.0000	1.0000	0.9998	0.9974	0.9861	0.9520	0.8782	0.7553	0.5914	0.4119
	10	1.0000	1.0000	1.0000	0.9994	0.9961	0.9829	0.9468	0.8725	0.7507	0.5881
	11	1.0000	1.0000	1.0000	0.9999	0.9991	0.9949	0.9804	0.9435	0.8692	0.7483
	12	1.0000	1.0000	1.0000	1.0000	0.9998	0.9987	0.9940	0.9790	0.9420	0.8684
	13	1.0000	1.0000	1.0000	1.0000	1.0000	0.9997	0.9985	0.9935	0.9786	0.9423
	14	1.0000	1.0000	1.0000	1.0000	1.0000	1.0000	0.9997	0.9984	0.9936	0.9793
	15	1.0000	1.0000	1.0000	1.0000	1.0000	1.0000	1.0000	0.9997	0.9985	0.9941
	16	1.0000	1.0000	1.0000	1.0000	1.0000	1.0000	1.0000	1.0000	0.9997	0.9987
	17	1.0000	1.0000	1.0000	1.0000	1.0000	1.0000	1.0000	1.0000	1.0000	0.9998
	18	1.0000	1.0000	1.0000	1.0000	1.0000	1.0000	1.0000	1.0000	1.0000	1.0000

The binomial cumulative distribution function (continued)

			p =	0.05	0.10	0.15	0.20	0.25	0.30	0.35	0.40	0.45	0.50
n = 25	x =	0		0.2774	0.0718	0.0172	0.0038	0.0008	0.0001	0.0000	0.0000	0.0000	0.0000
		1		0.6424	0.2712	0.0931	0.0274	0.0070	0.0016	0.0003	0.0001	0.0000	0.0000
		2		0.8729	0.5371	0.2537	0.0982	0.0321	0.0090	0.0021	0.0004	0.0001	0.0000
		3		0.9659	0.7636	0.4711	0.2340	0.0962	0.0332	0.0097	0.0024	0.0005	0.0001
		4		0.9928	0.9020	0.6821	0.4207	0.2137	0.0905	0.0320	0.0095	0.0023	0.0005
		5		0.9988	0.9666	0.8385	0.6167	0.3783	0.1935	0.0826	0.0294	0.0086	0.0020
		6		0.9998	0.9905	0.9305	0.7800	0.5611	0.3407	0.1734	0.0736	0.0258	0.0073
		7		1.0000	0.9977	0.9745	0.8909	0.7265	0.5118	0.3061	0.1536	0.0639	0.0216
		8		1.0000	0.9995	0.9920	0.9532	0.8506	0.6769	0.4668	0.2735	0.1340	0.0539
		9		1.0000	0.9999	0.9979	0.9827	0.9287	0.8106	0.6303	0.4246	0.2424	0.1148
		10		1.0000	1.0000	0.9995	0.9944	0.9703	0.9022	0.7712	0.5858	0.3843	0.2122
		11		1.0000	1.0000	0.9999	0.9985	0.9893	0.9558	0.8746	0.7323	0.5426	0.3450
		12		1.0000	1.0000	1.0000	0.9996	0.9966	0.9825	0.9396	0.8462	0.6937	0.5000
		13		1.0000	1.0000	1.0000	0.9999	0.9991	0.9940	0.9745	0.9222	0.8173	0.6550
		14		1.0000	1.0000	1.0000	1.0000	0.9998	0.9982	0.9907	0.9656	0.9040	0.7878
		15		1.0000	1.0000	1.0000	1.0000	1.0000	0.9995	0.9971	0.9868	0.9560	0.8852
		16		1.0000	1.0000	1.0000	1.0000	1.0000	0.9999	0.9992	0.9957	0.9826	0.9461
		17		1.0000	1.0000	1.0000	1.0000	1.0000	1.0000	0.9998	0.9988	0.9942	0.9784
		18		1.0000	1.0000	1.0000	1.0000	1.0000	1.0000	1.0000	0.9997	0.9984	0.9927
		19		1.0000	1.0000	1.0000	1.0000	1.0000	1.0000	1.0000	0.9999	0.9996	0.9980
		20		1.0000	1.0000	1.0000	1.0000	1.0000	1.0000	1.0000	1.0000	0.9999	0.9995
		21		1.0000	1.0000	1.0000	1.0000	1.0000	1.0000	1.0000	1.0000	1.0000	0.9999
		22		1.0000	1.0000	1.0000	1.0000	1.0000	1.0000	1.0000	1.0000	1.0000	1.0000
n = 30	x =	0		0.2146	0.0424	0.0076	0.0012	0.0002	0.0000	0.0000	0.0000	0.0000	0.0000
		1		0.5535	0.1837	0.0480	0.0105	0.0020	0.0003	0.0000	0.0000	0.0000	0.0000
		2		0.8122	0.4114	0.1514	0.0442	0.0106	0.0021	0.0003	0.0000	0.0000	0.0000
		3		0.9392	0.6474	0.3217	0.1227	0.0374	0.0093	0.0019	0.0003	0.0000	0.0000
		4		0.9844	0.8245	0.5245	0.2552	0.0979	0.0302	0.0075	0.0015	0.0002	0.0000
		5		0.9967	0.9268	0.7106	0.4275	0.2026	0.0766	0.0233	0.0057	0.0011	0.0002
		6		0.9994	0.9742	0.8474	0.6070	0.3481	0.1595	0.0586	0.0172	0.0040	0.0007
		7		0.9999	0.9922	0.9302	0.7608	0.5143	0.2814	0.1238	0.0435	0.0121	0.0026
		8		1.0000	0.9980	0.9722	0.8713	0.6736	0.4315	0.2247	0.0940	0.0312	0.0081
		9		1.0000	0.9995	0.9903	0.9389	0.8034	0.5888	0.3575	0.1763	0.0694	0.0214
		10		1.0000	0.9999	0.9971	0.9744	0.8943	0.7304	0.5078	0.2915	0.1350	0.0494
		11		1.0000	1.0000	0.9992	0.9905	0.9493	0.8407	0.6548	0.4311	0.2327	0.1002
		12		1.0000	1.0000	0.9998	0.9969	0.9784	0.9155	0.7802	0.5785	0.3592	0.1808
		13		1.0000	1.0000	1.0000	0.9991	0.9918	0.9599	0.8737	0.7145	0.5025	0.2923
		14		1.0000	1.0000	1.0000	0.9998	0.9973	0.9831	0.9348	0.8246	0.6448	0.4278
		15		1.0000	1.0000	1.0000	0.9999	0.9992	0.9936	0.9699	0.9029	0.7691	0.5722
		16		1.0000	1.0000	1.0000	1.0000	0.9998	0.9979	0.9876	0.9519	0.8644	0.7077
		17		1.0000	1.0000	1.0000	1.0000	0.9999	0.9994	0.9955	0.9788	0.9286	0.8192
		18		1.0000	1.0000	1.0000	1.0000	1.0000	0.9998	0.9986	0.9917	0.9666	0.8998
		19		1.0000	1.0000	1.0000	1.0000	1.0000	1.0000	0.9996	0.9971	0.9862	0.9506
		20		1.0000	1.0000	1.0000	1.0000	1.0000	1.0000	0.9999	0.9991	0.9950	0.9786
		21		1.0000	1.0000	1.0000	1.0000	1.0000	1.0000	1.0000	0.9998	0.9984	0.9919
		22		1.0000	1.0000	1.0000	1.0000	1.0000	1.0000	1.0000	1.0000	0.9996	0.9974
		23		1.0000	1.0000	1.0000	1.0000	1.0000	1.0000	1.0000	1.0000	0.9999	0.9993
		24		1.0000	1.0000	1.0000	1.0000	1.0000	1.0000	1.0000	1.0000	1.0000	0.9998
		25		1.0000	1.0000	1.0000	1.0000	1.0000	1.0000	1.0000	1.0000	1.0000	1.0000

The binomial cumulative distribution function (continued)

	$p =$	0.05	0.10	0.15	0.20	0.25	0.30	0.35	0.40	0.45	0.50
$n = 40$ $x =$	0	0.1285	0.0148	0.0015	0.0001	0.0000	0.0000	0.0000	0.0000	0.0000	0.0000
	1	0.3991	0.0805	0.0121	0.0015	0.0001	0.0000	0.0000	0.0000	0.0000	0.0000
	2	0.6767	0.2228	0.0486	0.0079	0.0010	0.0001	0.0000	0.0000	0.0000	0.0000
	3	0.8619	0.4231	0.1302	0.0285	0.0047	0.0006	0.0001	0.0000	0.0000	0.0000
	4	0.9520	0.6290	0.2633	0.0759	0.0160	0.0026	0.0003	0.0000	0.0000	0.0000
	5	0.9861	0.7937	0.4325	0.1613	0.0433	0.0086	0.0013	0.0001	0.0000	0.0000
	6	0.9966	0.9005	0.6067	0.2859	0.0962	0.0238	0.0044	0.0006	0.0001	0.0000
	7	0.9993	0.9581	0.7559	0.4371	0.1820	0.0553	0.0124	0.0021	0.0002	0.0000
	8	0.9999	0.9845	0.8646	0.5931	0.2998	0.1110	0.0303	0.0061	0.0009	0.0001
	9	1.0000	0.9949	0.9328	0.7318	0.4395	0.1959	0.0644	0.0156	0.0027	0.0003
	10	1.0000	0.9985	0.9701	0.8392	0.5839	0.3087	0.1215	0.0352	0.0074	0.0011
	11	1.0000	0.9996	0.9880	0.9125	0.7151	0.4406	0.2053	0.0709	0.0179	0.0032
	12	1.0000	0.9999	0.9957	0.9568	0.8209	0.5772	0.3143	0.1285	0.0386	0.0083
	13	1.0000	1.0000	0.9986	0.9806	0.8968	0.7032	0.4408	0.2112	0.0751	0.0192
	14	1.0000	1.0000	0.9996	0.9921	0.9456	0.8074	0.5721	0.3174	0.1326	0.0403
	15	1.0000	1.0000	0.9999	0.9971	0.9738	0.8849	0.6946	0.4402	0.2142	0.0769
	16	1.0000	1.0000	1.0000	0.9990	0.9884	0.9367	0.7978	0.5681	0.3185	0.1341
	17	1.0000	1.0000	1.0000	0.9997	0.9953	0.9680	0.8761	0.6885	0.4391	0.2148
	18	1.0000	1.0000	1.0000	0.9999	0.9983	0.9852	0.9301	0.7911	0.5651	0.3179
	19	1.0000	1.0000	1.0000	1.0000	0.9994	0.9937	0.9637	0.8702	0.6844	0.4373
	20	1.0000	1.0000	1.0000	1.0000	0.9998	0.9976	0.9827	0.9256	0.7870	0.5627
	21	1.0000	1.0000	1.0000	1.0000	1.0000	0.9991	0.9925	0.9608	0.8669	0.6821
	22	1.0000	1.0000	1.0000	1.0000	1.0000	0.9997	0.9970	0.9811	0.9233	0.7852
	23	1.0000	1.0000	1.0000	1.0000	1.0000	0.9999	0.9989	0.9917	0.9595	0.8659
	24	1.0000	1.0000	1.0000	1.0000	1.0000	1.0000	0.9996	0.9966	0.9804	0.9231
	25	1.0000	1.0000	1.0000	1.0000	1.0000	1.0000	0.9999	0.9988	0.9914	0.9597
	26	1.0000	1.0000	1.0000	1.0000	1.0000	1.0000	1.0000	0.9996	0.9966	0.9808
	27	1.0000	1.0000	1.0000	1.0000	1.0000	1.0000	1.0000	0.9999	0.9988	0.9917
	28	1.0000	1.0000	1.0000	1.0000	1.0000	1.0000	1.0000	1.0000	0.9996	0.9968
	29	1.0000	1.0000	1.0000	1.0000	1.0000	1.0000	1.0000	1.0000	0.9999	0.9989
	30	1.0000	1.0000	1.0000	1.0000	1.0000	1.0000	1.0000	1.0000	1.0000	0.9997
	31	1.0000	1.0000	1.0000	1.0000	1.0000	1.0000	1.0000	1.0000	1.0000	0.9999
	32	1.0000	1.0000	1.0000	1.0000	1.0000	1.0000	1.0000	1.0000	1.0000	1.0000

The binomial cumulative distribution function (continued)

$p =$		0.05	0.10	0.15	0.20	0.25	0.30	0.35	0.40	0.45	0.50
$n = 50$ $x =$	0	0.0769	0.0052	0.0003	0.0000	0.0000	0.0000	0.0000	0.0000	0.0000	0.0000
	1	0.2794	0.0338	0.0029	0.0002	0.0000	0.0000	0.0000	0.0000	0.0000	0.0000
	2	0.5405	0.1117	0.0142	0.0013	0.0001	0.0000	0.0000	0.0000	0.0000	0.0000
	3	0.7604	0.2503	0.0460	0.0057	0.0005	0.0000	0.0000	0.0000	0.0000	0.0000
	4	0.8964	0.4312	0.1121	0.0185	0.0021	0.0002	0.0000	0.0000	0.0000	0.0000
	5	0.9622	0.6161	0.2194	0.0480	0.0070	0.0007	0.0001	0.0000	0.0000	0.0000
	6	0.9882	0.7702	0.3613	0.1034	0.0194	0.0025	0.0002	0.0000	0.0000	0.0000
	7	0.9968	0.8779	0.5188	0.1904	0.0453	0.0073	0.0008	0.0001	0.0000	0.0000
	8	0.9992	0.9421	0.6681	0.3073	0.0916	0.0183	0.0025	0.0002	0.0000	0.0000
	9	0.9998	0.9755	0.7911	0.4437	0.1637	0.0402	0.0067	0.0008	0.0001	0.0000
	10	1.0000	0.9906	0.8801	0.5836	0.2622	0.0789	0.0160	0.0022	0.0002	0.0000
	11	1.0000	0.9968	0.9372	0.7107	0.3816	0.1390	0.0342	0.0057	0.0006	0.0000
	12	1.0000	0.9990	0.9699	0.8139	0.5110	0.2229	0.0661	0.0133	0.0018	0.0002
	13	1.0000	0.9997	0.9868	0.8894	0.6370	0.3279	0.1163	0.0280	0.0045	0.0005
	14	1.0000	0.9999	0.9947	0.9393	0.7481	0.4468	0.1878	0.0540	0.0104	0.0013
	15	1.0000	1.0000	0.9981	0.9692	0.8369	0.5692	0.2801	0.0955	0.0220	0.0033
	16	1.0000	1.0000	0.9993	0.9856	0.9017	0.6839	0.3889	0.1561	0.0427	0.0077
	17	1.0000	1.0000	0.9998	0.9937	0.9449	0.7822	0.5060	0.2369	0.0765	0.0164
	18	1.0000	1.0000	0.9999	0.9975	0.9713	0.8594	0.6216	0.3356	0.1273	0.0325
	19	1.0000	1.0000	1.0000	0.9991	0.9861	0.9152	0.7264	0.4465	0.1974	0.0595
	20	1.0000	1.0000	1.0000	0.9997	0.9937	0.9522	0.8139	0.5610	0.2862	0.1013
	21	1.0000	1.0000	1.0000	0.9999	0.9974	0.9749	0.8813	0.6701	0.3900	0.1611
	22	1.0000	1.0000	1.0000	1.0000	0.9990	0.9877	0.9290	0.7660	0.5019	0.2399
	23	1.0000	1.0000	1.0000	1.0000	0.9996	0.9944	0.9604	0.8438	0.6134	0.3359
	24	1.0000	1.0000	1.0000	1.0000	0.9999	0.9976	0.9793	0.9022	0.7160	0.4439
	25	1.0000	1.0000	1.0000	1.0000	1.0000	0.9991	0.9900	0.9427	0.8034	0.5561
	26	1.0000	1.0000	1.0000	1.0000	1.0000	0.9997	0.9955	0.9686	0.8721	0.6641
	27	1.0000	1.0000	1.0000	1.0000	1.0000	0.9999	0.9981	0.9840	0.9220	0.7601
	28	1.0000	1.0000	1.0000	1.0000	1.0000	1.0000	0.9993	0.9924	0.9556	0.8389
	29	1.0000	1.0000	1.0000	1.0000	1.0000	1.0000	0.9997	0.9966	0.9765	0.8987
	30	1.0000	1.0000	1.0000	1.0000	1.0000	1.0000	0.9999	0.9986	0.9884	0.9405
	31	1.0000	1.0000	1.0000	1.0000	1.0000	1.0000	1.0000	0.9995	0.9947	0.9675
	32	1.0000	1.0000	1.0000	1.0000	1.0000	1.0000	1.0000	0.9998	0.9978	0.9836
	33	1.0000	1.0000	1.0000	1.0000	1.0000	1.0000	1.0000	0.9999	0.9991	0.9923
	34	1.0000	1.0000	1.0000	1.0000	1.0000	1.0000	1.0000	1.0000	0.9997	0.9967
	35	1.0000	1.0000	1.0000	1.0000	1.0000	1.0000	1.0000	1.0000	0.9999	0.9987
	36	1.0000	1.0000	1.0000	1.0000	1.0000	1.0000	1.0000	1.0000	1.0000	0.9995
	37	1.0000	1.0000	1.0000	1.0000	1.0000	1.0000	1.0000	1.0000	1.0000	0.9998
	38	1.0000	1.0000	1.0000	1.0000	1.0000	1.0000	1.0000	1.0000	1.0000	1.0000

Percentage points of the normal distribution

The z-values in the table are those which a random variable
$Z \sim N(0, 1)$ exceeds with probability p, i.e. $P(Z > z) = 1 - \Phi(z) = p$.

p	z	p	z
0.5000	0.0000	0.0500	1.6449
0.4000	0.2533	0.0250	1.9600
0.3000	0.5244	0.0100	2.3263
0.2000	0.8416	0.0050	2.5758
0.1500	1.0364	0.0010	3.0902
0.1000	1.2816	0.0005	3.2905

Critical values for the Product Moment Correlation Coefficient, r

The r-values in the table are the minimum values of the Product Moment Correlation Coefficient for which a one-tailed hypothesis test at the given significance level on a data set of size n is statistically significant.

n	0.10	0.05	0.025	0.01	0.005
3	0.9511	0.9877	0.9969	0.9995	0.9999
4	0.8000	0.9000	0.9500	0.9800	0.9900
5	0.6870	0.8054	0.8783	0.9343	0.9587
6	0.6084	0.7293	0.8114	0.8822	0.9172
7	0.5509	0.6694	0.7545	0.8329	0.8745
8	0.5067	0.6215	0.7067	0.7887	0.8343
9	0.4716	0.5822	0.6664	0.7498	0.7977
10	0.4428	0.5494	0.6319	0.7155	0.7646
11	0.4187	0.5214	0.6021	0.6851	0.7348
12	0.3981	0.4973	0.5760	0.6581	0.7079
13	0.3802	0.4762	0.5529	0.6339	0.6835
14	0.3646	0.4575	0.5324	0.6120	0.6614
15	0.3507	0.4409	0.5140	0.5923	0.6411
16	0.3383	0.4259	0.4973	0.5742	0.6226
17	0.3271	0.4124	0.4821	0.5577	0.6055
18	0.3170	0.4000	0.4683	0.5425	0.5897
19	0.3077	0.3887	0.4555	0.5285	0.5751
20	0.2992	0.3783	0.4438	0.5155	0.5614

Critical values for Spearman's Rank Correlation Coefficient, r_s

The r_s-values in the table are the minimum values of Spearman's Rank Correlation Coefficient for which a one-tailed hypothesis test at the given significance level on a data set of size n is statistically significant.

n	0.05	0.025	0.01
4	1.0000	-	-
5	0.9000	1.0000	1.0000
6	0.8286	0.8857	0.9429
7	0.7143	0.7857	0.8929
8	0.6429	0.7381	0.8333
9	0.6000	0.7000	0.7833
10	0.5636	0.6485	0.7455
11	0.5364	0.6182	0.7091
12	0.5035	0.5874	0.6783
13	0.4835	0.5604	0.6484
14	0.4637	0.5385	0.6264
15	0.4464	0.5214	0.6036
16	0.4294	0.5029	0.5824
17	0.4142	0.4877	0.5662
18	0.4014	0.4716	0.5501
19	0.3912	0.4596	0.5351
20	0.3805	0.4466	0.5218

Answers

Chapter 1: Algebra

1. Proof

Exercise 1.1

Q1 **a)** Take two odd numbers $2l + 1$ and $2m + 1$ (where l and m are integers), then their sum is $2l + 1 + 2m + 1 = 2l + 2m + 2$ $= 2(l + m + 1) =$ even.

b) Take two even numbers, $2j$ and $2k$ (where j and k are integers), then their product is $2j \times 2k = 4jk$ $= 2(2jk) =$ even.

c) Take one even number, $2l$ and one odd number $2m + 1$ (where l and m are integers), then their product is $2l \times (2m + 1) = 4lm + 2l = 2(2lm + l) =$ even.

Q2 E.g. Let $p = 1 \Rightarrow \frac{1}{p^2} = \frac{1}{p}$, so the statement is not true.

Q3 $(x + 5)^2 + 3(x - 1)^2$
$= x^2 + 10x + 25 + 3(x^2 - 2x + 1)$
$= x^2 + 10x + 25 + 3x^2 - 6x + 3$
$= 4x^2 + 4x + 28$
$= 4(x^2 + x + 7)$

This has a factor of 4 outside the brackets, so it is always divisible by 4.

Q4 E.g. Proof by exhaustion:
Take three consecutive integers $(n - 1)$, n and $(n + 1)$. Their product is $(n - 1)$ $n(n + 1) = n(n^2 - 1) = n^3 - n$.
Consider the two cases
— n even and n odd.
For n even, n^3 is even (as even $\times$ even = even) so $n^3 - n$ is also even (as even − even = even). For n odd, n^3 is odd (as odd $\times$ odd = odd) so $n^3 - n$ is even (as odd − odd = even). So $n^3 - n$ is even when n is even and when n is odd, and n must be either odd or even, so the product of three consecutive integers is always even.

Q5 E.g. $n = 8 \Rightarrow n^2 - n - 1$
$= 8^2 - 8 - 1 = 55$ — not prime
$n^2 - n - 1$ is not prime when $n = 8$, so the statement is false.

Q6 E.g. take $x = -1$ and $y = 2$.
Then $\sqrt{x^2 + y^2} = \sqrt{(-1)^2 + 2^2}$
$= \sqrt{1 + 4} = \sqrt{5} = 2.236...$
and $x + y = -1 + 2 = 1$. $2.236... > 1$, so the statement is not true.

Q7 Take any two rational numbers a and b. By the definition of rational numbers we know that $a = \frac{p}{q}$ and $b = \frac{r}{s}$ where p, q, r, s are integers, and q and s are non-zero.
So, the sum of a and b is
$\frac{p}{q} + \frac{r}{s} = \frac{ps + rq}{qs}$.
ps and rq are the product of integers, so are also integers. This means $ps + rq$ is also an integer. qs is the product of non-zero integers, so must also be a non zero integer.
This shows that $a + b$ is the quotient of two integers, and has a non-zero denominator, so by definition $a + b$ is rational.

Q8 **a)** Proof by exhaustion:
Consider the two cases
— n even and n odd.
Let n be even. $n^2 - n = n(n - 1)$, so if n is even, $n - 1$ is odd so $n(n - 1)$ is even (as even $\times$ odd = even). So $n(n - 1) - 1$ is odd.
Let n be odd. If n is odd, $n - 1$ is even, so $n(n - 1)$ is even (as odd $\times$ even = even). So $n(n - 1) - 1$ is odd. As any integer n has to be either odd or even, $n^2 - n - 1$ is odd for any value of n.

b) As $n^2 - n - 1$ is odd, $n^2 - n - 2$ is even. The product of even numbers is also even, so as $(n^2 - n - 2)^3$ is the product of 3 even numbers, it will always be even.

2. Algebraic Expressions

Exercise 2.1

Q1 **a)** $5x + 20$ **b)** $4a - 2ab$
c) $-2x^2 - 2y$ **d)** $6m^2n + 6mn$
e) $-4ht^3 + 8h^2t^2 + 12h^4t$
f) $14z^2 + 7z^3$ **g)** $7x - 7$
h) $7p^3 - 2pq + q$
i) $7x^3y + 7xyz^2$ **j)** $3x - x^2$
k) $-s^2t - 5s$ **l)** $4x + x^2y - 4xy$

Q2 **a)** $x^2 + 2x - 15$ **b)** $6z^2 + 5z - 6$
c) $u^2 + 16u + 64$
d) $a^2bc + ab^2d + ac^2d + bcd^2$
e) $20f^2 - 30g + 2f^3 - 3fg$ **f)** $49 - q^2$
g) $4 - 12w + 9w^2$
h) $16r^2s^4 + 24rs^2 + 9$
i) $25k^4l^2 - 20k^3ln + 4k^2n^2$
j) $9g^2h^2 - 12gh + 6gh^2 - 8h$
k) $14y^2z - 4yz^2 + 49y - 14z$
l) $5c^4 + 19c^3 - 4c^2$

Q3 **a)** $l^3 + 7l^2 + 13l + 15$
b) $6 + q + 7q^2 + 4q^3$
c) $m^3 - m^2 - 10m - 8$
d) $r^3 + 3r^2s + 3rs^2 + s^3$
e) $4 - 3x - 3y - 2xy - x^2 - y^2$
f) $-10c^4 - 2c^3 + 5c^3d - 2cd^2 - cd + 2d^2$
g) $4x^3y + 16x^2y - 12x^2y^2 - 48xy^2 + 9xy^3 + 36y^3$

Q4 $x^2 + 7x + 3$ m^2
Carole's garden has an area of x^2 m^2. Mark's garden has an area of $(x + 3)(2x + 1) = 2x^2 + 7x + 3$ m^2.

Exercise 2.2

Q1 **a)** $3(3k + 5l)$ **b)** $u(u - v)$
c) $5(2w + 3)$ **d)** $2xy(x - 6y)$
e) $fg(fg - 1)$
f) $u^2v(3v + 5u^2v^3 + 12)$
g) $p(p^2 + 3q^3 + 2)$
h) $cde(ab - bf - fg)$
i) $11xy(y - x - xy)$
j) $mnp^2(1 + 7mp)$
k) $ab(2b^3 + 3a^2b - 4)$
l) $4z(9xy - 2x^2z + 5y^2z)$

Q2 **a)** $(x - y)(x + y)$
b) $(3a - 2b)(3a + 2b)$
c) $(5x - 7z)(5x + 7z)$
d) $c(a - 4b)(a + 4b)$
e) $\left(y - \sqrt{2}\right)\left(y + \sqrt{2}\right)$
f) $\left(2x - \sqrt{3}\right)\left(2x + \sqrt{3}\right)$

Q3 **a)** $(2 - z)[(4 - z)^2 + p]$
b) $(r - d)^2(r - d + 5)$
c) $(b + c)^5(a + b - 1)$
d) $(a - 2x)(l^2m - rp^2)$
e) $(h - 4g)(h - 4g + 1)$
f) $(x^2 + y)(2 + x)$

Q4 **a)** $(p + q)(p + 3q)$
b) $-2(2x - y)(x + y)$
c) $7s(r + 6s)$ **d)** $(l + w + h)(w + h)$
e) $x(1 - y)(x - xy + 2)$
f) $(a + b)^2(ab + b^2 + 3a)$

Q5 **a)** $m^3 + 125$ **b)** $p^3 - 8q^3$
c) $-2v(u + v)$
d) 0 **e)** $2s(2 + 2r + r^2 - s)$
f) $-4(4x^2 + z^2)(y^2 + z^2)$
Notice that this is actually a difference of two squares — it's the first bracket squared minus the second bracket squared. Use this to write the expression as the product of two brackets, simplify the terms within each bracket, then take out any common factors.

Exercise 2.3

Q1 a) $\dfrac{7x}{12}$ b) $\dfrac{2t+13}{t^2}$

c) $\dfrac{5q-2p}{10pq}$ d) $\dfrac{a^2b^2+b^2c^2+c^2a^2}{abc}$

e) $\dfrac{2-3m^2+n^3}{mn}$ f) $\dfrac{2a^2-9b^2}{a^3b^3}$

g) $\dfrac{xy+2x^3+4y}{x^2y}$

h) $\dfrac{2a^2b+a^4-2b^2}{a^2b}$

Q2 a) $\dfrac{8y-13}{(y-1)(y-2)}$ b) $\dfrac{3r+41}{(r-5)(r+3)}$

c) $\dfrac{7p-24}{p(p-3)}$ d) $\dfrac{w(7w-19)}{2(w-2)(w-7)}$

e) $\dfrac{-2}{(z+2)(z+4)}$ f) $\dfrac{4q+1}{(q+1)(q-2)}$

g) $\dfrac{x^2+xz+2z^2}{(x-z)(x+z)}$ h) $\dfrac{3y+5xy}{(2x+3)(x-3)}$

Q3 a) $\dfrac{x+5}{3}$ b) $2a-4b-5c$

c) $p-2n$ d) $\dfrac{s(4+6s+9s^2)}{2}$

e) $yz(1-4y^2+6y)$

f) $\dfrac{4-2c+c^2d}{4ce}$ g) $\dfrac{2+xy-x}{x+3}$

h) $\dfrac{4(g-h)}{g}$

3. Laws of Indices
Exercise 3.1

Q1 a) 10^5 b) y^4 c) 5^2 d) 6^3

e) 3^5 f) 6^{10} g) r^{-4} h) 3^6

i) k^{-10} j) $z^{\frac{1}{2}}$ k) 8^3 l) pq^3

m) $c^{-3}d^{-6}$ n) a^2b^4 o) $3z^{-1}$ p) m^4n^2

Q2 a) 16 b) $\dfrac{1}{2}$ c) 49

d) 3 e) 1 f) 64

g) 1 h) 1 i) 1

Q3 a) p^{-1} b) $q^{\frac{1}{2}}$ c) $r^{\frac{3}{2}}$

d) $s^{\frac{5}{4}}$ e) $t^{\frac{1}{3}}$ f) $x^{\frac{4}{3}}$

Q4 a) 3 b) 2 c) 8

d) $\dfrac{1}{3}$ e) $\dfrac{1}{8}$

Q5 a) $\dfrac{1}{4}q$ b) $\dfrac{32}{q^2}$ c) $\dfrac{1}{128}q^3$

d) $\dfrac{1}{256}q^5$ e) $\dfrac{1}{4q}$ f) $\dfrac{64}{q^2}$

Q6 a) $x=\dfrac{2}{3}$ b) $x=-\dfrac{1}{2}$

c) $x=-\dfrac{5}{2}$ d) $x=-\dfrac{1}{4}$

e) $x=-\dfrac{1}{2}$ f) $x=-3$

4. Surds
Exercise 4.1

Q1 a) $2\sqrt{2}$ b) $2\sqrt{6}$ c) $5\sqrt{2}$

d) $3\sqrt{7}$ e) $6\sqrt{2}$ f) $\dfrac{\sqrt{5}}{2}$

g) $\dfrac{\sqrt{7}}{10}$ h) $\dfrac{\sqrt{11}}{3}$

Q2 a) 24 b) 15 c) 7

d) $6\sqrt{10}$ e) 44 f) 40

g) 72 h) 120 i) $2\sqrt{2}$

j) $\dfrac{4}{9}$

Q3 a) $3\sqrt{5}$ b) $2\sqrt{2}$ c) $7\sqrt{3}$

d) $\sqrt{2}$ e) $8\sqrt{10}$ f) $50\sqrt{3}$

Q4 a) $4+3\sqrt{2}$ b) $5\sqrt{3}-6$

c) 7 d) 61

e) $7+4\sqrt{3}$ f) $61-24\sqrt{5}$

Q5 $4\sqrt{3}$ cm
You need to use Pythagoras here,
$AC^2 = AB^2 + BC^2.$

Exercise 4.2

Q1 a) $2\sqrt{3}$ b) $3\sqrt{7}$

c) $6\sqrt{5}$ d) $6\sqrt{5}$

e) $-\sqrt{6}$ f) $7\sqrt{3}$

Q2 a) $-2+2\sqrt{3}$ b) $2+2\sqrt{5}$

c) $-12-3\sqrt{10}$ d) $-3-\sqrt{6}$

Q3 a) $3+2\sqrt{2}$ b) $11+5\sqrt{5}$

c) $\dfrac{15}{13}-\dfrac{7}{13}\sqrt{3}$

d) $\dfrac{27}{11}+\dfrac{7}{11}\sqrt{5}$ e) $\dfrac{3}{5}+\dfrac{4}{15}\sqrt{6}$

f) $-\dfrac{24}{13}+\dfrac{5}{13}\sqrt{35}$

g) $-1-\dfrac{2}{3}\sqrt{6}$ h) $\dfrac{1}{5}\sqrt{15}$

Q4 a) $\sqrt{7}+\sqrt{3}$

b) $-4(\sqrt{11}+\sqrt{17})$

c) $\dfrac{1}{4}(\sqrt{13}-\sqrt{5})$

d) $-\dfrac{1}{8}(\sqrt{7}+\sqrt{15})$

Q5 $x=2+2\sqrt{5}$

Q6 $y=11+4\sqrt{7}$

Q7 Area of a rectangle
= length × width, so:
$(2+\sqrt{2})=l\times(3\sqrt{2}-4)$
$\Rightarrow l=\dfrac{(2+\sqrt{2})}{(3\sqrt{2}-4)}$
$=(7+5\sqrt{2})$ cm

Review Exercise — Chapter 1

Q1 Take one even number, $2l$ and one odd number $2m+1$ (where l and m are integers), then when the odd number is subtracted from the even number, the result is:
$2l-(2m+1)=2(l-m)-1$
$=2(l-m-2)+1=$ odd

Q2 Take two rational numbers $a=\dfrac{p}{q}$ and $b=\dfrac{r}{s}$.
The difference between them is
$\dfrac{p}{q}-\dfrac{r}{s}=\dfrac{ps-qr}{qs}$.

p, q, r and s are all integers, so $ps-qr$ is an integer. q and s are non-zero integers, so qs is a non-zero integer.

So $\dfrac{ps-qr}{qs}$ is a rational number.

Q3 Disproof by counter-example: Zero is a rational number, but dividing by zero does not give a rational result.

Q4 a) a^2-b^2 b) $a^2+2ab+b^2$

c) $25y^2+210xy$

d) $3x^2+10xy+3y^2+13x+23y+14$

e) $-c^2d-3c^3+8cd^2-4d^3$

f) $s^4-8s^2t^2+16t^4$

Q5 $5x^3-90x^2+400x$ cm^3
The side lengths of the box are x cm, $(x-10)$ cm and $(x-8)$ cm, so the volume of one box is $x(x-10)(x-8)$. Multiply out the brackets, and then multiply by 5, to get the expression for the volume of 5 boxes.

Q6 a) $xy(2x+a+2y)$ b) $a^2x(1+b^2x)$

c) $8(2y+xy+7x)$

d) $3s(8+20t+5st^2)$

e) $9c(3-c^2d-5d^2)$

f) $x^2y(yz^2+xy^2-z)$

Q7 a) $(x+1)(1-y)$ b) $z^2(z^2+3-z)$

c) $(x+y)(2x+y)$

d) $(x-2)(x-3)$ e) $(5+x^2)(5-x^2)$

f) $c^2(3bc+2d^3)(3bc-2d^3)$

Q8 a) $\dfrac{52x+5y}{60}$ b) $\dfrac{5x-2y}{x^2y^2}$

c) $\dfrac{x^3+x^2-y^2+xy^2}{x(x^2-y^2)}$

d) $\dfrac{a^3+4ab-7b}{a^2b}$ e) $\dfrac{9x^2y-4}{3xy}$

f) $\dfrac{4s^3+5s^2t-2t^3}{2s^2t^2}$

Q9 a) $\dfrac{3a}{2b}$ b) $\dfrac{2(p^2+q^2)}{p^2-q^2}$

c) $\dfrac{2(c^2+d^2)}{(c-d)^2(c+d)}$

d) $\dfrac{3x^2-1}{2x^2(1+x)}$

e) $\dfrac{k(k^2+k+2)}{k^2-1}$

f) $\dfrac{4y^2-8y-12z-2-6z^2}{(z+1)(y+z)(y-1)}$

Q10 Call the unknown side of the flower bed z.
Then $z=\dfrac{x^2}{x-3}$ and $y+z=\dfrac{3x^2}{x+6}$.
So $y=\dfrac{3x^2}{x+6}-z=\dfrac{3x^2}{x+6}-\dfrac{x^2}{x-3}$
$=\dfrac{3x^2(x-3)-x^2(x+6)}{(x+6)(x-3)}$
$=\dfrac{3x^3-9x^2-x^3-6x^2}{(x+6)(x-3)}$
$=\dfrac{2x^3-15x^2}{(x+6)(x-3)}$
$=\dfrac{x^2(2x-15)}{(x+6)(x-3)}$

Q11 a) x^8 b) a^{15} c) x^6

d) a^8 e) x^4y^3z f) $\dfrac{b^2c^5}{a}$

Q12 a) g^{-3} **b)** r^8p^{-1} **c)** k^2

    d) $m^{-10}n^6$ **e)** $s^{10}t^{18}$ **f)** ab^5c^{-1}

Q13 a) 4   **b)** 2   **c)** 8

    d) 1   **e)** $\frac{1}{7}$ **f)** 9

Q14 a) $2\sqrt{7}$ **b)** $\frac{\sqrt{5}}{6}$

    c) $3\sqrt{2}$ **d)** $\frac{3}{4}$

Q15 a) $-\sqrt{3}$ **b)** $6\sqrt{5}$ **c)** $9\sqrt{7}$

    d) $5\sqrt{13}$ **e)** $13\sqrt{6}$

Q16 $a = 2\sqrt{30}$

    a is the difference between the side lengths of the two squares — so that's

$$\sqrt{1920} - \sqrt{1080} = 8\sqrt{30} - 6\sqrt{30} = 2\sqrt{30}.$$

Q17 a) $\frac{8}{\sqrt{2}} = \frac{8}{\sqrt{2}} \times \frac{\sqrt{2}}{\sqrt{2}} = \frac{8\sqrt{2}}{2} = 4\sqrt{2}$

    b) $\frac{\sqrt{2}}{2} = \frac{\sqrt{2}}{(\sqrt{2})^2} = \frac{1}{\sqrt{2}}$

Q18 $136 + 24\sqrt{21}$

Q19 $3 - \sqrt{7}$

Q20 a) $\frac{17}{3} + \frac{4}{3}\sqrt{13}$

    b) $\frac{41}{2} + \frac{15}{2}\sqrt{7}$ **c)** $\frac{3}{2} + \sqrt{3}$

Chapter 2: Quadratics and Cubics

1. Quadratic Equations

Exercise 1.1

Q1 a) $(x - 5)(x - 1)$ **b)** $(x - 6)(x + 3)$

    c) $(x + 11)^2$ **d)** $x(x - 12)$

    e) $(y - 6)(y - 7)$ **f)** $(x + 48)(x + 3)$

    g) $(x + 11)(x - 11)$ **h)** $(x - 2)(x - 33)$

Q2 a) $(2x + 1)(2x - 3)$ **b)** $(2x + 1)(x + 11)$

    c) $(7x + 2)(x - 3)$ **d)** $(-x + 4)(x + 9)$

    e) $(3x + 1)(2x - 3)$ **f)** $2(x + 1)(x - 1)$

    g) $3(x + 1)(x - 1)$ **h)** $-(x - 7)(x - 2)$

Q3 a) $x = 4$ or $x = -2$ **b)** $x = -5$ or $x = 4$

    c) $p = -19$ or $p = -2$

    d) $x = 9$ or $x = 6$

    e) $x = -5$ or $x = -13$

    f) $x = 7$ or $x = -6$

    g) $x = -100$ or $x = -1000$

    h) $x = 2$ or $x = -1$

    i) $x = \frac{1}{5}$ or $x = 4$

Q4 a) $x = \frac{3}{5}$ or $x = -5$

    b) $x = -\frac{1}{4}$ or $x = -\frac{13}{8}$

    c) $a = \frac{3}{5}$ or $a = -3$

    d) $x = -\frac{5}{4}$ or $x = -\frac{3}{2}$

    e) $q = \frac{3}{4}$ or $q = 2$

    f) $y = -\frac{4}{3}$ or $y = \frac{3}{8}$

Q5 $x = 7$ or $x = -5$

Q6 f(x) meets the x-axis when $x = 10$ and $x = -3$.

Q7 The temperature is 0 °C after 2.5 hours and after 4 hours.

Q8 $(x + 4y)(x + 2y)$

Exercise 1.2

Q1 a) $x = 2 \pm \sqrt{2}$ **b)** $x = 1 \pm 3\sqrt{5}$

    c) $x = -\frac{3}{2} \pm \frac{1}{2}\sqrt{57}$ **d)** $x = 7 \pm \sqrt{7}$

    e) $x = -\frac{1}{2} \pm \frac{1}{2}\sqrt{2}$ **f)** $x = 1$ or 3

    g) $x = \frac{1}{2}$ or $\frac{1}{3}$ **h)** $x = \frac{1}{2} \pm \frac{1}{2}\sqrt{71}$

    i) $x = \sqrt{11}$

Q2 a) $x^2 - 4x - 1$ **b)** $x = 2 \pm \sqrt{5}$

    c) The roots produced by the quadratic formula in part b) are the same as the numbers subtracted from x in the expression from a) — it's just the same quadratic.

Q3 $A = -4$ and $B = 3$.

Q4 a) $x = -\frac{1}{2}$ **b)** $x = \frac{7}{8} \pm \frac{1}{24}\sqrt{57}$

    c) $x = \frac{3}{5} \pm \frac{1}{5}\sqrt{2}$

    d) $x = -\frac{3}{10} \pm \frac{1}{10}\sqrt{11}$

    e) $x = \frac{7}{2}$ or -1 **f)** $x = 2$ or $-\frac{4}{3}$

Exercise 1.3

Q1 a) $x = 1$ or -9 **b)** $x = -1$ or -4

    c) $x = \frac{3}{5} \pm \frac{\sqrt{21}}{5}$ **d)** $x = \frac{1}{3}(1 \pm 4\sqrt{2})$

Q2 a) $(x + 3)^2 - 1$ **b)** $(x + 4)^2 - 26$

    c) $\left(x - \frac{3}{2}\right)^2 - \frac{49}{4}$ **d)** $(x - 10)^2 - 85$

    e) $\left(x + \frac{9}{2}\right)^2 - \frac{89}{4}$ **f)** $\left(x - \frac{5}{2}\right)^2 + \frac{3}{4}$

    g) $(x - m)^2 + (-m^2 + n)$

    h) $(x + 3r)^2 + (-9r^2 + s)$

Q3 a) $x = 8$ or -2 **b)** $x = -2 \pm 2\sqrt{3}$

    c) $x = 1$ or 3   **d)** $x = 4$ or 6

    e) $p = 20$ or -10 **f)** $x = -1 \pm \sqrt{1 - k}$

    g) $q = -2$ or -1 **h)** $x = 2 \pm \sqrt{4 - k}$

Exercise 1.4

Q1 a) $3(x - 2)^2 - 5$ **b)** $2(x + 4)^2 - 27$

    c) $5(x + 2)^2 - 22$ **d)** $2(x - 1)^2 - 5$

    e) $6\left(x + \frac{5}{2}\right)^2 - \frac{115}{2}$

    f) $-\left(x + \frac{9}{2}\right)^2 + \frac{117}{4}$

    g) $4\left(x - \frac{11}{4}\right)^2 - \frac{101}{4}$

    h) $-3\left(x - \frac{3}{2}\right)^2 + \frac{31}{4}$

Q2 a) $x = \frac{1}{2}$ or $-\frac{13}{2}$ **b)** $x = \frac{2}{3}$ or $-\frac{8}{3}$

    c) $x = 3 \pm \frac{3\sqrt{2}}{2}$ **d)** $x = 9$ or -3

    e) $x = -1 \pm \frac{\sqrt{30}}{5}$ **f)** $x = -3 \pm \frac{\sqrt{87}}{3}$

Q1 g) $x = -\frac{1}{3} \pm \frac{\sqrt{2}}{2}$ **h)** $x = \frac{2}{5}$ or $\frac{1}{5}$

Q3 $ax^2 + bx + c = a\left(x^2 + \frac{b}{a}x + \frac{c}{a}\right)$

$$= a\left(x + \frac{b}{2a}\right)^2 - \frac{b^2}{4a} + c$$

$$a\left(x + \frac{b}{2a}\right)^2 - \frac{b^2}{4a} + c = 0$$

$$\Rightarrow \left(x + \frac{b}{2a}\right)^2 = \frac{b^2}{4a^2} - \frac{c}{a}$$

$$\Rightarrow \left(x + \frac{b}{2a}\right)^2 = \frac{b^2 - 4ac}{4a^2}$$

$$\Rightarrow x + \frac{b}{2a} = \pm\sqrt{\frac{b^2 - 4ac}{4a^2}}$$

$$\Rightarrow x = -\frac{b}{2a} \pm \frac{\sqrt{b^2 - 4ac}}{2a}$$

$$\Rightarrow x = \frac{-b \pm \sqrt{b^2 - 4ac}}{2a}$$

Congratulations, you've just proved the quadratic formula.

Exercise 1.5

Q1 a) $u = x^{\frac{1}{2}}$ **b)** $u = e^x$

    c) $u = 5^x$ **d)** $u = \cos x$

Q2 $x = -\frac{7}{25}$ or $-\frac{1}{2}$

    You can solve this problem by first using the substitution $u = \frac{1}{5x + 2}$ to get an equation in terms of u.

    Solve this equation, then put $\frac{1}{5x + 2}$ back into the solutions in u to get solutions in x.

2. Quadratic Functions and Roots

Exercise 2.1

Q1 a) 2 real roots.   **b)** 1 real root.

    c) no real roots.   **d)** 2 real roots.

Q2 $f(x) = (x + 3)^2 + 1 \Rightarrow$ no real roots and a line of symmetry at $x = -3$.

Q3 Comparing $f(x) = -\left(x + \frac{7}{2}\right)^2 + \frac{25}{4}$

    to $p(x + q)^2 + r$ gives $p = -1$, $r = \frac{25}{4}$

    These have different signs, so f(x) has two real roots.

Exercise 2.2

Q1 a) $b^2 - 4ac = 4$, 2 real roots.

    b) $b^2 - 4ac = 0$, 1 real root.

    c) $b^2 - 4ac = 121$, 2 real roots.

    d) $b^2 - 4ac = \frac{1}{25}$, 2 real roots.

    e) $b^2 - 4ac = 400$, 2 real roots.

    f) $b^2 - 4ac = 19$, 2 real roots.

    g) $b^2 - 4ac = -40$, no real roots

    h) $b^2 - 4ac = \frac{9}{4}$, 2 real roots

Q2 $b = \pm 7$ **Q3** $a = 49$

Q4 $p < 9$ **Q5** $q < 5$

Q6 $b^2 - 4ac = (10p + 1)^2 - 4 \times 2 \times 5$
$= 100p^2 + 20p - 39$

$100p^2 + 20p - 39 < 0$
$\Rightarrow 100p^2 + 20p < 39$
$\Rightarrow 20p(5p + 1) < 39$
$\Rightarrow p(5p + 1) < \dfrac{39}{20}$

Q7 **a)** $b^2 - 4ac = 10k + 25$
The equation has no real roots so the discriminant is negative so $10k + 25 < 0$.

b) $k < -\dfrac{5}{2}$

You can solve this problem by solving the equation from a).

Q8 **a)** $k = \dfrac{6}{4} = \dfrac{3}{2}$ **b)** $k > \dfrac{3}{2}$

c) $k < \dfrac{3}{2}$

You can solve these problems by first finding the discriminant. Then solve discriminant = 0 for a), discriminant < 0 for b) and discriminant > 0 for c).

3. Quadratic Graphs

Exercise 3.1

Q1 a)-c)

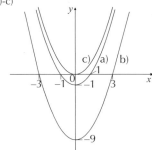

Q2 **a)** $(x - 9)(x - 1)$

b) & c)

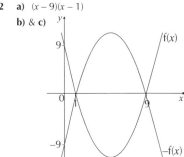

Q3 **a)**

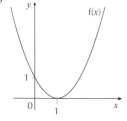

b)

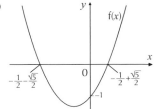

c)

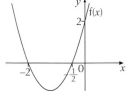

d)

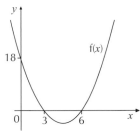

e)

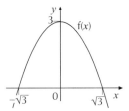

f)

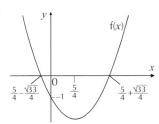

Q4 **a)** The roots are $x = -2$ and $x = 1$.

b) $p = -1$ and $q = 2$.

Exercise 3.2

Q1 **a)** (i) - (iii)

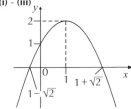

b) (i) - (iii)

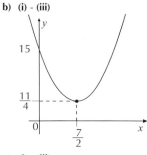

c) (i) - (iii)

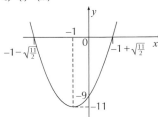

d) (i) - (iii)

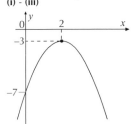

Q2 **a)** $q = 4$ and $r = 2$.

b)

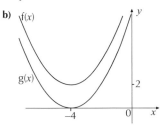

c) $f(x)$ has no real roots.
$g(x)$ has one real root.

Q3 **a)** $(x - 3)^2 - 4$

b) $x = 5$ or 1

c)

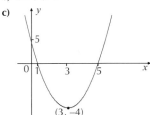

Exercise 3.3

Q1

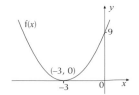

Q2 a)

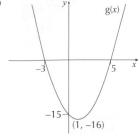

e) $x = 0$, $x = \frac{2}{3}$ or $x = -\frac{4}{3}$

f) $x = 0$, $x = \frac{5}{9}$ or $x = \frac{2}{9}$

g) $x = 0$ **h)** $x = 0$, $x = 2$ or $x = -2$

i) $x = 0$ or $x = \frac{-7 \pm \sqrt{109}}{10}$

j) $x = 0$, $x = \frac{1}{4}$ or $x = -1$

k) $x = 0$ or $x = -2 \pm \frac{1}{2}\sqrt{10}$

l) $x = 0$

Exercise 4.2

Q1 a) -20 **b)** -6 **c)** -2

    d) 10 **e)** -2 **f)** $\frac{35}{8}$

Q2 a) 106 **b)** 106

    c) 41 **d)** 41

Q3 a) 44 **b)** $-\frac{129}{16}$

    c) 0 **d)** $-\frac{209}{81}$

Q4 $c = 8$ **Q5** $p = 3$

Q6 $d = 3$ **Q7** $k = 2$

Q8 $p = 3$

You can solve this problem by finding f(1) and f(−1) in terms of p. Then set these equal to each other and solve to find p.

Q9 $q = -20$

You can solve this problem by finding f(2) and f(−1) in terms of q. Then set these equal to each other and solve to find q.

Exercise 4.3

Q1 a) $f(1) = (1)^3 - (1)^2 - 3(1) + 3 = 0$
So by the Factor Theorem,
$(x - 1)$ is a factor.

    b) $f(-1) = (-1)^3 + 2(-1)^2 + 3(-1) + 2 = 0$
So by the Factor Theorem,
$(x + 1)$ is a factor.

    c) $f(-2) = (-2)^3 + 3(-2)^2 - 10(-2) - 24$
$= 0$ So by the Factor Theorem,
$(x + 2)$ is a factor.

    d) $f(3) = (3)^3 + 2(3)^2 - 9(3) - 18 = 0$
So by the Factor Theorem,
$(x - 3)$ is a factor.

Q2 a) $f\left(\frac{1}{2}\right) = 2\left(\frac{1}{2}\right)^3 - \left(\frac{1}{2}\right)^2 - 8\left(\frac{1}{2}\right) + 4 = 0$
So by the Factor Theorem,
$(2x - 1)$ is a factor.

    b) $f\left(\frac{2}{3}\right)$

$= 3\left(\frac{2}{3}\right)^3 - 5\left(\frac{2}{3}\right)^2 - 16\left(\frac{2}{3}\right) + 12 = 0$
So by the Factor Theorem,
$(3x - 2)$ is a factor.

    c) $f\left(-\frac{1}{5}\right)$

$= 5\left(-\frac{1}{5}\right)^3 - 44\left(-\frac{1}{5}\right)^2 + 61\left(-\frac{1}{5}\right) + 14$
$= 0$

So by the Factor Theorem,
$(5x + 1)$ is a factor.

---

d) $f\left(\frac{1}{2}\right)$

$= -2\left(\frac{1}{2}\right)^3 + 3\left(\frac{1}{2}\right)^2 + 11\left(\frac{1}{2}\right) - 6 = 0$

So by the Factor Theorem,
$(1 - 2x)$ is a factor.

Q3 a) $f(3) = (3)^3 - 2(3)^2 - 5(3) + 6 = 0$
So by the Factor Theorem,
$(x - 3)$ is a factor.

    b) $1 - 2 - 5 + 6 = 0$
So by the Factor Theorem
$(x - 1)$ is a factor.

Q4 a) $f(-4)$
$= 3(-4)^3 - 5(-4)^2 - 58(-4) + 40 = 0$
So by the Factor Theorem,
$(x + 4)$ is a factor.

    b) $f\left(\frac{2}{3}\right)$

$= 3\left(\frac{2}{3}\right)^3 - 5\left(\frac{2}{3}\right)^2 - 58\left(\frac{2}{3}\right) + 40 = 0$

So by the Factor Theorem,
$(3x - 2)$ is a factor.

    c) $f(5) = 3(5)^3 - 5(5)^2 - 58(5) + 40$
So by the Factor Theorem,
$(x - 5)$ is a factor.

Q5 a) $p = -4$ **b)** $q = 4$

You can solve these problems by finding f(2) in terms of p and f(3) in terms of q. Then set the equations equal to zero and solve to find p and q.

Q6 $c = -4$ and $d = 5$
You can solve this problem by using f(1) = 0 and f(2) = 0 to set up equations in terms of c and d. Then solve these equations simultaneously to find c and d.

Exercise 4.4

Q1 a) $x(x - 1)(x - 2)$

    b) $(x - 2)(x + 3)(2x + 1)$

    c) $(x - 1)^3$ **d)** $(x - 2)(x - 2)(x + 1)$

    e) $(x - 1)(x + 5)(x - 7)$

    f) $(x - 2)(x - 4)(x + 6)$

    g) $(x - 1)(x^2 - 7)$ or $(x - 1)(x + \sqrt{7})(x - \sqrt{7})$

    h) $(x - 2)(x + 1)(x + 3)$

Q2 a) $(x + 2)(x^2 + 2x - 4)$

    b) $x = -2$, $x = -1 + \sqrt{5}$
and $x = -1 - \sqrt{5}$

Q3 $x = 1$ and $x = \pm\sqrt{3}$

Q4 $x = 1$, $x = -1$, $x = 2$

Q5 $(3x - 1)(2x + 1)(x + 6)$

Q6 a) $p = 8$ **b)** $(x - 5)(x - 1)(x - 2)$

    c) $x = 5$, 1 and 2.

Q7 a) $(x - 1)(3x - 1)(x + 2)$

    b) $(x - 1)(5x + 2)(x - 2)$

    c) $(x - 1)(2x + 3)(2x - 1)$

Q8 $f(2) = 2(2)^3 - 2^2 - 2(2) - 8 = 0$
So $x = 2$ is a root, and $(x - 2)$ is a factor.
$(x - 2)(2x^2 + 3x + 4) = 0$.
$b^2 - 4ac = 3^2 - 4 \times 2 \times 4 = -23$.
The discriminant is negative so the quadratic has no real roots. Hence the only real root of the cubic is $x = 2$.

Q3 a)

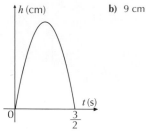   **b)** 9 cm

Q4 a)

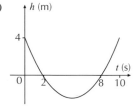

    b) (i) 4 m   **(ii)** −2.25 m

    (iii) 6 seconds

Q5 a)

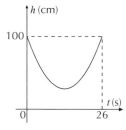

    b) 15.5 m

4. Factorising Cubics
Exercise 4.1

Q1 a) $x(x + 2)(x + 3)$ **b)** $x(x + 7)(x - 1)$

    c) $x(x - 9)^2$ **d)** $x(x + 5)(x + 2)$

    e) $x(x + 1)(x + 3)$ **f)** $x(x + 7)(x - 5)$

    g) $x(x + 2)(x - 8)$ **h)** $-x(x - 3)(x - 1)$

    i) $-x(x + 4)(x - 1)$ **j)** $x(2x + 5)(x + 5)$

    k) $x(2x - 3)(x - 2)$ **l)** $x(4x - 3)(x + 4)$

    m) $x(x + 6)(x - 6)$

    n) $x\left(x + \frac{2}{5}\right)\left(x - \frac{2}{5}\right)$

    o) $x(x + 7)(x - 7)$

    p) $x\left(x + \frac{3}{2}\right)\left(x - \frac{3}{2}\right)$

Q2 a) $x = 0$, $x = 6$ or $x = -4$

    b) $x = 0$, $x = 3$ or $x = -7$

    c) $x = 0$, $x = -\frac{1}{2}$ or $x = -4$.

    d) $x = 0$, $x = \frac{1}{3}$ or $x = -9$

Exercise 4.5

Q1 **a)** $(x - 3)^2(x + 4)$

b) $(x + 2)(x^2 - 3x - 5)$

c) $(x - 2)(2x + 1)(x + 7)$

d) $(x + 5)(x + 2)(x + 3)$

Q2 $(x - 1)(x^2 + x - 4)$

Q3 **a)** -49

b) $f(-3) = (-3)^3 - 2(-3)^2 + (-3) - 1 = -49$

Q4 $f(x) = (x - 2)(x^2 + 4x + 1)$.

Q5 $x = -2$, $x = 3$ and $x = -1$.

Q6 $(x - 2)(x^2 + 3x + 6)$

Q7 **a)** 13

You can solve this problem by using algebraic long division to get 13. Use the Factor Theorem to check your answer.

b) $x = 2$ or $x = 4$

You can solve this problem by using your calculations from part a) to write $f(x)$ as $(x - 2)(x^2 - 6x + 8) + 13$. Then to solve $f(x) - 13 = 0$, just solve $(x - 2)(x^2 - 6x + 8) = 0$. The quadratic factorises to $(x - 2)(x - 4)$, so the solutions are $x = 2$ (a repeated factor) and $x = 4$.

Review Exercise — Chapter 2

Q1 **a)** $(x + 1)^2$ **b)** $(x - 10)(x - 3)$

c) $(x + 2)(x - 2)$ **d)** $(3 - x)(x + 1)$

e) $(2x + 1)(x - 4)$

f) $(5x - 3)(x + 2)$

Q2 **a)** $x = 2$ or 1 **b)** $x = -4$ or 3

c) $x = 2$ or -1 **d)** $x = \pm 4$

e) $x = -\frac{2}{3}$ or 7 **f)** $x = \pm\frac{1}{2}$

g) $x = \frac{3}{2}$ or 1 **h)** $x = \pm\frac{2}{3}$

i) $x = \frac{2}{3}$ or $-\frac{5}{2}$

Q3 **a)** $x = \frac{7 \pm \sqrt{13}}{6}$ **b)** $x = \frac{3 \pm \sqrt{13}}{2}$

c) $x = -2 \pm \sqrt{10}$

Q4 **a)** $(x + 3)^2 - 2$ **b)** $x = -2 \pm \frac{\sqrt{2}}{2}$

Q5 $x = 1$, $x = -1$, $x = 4$ and $x = -4$
Use the substitution $u = x^2$, and solve $u^2 - 17u + 16 = 0$.

Q6 $k > 4$ or $k < -4$.

Q7 **a)** $(x - 2)^2 - 7$;
minimum value = -7 at $x = 2$,
and the graph crosses the x-axis
at $x = 2 \pm \sqrt{7}$.

b) $\left(x + \frac{5}{2}\right)^2 + \frac{7}{4}$;
minimum value = $\frac{7}{4}$ at $x = -\frac{5}{2}$,
and the graph doesn't cross the
x-axis.

c) $\frac{21}{4} - \left(x + \frac{3}{2}\right)^2$;
maximum value = $\frac{21}{4}$ at $x = -\frac{3}{2}$,
and the graph crosses the x-axis
at $-\frac{3}{2} \pm \frac{\sqrt{21}}{2}$.

d) $2(x - 1)^2 + 9$;
minimum value = 9 at $x = 1$,
and the graph doesn't cross the
x-axis.

e) $4\left(x - \frac{7}{2}\right)^2 - 1$;
minimum value = -1 at $x = \frac{7}{2}$,
and the graph crosses the x-axis
at $x = 4$ or $x = 3$.

f) $-3(x - 2)^2 + 26$;
maximum value = 26 at $x = 2$
and the graph crosses the x-axis at
$x = 2 \pm \frac{\sqrt{78}}{3}$.

Q8 **a)** 2 roots

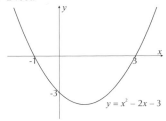

$y = x^2 - 2x - 3$

b) 1 root

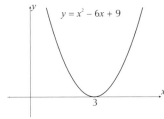

$y = x^2 - 6x + 9$

c) no roots

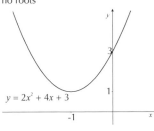

$y = 2x^2 + 4x + 3$

Q9 **a)** $(0, 0)$ and $(2, 0)$. **b)** $x(x - 2)(5x - 3)$.

Q10 **a)**

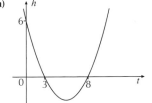

b) **(i)** 6 m

(ii) $-\frac{25}{16}$ m **(iii)** 5 seconds

Q11 **a)** Set the equations equal to each
other:
$x(x - 6)^2 = -x(2x - 31)$
$\Rightarrow x(x^2 - 12x + 36) = -2x^2 + 31x$
$\Rightarrow x^3 - 12x^2 + 36x = -2x^2 + 31x$
$\Rightarrow x^3 - 10x^2 + 5x = 0$

b) $x = 0$ and $x = 5 \pm 2\sqrt{5}$.
You can solve this problem by using the quadratic formula or completing the square to solve the equation in part a).

Q12 **a)** $x = 0$ or $x = 4$

b) $x = 0$, $x = 1$ or $x = -6$

c) $x = 0$ or $x = 3$

d) $x = 0$, $x = -3$ or $x = -5$

e) $x = 0$, $x = 6$ or $x = -\frac{2}{7}$

f) $x = 0$, $x = \frac{4}{3}$ or $x = -\frac{1}{2}$

Q13 **a)** **(i)** -16 **(ii)** -10 **(iii)** 26

b) **(i)** -1 **(ii)** 9 **(iii)** 38

c) **(i)** -2 **(ii)** 0 **(iii)** 37

Q14 **a)** -24 **b)** 18 **c)** 28 **d)** $\frac{241}{16}$

Q15 $c = 6$

Q16 **a)** $(x - 1)$ is a factor

b) $(x + 1)$ is not a factor

c) $(x - 2)$ is not a factor

d) $(2x - 2)$ is a factor

Q17 $k = -36$

Q18 **a)** Quotient: $x^2 - 4x + 9$,
remainder: -24

b) Quotient: $x^2 - x - 7$, remainder: -8

c) Quotient: $x^2 + 3$, remainder: -4

Q19 **a)** $f(x) = (x + 2)(3x^2 - 10x + 15) - 36$

b) $f(x) = (x + 2)(x^2 - 3) + 10$

c) $f(x) = (x + 2)(2x^2 - 4x + 14) - 31$

Q20 $c = 10$ and $d = -96$.
You can solve this problem by using $f(2) = 0$ and $f(-3) = 0$ to set up equations in terms of c and d. Then solve these equations simultaneously to find c and d.

Q21 3 and $3 \pm 2\sqrt{5}$
You can solve this problem by using algebraic long division or the factorising cubics method to get $(x - 3)(x^2 - 6x - 11)$.
So one root is $x = 3$. Then find the roots of the quadratic using the quadratic formula, leaving your answers in surd form.

Q22 -1, -2 and -3.
You can solve this problem by using trial and error to find $(x + 1)$ as a factor. Then use algebraic long division or the factorising cubics method to get $(x + 1)(x^2 + 5x + 6)$. Then factorise the quadratic to get the roots.

Q23 **a)** $(x + 2)(x^2 - 7x + 14) - 30$
You can solve this problem by using algebraic long division to get quotient $x^2 - 7x + 14$ and remainder -30.

b) $f(x) + 30 = (x + 2)(x^2 - 7x + 14)$
So when $f(x) + 30 = 0$,
$x = -2$ is a solution.
Show that $x^2 - 7x + 14 = 0$
has no real solutions:
$b^2 - 4ac = 7^2 - 4 \times 1 \times 14 = -7 < 0$.
Hence $x = -2$ is the only
solution to $f(x) + 30 = 0$.

Chapter 3: Inequalities and Simultaneous Equations

1. Inequalities

Exercise 1.1

Q1
  a) $x < 5$ b) $x \geq 3$
  c) $x > -3$ d) $x \geq 1$
  e) $x \leq \dfrac{1}{2}$ f) $x \leq 2.5$
  g) $x > 2$ h) $x < \dfrac{16}{3}$

Q2
  a) $\{x : x < 0\}$ b) $\left\{x : x \leq \dfrac{2}{15}\right\}$
  c) $\left\{x : x \geq -\dfrac{1}{2}\right\}$

Q3 a) $x < -10$ b) $x \leq -\dfrac{1}{5}$ c) $x > -54$

Q4
  a) $\{x : -1 < x < 9\}$
    or $\{x : x > -1\} \cap \{x : x < 9\}$
  b) $\{x : -5 < x \leq 3\}$
    or $\{x : x > -5\} \cap \{x : x \leq 3\}$
  c) $\left\{x : -\dfrac{1}{3} \leq x \leq \dfrac{2}{3}\right\}$ or
    $\left\{x : x \geq -\dfrac{1}{3}\right\} \cap \left\{x : x \leq \dfrac{2}{3}\right\}$

Q5 a) $x \geq 1$

  b) $x < 3$

  c) $x \leq -1$

  d) $x \geq -2$

  e) $x \leq -2$

  f) $x > -\dfrac{3}{2}$

Q6 $3 \leq x < 6$

Q7 $\{x : -3 < x < 4\}$
    or $\{x : x > -3\} \cap \{x : x < 4\}$

Q8
  a) $-2 \leq x \leq 5$
  b) $1 < x \leq 2$ c) $x > 7$
  d) There is no solution that satisfies both inequalities.

Exercise 1.2

Q1
  a) $-3 < x < 1$ b) $x < 0$ or $x > 4$
  c) $x \leq -5$ or $x \geq \dfrac{1}{2}$
  d) $x < 1 - \sqrt{6}$ or $x > 1 + \sqrt{6}$

Q2
  a) $\{x : -2 \leq x \leq 2\}$
    or $\{x : x \geq -2\} \cap \{x \leq 2\}$
  b) $\left\{x : x < \dfrac{1}{3}\right\} \cup \{x : x > 4\}$
  c) $\{x : 3 - \sqrt{5} < x < 3 + \sqrt{5}\}$
    or $\{x : x > 3 - \sqrt{5}\} \cap \{x < 3 + \sqrt{5}\}$

Q3 a)

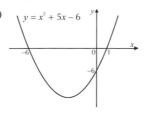

$x \leq -6$ or $x \geq 1$

  b)

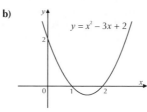

$1 < x < 2$

  c)

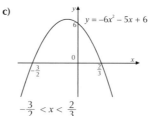

$-\dfrac{3}{2} < x < \dfrac{2}{3}$

You could also have rearranged the inequality into $6x^2 + 5x - 6 < 0$ and sketched the corresponding graph.

  d)

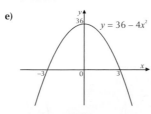

$3 \leq x \leq 7$

  e)

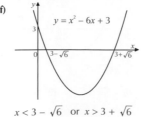

$x \leq -3$ or $x \geq 3$

  f)

$y = x^2 - 6x + 3$

$x < 3 - \sqrt{6}$ or $x > 3 + \sqrt{6}$

  g)

$y = x^2 - x + 3$

x can take any real value

  h) $y = -5x^2 - 13x + 6$

$-3 \leq x \leq \dfrac{2}{5}$

Again, you might have rearranged the inequality differently and ended up with the graph the other way up.

  i) $y = 2x^2 - 3x - 9$

$x < -\dfrac{3}{2}$ or $x > 3$

  j) $y = x^2 + 3x + 16$

No real solutions.

  k) $y = x^2 + 5x - \dfrac{1}{2}$

$-\dfrac{5}{2} - \dfrac{3}{2}\sqrt{3} < x < -\dfrac{5}{2} + \dfrac{3}{2}\sqrt{3}$

  l) $y = \dfrac{3}{4}x^2 - \dfrac{1}{4}x - 1$

$x \leq -1$ or $x \geq \dfrac{4}{3}$

Q4 $x \geq 13$ metres

Q5 a) $-3 < k < 3$

b) $\{k : 0 < k < 4\}$
or $\{k : k > 0\} \cap \{k : k < 4\}$

To answer this question you need to use the discriminant for each quadratic — in part a), the discriminant needs to be greater than zero, and in b) you need it to be less than zero.

Q6 a) $1 \leq x \leq 3$ **b)** $x > \dfrac{5 + \sqrt{13}}{2}$

Exercise 1.3

Q1 a) False **b)** False **c)** True
d) False **e)** False

Q2 a)
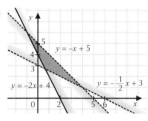

b)
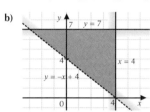

c)
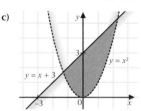

d)
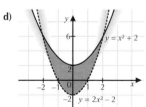

e)
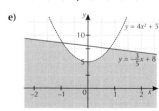

f)
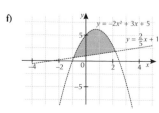

Q3 Region A is larger.

To solve this, accurately draw the two regions on graph paper. Then find the areas of regions A and B — they're both triangles. You should have found that area A = 12 and area B = 10.5.

Q4 a) $3x + y \leq 42$

b)
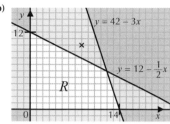

c) The bakery has enough eggs, but not enough flour to meet the order.

2. Simultaneous Equations

Exercise 2.1

Q1 a) $x = 3, y = 1$ **b)** $x = -1, y = 5$

c) $x = \dfrac{1}{2}, y = -2$ **d)** $x = 0, y = -\dfrac{2}{3}$

e) $x = 3, y = -5$ **f)** $x = -21, y = \dfrac{7}{2}$

g) $x = 7, y = -\dfrac{1}{4}$

h) $x = -\dfrac{111}{7}, y = -\dfrac{183}{7}$

Q2 a) $(4, 5)$ **b)** $(-3, 9)$ **c)** $(-1, -2)$

d) These lines do not intersect.

e) $\left(\dfrac{3}{2}, -\dfrac{2}{3}\right)$ **f)** $(0, -3)$

g) $\left(\dfrac{107}{60}, -\dfrac{7}{30}\right)$ **h)** $\left(-\dfrac{7}{13}, \dfrac{23}{65}\right)$

i) $\left(\dfrac{92}{39}, \dfrac{82}{39}\right)$ **j)** $\left(-300, -\dfrac{2200}{3}\right)$

Q3 The three signposts are at $(-1, -3)$, $(2, 3)$ and $(-3, 2)$.

Exercise 2.2

Q1 a) $x = -1, y = -1$ **b)** $x = 2, y = 3$

Q2 a) $x = 4, y = 13$ or $x = -1, y = 3$

b) $x = \dfrac{5}{2}, y = \dfrac{19}{2}$ or $x = -1, y = -1$

c) $x = 6, y = 11$ or $x = 1, y = -4$

d) $x = -2, y = -3$ or $x = 6, y = 1$

e) There are no solutions for the simultaneous equations.

f) $x = 2, y = 7$

g) $x = -1, y = 11$ or $x = 4, y = -9$

h) $x = -3, y = 8$ or $x = \dfrac{1}{2}, y = 1$

i) $x = -9, y = \dfrac{5}{4}$ or $x = \dfrac{10}{3}, y = -\dfrac{35}{9}$

j) $x = -\dfrac{13}{2}, y = -11$ or $x = 2, y = 6$

Q3 a) $(-8, -8)$ and $\left(3, \dfrac{17}{2}\right)$

b) $(4, 30)$ and $(-2, 0)$

c) $(-5, 5)$ and $(7, -1)$

d) $(-2, 3)$ and $(1, 6)$

e) $\left(-5, \dfrac{31}{6}\right)$ and $\left(\dfrac{2}{3}, \dfrac{25}{18}\right)$

f) $\left(-\dfrac{1}{2}, 8\right)$ and $\left(\dfrac{1}{2}, 12\right)$

Q4 a) $x = -1, y = 3$

b) $x^2 + y^2 = 10$ is a circle and $x - 3y + 10 = 0$ is a straight line. They intersect at a single point, so the line is a tangent to the circle.

Q5 a) The graphs will intersect at two points.

b) The graphs will intersect only once.

c) The graphs will not intersect.

You can answer this question by solving the simultaneous equations (you'd need to use the quadratic formula) — but as you only need to find the number of solutions, there's a quicker way. If you use the substitution method to get a quadratic in the form $ax^2 + bx + c = 0$ you can then find the discriminant of this equation to find the number of solutions (see p.18).

Review Exercise
— Chapter 3

Q1 a) $x > -\dfrac{38}{5}$ **b)** $y \leq \dfrac{7}{8}$

c) $y \leq -\dfrac{3}{4}$ **d)** $x > \dfrac{5}{2}$

e) $x > -4$ **f)** $x \leq -3$

g) $x < \dfrac{4}{11}$ **h)** $y \geq -\dfrac{13}{3}$

Q2 a) $-\dfrac{1}{3} \leq x \leq 2$

b) $x < 1 - \sqrt{3}$ or $x > 1 + \sqrt{3}$

c) $x \leq -3$ or $x \geq -2$

d) $x \leq -3$ or $x \geq 1$

e) $x < -\dfrac{1}{2}$ or $x > 1$

f) $-3 < x < 2$

g) $-3 - 2\sqrt{3} \leq x \leq -3 + 2\sqrt{3}$

h) $x \leq -\dfrac{7}{4}$ or $x \geq 2$

Q3 a)
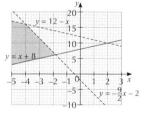

b)
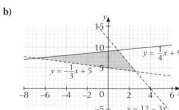

c)

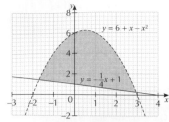

d)

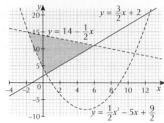

e)

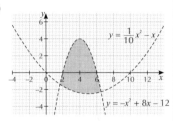

Q4 a) $x = -3$, $y = -4$

b) $x = -\frac{1}{6}$, $y = -\frac{5}{12}$

c) no solutions

d) $x = \frac{17}{3}$, $y = 5$

e) $x = 115$, $y = -\frac{45}{2}$

f) $x = \frac{11}{140}$, $y = \frac{3}{70}$

Q5 a) $\left(\frac{1}{4}, -\frac{13}{4}\right)$ b) $(4, 5)$ c) $(-5, -2)$

d) $\left(-\frac{157}{13}, -\frac{153}{13}\right)$ e) $\left(\frac{333}{10}, -\frac{33}{20}\right)$

f) $\left(-\frac{1}{198}, \frac{14}{99}\right)$

Q6 a) There are two solutions, $x = 2$, $y = -6$ and $x = 7$, $y = 4$, so the line and the curve meet at the points $(2, -6)$ and $(7, 4)$.

b) There is one solution, $x = 2$, $y = 26$, so the line is a tangent to the parabola at the point $(2, 26)$.

c) The line and the curve never meet.

d) There are two solutions, $x = -2$, $y = \frac{7}{2}$ and $x = -\frac{3}{4}$, $y = \frac{41}{16}$, so the line and the curve meet at $\left(-2, \frac{7}{2}\right)$ and $\left(-\frac{3}{4}, \frac{41}{16}\right)$.

e) There is one solution, $x = 6$, $y = \frac{21}{2}$, so the line is a tangent to the parabola at the point $\left(6, \frac{21}{2}\right)$.

f) There are two solutions, $x = -1$, $y = -1$, and $x = 6$, $y = 0$, so the line crosses the circle at the points $(-1, -1)$ and $(6, 0)$.

Q7 There will be two points of intersection.

Chapter 4:
Coordinate Geometry, Graphs and Circles

1. The Equation of a Straight Line

Exercise 1.1

Q1 a) gradient = -4, y-intercept = $(0, 11)$

b) gradient = -1, y-intercept = $(0, 4)$

c) gradient = 1.7, y-intercept = $(0, -2.3)$

Q2 a) $y = -3x + 2$ b) $y = 5x - 3$

c) $y = \frac{1}{2}x + 6$ d) $y = 0.8x + 1.2$

Q3 a) $5x - y + 2 = 0$ b) $x + 6y - 6 = 0$

c) $2x - 4y - 1 = 0$

d) $7x - 2y - 9 = 0$

e) $4x - 6y + 15 = 0$

f) $4x - 3y = 0$ g) $20x + 20y - 1 = 0$

h) $5x - 3y - 32 = 0$

i) $x - 26y + 220 = 0$

Q4 a) $y = 2x + 8$ b) $y = -8x - 5$

c) $y = -x - 5$ d) $y = \frac{2}{3}x - 2$

Q5 a) (i) $y - 1 = x - 4$ or $y + 3 = x$

(ii) $y = x - 3$

(iii) $x - y - 3 = 0$

b) (i) $y + 3 = 2(x - 12)$ or $y - 1 = 2(x - 14)$

(ii) $y = 2x - 27$ (iii) $2x - y - 27 = 0$

c) (i) $y - 7 = \frac{2}{7}(x - 5)$ or $y - 5 = \frac{2}{7}(x + 2)$

(ii) $y = \frac{2}{7}x + \frac{39}{7}$

(iii) $2x - 7y + 39 = 0$

d) (i) $y - 6 = -\frac{8}{7}(x + 3)$ or $y + 2 = -\frac{8}{7}(x - 4)$

(ii) $y = -\frac{8}{7}x + \frac{18}{7}$

(iii) $8x + 7y - 18 = 0$

e) (i) $y - 2 = -(x - 5)$ or $y - 4 = -(x - 3)$

(ii) $y = -x + 7$

(iii) $x + y - 7 = 0$

f) (i) $y + 1 = -\frac{3}{2}(x - 9)$ or $y - 2 = -\frac{3}{2}(x - 7)$

(ii) $y = -\frac{3}{2}x + \frac{25}{2}$

(iii) $3x + 2y - 25 = 0$

g) (i) $y - 1 = -\frac{1}{10}(x + 6)$ or $y = -\frac{1}{10}(x - 4)$

(ii) $y = -\frac{1}{10}x + \frac{4}{10}$

(iii) $x + 10y - 4 = 0$

h) (i) $y - 3 = \frac{4}{17}(x + 12)$ or $y - 7 = \frac{4}{17}(x - 5)$

(ii) $y = \frac{4}{17}x + \frac{99}{17}$

(iii) $4x - 17y + 99 = 0$

i) (i) $y - 1 = 2x$ or $y + 1 = 2(x + 1)$

(ii) $y = 2x + 1$

(iii) $2x - y + 1 = 0$

j) (i) $y + 4 = -\frac{4}{7}(x - 21)$ or $y - 16 = -\frac{4}{7}(x + 14)$

(ii) $y = -\frac{4}{7}x + 8$

(iii) $4x + 7y - 56 = 0$

k) (i) $y - 5 = 0.96(x - 5)$ or $y - 0.2 = 0.96x$

(ii) $y = 0.96x + 0.2$

(iii) $24x - 25y + 5 = 0$

l) (i) $y - 0.05 = -\frac{165}{67}(x - 0.01)$ or $y - 5 = -\frac{165}{67}(x + 2)$

(ii) $y = -\frac{165}{67}x + \frac{5}{67}$

(iii) $165x + 67y - 5 = 0$

Q6 $y = \frac{1}{4}x - 2$

Q7 a) gradient = 3, y-intercept = $\left(0, \frac{3}{2}\right)$

b) gradient = 3, y-intercept = $(0, 4)$

c) gradient = $-\frac{1}{4}$, y-intercept = $\left(0, -\frac{1}{2}\right)$

d) gradient = $-\frac{7}{8}$, y-intercept = $\left(0, -\frac{11}{8}\right)$

e) gradient = $\frac{1}{7}$, y-intercept = $\left(0, \frac{1}{14}\right)$

f) gradient = $\frac{3}{28}$, y-intercept = $\left(0, \frac{4}{7}\right)$

g) gradient = -0.5, y-intercept = $(0, -1.5)$

h) gradient = 100, y-intercept = $(0, -110)$

i) gradient = $\frac{2}{7}$, y-intercept = $\left(0, \frac{1}{4}\right)$

j) gradient = $-\frac{1}{9}$, y-intercept = $\left(0, \frac{2}{9}\right)$

k) gradient = $-\frac{1}{12}$, y-intercept = $(0, 1)$

l) gradient = $\frac{11}{29}$, y-intercept = $\left(0, \frac{17}{29}\right)$

Q8 The points a), c) and e) lie on the line ($y = 3x - 13$).

Q9 The points a), c), d) and f) lie on the line ($y = -2x + 18$).

Q10 a) $d = 32t$ b) 18 minutes

c) Some possible answers include:
  – The car's speed is likely to vary, rather than stay constant.
  – External factors would affect the car's speed, such as bends in the road, or other vehicles.
  – The car wouldn't start at 32 km/h — it would take time for it to reach this speed.

Q11 a) $3x + 4y = 18 \Rightarrow 3x + 4y - 18 = 0$

b)

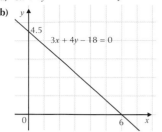

c) $x + 2y = 8 \Rightarrow x + 2y - 8 = 0$

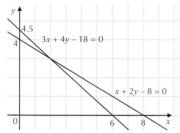

d) The cost of a small cup is £2 and a large cup is £3.

Exercise 1.2

Q1 a) (i) $(1, 2.5)$ **(ii)** $\sqrt{29}$

b) (i) $(0.5, 7.5)$ **(ii)** $5\sqrt{2}$

c) (i) $(-5, -4.3)$ **(ii)** 15

d) (i) $\left(-\frac{5}{2}, \frac{11}{6}\right)$ **(ii)** $3\sqrt{26}$

e) (i) $(3, 12)$ **(ii)** $4\sqrt{5}$

f) (i) $(3, -5)$ **(ii)** $\sqrt{13}$

g) (i) $(-0.5, -9)$ **(ii)** $5\sqrt{17}$

h) (i) $(-2.5, -11)$ **(ii)** $3\sqrt{5}$

Q2 a) (i) $(1.5, -0.5)$ **(ii)** $\sqrt{10}$

b) (i) $(4.25, 2.5)$ **(ii)** $\frac{\sqrt{5}}{2}$

c) (i) $(-5, 3)$ **(ii)** $4\sqrt{29}$

d) (i) $(6, 3)$ **(ii)** 30

First use the equation of the line to find the values of a and b, then find the midpoint and length with the formulas.

Q3 They are still closer to point A.
Find the distance from A to B using the distance formula and compare it with the distance travelled so far.

Q4 a) $4\sqrt{5}$
Start by finding a and b. One way to do this is it use the gradient and midpoint formulas to form simultaneous equations for a and b. Then use the length formula to find the distance between A and B.

b) $4\sqrt{26}$
Use the midpoint formula to find a = −1, then the gradient formula to find b = −21. Then use the length formula.

Q5 $(-1, 0.5)$ and $(3, 3.5)$
The gradient formula tells you that 3(change in x) = 4(change in y), and the length formula tells you that (change in x)² + (change in y)² = 25. Solve these simultaneously to get (change in x) = 4 and (change in y) = 3. Since the midpoint is at (1, 2), C and D must be either at (−1, 0.5) and (3, 3.5), or at (−1, 3.5) and (3, 0.5). Since the gradient is positive, it must be the first pair. You might notice that CD is the hypotenuse of a right-angled triangle with sides 3, 4, 5, which can make the working easier.

2. Parallel and Perpendicular Lines

Exercise 2.1

Q1 a), c) and e) are parallel.

Q2 a) $4x - y - 10 = 0$ **b)** $2x - y + 3 = 0$

Q3 a) no **b)** yes **c)** yes

Q4 a) $y = \frac{1}{2}x + 1$ **b)** $x - 2y + 2 = 0$

Q5 a) $2x - y - 3 = 0$ **b)** $5x + y - 14 = 0$

c) $x - 9y + 24 = 0$ **d)** $4x - y + 19 = 0$

e) $x - y = 0$ **f)** $x + 5y - 300 = 0$

g) $5x + 22y - 196 = 0$

h) $3x - 2y + 10 = 0$

i) $9x - y - 15 = 0$

Exercise 2.2

Q1 a) $y = -\frac{1}{2}x + 4$ **b)** $y = -5x + 27$

Q2 a) $4x + y + 2 = 0$ **b)** $3x - 2y + 7 = 0$

c) $2x + 3y - 7 = 0$ **d)** $2x + y - 7 = 0$

e) $42x + 8y - 77 = 0$

f) $3x + y + 16 = 0$

g) $28x + y - 204 = 0$

h) $x + 5y - 25 = 0$

i) $4x + 3y - 216 = 0$

Q3 a) AB: $y = \frac{1}{4}x + 2$, BC: $y = -4x + 19$,
AC: $y = -\frac{3}{5}x + 2$

b) The triangle is right-angled, since AB is perpendicular to BC:
$m_{AB} \times m_{BC} = \frac{1}{4} \times -4 = -1$

Q4 $y = -\frac{2}{3}x + \frac{2}{3}a + b$
(or $2x + 3y - 2a - 3b = 0$)
Rearrange 3x − 2y = 6 to find the gradient and hence get the gradient of A. Then substitute (a, b) into the equation y = mx + c to find c in terms of a and b.

Q5 $y = 2x - 3$
Find the midpoint and gradient of AB, then find the equation of the line that passes through the midpoint with gradient $-1 \div m_{AB}$

3. Proportion

Exercise 3.1

Q1 a) 15 **b)** 7 **c)** 24
d) 10.5 **e)** 18

Q2 a) 2 **b)** 8 **c)** 4 **d)** 7.5

Q3 a)

b) 10 **c)** 62.5 **d)** $3\sqrt{2}$

Q4 If $y \propto x$ and $y \propto z$,
then you can write $y = k_1x$ and $y = k_2z$,
where k_1 and k_2 are constants.
Equating y's: $k_1x = k_2z \Rightarrow x = \frac{k_2}{k_1}z$
$\frac{k_2}{k_1}$ must be a constant, since k_1 and k_2
are both constants.
So $x \propto z$ with constant of
proportionality $\frac{k_2}{k_1}$.

Q5 1.1×10^{-7} N

4. Curve Sketching

Exercise 4.1

Q1 a) D **b)** B **c)** A **d)** C

Q2 a) $x^3 - 7x^2 + 12x = x(x - 3)(x - 4)$.

b)

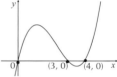

Q3 a)

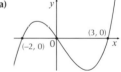

b)

c)

d)

e)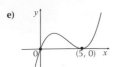

f)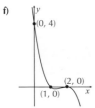

g)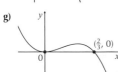

h)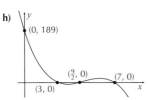

i)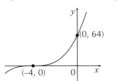

j)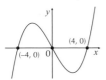

k)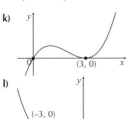

l)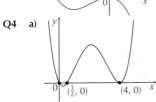

Q4 a)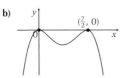

b) (page continued)

c)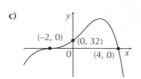

d)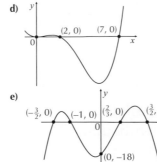

e)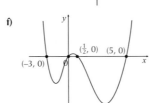

f)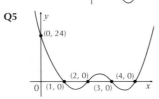

Q5

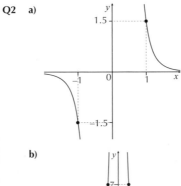

Use trial and error to find a root, then use algebraic division to factorise it out of the expression. Repeat this process until the expression is fully factorised.

Exercise 4.2

Q1 a) D b) A c) B d) C

Q2 a)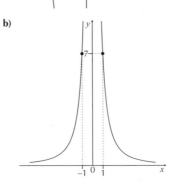

b)

c)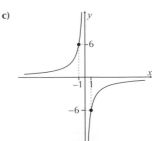

d)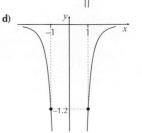

e)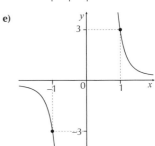

f)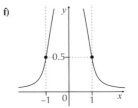

g)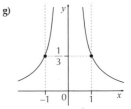

h)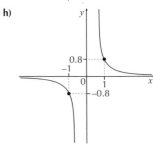

Q3 **a)**

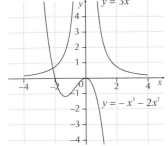

b) The equation has 1 real root.

Q4 **a)**

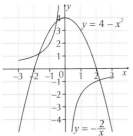

b) $x = -0.54, -1.68$ and 2.21 (to 2 d.p.)
(accept: -0.4 to -0.7, -1.6 to -1.8
and 2.1 to 2.3)

5. Graph Transformations
Exercise 5.1

Q1 **a)**

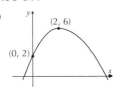

b)

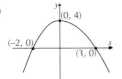

Q2 **a)** Asymptotes are $x = 0$ and $y = 0$.

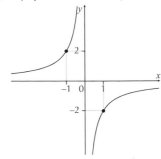

b) Asymptotes are $x = -3$ and $y = 0$.

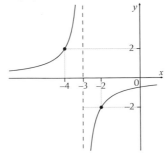

c) Asymptotes are $x = 0$ and $y = 3$.

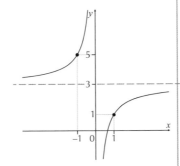

Q3 **a)** 1 unit up

b) 2 units right   **c)** 4 units left

Q4 Translation by 5 units down,
i.e. by the vector $\begin{pmatrix} 0 \\ -5 \end{pmatrix}$.

Q5 **a)** $y = x^2 - 3x + 13$

b) $y = x^2 - 3x + 2$ or $y = (x - 2)(x - 1)$

c) $y = x^2 - x + 5$

d) $y = x^2 - 9x + 25$

Q6 **a)** and **b)**

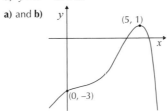

Q7 **a)**

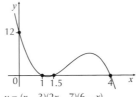

b) $y = (x - 3)(2x - 7)(6 - x)$

c)

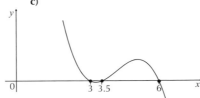

Q8 **a)** $g(x) = x^2 + 6x + 14$

b) $h(x) = x^2 + 6x + 10$

Q9 **a)** $x = 0, y = -4$

b) $x = -3, y = 0$ **c)** $x = 1, y = 7$

Exercise 5.2

Q1 **a)**

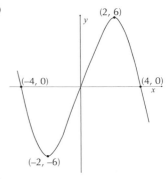

b)

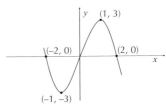

c)

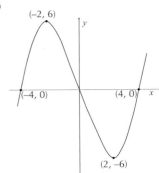

d)

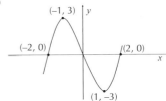

Q2 B   **Q3** B

Q4 **a)**

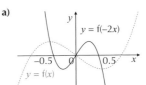

b)

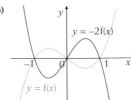

c)

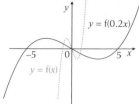

d)

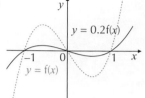

Q5 **a)**

b)

c)

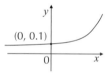

d)

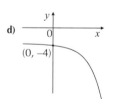

e)

Q6 **a)** $g(x) = 2x^2 - 6x + 6 \ (= 2(x^2 - 3x + 3))$
b) $g(x) = x^2 + 3x + 3$
c) $g(x) = 16x^2 - 12x + 3$

Q7 **a)**

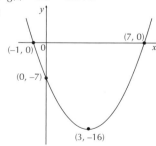

b) $y = -2x^2 + 12x + 14$

c)

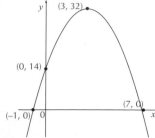

6. Circles

Exercise 6.1

Q1 **a)** $x^2 + y^2 = 25$ **b)** $x^2 + y^2 = 49$
   c) $x^2 + y^2 = 23$ **d)** $x^2 + y^2 = 18$
   e) $x^2 + y^2 = 7776$

Q2 **a)** $(x - 2)^2 + (y - 5)^2 = 9$
   b) $(x + 3)^2 + (y - 2)^2 = 25$
   c) $(x + 2)^2 + (y + 3)^2 = 49$
   d) $(x - 3)^2 + y^2 = 16$
   e) $(x - 5)^2 + (y - 3)^2 = 64$
   f) $(x - 3)^2 + (y - 1)^2 = 31$
   g) $(x + 3)^2 + (y + 2)^2 = 5$
   h) $(x + 10)^2 + (y - 7)^2 = 121$
   i) $(x - 8)^2 + y^2 = 17$

Q3 **a)** centre $(1, 5)$, $r = 2$
   b) centre $(3, 5)$, $r = 8$
   c) centre $(3, -2)$, $r = 5$
   d) centre $(6, 4)$, $r = 2\sqrt{5}$
   e) centre $(-8, -1)$, $r = 3\sqrt{3}$
   f) centre $(0, 12)$, $r = 7\sqrt{3}$

Q4 $r = 5\sqrt{2}$,
equation $(x - 3)^2 + (y - 5)^2 = 50$

Q5 **a)** $(x - 1)^2 + (y - 1)^2 = 2$
   b) $(x + 7)^2 + (y - 13)^2 = 218$
   c) $(x - 8)^2 + (y + 6)^2 = 100$
   d) $(x - 14)^2 + (y - 22)^2 = 680$

Exercise 6.2

Q1 **a)** centre $(-1, 2)$ **b)** $r = 2\sqrt{2}$

Q2 **a)** centre $\left(\frac{3}{2}, 0\right)$ **b)** $r = = \frac{\sqrt{5}}{2}$

Q3 **a)** $r = 4$, centre $(-1, 3)$
   b) $r = \sqrt{5}$, centre $(0, 1)$
   c) $r = 5$, centre $(3, 2)$
   d) $r = \sqrt{21}$, centre $(5, -3)$
   e) $r = \sqrt{66}$, centre $(-7, 4)$
   f) $r = 2\sqrt{2}$, centre $(2, -0.5)$
   g) $r = \frac{3\sqrt{2}}{2}$, centre $(-1, -1.5)$
   h) $r = \sqrt{13}$, centre $(1, -2)$
   i) $r = \sqrt{21}$, centre $(-4, 2)$

Q4 $x^2 + y^2 + 6y - 1 = 0$, $f = 0$, $g = 3$, $c = -1$

Q5 $x^2 + y^2 + 8x - 4y = 0$, $f = 4$, $g = -2$, $c = 0$

Q6 **a)** $x^2 + y^2 + 2fx + 2gy + c = 0$
$(x + f)^2 - f^2 + (y + g)^2 - g^2 + c = 0$
$(x + f)^2 + (y + g)^2 = f^2 + g^2 - c$
So $a = -f$, $b = -g$ and
$r^2 = f^2 + g^2 - c$
i.e. centre $(-f, -g)$ and
$r = \sqrt{f^2 + g^2 - c}$ as required.

   b) centre $(2.5, 2.5)$, $r = \frac{\sqrt{10}}{2}$

Exercise 6.3

Q1 **a)** $(3, 1)$ **b)** 3 **c)** $x + 3y = 16$

Q2 **a)** $2x + 3y + 9 = 0$ **b)** $x - y + 5 = 0$
   c) $x - 3y - 15 = 0$ **d)** $2x - y - 16 = 0$
   e) $5x - y - 48 = 0$ **f)** $x - 2y + 29 = 0$
   g) $2x + 3y + 22 = 0$
   h) $11x + 5y + 39 = 0$

Q3 $n = 3$
*Find the gradient of the line from the centre of
the circle to A in terms of n, then use the fact
that it is perpendicular to the tangent to solve
for n. You could also find the equation of this
radius in the form y = mx + c, then substitute
in the point (n, 1).*

Q4 **a)** $x - 3y + 4 = 0$
*Use the gradient formula with points A
and M to find the gradient of AB. Line l
is perpendicular to AB and passes through
M, so use this to find its equation.*

   b) $(x - 2)^2 + (y - 2)^2 = 50$
*Use the length formula to find the
distance between A and C, then substitute
this and the coordinates of C into the
general equation of a circle.*

Q5 **a)** Gradient of AB $= \frac{14 - 12}{4 - (-2)} = \frac{2}{6} = \frac{1}{3}$
Gradient of BC $= \frac{2 - 14}{8 - 4} = \frac{-12}{4}$
$= -3$
$\frac{1}{3} \times -3 = -1$ so AB and BC
are perpendicular.
So angle ABC is $90°$. By circle
properties, AC must be a diameter of
the circle.

   b) $(x - 3)^2 + (y - 7)^2 = 50$
*AC is a diameter, so the centre of the
circle is the midpoint of AC. Then use
the length formula to find the distance
from the centre to A, B or C, which is the
radius of the circle.*

Q6 $(x + 2)^2 + (y - 4)^2 = 65$
*Find the equations of two of the
perpendicular bisectors:
AB (y = -x + 2), BC (y = -3x - 2)
and AC (y = $\frac{2}{3}$ x + $\frac{16}{3}$)
Then solve the two equations simultaneously
to find the centre of the circle, (-2, 4).
Find the distance from the centre to A, B or C
with the length formula to get the radius.*

Q7 **a)** $(x - 1)^2 + (y - 1)^2 = 50$
   b) $x^2 + (y - 11)^2 = 29$
   c) $(x - 16)^2 + (y - 8)^2 = 40$
   d) $(x - 6)^2 + (y + 1)^2 = 290$
Use the same method as in Q6.

Review Exercise —
Chapter 4

Q1 **a)** (i) $y + 1 = 3(x - 2)$ or $y + 19 = 3(x + 4)$
  (ii) $y = 3x - 7$
  (iii) $3x - y - 7 = 0$

b) (i) $y + \frac{1}{3} = \frac{1}{5}x$ or $y - \frac{2}{3} = \frac{1}{5}(x - 5)$
  (ii) $y = \frac{1}{5}x - \frac{1}{3}$
  (iii) $3x - 15y - 5 = 0$

c) (i) $y - 7 = \frac{3}{5}(x - 8)$
  or $y + 2 = \frac{3}{5}(x + 7)$
  (ii) $y = \frac{3}{5}x + \frac{11}{5}$
  (iii) $3x - 5y + 11 = 0$

d) (i) $y - 5 = \frac{5}{6}(x - 5)$
  or $y - \frac{5}{2} = \frac{5}{6}(x - 2)$
  (ii) $y = \frac{5}{6}x + \frac{5}{6}$
  (iii) $5x - 6y + 5 = 0$

e) (i) $y - 2 = -4(x - 1.3)$
  or $y = -4(x - 1.8)$
  (ii) $y = -4x + 7.2$
  (iii) $20x + 5y - 36 = 0$

f) (i) $y + 2.3 = -0.2(x - 4.6)$
  or $y + 0.3 = -0.2(x + 5.4)$
  (ii) $y = -0.2x - 1.38$
  (iii) $10x + 50y + 69 = 0$

Q2 **a)** $y = \frac{3}{2}x - 4$ **b)** $y = -\frac{1}{2}x + 4$

Q3 $y = \frac{3}{2}x + \frac{15}{2}$

Q4 **a)** The +2 means that the equation cannot be written in the form $y = kx$ (the graph also does not pass through the origin), so y is not directly proportional to x.

b) The equation can be written as $y = (a - b)x$, where the constant of proportionality is equal to $(a - b)$, so y is directly proportional to x.

c) Simplifying the equation gives $y = x - 2$, which cannot be written as $y = kx$, so y is not directly proportional to x.

d) Expanding the brackets gives:
$y = x^2 + 6x + 9 - (x^2 - 6x + 9)$
$\Rightarrow y = x^2 + 6x + 9 - x^2 + 6x - 9$
$\Rightarrow y = 12x$, so they are in direct proportion.

Q5 22.5 N

Q6 **a)** 144 **b)** 31 104 **c)** 2

Q7 **a)**

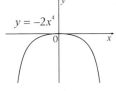

b)

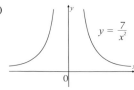

c)

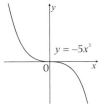

d)

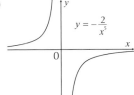

e)

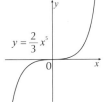

f)

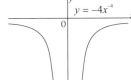

g)

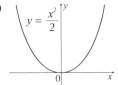

h)

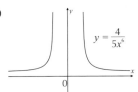

Q8 **a)**

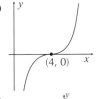

b)

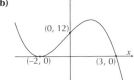

c)

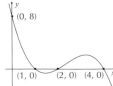

d)

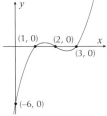

e)

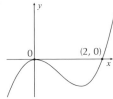

f)

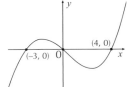

Q9 **a)**

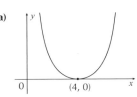

b)

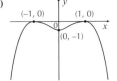

c)

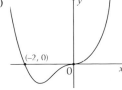

d)

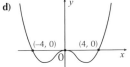

e)

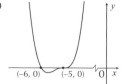

$(-6, 0)$ $(-5, 0)$ 0 x

f)

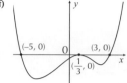

$(-5, 0)$ 0 $(3, 0)$ x
$(\frac{1}{3}, 0)$

Q10

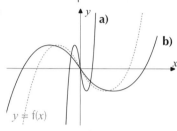

a) b)

$y = f(x)$

c) d)

$y = f(x)$

e) f)

$y = f(x)$

g) h)

$y = f(x)$

Q11 **a)** Vertical stretch, scale factor 3

b) Horizontal stretch, scale factor $\frac{1}{2}$

c) Horizontal translation by 1 to the right

d) Vertical translation by 12 downwards

e) Vertical translation by 2 upwards

f) Horizontal translation by 3 to the left

Q12 a)

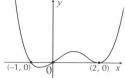

$(-1, 0)$ 0 $(2, 0)$ x

Since x = 2 is a root, (x − 2) is a factor by the Factor Theorem, so use algebraic division (or another suitable method) to factorise (x − 2) out of f(x). You can also see that x will factorise out of the function, so you are left with a quadratic which you can factorise as usual.

b)

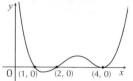

0 $(1, 0)$ $(2, 0)$ $(4, 0)$ x

c) $g(x) = (x − 2)^4 − 3(x − 2)^3 + 4(x − 2)$
or $g(x) = (x − 1)(x − 2)(x − 4)^2$
Substitute (x − 2) in place of x in f(x), or write down g(x) in its factorised form using the roots you know from the graph (or from part a)).

Q13 a)

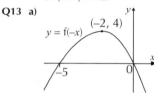

$y = f(-x)$ $(-2, 4)$
-5 0 x

b)

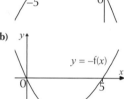

$y = -f(x)$
0 5 x
$(2, -4)$

c)

$(2, 8)$
$y = 2f(x)$
0 5 x

d)

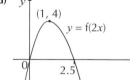

$(1, 4)$
$y = f(2x)$
0 2.5 x

Q14 a) $r = 3$, centre $(0, 0)$

b) $r = 2$, centre $(2, -4)$

c) $r = 5$, centre $(-3, 4)$

Q15 a) $(x - 3)^2 + (y - 2)^2 = 36$

b) $(x + 4)^2 + (y + 8)^2 = 64$

c) $x^2 + (y + 3)^2 = 14$

Q16 centre $(2, -3)$, $r = 9$

Q17 $4x + 3y - 61 = 0$

Q18 $5x + y - 3 = 0$

Q19 12
X is the midpoint of AB, so the length of AX is 9. AC is a radius, so the length of AC is 15. Since CX bisects the chord AB, the angle AXC is 90°. So triangle ACX is a right-angled triangle with hypotenuse AC and you can use Pythagoras' theorem to find CX.

Q20 $(x - 3)^2 + (y - 6.5)^2 = 3.25$
Find the equations of two of the perpendicular bisectors: AB (y = −x + 9.5), BC (x = 3) and AC (y = −0.2x + 7.1)
Then solve the two equations simultaneously to find the centre of the circle, (3, 6.5).
Find the distance from the centre to A, B or C with the length formula to get the radius.

Q21 a) Length $= 5\sqrt{2}$, midpoint $= (0.5, 6.5)$

b) $(x - 3)^2 + (y - 4)^2 = 25$

c) 12.5
CM bisects XY, so it is perpendicular. So the triangle CXY has base XY and perpendicular height CM.
Use the length formula to find the length of CM (you have already found the length of XY in part a).
Alternatively, you might notice that CX and CY are perpendicular, so you can also work out the area of CXY using CX and CY as the base and perpendicular height, both of which have length 5.

Chapter 5: The Binomial Expansion

1. Binomial Expansions

Exercise 1.1

Q1 $1 + 4x + 6x^2 + 4x^3 + x^4$

Q2 **a)** 15   **b)** 792   **c)** 27 405
       d) 1

Q3 **a)** 126   **b)** 120   **c)** 1365
       d) 28   **e)** 100

Q4 $1 + 10x + 45x^2 + 120x^3 + ...$

Q5 $1 + 6x + 15x^2 + 20x^3 + 15x^4 + 6x^5 + x^6$

Q6 $1 + 7x + 21x^2 + 35x^3 + ...$

Q7 **a)** $1 + 11x + 55x^2 + ...$
       b) $1 + 12x + 66x^2 + ...$
       c) $1 + 15x + 105x^2 + ...$
       d) $1 + 30x + 435x^2 + ...$

Exercise 1.2

Q1 **a)** $1 + 12x + 54x^2 + 108x^3 + 81x^4$
       b) $1 - 4x + 6x^2 - 4x^3 + x^4$
       c) $1 - 6x + 15x^2 - 20x^3 + 15x^4 - 6x^5 + x^6$
       d) $1 - 10x + 40x^2 - 80x^3 + 80x^4 - 32x^5$
       e) $1 - 12x + 48x^2 - 64x^3$
       f) $1 - 25x + 250x^2 - 1250x^3$
              $+ 3125x^4 - 3125x^5$
       g) $1 + 12x + 60x^2 + 160x^3 + 240x^4$
              $+ 192x^5 + 64x^6$
       h) $18x + 168x^3 + 252x^5 + 72x^7 + 2x^9$

Q2 $1 - x - 3x^2 + ...$

Q3 210

Q4 $1 + 8kx + 28k^2x^2 + 56k^3x^3 + ...$

Q5 $k = 3$

Exercise 1.3

Q1 $729 + 1458x + 1215x^2 + 540x^3 + ...$

Q2 **a)** $16 + 32x + 24x^2 + 8x^3 + x^4$

b) $16 + 64x + 96x^2 + 64x^3 + 16x^4$

c) $16 - 64x + 96x^2 - 64x^3 + 16x^4$

d) $\frac{1}{16} + \frac{1}{4}x + \frac{3}{8}x^2 + \frac{1}{4}x^3 + \frac{1}{16}x^4$

Q3 **a)** $\lambda = 4$ **b)** $1 + 32x + 448x^2 + ...$

Q4 $2187 + 25\,515x + 127\,575x^2 + 354\,375x^3 + ...$

Q5 $729 + 3645x + 7776x^2 + 9180x^3 + 6480x^4 + ...$

Q6 **a)** $n = 22$ **b)** $1540x^3$

Q7 **a)** 2560 **b)** 44 800

c) 7 **d)** −1593

Q8 **a)** $32 + 16x - 160x^2 + 200x^3 - 110x^4 + 29x^5 - 3x^6$

b) $2 + 29x + 165x^2 + 450x^3 + 540x^4 + 81x^5 - 243x^6$

c) $16 + 64x - 24x^2 - 152x^3 + 169x^4 - 66x^5 + 9x^6$

d) $8 + 60x + 114x^2 - 55x^3 - 171x^4 + 135x^5 - 27x^6$

Q9 $a = 4$
Find the coefficients of x^2 and x^5 in terms of a, then use the fact given in the question to solve for a.

Q10 2688

Q11 **a)** $n = 11$
Find the coefficients of x^2 and x^3 in terms of n, then solve for n.

b) $a = 5$
Find the coefficients of x and x^2, then solve for a.

Q12 $\mu = 7$ or −7
Using the expansion, the coefficient of x^2 is $1792\mu^2$. Set this equal to 87 808 from the question, and don't forget to include the negative root at the end.

Q13 43 632
Expand the outer brackets first — $[(x + 2)^3(x + 3)^2]^2 = (x + 2)^6(x + 3)^4$ — then expand each of these using the formula, and multiply the expressions together (you can ignore any powers of x greater than 2).

Exercise 1.4

Q1 **a)** $64 + 192x + 240x^2 + ...$

b) **(i)** 65.944 **(ii)** 85.6

(iii) 112 **(iv)** 220

(v) 47.2 **(vi)** 62.104

Q2 **a)** 13722.9 (1 d.p.)

b) 16099.4 (1 d.p.)

c) 16355.3 (1 d.p.)

Q3 **a)** $1 + 6x + \frac{33}{2}x^2 + \frac{55}{2}x^3 + \frac{495}{16}x^4 + ...$

b) 1.0616778 (7 d.p.)

Q4 $(1 - 3x)^6$
$= 1 + {}^6C_1(-3x) + {}^6C_2(-3x)^2 + {}^6C_3(-3x)^3 + ...$
$= 1 - 18x + 135x^2 - 540x^3 + ...$
$(1 + x)(1 - 3x)^6 = (1 + x)(1 - 18x + ...)$
$= 1 - 18x + ... + x - 18x^2 + ...$
$\approx 1 - 17x$ as required.

Q5 **a)** 2176.81 (2 d.p.)

b) 1347.84

c) 1898.58 (2 d.p.)

d) 2197.23 (2 d.p.)

e) 2344.76 (2 d.p.)

Q6 Because $x > 1$, higher powers of x will not be small enough to ignore, so only taking the terms up to x^3 will not provide an accurate estimate.

Review Exercise — Chapter 5

Q1 $1 + 12x + 66x^2 + 220x^3 + ...$

Q2 **a)** $1 + 40x + 780x^2 + ...$

b) $1 - 20x + 190x^2 - ...$

c) $1 + 60x + 1710x^2 + ...$

d) $1024 - 5120x + 11\,520x^2 - ...$

e) $1024 + 15\,360x + 103\,680x^2 + ...$

Q3 $29120x^4$

Q4 **a)** $1 + 3x + 4x^2 + \frac{28}{9}x^3 + ...$

b) 1.027326 (6 d.p.)

Q5 $1 + 15x + 90x^2 + 270x^3 + 405x^4 + 243x^5$

Q6 **a)** $1 + 8ax + 28a^2x^2 + 56a^3x^3 + 70a^4x^4 + ...$

b) $a = \frac{1}{4}$, coefficient of x is 2

Q7 $16\,384 - 143\,360x + 537\,600x^2 + ...$

Q8 720

Q9 **a)** $177\,147 + \frac{649\,539}{4}x + \frac{1\,082\,565}{16}x^2 + \frac{1\,082\,565}{64}x^3 + \frac{721\,710}{256}x^4 + ...$

b) 178 450.417 (3 d.p.)

Q10 **a)** $8192 + 53\,248kx + 159\,744k^2x^2 + ...$

b) $k = 2$

Q11 0.784 (3 d.p.)

Q12 **a)** $64 - 64x + \frac{80}{3}x^2 - \frac{160}{27}x^3 + ...$

b) **(i)** $256x - 256x^2$

(ii) $192 - 256x + 144x^2$

(iii) $64 + 960x + \frac{20\,048}{3}x^2$
Find the expansion of $(x + 1)^{16}$ up to the term in x^2, then multiply this by your expansion from part a).

Q13 **a)** $1 + 15x + 105x^2 + 455x^3 + 1365x^4 + ...$

b) To find 2.01^{15}, you would need to substitute $x = 1.01$. Since $x > 1$, x^n is not small enough to ignore for large n, so the estimate would be inaccurate.

Q14 **a)** **(i)** 240 **(ii)** 236.25

b) $(2 + x)^6$

Chapter 6: Trigonometry

1. The Sine and Cosine Rules

Exercise 1.1

Q1 P: (−0.656, 0.755) (3 s.f.), Q: (−0.616, −0.788) (3 s.f.), R: (0.921, −0.391) (3 s.f.)

Q2 **a)** 26.0° (3 s.f.) **b)** 48.0° (3 s.f.)

c) 84.9° (3 s.f.)

Exercise 1.2

Q1 **a)** $QR = 6.87$ cm (3 s.f.)

b) $TW = 9.53$ cm (3 s.f.)

Q2 **a)** $D = 60.6°$ (3 s.f.)

b) $V = 61.1°$ (3 s.f.)

Q3 $JK = 27.6$ cm (3 s.f.)

Q4 $PQ = 33.1$ m (3 s.f.)

Q5 $BC = 14.3$ cm (3 s.f.)

Q6 Smallest angle = 27.2° (3 s.f.)

Q7 $XYZ = 38.1°$ (3 s.f.)
Use Pythagoras' Theorem to find the lengths of XY, YZ and ZX, then put these values into the cosine rule.

Q8 **a)** Area = 50.3 cm² (3 s.f.)

b) Area = 10.4 cm² (3 s.f.)

Exercise 1.3

Q1 4.95 m (3 s.f.)

Q2 **a)** $BM = 2.91$ km (3 s.f.)

b) Height = 851 m (to the nearest m)

Q3 **a)**

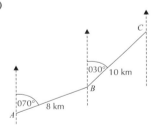

b) 16.9 km (3 s.f.)

c) 228° (3 s.f.)

Q4 Area = 102 m² (3 s.f.)

2. Trig Identities

Exercise 2.1

Q1 $\frac{\sin\theta}{\tan\theta} - \cos\theta \equiv \frac{\sin\theta}{\left(\frac{\sin\theta}{\cos\theta}\right)} - \cos\theta \equiv \cos\theta - \cos\theta \equiv 0$

Q2 $\cos^2\theta \equiv 1 - \sin^2\theta \equiv (1 - \sin\theta)(1 + \sin\theta)$

Q3 $\cos x = \frac{\sqrt{3}}{2}$

Q4 $4 \sin^2 x - 3 \cos x + 1$
$\equiv 4(1 - \cos^2 x) - 3 \cos x + 1$
$\equiv 4 - 4 \cos^2 x - 3 \cos x + 1$
$\equiv 5 - 3 \cos x - 4 \cos^2 x$

Q5 $\tan x = \sqrt{3}$

Q6 $(\tan x + 1)(\tan x - 1) \equiv \tan^2 x - 1$
$\equiv \dfrac{\sin^2 x}{\cos^2 x} - 1 \equiv \dfrac{1 - \cos^2 x}{\cos^2 x} - 1$
$\equiv \dfrac{1}{\cos^2 x} - \dfrac{\cos^2 x}{\cos^2 x} - 1 \equiv \dfrac{1}{\cos^2 x} - 2$

Q7 Here the student has divided both sides by $\sin \theta$. But $\sin \theta$ could equal 0, so you shouldn't divide by it. Instead the student should have rearranged:
$\cos \theta \sin \theta = \dfrac{1}{2} \sin \theta$
$\Rightarrow \cos \theta \sin \theta - \dfrac{1}{2} \sin \theta = 0$
$\Rightarrow \sin \theta (\cos \theta - \dfrac{1}{2}) = 0$.

So there's a solution when
$\cos \theta = \dfrac{1}{2} \Rightarrow \theta = 60°$,
as the student found.

But there's also a solution when
$\sin \theta = 0 \Rightarrow \theta = 0°$. This was not found because the student had cancelled the sin terms.

Q8 $\tan x + \dfrac{1}{\tan x} \equiv \dfrac{\sin x}{\cos x} + \dfrac{\cos x}{\sin x}$
$\equiv \dfrac{\sin^2 x + \cos^2 x}{\sin x \cos x} \equiv \dfrac{1}{\sin x \cos x}$

Q9 $4 + \sin x - 6 \cos^2 x$
$\equiv 4 + \sin x - 6(1 - \sin^2 x)$
$\equiv -2 + \sin x + 6 \sin^2 x$
$\equiv (2 \sin x - 1)(3 \sin x + 2)$

Q10 $\sin^2 x \cos^2 y - \cos^2 x \sin^2 y$
$\equiv (1 - \cos^2 x)\cos^2 y - \cos^2 x(1 - \cos^2 y)$
$\equiv \cos^2 y - \cos^2 x \cos^2 y$
$\quad - \cos^2 x + \cos^2 x \cos^2 y$
$\equiv \cos^2 y - \cos^2 x$

Q11 Look at the right-angled triangle below:

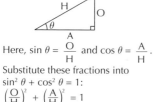

Here, $\sin \theta = \dfrac{O}{H}$ and $\cos \theta = \dfrac{A}{H}$.
Substitute these fractions into
$\sin^2 \theta + \cos^2 \theta = 1$:
$\left(\dfrac{O}{H}\right)^2 + \left(\dfrac{A}{H}\right)^2 = 1$
$\Rightarrow \dfrac{O^2}{H^2} + \dfrac{A^2}{H^2} = 1 \Rightarrow O^2 + A^2 = H^2$
— this is Pythagoras' theorem.

3. Trig Graphs
Exercise 3.1

Q1

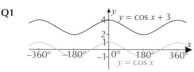

Q2 **a)**

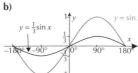

b)

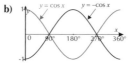

Q3 **a)**

$y = \sin 3x$

b)

$y = \cos x$ $y = -\cos x$

Q4 **a)-b)**

$f(x) = \tan x$

translation of $f(x) = \tan x$

c) $f(x) = \tan (x + 90°)$

Q5 **a)-b)**

$y = \sin x$

stretch of $y = \sin x$

c) $y = \sin \dfrac{1}{2} x$.

Q6 **a)** The graph has been translated to the left by 90°.

b) $y = \sin (x + 90°)$ (or $y = \cos x$)

Q7 **a)** The graph is stretched vertically by a factor of 2.

b) $y = 2 \cos x$

4. Solving Trig Equations
Exercise 4.1

Q1 **a)** $x = 48.6°$ and $x = 131.4°$ (both to 1 d.p.)

b) $x = 71.9°$ and $x = 288.1°$ (both to 1 d.p.)

c) $x = 123.7°$ and $x = 303.7°$ (both to 1 d.p.)

d) $x = 335.2°$ and $x = 204.8°$ (both to 1 d.p.)

e) $x = 124.1°$ and $x = 235.9°$ (both to 1 d.p.)

f) $x = 146.2°$ and $x = 326.2°$ (both to 1 d.p.)

g) $x = 45°$ and $x = 315°$

h) $x = 60°$ and $x = 240°$

i) $x = 30°$ and $x = 150°$

j) $x = 30°$ and $x = 210°$

---

k) $x = 45°$ and $x = 225°$

l) $x = 30°$ and $x = 330°$

Q2 $x = 143.1°$ (given in question), $216.9°$ (1 d.p.)

Q3 $x = 68.2°, 248.2°, 428.2°, 608.2°, 788.2°, 968.2°$ (all to 1 d.p.)

Q4 $x = 54.1°, 126°, -306°, -234°$ (all to 3 s.f.)

Exercise 4.2

Q1 $x = 153.3°$

Q2 **a)** $x = 36.9°$ and $x = 323.1°$ (both to 1 d.p.)

b) $x = 69.7°$ and $x = 249.7°$ (both to 1 d.p.)

c) $x = 188.6°$ and $x = 351.4°$ (both to 1 d.p.)

d) $x = 16.7°$ and $x = 196.7°$ (both to 1 d.p.)

e) $x = 149.0°$ and $x = 329.0°$ (both to 1 d.p.)

f) $x = 196.9°$ and $x = 343.1°$ (both to 1 d.p.)

g) $x = 14.5°$ and $x = 165.5°$ (both to 1 d.p.)

h) $x = 41.4°$ and $x = 318.6°$ (both to 1 d.p.)

i) $x = 125.5°$ and $x = 305.5°$ (both to 1 d.p.)

Q3 $x = 96.8°$ and $x = 277°$ (both to 3 s.f.)

Q4 $x = 48.6°, 131.4°, 408.6°, 491.4°$ (all to 1 d.p.)

Q5 $x = 71.9°$ and $x = -71.9°$ (both to 1 d.p.)

Q6 $x = 55.1°, 125°, 415°, 485°$ (all to 3 s.f.)

Q7 $x = 183.4°, 356.6°, 543.4°, 716.6°, 903.4°, 1076.6°$ (all to 1 d.p.)

Q8 $x = -274.8°, -94.8°, 85.2°, 265.2°$ (all to 1 d.p.)

Exercise 4.3

Q1 **a)** $x = 18.4°, 71.6°, 198.4°, 251.6°$ (all to 1 d.p.)

b) $x = 19.4°, 64.4°, 109.4°, 154.4°, 199.4°, 244.4°, 289.4°, 334.4°$ (all to 1 d.p.)

c) $x = 34.6°, 85.4°, 154.6°, 205.4°, 274.6°, 325.4°$ (all to 1 d.p.)

d) $x = 23.4°, 36.6°, 143.4°, 156.6°, 263.4°, 276.6°$ (all to 1 d.p.)

e) $x = 12°, 60°, 84°, 132°, 156°, 204°, 228°, 276°, 300°, 348°$

f) $x = 49.2°, 139.2°, 229.2°, 319.2°$ (all to 1 d.p.)

Q2 $x = 22.0°, 158.0°, 202.0°, 338.0°$ (all to 1 d.p.)

Q3 $x = 65.4°, 114.6°, 185.4°, 234.6°, 305.4°, 354.6°$ (all to 1 d.p.)

Q4 $x = 129.1°$ (1 d.p.)

Q5 $x = -90°, 90°$

Exercise 4.4

Q1 $x = 77.2°$ and $336.8°$ (both to 1 d.p.)
Q2 $x = 102.8°$ and $282.8°$ (both to 1 d.p.)
Q3 $x = 117.3°$ and $350.7°$ (both to 1 d.p.)
Q4 $x = 168.5°$ and $348.5°$ (both to 1 d.p.)
Q5 $x = -120.5°, 30.5°, 239.5°$ (all to 1 d.p.)
Q6 $x = 60.0°$ and $255.0°$ (both to 1 d.p.)

Exercise 4.5

For the questions in this exercise, you might have to use trig identities to get the equation in terms of a single trig function, then solve this equation. For some of the questions you'll have to factorise a quadratic equation before you can solve it.

Q1 **a)** $x = 78.7°, 19.5°, 160.5°, 258.7°$
(all to 1 d.p.)
b) $x = 0°, 53.1°$ (1 d.p.), $126.9°$ (1 d.p.), $180°, 360°$
c) $x = 71.6°, 108.4°, 251.6°, 288.4°$
(all to 1 d.p.)
d) $x = 90°, 41.4°$ (1 d.p.), $270°, 318.6°$
(1 d.p.)
e) $x = 59.0°, 239.0°$ (both 1 d.p.)
f) $x = 0°, 21.8°$ (1 d.p.), $180°, 201.8°$ (1 d.p.), $360°$
g) $x = 48.2°$ (1 d.p.), $120°, 240°, 311.8°$ (1 d.p.)
h) $x = 156.8°, 336.8°$ (both to 1 d.p.)

Q2 **a)** $x = 0°, 180°$ and $360°$
b) $x = -348.5°, -191.5°, 11.5°, 168.5°, 371.5°, 528.5°$ (all to 1 d.p.)
c) $x = -330°, -210°, -90°, 30°, 150°, 270°$

Q3 **a)** $4 \sin^2 x = 3 - 3\cos x$
$4(1 - \cos^2 x) = 3 - 3\cos x$
$4 - 4\cos^2 x = 3 - 3\cos x$
$\Rightarrow 4\cos^2 x - 3\cos x - 1 = 0$,
as required.
b) $x = 0°, 104.5°$ (1 d.p.), $255.5°$
(1 d.p.), $360°$

Q4 $x = 24.1°, 54.7°, 125.3°, 155.9°, 204.1°, 234.7°, 305.3°, 335.9°$ (all to 1 d.p.)

Q5 $x = -340.5°, -199.5°, 19.5°, 160.5°$ (all to 1 d.p.)

Review Exercise — Chapter 6

Q1 $\cos 30° = \dfrac{\sqrt{3}}{2}$, $\sin 30° = \dfrac{1}{2}$,
$\tan 30° = \dfrac{1}{\sqrt{3}}$
$\cos 45° = \dfrac{1}{\sqrt{2}}$, $\sin 45° = \dfrac{1}{\sqrt{2}}$,
$\tan 45° = 1$
$\cos 60° = \dfrac{1}{2}$, $\sin 60° = \dfrac{\sqrt{3}}{2}$,
$\tan 60° = \sqrt{3}$

Q2 **a)** $60°$ **b)** $30°$ **c)** $180°$

Q3 **a)** Angle $B = 125°$,
side $c = 3.10$ m (3 s.f.),
side $a = 3.66$ m (3 s.f.)
b) Area $= 4.64$ m^2 (3 s.f.)

Q4 **a)** Side $r = 11.7$ km (1 d.p.),
angle $P = 22.4°$ (1 d.p.),
angle $Q = 137.6°$ (1 d.p.)
b) Area $= 51.1$ km^2 (1 d.p.)

Q5 $22.3°, 49.5°, 108.2°$
(all to 1 d.p.)

Q6 For one triangle, $B = 72.9°$, $C = 72.1°$,
$c = 4.98$ m (all to 3 s.f.)
For the other triangle: $B = 107°$,
$C = 37.9°$, $c = 3.22$ m (all to 3 s.f.)

Q7 $\tan x - \sin x \cos x \equiv \dfrac{\sin x}{\cos x} - \sin x \cos x$
$\equiv \dfrac{\sin x - \sin x \cos^2 x}{\cos x}$
$\equiv \dfrac{\sin x(1 - \cos^2 x)}{\cos x}$
$\equiv \dfrac{\sin x(\sin^2 x)}{\cos x}$
$\equiv \sin^2 x \tan x$

Q8 $\tan^2 x - \cos^2 x + 1 \equiv \dfrac{\sin^2 x}{\cos^2 x} - (1 - \sin^2 x) + 1$
$\equiv \dfrac{\sin^2 x}{\cos^2 x} + \sin^2 x$
$\equiv \dfrac{\sin^2 x + \sin^2 x \cos^2 x}{\cos^2 x}$
$\equiv \dfrac{\sin^2 x(1 + \cos^2 x)}{\cos^2 x}$
$\equiv \tan^2 x(1 + \cos^2 x)$

Q9 2

Q10 $\dfrac{\sin^4 x + \sin^2 x \cos^2 x}{\cos^2 x - 1}$
$\equiv \dfrac{\sin^4 x + \sin^2 x(1 - \sin^2 x)}{1 - \sin^2 x - 1}$
$\equiv \dfrac{\sin^4 x + \sin^2 x - \sin^4 x}{-\sin^2 x}$
$\equiv \dfrac{\sin^2 x}{-\sin^2 x} \equiv -1$

Q11 a)

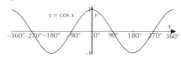

b)

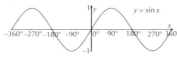

c)

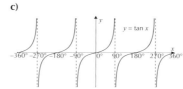

Q12 $y = -\dfrac{1}{2}\cos x$
Q13 $y = \sin 2x$

Q14 a)

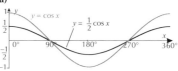

b)

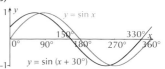

c)

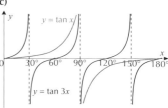

Q15 **a)** **(i)** $\theta = 60°$ and $\theta = 120°$
(ii) $\theta = 135°$ and $\theta = 315°$
(iii) $\theta = 135°$ and $\theta = 225°$.
b) **(i)** $\theta = -147.0°, -123.0°, -57.0°, -33.0°, 33.0°, 57.0°, 123.0°$
and $147.0°$ (all to 1 d.p.)
(ii) $\theta = -17.5°$ and $127.5°$
(both to 1 d.p.)
(iii) $\theta = 179.8°$ (1 d.p.)

Q16 $x = 70.5°$ (1 d.p.), $120°, 240°, 289.5°$
(1 d.p.)

Q17 $x = -30°$

Q18 $x = 14.5°$ (1 d.p.), $165.5°$ (1 d.p.), $210°, 330°$

Q19 $x = 0°, 70.5°$ (1 d.p.), $180°, 289.5°$
(1 d.p.), $360°, 430.5°$ (1 d.p.), $540°, 649.5°$ (1 d.p.), $720°$
For questions 16-19, you either have to use the trig identities or factorise a quadratic equation (or both) to find the solutions.

Chapter 7: Exponentials and Logarithms

1. Exponentials

Exercise 1.1

Q1 **a)** **(i)-(iii)**

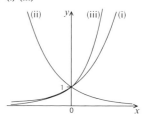

Q8 a)

x	−3	−2	−1	0	1	2	3
y	0.0156	0.0625	0.25	1	4	16	64

b)

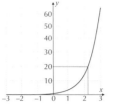

c) 2.2   **d)** 2.16 (3 s.f.)

Q9 a) 2.38 (3 s.f.)
b) 200 000 (3 s.f.)
c) 1.09 (3 s.f.)   **d)** 4.82 (3 s.f.)

Q10 a) 0.8959 (4 d.p.)   **b)** −0.8830 (4 d.p.)
c) 0.1223 (4 d.p.)   **d)** 0.8000 (4 d.p.)

Q11 a) $x = 2e^2$

b) $x = \dfrac{e^{-3} + 28}{8}$ or $\dfrac{1}{8e^3} + \dfrac{7}{2}$

c) $x = 0$ **d)** $x = \dfrac{1}{4}\ln 3$

You had to use quadratics again for parts c) and d) (like in Exercise 4.1).

Q12 $x = \log 2.5$ or $x = 0$
You need to rewrite the equation as a quadratic again here.

Q13 $P = 35$

Q14 The spiders are in danger of extinction in the 8th year.

Q15 a) £1015 to the nearest £

b) After 14 years old the value will have fallen below £500.

c)

Q16 a) 46 leopards

b) 13 years

c) The model predicts that only 2 leopards will be left in the wild after 5 years.

Q17 a) 30 zombies

b) 158

c) 15 weeks

Q18 Area = length × width. The area is always 120 m², so $lw = 120$. Take logs:
$\log lw = \log 120$
$\Rightarrow \log l + \log w = \log 120$
$\Rightarrow \log l = \log 120 - \log w$

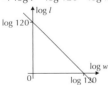

Q19 a) $y = e^{7.5 - 0.5t}$ (or $y = e^{7.5}e^{-0.5t}$)
Find an equation in the form $\ln y = mt + c$. The y-intercept (c) is 7.5 and the gradient (m) is −0.5. Then take exponentials of both sides of $\ln y = -0.5t + 7.5$ to get the exponential equation.

b) $y = e^{3.5 + 0.25t}$ (or $y = e^{3.5}e^{0.25t}$)
Use the same method as for part a) — this time, the equation of the line is $\ln y = 0.25t + 3.5$.

c) The 9th month

d) E.g. the model predicts that the population of grey squirrels will continue to grow exponentially with time. However, in reality, factors such as the availability of resources will begin to slow the growth after a certain time.

Chapter 8: Differentiation

1. The Gradient of a Curve

Exercise 1.1

Q1 a) (i) 7   **(ii)** 4.75   **(iii)** 3.31

b) The gradients of the straight lines in part a) move closer to 3 as the value of x moves closer to 1.

Q2 a) $\dfrac{dy}{dx} = 1$ **b)** $f'(x) = 3x^2$

c) $f'(x) = 2$ **d)** $f'(x) = 4x$

Q3 a) $\dfrac{dy}{dx} = 10x$ **b)** $\dfrac{dy}{dx} = 1 - 2x$

c) $\dfrac{dy}{dx} = 9x^2$ **d)** $\dfrac{dy}{dx} = 6x^2 + 3$

2. Differentiating $y = f(x)$

Exercise 2.1

Q1 a) $\dfrac{dy}{dx} = 6x^5$ **b)** $\dfrac{dy}{dx} = -\dfrac{2}{x^3}$

c) $\dfrac{dy}{dx} = 6x$ **d)** $\dfrac{dy}{dx} = 7$

e) $\dfrac{dy}{dx} = \dfrac{3}{2\sqrt{x}}$ **f)** $\dfrac{dy}{dx} = -\dfrac{2}{x^2}$

Q2 a) $f'(x) = 7x^6$ **b)** $f'(x) = -\dfrac{4}{x^5}$

c) $f'(x) = 12x^2$ **d)** $f'(x) = \dfrac{1}{\sqrt[3]{x^2}}$

e) $f'(x) = 0$ **f)** $f'(x) = -\dfrac{8}{x^3}$

Q3 a) 16   **b)** $-\dfrac{1}{4}$ **c)** −20

d) $\dfrac{1}{3}$ **e)** −32   **f)** −150

Exercise 2.2

Q1 a) $\dfrac{dy}{dx} = 12x^2 - 2x$

b) $\dfrac{dy}{dx} = 1 - \dfrac{1}{x^2}$

c) $\dfrac{dy}{dx} = 6x + \dfrac{1}{2\sqrt{x}}$

d) $f'(x) = -10x^4 + 4 + \dfrac{2}{x^3}$

e) $f'(x) = \dfrac{3}{2}\sqrt{x} - 1$

f) $f'(x) = 5 + \dfrac{6}{x^4} + \dfrac{1}{3\sqrt[3]{x^2}}$

Q2 a) $\dfrac{d}{dx}(x(x^6 - 1)) = 7x^6 - 1$

b) $\dfrac{d}{dx}((x - 3)(x + 4)) = 2x + 1$

c) $\dfrac{d}{dx}(x(x - 1)(x - 2)) = 3x^2 - 6x + 2$

d) $\dfrac{d}{dx}((x - 3)(x + 4)(x - 1)) = 3x^2 - 13$

e) $\dfrac{d}{dx}(x^2(x - 4)(3 - x^3))$
$= 9x^2 - 6x^5 - 24x + 20x^4$

f) $\dfrac{d}{dx}((x - 3)^2(x^2 - 2))$
$= 4x^3 - 18x^2 + 14x + 12$

Q3 a) 102   **b)** 159.75   **c)** 47
d) 5   **e)** 2.75   **f)** −10
g) $\dfrac{26}{25}$ **h)** −6

Q4 a)

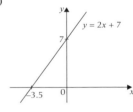

b)

c)

d)

Q5 a) (1, −1)   **b)** $(-\dfrac{2}{3}, -\dfrac{4}{3})$
c) $(\dfrac{3}{10}, -\dfrac{9}{20})$ **d)** (1, 6) and (−1, −6)
e) (0, 0) and $(\dfrac{1}{3}, -\dfrac{1}{27})$
f) (−2, 20) and (1, −7)

Q6 a) $\dfrac{dy}{dx} = 1$ **b)** $f'(x) = 2x$
c) $f'(x) = 4x^3 - 12x^2$ **d)** $\dfrac{dy}{dx} = 1 - \dfrac{12}{x^2}$
e) $\dfrac{dy}{dx} = \dfrac{7}{2}\sqrt{x^5} - 1$ **f)** $f'(x) = -\dfrac{3}{2\sqrt{x^3}}$
g) $f'(x) = \dfrac{1}{2\sqrt{x}}$ **h)** $f'(x) = \dfrac{1}{2\sqrt{x}}$
i) $\dfrac{dy}{dx} = -\dfrac{1}{2\sqrt{x}}$

Exercise 2.3

Q1 a) $y = 5x + 2$ **b)** $y = 10x - 13$
c) $y = 9x - 14$ **d)** $y = 8x + 4$
e) $y = 24x - 38$ **f)** $y = -2x + 6$

Q2 **a)** $3x - 4y + 16 = 0$
b) $13x - 2y - 11 = 0$
c) $5x - 16y + 56 = 0$
d) $5x + 4y - 16 = 0$
e) $5x - 3y - 29 = 0$
f) $13x - 9y + 21 = 0$

Q3 **a)** $x + 8y - 50 = 0$
b) $x - 10y + 81 = 0$
c) $x + 11y - 69 = 0$
d) $x - 4y + 42 = 0$
e) $x + 3y + 25 = 0$

Q4 **a)** $3x - 10y + 46 = 0$
b) $16x - 4y - 13 = 0$
c) $4x - 9y - 34 = 0$ **d)** $y = 4x + 9$
e) $8x + 7y - 67 = 0$ **f)** $x + 2y + 4 = 0$

Q5 **a)** $(3, 3)$ **b)** $y = 9x - 24$
c) $x + 9y - 30 = 0$

Q6 **a)** Putting $x = -2$ into the equation gives:

$$y = \frac{x^3 + x^2 + x + 5}{x^2}$$

$$= \frac{(-2)^3 + (-2)^2 + (-2) + 5}{(-2)^2}$$

$$= \frac{-8 + 4 - 2 + 5}{4} = -\frac{1}{4}$$

so $(2, -\frac{1}{4})$ is a point on the curve.
b) $8x - 4y + 15 = 0$
c) $2x + 4y + 5 = 0$

3. Second Order Derivatives

Exercise 3.1

Q1 **a)** $\frac{dy}{dx} = 3x^2$ and $\frac{d^2y}{dx^2} = 6x$

b) $\frac{dy}{dx} = 5x^4$ and $\frac{d^2y}{dx^2} = 20x^3$

c) $\frac{dy}{dx} = 4r^3$ and $\frac{d^2y}{dx^2} = 12x^2$

d) $\frac{dy}{dx} = 1$ and $\frac{d^2y}{dx^2} = 0$

e) $\frac{dy}{dx} = -\frac{1}{x^2}$ and $\frac{d^2y}{dx^2} = \frac{2}{x^3}$

f) $\frac{dy}{dx} = \frac{1}{2\sqrt{x}}$ and $\frac{d^2y}{dx^2} = -\frac{1}{4(\sqrt{x})^3}$

g) $\frac{dy}{dx} = -\frac{2}{x^3}$ and $\frac{d^2y}{dx^2} = \frac{6}{x^4}$

h) $\frac{dy}{dx} = \frac{3}{2}\sqrt{x}$ and $\frac{d^2y}{dx^2} = \frac{3}{4\sqrt{x}}$

Q2 **a)** $f'(x) = 12x^2 - 2x$ and $f''(x) = 24x - 2$
b) $f'(x) = 3x^2 - 8x - 3$ and $f''(x) = 6x - 8$
c) $f'(x) = 3x^2 - 2$ and $f''(x) = 6x$
d) $f'(x) = \frac{3}{2\sqrt{x}} + \frac{3}{2}\sqrt{x}$ and

$$f''(x) = -\frac{3}{4(\sqrt{x})^3} + \frac{3}{4\sqrt{x}}$$

$$\left(= -\frac{3}{4x\sqrt{x}} + \frac{3}{4\sqrt{x}}\right)$$

e) $f'(x) = 9x^2 - 4x$ and $f''(x) = 18x - 4$
f) $f'(x) = \frac{3}{2}\sqrt{x} - 1 + \frac{7}{2\sqrt{x}}$ and

$$f''(x) = \frac{3}{4\sqrt{x}} - \frac{7}{4(\sqrt{x})^3}$$

Q3 **a)** 16 **b)** $\frac{11}{32}$ **c)** -38
d) 240 **e)** 2 **f)** $\frac{2}{27}$

4. Derivatives and Graphs

Exercise 4.1

Q1 **a)** 2 stationary points
b) 3 stationary points

Q2 **a)** $x = -\frac{3}{2}$ **b)** $x = \frac{1}{2}$
c) $x = \frac{1}{3}$ and $x = -3$
d) $x = 0$ and $x = 9$

Q3 **a)** $(\frac{5}{4}, -\frac{9}{8})$ **b)** $(\frac{3}{2}, -\frac{7}{4})$
c) $(-1, 10)$ **d)** $(-\frac{1}{4}, -\frac{25}{8})$

Q4 **a)** $(1, 0)$ and $(-1, 4)$ **b)** $(0, 5)$
c) $(0, 0)$ and $\left(-\frac{4}{3}, \frac{32}{9}\right)$
d) $(0, 8)$ and $(-2, 24)$

Q5 $f'(x) = 5x^4 + 3$. When $f'(x) = 0$,
$5x^4 + 3 = 0 \Rightarrow x^4 = -\frac{3}{5}$.
Finding a solution would involve finding the fourth root of a negative number. But $x^4 = (x^2)^2$, so x^4 is always positive and so there are no stationary points.

Q6 **a)** $\frac{dy}{dx} = 3x^2 - 14x - 5$
b) $(-\frac{1}{3}, \frac{77}{27})$ and $(5, -73)$

Q7 $k > 0$
For stationary points to occur, f'(x) must equal zero, so f'(x) = 3x² + k = 0 ⇒ -$\frac{k}{3}$ = x². For this equation to have a solution, k can't be positive (or it would be taking the square root of a negative number), so k ≤ 0. Therefore, if the graph has no stationary points, k > 0.

Exercise 4.2

Q1 **a)** negative **b)** positive
c) negative **d)** negative
e) positive

Q2 **a)** $\frac{d^2y}{dx^2} = 6x$, $(2, -12)$ is a minimum
b) $\frac{d^2y}{dx^2} = 24x^2 - 96x$,
$(6, 36)$ is a minimum
c) $\frac{d^2y}{dx^2} = 80x^3 + 180x^2$,
$(-3, -7)$ is a maximum
d) $\frac{d^2y}{dx^2} = 20x^3 - 60x^2 + 10$,
$(4, 64)$ is a minimum

Q3 **a)** $(1, 3)$
b) The second derivative at $x = 1$ is positive, so it's a minimum.

Q4 **a)** $(0, 5)$, maximum
b) $(1, -2)$, minimum $(-1, 6)$, maximum
c) $(4, -65)$, minimum
$(-2, 43)$, maximum
d) $(0, -10)$, minimum
$(-1, -9)$, maximum
$(-2, -10)$, minimum

e) $(-1, 1)$, maximum
$(-\frac{1}{3}, -\frac{5}{27})$, minimum
f) $(3, 4)$, minimum
$(-3, -4)$, maximum

Q5 **a)** $f'(x) = 3x^2 - 6x$ and $f''(x) = 6x - 6$.
b) $(0, 4)$, maximum
$(2, 0)$, minimum

Q6 **a)** $x = 10$ **b)** minimum

Q7 $a = -9$, $b = 27$, $c = -17$
(so $f(x) = x^3 - 9x^2 + 27x - 17$)
Find f'(x) and f''(x) in terms of a and b. Then use the coordinates of the stationary point and the value of f''(x) at this point to form equations that you can solve to find a, b and c.

Q8 **a)** $\frac{dy}{dx} = 4x^3 + 3kx^2 + 2x$. Stationary points occur when $\frac{dy}{dx} = 0$,
so $4x^3 + 3kx^2 + 2x = 0$
$\Rightarrow x(4x^2 + 3kx + 2) = 0$
so $x = 0$ or $4x^2 + 3kx + 2 = 0$.
As you know the only stationary point occurs at $x = 0$, the part in brackets can't have any solutions. This gives you information about the discriminant of the quadratic equation:
$b^2 - 4ac < 0 \Rightarrow 9k^2 < 32$
$\Rightarrow k^2 < \frac{32}{9}$.
b) $(0, 17)$, minimum turning point

Exercise 4.3

Q1 **a)** $\frac{dy}{dx} = 2x + 7$. The function is increasing for $x > -\frac{7}{2}$.
b) $\frac{dy}{dx} = 10x + 3$. The function is increasing for $x > -\frac{3}{10}$.
c) $\frac{dy}{dx} = -18x$.
The function is increasing for $x < 0$.

Q2 **a)** $f'(x) = -3 - 4x$. The function is decreasing for $x > -\frac{3}{4}$.
b) $f'(x) = -18x$. The function is decreasing for $x > 0$.
c) $f'(x) = -17 + 12x$. The function is decreasing for $x < \frac{17}{12}$.

Q3 **a)** $\frac{dy}{dx} = 3x^2 - 12x - 15$.
The function is increasing when $x < -1$ and when $x > 5$.
b) $\frac{dy}{dx} = 3x^2 + 12x + 12$.
The function is increasing for all values of x except $x = -2$.
c) $\frac{dy}{dx} = 2x + \frac{1}{2\sqrt{x}}$. The function is increasing for all $x > 0$.
d) $\frac{dy}{dx} = 8x - \frac{1}{x^2}$. The function is increasing when $x > \frac{1}{2}$

Chapter 9: Integration

1. Indefinite Integration

Exercise 1.1

Q1 a) $y = \frac{x^8}{8} + C$ b) $y = \frac{x^4}{2} + C$

c) $y = 4x^2 + C$ d) $y = -x^5 + C$

e) $y = 2x^{100} + C$ f) $y = -\frac{1}{2x^2} + C$

g) $y = -\frac{4}{3x^3} + C$ h) $y = \frac{3}{2x^4} + C$

i) $y = -12x + C$ j) $y = \frac{2x^{\frac{3}{2}}}{3} + C$

k) $y = \frac{3x^{\frac{4}{3}}}{4} + C$ l) $y = \frac{24}{5}x^{\frac{5}{2}} + C$

Q2 a) $\frac{3x^{\frac{5}{3}}}{5} + C$ b) $3x^{\frac{7}{3}} + C$

c) $2x^{\frac{1}{2}} + C$ d) $3x^{\frac{2}{3}} + C$

e) $10x^{1.4} + C$ f) $-3x^{0.4} + C$

g) $8x^{\frac{1}{4}} + C$ h) $-3x^{\frac{1}{3}} + C$

i) $4x^{-\frac{1}{3}} + C$ j) $\frac{1}{7}x^{\frac{7}{2}} + C$

k) $\frac{5}{18}x^{\frac{12}{5}} + C$ l) $50x^{1.01} + C$

Exercise 1.2

Q1 a) $f(x) = \frac{5x^2}{2} - x^3 + C$

b) $f(x) = x^4 - 2x^2 + C$

c) $f(x) = \frac{x^3}{3} - 3x^2 + 9x + C$

d) $f(x) = 2x^3 - \frac{2}{x^2} + C$

e) $f(x) = \frac{x^3}{3} + 4x - \frac{4}{x} + C$

f) $f(x) = \frac{6}{5}x^{\frac{5}{2}} - 3x^{\frac{2}{3}} + C$

g) $f(x) = 4x^{\frac{3}{2}} + \frac{1}{x} + C$

h) $f(x) = 4x^{\frac{1}{2}} - 2x^{\frac{7}{2}} + C$

i) $f(x) = 2x^{\frac{5}{2}} - 2x^{\frac{3}{2}} + C$

j) $f(x) = \frac{2}{3}x^3 - \frac{2}{5}x^{\frac{5}{2}} + C$

k) $f(x) = \frac{12}{7}x^{\frac{7}{6}} + C$

l) $f(x) = \frac{2}{7}x^{\frac{7}{2}} - \frac{4}{5}x^{\frac{5}{2}} + C$

Q2 a) $0.5x^{1.1} - 6x^{0.5} + C$

b) $2x^4 - 4\sqrt{x} - \frac{5}{x} + C$

c) $\frac{2}{7}x^{\frac{7}{2}} + x^{\frac{1}{2}} + C$

d) $2x^{\frac{7}{2}} - \frac{2}{3}x^{\frac{3}{2}} - 4x^{\frac{1}{2}} + C$

e) $3x^3 - 12x^{\frac{5}{2}} + \frac{25}{2}x^2 + C$

f) $\frac{2}{3}x^3 - 2\sqrt{x} + C$

g) $10x^{\frac{5}{2}} - 20x^{\frac{1}{2}} + 18x^{\frac{1}{3}} + C$

h) $2x^{\frac{1}{2}} - 2x^{\frac{3}{2}} - 2x + C$

i) $x^4 + \frac{8}{7}x^{\frac{7}{2}} + \frac{1}{3}x^3 + C$

Q3 a) $y = \frac{x^3}{2} + \frac{2}{x^2} + C$

b) $f(x) = -4x^{-\frac{1}{3}} + 2x^{\frac{5}{2}} + C$

Q4 a) $\frac{2}{3}x^{\frac{3}{2}} + 2x - 6x^{\frac{1}{2}} + C$

b) $\frac{2}{5}x^{\frac{5}{2}} - \frac{4}{3}x^{\frac{3}{2}} + 2x^{\frac{1}{2}} + C$

Exercise 1.3

Q1 a) $f(x) = x^4 + 5$

b) $f(x) = x^3 - 2x^2 + 3x - 5$

c) $f(x) = 2x^3 + 6x^2 - 3$

d) $f(x) = -\frac{5}{x} + x^2 - 20$

e) $f(x) = \frac{3}{4}x^4 - 4x^3 + 10$

f) $f(x) = x^3 - x^2 - x - 18$

g) $f(x) = \frac{x^3}{3} - \frac{3}{x} + 13$

h) $f(x) = 3x^3 - \frac{1}{x^2} + 6$

i) $f(x) = 2x^{\frac{3}{2}} - \frac{2}{5}x^{\frac{5}{2}} + \frac{12}{5}$

Q2 $f(x) = 6\sqrt{x} + x^2 - 19$

Q3 $y = 2x^{\frac{3}{2}} - \frac{1}{x} + 6$

Q4 $y = \frac{t^2}{2} - 4t^{\frac{3}{2}} + 9t - 3$

Q5 $f(x) = 2x^{\frac{5}{2}} - \frac{2}{3}x^{\frac{3}{2}} - 1$

Q6 $f(x) = \frac{x^3}{3} - \frac{4}{\sqrt{x}} + 2$

Q7 $y = -\frac{1}{x} + \frac{3}{x^2} + 2x - 7$

Q8 $v = \frac{100}{3} = 33.3 \text{ ms}^{-1}$ (3 s.f.)

Q9 $k = 6$, $f(x) = x^3 + 3x^2 - 6x - 1$
When $x = 2$, $f'(x) = 18$, so use this fact to find the value of k. Then integrate and find C using the normal method.

2. Definite Integration

Exercise 2.1

Q1 a) -20 b) $\frac{651}{4}$ c) 21

d) $\frac{109}{864}$ e) $\frac{17}{6}$ f) $\frac{1085}{192}$

g) $\frac{61}{6}$ h) $\frac{82}{5}$ i) $\frac{1319}{36}$

j) $\frac{5}{16}$ k) 476 l) $\frac{1364}{21}$

Q2 -56 **Q3** $\frac{1}{2}$

Q4 a) $a = 4$ b) $a = 10$
Evaluate the integral in terms of a, and solve to find a. You can ignore the solution $a = -4$ in part a) since $a > 0$.

Q5 a) $A = \frac{1}{6}$ or $A = -1$

b) $A = -\frac{7}{3}$ or $A = 2$

Evaluate the integral in terms of A, then form a quadratic and solve for A.

Q6 a) $a = 2$ b) $a = -3$
c) $a = -2$ d) $a = -\frac{1}{2}$
$\int_0^1 ax^a \, dx = \frac{a}{a+1}$, so you can use this to find a in each part.

Exercise 2.2

Q1 a) $\frac{40}{3}$ b) $\frac{32}{3}$ c) $\frac{37}{12}$

Q2 a) 160 b) 7 c) 34

Q3 $\frac{75}{16}$

Q4 $\frac{45}{2}$
The lines cross at $x = 3$ (and again at $x = 12$) and $(x - 6)^2 = 0$ when $x = 6$. So split the area into two parts — one under the line $y = 3x$ (between $x = 0$ and $x = 3$) and one under the curve $y = (x - 6)^2$ (between $x = 3$ and $x = 6$). Then integrate to find each area (or use the area of a triangle formula for the area under $y = 3x$).

Q5 $\frac{3}{2}$
Factorise the cubic — you should get $x(x + 1)(x + 3)$, so the graph crosses the x-axis at $x = 0$, -1 and -3. You can see from the sketch that the area is above the x-axis between $x = -3$ and $x = -1$, and below the x-axis between $x = -1$ and $x = 0$. Split the area and integrate between $x = -2$ and $x = -1$, and then between $x = -1$ and $x = 0$. Then add these areas together.

Q6 a) $\frac{94}{3}$ m (or $31\frac{1}{3}$ m)

b) $\frac{500}{3}$ m (or $166\frac{2}{3}$ m)

Review Exercise — Chapter 9

Q1 a) $f(x) = 2x^{\frac{1}{2}} + 4x - \frac{5x^4}{4} + C$

b) $f(x) = x^2 - \frac{3}{x} + C$

c) $f(x) = 2x^3 + \frac{2}{3}\sqrt{x} + C$

Q2 a) $\frac{x^5}{7} + \frac{x^2}{3} + \frac{x}{4} + C$

b) $2\sqrt{x} + \frac{2}{3}\sqrt{x^3} + C$

c) $-\frac{3}{x} + \frac{9}{2}\sqrt{x^2} + C$

Q3 a) $\frac{4}{3}x^3 + 6\sqrt{x} - 2x + C$

b) $\frac{9}{2}x^2 + 12\sqrt{x^3} + 9x + C$

Q4 $y = 3x^2 - 7x + 4$

Q5 a) $y = 3x^2 - 13x + 12$

b)
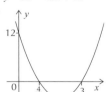

Q6 a) $f(x) = 2x^3 + 3x^2 - 5x$

b)

Q7 a) $\dfrac{dy}{dx} = \dfrac{(x+2)(x-2)}{\sqrt{x}}$

$= \dfrac{x^2 - 4}{\sqrt{x}} = \dfrac{x^2}{x^{\frac{1}{2}}} - \dfrac{4}{x^{\frac{1}{2}}}$

$= x^{\frac{3}{2}} - 4x^{-\frac{1}{2}}$

So $A = 1$ and $B = -4$

b) $y = \dfrac{2}{5}x^{\frac{5}{2}} - 8x^{\frac{1}{2}} + 9$

Q8 $f(x) = 2x^3 - 12x + \dfrac{8}{x} + 1$

Q9 $f(x) = 2x^{\frac{5}{2}} + 2x^{\frac{1}{2}} - 10x - 3$

Q10 a) 4   **b)** $\dfrac{5}{2}$ **c)** $-\dfrac{33}{8} + 6\sqrt{2}$

d) $-\dfrac{157}{3}$ **e)** 45   **f)** $-\dfrac{3}{20}$

Q11 a) 36

b)

Q12 a) $A = 61$ or $A = -1$

b) $A = 3$ or $A = \dfrac{5}{3}$

Evaluate the integral in terms of A, then form a quadratic and solve for A.

Q13 a) $\dfrac{9}{2}$ **b)** $\dfrac{118}{3}$ **c)** $\dfrac{71}{3}$

Q14 a) $\dfrac{8}{3}$ **b)** $\dfrac{28}{3}$

c) $\dfrac{64}{3}$

Split the area into two — integrate $2x^2$ between $x = 0$ and $x = 2$, and integrate $12 - 2x$ between $x = 2$ and $x = 6$ (or use the formula for the area of a triangle).

d) $\dfrac{9}{2}$

Find the area under the line $y = x + 3$ (either by integrating between $x = 1$ and $x = 4$ or by using the trapezium formula), then subtract the area under $x^2 - 4x + 7$ to find the shaded area.

Q15 a) $\dfrac{253}{12}$ **b)** 16

Q16 $a = 2$, area $= 16$

Factorise the cubic using the Factor Theorem and algebraic division (or another suitable method) — you should get $y = (x - 2)^2(2x - 7)$. The double root is at $x = 2$, so integrate the function between $x = 0$ and $x = 2$ to find the area.

Q17 a) The total area is 48.6 m², so the plan meets the requirement.

b) 45.9 m² (3 s.f.)

Chapter 10: Vectors

1. Vectors

Exercise 1.1

Q1 a) vector   **b)** scalar   **c)** vector

Q2 a)   **b)**

c) $a + b$ **d)** $a - b$

Q3 a) $\overrightarrow{AC}$ **b)** $\overrightarrow{BA}$ **c)** $\overrightarrow{DB}$

Q4 a) $-\mathbf{q}$ **b)** $\mathbf{q} + \mathbf{p}$

c) $-\mathbf{p} - \mathbf{q}$ or $-\mathbf{q} - \mathbf{p}$

Q5 $\overrightarrow{JL} = \overrightarrow{JD} + \overrightarrow{DL}$.

J is the midpoint of ED,

so $\overrightarrow{JD} = \dfrac{1}{2}\overrightarrow{ED} = \dfrac{1}{2}\mathbf{d}$.

And L is the midpoint of DF,

so $\overrightarrow{DL} = \dfrac{1}{2}\overrightarrow{DF}$.

$\overrightarrow{DF} = \overrightarrow{DE} + \overrightarrow{EF} = -\mathbf{d} + \mathbf{f}$

$\Rightarrow \overrightarrow{DL} = \dfrac{1}{2}(\mathbf{f} - \mathbf{d})$

So, $\overrightarrow{JL} = \dfrac{1}{2}\mathbf{d} + \dfrac{1}{2}(\mathbf{f} - \mathbf{d}) = \dfrac{1}{2}\mathbf{f}$.

Exercise 1.2

Q1 E.g. $6\mathbf{t} - 4\mathbf{u}$ and $9\mathbf{t} - 6\mathbf{u}$.

Q2 $4\mathbf{b} + 8\mathbf{a}$, $2\mathbf{a} + \mathbf{b}$, and $-\mathbf{b} - 2\mathbf{a}$ are parallel.

$2\mathbf{p} + \mathbf{q}$, and $\dfrac{1}{2}\mathbf{q} + \mathbf{p}$ are parallel.

$10\mathbf{a} - 5\mathbf{b}$, and $2\mathbf{a} - \mathbf{b}$ are parallel.

Q3 $\overrightarrow{AB} = \overrightarrow{CD}$ because they're parallel, so $\overrightarrow{BC} = \mathbf{m} - \mathbf{n}$.

Q4 a) $\overrightarrow{DF} = \dfrac{2}{3}\mathbf{b}$ **b)** $-\mathbf{b} + \dfrac{1}{2}\mathbf{d}$

c) $\dfrac{1}{2}\mathbf{d} + \dfrac{2}{3}\mathbf{b}$

Q5 $\overrightarrow{YZ} = -\mathbf{a} + \mathbf{b}$, so $\overrightarrow{YP} = \dfrac{1}{2}\overrightarrow{YZ}$

$= \dfrac{1}{2}(-\mathbf{a} + \mathbf{b})$.

This means, $\overrightarrow{PQ} = -\overrightarrow{YP} + \overrightarrow{YQ}$

$= -\dfrac{1}{2}(-\mathbf{a} + \mathbf{b}) + \dfrac{1}{2}(-\mathbf{a})$

$= -\dfrac{1}{2}\mathbf{b}$.

This shows $\overrightarrow{PQ}$ is a scalar multiple of $\overrightarrow{XZ}$, so they're parallel vectors.

Q6 $\overrightarrow{US} = \overrightarrow{UT} + \overrightarrow{TS} = -\overrightarrow{TU} - \overrightarrow{ST}$

$= -(\mathbf{v} - \mathbf{w}) - (2\mathbf{v} - \mathbf{w}) = -3\mathbf{v}$.

This is a scalar multiple of $\mathbf{v}$, so is parallel to $\mathbf{v}$.

Q7 $\overrightarrow{YZ} = \overrightarrow{YX} + \overrightarrow{XZ} = -\overrightarrow{XY} + \overrightarrow{XZ}$

$= -(3\mathbf{a} - 4\mathbf{b} + 2\mathbf{c}) + \mathbf{a} - 2\mathbf{b} - 2\mathbf{c}$

$= -2\mathbf{a} + 2\mathbf{b} - 4\mathbf{c} = 2(\mathbf{a} - \mathbf{b} + 2\mathbf{c})$

This is a scalar multiple of $\mathbf{a} - \mathbf{b} + 2\mathbf{c}$, so they're parallel.

Exercise 1.3

Q1 $\overrightarrow{YZ} = \mathbf{t} + \mathbf{u} = \overrightarrow{XY}$. These are the same vector, so X, Y and Z are collinear.

Q2 $\overrightarrow{AB} = \mathbf{b} - \mathbf{a}$ and $\overrightarrow{BC} = 5(\mathbf{a} - \mathbf{b})$.

This shows they're scalar multiples, so they are parallel. Therefore, A, B and C are collinear.

Q3 $\overrightarrow{QR} = 2\mathbf{m} + 3\mathbf{n}$ and

$\overrightarrow{RS} = \mathbf{m} + \dfrac{3}{2}\mathbf{n} = \dfrac{1}{2}\overrightarrow{QR}$. This shows they're scalar multiples, so they are parallel. Therefore, Q, R and S are collinear.

Q4 $\overrightarrow{OA} = 4\mathbf{a} - 2\mathbf{b}$.

$\overrightarrow{AC} = \overrightarrow{AB} + \overrightarrow{BD} + \overrightarrow{DC}$

$= 2\mathbf{b} + 4\mathbf{a} - \mathbf{b} - \dfrac{5}{2}\mathbf{b} - \mathbf{a} = 3\mathbf{a} - \dfrac{3}{2}\mathbf{b}$

$= \dfrac{3}{4}\overrightarrow{OA}$

This shows that $\overrightarrow{OA}$ and $\overrightarrow{AC}$ are scalar multiples of one another, so they're parallel. Therefore, O, A and C are collinear and OAC is a straight line.

Q5 X is the midpoint of AC, so $\overrightarrow{AX} = \overrightarrow{XC} = \mathbf{a}$.

So, $\overrightarrow{DX} = \mathbf{a} - \mathbf{b} + \mathbf{a} = 2\mathbf{a} - \mathbf{b}$ and $\overrightarrow{XB} = -\mathbf{a} + 3\mathbf{a} - 2\mathbf{b} = 2\mathbf{a} - 2\mathbf{b}$.

This shows $\overrightarrow{DX}$ and $\overrightarrow{XB}$ are not scalar multiples of one another, so are not parallel. Therefore, D, X and B are not collinear and DXB is not a straight line.

Exercise 1.4

Q1 Jack's house: $\begin{pmatrix} 2 \\ 3 \end{pmatrix}$ Jack's School: $\begin{pmatrix} 4 \\ -5 \end{pmatrix}$

Q2 a) $\begin{pmatrix} 6 \\ -1 \end{pmatrix}$ **b)** $\begin{pmatrix} -2 \\ 7 \end{pmatrix}$

c) $\begin{pmatrix} 2 \\ 2 \end{pmatrix}$ **d)** $\begin{pmatrix} -25 \\ -25 \end{pmatrix}$

Q3 a) C (–1, 2), D (4, –3)

b) $\overrightarrow{CD} = 5\mathbf{i} - 5\mathbf{j}$, $\overrightarrow{DC} = -5\mathbf{i} + 5\mathbf{j}$

Q4 $\mathbf{p} + 3\mathbf{q} + \mathbf{r} = \begin{pmatrix} 4 \\ -3 \end{pmatrix} = \dfrac{1}{3}(12\mathbf{i} - 9\mathbf{j})$.

This shows they're parallel.

Q5 $\overrightarrow{OB} = 3\mathbf{i} + 6\mathbf{j}$,

$\overrightarrow{OD} = -4\mathbf{i} - \mathbf{j}$ (or vice versa).

Q6 $7\mathbf{i} - 11\mathbf{j}$

Q7 $\overrightarrow{AB} = -2\mathbf{i} - 3\mathbf{j}$, $\overrightarrow{BC} = -\mathbf{i} + 2\mathbf{j}$, $\overrightarrow{CA} = 3\mathbf{i} + \mathbf{j}$.

Q8 a) $\overrightarrow{DE} = \begin{pmatrix} 4 \\ 1 \end{pmatrix}$, $\overrightarrow{EF} = \begin{pmatrix} 2 \\ 6 \end{pmatrix}$,

$\overrightarrow{FG} = \begin{pmatrix} -2 \\ 5 \end{pmatrix}$, $\overrightarrow{GD} = \begin{pmatrix} -4 \\ -12 \end{pmatrix}$

b) $\begin{pmatrix} 6 \\ 7 \end{pmatrix}$

Q9 R = (7, 7), $\overrightarrow{QR} = \begin{pmatrix} 4 \\ 4 \end{pmatrix}$

2. Calculating with Vectors

Exercise 2.1

Q1 a) 10   **b)** 13   **c)** $2\sqrt{5}$

d) $\sqrt{10}$ **e)** 25   **f)** 7

g) 4   **h)** 7   **i)** $\sqrt{5}$

j) 9   **k)** $\sqrt{17}$

Q2 $|\overrightarrow{OS}| = 5\sqrt{5}$

Q3 a) $\sqrt{5}$ **b)** $5\sqrt{2}$ **c)** $\sqrt{26}$

Q4 a) 5   **b)** $4\sqrt{2}$ **c)** 26

d) $3\sqrt{5}$ **e)** 5   **f)** 9

Q5 a) $\mathbf{i}$ **b)** $\begin{pmatrix} \frac{1}{\sqrt{5}} \\ \frac{2}{\sqrt{5}} \end{pmatrix}$

c) $\dfrac{5}{\sqrt{41}}\mathbf{i} - \dfrac{4}{\sqrt{41}}\mathbf{j}$ **d)** $\begin{pmatrix} -\frac{1}{\sqrt{10}} \\ -\frac{3}{\sqrt{10}} \end{pmatrix}$

This is convenient as she does not need to identify the population of 'people who visit the park', and would save time compared to going to survey people in person.

Q2 Advantage: E.g. if there are differences in the reading habits of the boys and girls, making the sample more representative would prevent the higher number of responses from boys influencing the overall trends in the sample data.

Disadvantage: E.g. if there is no overall difference in reading habits between boys and girls, then taking a sample of the data is unnecessary and is a waste of already collected data.

2. Representing Data

Exercise 2.1

Q1 **a)** Make, Colour

b) Mileage, Number of doors, Cost of service

Q2 **a)** Number of medals won last season, Shoe size

b) Height, Mass

Q3 **a)** Discrete **b)** 35 people

Q4 **a)** There are no 'gaps' between possible heights.

b)

Height, h (cm)	No. of members	Lower class b'dary (cm)	Upper class b'dary (cm)	Class width (cm)	Class mid-point (cm)
$140 \le h < 150$	3	140	150	10	145
$150 \le h < 160$	9	150	160	10	155
$160 \le h < 170$	17	160	170	10	165
$170 \le h < 180$	12	170	180	10	175
$180 \le h < 190$	5	180	190	10	185
$190 \le h < 200$	1	190	200	10	195

c)

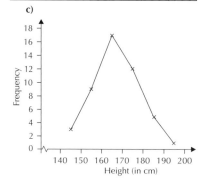

Exercise 2.2

Q1

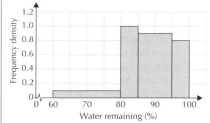

Q2 **a)** 12 **b)** 190 **c)** 48

d) 0.221 (3 s.f.) **e)** 0.0474 (3 s.f.)

Q3 **a)** The area of the bar is 13.5 cm². This represents 12 butterflies. So each butterfly is represented by 13.5 ÷ 12 = 1.125 cm² on the histogram.

b) 20

c) 2.5 cm wide, 6.3 cm high

Exercise 2.3

Q1 **a)** 30 **b)** 2

c) 5 **d)** 73 members

Q2
```
27 | 1 2 2 3 5 5 5 5 9
28 | 0 0 2 3 5 7 9 9 9
29 | 0 0 5 7
30 | 1 1 2 3 3 3 6 7
31 | 0 6 7 9
```
Key: 29 | 0 means 290

Q3 **a)** 7 **b)** 10.7 °C **c)** 5.5 °C

Q4 **a)**
```
0 | 8
1 | 2 5 6
2 | 1 4 5 6 7 9
3 | 5 7
4 | 0 3
5 | 6
6 | 4
```
Key: 2 | 1 means 2.1 km

b) **(i)** 6.4 km **(ii)** 4 children

Q5 **a)** 60 minutes **b)** 17 **c)** 7

Exercise 2.4

Q1 A is positively skewed, B is symmetrical.

Q2 The average height for men and for women will be different, so the data for each will be concentrated around a different mode, making the data bimodal.

3. Location: Mean, Median and Mode

Exercise 3.1

Q1 £1.16 **Q2** 38.2 points (3 s.f.)

Q3 1.4 goals

Q4 **a)** 49.6 years (3 s.f.)
Work out the total age in the group (15 × 47.4 = 711), then subtract 17 and divide by 14.

b) 20 years old
Find the new total age (15 × 47.6 = 714), and subtract the previous total (694) to find the new member's age.

Exercise 3.2

Q1 **a)** £110

b) All the values occur just once.

Q2 mode = 6.9%, median = 6.7%

Q3 mode = 5, median = 4

Q4 **a)** mode = 5 **b)** median = 20

Q5 **a)** modes = 4.0 Mbit/s, 5.8 Mbit/s and 6.9 Mbit/s
median = 5.8 Mbit/s

b) mode = 6.2 Mbit/s
median = 5.7 Mbit/s

Exercise 3.3

Q1 **a)** 0-2 letters **b)** 4.18 letters

Q2 **a)**

Time (t, mins)	Freq., f	C. freq.	x	fx
$3 \le t < 4$	7	7	3.5	24.5
$4 \le t < 5$	14	21	4.5	63
$5 \le t < 6$	24	45	5.5	132
$6 \le t < 8$	10	55	7	70
$8 \le t < 10$	5	60	9	45

b) mean = 5.58 mins (3 s.f.), median = 5.38 mins (3 s.f.)

Q3 **a)** mean = 279 mins

b) median = 274 mins (3 s.f.)

Exercise 3.4

Q1 **a)** Median — most employees will earn relatively low salaries but a few may earn much higher salaries, so the mean could be heavily affected by a few high salaries.

b) Mean — the data should be reasonably symmetrical about the mean, so the mean would be a good measure of location. The median would be good as well (for a symmetrical data set, it should be roughly equal to the mean).

c) Mode — make of car is qualitative data so the mode is the only average that can be found.

d) Mean — the data should be reasonably symmetrical about the mean, so the mean would be a good measure of location. The median would be good as well (for a symmetrical data set, it should be roughly equal to the mean).

e) Median — most employees will perhaps travel fairly short distances to work but a few employees may live much further away. The median would not be affected by these few high values.
The mode is unlikely to be suitable in b), d) and e) (and possibly a) as well) because all the values may be different.

Q2 There is a very extreme value of 8 that would affect the mean quite heavily.

4. Dispersion
Exercise 4.1

Q1 Range = 45, IQR = 24.5

Q2 **a)** Range = 85 814 miles

    b) Q_1 = 5871.5 miles, Q_3 = 53 330.5 miles

    c) IQR = 47 459 miles

Q3 **a)** 8.45 am:
Range = 5 mph, IQR = 2 mph
10.45 am:
Range = 14 mph, IQR = 5 mph
1 pm:
Range = 28 mph, IQR = 5 mph

    b) 8.45 am: 1 mph, 10.45 am: 4 mph, 1 pm: 3 mph

    c) 8.45 am: 4 mph, 10.45 am: 9 mph, 1 pm: 19 mph

    d) 8.45 am: 0 mph, 10.45 am: 1 mph, 1 pm: 1 mph

Q4 **a)** 11.7 mm (3 s.f.) **b)** 15.8 mm (3 s.f.)

    c) 37.3 mm (3 s.f.) **d)** 6.27 mm (3 s.f.)

    e) 47.9 mm (3 s.f.)

Exercise 4.2

Q1 **a)** 5   **b)** 7

    c) The data is grouped so you don't know the actual values.

Q2

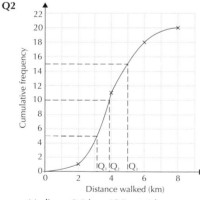

Median ≈ 3.9 km, IQR ≈ 1.8 km

Q3 **a)** 84 people   **b)** Median ≈ £67

    c) IQR ≈ 79 − 52 = £27

    d) **(i)** 70   **(ii)** 4   **(iii)** 54

Exercise 4.3

Q1 4 is not an outlier, but 52 is.

Q2 **a)** 21   **b)** No

    c)

Q3 **a)** No

    b)

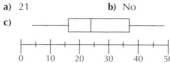
No. of items of junk mail received

    c)

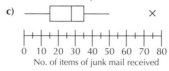
No. of items of junk mail received

Exercise 4.4

Q1 **a)** 761   **b)** 3 475 138

    c) variance = 68.7 (3 s.f.), s.d. = 8.29 (3 s.f.)

Q2 **a)** 1.95   **b)** 91

    c) variance = 0.7475, s.d. = 0.865 (3 s.f.)

Q3 **a)** 1.05 (3 s.f.)

    b) 0.35 is not an outlier.

Q4 **a)** 3.73 minutes (3 s.f.)
Use the formula from p.147 to find the combined mean of the two data sets.

    b) variance = 1.08 mins² (3 s.f.), s.d. = 1.04 mins (3 s.f.)
Work backwards from the s.d. of each data set to find Σx^2 for each data set. Then add these together to get the combined sum of squares, and use this in the variance formula.

Exercise 4.5

Q1 mean = 45.0 (3 s.f.)
sample standard deviation = 19.6 (3 s.f.)

Q2 sample variance = 43.2 (3 s.f.)
sample standard deviation = 6.57 (3 s.f.)

Exercise 4.6

Q1 **a)** variance = 135 kg² (3 s.f.), s.d. = 11.6 kg (3 s.f.)

    b) Because the data is grouped.

Q2 s.d. = 0.172 (3 s.f.)

Exercise 4.7

Q1 Possible answers include:

    – It won't be affected by outliers in the data.

    – Since there are only 20 data points, it will be fairly easy to calculate.

Q2 The interquartile range, as it is not affected by outliers.

Exercise 4.8

Q1 $\bar{x}$ = 20 186, s.d. of x = 20.1

Q2 **a)** Using $y = 100(x − 0.6)$ gives: 1, 7, 3, 3, 6, 5, 4, 8, 4, 2

    b) $\bar{x}$ = 0.643 cm, s.d. of x = 0.021 cm

Q3 $\bar{x}$ = 108.25 g, s.d. of x = 4.15 g (3 s.f.)

Q4 $\bar{x}$ = −1.65, s.d. of x = 1.97 (3 s.f.)
Use the coding $y = x + 2$ to get $\Sigma y = 7$ and $\Sigma y^2 = 80$. Find the mean and standard deviation of y, then uncode them to get the mean and standard deviation of x.

Exercise 4.9

Q1 The median is higher for Shop B. This shows that the prices in Shop B are generally higher. The median in Shop A is approximately £37 while the median in Shop B is roughly £63, so the difference between the average prices is around £26.

Although the ranges in the two shops are quite similar, the interquartile range (IQR) for Shop B is higher than that for Shop A. This shows that the prices of shoes in Shop B are more varied than the prices in Shop A.

Q2 For the men: mean = 7.3 hrs,
                 median = 7 hrs
For the women: mean = 8.5 hrs
                   median = 8.5 hrs
The mean and median are both higher for the women, so they get between 1 and 1.5 hours more sleep per night, on average, than the men.
For the men: s.d. = 1.42 hrs (3 s.f.)
For the women: s.d. = 1.63 hrs (3 s.f.)
The standard deviation is slightly higher for the women, so the number of hours of sleep for the women varies slightly more from the mean than it does for the men.

5. Correlation and Regression
Exercise 5.1

Q1 **a)**

b) Negative correlation.
(2, 6.3) appears to be an outlier.

Q2 The conclusion is not supported by the data. The correlation might be a coincidence, or it could be caused by another factor (such as amount of wind, or temperature, etc).

Q3 a)

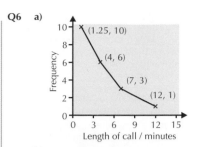

b) The data shows overall positive correlation, but there are two clusters of data. One shows some positive correlation, while the other does not look correlated at all.

c) The circumference of 3.5 cm or the length of 8.9 cm.

Exercise 5.2

Q1 a) Explanatory variable: time spent practising
Response variable: number of mistakes made

b) Explanatory variable: age
Response variable: value

c) Explanatory variable: population
Response variable: number of phone calls made

d) Explanatory variable: amount of sunlight
Response variable: growth rate

Q2 a) y is the response variable.

b) (i) 2.205   **(ii)** 3.81

Q3 a) $58.8 - 2.47 \times 7 = 41.51$ — so the volunteer would be predicted to have approximately 42 spots. This is interpolation (since 7 is between 2 and 22, which are the values of x between which data was collected). This estimate should be reliable.

b) $58.8 - 2.47 \times 0 = 58.8$ — so the volunteer would be predicted to have approximately 59 spots. This is extrapolation (since 0 is less than 2, which was the smallest value of d for which data was collected). This estimate may not be reliable.

c) Using the formula for $d = 30$ is extrapolation, since 30 is greater than 22, the largest value of d for which data was collected. The model isn't valid for $d = 30$, since you can't have a negative number of spots, but this doesn't mean that the regression equation is wrong.

Exercise 5.3

Q1 Cubic, as the shape of the data resembles a cubic graph.

Q2 $t = 3.64$ (3 s.f.)
The estimate is interpolated (2 is between 1.6 and 7.9), so it should be reliable, although since the sample is small, the regression curve may not be very accurate.

Review Exercise — Chapter 11

Q1 a) All the members of the tennis club.

b) Finite

Q2 a) The population is the 1200 students at the school.

b) One reason for using a sample is that it would be time-consuming and difficult to test every student in the school. Another reason is that it would be difficult to process the large amount of data.

Q3 E.g. Give each house a 3-digit number between 001 and 173 corresponding to its house number. Using a random-number table, choose a starting point on the table and move along it 3 digits at a time. For each 3 digits, see if it is a 3-digit number between 001 and 173. If it is, include the house with that number. Choose the first 40 distinct numbers between 001 and 173 that you come across in the table. Survey the 40 houses which match the numbers you have chosen.

Q4 Possible answers include:
– Cluster sample — using schools as clusters, randomly select schools to sample, then use another method, e.g. stratified sampling, to select students to collect data from.
– Quota sample — divide the population into groups, e.g. age or year group, then collect data where possible until the quotas are met.
– Opportunity sample — collect data in the most convenient way, e.g. by visiting a single school.

Q5 a) Quota sample. The sample is non-random, so it could be biased. For example: the interviewer is not told which ages to sample, so they might ask younger people, whose tea-drinking habits might be different from those of older people.

b) Systematic sample. There could be a pattern making the sample biased. For example: every 100th ticket number could correspond to a seat with a bad view — every 100th seat could be at the end of a row, which could have a worse view than seats in the middle.

c) Opportunity/convenience sample. The sample isn't representative of the population. For example, many people work between the hours of 9 am and 5 pm on a Monday — these people are excluded from the sample.

Q6 a)

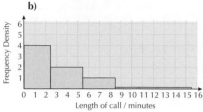

b)

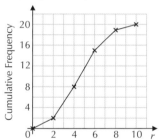

Q7 a) 12%   **b)** 0.14   **c)** 23%

d) You have to assume that the data is evenly distributed in the range 32-36, which it may not be.

Q8 12.8, 13.2, 13.5, 14.3, 14.3, 14.6, 14.8, 15.2, 15.9, 16.1, 16.1, 16.2, 16.3, 17.0, 17.2 (all in cm)

Q9 a) Positively skewed, unimodal

b) Symmetrical, unimodal

c) Negatively skewed, bimodal

Q10 mean = 1.375,   median = 1,   mode = 0

Q11 mean = 37.1 mph,
median = 36.9 mph (3 s.f.)
modal class: 35 - 39 mph.

Q12 a) 36   **b)** 17   **c)** 22

Q13 a)

b) (i) 5   **(ii)** 8 or 9   **(iii)** 10 or 11

c) (i) 3   **(ii)** 5.5

Q14 a)

Duration, t (sec)	Frequency, f
$400 < t \le 600$	6
$600 < t \le 800$	11
$800 < t \le 1000$	14
$1000 < t \le 1200$	28
$1200 < t \le 1400$	22
$1400 < t \le 1600$	10
$1600 < t \le 1800$	7
$1800 < t \le 2000$	2

E.g. level 3 starts after 400 seconds, and lasts until 600 seconds, etc. So use these as the ranges in the table.

b)

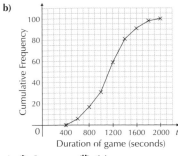

c) (i) 3   **(ii)** 14

d) IQR = 431 (3 s.f.)

n = 100, so Q_1 is in the 800-1000 class and Q_3 is in the 1200-1400 class.

Q15 a) (i) median = 5 minutes

    (ii) Q_1 = 4 minutes, Q_3 = 7 minutes.

    (iii) lower fence = –0.5,
      upper fence = 11.5
      so 12 is an outlier.

b)

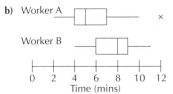

c) Possible answers include:

– The times for Worker B are 3 minutes longer than those for Worker A, on average.

– The IQR for both workers is the same — generally they both work with the same consistency. The range for Worker A is larger than that for Worker B. Worker A had a few items he/she could iron very quickly and a few which took a long time.

d) E.g. Worker A would be better to employ, as the median time is less than for Worker B, and the upper quartile is less than the median of Worker B, suggesting that Worker A would generally iron items quicker than Worker B.

Q16 mean = 17.9 (3 s.f.), s.d. = 5.57 (3 s.f.)

Q17 mean = 115.6, variance = 49

Q18 a) mean = 21.25, s.d. = 0.805 (3 s.f.)

b) 19.6 is an outlier

Q19 mean = 37.9 mins,
s.d. = 3.88 mins (3 s.f.)

Q20 Read the quartiles off the graphs:

Island A: $Q_1 \approx 8$ °C, $Q_2 \approx 15$ °C,
        $Q_3 \approx 19$ °C $\Rightarrow$ IQR ≈ 11 °C

Island B: $Q_1 \approx 9.5$ °C, $Q_2 \approx 12$ °C,
        $Q_3 \approx 15.5$ °C $\Rightarrow$ IQR ≈ 6 °C

Island A has a higher median temperature, suggesting that the temperatures on island A are generally higher than island B.

The data for island A has a larger interquartile range than that of island B — the data for island B is grouped more closely about the median, while the data for island A is more spread out. This suggests that the temperatures on island A tend to vary more than on island B.

Q21 a)

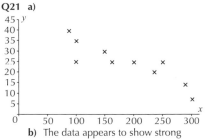

b) The data appears to show strong negative correlation.

Q22 a) Explanatory: number of sunny days
Response: number of volleyball-related injuries

b) Explanatory: number of rainy days
Response: number of board game-related injuries

c) Explanatory: disposable income
Response: amount spent on luxuries

d) Explanatory: number of cups of tea
Response: number of trips to the loo

e) Explanatory: number of tickets sold
Response: number of pairs of boots bought

Q23 a) *m* = 142.4 g

b) This estimate might not be very reliable because it uses an *r*-value from outside the range of the original data. It is extrapolation.

Chapter 12: Probability

1. Elementary Probability

Exercise 1.1

Q1 a) $\frac{1}{52}$ **b)** $\frac{1}{52}$ **c)** $\frac{1}{13}$ **d)** $\frac{1}{2}$

Q2 a)

×	1	2	3	4	5	6
1	1	2	3	4	5	6
2	2	4	6	8	10	12
3	3	6	9	12	15	18
4	4	8	12	16	20	24
5	5	10	15	20	25	30
6	6	12	18	24	30	36

b) $\frac{1}{6}$ **c)** $\frac{7}{18}$ **d)** 10

Q3 a) E.g.

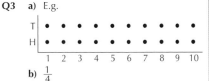

b) $\frac{1}{4}$

Q4 a) E.g.

–	1	2	3	4	5	6
1	0	1	2	3	4	5
2	1	0	1	2	3	4
3	2	1	0	1	2	3
4	3	2	1	0	1	2
5	4	3	2	1	0	1
6	5	4	3	2	1	0

b) $\frac{1}{6}$ **c)** 0

d) The most likely score is 1.
P(1) = $\frac{5}{18}$

Q5 $\frac{13}{25}$

2. Solving Probability Problems

Exercise 2.1

Q1 a)

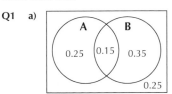

b) 0.25   **c)** 0.35   **d)** 0.75   **e)** 0.25

Q2 a) 0.1   **b)** 0   **c)** 0.25   **d)** 0.25

    e) 0.5   **f)** 0.75   **g)** 0   **h)** 0.15

Q3 a) $\frac{37}{200}$ **b)** $\frac{31}{61}$ **c)** $\frac{7}{40}$ **d)** $\frac{9}{40}$

Q4 a) 0.26   **b)** 0.46   **c)** 0.76

Draw a Venn diagram to represent the information. Draw a circle for each of the events 'goes to home league matches', 'goes to away league matches' and 'goes to cup matches' — then start by filling in the number of supporters who go to all three types of match and work outwards.

Exercise 2.2

Q1 a) 0.76   **b)** 0.66

Q2 a)

	BC Tops	Cumbria	No tea	Total
Nenco	0.16	0.07	**0.09**	**0.32**
Yescafé	0.11	**0.03**	**0.04**	0.18
No coffee	**0.24**	0.12	0.14	**0.50**
Total	0.51	**0.22**	0.27	1

b) (i) 0.03   **(ii)** 0.50

    (iii) 0.36   **(iv)** 0.68

Q3 a)

	M	not M	Total
P	19	19	38
not P	27	79	106
Total	46	98	144

b) $\frac{65}{144}$ **c)** $\frac{19}{46}$

3. Laws of Probability

Exercise 3.1

Q1 **a)** 0.7 **b)** 0.65 **c)** 0.35
Q2 **a)** 0.56 **b)** 0.81 **c)** 0.37 **d)** 0.83
Q3 **a)** 0.75 **b)** 0.32 **c)** 0.68
Q4 **a)** 0.44 **b)** 0.22 **c)** 0.23 **d)** 0.78
Q5 **a)** 0.26 **b)** 0.21 **c)** 0.82 **d)** 0.18
Q6 **a)** 0.17 **b)** 0.17 **c)** 0.21

Exercise 3.2

Q1 **a)** 0 **b)** 0.85 **c)** 0.15
Q2 **a)** 0.7 **b)** 0.61 **c)** 0.59 **d)** 0
e)

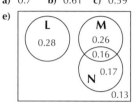

Q3 **a)** 0.6 **b)** 0.18
Q4 **a)** $P(A \text{ and } B) = 0.08 \neq 0$, so A and B aren't mutually exclusive.
b) $P(A \text{ and } C) = 0$, so A and C are mutually exclusive.
c) $P(B \text{ and } C) = 0.23 \neq 0$, so B and C aren't mutually exclusive.
Q5 **a)** $P(C) = 1 - 0.6 = 0.4$
$P(C \text{ and } D) = P(C) - P(C \text{ and } D')$
$= 0.4 - 0.4 = 0$,
so C and D are mutually exclusive.
b) 0.65
Q6 Out of the total of 50 biscuits, 30 are plain, and 20 are chocolate-coated. Half of the biscuits are in wrappers, so 25 biscuits are in wrappers. Since there are more biscuits in wrappers than there are chocolate-coated ones, there must be some biscuits (at least 5) which are plain and in wrappers. So events P and W can happen at the same time (i.e. $P(P \text{ and } W) \neq 0$), which means they are not mutually exclusive.

Exercise 3.3

Q1 0.1984 **Q2** 0.6
Q3 **a)** 0.5712 **b)** 0.1664
c) 0.4368 **d)** 0.1536
Q4 **a)** 0.28 **b)** 0.82 **c)** 0.12
Q5 **a)** $\frac{1}{16}$ **b)** $\frac{1}{2704}$
Q6 A and B: $P(A) \times P(B) = \frac{3}{11} \times \frac{1}{3} = \frac{1}{11}$
$P(A) \times P(B) = \frac{1}{11} = P(A \text{ and } B)$,
so A and B are independent.
A and C: $P(A) \times P(C) = \frac{3}{11} \times \frac{15}{28} = \frac{45}{308}$
$P(A) \times P(C) = \frac{45}{308} \neq \frac{2}{15} = P(A \text{ and } C)$,
so A and C are not independent.

B and C: $P(B) \times P(C) = \frac{1}{3} \times \frac{15}{28} = \frac{5}{28}$
$P(B) \times P(C) = \frac{5}{28} = P(B \text{ and } C)$,
so B and C are independent.
Q7 **a)** 0.099 **b)** 0.48

Exercise 3.4

Q1 **a)** The events are not independent because the probability that Jake wins his 2nd match depends on whether or not he won his 1st match.
b) **(i)** 0.45 **(ii)** 0.74
Q2 **a)**

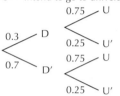

b) $\frac{1}{12}$ **c)** $\frac{11}{12}$
Q3 **a)** Let D = 'passed driving test' and U = 'intend to go to university'.

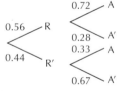

b) 0.225 **c)** 0.175
Q4 Let R = 'orders roast dinner' and let A = 'orders apple pie for pudding'.

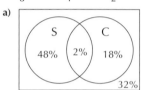

$P(A) = 0.5484$
Q5 **a)** Let R_i = 'ball i is red', Y_i = 'ball i is yellow' and G_i = 'ball i is green', for i = 1 and 2.

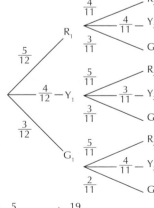

b) $\frac{5}{33}$ **c)** $\frac{19}{66}$

d) If the first ball is replaced, the probability of winning becomes:
$\left(\frac{5}{12} \times \frac{5}{12}\right) + \left(\frac{4}{12} \times \frac{4}{12}\right) + \left(\frac{3}{12} \times \frac{3}{12}\right)$
$= \frac{25}{144} + \frac{16}{144} + \frac{9}{144} = \frac{50}{144} = \frac{25}{72}$
Since $\frac{25}{72} > \frac{19}{66}$, a player is more likely to win now that the game has been changed.
Q6 **a)** 0.46 **b)** 0.42 **c)** 0.432
d) 0.448 **e)** 0.444
Sketch a tree diagram for each situation, then find the probability for each 'path' that has exactly one positive review and add them together. It doesn't matter which order you put the trials in, as the probabilities are independent.

Review Exercise — Chapter 12

Q1 **a)**

		Dice					
		1	2	3	4	5	6
Coin	H	2	4	6	8	10	12
	T	5	6	7	8	9	10

b) $\frac{1}{6}$ **c)** $\frac{3}{4}$ **d)** $\frac{1}{2}$
Q2 **a)**

S 48% | 2% | C 18%
32%

b) 18% **c)** 66% **d)** 0.48
e) 0.32 **f)** 0.1
Q3 $\frac{19}{50}$ or 0.38
Show the information you're given in a Venn diagram. Draw a circle for each of the events 'likes activity holidays', 'likes beach holidays' and 'likes skiing holidays', and label each area with the number of people who like that type of holiday. Start with the number of people who like all three types of holiday and work outwards.
Q4 **a)** $\frac{2}{5}$ **b)** $\frac{7}{30}$ **c)** $\frac{7}{10}$
Q5 **a)** 0.9 **b)** 0.1 **c)** 0.8
Q6 **a)** 0.5 **b)** 0.5
c) **(i)** 0.09 **(ii)** 0.06 **(iii)** 0.1
Q7 **a)** 0.72 **b)** 0.98 **c)** 0.02 **d)** 0.28
Q8 **a)** $\frac{5}{12}$ **b)** $\frac{7}{36}$
c) It isn't possible for her score to be both a prime number and a square number, so the events P and S are mutually exclusive.
d) $\frac{11}{18}$
e) The score from the second experiment is unaffected by the score from the first experiment, so the events S_1 and S_2 are independent.
f) $\frac{49}{1296}$

Q9 a)

1st Sat   2nd Sat

b) 0.84   **c)** 0.37

Chapter 13: Statistical Distributions

1. Probability Distributions

Exercise 1.1

Q1 **a)** X is 'number of tails'.
x could be 0, 1, 2, 3 or 4.

b) X is 'number of heads'.
x could be 0, 1, 2, 3, 4, 5 or 6.

c) X is 'sum of the two dice scores'.
x could be 2, 3, 4, 5, 6, 7 or 8.

Q2 **a)**

x	1	2	3	4
$P(X = x)$	0.1	0.2	0.3	0.4

b)

x	0	3	4	5
$P(X = x)$	0.55	0.25	0.15	0.05

c)

x	10	20	30	40	50
$P(X = x)$	0.2	0.2	0.2	0.2	0.2

d)

x	1	3	4	5	7
$P(X = x)$	0.01	0.09	0.16	0.25	0.49

Q3 **a)**

a	2	3	4	5	6	7
$P(A = a)$	$\frac{1}{6}$	$\frac{1}{6}$	$\frac{1}{6}$	$\frac{1}{6}$	$\frac{1}{6}$	$\frac{1}{6}$

b)

b	0	1
$P(B = b)$	$\frac{1}{2}$	$\frac{1}{2}$

c)

c	5	10	15	20	25	30
$P(C = c)$	$\frac{1}{6}$	$\frac{1}{6}$	$\frac{1}{6}$	$\frac{1}{6}$	$\frac{1}{6}$	$\frac{1}{6}$

d)

d	0	1
$P(D = d)$	$\frac{1}{2}$	$\frac{1}{2}$

Q4 $P(X = x) = \begin{cases} \frac{1}{3} & x = 0 \\ \frac{2}{3} & x = 1 \end{cases}$

Q5

x	1	2	3	4	5	7	9
$P(X = x)$	$\frac{5}{13}$	$\frac{1}{13}$	$\frac{2}{13}$	$\frac{1}{13}$	$\frac{2}{13}$	$\frac{1}{13}$	$\frac{1}{13}$

Exercise 1.2

Q1 **a)** $a = 0.3$ **b)** 0.8   **c)** 0.2

Q2 **a)** **(i)** $k = \frac{1}{14}$

(ii)

x	1	2	3
$P(X = x)$	$\frac{1}{14}$	$\frac{2}{7}$	$\frac{9}{14}$

(iii) $\frac{5}{14}$

b) **(i)** $k = \frac{6}{11}$

(ii)

x	1	2	3
$P(X = x)$	$\frac{6}{11}$	$\frac{3}{11}$	$\frac{2}{11}$

(iii) $\frac{9}{11}$

c) **(i)** $k = \frac{1}{16}$

(ii)

x	1	2	3	4	5	6	7
$P(X = x)$	$\frac{1}{16}$	$\frac{1}{8}$	$\frac{3}{16}$	$\frac{1}{4}$	$\frac{3}{16}$	$\frac{1}{8}$	$\frac{1}{16}$

(iii) $\frac{3}{16}$

Q3

x	0	2	5	10
$P(X = x)$	$\frac{1}{10}$	$\frac{3}{5}$	$\frac{1}{5}$	$\frac{1}{10}$

$P(X > 0) = \frac{9}{10}$

Q4

x	0	1	2
$P(X = x)$	$\frac{4}{7}$	$\frac{2}{7}$	$\frac{1}{7}$

$P(X \geq 1) = \frac{3}{7}$

Let $k = P(X = 2)$. Then $P(X = 1) = 2k$ and $P(X = 0) = 4k$. Since the total probability must be 1, you know that $k + 2k + 4k = 1$, i.e. $k = \frac{1}{7}$.

Exercise 1.3

Q1 $\frac{1}{2}$

Q2 **a)** $\frac{1}{4}$ **b)** $\frac{5}{8}$ **c)** $\frac{5}{8}$ **d)** $\frac{1}{4}$

Q3 **a)**

x	0	5	10
$P(X = x)$	$\frac{1}{3}$	$\frac{1}{2}$	$\frac{1}{6}$

b) $\frac{2}{3}$

Q4

x	12	13	14	15
$P(X = x)$	$\frac{1}{4}$	$\frac{1}{4}$	$\frac{1}{4}$	$\frac{1}{4}$

$P(X \leq 14) = \frac{3}{4}$

Q5 **a)** $k = \frac{1}{6}$ **b)** $\frac{2}{3}$ **c)** $\frac{1}{2}$

d) $\frac{1}{3}$ **e)** $\frac{1}{3}$

Q6 $P(Y = y) = \frac{1}{150}$ $y = 1, 2, ..., 150$

$P(60 < Y \leq 75) = \frac{1}{10}$

Q7 $p(1) = k(1^3 - 6(1^2) + 11(1))$
$= k(1 - 6 + 11) = 6k$
$p(2) = k(2^3 - 6(2^2) + 11(2))$
$= k(8 - 24 + 22) = 6k$
$p(3) = k(3^3 - 6(3^2) + 11(3))$
$= k(27 - 54 + 33) = 6k$

So $p(x)$ is the same for all x, meaning that X has a discrete uniform distribution. The probabilities add up to 1, so:
$6k + 6k + 6k = 1 \Rightarrow 18k = 1 \Rightarrow k = \frac{1}{18}$

Exercise 1.4

Q1 **a)**

x	1	2	3	4	5
$F(x)$	0.1	0.3	0.6	0.8	1

b)

x	1	2	3	4
$F(x)$	0.3	0.5	0.8	1

c)

x	-2	-1	0	1	2
$F(x)$	$\frac{1}{5}$	$\frac{2}{5}$	$\frac{3}{5}$	$\frac{4}{5}$	1

d)

x	2	4	8	16	32	64
$F(x)$	$\frac{1}{2}$	$\frac{3}{4}$	$\frac{7}{8}$	$\frac{15}{16}$	$\frac{31}{32}$	1

Q2 **a)**

x	1	2	3	4
$F(x)$	0.3	0.4	0.85	1

(i) 0.85   **(ii)** 0.55

b)

x	-2	-1	0	1	2
$F(x)$	$\frac{1}{10}$	$\frac{1}{2}$	$\frac{3}{5}$	$\frac{4}{5}$	1

(i) $\frac{3}{5}$ **(ii)** $\frac{2}{5}$

Q3 **a)**

x	1	2	3	4	5	6	7	8
$F(x)$	$\frac{1}{8}$	$\frac{1}{4}$	$\frac{3}{8}$	$\frac{1}{2}$	$\frac{5}{8}$	$\frac{3}{4}$	$\frac{7}{8}$	1

b) **(i)** $\frac{3}{8}$ **(ii)** $\frac{1}{2}$

2. Binomial Distributions

Exercise 2.1

Q1 **a)** 720   **b)** 40 320   **c)** 12

d) 60   **e)** 181 440   **f)** 1680

g) 1260   **h)** 15 120

Exercise 2.2

Q1 167 960

Q2 **a)** 120   **b)** 252   **c)** 120

Q3 **a)** 184 756   **b)** 38 760   **c)** 190

Q4 **a)** 330   **b)** 462   **c)** 165

d) 1   **e)** 462

Exercise 2.3

Q1 **a)** Not a binomial distribution
— the number of trials is not fixed.

b) X follows a binomial distribution.
$X \sim B(2000, 0.005)$.

c) Y follows a binomial distribution.
$Y \sim B(10, 0.5)$.

Q2 The number of trials is fixed (650), each trial can either succeed or fail, X is the total number of successes, and the probability of each button falling off is the same if the trials are independent. So to model this situation with a binomial distribution, you would need to assume that all the trials are independent — then $X \sim B(650, 0.001)$.

Q3 E.g. Kaitlin is assuming that there is a constant probability of it being sunny on a given day, which isn't valid.

Q4 To model this situation with a binomial distribution, you would need to assume that all the trials (the acts) are independent.

Q5 The number of trials is fixed, each trial can either succeed or fail, and X is the total number of successes. To make the probability of success the same each time, the cards would need to be replaced, and to make each pick independent you could shuffle the pack after replacing the picked cards.
If this is done, then $X \sim B(10, \frac{3}{13})$.

Exercise 2.4

Q1 a) (i) 0.264 (3 s.f.) (ii) 0.0326 (3 s.f.)
(iii) 0.00638 (3 s.f.)

b) (i) 0.229 (3 s.f.) (ii) 0.0313 (3 s.f.)
(iii) 0.000611 (3 s.f.)

c) (i) 0.113 (3 s.f.) (ii) 0.0812 (3 s.f.)
(iii) 0.000300 (3 s.f.)

Q2 a) (i) 0.0850 (3 s.f.) (ii) 0.639 (3 s.f.)
(iii) 0.253 (3 s.f.)

b) (i) 0.147 (3 s.f.) (ii) 0.599 (3 s.f.)
(iii) 0.647 (3 s.f.)

c) (i) 0.110 (3 s.f.) (ii) 0.427 (3 s.f.)
(iii) 0.507 (3 s.f.)

Q3 a) 0.161 (3 s.f.) b) 0.402 (3 s.f.)
c) 0.965 (3 s.f.) d) 0.969 (3 s.f.)
e) 0.00334 (3 s.f.) f) 0.188 (3 s.f.)

Exercise 2.5

Q1 a) (i) 0.969 (3 s.f.) (ii) 0.813 (3 s.f.)
(iii) 0.938 (3 s.f.)

b) (i) 0.805 (3 s.f.) (ii) 0.997 (3 s.f.)
(iii) 1

Q2 a) There are 12 answers, which are either 'correct' or 'incorrect'. The student guesses at random so the questions are answered independently of each other and the probability of a correct answer is $\frac{1}{3}$.
So $X \sim B(12, \frac{1}{3})$.

b) 0.181 (3 s.f.) c) 4

Q3 0.161 (3 s.f.)
Mean of X = np so 25p = 1O, i.e. p = O.4.
So find P(X = 1O) for X ~ B(25, O.4).

Q4 0.531 (3 s.f.)

Q5 a) 0.844 (3 s.f.) b) 0.0979 (3 s.f.)
c) 22.5
Let X represent the number of 'treble-2O's'.
Then X ~ B(n, O.75). For a), n = 3 and for b) and c), n = 3O.

3. The Binomial Cumulative Distribution Function

Exercise 3.1

Q1 a) 0.5256 (4 d.p.) b) 0.9996 (4 d.p.)
c) 1.0000 (4 d.p.) d) 1.0000 (4 d.p.)
e) 0.9219 (4 d.p.) f) 0.7759 (4 d.p.)
g) 0.9803 (4 d.p.) h) 0.2440 (4 d.p.)

Q2 a) 0.4417 (4 d.p.) b) 0.0194 (4 d.p.)
c) 0.0726 (4 d.p.) d) 0.9313 (4 d.p.)
e) 0.0726 (4 d.p.) f) 0.0006 (4 d.p.)
g) 0.0039 (4 d.p.) h) 0.2054 (4 d.p.)

Q3 a) 0.9941 (4 d.p.) b) 0.5881 (4 d.p.)
c) 0.9793 (4 d.p.) d) 0.0059 (4 d.p.)
e) 0.9423 (4 d.p.) f) 0.8684 (4 d.p.)
g) 0.9987 (4 d.p.) h) 0.0013 (4 d.p.)

Q4 a) 0.1163 (4 d.p.) b) 0.9604 (4 d.p.)
c) 0.0067 (4 d.p.) d) 0.5060 (4 d.p.)
e) 0.9993 (4 d.p.) f) 0.6216 (4 d.p.)
g) 0.8813 (4 d.p.) h) 0.0342 (4 d.p.)

Q5 0.9677 (4 d.p.)

Q6 0.9988 (4 d.p.)

Exercise 3.2

Q1 a) 0.9095 (4 d.p.) b) 0.3902 (4 d.p.)
c) 0.0093 (4 d.p.) d) 0.7827 (4 d.p.)
e) 0.9729 (4 d.p.) f) 0.0003 (4 d.p.)

Q2 a) 0.1844 (4 d.p.) b) 0.0136 (4 d.p.)
c) 0.1061 (4 d.p.) d) 0.0531 (4 d.p.)
e) 0.5302 (4 d.p.) f) 0.9347 (4 d.p.)

Q3 a) 0.9532 (4 d.p.) b) 0.6167 (4 d.p.)
c) 0.9944 (4 d.p.) d) 0.1867 (4 d.p.)
e) 0.0015 (4 d.p.) f) 0.1090 (4 d.p.)

Q4 a) 0.8935 (4 d.p.) b) 0.7339 (4 d.p.)
c) 0.0234 (4 d.p.) d) 0.2544 (4 d.p.)

Q5 0.6197 (4 d.p.)

Q6 0.0444 (4 d.p.)

Exercise 3.3

Q1 a) $a = 2$ b) $b = 6$
c) $c = 1$ d) $d = 5$

Q2 a) $a = 22$ b) $b = 9$
c) $c = 11$ d) $d = 17$

Q3 a) 12 b) 14

Q4 15

4. Modelling Real Problems

Exercise 4.1

Q1 a) There's a fixed number of independent trials (50) with 'success' meaning a person who passes takes a leaflet and 'failure' meaning they don't, a constant probability of success (0.25) and X is the total number of successes.
$X \sim B(50, 0.25)$.

b) 0.9979 (4 d.p.) c) 0.0985 (4 d.p.)

Q2 a) 0.2123 (4 d.p.) b) 0.1132 (4 d.p.)

Q3 a) The probability of Simon being able to solve each crossword needs to remain the same, and all the outcomes need to be independent.

b) $p = \frac{5}{19} = 0.263$ (to 3 s.f.)
To solve part b), use the binomial probability function to find P(X = 4) and P(X = 5) in terms of p. Then set these expressions equal to each other and solve to find p.

Q4 a) $X \sim B\left(74, \frac{1}{37}\right)$

b) $P(X \geq 2) = 0.598$ (3 s.f.)

c) The expected number of times Ricky will win is $np = 74 \times \frac{1}{37} = 2$, which means that he can expect to win 2 games and lose 72.
When he wins, he gains £175, and when he loses, he loses £5.
So his total earnings would be
$2 \times £175 + 72 \times (-£5)$
$= £350 - £360 = -£10$
I.e. he can expect to make a loss of £10 over the course of 74 games.

Review Exercise — Chapter 13

Q1 a) $k = 0.1$ b) 0.6

Q2

x	2	3	5	7
$P(X = x)$	$\frac{11}{36}$	$\frac{1}{3}$	$\frac{7}{36}$	$\frac{1}{6}$

$P(X \leq 5) = \frac{5}{6}$

Q3

w	0.2	0.3	0.4	0.5
$P(W \leq w)$	0.2	0.4	0.7	1

Q4 a)

x	1	2	3	4	5
$F(x)$	$\frac{3}{25}$	$\frac{7}{25}$	$\frac{12}{25}$	$\frac{18}{25}$	1

(i) $\frac{12}{25}$ (ii) $\frac{9}{25}$

b)

x	1	2	3	4	5	6
$F(x)$	$\frac{1}{6}$	$\frac{1}{3}$	$\frac{1}{2}$	$\frac{2}{3}$	$\frac{5}{6}$	1

(i) $\frac{1}{2}$ (ii) $\frac{1}{3}$

Q5 a) 39 070 080 b) 63 063 000
c) 792 d) 35

Q6 a) Binomial — there are a fixed number of independent trials (30) with two possible results ('prime' / 'not prime'), a constant probability of success, and the random variable is the total number of successes.

b) Binomial — there are a fixed number of independent trials (the number of students in the class) with two possible results ('heads' / 'tails'), a constant probability of success, and the random variable is the total number of successes.

c) Not binomial — the probability of being dealt an ace changes with each card dealt, since the total number of cards decreases as each card is dealt.

d) Not binomial — the number of trials is not fixed.

Q7 a) 0.2461 (4 d.p.) **b)** 0.0098 (4 d.p.)
c) 0.6230 (4 d.p.) **d)** 0.0107 (4 d.p.)

Q8 a) 0.2286 (4 d.p.) **b)** 0.0754 (4 d.p.)
c) 0.1463 (4 d.p.) **d)** 0.0001 (4 d.p.)

Q9 a) 8 **b)** 6 **c)** 11.25
d) 40 **e)** 21 **f)** 0.54
g) 6 **h)** 10.35

Q10 a) 0.4711 (4 d.p.) **b)** 0.9745 (4 d.p.)
c) 1.0000 (4 d.p.) **d)** 0.7208 (4 d.p.)
e) 0.0005 (4 d.p.) **f)** 0.1132 (4 d.p.)
g) 1 **h)** 0.8250 (4 d.p.)

Q11 a) 0.9997 (4 d.p.) **b)** 0.1302 (4 d.p.)
c) 0.9361 (4 d.p.) **d)** 0.5836 (4 d.p.)
e) 0.1416 (4 d.p.) **f)** 0.2503 (4 d.p.)

Q12 a) $a = 13$ **b)** $b = 8$ **c)** $c = 5$

Q13 a) $a = 3$ **b)** $b = 7$ **d)** $c = 9$

Q14 a) There's a fixed number of independent trials (40) with 'success' meaning a person uses the voucher and 'failure' meaning they don't, a constant probability of success (0.15) and X is the total number of successes. $X \sim B(40, 0.15)$.

b) 0.0672 (4 d.p.) **c)** 0.1742 (4 d.p.)

Q15 a) 0.1678 (4 d.p.) **b)** 0.8822 (4 d.p.)

Q16 7 or more

Q17 a) The probability of Messy being able to dribble past the player needs to remain the same each time, and all the outcomes need to be independent.

b) $p = \frac{1}{3}$
To solve part b), use the binomial probability function to find $P(X = 3)$ and $P(X = 4)$ in terms of p. Then set these expressions equal to each other and solve to find p.

Chapter 14: Statistical Hypothesis Testing

1. Hypothesis Tests

Exercise 1.1

Q1 a) The probability that a seed germinates.
b) 0.9
c) Call the probability p. Then **(i)** $H_0: p = 0.9$ **(ii)** $H_1: p > 0.9$
d) One-tailed

Q2 Let p be the probability that a randomly selected resident knows about the grants. Then $H_0: p = 0.16$ and $H_1: p > 0.16$.

Q3 Let p be the proportion of customers who buy a jar of chilli chutney. Then $H_0: p = 0.03$ and $H_1: p \neq 0.03$.

Q4 Let p be the probability that a randomly selected gym member watches Australian soaps. Then $H_0: p = 0.4$ and $H_1: p > 0.4$.

2. Hypothesis Tests for a Binomial Distribution

Exercise 2.1

Q1 a) Let p be the probability of the spinner landing on 7. Then $H_0: p = 0.1$ and $H_1: p > 0.1$. Let X be the number of times the spinner lands on 7 in 50 spins. Then under H_0, $X \sim B(50, 0.1)$.

b) Let p be the probability of Eli being stopped at the traffic lights. Then $H_0: p = 0.25$ and $H_1: p < 0.25$. Let X be the number of times Eli is stopped in 2 weeks. Then under H_0, $X \sim B(14, 0.25)$.

c) Let p be the probability that a driver gets lost on any journey. Then $H_0: p = 0.025$ and $H_1: p \neq 0.025$. Let X be the number of journeys where the driver gets lost in the sample of 100. Then under H_0, $X \sim B(100, 0.025)$.

d) Let p be the probability that a randomly selected teenager from the Scottish island has the antibody present. Then $H_0: p = 0.35$ and $H_1: p \neq 0.35$. Let X be the number of teenagers in the sample who have the antibody present. Then under H_0, $X \sim B(40, 0.35)$.

e) Let p be the probability that a randomly selected student has seen the film. Then $H_0: p = 0.5$ and $H_1: p > 0.5$. Let X be the number of students in the sample who have seen the film. Then under H_0, $X \sim B(30, 0.5)$.

f) Let p be the probability that a mouse is caught on any day. Then $H_0: p = 0.7$ and $H_1: p < 0.7$. Let X be the number of days a mouse is caught in the sample of 21. Then under H_0, $X \sim B(21, 0.7)$.

Exercise 2.2

Q1 a) Let p be the probability of Charlotte guessing correctly. Then $H_0: p = 0.2$ and $H_1: p > 0.2$.

b) Let X be the number of times Charlotte is correct in the sample. Then under H_0, $X \sim B(10, 0.2)$.

c) $P(X \geq 4) = 0.1209 > 0.05$. So there is not significant evidence at the 5% level to reject H_0 in favour of Charlotte's claim.

Q2 There is significant evidence at the 10% level to reject H_0 in favour of Ellen's claim that fewer people think chicken dinosaurs are good value.

Q3 There is not significant evidence at the 1% level to reject H_0 in favour of H_1, so Hati's claim is not upheld at the 1% level.

Exercise 2.3

Q1 There is not significant evidence at the 1% level to reject H_0 in favour of the alternative hypothesis that the number of distinctions has changed.

Q2 There is significant evidence at the 10% level to reject H_0 in favour of the alternative hypothesis that the number of rare birds is different with the new birdseed.

Q3 There is not significant evidence at the 5% level to reject H_0 in favour of the alternative hypothesis that the number of customers buying the magazine is different in the new shop.

Exercise 2.4

Q1 a) Critical region: $X \geq 9$
b) Actual significance level: 0.0409 (4 d.p.) or 4.09%
c) Acceptance region: $X < 9$ (or $X \leq 8$)

Q2 Critical region: $X \leq 2$
Actual significance level: 0.0442 (4 d.p.) or 4.42%.

Q3 Critical region: $X \leq 5$ or $X \geq 15$
Actual significance level: 0.0638 (4 d.p.) or 6.38%

Q4 a) Critical region: $X \leq 1$
b) Actual significance level: 0.0142 (4 d.p.) or 1.42%.
c) 3 does not lie in the critical region, so the result is not significant at the 5% level.

Q5 Critical region: $X \geq 15$
Actual significance level: 0.0053 (4 d.p.) or 0.53%

Q6 Critical region: $X \geq 6$
Actual significance level: 0.0378
(4 d.p) or 3.78%.

Q7 **a)** Critical region: $X \geq 11$

b) Actual significance level: 0.0196
(4 d.p.) or 1.96%

c) 10 doesn't lie in the critical region so this result is not significant at the 5% level.

d) Critical region: $X \geq 10$
Actual significance level: 0.0834
(4 d.p.) or 8.34%
10 lies in the critical region so this result is significant at the 10% level.

Review Exercise — Chapter 14

Q1 Let p be the probability that a battery from the new brand lasts for more than 18 months. Then $H_0: p = 0.64$, $H_1: p > 0.64$. This is a one-tailed test.

Q2 A two-tailed test should be used. Let p be the probability of getting 'heads'. Then $H_0: p = 0.5$, $H_1: p \neq 0.5$.

Q3 Let p be the probability that an item is faulty. Then $H_0: p = 0.05$, $H_1: p \neq 0.05$. Let X be the number of faulty items in the sample. Then under H_0, $X \sim B(50, 0.05)$.

Q4 **a)** The population parameter is p, the probability that Tina answers a question correctly. Then $H_0: p = 0.84$, $H_1: p > 0.84$.

b) The test statistic, X, is the number of questions in the sample that Tina answers correctly. Then under H_0, $X \sim B(10, 0.84)$.

c) $P(X \geq 9) = 0.5080$ (4 d.p.) > 0.05. So there is not significant evidence at the 5% level to reject H_0 in favour of Tina's claim.

Q5 **a)** There is insufficient evidence at the 5% level of significance to reject H_0.

b) There is sufficient evidence at the 1% level of significance to reject H_0.

Q6 There is not significant evidence at the 5% level to reject H_0.

Q7 **a)** Critical region: $X \geq 15$

b) Actual significance level: 0.0064 (4 d.p.) or 0.64%

c) Acceptance region: $X < 15$ (or $X \leq 14$)

Q8 Critical region: $X = 0$

Q9 **a)** Critical region: $X \leq 78$ or $X \geq 91$

b) Actual significance level: 0.0944 (4 d.p.) or 9.44%

c) 75 lies in the critical region, so the result is significant at the 10% level.

Chapter 15: Kinematics

1. Motion Graphs

Exercise 1.1

Q1 First stage: $v = 80$ kmh^{-1}, Second stage: $v = 40$ kmh^{-1}, Third stage: $v = 0$ kmh^{-1}, Fourth stage: $v = -120$ kmh^{-1}

Q2 **a)** 400 m

b)
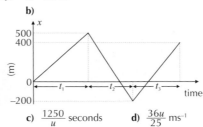

c) $\dfrac{1250}{u}$ seconds   **d)** $\dfrac{36u}{25}$ ms^{-1}

Q3
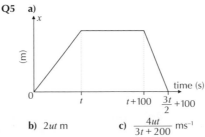

Q4 **a)**
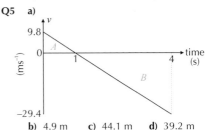

b) -36 kmh^{-1} **c)** 30 kmh^{-1}

Q5 **a)**

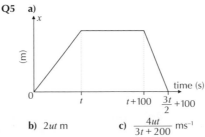

b) $2ut$ m   **c)** $\dfrac{4ut}{3t + 200}$ ms^{-1}

Exercise 1.2

Q1 The bus accelerates uniformly from rest to a speed of 20 kmh^{-1} in 2 min. It then travels at this speed for 18 min, before decelerating uniformly to 10 kmh^{-1} in 5 min. Finally, it decelerates uniformly to rest in 10 min.

Q2 **a)** 3 ms^{-2} **b)** -0.75 ms^{-2}

c) 1.5 ms^{-2}

Q3 **a)**
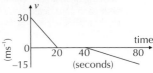

b) $30T$

c) $x = 300$ m, $y = 120$ m, $T = 14$ s

Q4 **a)** It takes the train 40 s to reach the signal box.

b) 1.5 ms^{-2} **c)** 300 m

Q5 **a)**

b) 4.9 m   **c)** 44.1 m   **d)** 39.2 m

Exercise 1.3

Q1 **a)** -15 ms^{-1} **b)** 62 ms^{-1}

c) 84 ms^{-1}

Q2 **a)**
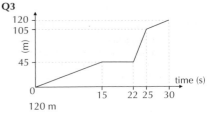

b) 28 ms^{-1} **c)** 840 m

d)

Q3

120 m

2. Constant Acceleration Equations

Exercise 2.1

Q1 **a)** 2.4 ms^{-2} **b)** 30 m

Q2 **a)** 5 ms^{-1} **b)** 20 s
c) 0.25 ms^{-2}

Q3 **a)** 5 ms^{-2}
b) Acceleration is constant. The skier is modelled as a particle travelling in a straight line.

Q4 **a)** 6 ms^{-2} **b)** 3 ms^{-1}
You can solve this problem by first calculating the motion between the first and second posts to get an equation in terms of u and a. Do the same for the motion between the first and third posts. Then solve the equations simultaneously. For b) use your calculations from a).

Q5 **a)** 500 m **b)** 28 ms^{-1}
You can solve part a) by calculating the motion while the bus is in the tunnel. To solve part b) find the distance travelled before the tunnel, s_1, and after the tunnel, s_2 (both in terms of U). Then the total distance travelled is $s_1 + 500 + s_2$, so make an equation by setting this equal to 1580. Finally solve this equation to find U.

Exercise 2.2

Q1 44.1 m
Q2 1.43 s (3 s.f.)
Q3 **a)** 1.01 s (3 s.f.) **b)** 9.90 ms^{-1} (3 s.f.)
Q4 **a)** 45.9 m (3 s.f.) **b)** 6.12 s (3 s.f.)
c) 10.4 ms^{-1} upwards
Q5 **a)** 9.4 ms^{-1} **b)** 15.9 m
Q6 **a)** 8.27 m (3 s.f.) **b)** 0.465 s (3 s.f.)
Q7 **a)** 7.35 m (3 s.f.) **b)** 1.22 s (3 s.f.)
c) 19.6 ms^{-1} (3 s.f.)
Q8 **a)** 2.5 s **b)** 6 s **c)** 60.025 m
Q9 **a)** 77.0 ms^{-1} (3 s.f.)
You can solve this problem by first considering the motion between the two targets to find the speed as the projectile passes the first target. Then use this value when calculating the speed of projection.
b) 253 m (3 s.f.) **c)** 2.28 s (3 s.f.)
For b) and c) use the suvat equations with values from a).
Q10 **a)** 6.08 ms^{-1} (3 s.f.) **b)** 1.49 s (3 s.f.)
c) Any suitable reason — e.g. the carriage is likely to be affected by air resistance (or friction), the carriage is too large to be modelled as a particle.

Exercise 2.3

Q1 **a)**

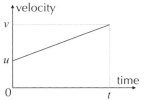

Displacement is the area under the graph. Using area of a trapezium
$$s = \left(\frac{u+v}{2}\right)t$$

b) Substitute $t = \frac{v-u}{a}$ into $s = \left(\frac{u+v}{2}\right)t$:

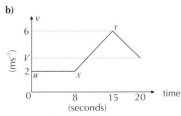

$$s = \left(\frac{u+v}{2}\right)\left(\frac{v-u}{a}\right)$$
$$\Rightarrow 2as = (u+v)(v-u)$$
$$\Rightarrow 2as = uv - u^2 + v^2 - vu$$
$$\Rightarrow v^2 = u^2 + 2as$$

Q2 **a)** $t = 7 \text{ s}$
b)

c) 3.2 ms^{-1}

Q3 **a)**

b) 45 seconds

Q4 **a)** 0.828 s (3 s.f.)
You can solve this problem by finding the distance that each car travels (s_X and s_Y) separately, in terms of t. The cars collide when $s_X + s_Y = 30$. This gives a quadratic in t which you can solve using the quadratic formula.
b) $v_X = 15.8 \text{ ms}^{-1}$ (3 s.f.), $v_Y = 21.7 \text{ ms}^{-1}$ (3 s.f.)
c) 12.8 m (3 s.f.)
For b) and c) use the suvat equations with values from a).

Q5 **a)**

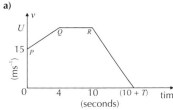

b) 27 ms^{-1} **c)** 21.8 s (3 s.f.)
d) 2.29 ms^{-2} (3 s.f.)

Q6 **a)** 9.21 s (3 s.f.)
You can solve this problem by finding the distance that each ball travels (s_1 and s_2) separately, in terms of t. The balls are level when $s_1 = s_2$. This gives a quadratic in t which you can solve using the quadratic formula.
b) 24.8 m (3 s.f.)
Put $t = 9.211...$ into your expression for s_1 or s_2.
c) 23 m
You can solve this problem by finding the time that the first ball comes to rest and the distance it travels in this time. Then find the distance the second ball travels in 15 seconds. Finally calculate the difference between the two distances.

Q7 **a)** 11.2 m (3 s.f.)
You can solve this problem by finding the time that B is at its highest point. Then find the displacement of A at this time.
b) 2.70 s (3 s.f.)
You can solve this problem by calculating the distance that each particle travels (s_A and s_B) separately, in terms of t. The balls are level when $s_A + s_B = 30$ (as they start 30 m apart). This gives an equation in t that you can solve.
c) 4.39 m (3 s.f.)
Use your calculations from b).

3. Non-Uniform Acceleration

Exercise 3.1

Q1 **a)** 21 m **b)** $v = 6t^2 - 8t$
c) 30 ms^{-1}
Q2 **a)** 5.33 m (3 s.f.) **b)** 6 ms^{-2}
Q3 **a)** 2 ms^{-1} **b)** 1.86 ms^{-2} (3 s.f.)
Q4 **a)** 5 ms^{-1} **b)** 0 ms^{-2}

Exercise 3.2

Q1 **a)** $s = t + 3t^2 + 2t^3 - t^4$
b) Displacement is 14 cm, velocity is 5 cms^{-1}.
Q2 **a)** $s = 3t^4 - 6t^3 + t^2 + 2$
b) Displacement is 6 m, velocity is 28 ms^{-1}.
Q3 -5 ms^{-1}
Q4 $s = -\frac{1}{4}t^4 + t^3 - 2t^2 + 2t + 2$

Exercise 3.3

Q1 **a)** 1 s **b)** 11 m
Q2 **a)** 27 ms^{-1} **b)** 11 ms^{-1}
Q3 14.7 ms^{-1} (in the negative direction)
Q4 0.148 m (3 s.f.)
You can solve this problem by integrating twice to get an equation for the displacement with two unknown values. Then use the two conditions to find these values.

The maximum displacement occurs when v = 0. So solve v = 0 and find the time when the maximum displacement occurs. Finally substitute this value of t into the displacement formula.

Review Exercise — Chapter 15

Q1 A: 80 kmh^{-1}, B: 26.7 kmh^{-1} (3 s.f.), C: 0 kmh^{-1}, D: 80 kmh^{-1}

Q2

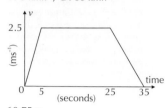

68.75 m

Q3 **a)** 1.67 ms^{-2} (3 s.f.)   **b)** 5 ms^{-2}
c) 12.5 m

Q4 The parachutist accelerates uniformly for 16 seconds at a rate of 9 ms^{-2}, reaching a velocity of 144 ms^{-1}. He then decelerates uniformly at a rate of 6 ms^{-2} for 14 seconds, until he reaches 60 ms^{-1}. After this he is no longer accelerating, so his final velocity is 60 ms^{-1}.

Q5 12 m

Q6 **a)** 160 m   **b)** 10 ms^{-1}

Q7 $s = 15.9$ (3 s.f.) so yes.

Q8 **a)** 62.5 m   **b)** 7.14 s (3 s.f.)

Q9 **a)** 34.7 ms^{-1} (3 s.f.) **b)** 51.4 m (3 s.f.)
c) 1.01 s (3 s.f.)

Q10 a)

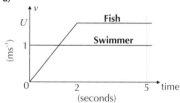

b) 1.25 ms^{-1}

Q11 **a)** 26.1 m (3 s.f.)   **b)** 2.46 s (3 s.f.)
c) 5.34 m (3 s.f.)

Q12 **a)** 6.25 m   **b)** −2 ms^{-2}

Q13 **a)** $s = 3t + \frac{5}{2}t^2 + \frac{4}{3}t^3 - \frac{3}{4}t^4$
b) $s = 14.7$ cm (3 s.f.), $v = 5$ cms^{-1}

Q14 **a)** 3.125 m **b)** 0.75 m   **c)** 16 m

Q15 **a)** The yo-yo is released from $s = 0$ when $t = 0$, and at time $t = 2$, the yo-yo returns to $s = 0$.
b) 2 feet

Q16 7.50 ms^{-1} (3 s.f.)

Chapter 16: Forces and Newton's Laws

1. Understanding Units

Exercise 1.1

Q1 **a)** m^3 **b)** kgm^{-3} or kg/m^3
c) kgms^{-1} or kgm/s
d) kgms^{-2} or kgm/s^2
e) kgm^{2}s^{-2} or kgm^2/s^2
f) kgm^{-1}s^{-2} or kg/(ms^2)

2. Models in Mechanics

Exercise 2.1

Q1 The apple is modelled as a particle. The apple is initially at rest. Air resistance can be ignored. There are no other external forces acting. The effect of gravity (g) is constant.

Q2 The conker is modelled as a particle. The shoelace is a light, inextensible string. There are no other external forces acting.

Q3  The sledge is modelled as a particle.
The surface of the slope is smooth. The rope is a light, inextensible string. The rope is parallel to the slope. No other external forces are acting.

Q4 **a)** The box is modelled as a particle. The floor is smooth (it's polished). There are no other external forces acting.

b) The crate is modelled as a particle.
The rope is light and inextensible. The floor is rough. There are no other external forces acting.

Q5 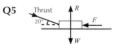 The package is modelled as a particle.
The stick is light and rigid. The ground is rough. There are no other external forces acting.

Q6 **a)** The car is modelled as a particle. The angle of the slope is constant.
The surface is rough. There are no other external forces acting.

b) 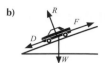 The car is modelled as a particle. The angle of the slope is constant.
The surface is rough. There are no other external forces acting.

Q7 **a)**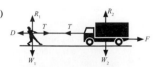
The man and the lorry are both modelled as particles. The rope is light and inextensible, and remains taut. The road is rough. No resistance forces slow the strongman's motion. There are no other external forces acting.

b)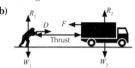
The assumptions about the man, lorry, road, resistance and external forces are the same as in a). The rod is light and rigid.

Q8 The weight is modelled as a particle. The rod is light and rigid. There are no other external forces acting.

3. Forces

Exercise 3.1

Q1 **a)** Magnitude = 7 N. Direction $\theta = 0°$
b) Magnitude = 2.83 N (3 s.f.) Direction $\theta = 45°$
c) Magnitude = 5 N. Direction $\theta = 53.1°$ (3 s.f.)
d) Magnitude = 5 N. Direction $\theta = 127°$ (3 s.f.)
e) Magnitude = 13 kN. Direction $\theta = 337°$ (3 s.f.)

Q2 **a)** Magnitude = 3.16 N (3 s.f.) Direction $\theta = 18.4°$ (3 s.f.)
b) Magnitude = 4.47 N (3 s.f.) Direction $\theta = 207°$ (3 s.f.)
c) Magnitude = 12.4 N (3 s.f.) Direction $\theta = 346°$ (3 s.f.)
d) Magnitude = 0.707 kN (3 s.f.) Direction $\theta = 135°$
e) Magnitude = 11 N Direction $\theta = 270°$

Q3 60°

Q4 $a = 0.5$

Q5 16.3° (to 3 s.f.)
Find the direction of each of the vectors. Because they both act from the same point, the difference between these two angles will be the angle between the vectors.

Exercise 3.2

Q1 $T = 8$ N

Q2 **a)** $11\mathbf{i} + 3\mathbf{j}$ N **b)** $\mathbf{i} + 2\mathbf{j}$ N
   c) $4\mathbf{i} + \mathbf{j}$ N

Q3 $x = 2$

Q4 **a)**

   b) $-4\mathbf{i} - 2\mathbf{j}$ N
   c) $\mathbf{j}$ N

4. Newton's Laws of Motion

Exercise 4.1

Q1 60 N

Q2 1.5 N

Q3 **a)** $a = 2$ ms^{-2} **b)** 16 ms^{-1}

Q4 $T = 183.6$ N

Q5 $T = 15.6$ N (1 d.p.)

Q6 **a)** 3.6 kg **b)** 20 ms^{-1}
   c) 35.28 N

Q7 **a)** 0.625 ms^{-2}
   b) 693 N (3 s.f.)
   Resolve vertically using F = ma, and solve for T. Remember that the resistance force is non-gravitational, so the weight of the sack acts in addition to this 120 N.

Q8 345.6 m
   Resolve vertically using F = ma (including the upwards resistance of 1.5 N) to find the acceleration, then use the equation $s = ut + \frac{1}{2}at^2$ to find the displacement. Remember that if something is dropped, its initial velocity u = 0.

Q9 **a)** $(0.8\mathbf{i} - 0.2\mathbf{j})$ ms^{-2}
   b) 0.825 ms^{-2} (3 s.f.)
   c) 4.95 ms^{-1} (3 s.f.)

Q10 0.5 kg
   Use $\mathbf{v} = \mathbf{u} + \mathbf{a}t$ (i.e. the vector form) to find $\mathbf{a}$, then use this with $\mathbf{F} = m\mathbf{a}$ to find m.

Q11 **a)** $(6\mathbf{i} + 4\mathbf{j})$ N
   Use $\mathbf{v} = \mathbf{u} + \mathbf{a}t$ to find $\mathbf{a}$, then use this with $\mathbf{F} = m\mathbf{a}$ to find the force.
   b) 8.06 N (3 s.f.)
   The sum of the two forces must be equal to the resultant force. Take the known force away from the resultant force to find the other force, and then find its magnitude.

Q12 **a)** 5 kg
   Find $\mathbf{a}$ with $\mathbf{v} = \mathbf{u} + \mathbf{a}t$, then put this into $\mathbf{F} = m\mathbf{a}$. Solve for x.
   b) 23.8 N (3 s.f.)
   Take the known force away from the resultant force to find the other force, and then find its magnitude.

Exercise 4.2

Q1 **a)** 24 100 N (3 s.f.)
   b) 4080 N (3 s.f.)

Q2 **a)** 19 920 N **b)** 11 620 N
   c) 24.2 ms^{-1} (3 s.f.)

Q3 **a)** 1050 N **b)** 450 N
   c) E.g. The tractor and trailer are modelled as particles, there are no external forces (e.g. air resistance) acting, the coupling is horizontal, the braking force generated by the tractor is constant, the tractor and trailer are moving in a straight line on horizontal ground.

Q4 **a)** 1500 N **b)** 660 N
   c) 32 s
   Apply F = ma to the caravan (which now only has the 500 N force acting horizontally) to find a, then plug this into v = u + at to find t.

Exercise 4.3

Q1 **a)**

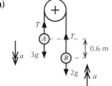

   b) 0.553 s (3 s.f.)

Q2 **a)** 255.5 N **b)** 20.8 kg (3 s.f.)

Q3 **a)** 5.72 ms^{-2} (3 s.f.) **b)** 28.6 N (3 s.f.)
   Resolve horizontally and vertically to create two simultaneous equations for T and a.
   c) E.g. String is light and inextensible, pulley is fixed and smooth, horizontal surface is smooth, no other external forces are acting, A doesn't hit the pulley, B doesn't hit the floor, string doesn't break, pulley doesn't break, string between A and the pulley is horizontal, string is initially taut, acceleration due to gravity is constant at 9.8 ms^{-2}.

Q4 **a)**

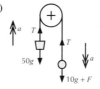

   b) 493 N **c)** 395.6 N
   d) $v = 3.35$ ms^{-1} (3 s.f.)
   Redraw the diagram with new forces (11g down and T up on the bucket, 10g down and T up on the counterweight). Resolve vertically for the bucket and the counterweight to get a pair of simultaneous equations in T and a. Solve to find a, then substitute this into $v^2 = u^2 + 2as$ to find v.

Q5 8.89 kg (2 d.p.)

Q6 **a)** 1.09 ms^{-2} (3 s.f.) **b)** 261 N (3 s.f.)
   c) 0.369 s (3 s.f.)

Q7 1.75 s (3 s.f.)

Exercise 4.4

Q1 **a)** 0.333 ms^{-2} (3 s.f.)
   b) 1.27 kg (3 s.f.)

Q2 7460 N

Q3 **a)** 5500 N **b)** 1.25 ms^{-2}
   c) 1.58 s (3 s.f.)
   First, find how far the crate travelled in the first five seconds (its displacement) using one of the suvat equations. Then use the suvat equation $s = ut + \frac{1}{2}at^2$ to make a quadratic in t. Solve this using the quadratic formula, and take the positive value of t as the answer.

   d) Some possible answers include: The pulley is assumed to be smooth, which is likely to be inaccurate. The model could be improved by accounting for the friction in the pulley. The driving force and the resistance force are given as constant, but it would be more accurate to assume that they vary with time and include that in the model. The falling crate would experience air resistance as it fell, so if the model were updated to include that, it would be more realistic.

Review Exercise — Chapter 16

Q1 **a)** ms^{-1} or m/s **b)** m^3
   c) ms^{-3} or m/s^3 **d)** Am^{-2} or A/m^2

Q2 **a)**

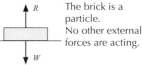

   The brick is a particle. No other external forces are acting.

   b)   The ball is a particle. No other external forces are acting (e.g. no air resistance).

   c)

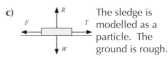

   The sledge is modelled as a particle. The ground is rough.
   The rope is a light, inextensible string. The rope is parallel to the ground.

   d)

   The toboggan is modelled as a particle. The slope is smooth.
   No other external forces are acting.

   e)

   The pendulum is modelled as a particle. The string is light and inextensible.
   The rod is thin, straight and rigid. The rod is horizontal.

Q3 15.9° (3 s.f.)

Q4 a) Magnitude = 5 N,
Direction $\theta = 307°$ (3 s.f.)

b) Magnitude = 11.4 N (3 s.f.)
Direction $\theta = 22.4°$ (3 s.f.)

c) Magnitude = 5.77 N (3 s.f.)
Direction $\theta = 161°$ (3 s.f.)

d) Magnitude = 14.3 N (3 s.f.)
Direction $\theta = 21.1°$ (3 s.f.)

e) Magnitude = 5.54 N (3 s.f.)
Direction $\theta = 74.3°$ (3 s.f.)

f) Magnitude = 5.21 N (3 s.f.)
Direction $\theta = 347°$ (3 s.f.)

Q5 4 ms⁻¹

Q6 3.5 N

Q7 a) 34.6 N   b) 4.08 kg (3 s.f.)

Q8 a) 16 N

b) Magnitude = 32.8 N (3 s.f.)
Direction $\theta = 74.1°$ (3 s.f.)

Q9 a) 5.6 ms⁻²   b) 16.8 N

c) E.g. No other external forces are
acting, A doesn't hit the pulley,
B doesn't hit the floor, string doesn't
break, pulley doesn't break, string
between A and pulley is horizontal,
string is initially taut, acceleration
due to gravity is constant at 9.8 ms⁻².

Q10 a) Acceleration = 6.25 ms⁻².
Direction $\theta = 53.1°$ (3 s.f.)

b) 28.125 m

Q11 a) 350 N   b) 400 N

Q12 3.13 kg (3 s.f.)

Q13 69.4 N

Q14 1.00 s (3 s.f.)
*Split the motion into two parts. The first
part is from the particles being released,
to A striking the pulley. By resolving the
horizontal and vertical forces and then using
$s = ut + \frac{1}{2}at^2$ you can find how long it is
before A hits the pulley. Then calculate
how long it takes B to fall to the ground
accelerating under gravity, again using
$s = ut + \frac{1}{2}at^2$.
Remember that B is not starting from rest,
so you'll need to find out how fast it was
travelling when the string snapped. Add these
two times together to find the answer.*

Chapter 17: Algebra and Functions

1. Proof by Contradiction
Exercise 1.1

Q1 Suppose that there is a number x that
is the largest multiple of 3, so it can be
written as $x = 3k$ for some integer k.

Then $x + 3 = 3k + 3 = 3(k + 1)$ is also a
multiple of 3 and is larger than x, which
contradicts the initial assumption. So
there cannot be a largest multiple of 3.

Q2 Suppose that there is some even number
x for which x^2 is odd. Since x is even, it
can be written as $x = 2n$ for some integer
n.
Then $x^2 = (2n)^2 = 4n^2 = 2(2n^2)$ which is
even, which contradicts the assumption
that x^2 is odd.
So if x^2 is odd, then x must also be odd.

Q3 a) Suppose that there is a rational
number $x \neq 0$ and an irrational
number y such that xy is rational.
This means that x can be written
as $x = \frac{a}{b}$ and xy can be written as
$xy = \frac{c}{d}$, where a, b, c and d are all
non-zero integers.
So $xy = \frac{a}{b}y = \frac{c}{d} \Rightarrow y = \frac{bc}{ad}$
Since bc and ad are both integers,
this means that y is a rational
number, which contradicts the
assumption that y is irrational. So the
statement must be true.

b) To disprove the statement, find a
counter-example. $\sqrt{2}$ is an irrational
number, but $\sqrt{2} \times \sqrt{2} = 2$ which is
rational, so the statement is false.

Q4 Suppose that there is a smallest positive
rational number, and call it x.
Since x is rational, it can be written as
$x = \frac{a}{b}$, and since it is positive, a and
b are both positive integers (or both
negative, in which case you can simplify
the fraction by dividing top and bottom
by –1 to get a and b positive).

Then $\frac{a}{b+1}$ is also a positive rational
number, and is smaller than x, which
contradicts the assumption that x is the
smallest positive rational number.
So there cannot be a smallest positive
rational number.

Q5 Assume that $1 + \sqrt{2}$ is rational, so it can
be written as $\frac{a}{b}$ where a and b are non-
zero integers.
So $1 + \sqrt{2} = \frac{a}{b} \Rightarrow \sqrt{2} = \frac{a}{b} - 1$
$\Rightarrow \sqrt{2} = \frac{a-b}{b}$
Since a and b are integers, $(a - b)$ is also
an integer, which means that $\sqrt{2}$ is
rational, which is not true.
So $1 + \sqrt{2}$ must be irrational.

Q6 a) Suppose that there is an integer x
such that x^2 is a multiple of 3 but
x is not. If x is not a multiple of 3,
then there are two cases to consider:
$x = 3k + 1$ and $x = 3k + 2$
for some integer k.
If $x = 3k + 1$,
then $x^2 = (3k + 1)^2 = 9k^2 + 6k + 1$
$= 3(3k^2 + 2k) + 1$
So x^2 is not a multiple of 3.
If $x = 3k + 2$,
then $x^2 = (3k + 2)^2 = 9k^2 + 12k + 4$
$= 3(3k^2 + 4k + 1) + 1$
So x^2 is not a multiple of 3.

Therefore, by exhaustion, x^2 cannot
be a multiple of 3, which contradicts
the initial assumption.
So if x^2 is a multiple of 3, then x must
also be a multiple of 3.

b) Suppose that $\sqrt{3}$ is rational, so
$\sqrt{3} = \frac{a}{b}$ for some non-zero integers
a and b that share no common
factors. So $b\sqrt{3} = a \Rightarrow 3b^2 = a^2 \Rightarrow$
a^2 is a multiple of 3.
From part a), this means that a is also
a multiple of 3, so write $a = 3k$ for
some integer k.
$3b^2 = (3k)^2 \Rightarrow 3b^2 = 9k^2$
$\Rightarrow b^2 = 3k^2$
$\Rightarrow b^2$ is a multiple of 3.
Again, from part a), this means b is a
multiple of 3. But it was assumed at
the start that a and b had no common
factors.
So $\sqrt{3}$ cannot be written as an
integer fraction, so it is irrational.

2. Simplifying Expressions
Exercise 2.1

Q1 a) $\frac{3}{x+1}$ b) $\frac{x}{x-2}$ c) $\frac{2}{x+3}$

d) $\frac{5x}{2x+3}$ e) $\frac{3x+2}{2x+5}$ f) $x+2$

g) $\frac{x}{x+2}$ h) $\frac{1}{x}$ i) $\frac{3x+1}{2x+1}$

j) $\frac{1}{2}$ k) $-\frac{1}{3x^2}$ l) $\frac{1}{3x^2}$

m) $\frac{3x}{x+1}$ n) $\frac{2x+3}{3x+4}$

o) $\frac{x+1}{(x+2)(x+3)}$ p) $\frac{2x-1}{x-1}$

Exercise 2.2

Q1 a) $\frac{5x+8}{(x+1)(x+2)}$ b) $\frac{3x+19}{(x-3)(x+4)}$

c) $\frac{12x}{(x+2)(x-2)}$ d) $\frac{x+19}{(x-2)(2x+3)}$

e) $\frac{x^2+5x+3}{(x+2)(x+1)}$ f) $\frac{2x-3}{(x+1)^2}$

g) $\frac{3x^2+14x+10}{x(x+3)(x+2)}$ h) $\frac{15x^2-8x+4}{20x}$

i) $\frac{2}{(x+2)(x-2)}$ j) $\frac{3(2x+1)}{(x+1)(2x-1)}$

k) $\frac{9x^2+16x+4}{x(x+1)(x+2)}$

l) $\frac{2(x^2-x+7)}{(x+4)(x+1)(x-2)}$

m) $\frac{2x^2+x+3}{(x+1)^2}$

n) $\frac{2x-1}{x}$

Exercise 2.3

Q1 a) $\frac{5x^2}{6}$ b) $\frac{12x}{7}$ c) $\frac{2x^5}{3y^3}$

d) $\frac{16x^3y}{5}$ e) $\frac{x^2}{9}$ f) $\frac{8x^2}{3}$

g) $\frac{x^2}{4}$ h) $\frac{x^2y}{6}$ i) $\frac{x}{12}$

j) $\frac{3}{(x+2)}$ k) $\frac{10(x+1)}{3}$

l) $\dfrac{2(x-1)}{x-2}$ **m)** $\dfrac{x+2}{3}$ **n)** $\dfrac{2}{x}$

o) x **p)** $\dfrac{3(x+3)}{x(x-3)}$

q) $\dfrac{(x-2)(x+3)}{3x}$ **r)** $\dfrac{x(x+1)}{4(x+2)}$

s) $\dfrac{2(x+2)(x+1)}{x^2(x-1)}$ **t)** $\dfrac{1}{2(x+1)}$

Q2 $\dfrac{x-2}{x(x-1)}$

Exercise 2.4

Q1 **a)** $(x^2 - 15x + 21)(x+1) - 10.$
Quotient: $x^2 - 15x + 21$,
remainder: -10

b) $(2x^2 + 9x + 10)(x-2) + 3.$
Quotient: $2x^2 + 9x + 10$,
remainder: 3

c) $(3x^2 - x - 5)(2x+1).$
Quotient: $3x^2 - x - 5$,
remainder: 0

d) $(x^2 - 15x + 21)(x+1) - 10.$
Quotient: $x^2 - 15x + 21$,
remainder: -10

e) $(x^2 + 7x - 6)(x+3) + 5.$
Quotient: $x^2 + 7x - 6$,
remainder: 5

f) $(2x^2 + 9x + 10)(x-2) + 3.$
Quotient: $2x^2 + 9x + 10$,
remainder: 3

g) $(3x^2 - 15x - 3)(x+5) + 24.$
Quotient: $3x^2 - 15x - 3$,
remainder: 24

h) $(x^3 + x^2 + x + 1)(x-1)$
Quotient: $x^3 + x^2 + x + 1$,
remainder: 0

i) $(4x^2 + 3x + 5)(2x-3) + 25.$
Quotient: $4x^2 + 3x + 5$,
remainder: 25

j) $(5x^2 + x - 3)(2x+1) + 24.$
Quotient: $5x^2 + x - 3$,
remainder: 24

k) $(3x^2 - 2x + 11)(x-2) + 10.$
Quotient: $3x^2 - 2x + 11$,
remainder: 10

l) $(8x^3 + 12x^2 + 18x + 27)(2x-3) + 81.$
Quotient: $8x^3 + 12x^2 + 18x + 27$,
remainder: 81

Q2 $3x^4 - 8x^3 - 6x - 4$
$\equiv (3x^3 + x^2 + 3x + 3)(x-3) + 5$ or
$(3x^4 - 8x^3 - 6x - 4) \div (x-3)$
$= 3x^3 + x^2 + 3x + 3$ remainder 5

Q3 $2x^3 - 5x^2 - 21x + 36$
$\equiv (x^2 - x - 12)(2x-3)$
Solutions of $2x^3 - 5x^2 - 21x + 36 = 0$ are:
$x = \dfrac{3}{2}$, 4 and -3.

Q4 $x^4 + 3x^3 + x^2 + 1$
$\equiv (x^3 + 2x^2 - x + 1)(x+1)$
One solution to $x^4 + 3x^3 + x^2 = -1$
is $x = -1$

Q5 $x^3 + x^2 - x - 2$

Q6 $3x^4 + 7x^3 - 22x^2 - 8x$
$\equiv x(3x+1)(x+4)(x-2)$
$x = 0$, $x = -\dfrac{1}{3}$, $x = -4$ and $x = 2$

3. Mappings and Functions
Exercise 3.1

Q1

1	→	6
2	→	12
3	→	18
4	→	24

Q2

1	→	5
2	→	6
3	→	7
4	→	8
5	→	9
6	→	10
7	→	11

Q3 **a)**

$\dfrac{x}{x+1}$

0	→	0
1	→	$\frac{1}{2}$
2	→	$\frac{2}{3}$
3	→	$\frac{3}{4}$

b)

$3x + 2$

3	→	11
7	→	23
11	→	35
20	→	62

Q4 $g(0) = 1$ $g(2) = \dfrac{1}{5}$

Q5 $f(1) = \dfrac{1}{2}$ $f(100) = \dfrac{1}{4}$

Q6 **a)** $0 \le h(x) \le 1$ **b)** $-1 \le j(x) \le 1$

Q7 **a)** $x \in \mathbb{R}$, $f(x) > -1$
b) $x > 0$, $g(x) \ge 0$.

Q8 **a)** Yes, it is a function.
b) No, because the map is not defined for elements 4 and 5 of the domain.
c) No, because a value in the domain can map to more than one value in the range.

Exercise 3.2

Q1 **a)** Yes, it is a function.
b) No, because a value of x can map to more than one value of $f(x)$.

Q2 **a)**

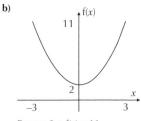

Range: $f(x) \ge -2$

b)

Range: $2 \le f(x) \le 11$

c)

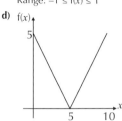

Range: $-1 \le f(x) \le 1$

d)

Range: $0 \le f(x) \le 5$

Q3 **a)** Range: $3 \le f(x) \le 11$, domain: $1 \le x \le 5$.
b) Range: $1 \le f(x) \le 10$,
domain: $-1 \le x \le 4$.

Q4 $1 < f(x) \le 2$.

Q5 $a = 2$.

Q6 $a = -3$ and $b = 3$

Q7 Restricting the domain to $x \ge -1$ would make $h(x)$ a function.

Q8 Restricting the domain to e.g. $-90° < x < 90°$ would make this a function.

Q9 Either $x > 2$ or $x < -2$.

Q10 **a)** It is not a function because it is not defined for all values of x in the domain (it's not defined at $x = 0$ or $x = 4$).
b) $x \in \mathbb{R}$, $x \ne 0$, $x \ne 4$

4. Composite Functions
Exercise 4.1

Q1 **a)** $fg(3) = 49$ **b)** $gf(3) = 19$
c) $f^2(5) = 625$ **d)** $g^2(2) = 11$

Q2 $fg(90°) = 0$, $gf(90°) = 2$

Q3 **a)** $gf(1) = 2$, $fg(1) = \dfrac{3}{4}$, $f^2(4) = \dfrac{6}{5}$
b) $g(-1) = -2$, and $f(-2)$ has a denominator of 0 (which is undefined).

Q4 **a)** $fg(x) = \cos 2x$ **b)** $gf(x) = 2 \cos x$

Q5 **a)** $fg(x) = 2(2^x) - 1 \ (= 2^{x+1} - 1)$
b) $gf(x) = 2^{(2x-1)}$
c) $f^2(x) = 4x - 3$

Q6 $fg(x) = \dfrac{2}{x+3}$, $gf(x) = \dfrac{2(2x-1)}{x-1}$

Q7 $f^2(x) = \dfrac{x}{1-2x}$, $gfg(x) = \dfrac{x^4}{(1-x^2)^2}$

Q8 **a)** $fg(x) = (2x-3)^2$, range: $fg(x) \ge 0$.
b) $gf(x) = 2x^2 - 3$, range: $gf(x) \ge -3$.

Q9 **a)** $gf(x) = \ln\left(\dfrac{1}{x} + 1\right)$
Domain: $\{x > 0\}$, range: $gf(x) > 0$.
b) $fg(x) = \dfrac{1}{\ln(x+1)}$
Domain: $\{x > 0\}$, range: $fg(x) > 0$

Q10 $fgh(x) = 15x^2 + 14$

Exercise 4.2

Q1 **a)** $x = 5$ **b)** $x = 2$

    c) $x = 2$ or $x = -2$

    d) $x = 3$ or $x = -\dfrac{5}{3}$

    e) $x = \pm 2\sqrt{5}$ **f)** $x = 64$

    g) $x = 2$ **h)** $x = 1$ or $x = -3$

    i) $x = \dfrac{1}{3}$ **j)** $x = 0$

    k) $x = \dfrac{1}{\sqrt{2}} = \dfrac{\sqrt{2}}{2}$ or $x = -\dfrac{1}{\sqrt{2}} = \dfrac{-\sqrt{2}}{2}$

Q2 **a)** $\mathrm{fg}(x) = (b - 3x)^2 + b$, range: $\mathrm{fg}(x) \geq b$

    $\mathrm{gf}(x) = -3x^2 - 2b$, range: $\mathrm{gf}(x) \leq -2b$

    b) $\mathrm{gf}(2) = 62$

5. Inverse Functions

Exercise 5.1

Q1 **a)** Yes, as the graph shows a one-to-one function.

    b) No, as it is a many-to-one map, and many-to-one functions do not have inverse functions.

Q2 **a)** No, as $\sin x$ is a many-to-one function over the domain $x \in \mathbb{R}$.

    b) No, as it is a many-to-one function over the domain $x \in \mathbb{R}$.

    c) Yes, as it is a one-to-one function over the domain $x \geq 4$.

Q3 **a)** $\mathrm{f}^{-1}(x) = \dfrac{x - 4}{3}$

    Domain: $x \in \mathbb{R}$, range: $\mathrm{f}^{-1}(x) \in \mathbb{R}$.

    b) $\mathrm{f}^{-1}(x) = \dfrac{x}{5} + 2$

    Domain: $x \in \mathbb{R}$, range: $\mathrm{f}^{-1}(x) \in \mathbb{R}$.

    c) $\mathrm{f}^{-1}(x) = \dfrac{1}{x} - 2$

    Domain: $x > 0$, range: $\mathrm{f}^{-1}(x) > -2$.

    d) $\mathrm{f}^{-1}(x) = \sqrt{x - 3}$

    Domain): $x > 3$, range: $\mathrm{f}^{-1}(x) > 0$.

Q4 **a)** $\mathrm{f}^{-1}(x) = \dfrac{x}{3 - x}$

    Domain: $x < 3$, range: $\mathrm{f}^{-1}(x) > -1$.

    b) $\mathrm{f}^{-1}(2) = 2$ **c)** $\mathrm{f}^{-1}\left(\dfrac{1}{2}\right) = \dfrac{1}{5}$

Q5 **a)** $\mathrm{f}^{-1}(x) = \dfrac{3x + 4}{1 - x}$

    Domain: $x < 1$, range: $\mathrm{f}^{-1}(x) > -3$.

    b) $\mathrm{f}^{-1}(0) = 4$ **c)** $\mathrm{f}^{-1}\left(-\dfrac{2}{5}\right) = 2$

Q6 **a)** Domain: $x \in \mathbb{R}$, range: $\mathrm{f}^{-1}(x) > 3$.

    b) Domain: $2 \leq x \leq 26$, range: $1 \leq \mathrm{f}^{-1}(x) \leq 7$.

    c) Domain: $x < 1$, range: $\mathrm{f}^{-1}(x) < 2$.

    d) Domain: $x \geq 3$, range: $\mathrm{f}^{-1}(x) \geq 2$.

    e) Domain $x \geq 0$, range: $0° \leq \mathrm{f}^{-1}(x) < 90°$.

    f) Domain $\ln 9 \leq x \leq \ln 16$, range: $3 \leq \mathrm{f}^{-1}(x) \leq 4$.

Q7 **a)** $\mathrm{f}^{-1}(x) = (\ln x) - 1$

    Domain: $x > 0$, range: $\mathrm{f}^{-1}(x) \in \mathbb{R}$.

    b) $\mathrm{f}^{-1}(x) = \sqrt[3]{x}$

    Domain: $x < 0$, range: $\mathrm{f}^{-1}(x) < 0$.

    c) $\mathrm{f}^{-1}(x) = 2^{2-x}$

    Domain: $x \leq 2$, range: $\mathrm{f}^{-1}(x) \geq 1$.

    d) $\mathrm{f}^{-1}(x) = \dfrac{1}{x} + 2$

    Domain: $x \neq 0$, range: $\mathrm{f}^{-1}(x) \neq 2$.

Q8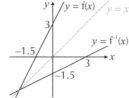

Q9 **a)**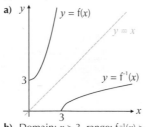

    b) Domain: $x > 3$, range: $\mathrm{f}^{-1}(x) > 0$.

Q10 **a)**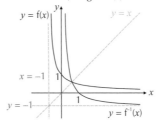

    b) There is one point where the graphs intersect.

Q11 **a)** $\mathrm{f}^{-1}(x) = \dfrac{1}{x} + 3$.

    Domain: $x > 0$, range: $\mathrm{f}^{-1}(x) > 3$.

    b)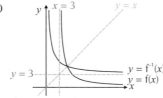

    c) There is one solution.

    d) $x = \dfrac{3 + \sqrt{13}}{2}$

6. Modulus

Exercise 6.1

Q1 **a)**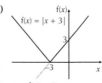

    Range: $\mathrm{f}(x) \geq 0$

    b)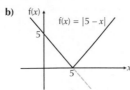

    Range: $\mathrm{f}(x) \geq 0$

    c)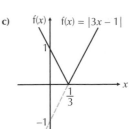

    Range: $\mathrm{f}(x) \geq 0$

    d)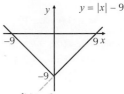

    Range: $\mathrm{f}(x) \geq -9$

    e)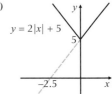

    Range: $\mathrm{f}(x) \geq 5$

Q2 **a)**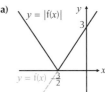

    b)

    c)

    d)

    e)

Q3 **a)** 2 **b)** 1 **c)** 4 **d)** 3

Q4 **a)**

b)

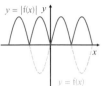

c)

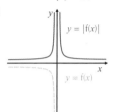

Q5

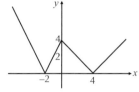

Q6 **a)**

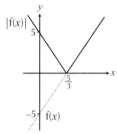

b)

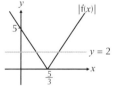

The line $y = 2$ intersects with the line $|3x - 5|$ in two places so there are 2 solutions to $|3x - 5| = 2$.

Q7 **a)**

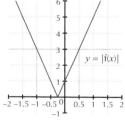

b) $x = 0.5$ and $x = -1$

Exercise 6.2

Q1 **a)** $x = 8$ and $x = -4$
b) $x = 2$ and $x = -3$
c) $x = \frac{5}{3}$ and $x = 1$
d) $x = -12$ and $x = 6$
e) $x = -2$ and $x = -1$
f) $x = 1$ and $x = 3$
g) $x = -1$ and $x = 5$
h) $x = \frac{3}{2}$ and $x = -\frac{3}{2}$

Q2 17 or 13

Q3 6 or 8

Q4 5 or 7

Q5 **a)**

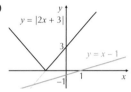

b) There are no solutions.

Q6 4 or 7
First you need to find what possible values x can take, then plug those numbers into $2|x - 1| + 3$.

Exercise 6.3

Q1 **a)**

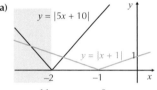

b) $x = -\frac{11}{6}$ and $x = -\frac{9}{4}$

Q2 **a)** $x = 2$ and $x = -\frac{2}{3}$
b) $x = 2$ and $x = -\frac{1}{3}$ **c)** $x = 2$

Q3 **a)** $-8 < x < 8$
b) $x \leq -5$ and $x \geq 5$
c) $x < -6$ and $x > 6$
d) $-2 \leq x \leq 1$
e) $0 \leq x \leq 2$
f) $x < -7$ and $x > -1$
g) $x < -2$
h) $x \leq \frac{8}{3}$ and $x \geq 8$
i) $-6 \leq x \leq 0$

Q4 $\{x : x \geq 2\} \cup \{x : x \leq -2\}$

Q5 $-2 \leq x \leq 1$. The possible values are $0 \leq |5x + 4| \leq 9$.
Draw a graph of $y = |5x + 4|$ for $-2 \leq x \leq 1$. Use the graph to find the maximum and minimum values for $|5x + 4|$.

7. Transformations of Graphs

Exercise 7.1

Q1

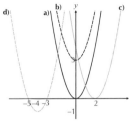

a) Turning point at $(0, 0)$
b) Turning point at $(0, 3)$, translation vector $\begin{pmatrix} 0 \\ 3 \end{pmatrix}$
c) Turning point at $(2, 0)$, translation vector $\begin{pmatrix} 2 \\ 0 \end{pmatrix}$
d) Turning point at $(-4, -1)$, translation vector $\begin{pmatrix} -4 \\ -1 \end{pmatrix}$

Q2 **a)**

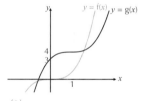

b) $\begin{pmatrix} 1 \\ 4 \end{pmatrix}$
c) $y = (x - 1)^3 + 4 \ (= x^3 - 3x^2 + 3x + 3)$

Q3

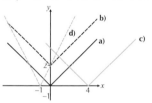

Q4

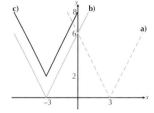

Q5

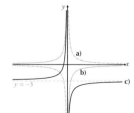

Q6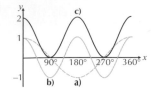

d) The minimum points on c) are (90°, 0) and (270°, 0).

Q7 **a)**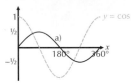

b) $y = \frac{1}{2}\cos(x - 90°) \left(= \frac{1}{2}\sin x\right)$

Q8 The point of inflection of x^3 is at (0, 0), so:

Transformed Function	New equation	Coordinates of point of inflection
$f(x - 2)$	$(x - 2)^3$	(2, 0)
$-f(x) - 3$	$-x^3 - 3$	(0, -3)
$f(-x) + 4$	$-x^3 + 4$	(0, 4)

Q9 **a)**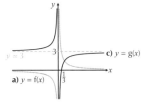

b) Reflect in the y-axis (or x-axis) and translate by $\begin{pmatrix} 0 \\ 3 \end{pmatrix}$ (3 upwards).

Q10

Original graph	...	Sequence of transformations
$y = x^3$	...	Translate by $\begin{pmatrix} 4 \\ 5 \end{pmatrix}$ i.e. 4 right and 5 up.
$y = 4^x$	...	Stretch horizontally by a factor of $\frac{1}{3}$ and translate by $\begin{pmatrix} 0 \\ -1 \end{pmatrix}$ i.e. 1 down.
$y = \lvert x + 1 \rvert$	...	Stretch horizontally by a factor of $\frac{1}{2}$, reflect in the x-axis and translate by $\begin{pmatrix} 0 \\ 1 \end{pmatrix}$ i.e. 1 up.
$y = \sin x$	...	Stretch horizontally by a factor of $\frac{1}{2}$, stretch vertically by a factor of 3, reflect in the x-axis and translate by $\begin{pmatrix} 0 \\ 1 \end{pmatrix}$ i.e. 1 up.

Q11 **a)** $y = 2x^2 - 4x + 6$
$= 2[x^2 - 2x + 3] = 2[(x - 1)^2 + 2]$

b) Translate by $\begin{pmatrix} 1 \\ 2 \end{pmatrix}$ i.e. 1 right, then 2 up, then stretch vertically by a factor of 2.

---

c)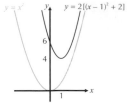

d) The minimum point is at (1, 4).

Q12 **a)** Stretch horizontally, scale factor $\frac{1}{3}$, then stretch vertically, scale factor 4.

b) Stretch horizontally, scale factor $\frac{1}{2}$, then reflect in the x-axis, then translate by $\begin{pmatrix} 0 \\ 4 \end{pmatrix}$ i.e. 4 up.

c) Translate by $\begin{pmatrix} 60° \\ 0 \end{pmatrix}$ i.e. 60° right, then stretch vertically, scale factor 2.

Q13 **a)**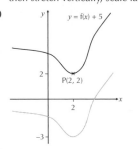

b)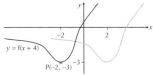

c)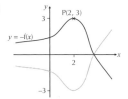

8. Partial Fractions

Exercise 8.1

Q1 $\dfrac{3x + 3}{(x - 1)(x - 4)} \equiv -\dfrac{2}{(x - 1)} + \dfrac{5}{(x - 4)}$

Q2 $\dfrac{5x - 1}{x(2x + 1)} \equiv -\dfrac{1}{x} + \dfrac{7}{(2x + 1)}$

Q3 $\dfrac{3x - 2}{x^2 + x - 12} \equiv \dfrac{2}{(x + 4)} + \dfrac{1}{(x - 3)}$

Q4 $\dfrac{2}{x^2 - 16} \equiv -\dfrac{1}{4(x + 4)} + \dfrac{1}{4(x - 4)}$

Q5 $\dfrac{5}{x^2 - x - 6} \equiv \dfrac{1}{(x - 3)} - \dfrac{1}{(x + 2)}$

Q6 $\dfrac{11x}{2x^2 + 5x - 12} \equiv \dfrac{3}{(2x - 3)} + \dfrac{4}{(x + 4)}$

Q7 **a)** $x(x - 3)(x + 3)$

b) $\dfrac{12x + 18}{x^3 - 9x} \equiv -\dfrac{2}{x} - \dfrac{1}{(x + 3)} + \dfrac{3}{(x - 3)}$

Q8 $\dfrac{3x + 9}{x^3 - 36x} \equiv -\dfrac{1}{4x} - \dfrac{1}{8(x + 6)} + \dfrac{3}{8(x - 6)}$

Q9 **a)** $x^3 - 7x - 6 = (x + 1)(x - 3)(x + 2)$

---

b) $\dfrac{6x + 2}{x^3 - 7x - 6}$
$\equiv \dfrac{1}{(x + 1)} + \dfrac{1}{(x - 3)} - \dfrac{2}{(x + 2)}$

Q10 $\dfrac{6x + 4}{(x + 4)(x - 1)(x + 1)}$
$\equiv -\dfrac{4}{3(x + 4)} + \dfrac{1}{(x - 1)} + \dfrac{1}{3(x + 1)}$

Q11 $\dfrac{15x - 27}{x^3 - 6x^2 + 3x + 10}$
$\equiv -\dfrac{7}{3(x + 1)} - \dfrac{1}{3(x - 2)} + \dfrac{8}{3(x - 5)}$

Exercise 8.2

Q1 $\dfrac{3x}{(x + 5)^2} \equiv \dfrac{3}{(x + 5)} - \dfrac{15}{(x + 5)^2}$

Q2 $\dfrac{5x + 2}{x^2(x + 1)} \equiv \dfrac{3}{x} + \dfrac{2}{x^2} - \dfrac{3}{(x + 1)}$

Q3 **a)** $\dfrac{2x - 7}{(x - 3)^2} \equiv \dfrac{2}{(x - 3)} - \dfrac{1}{(x - 3)^2}$

b) $\dfrac{3x + 7}{(2x + 3)^2} \equiv \dfrac{3}{(2x + 3)} - \dfrac{2}{(2x + 3)^2}$

c) $\dfrac{7x}{(x + 4)^2(x - 3)}$
$\equiv -\dfrac{3}{7(x + 4)} + \dfrac{4}{(x + 4)^2} + \dfrac{3}{7(x - 3)}$

d) $\dfrac{11x - 10}{x(x - 5)^2} \equiv -\dfrac{2}{5x} + \dfrac{2}{5(x - 5)} + \dfrac{9}{(x - 5)^2}$

e) $\dfrac{x + 5}{(x - 1)^2 x} \equiv \dfrac{5}{x} - \dfrac{5}{x - 1} + \dfrac{6}{(x - 1)^2}$

Q4 $\dfrac{5x + 10}{x^3 - 10x^2 + 25x}$
$\equiv \dfrac{2}{5x} - \dfrac{2}{5(x - 5)} + \dfrac{7}{(x - 5)^2}$

Q5 $\dfrac{3x + 2}{(x - 2)(x^2 - 4)}$
$\equiv -\dfrac{1}{4(x + 2)} + \dfrac{1}{4(x - 2)} + \dfrac{2}{(x - 2)^2}$

Q6 $c = -3$
Write the equation in the form:
$x + 17 \equiv (x + c)^2 - (x + c)(x + 1) + 5(x + 1)$.
Then find c by multiplying out the brackets and equating coefficients.

Review Exercise — Chapter 17

Q1 Suppose that there is some even number x for which x^3 is odd. Since x is even, it can be written as $x = 2n$ for some integer n. Then $x^3 = (2n)^3 = 8n^3 = 2(4n^3)$ which is even, which contradicts the assumption that x^3 is odd. So if x^3 is odd, then x must also be odd.

Q2 **a)** $\dfrac{2x + 5}{3}$ **b)** $\dfrac{4}{x - 3}$

c) $\dfrac{2(x - 3)}{x + 1}$

Q3 **a)** $\dfrac{x^3 + 2x^2 + 7x + 3}{x^2(2x + 1)}$

b) $\dfrac{2(1 - 2x - x^2)}{(x + 1)(x - 1)}$

c) $-\dfrac{3x^3 + 2x^2 - 8x - 1}{3x(x + 1)^2}$

Q4 $2x^3 + 8x^2 + 7x + 8$
$= (2x^2 + 2x + 1)(x + 3) + 5.$
The result when $2x^3 + 8x^2 + 7x + 8$ is divided by $(x + 3)$ is $2x^2 + 2x + 1$ remainder 5.

Q5 $x^3 - 5x - 2$ remainder 0.
One solution of $x^4 + x^3 - 5x^2 - 7x = 2$
is $x = -1$.
This tells you that $x^4 + x^3 - 5x^2 - 7x - 2$
$= (x^3 - 5x - 2)(x + 1)$. Setting the divisor
equal to zero gives a solution.

Q6 **a)** Range $f(x) \geq -16$. This is a function,
and it's one-to-one (the domain
is restricted so every x-value is
mapped to only one value of $f(x)$).

b) Range is $f(x) \geq -2.25$. This is a
function, and it's many-to-one.

c) Range $f(x) \geq 0$. This is not a function
as $f(x)$ doesn't exist for $x < 0$.

Q7 **a)** $f(0) = 5$, $f\left(\frac{1}{2}\right) = 2\frac{1}{2}$

b)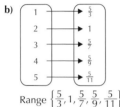

Range $\left\{\frac{5}{3}, 1, \frac{5}{7}, \frac{5}{9}, \frac{5}{11}\right\}$

c) Yes.

d) No — the mapping is
not defined for $x = -\frac{1}{2}$.

Q8 **a)**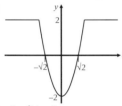

b) $-2 \leq f(x) \leq 2$

Q9 **a)** $fg(2) = \frac{3}{7}$, $gf(1) = 9$, $fg(x) = \frac{3}{2x+3}$

b) $fg(2) = 108$, $gf(1) = 7$,
$fg(x) = 3(x + 4)^2$

Q10 **a)** $fg(1) = 2$ $gf(1) = 10$
$f^2(10) - 0$ $g^2(-1) = 100$

b) Because $f(1) = \log_{10} 1 = 0$, and
$f(0) = \log_{10} 0$, which is undefined.

Q11 $fg(x) = 3x + 21$ $gf(x) = 3x + 7$
$g^2(x) = x + 14$

Q12 f is a one-to-one function
so it has an inverse.
Domain: $x \geq 3$, range: $f^{-1}(x) \in \mathbb{R}$.

Q13 $f^{-1}(x) = \frac{x^2}{2} + 2$
Domain: $x \geq 0$, range $f^{-1}(x) \geq 2$.

Q14 In the domain $0 \leq x \leq \frac{\pi}{2}$, $\cos x$ is a
one-to-one function, as shown:

so $f^{-1}(x)$ does exist.

Q15 $y = \frac{x}{x-1} \Rightarrow y(x-1) = x \Rightarrow yx - y = x$
$\Rightarrow yx - x = y$
$\Rightarrow x(y - 1) = y$
$\Rightarrow x = \frac{y}{y-1}$

This shows that $f(x) = f^{-1}(x)$.
Therefore, $f^2(x) = x$.
You've shown that $f(x) = f^{-1}(x)$,
so $f^2(x) = ff^{-1}(x) = x$.

Q16 $f^{-1}(x) = 10^x - 4$

Q17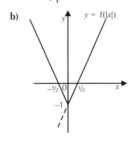

Q18 **a)**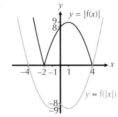

b)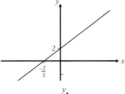

Q19 $x = \frac{5}{4}$ and $x = -\frac{3}{2}$

Q20 **a)**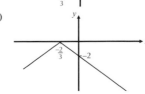

b) $x = -3$ or $x = 3$

Q21 **a)**

b)

c)

Q22 $\frac{2x}{(x-5)(x+5)} \equiv \frac{1}{(x-5)} + \frac{1}{(x+5)}$

Q23 $A = 8$, $B = -3$

Q24 $A = -4$, $B = 5$

Q25 **a)** $\frac{4}{x} - \frac{4}{(x+1)}$

b) $\frac{1}{(x+4)} + \frac{2}{(2x-3)}$

c) $\frac{3}{(x+3)} + \frac{2}{(x-2)}$

d) $\frac{15}{(x+3)} - \frac{10}{(x+2)}$

e) $\frac{2}{2x+1} - \frac{6}{3x-2}$

f) $\frac{5}{3(x+3)} + \frac{1}{3x}$

Q26 $\frac{2x-5}{(x-5)^2} = \frac{A}{(x-5)} + \frac{B}{(x-5)^2}$,
so $A(x-5) + B = 2x - 5$.
$\Rightarrow Ax - 5A + B = 2x - 5$. Equating
coefficients gives $A = 2 \Rightarrow B = 5$.
This gives $\frac{2}{(x-5)} + \frac{5}{(x-5)^2}$,
as required.

Q27 **a)** $\frac{2}{(x+3)} - \frac{4}{(x+3)^2}$

b) $\frac{-4}{(2x-1)} + \frac{2}{(2x-1)^2} + \frac{2}{(x+2)}$

c) $\frac{5}{x^2} + \frac{4}{x} - \frac{4}{(x-1)}$

Q28 $b = 5$
Combine the partial fraction back into one
fraction, and then equate the coefficients of the
numerators to find b.

Chapter 18: Trigonometry

1. Arcs and Sectors

Exercise 1.1

Q1 **a)** π **b)** $\frac{3\pi}{4}$ **c)** $\frac{3\pi}{2}$
    d) $\frac{7\pi}{18}$ **e)** $\frac{5\pi}{6}$ **f)** $\frac{5\pi}{12}$

Q2 **a)** $45°$ **b)** $90°$ **c)** $60°$
    d) $450°$ **e)** $135°$ **f)** $420°$

Exercise 1.2

Q1 $s = 12$ cm, $A = 36$ cm^2

Q2 $s = 6.4$ cm (1 d.p.), $A = 25.7$ cm^2 (1 d.p.)

Q3 $\theta = \frac{3\pi}{4}$

Q4 **a)** $s = 6$ cm, $A = 15$ cm^2

b) $s = 2.4$ cm, $A = 4.8$ cm^2

c) $s = 12.6$ cm (3 s.f.), $A = 56.5$ cm^2
(3 s.f.)

d) $s = 5.24$ cm (3 s.f.), $A = 10.5$ cm^2
(3 s.f.)

Q5 $s = 5.4$ cm

Q6 $\frac{\pi}{3}$ cm, $A = \frac{\pi}{2}$ cm^2

Q7 $A = 17.5$ cm^2

Q8 $r = 10$ cm, $\theta = 5.03$ radians (3 s.f.)
Use the information you're given to form equations for s and A in terms of r and θ, then solve simultaneously.

Q9 $\theta = \dfrac{3\pi}{7}$
Find the areas of A and B in terms of θ (the angle of the missing sector is $\pi - \theta$, since they lie on a straight line). Then set these areas equal to equal other and solve for θ.

2. Small Angle Approximations

Exercise 2.1

Q1 a) $\sin 0.23 \approx 0.23$
From a calculator,
$\sin 0.23 = 0.228$ (3 d.p.)

   b) $\sin 0.12 \approx 0.12$
From a calculator,
$\sin 0.12 = 0.120$ (3 d.p.)

   c) $\cos 0.01 \approx 0.99995$
From a calculator,
$\cos 0.01 = 0.999950$ (6 d.p.)

   d) $\cos 0.24 \approx 0.9712$
From a calculator,
$\cos 0.24 = 0.97134$ (5 d.p.)

   e) $\tan 0.18 \approx 0.18$
From a calculator,
$\tan 0.18 = 0.182$ (3 d.p.)

Q2 a) $f(0.3) \approx 1.255$
From a calculator,
$f(0.3) = 1.2509$ (4 d.p.)

   b) $f(0.5) \approx 1.375$
From a calculator,
$f(0.5) = 1.3570$ (4 d.p.)

   c) $f(0.25) \approx 1.21875$
From a calculator,
$f(0.25) = 1.216316$ (6 d.p.)

   d) $f(0.01) \approx 1.00995$
From a calculator,
$f(0.01) = 1.009950$ (6 d.p.)

   e) $f(0.03) \approx 1.02955$
From a calculator,
$f(0.03) = 1.029546$ (6 d.p.)

Q3 a) $\theta - \dfrac{1}{2}\theta^3$ b) $5\theta^3$
   c) $2 - 9\theta^2$ d) $1 + 3\theta - 2\theta^2$
   e) $\dfrac{1}{2}(\theta^2 + \theta - 2)$ f) 1

Q4 a) $\mathbf{d} = 6\sin\theta\,\mathbf{i} + 6(1 - \cos\theta)\mathbf{j}$
$|\mathbf{d}| = \sqrt{(6\sin\theta)^2 + (6 - 6\cos\theta)^2}$
$= \sqrt{36\sin^2\theta + 36 - 72\cos\theta + 36\cos^2\theta}$
$= \sqrt{36(\sin^2\theta + \cos^2\theta) + 36 - 72\cos\theta}$
$= \sqrt{36 + 36 - 72\cos\theta}$
$= \sqrt{72(1 - \cos\theta)} = 6\sqrt{2(1 - \cos\theta)}$
as required

   b) Arc length $s = 6\theta$
$|\mathbf{d}| = 6\sqrt{2(1 - \cos\theta)}$
$\approx 6\sqrt{2\left(1 - \left(1 - \dfrac{1}{2}\theta^2\right)\right)}$
$= 6\sqrt{2\left(\dfrac{1}{2}\theta^2\right)} = 6\sqrt{\theta^2} = 6\theta = s$
as required

3. Inverse Trig Functions

Exercise 3.1

Q1 a) 0 b) $\dfrac{\pi}{3}$ c) $\dfrac{\pi}{3}$
   d) $\dfrac{\pi}{4}$ e) 0

Q2 a)
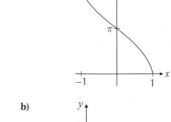
$y = 2\arccos x$

   b)
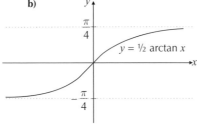
$y = \frac{1}{2}\arctan x$
Range: $-\dfrac{\pi}{4} < \dfrac{1}{2}\arctan x < \dfrac{\pi}{4}$.

Q3
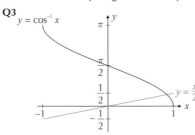
$y = \cos^{-1} x$
The graphs intersect once, so there is one real root of the equation $\cos^{-1} x = \dfrac{x}{2}$.

Q4 a) $-\dfrac{\pi}{2}$ b) $\dfrac{5\pi}{6}$ c) $-\dfrac{\pi}{6}$ d) $-\dfrac{\pi}{6}$

Q5 a) $\dfrac{1}{\sqrt{3}}$ b) $\dfrac{2\pi}{3}$ c) $\dfrac{\sqrt{3}}{2}$

Q6 $f^{-1}(x) = \dfrac{1}{2}\arcsin(x - 1)$
First write f(x) as y = 1 + sin 2x, then rearrange to make x the subject. Then replace x with $f^{-1}(x)$ and y with x.

4. Cosec, Sec and Cot

Exercise 4.1

Q1 a)
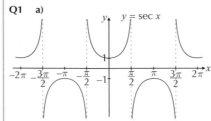
$y = \sec x$

   b) Maximum points: $(-\pi, -1)$ and $(\pi, -1)$
Minimum points: $(-2\pi, 1)$, $(0, 1)$ and $(2\pi, 1)$

   c) $y \geq 1$ or $y \leq -1$

Q2 a)
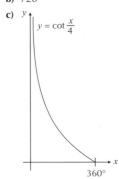
$y = \operatorname{cosec} x$

   b) Maximum: $\left(\dfrac{3\pi}{2}, -1\right)$,
minimum: $\left(\dfrac{\pi}{2}, 1\right)$

   c) Domain: $x \in \mathbb{R}$, $x \neq n\pi$ (where n is an integer).
Range: $y \geq 1$ or $y \leq -1$.

Q3 A horizontal translation right by $\dfrac{\pi}{2}$ (or 90°) or a horizontal translation left by $\dfrac{3\pi}{2}$ (or 270°).

Q4 a) A horizontal stretch scale factor 4.
   b) $720°$
   c)
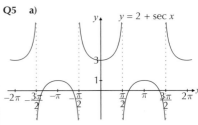
$y = \cot\dfrac{x}{4}$

Q5 a)
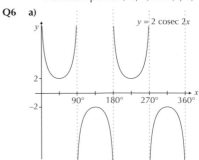
$y = 2 + \sec x$

Domain: $x \in \mathbb{R}$, $x \neq \left(n\pi + \dfrac{\pi}{2}\right)$ (where n is an integer)
Range: $y \geq 3$ or $y \leq 1$

   b) Minimum points: $(-2\pi, 3)$, $(0, 3)$ and $(2\pi, 3)$
Maximum points: $(-\pi, 1)$ and $(\pi, 1)$

Q6 a)

$y = 2\operatorname{cosec} 2x$

b) Maximum points: $(135°, -2)$ and $(315°, -2)$
Minimum points: $(45°, 2)$ and $(225°, 2)$

c) $x = 0°, 90°, 180°, 270°$ and $360°$.

Q7 a) $x = n\pi$ or $180n°$, where n is an integer

b) $360°$

c)

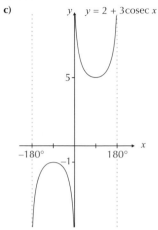

$y = 2 + 3\text{cosec}\, x$

Range: $y \geq 5$ or $y \leq -1$

Exercise 4.2

Q1 a) 1.02   **b)** 3.86
c) 1.73   **d)** –3.86
e) 2.92   **f)** 2.64
g) 4.73   **h)** –4.26

Q2 a) –1.01   **b)** 1.46
c) 1.03   **d)** 1.85
e) 2.61   **f)** 10.4
g) 0.487   **h)** 0.136

Q3 a) 2   **b)** 2
c) 1   **d)** $\dfrac{2\sqrt{3}}{3}$
e) –1   **f)** $\sqrt{2}$
g) $-\sqrt{3}$ **h)** $-\sqrt{2}$
i) $-\dfrac{2\sqrt{3}}{3}$ **j)** $\dfrac{2\sqrt{3}}{3}$
k) 4   **l)** 1

Q4 a) $\dfrac{1}{3}$ **b)** $\dfrac{2}{5}$ **c)** $\sqrt{3}$
d) $\dfrac{3+\sqrt{3}}{3}$ **e)** $\dfrac{1}{2}$

Exercise 4.3

Q1 a) $2\sec x$ **b)** 1
c) $3\cot x$ **d)** $\tan x$
e) $\cot x$ **f)** $\sec x \,\text{cosec}\, x$
g) $4\cot x$ **h)** 1

Q2 a) $\sin x \cot x = \sin x \left(\dfrac{1}{\tan x}\right)$
$= \sin x \left(\dfrac{\cos x}{\sin x}\right) = \cos x$

b) $\sec x - \cos x = \dfrac{1}{\cos x} - \cos x$
$= \dfrac{1 - \cos^2 x}{\cos x} = \dfrac{\sin^2 x}{\cos x}$
$= \left(\dfrac{\sin x}{\cos x}\right)\sin x = \tan x \sin x$

c) $\dfrac{\sec x}{\cot x} = \dfrac{\frac{1}{\cos x}}{\frac{1}{\tan x}} = \dfrac{\tan x}{\cos x} = \dfrac{\frac{\sin x}{\cos x}}{\cos x}$
$= \dfrac{\sin x}{\cos^2 x} = \sin x \sec^2 x$

d) $\tan x \,\text{cosec}\, x = \left(\dfrac{\sin x}{\cos x}\right)\left(\dfrac{1}{\sin x}\right)$
$= \dfrac{1}{\cos x} = \sec x$

e) $\dfrac{(\tan^2 x)(\text{cosec}\, x)}{\sin x}$
$= \dfrac{\left(\frac{\sin^2 x}{\cos^2 x}\right)\left(\frac{1}{\sin x}\right)}{\sin x} = \dfrac{\left(\frac{\sin x}{\cos^2 x}\right)}{\sin x}$
$= \dfrac{1}{\cos^2 x} = \sec^2 x$

f) $\text{cosec}\, x (\sin x + \cos x)$
$= \dfrac{1}{\sin x}(\sin x + \cos x)$
$= 1 + \dfrac{\cos x}{\sin x} = 1 + \dfrac{1}{\tan x} = 1 + \cot x$

Q3 All answers given to 1 d.p.
a) $x = 58.2°$ and $x = 301.8°$
b) $x = 22.6°$ and $x = 202.6°$
c) $x = 210°$ and $330°$
d) $x = 140.3°$ and $219.7°$
e) $x = 157.4°$ and $337.4°$
f) $x = 45.6°$ and $134.4°$
g) $x = 62.4°, 117.6°, 242.4°$ and $297.6°$
h) $x = 17.1°, 77.1°, 137.1°, 197.1°,$
$257.1°,$ and $317.1°$

Q4 a) $x = \dfrac{\pi}{3}$ and $x = \dfrac{5\pi}{3}$
b) $x = \dfrac{7\pi}{6}$ and $\dfrac{11\pi}{6}$
c) $x = \dfrac{\pi}{8}, \dfrac{5\pi}{8}, \dfrac{9\pi}{8}$ and $\dfrac{13\pi}{8}$
d) $x = \dfrac{\pi}{5}, \dfrac{3\pi}{5}, \pi, \dfrac{7\pi}{5}$ and $\dfrac{9\pi}{5}$

Q5 $x = \dfrac{3\pi}{8}, \dfrac{7\pi}{8}, \dfrac{11\pi}{8}$ and $\dfrac{15\pi}{8}$

Q6 $x = 20.9°, 69.1°, 200.9°$ and $249.1°$ (all to 1 d.p.)

Q7 $x = \dfrac{2\pi}{3}$ and $\dfrac{4\pi}{3}$

Q8 $x = \dfrac{\pi}{9}, \dfrac{2\pi}{9}, \dfrac{7\pi}{9}, \dfrac{8\pi}{9}, \dfrac{13\pi}{9}$
and $\dfrac{14\pi}{9}$

Q9 a) $x = 45°$
b) $x = 63.4°$ and $153.4°$ (to 1 d.p.)
For each of these, you need to factorise the equation, then solve the factorised equation.

Q10 $x = 19.5°, 160.5°, 153.4°, 333.4°$ (all to 1 d.p.)

5. Identities Involving Cosec, Sec and Cot

Exercise 5.1

Q1 a) $\sin^2 \theta + \cos^2 \theta \equiv 1$
$\Rightarrow \dfrac{\sin^2 \theta}{\cos^2 \theta} + \dfrac{\cos^2 \theta}{\cos^2 \theta} \equiv \dfrac{1}{\cos^2 \theta}$
$\Rightarrow \tan^2 \theta + 1 \equiv \sec^2 \theta$

b) $\sin^2 \theta + \cos^2 \theta \equiv 1$
$\Rightarrow \dfrac{\sin^2 \theta}{\sin^2 \theta} + \dfrac{\cos^2 \theta}{\sin^2 \theta} \equiv \dfrac{1}{\sin^2 \theta}$
$\Rightarrow 1 + \cot^2 \theta \equiv \text{cosec}^2 \theta$

Q2 $3\,\text{cosec}^2 x - 2$

Q3 –1

Q4 $x + \dfrac{1}{x} = \sec \theta + \tan \theta + \dfrac{1}{\sec \theta + \tan \theta}$
$= \dfrac{(\sec \theta + \tan \theta)^2 + 1}{\sec \theta + \tan \theta}$
$= \dfrac{\sec^2 \theta + 2\sec \theta \tan \theta + \tan^2 \theta + 1}{\sec \theta + \tan \theta}$
But since $\sec^2 \theta = \tan^2 \theta + 1$:
$x + \dfrac{1}{x} = \dfrac{\sec^2 \theta + 2\sec \theta \tan \theta + \sec^2 \theta}{\sec \theta + \tan \theta}$
$= \dfrac{2\sec \theta(\sec \theta + \tan \theta)}{\sec \theta + \tan \theta}$
$= 2\sec \theta$ as required.

Q5 a) $\tan^2 x = 2\sec x + 2$
$\Rightarrow \sec^2 x - 1 = 2\sec x + 2$
$\Rightarrow \sec^2 x - 2\sec x - 3 = 0$
b) $x = 70.5°$ (1 d.p.), $180°$ and $289.5°$ (1 d.p.)

Q6 a) $2\,\text{cosec}^2 x = 5 - 5\cot x$
$\Rightarrow 2(1 + \cot^2 x) = 5 - 5\cot x$
$\Rightarrow 2\cot^2 x + 5\cot x - 3 = 0$
b) $x = -2.03, -0.32, 1.11, 2.82$ (all to 2 d.p.)

Q7 a) $2\cot^2 A + 5\,\text{cosec}\, A = 10$
$\Rightarrow 2(\text{cosec}^2 A - 1) + 5\,\text{cosec}\, A = 10$
$\Rightarrow 2\,\text{cosec}^2 A - 2 + 5\,\text{cosec}\, A = 10$
$\Rightarrow 2\,\text{cosec}^2 A + 5\,\text{cosec}\, A - 12 = 0$
b) $A = 194.5°, 345.5°, 41.8°, 138.2°$ (all to 1 d.p.)

Q8 $x = 0, \dfrac{3\pi}{4}, \pi, \dfrac{7\pi}{4}, 2\pi$

Q9 a) $\sin \theta = \pm\dfrac{\sqrt{3}}{2}$
b) $\theta = 60°, 120°$

Q10 $x = 63.4°, 135°, 243.4°$ and $315°$ (all to 1 d.p.)

Q11 $x = \dfrac{\pi}{6}, \dfrac{5\pi}{6}, \dfrac{7\pi}{6}, \dfrac{11\pi}{6}$

Q12 $x = 1.91, 2.09, 4.19$ and 4.37 (all to 2 d.p.)

Q13 a) (i) $-\dfrac{60}{61}$ **(ii)** $-\dfrac{61}{11}$ **(iii)** $-\dfrac{61}{60}$
b) (i) $-\dfrac{8}{17}$ **(ii)** $-\dfrac{17}{8}$ **(iii)** $\dfrac{8}{15}$

Q14 $\tan x = \perp\sqrt{35}$

Exercise 5.2

Q1 $\tan^2 \theta \equiv \sec^2 \theta - 1 \equiv (\sec \theta + 1)(\sec \theta - 1)$

Q2 a) $\sec^2 \theta - \text{cosec}^2 \theta$
$\equiv (1 + \tan^2 \theta) - (1 + \cot^2 \theta)$
$\equiv \tan^2 \theta - \cot^2 \theta$

b) $\tan^2 \theta - \cot^2 \theta$ is the difference of two squares, and so can be written as $(\tan \theta + \cot \theta)(\tan \theta - \cot \theta)$. So is $\sec^2 \theta - \text{cosec}^2 \theta$, so it can be written $(\sec \theta + \text{cosec}\, \theta)(\sec \theta - \text{cosec}\, \theta)$. So using the result from part a), $(\sec \theta + \text{cosec}\, \theta)(\sec \theta - \text{cosec}\, \theta)$ $\equiv (\tan \theta + \cot \theta)(\tan \theta - \cot \theta)$.

Q3 $(\tan x + \cot x)^2$
$\equiv \tan^2 x + \cot^2 x + 2\tan x \cot x$
$\equiv \tan^2 x + \cot^2 x + \dfrac{2\tan x}{\tan x}$
$\equiv \tan^2 x + \cot^2 x + 2$
$\equiv (1 + \tan^2 x) + (1 + \cot^2 x)$
$\equiv \sec^2 x + \text{cosec}^2 x$

Q4 $\sec^2\theta\,\operatorname{cosec}^2\theta \equiv (1 + \tan^2\theta)(1 + \cot^2\theta)$
$\equiv 1 + \cot^2\theta + \tan^2\theta + \cot^2\theta\tan^2\theta$
$\equiv 1 + \cot^2\theta + \tan^2\theta + 1$
$\equiv 2 + \cot^2\theta + \tan^2\theta$

Q5 $\cot^2 x + \sin^2 x$
$\equiv (\operatorname{cosec}^2 x - 1) + (1 - \cos^2 x)$
$\equiv \operatorname{cosec}^2 x - \cos^2 x$
$\equiv (\operatorname{cosec} x + \cos x)(\operatorname{cosec} x - \cos x)$

Q6 $\dfrac{1 - \cot^4 x}{\operatorname{cosec}^2 x} \equiv \dfrac{(1 + \cot^2 x)(1 - \cot^2 x)}{1 + \cot^2 x}$
$\equiv 1 - \cot^2 x \equiv 1 - (\operatorname{cosec}^2 x - 1)$
$\equiv 2 - \operatorname{cosec}^2 x$

Q7 $\dfrac{(\sec x - \tan x)(\tan x + \sec x)}{\operatorname{cosec} x - \cot x}$
$\equiv \dfrac{\sec^2 x - \tan^2 x}{\operatorname{cosec} x - \cot x} \equiv \dfrac{(1 + \tan^2 x) - \tan^2 x}{\operatorname{cosec} x - \cot x}$
$\equiv \dfrac{1}{\operatorname{cosec} x - \cot x}$
$\equiv \dfrac{\operatorname{cosec} x + \cot x}{(\operatorname{cosec} x - \cot x)(\operatorname{cosec} x + \cot x)}$
$\equiv \dfrac{\operatorname{cosec} x + \cot x}{\operatorname{cosec}^2 x - \cot^2 x} \equiv \dfrac{\operatorname{cosec} x + \cot x}{(1 + \cot^2 x) - \cot^2 x}$
$\equiv \cot x + \operatorname{cosec} x$

Q8 $\dfrac{\cot x}{1 + \operatorname{cosec} x} + \dfrac{1 + \operatorname{cosec} x}{\cot x}$
$\equiv \dfrac{\cot^2 x + (1 + \operatorname{cosec} x)^2}{\cot x(1 + \operatorname{cosec} x)}$
$\equiv \dfrac{(\operatorname{cosec}^2 x - 1) + (1 + 2\operatorname{cosec} x + \operatorname{cosec}^2 x)}{\cot x(1 + \operatorname{cosec} x)}$
$\equiv \dfrac{2\operatorname{cosec} x(1 + \operatorname{cosec} x)}{\cot x(1 + \operatorname{cosec} x)} \equiv \dfrac{2\operatorname{cosec} x}{\cot x}$
$\equiv \dfrac{2\tan x}{\sin x} \equiv \dfrac{2\sin x}{\sin x \cos x}$
$\equiv \dfrac{2}{\cos x} \equiv 2\sec x$

Q9 $\dfrac{\operatorname{cosec} x + 1}{\operatorname{cosec} x - 1} \equiv \dfrac{(\operatorname{cosec} x + 1)(\operatorname{cosec} x + 1)}{(\operatorname{cosec} x - 1)(\operatorname{cosec} x + 1)}$
$\equiv \dfrac{\operatorname{cosec}^2 x + 2\operatorname{cosec} x + 1}{\operatorname{cosec}^2 x - 1}$
$\equiv \dfrac{\operatorname{cosec}^2 x + 2\operatorname{cosec} x + 1}{(1 + \cot^2 x) - 1}$
$\equiv \dfrac{\operatorname{cosec}^2 x + 2\operatorname{cosec} x + 1}{\cot^2 x}$
$\equiv \dfrac{\operatorname{cosec}^2 x}{\cot^2 x} + \dfrac{2\operatorname{cosec} x}{\cot^2 x} + \dfrac{1}{\cot^2 x}$
$\equiv \dfrac{\tan^2 x}{\sin^2 x} + \dfrac{2\tan^2 x}{\sin x} + \tan^2 x$
$\equiv \dfrac{\sin^2 x}{\cos^2 x \sin^2 x} + \dfrac{2\sin^2 x}{\cos^2 x \sin x} + \tan^2 x$
$\equiv \dfrac{1}{\cos^2 x} + \dfrac{2\sin x}{\cos x \cos x} + \tan^2 x$
$\equiv \dfrac{1}{\cos^2 x} + \dfrac{2\tan x}{\cos x} + \tan^2 x$
$\equiv \sec^2 x + 2\tan x \sec x + (\sec^2 x - 1)$
$\equiv 2\sec^2 x + 2\tan x \sec x - 1$

6. The Addition Formulas

Exercise 6.1

Q1 a) $\dfrac{1}{2}$ b) $\dfrac{\sqrt{3}}{2}$ c) $\dfrac{1}{\sqrt{3}}$
d) 0 e) $\dfrac{1}{\sqrt{2}}$ f) $\dfrac{\sqrt{3}}{2}$

Q2 a) $\dfrac{1}{2}$ b) -1 c) $-\sqrt{3}$

Q3 a) $\sin 3x$ b) $\cos 10x$
c) $\tan 10x$ d) $5\sin 5x$
e) $8\cos 2x$ f) $\tan 3x$

Q4 a) $\dfrac{36}{325}$ b) $\dfrac{253}{325}$
c) $\dfrac{323}{325}$ d) $\dfrac{204}{253}$

Q5 a) $\dfrac{9\sqrt{10} + \sqrt{70}}{40}$ b) $\dfrac{3\sqrt{70} + 3\sqrt{10}}{40}$
c) $\dfrac{18\sqrt{10} - 2\sqrt{70}}{37}$ d) $\dfrac{2\sqrt{70} - 2\sqrt{10}}{9}$

Q6 $\cos\dfrac{\pi}{12} = \cos\left(\dfrac{\pi}{4} - \dfrac{\pi}{6}\right)$
$= \cos\dfrac{\pi}{4}\cos\dfrac{\pi}{6} + \sin\dfrac{\pi}{4}\sin\dfrac{\pi}{6}$
$= \left(\dfrac{1}{\sqrt{2}} \times \dfrac{\sqrt{3}}{2}\right) + \left(\dfrac{1}{\sqrt{2}} \times \dfrac{1}{2}\right) = \dfrac{\sqrt{3} + 1}{2\sqrt{2}}$
$= \dfrac{\sqrt{6} + \sqrt{2}}{4}$

Q7 $\sin 75° = \sin(30° + 45°)$
$= \sin 30°\cos 45° + \cos 30°\sin 45°$
$= \left(\dfrac{1}{2} \times \dfrac{1}{\sqrt{2}}\right) + \left(\dfrac{\sqrt{3}}{2} \times \dfrac{1}{\sqrt{2}}\right)$
$= \dfrac{1 + \sqrt{3}}{2\sqrt{2}} = \dfrac{\sqrt{6} + \sqrt{2}}{4}$

Q8 $\tan 75° = \tan(45° + 30°)$
$= \dfrac{\tan 45° + \tan 30°}{1 - \tan 45°\tan 30°}$
$= \dfrac{1 + \dfrac{1}{\sqrt{3}}}{1 - 1 \times \dfrac{1}{\sqrt{3}}} = \dfrac{\sqrt{3} + 1}{\sqrt{3} - 1}$

Exercise 6.2

Q1 $\tan(A - B) \equiv \dfrac{\sin(A - B)}{\cos(A - B)}$
$\equiv \dfrac{\sin A\cos B - \cos A\sin B}{\cos A\cos B + \sin A\sin B}$
$\equiv \dfrac{\left(\dfrac{\sin A\cos B}{\cos A\cos B}\right) - \left(\dfrac{\cos A\sin B}{\cos A\cos B}\right)}{\left(\dfrac{\cos A\cos B}{\cos A\cos B}\right) + \left(\dfrac{\sin A\sin B}{\cos A\cos B}\right)}$
$\equiv \dfrac{\left(\dfrac{\sin A}{\cos A}\right) - \left(\dfrac{\sin B}{\cos B}\right)}{1 + \left(\dfrac{\sin A}{\cos A}\right)\left(\dfrac{\sin B}{\cos B}\right)}$
$\equiv \dfrac{\tan A - \tan B}{1 + \tan A\tan B}$

Q2 a) $\dfrac{\cos(A - B) - \cos(A + B)}{\cos A\sin B}$
$\equiv \dfrac{(\cos A\cos B + \sin A\sin B)}{\cos A\sin B}$
$\qquad - \dfrac{(\cos A\cos B - \sin A\sin B)}{\cos A\sin B}$
$\equiv \dfrac{2\sin A\sin B}{\cos A\sin B} \equiv \dfrac{2\sin A}{\cos A} \equiv 2\tan A$

b) $\dfrac{1}{2}[\cos(A - B) - \cos(A + B)]$
$\equiv \dfrac{1}{2}[(\cos A\cos B + \sin A\sin B) - (\cos A\cos B - \sin A\sin B)]$
$\equiv \dfrac{1}{2}(2\sin A\sin B) \equiv \sin A\sin B$

c) $\sin(x + 90°)$
$\equiv \sin x\cos 90° + \cos x\sin 90°$
$\equiv \sin x(0) + \cos x(1) \equiv \cos x$

d) $\cos(x + 180°)$
$\equiv \cos x\cos 180° - \sin x\sin 180°$
$\equiv \cos x(-1) - \sin x(0) \equiv -\cos x$

Q3 $x = -1.99$ and $x = 1.15$ (both to 2 d.p.)

Q4 a) $\tan\left(-\dfrac{\pi}{12}\right) = \tan\left(\dfrac{\pi}{6} - \dfrac{\pi}{4}\right)$
$\equiv \dfrac{\tan\dfrac{\pi}{6} - \tan\dfrac{\pi}{4}}{1 + \tan\dfrac{\pi}{6}\tan\dfrac{\pi}{4}}$
$\equiv \dfrac{\dfrac{1}{\sqrt{3}} - 1}{1 + \dfrac{1}{\sqrt{3}}} \equiv \dfrac{1 - \sqrt{3}}{\sqrt{3} + 1}$
$\equiv \dfrac{1 - \sqrt{3}}{\sqrt{3} + 1} \times \dfrac{\sqrt{3} - 1}{\sqrt{3} - 1}$
$\equiv \dfrac{2\sqrt{3} - 4}{2} \equiv \sqrt{3} - 2$

b) $x = \dfrac{11\pi}{12}$

Q5 $2\sin(x + 30°)$
$\equiv 2\sin x\cos 30° + 2\cos x\sin 30°$
$\equiv 2\sin x\left(\dfrac{\sqrt{3}}{2}\right) + 2\cos x\left(\dfrac{1}{2}\right)$
$\equiv \sqrt{3}\,\sin x + \cos x$

Q6 $\dfrac{\sqrt{3} - \tan x}{1 + \sqrt{3}\tan x}$

Q7 a) $\tan B = -\dfrac{4}{35}$
b) $\tan(A - B) = \dfrac{137}{268}$

Q8 a) $\tan x = \dfrac{4 - \tan y}{1 - 4\tan y}$
b) $x = \dfrac{3\pi}{4}$ and $x = \dfrac{7\pi}{4}$

Q9 a) $\theta = 63.43°$ and $\theta = 243.43°$ (both to 2 d.p.)
b) $\theta = 2.84$ and $\theta = 5.99$ (both to 2 d.p.)
c) $\theta = 30°$ and $\theta = 210°$

Q10 Use the sin addition formula for $\sin\left(x + \dfrac{\pi}{6}\right)$:
$\sin\left(x + \dfrac{\pi}{6}\right) = \sin x\cos\dfrac{\pi}{6} + \cos x\sin\dfrac{\pi}{6}$
$= \dfrac{\sqrt{3}}{2}\sin x + \dfrac{1}{2}\cos x$
Now use the small angle approximations for sin and cos:
$\approx \dfrac{\sqrt{3}}{2}x + \dfrac{1}{2}\left(1 - \dfrac{1}{2}x^2\right)$
$= \dfrac{\sqrt{3}}{2}x + \dfrac{1}{2} - \dfrac{1}{4}x^2$
$= \dfrac{1}{2} + \dfrac{\sqrt{3}}{2}x - \dfrac{1}{4}x^2$

7. The Double Angle Formulas

Exercise 7.1

Q1 a) 1 b) $-\dfrac{1}{2}$ c) $\dfrac{\sqrt{3}}{4}$
d) $\dfrac{\sqrt{3}}{12}$ e) $-\dfrac{\sqrt{3}}{2}$

Q2 a) $\dfrac{17}{18}$ b) $\dfrac{\sqrt{35}}{18}$ c) $\dfrac{\sqrt{35}}{17}$
d) $\dfrac{18}{17}$ e) $\dfrac{18}{\sqrt{35}}\left(= \dfrac{18\sqrt{35}}{35}\right)$
f) $\dfrac{17}{\sqrt{35}}\left(= \dfrac{17\sqrt{35}}{35}\right)$

Q3 a) $\dfrac{7}{8}$ b) $\dfrac{\sqrt{15}}{8}$ c) $\dfrac{\sqrt{15}}{7}$
d) $\dfrac{8}{7}$ e) $\dfrac{8}{\sqrt{15}}\left(= \dfrac{8\sqrt{15}}{15}\right)$

f) $\dfrac{7}{\sqrt{15}}\ \left(=\dfrac{7\sqrt{15}}{15}\right)$

Q4 **a)** $\dfrac{\sin 6\theta}{6}$ **b)** $-\cos\left(\dfrac{4y}{3}\right)$ **c)** $\cot x$

Exercise 7.2

Q1 All answers given to 1 d.p.
 a) $x = 14.5°$ and $x = 165.5°$
 b) $x = 113.6°, 120°, 240°, 246.4°$
 c) $x = 26.6°, 108.4°, 206.6°, 288.4°$
 d) $x = 0°, 71.6°, 108.4°, 180°, 251.6°,$
 $288.4°, 360°$

Q2 **a)** $x = 1.82$ and $x = 4.46$ (both to 3 s.f.)
 b) $x = 0.361, 2.78, 3.50, 5.92$
 (all to 3 s.f.)
 c) $x = 0.663, 2.23, 3.80, 5.38$
 (all to 3 s.f.)

Q3 **a)** $x = \dfrac{2\pi}{3}$ and $x = \dfrac{4\pi}{3}$
 b) $x = \pi$
 c) $x = \dfrac{\pi}{6}, \dfrac{5\pi}{6}, \dfrac{3\pi}{2}$

Q4 **a)** $\sin 2x \sec^2 x$
 $\equiv (2\sin x\cos x)\left(\dfrac{1}{\cos^2 x}\right)$
 $\equiv \dfrac{2\sin x}{\cos x} \equiv 2\tan x$
 b) $\dfrac{2}{1+\cos 2x} \equiv \dfrac{2}{1+2\cos^2 x - 1}$
 $\equiv \dfrac{2}{2\cos^2 x} \equiv \dfrac{1}{\cos^2 x} \equiv \sec^2 x$
 c) $\cot x - 2\cot 2x \equiv \dfrac{1}{\tan x} - \dfrac{2}{\tan 2x}$
 $\equiv \dfrac{1}{\tan x} - \dfrac{2(1-\tan^2 x)}{2\tan x}$
 $\equiv \dfrac{1-(1-\tan^2 x)}{\tan x} \equiv \dfrac{\tan^2 x}{\tan x} \equiv \tan x$
 d) $\tan 2x + \cot 2x \equiv \dfrac{\sin 2x}{\cos 2x} + \dfrac{\cos 2x}{\sin 2x}$
 $\equiv \dfrac{\sin^2 2x + \cos^2 2x}{\sin 2x\cos 2x}$
 $\equiv \dfrac{1}{\frac{1}{2}\sin 4x} \equiv \dfrac{2}{\sin 4x} \equiv 2\operatorname{cosec} 4x$

Q5 **a)** $\dfrac{1+\cos 2x}{\sin 2x} \equiv \dfrac{1+(2\cos^2 x - 1)}{2\sin x\cos x}$
 $\equiv \dfrac{2\cos^2 x}{2\sin x\cos x} \equiv \dfrac{\cos x}{\sin x} \equiv \cot x$
 b) $\theta = 4.1°, 94.1°, 184.1°, 274.1°$
 (all to 1 d.p.)

Q6 **a)** $\operatorname{cosec} x - \cot\dfrac{x}{2} \equiv \dfrac{1}{\sin x} - \dfrac{\cos\frac{x}{2}}{\sin\frac{x}{2}}$

 $\equiv \dfrac{1}{2\sin\frac{x}{2}\cos\frac{x}{2}} - \dfrac{\cos\frac{x}{2}}{\sin\frac{x}{2}}$
 $\equiv \dfrac{1-2\cos^2\frac{x}{2}}{2\sin\frac{x}{2}\cos\frac{x}{2}}$
 $\equiv \dfrac{-\left(2\cos^2\frac{x}{2}-1\right)}{2\sin\frac{x}{2}\cos\frac{x}{2}} \equiv \dfrac{-\cos x}{\sin x}$
 $\equiv -\dfrac{1}{\left(\frac{\sin x}{\cos x}\right)} \equiv -\dfrac{1}{\tan x} \equiv -\cot x$
 b) $y = 0.464$ and $y = 0.464 - \pi = -2.68$
 (both to 3 s.f.)

Q7 **a)** **(i)** $\dfrac{5}{\sqrt{26}}$ **(ii)** $\dfrac{1}{\sqrt{26}}$ **b)** $\dfrac{1}{5}$

8. The R Addition Formulas

Exercise 8.1

Q1 $3\sin x - 2\cos x \equiv \sqrt{13}\,\sin(x - 33.7°)$

Q2 $6\cos x - 5\sin x \equiv \sqrt{61}\,\cos(x + 39.8°)$

Q3 $\sin x + \sqrt{7}\,\cos x \equiv 2\sqrt{2}\,\sin(x + 1.21)$

Q4 $\sqrt{2}\,\sin x - \cos x \equiv R\sin(x - \alpha)$
 $\Rightarrow \sqrt{2}\,\sin x - \cos x$
 $\equiv R\sin x\cos\alpha - R\cos x\sin\alpha$
 $\Rightarrow \textcircled{1}\ R\cos\alpha = \sqrt{2}$
 and $\textcircled{2}\ R\sin\alpha = 1$
 $\textcircled{2} \div \textcircled{1}$ gives $\tan\alpha = \dfrac{1}{\sqrt{2}}$
 $\textcircled{1}^2 + \textcircled{2}^2$ gives:
 $R^2\cos^2\alpha + R^2\sin^2\alpha = (\sqrt{2})^2 + 1^2 = 3$
 $\Rightarrow R^2(\cos^2\alpha + \sin^2\alpha) = 3$
 $\Rightarrow R^2 = 3 \Rightarrow R = \sqrt{3}$
 So $\sqrt{2}\,\sin x - \cos x \equiv \sqrt{3}\,\sin(x - \alpha)$,
 where $\tan\alpha = \dfrac{1}{\sqrt{2}}$

Q5 $3\cos 2x + 5\sin 2x \equiv R\cos(2x - \alpha)$
 $\Rightarrow 3\cos 2x + 5\sin 2x$
 $\equiv R\cos 2x\cos\alpha + R\sin 2x\sin\alpha$
 $\Rightarrow \textcircled{1}\ R\cos\alpha = 3$ and $\textcircled{2}\ R\sin\alpha = 5$
 $\textcircled{2} \div \textcircled{1}$ gives $\tan\alpha = \dfrac{5}{3}$
 $\textcircled{1}^2 + \textcircled{2}^2$ gives:
 $R^2\cos^2\alpha + R^2\sin^2\alpha = 3^2 + 5^2 = 34$
 $\Rightarrow R = \sqrt{34}$
 So $3\cos 2x + 5\sin 2x \equiv \sqrt{34}\,\cos(2x - \alpha)$
 where $\tan\alpha = \dfrac{5}{3}$.

Q6 **a)** $\sqrt{3}\,\sin x + \cos x \equiv 2\sin\left(x + \dfrac{\pi}{6}\right)$
 b)

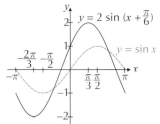

 $y = 2\sin\left(x + \dfrac{\pi}{6}\right)$
 $y = \sin x$

 The graph of $y = 2\sin\left(x + \dfrac{\pi}{6}\right)$ is the graph of $y = \sin x$ transformed by a horizontal translation left by $\dfrac{\pi}{6}$, then a vertical stretch by a factor of 2.

 c) The graph of $y = 2\sin\left(x + \dfrac{\pi}{6}\right)$ has a minimum at $\left(-\dfrac{2\pi}{3}, -2\right)$, a maximum at $\left(\dfrac{\pi}{3}, 2\right)$, and cuts the x-axis at $\left(-\dfrac{\pi}{6}, 0\right)$ and $\left(\dfrac{5\pi}{6}, 0\right)$.
 The y-intercept is at $(0, 1)$.
 The graph of $y = \sin x$ has a minimum at $\left(-\dfrac{\pi}{2}, -1\right)$, a maximum at $\left(\dfrac{\pi}{2}, 1\right)$, and cuts the x-axis at $(-\pi, 0)$, $(0, 0)$ and $(\pi, 0)$. To describe the graph of $y = 2\sin\left(x + \dfrac{\pi}{6}\right)$, each of these points needs to have $\dfrac{\pi}{6}$ subtracted from the x-coordinates, and the y-coordinates multiplied by 2. To find the y-intercept, just put $x = 0$ into the equation.

Exercise 8.2

Q1 **a)** $5\cos\theta - 12\sin\theta \equiv 13\cos(\theta + 67.4°)$
 b) $\theta = 4.7°$ and $\theta = 220.5°$
 (both to 1 d.p.)
 c) The maximum and minimum values of $13\cos(\theta + 67.4°)$ are at ± 13.

Q2 **a)** $2\sin 2\theta + 3\cos 2\theta$
 $\equiv \sqrt{13}\,\sin(2\theta + 0.983)$
 b) $\theta = 0.939, 2.79, 4.08, 5.93$
 (all to 3 s.f.)

Q3 **a)** $3\sin\theta - 2\sqrt{5}\,\cos\theta$
 $\equiv \sqrt{29}\,\sin(\theta - 56.1°)$
 b) $\theta = 124.3°$ and $\theta = 167.9°$
 (both 1 d.p.)
 c) The maximum value of $f(x)$ is $f(x) = \sqrt{29}$, which occurs at $x = 146.1°$ (1 d.p.)

Q4 **a)** $3\sin x + \cos x \equiv \sqrt{10}\,\sin(x + 18.4°)$
 b) $x = 20.8°$ and $x = 122.4°$
 (both to 1 d.p.)
 c) The maximum and minimum values of $f(x)$ are $\pm\sqrt{10}$

Q5 **a)** $4\sin x + \cos x \equiv \sqrt{17}\,\sin(x + 0.245)$
 b) Maximum value of $(4\sin x + \cos x)^4 = 289$
 c) $x = 0$ and $x = 2.65$ (3 s.f.)

Q6 **a)** $8\cos x + 15\sin x \equiv 17\cos(x - 1.08)$
 b) $x = 2.35$ and $x = 6.09$ (both to 3 s.f.)
 c) The minimum value of $g(x)$ is $g(x) = 0$, which occurs at $x = 2.65$ (3 s.f.).

Q7 **a)** $2\cos x + \sin x \equiv R\cos(x - \alpha)$
 $\equiv R\cos x\cos\alpha + R\sin x\sin\alpha$
 $\Rightarrow R\cos x = 2$, $R\sin\alpha = 1$
 $\tan\alpha = \dfrac{1}{2} \Rightarrow \alpha = 26.6°$ (3 s.f.)
 $R - \sqrt{2^2 + 1^2} - \sqrt{5}$
 b) Range: $-\sqrt{5} \le g(x) \le \sqrt{5}$

Q8 $3\sin\theta - \dfrac{3}{2}\cos\theta \equiv \dfrac{3\sqrt{5}}{2}\sin(\theta - 0.464)$
 $\theta = 1.57$ and $\theta = 2.50$ (both to 3 s.f.)

Q9 $\theta = 1.04$ and $\theta = 3.03$ (both to 3 s.f.)

9. Modelling with Trig Functions

Exercise 9.1

Q1 Sector with angle 120°:
 Area = 419 m² (3 s.f.)
 Perimeter = 81.9 m (3 s.f.)
 Sector with angle 144°:
 Area = 503 m² (3 s.f.)
 Perimeter = 90.3 m (3 s.f.)
 Sector with angle 96°:
 Area = 335 m² (3 s.f.)
 Perimeter = 73.5 m (3 s.f.)

Q2 **a)** $A = 12$, $B = 5$ (so $f(\theta) = 12 + 5\cos\theta$)

b) $C = \frac{\pi}{6}$, $D = 0$
(so $g(t) = 12 + 5 \cos\left(\frac{\pi}{6}t\right)$)
The longest day (t = O) will have 17 hours
of daylight, which is the maximum of the
function. This will occur when
cos (Ct + D) = 1, i.e. when Ct + D = O.
Similarly, the shortest day (t = 6) will
occur when cos (Ct + D) = −1
i.e. when Ct + D = π, so solve these
equations simultaneously to find C and
D. Because cos is periodic, you might
have found D = 2π. Also, because cos is
symmetrical, C = $-\frac{\pi}{6}$ will give you the
same answer — either one is fine.

Q3 Maximum of $h(t) = 21.1$ m (1 d.p.)
Minimum of $h(t) = 6.9$ m (1 d.p.)
You should find that h(t)
$\equiv 14 + 5\sqrt{2}\ \cos\left(t - \frac{\pi}{4}\right)$
The maximum and minimum of cos are 1 and
−1, so the maximum and minimum values of
h(t) are 14 ±5√2.

Q4 **a)** $H \equiv 10 + 7 \sin\left(t - \frac{\pi}{3}\right)$

b) Replace $\left(t - \frac{\pi}{3}\right)$ with x:
$h = 10 + 7 \sin x - \cos 2x$
$= 10 + 7 \sin x - (1 - 2 \sin^2 x)$
$= 10 + 7 \sin x - 1 + 2 \sin^2 x$
$= 9 + 7 \sin x + 2 \sin^2 x$
i.e. $A = 9$ and $B = 2$

c) $t = 1.57$ s (3 s.f.)
You need to find h = 13,
i.e. 9 + 7 sin x + 2 sin² x = 13,
so factorise and solve the quadratic for t.

Review Exercise —
Chapter 18

Q1 **a)** **(i)** $\frac{\pi}{12}$ **(ii)** $\frac{5\pi}{18}$

(iii) $\frac{11\pi}{6}$ **(iv)** $\frac{5\pi}{4}$

b) **(i)** 105°   **(ii)** 210°

(iii) 300°   **(iv)** 195°

Q2 BC = 7 cm, area = 35 cm²

Q3 BC = $\frac{10\pi}{3}$ cm

Q4 **a)** **(i)** 0.42   **(ii)** 0.98555
(iii) 0.22

b) **(i)** −0.86155   **(ii)** −0.92755
(iii) −0.7062

Q5 **a)** $12\theta^2$ **b)** $2 - 40\theta^2$ **c)** $\frac{2\theta^2}{2 - \theta^2}$

Q6 **a)** $\frac{\pi}{4}$ **b)** $\frac{\pi}{2}$ **c)** $\frac{\pi}{3}$

Q7
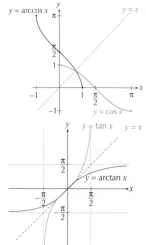

Q8 **a)** Rearrange to make x the subject:
$1 + \cos x = \frac{1}{y} \implies \cos x = \frac{1}{y} - 1$
$\implies x = \cos^{-1}(\frac{1}{y} - 1)$
Replace x with $f^{-1}(x)$ and y with x:
$f^{-1}(x) = \cos^{-1}(\frac{1}{x} - 1) = \arccos(\frac{1}{x} - 1)$

b) Domain: $\frac{1}{2} \le x \le 1$,
range: $0 \le f^{-1}(x) \le \frac{\pi}{2}$

c)
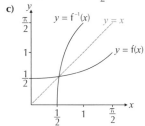

Q9 **a)** $\frac{3\pi}{4}$ **b)** $\frac{\pi}{4}$

Q10 **a)** 2   **b)** $\frac{2}{\sqrt{3}}$ **c)** $\sqrt{3}$

Q11
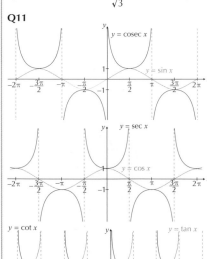

Q12 **a)** A horizontal stretch with scale factor $\frac{1}{4}$.

b) $\frac{\pi}{2}$

c)
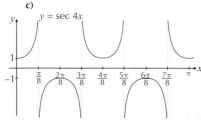

d) $y = \sec 4x$ is undefined when $x = \frac{\pi}{8}$, $\frac{3\pi}{8}, \frac{5\pi}{8}$ and $\frac{7\pi}{8}$.

Q13 $\cot^2\theta + \sin^2\theta$
$\equiv (\text{cosec}^2\theta - 1) + (1 - \cos^2\theta)$
$\equiv \text{cosec}^2\theta - \cos^2\theta$

Q14 $y = \cot^2\theta = \text{cosec}^2\theta - 1 = x^2 - 1$

Q15 $y^2 = 4 \tan^2\theta = 4(\sec^2\theta - 1) = 4(x^2 - 1)$
$\implies y = \pm 2\sqrt{x^2 - 1}$

Q16 **a)** $\text{cosec}^2 x = \frac{3\cot x + 4}{2}$
$\implies 2\ \text{cosec}^2 x = 3 \cot x + 4$
$\implies 2(1 + \cot^2 x) = 3 \cot x + 4$
$\implies 2 \cot^2 x - 3 \cot x + 2 - 4 = 0$
$\implies 2 \cot^2 x - 3 \cot x - 2 = 0$

b) $x = 0.46$, 3.61, 2.03 and 5.18
(all to 2 d.p.)

Q17 **a)** 2   **b)** $\sqrt{3}$

c) From a), sec $\theta = 2$, so sec² $\theta = 4$
$\implies 1 + \tan^2\theta = 4 \implies \tan^2\theta = 3$
$\implies \tan\theta = \sqrt{3}$

d) $\frac{1}{\sqrt{3}}$ **e)** $\frac{\sqrt{3}}{2}$

Q18 **a)** $\sin 11x$ **b)** $3 \cos 12x$
c) $\tan 4x$ **d)** $12 \sin 2x$

Q19 $\frac{\sqrt{2} + \sqrt{6}}{4}$

Q20 $\sin(A + B) = \frac{117}{125}$ (= 0.936)

Q21 $\theta = 0°$, 150°, 180°, 210°, 360°.

Q22 **a)** $x = 0$, 2.89, 6.28 (all to 3 s.f.)
b) $x = 1.23$, 5.05 (all to 3 s.f.)

Q23 **a)** $x = 0$, π, 2π

b) $x = \frac{\pi}{6}, \frac{\pi}{2}, \frac{5\pi}{6}, \frac{7\pi}{6}, \frac{3\pi}{2}, \frac{11\pi}{6}, \frac{\pi}{18},$
$\frac{5\pi}{18}, \frac{13\pi}{18}, \frac{17\pi}{18}, \frac{25\pi}{18}, \frac{29\pi}{18}$

Q24 $\frac{\cos\theta}{\sin\theta} + \frac{\sin\theta}{\cos\theta} \equiv \frac{\cos\theta\cos\theta}{\sin\theta\cos\theta} + \frac{\sin\theta\sin\theta}{\sin\theta\cos\theta}$
$\equiv \frac{\cos^2\theta + \sin^2\theta}{\sin\theta\cos\theta} \equiv \frac{1}{\sin\theta\cos\theta}$
$\equiv \frac{1}{\frac{1}{2}\sin 2\theta} \equiv 2\ \text{cosec}\ 2\theta$

Q25 $5 \sin\theta - 6\cos\theta \equiv \sqrt{61}\sin(\theta - 50.19°)$

Q26 **a)** $3\cos\theta - 8\sin\theta \equiv \sqrt{73}\cos(\theta + 69.4°)$
b) $\theta = 12.5°$ and $\theta = 208.6°$
(both to 1 d.p.)

Q27 7.83 m
First, write the 5 sin t + 3 cos t bit in the form
R sin (t + α). Find the maximum point of
this function, then add on the 2.

Chapter 19: Parametric Equations

1. Parametric Equations of Curves

Exercise 1.1

Q1 a) $(15, 25)$ b) $t = 6$ c) $x = \pm 18$

Q2 a) $(13, -45)$ b) $t = 8$ c) $x = -7$ or 5

Q3 a) $\left(\dfrac{4+\sqrt{2}}{2}, \dfrac{\sqrt{2}-6}{2}\right)$ b) $\theta = \dfrac{\pi}{3}$

c) $\theta = \dfrac{2\pi}{3}$

Q4 a) $t = \pm 3$ b) $y = 9$ or 114

Q5

t	-5	-4	-3	-2	-1
x	-25	-20	-15	-10	-5
y	$-\frac{2}{5}$	$-\frac{1}{2}$	$-\frac{2}{3}$	-1	-2

t	1	2	3	4	5
x	5	10	15	20	25
y	2	1	$\frac{2}{3}$	$\frac{1}{2}$	$\frac{2}{5}$

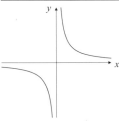

When t = 0, y is undefined, so there must be an asymptote.

Q6

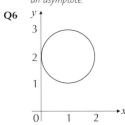

Q7 a) $a = 39$

b) At $(-6, 4)$, $x = -6 \Rightarrow 2t^2 - 7t = -6$
$\Rightarrow 2t^2 - 7t + 6 = 0$
$\Rightarrow (2t - 3)(t - 2) = 0$
$\Rightarrow t = \dfrac{3}{2}, t = 2$
$t = \dfrac{3}{2} \Rightarrow y = 10 - \left(\dfrac{3}{2}\right)^2 = \dfrac{31}{4} \neq 4$
$t = 2 \Rightarrow y = 10 - 2^2 = 6 \neq 4$
So neither of the t-values when $x = -6$ corresponds to $y = 4$, so $(-6, 4)$ is not on the curve.
You could have started with y = 4 and used a similar method to show that x ≠ −6 at this point.

Q8 a) 16 AU b) 7.62 AU (to 3 s.f.)

Q9 a) 12 m b) 16 m

Exercise 1.2

Q1 $A(5, 0)$ and $B(0, -5)$.

Q2 a) $t = 2$ b) $t = \pm 5$

Q3 $\left(0, \dfrac{1}{4}\right)$

Q4 $(-1, -4)$

Q5 $(8, 96)$ and $(-8, 96)$

Q6 $(4, 4)$ and $(4, -4)$

Q7 a) $a = \dfrac{1}{8}$
b) The curve does not meet the x-axis.

Q8 a) $\left(\dfrac{2}{3}, 0\right)$ and $\left(-\dfrac{2}{3}, 0\right)$
b) The curve would meet the y-axis when $x = 0$, i.e. when $\dfrac{2}{t} = 0$. This has no solutions, so the curve does not meet the y-axis.
c) $(-2, -8)$ and $\left(\dfrac{1}{3}, 27\right)$

Q9 a) The curve meets the x-axis at $(3, 0)$ and $(-3, 0)$. The curve meets the y-axis at $(0, -5)$ and $(0, 5)$.
b) $\left(\dfrac{3\sqrt{3}}{2}, \dfrac{5}{2}\right)$ and $\left(-\dfrac{3\sqrt{3}}{2}, -\dfrac{5}{2}\right)$

Q10 The ships will not collide.
They'll collide if they have the same x- and y-coordinates at the same time. Set $x_1 = x_2$, solve to find the value of t when they both have the same x-coordinate (it's t = 7), then sub this into the equations for y and see if the y-coordinates match — they don't.

2. Parametric and Cartesian Equations

Exercise 2.1

Q1 a) $y = x^2 - 6x + 9$ b) $y = \dfrac{18}{x}$
c) $y = \left(\dfrac{x}{2}\right)^{\frac{2}{3}}$ d) $y = 26 - 2x$
e) $y = x^2 - 8x + 7$
f) $y = 9x^2 - 15x + 6$
g) $\left(\dfrac{5-y}{8}\right)^2 - \dfrac{5-y}{16} = x$ or $\dfrac{y^2 - 6y + 5}{64} = x$
h) $x^2 + y^2 = 1$
i) $(x - 1)^2 + (y - 2)^2 = 1$ j) $y = 1 - 2x^2$
k) $y = 2x^2 - 1$ l) $y = 2x^2 + 20x + 49$

Q2 $y^2 = 1 + x^2$

Q3 $y^2 = 9 + \dfrac{9x^2}{4}$

Q4 a) The centre of the circle is $(5, -3)$, and the radius is 1.
b) $(x - 5)^2 + (y + 3)^2 = 1$

Q5 a) $t = \dfrac{1}{(x-2)}$
b) $y = \dfrac{3+t}{t^2} = \dfrac{3 + \dfrac{1}{(x-2)}}{\dfrac{1}{(x-2)^2}}$
$= 3(x - 2)^2 + (x - 2)$
$= 3(x^2 - 4x + 4) + x - 2$
$= 3x^2 - 11x + 10$
$= (3x - 5)(x - 2)$
c)

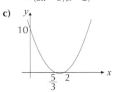

Q6 $y = \dfrac{6x + 13}{11 - 3x}$
You could also write this as
$6x - 11y + 3xy + 13 = 0$

Q7 $y^2 = 1 - \dfrac{x}{5}$

Q8 a) $\left(\dfrac{x}{a}\right)^2 + \left(\dfrac{y}{b}\right)^2 = 1$

b)

c) An ellipse.

Q9 a) $y = 2t - 1 \Rightarrow t = \dfrac{y+1}{2}$
$x = 3t^2 = 3\left(\dfrac{y+1}{2}\right)^2 = \dfrac{3}{4}(y + 1)^2$
b) $\left(\dfrac{1}{3}, -\dfrac{5}{3}\right)$ and $\left(\dfrac{3}{4}, 0\right)$

Q10 $y = \dfrac{35}{x - 2}$

Review Exercise — Chapter 19

Q1 a) $t = 4$, $y = \dfrac{1}{8}$ b) $t = \pm 10$

Q2 $(0, -17)$, $(0, -5)$, $(0, 3)$

Q3 a) $t = 0 \Rightarrow x = 3, y = 4$,
$t = 1 \Rightarrow x = 2.5, y = 7$
$t = 2 \Rightarrow x = 2, y = 14$,
$t = 3 \Rightarrow x = 1.5, y = 25$
b) (i) $t = 20$ (ii) $t = 2.5, t = -3$
c) $y = 8x^2 - 50x + 82$

Q4 $\left(\dfrac{4}{5}, 0\right)$ and $(1, 2)$

Q5 a) (i) $\left(\sqrt{2}, \dfrac{9}{2}\right)$ (ii) $\left(1, \dfrac{19}{4}\right)$
b) $y = 5 - \dfrac{x^2}{4}$ c) $-2 \leq x \leq 2$

Q6 $y = 5 - 36x^2$

Q7 a) $(0, 1)$ and $(0, 7)$
b) $(0, 7)$, $(3, 5.5)$ and $(8, 3)$

Q8 a) $\left(\dfrac{9}{2}, \dfrac{1}{16}\right)$
b) $x = 0$ on the y-axis, but $x = 4 - \cos 2\theta$ can never be zero, as $-1 \leq \cos 2\theta \leq 1$, so $3 \leq x \leq 5$.
c) $y = \dfrac{x^2 - 6x + 7}{4}$

Q9 a) $-e^{\frac{\pi}{4}}, e^{\frac{3\pi}{4}}, -e^{\frac{5\pi}{4}}, e^{\frac{7\pi}{4}}$
b) (i) $d = e^t$ (ii) $\left(-\dfrac{\sqrt{2}}{2}e^{\frac{\pi}{8}}, \dfrac{\sqrt{2}}{2}e^{\frac{\pi}{8}}\right)$
For part b)(i), use $d = \sqrt{x^2 + y^2}$ to find the distance of the particle from the origin. Substitute in the equations for x and y, and use the identity $\sin^2 \theta + \cos^2 \theta \equiv 1$ to get rid of θ.

Chapter 20:
Sequences and Series

1. Sequences
Exercise 1.1

Q1 **a)** **(i)** 55 **(ii)** 22 **(iii)** 145
b) Increasing

Q2 24

Q3 0, 3, 8, 15, 24

Q4 $k = 8$

Q5 $u_k = 13 - 6k$ and
$u_{k+1} = 13 - 6(k+1) = 7 - 6k$
The sequence is decreasing if $u_{k+1} < u_k$ for all values of k.
$7 - 6k < 13 - 6k \Rightarrow 7 < 13$, which is true so the sequence is decreasing.

Q6 $a = 4, b = -1$

Q7 $e = 3, f = 2, g = 4$
Form equations for the first 3 terms — you should get
$9 = (1^2)e + f + g, 20 = (2^2)e + 2f + g$
and $37 = (3^2)e + 3f + g$.
Solve the equations simultaneously (to solve simultaneous equations with 3 unknowns, you use a similar method to when there are 2 unknowns — it just takes a few more steps).

Q8 $n = 8$

Q9 **a)** 7 terms are positive **b)** Decreasing

Exercise 1.2

Q1 10, 30, 90, 270, 810

Q2 2, 4, 16, 256

Q3 $u_{n+1} = 2u_n, u_1 = 3$

Q4 **a)** $u_{n+1} = u_n + 4, u_1 = 12$
b) 23 terms

Q5 E.g. $u_{n+1} = 11 - u_n$ or $u_{n+1} = 28 \div u_n$, with $u_1 = 7$

Q6 $k = 4$

Q7 $r = 6$

Q8 7, 8, 10, 13, 17 **Q9** $a = 1.5, b = -2$

Q10 8, 4, 2, 1, $\frac{1}{2}$, $u_n = 2^{(4-n)}$ or $u_n = 16 \div 2^n$

2. Arithmetic Sequences
Exercise 2.1

Q1 52

Q2 **a)** $3n + 3$ **b)** $5n - 1$
c) $-4n + 16$ **d)** $2n - 0.5$
e) $85 - 8n$ **f)** $-0.5n - 1.5$

Q3 First term = 7, common difference = 4

Q4 49 **Q5** 6 **Q6** $k = 20$

Q7 $x = 2$, next term = ln 250
The difference between all the terms is the same in an arithmetic sequence. Use this fact to set up an equation — you should end up with
$\ln (x + 8) - \ln x = \ln (x + 48) - \ln (x + 8).$

Use the laws of log to solve for x. Once you've found x, use it to find the common difference, then add it onto the third term to find the next term in the sequence.

3. Arithmetic Series
Exercise 3.1

Q1 10th term = 35, $S_{10} = 215$

Q2 1560

Q3 $a = 18, d = -2, S_8 = 88$

Q4 9

Q5 $u_{100} = 606, S_{100} = 30\,900$

Q6 559 **Q7** 366

Q8 90 **Q9** $n = 30$

Q10 $a = 5(1) + 2 = 7$ and $l = 5k + 2$
$$S_n = \frac{1}{2}n(a + l) \Rightarrow 553 = \frac{1}{2}k(7 + 5k + 2)$$
$1106 = 5k^2 + 9k$
$5k^2 + 9k - 1106 = 0$
$(5k + 79)(k - 14) = 0$
Ignore the negative solution, so $k = 14$.

Q11 -968
Use the fact that it's an arithmetic progression to write down some equations in terms of d and x:
$x + 11 + d = 4x + 4 \Rightarrow -3x + d = -7$
$x + 11 + 2d = 9x + 5 \Rightarrow -8x + 2d = -6$
Solve these simultaneous equations to find d and x, and use these values to find a. Finally, put your values of a, d and n into the sum formula to find S_{11}.

Q12 $n = 8$ or $n = 11$
You know the first term (36), the sum (176) and you can work out the common difference (−4). Put these values into the formula for S_n — you'll end up with a quadratic to solve, which will give you the two different values of n. There are two possible values because the series goes into negative numbers, so the sum is reached twice.

Exercise 3.2

Q1 **a)** **(i)** 120 **(ii)** 325 **(iii)** 2 001 000
b) 528

Q2 $S_{10} = 55, S_{20} = 210$, so $\sum_{n=11}^{20} n = 155$

Q3 **a)** $n = 11$ **b)** $k = 15$

Q4 510 **Q5** 1414

4. Geometric Sequences and Series
Exercise 4.1

Q1 22.78125

Q2 **a)** 9 **b)** 177 147

Q3 0.09375 **Q4** $r = 2$

Q5 15 terms are less than 4

Q6 −0.04647 (5 d.p.)

Q7 u_{16} is the first term that's less than 1000.

Q8 $r = -1$

Q9 **a)** $\frac{3}{4}$ **b)** $\frac{2187}{65536}$

Q10 750

Q11 **a)** −0.8
b) There are 5 terms in the series before a term has modulus less than 1.
You could answer this part of the question by writing a new series where each term is the modulus of the term in the original series, then using logs to find the first term less than 1. But here it's much easier to just find the next few terms.

Exercise 4.2

Q1 576.28 (2 d.p.) **Q2** 80.98 (2 d.p.)

Q3 $n = 16$ **Q4** $x = 9.00$ (2 d.p.)

Q5 **a)** 2 **b)** 1.5 **c)** 49 150.5

Q6 **a)** Common ratio:
$$\frac{\text{2nd term}}{\text{1st term}} = \frac{\text{3rd term}}{\text{2nd term}}, \text{ so:}$$
$$\frac{m}{m + 10} = \frac{2m - 21}{m}$$
$\Rightarrow m^2 = (m + 10)(2m - 21)$
$\Rightarrow m^2 = 2m^2 - 21m + 20m - 210$
$\Rightarrow 0 = m^2 - m - 210$
b) Factorising $m^2 - m - 210 = 0$ gives:
$(m - 15)(m + 14) = 0$,
so $m = 15$ or $m = -14$,
since $m > 0, m = 15$.
c) 0.6 **d)** 62.12 (2 d.p.)

Q7 **a)** $x = -2$ **b)** 43

Q8 11.61 (2 d.p.)

Q9 1.60 (2 d.p.)

Q10 −2.1

Exercise 4.3

Q1 **a)** Does not converge
b) Converges
c) Converges
d) Does not converge
e) Converges
f) Does not converge

Q2 90

Q3 $r = 0.5$

Q4 **a)** $r = \frac{1}{3}$ **b)** $a = 9$

Q5 $r = 0.5, a = 6$

Q6 **a)** $r = 0.4$ **b)** $u_5 = 0.1536$

Q7 **a)** $r = -0.25$ **b)** $a = 192$
c) $S_\infty = 153.6$

Q8 The sum of terms after the 10th is $S_\infty - S_{10}$
$$S_\infty - S_{10} < \frac{1}{100} S_\infty \Rightarrow \frac{99}{100} S_\infty - S_{10} < 0$$
$$\Rightarrow \frac{99}{100} S_\infty < S_{10}$$
So $0.99(S_\infty) = \frac{0.99a}{1 - r} < \frac{a(1 - r^{10})}{(1 - r)} = S_{10}$
You can cancel and keep the inequality sign because the series is convergent so $|r| < 1 \Rightarrow 1 - r > 0$, and you know $a > 0$ from the question:
$\Rightarrow 0.99 < 1 - r^{10} \Rightarrow r^{10} < 0.01$
$\Rightarrow |r| < {}^{10}\sqrt{0.01} \Rightarrow |r| < 0.631$ (3 s.f.)

Q9 $r = \dfrac{\sqrt{3}}{3}$

Use the formulas for S_∞ and S_4 to form an equation in terms of a and r. Cancel $(1 - r)$ and a to find r, then rationalise the denominator (you're told that r is positive and real).

5. Modelling Problems

Exercise 5.1

Q1 £93

Q2 14.3 cm (1 d.p.)

Q3 The 9th day

Q4 After 10 months

Q5 £11 997.50 (to the nearest penny)

Q6 a) £123.60

b) £776.21 (to the nearest penny).

Q7 204 000 copies

Q8 The compost has not done what it has claimed.
If the claim were true, the leeks would be 35.3738... cm tall (this is the value of u_{15}). Since the leeks only reach a height of 25 cm, the claim on the compost is not justified.

Q9 a) £ 81 600   b) 1.02

c) £97 519.55 (to the nearest penny)

d) 21 years

Q10 496 dots

Q11 After 42 folds the paper would reach the moon

Q12 a) 15.7 miles (1 d.p.).

b) 322 miles (to the nearest mile)

Q13 On the 45th day she'll have over £10
This series is the natural numbers. You need to find how many are needed to exceed 1000 (£10 in pence), so set up a quadratic inequality using the formula for the sum of the natural numbers, and solve it to find the value of n.

Q14 7.17 % (3 s.f.)
After 0 years, u_1 = a and after 1 year, u_2 = ar. So after 10 years, u_{11} = ar^{10}. She wants her investment to double so u_{11} = ar_{10} = 2a — solve this equation to find r (and don't forget to subtract 1 to get the interest rate).

Review Exercise — Chapter 20

Q1 a) $4n - 2$ b) $0.5n - 0.3$

c) $-3n + 24$ d) $-6n + 82$

e) $5.2 - 0.3n$ f) $2.5n - 21.5$

Q2 a) 0.75   b) Increasing

Q3 61, increasing

Q4 $r = 4$ **Q5** $k = 5$

Q6 $-1, 2, -3, 4, -5$ **Q7** $a = 1, b = 3$

Q8 $u_{k+1} = u_k + 5, u_1 = 32$

Q9 a) 7, 10, 13, 16, 19

b) 2, 3, 2, 3, 2

Q10 a) $u_{k+1} = \sqrt{u_k}, u_1 = 65\ 536$

b) $u_{k+1} = u_k - 2k, u_1 = 40$

c) $u_{n+2} = u_n + u_{n+1}, u_1 = 1, u_2 = 1$

Q11 5, 7, 2, −5, −7, −2, 5, 7, 2, −5.
The sequence is periodic with order 6

Q12 $a = 3, b = 2$

Q13 $k = 2, u_3 = 25, u_4 = 53$

Q14 8, 10, 8, 10, 8, $u_n = 9 + (-1)^n$, periodic

Q15 $d = 0.75$

Q16 6

Q17 $k = 24$

Q18 n^{th} term $= -2n + 50, S_5 = 220$

Q19 610

Q20 a) 300   b) 222

Q21 $k = 35$

Q22 0.6

Q23 $u_n = 3(-3)^{n-1} = -(-3)^n$

Q24 a) $u_{10} = -39366$ b) $S_{10} = -29\ 524$

Q25 a) 11 184 810

b) 59.985 (3 d.p.)

c) 132 860

Q26 16.68 (2 d.p.)

Q27 7th term

Q28 The sum of the first n terms of a geometric series is S_n:
$S_n = a + ar + ar^2 + ar^3 + ... + ar^{n-1}$
Then: $rS_n = ar + ar^2 + ar^3 + ar^4 ... + ar^n$
Subtracting rS_n from S_n gives:
$(1 - r)S_n = a - ar^n = a(1 - r^n)$
$\Rightarrow S_n = \dfrac{a(1 - r^n)}{1 - r}$

Q29 a) $r = 2$ so series is divergent

b) $r = \dfrac{1}{3}$, so series is convergent

c) $r = \dfrac{1}{3}$, so series is convergent

d) $r = \dfrac{1}{4}$, so series is convergent

e) $r = 2.5$, so series is divergent

f) $r - \dfrac{1}{10}$, so series is convergent

Q30 a) $r = \dfrac{1}{2}$

b) 7th term $= 0.375 \left(= \dfrac{3}{8}\right)$

c) $S_{10} = 47.953$ (3 d.p.)

d) $S_\infty = 48$

Q31 $\displaystyle\sum_{k=0}^{\infty} ar^k = 44$

Q32 £1.2 million

Q33 The shop will take over £500 on the 15th day.

Q34 Last week: 2 hours 20 minutes
Total: 17 hours

Q35 2145 stones

Q36 a) The Year 1 donations are £20 000. The donations increase by 8% each year, so the second year the donations will be:
$1.08 \times 20\ 000 = £21\ 600$

b) 1.08

c) $u_n = 20\ 000(1.08)^{n-1}$

d) £289 731 (to the nearest £)

Chapter 21: The Binomial Expansion 2

1. The Binomial Expansion

Exercise 1.1

Q1 a) $1 - 4x + 10x^2 - 20x^3 + ..., |x| < 1$

b) $1 + 18x + 216x^2 + 2160x^3 + ..., |x| < \dfrac{1}{6}$

c) $1 + \dfrac{4x}{3} - \dfrac{16x^2}{9} + \dfrac{320x^3}{81} - ..., |x| < \dfrac{1}{4}$

d) $1 - 2x + 6x^2 - 20x^3 + ..., |x| < \dfrac{1}{4}$

e) $1 - 2x - x^2 - \dfrac{4x^3}{3} ..., |x| < \dfrac{1}{3}$

f) $1 + 8x + 48x^2 + 256x^3 + ..., |x| < \dfrac{1}{4}$

g) $1 + 3x - \dfrac{9x^2}{2} + \dfrac{27x^3}{2} - ..., |x| < \dfrac{1}{6}$

h) $1 + \dfrac{3x}{2} + \dfrac{27x^2}{8} + \dfrac{135x^3}{16} + ..., |x| < \dfrac{1}{3}$

i) $1 + \dfrac{x}{6} - \dfrac{x^2}{36} + \dfrac{5x^3}{648} - ..., |x| < 2$

j) $1 + \dfrac{2x}{3} + \dfrac{5x^2}{9} + \dfrac{40x^3}{81} + ..., |x| < 1$

Q2 a) −6860   b) valid for $|x| < \dfrac{1}{7}$

Q3 a) $-\dfrac{231}{8}$ b) valid for $|x| < \dfrac{1}{4}$

Exercise 1.2

Q1 a) $1 - \dfrac{5x}{6} - \dfrac{125x^2}{72} - ...$

b) $1 + \dfrac{91x}{6} + \dfrac{5827x^2}{72} + ...$

c) valid for $|x| < \dfrac{1}{5}$

Q2 a) $1 + 6x + 21x^2 + ...$
Valid for $|x| < \dfrac{1}{2}$

b) $1 - 5x + 22x^2 - ...$
Valid for $|x| < \dfrac{1}{3}$

c) $1 - \dfrac{47x}{7} - \dfrac{110x^2}{49} + ...$
Valid for $|x| < \dfrac{1}{2}$

d) $1 - \dfrac{10x}{3} + \dfrac{65x^2}{9} - ...$
Valid for $|x| < \dfrac{1}{4}$

Q3 $1 + 9x + 24x^2 + ...,$ valid for $|x| < 1$

Q4 a) (i) $1 + 4ax + 6a^2x^2 + 4a^3x^3 + a^4x^4$

(ii) $1 + 3bx + 6b^2x^2 + ...$

b) $1 + (4a + 3b)x + (6a^2 + 12ab + 6b^2)x^2 + ...$

c) $a = -5, b = 7$ and $a = 7, b = -9$
Equating coefficients of x^2 and factorising the left hand side, you get $6(a + b)^2 = 24 \Rightarrow a + b = \pm 2$. Form simultaneous equations by equating coefficients of x, then solve once for $a + b = 2$ and once for $a + b = -2$.

Exercise 1.3

Q1 a) $8 + 48x + 96x^2 + 64x^3 + ...$

b) $243 + 1620x + 4320x^2 + 5760x^3 + ...$

c) $2 + \dfrac{x}{4} - \dfrac{x^2}{64} + \dfrac{x^3}{512} - ...$

Answers   **527**

d) $\frac{1}{2} - \frac{x}{24} + \frac{x^2}{144} - \frac{7x^3}{5184} + ...$

e) $\frac{1}{81} + \frac{8x}{243} + \frac{40x^2}{729} + \frac{160x^3}{2187} + ...$

f) $3 + \frac{x}{6} - \frac{x^2}{216} + \frac{x^3}{3888} - ...$

Q2 $a = 2$
Find the coefficient of x^2 in the expansion in terms of a, then set this equal to 2000 and solve for a.

Q3 a) $128 - 2240x + 16\,800x^2 - ...$
b) $128 + 64x - 9696x^2 + ...$

Q4 a) $1 - \frac{3x}{5} + \frac{27x^2}{50} - \frac{27x^3}{50} + ...$,
valid for $|x| < \frac{5}{6}$
b) $2 - \frac{6x}{5} + \frac{27x^2}{25} - \frac{27x^3}{25} + ...$
Simplify the expression by applying surd rules and factorising until you find that it's equal to 2 × the expression from part a).

Q5 a) $\frac{1}{\sqrt{5}} + \frac{x}{5\sqrt{5}} + \frac{3x^2}{50\sqrt{5}} + ...$
b) $\frac{3+x}{\sqrt{5-2x}} \approx (3+x)\left(\frac{1}{\sqrt{5}} + \frac{x}{5\sqrt{5}} + \frac{3x^2}{50\sqrt{5}}\right)$
$\approx 3\left(\frac{1}{\sqrt{5}} + \frac{x}{5\sqrt{5}} + \frac{3x^2}{50\sqrt{5}}\right)$
$+ x\left(\frac{1}{\sqrt{5}} + \frac{x}{5\sqrt{5}}\right)$
$= \frac{3}{\sqrt{5}} + \frac{3x}{5\sqrt{5}} + \frac{9x^2}{50\sqrt{5}}$
$+ \frac{x}{\sqrt{5}} + \frac{x^2}{5\sqrt{5}}$
$= \frac{3}{\sqrt{5}} + \frac{8x}{5\sqrt{5}} + \frac{19x^2}{50\sqrt{5}}$

Q6 a) $\frac{1}{3} - \frac{2x}{27} + \frac{2x^2}{81} - ...$
b) $\frac{1}{3} + \frac{214x}{27} + \frac{5690x^2}{81}$

Q7 a) $1 - 6x + 7x^2 - ...$
Valid for $|x| < \frac{1}{3}$
b) $2 - \frac{47x}{4} + \frac{3359x^2}{64} - ...$
Valid for $|x| < \frac{1}{3}$
c) $1 + \frac{x}{4} + \frac{3x^2}{128} + ...$
Valid for $|x| < \frac{8}{3}$
d) $\frac{27}{256} + \frac{189x}{256} + \frac{4959x^2}{2048} + ...$
Valid for $|x| < \frac{3}{4}$

2. Binomial Expansions as Approximations

Exercise 2.1
Q1 a) $1 - 6x + 36x^2 - ...$
b) Valid for $|x| < \frac{1}{6}$
c) (i) 0.9436 (ii) 0.8944
(iii) 1.0636 (iv) 0.76

Q2 a) $1 + \frac{3x}{4} - \frac{27x^2}{32} + \frac{189x^3}{128} - ...$
b) Valid for $|x| < \frac{1}{3}$.
c) 1.1889 (4 d.p.)
d) 1.26% (3 s.f.)

Q3 a) $1 + x + \frac{3x^2}{2} + \frac{5x^3}{2} + ...$
b) Valid for $|x| < \frac{1}{2}$

---

c) 2.235   d) 0.048% (2 s.f.)

Q4 a) $64 - 960x + 6000x^2 - ...$
b) 55   c) 0.036% (2 s.f.)

Q5 a) $\sqrt{3} - \frac{2\sqrt{3}x}{3} - \frac{2\sqrt{3}x^2}{9} - ...$
b) Valid for $|x| < \frac{3}{4}$
c) $\frac{759}{800}$ d) 0.007% (1 s.f.)

3. Binomial Expansions and Partial Fractions

Exercise 3.1
Q1 a) $A = 2,\ B = -3$
b) $(1 + 6x)^{-1} = 1 - 6x + 36x^2 - ...$
$(4 + 3x)^{-1} = \frac{1}{4} - \frac{3x}{16} + \frac{9x^2}{64} - ...$
c) $\frac{5}{4} - \frac{183x}{16} + \frac{4581x^2}{64}$
d) Valid for $|x| < \frac{1}{6}$

Q2 a) $\frac{6}{(1-x)(1+x)(1+2x)}$
$\equiv \frac{A}{(1-x)} + \frac{B}{(1+x)} + \frac{C}{(1+2x)}$
$6 \equiv A(1+x)(1+2x) + B(1-x)(1+2x)$
$+ C(1-x)(1+x)$
Using the substitution method:
When $x = 1$, $6 = 6A \Rightarrow A = 1$
When $x = -1$, $6 = -2B \Rightarrow B = -3$
When $x = -\frac{1}{2}$, $6 = \frac{3}{4}C \Rightarrow C = 8$
Putting these values back into the expression gives:
$\frac{6}{(1-x)(1+x)(1+2x)}$
$\equiv \frac{1}{(1-x)} - \frac{3}{(1+x)} + \frac{8}{(1+2x)}$
b) $6 - 12x + 30x^2$
c) 0.0010% (2 s.f.)

Q3 a) $2x^3 + 5x^2 - 3x = x(2x-1)(x+3)$
$\frac{5x-6}{2x^3 + 5x^2 - 3x}$
$\equiv \frac{2}{x} - \frac{2}{(2x-1)} - \frac{1}{(x+3)}$
b) $\frac{2}{x} + \frac{5}{3} + \frac{37x}{9} + \frac{215x^2}{27}$
c) $|x| < \frac{1}{2}, x \neq 0$.

Q4 a) $\frac{55x+7}{(2x-5)(3x+1)^2}$
$\equiv \frac{2}{(2x-5)} - \frac{3}{(3x+1)} + \frac{2}{(3x+1)^2}$
b) $-\frac{7}{5} - \frac{79x}{25} - \frac{3367x^2}{125}$

Review Exercise — Chapter 21

Q1 a) $1 + 6x + 12x^2 + 8x^3$
b) $1 - 5x + 10x^2 - 10x^3 + 5x^4 - x^5$
c) $1 - 16x + 96x^2 - 256x^3 + 256x^4$
d) $1 - \frac{8x}{3} + \frac{8x^2}{3} - \frac{32x^3}{27} + \frac{16x^4}{81}$

Q2 Positive integer values (and zero).

Q3 a) $a = 4$ b) $a = 3$

Q4 $\left|\frac{dx}{c}\right| < 1$ or $|x| < \left|\frac{c}{d}\right|$

Q5 a) $1 - 5x + 15x^2 - 35x^3 + ...$, $|x| < 1$
b) $1 + 9x + 54x^2 + 270x^3 + ...$, $|x| < \frac{1}{3}$
c) $1 - \frac{5x}{2} - \frac{25x^2}{8} - \frac{125x^3}{16} + ...$,
$|x| < \frac{1}{5}$
d) $1 - \frac{2x}{3} + \frac{8x^2}{9} - \frac{112x^3}{81} + ...$, $|x| < \frac{1}{2}$

Q6 a) (i) $\frac{1}{9} - \frac{4}{27}x + \frac{4}{27}x^2 - ...$,
valid for $|x| < \frac{3}{2}$
(ii) $2 - \frac{1}{12}x - \frac{1}{288}x^2 - ...$,
valid for $|x| < 8$
b) $\frac{2}{9} - \frac{11x}{36} + \frac{799x^2}{2592} - ...$,
valid for $|x| < \frac{3}{2}$
c) (i) $\frac{551}{288}$ (ii) 0.014% (to 2 s.f.)

Q7 a) Write as an identity:
$\frac{5-10x}{(1+2x)(2-x)} \equiv \frac{A}{(1+2x)} + \frac{B}{(2-x)}$
So $5 - 10x \equiv A(2-x) + B(1+2x)$
$x = 2 \Rightarrow 5 - 20 = 5B \Rightarrow B = -3$
$x = -0.5 \Rightarrow 5 + 5 = 2.5A \Rightarrow A = 4$
So $\frac{5-10x}{(1+2x)(2-x)}$
$\equiv \frac{4}{(1+2x)} - \frac{3}{(2-x)}$ as required
b) $\frac{5}{2} - \frac{35x}{4} + \frac{125x^2}{8}$
c) 1.5% (to 2 s.f.)

Q8 a) $\frac{1}{a^2} + \frac{4x}{a^3} + \frac{12x^2}{a^4} + ...$
b) valid for $|x| < \left|\frac{a}{2}\right|$
c) $\frac{1}{2} + \frac{ax}{16} + \frac{3a^2x^2}{256} + ...$
d) valid for $|x| < \left|\frac{4}{a}\right|$
e) $\frac{1}{2a^2} + \frac{(a^2+32)x}{16a^3} + ...$ f) $\frac{9}{32}$
Treat a as a constant throughout this question. Multiply the two expressions together for part e), ignoring all the x^2 or higher power terms. Then for part f), substitute a = 2 into the expression you obtained for the coefficient of x in part e).

Chapter 22: Differentiation 2

1. Points of Inflection

Exercise 1.1
Q1 a) The graph is concave when $x < 1$
b) The graph is concave when $x < 5$
c) The graph is concave when
$x < -\sqrt{\frac{2}{3}}$ or $x > \sqrt{\frac{2}{3}}$

Q2 a) The graph is convex for all values of x (i.e. $x \in \mathbb{R}$)
b) The graph is convex when $x > -3$
c) The graph is convex when $x < -\sqrt{2}$ or $x > \sqrt{2}$

Q3 $f(x)$ is convex for $x < -7$ and $x > 1$, and concave for $-7 < x < 1$.

Exercise 1.2

Q1 $x = \pm\dfrac{1}{3}$

Q2 $y = x^2 - \dfrac{1}{x} \Rightarrow \dfrac{dy}{dx} = 2x + \dfrac{1}{x^2}$

$\Rightarrow \dfrac{d^2y}{dx^2} = 2 - \dfrac{2}{x^3}$

At a point of inflection, $\dfrac{d^2y}{dx^2} = 0$

$\Rightarrow 2 - \dfrac{2}{x^3} = 0 \Rightarrow 2 = \dfrac{2}{x^3}$

$\Rightarrow x^3 = 1 \Rightarrow x = 1$

If $x < 1$, $x^3 < 1$, so $\dfrac{2}{x^3} > 2$,

so $\dfrac{d^2y}{dx^2}$ is negative.

If $x > 1$, $x^3 > 1$, so $\dfrac{2}{x^3} < 2$,

so $\dfrac{d^2y}{dx^2}$ is positive.

So at $x = 1$, $\dfrac{d^2y}{dx^2} = 0$ and the sign

of $\dfrac{d^2y}{dx^2}$ changes, so this is a point
of inflection.
When $x = 1$, $y = 1^2 - \dfrac{1}{1} = 0$, so $(1, 0)$
is a point of inflection of $y = x^2 - \dfrac{1}{x}$.

Q3 $(-1, 2)$

Q4 $y = x^5 - 6x^4 - \dfrac{16}{3}x^3 + 4$

$\Rightarrow \dfrac{dy}{dx} = 5x^4 - 24x^3 - 16x^2$

$\Rightarrow \dfrac{d^2y}{dx^2} = 20x^3 - 72x^2 - 32x$

At a point of inflection, $\dfrac{d^2y}{dx^2} = 0$

$\Rightarrow 20x^3 - 72x^2 - 32x = 0$
$\Rightarrow 5x^3 - 18x^2 - 8x = 0$
$\Rightarrow x(5x + 2)(x - 4) = 0$
$\Rightarrow x = 0, -0.4$ or 4
The question only asks for $x = 0$,
so ignore the other two points.
If x is small and positive,
$20x^3 - 72x^2 - 32x < 0$ and if x is small
and negative, $20x^3 - 72x^2 - 32x > 0$.

So at $x = 0$, $\dfrac{d^2y}{dx^2} = 0$ and the sign of $\dfrac{d^2y}{dx^2}$

changes, so this is a point of inflection.
When $x = 0$, $y = 4$, so $(0, 4)$ is a point of
inflection.

Exercise 1.3

Q1 **a)** $f(x) = x^3 + 2x^2 + 3x + 3$
$\Rightarrow f'(x) = 3x^2 + 4x + 3$
$\Rightarrow f''(x) = 6x + 4$
At a point of inflection, $f''(x) = 0$
$\Rightarrow 6x + 4 = 0 \Rightarrow x = -\dfrac{2}{3}$

When $x > -\dfrac{2}{3}$, $6x + 4 > 0$

and when $x < -\dfrac{2}{3}$, $6x + 4 < 0$

So the graph of $y = f(x)$ has one point

of inflection, at $x = -\dfrac{2}{3}$.

b) $f'(x) = 3x^2 + 4x + 3$, so at $x = -\dfrac{2}{3}$,

$f'(x) = 3\left(-\dfrac{2}{3}\right)^2 + 4\left(-\dfrac{2}{3}\right) + 3$

$= \dfrac{4}{3} - \dfrac{8}{3} + 3 = \dfrac{5}{3}$

$f'(x) \neq 0$ at the point of inflection,
so it is not a stationary point.

Q2 There is a stationary point at $(0, 1)$ which
is a point of inflection and another at
$\left(\dfrac{3}{2}, -\dfrac{11}{16}\right)$ which is a minimum.

Q3 There are stationary points at $\left(-1, \dfrac{56}{15}\right)$
and $\left(1, \dfrac{64}{15}\right)$, and both are points of
inflection.

Q4 There is a stationary point at
$(-10, 4\,000\,000)$ which is a maximum,
another at $(0, 0)$ which is a point of
inflection and another at
$(10, -4\,000\,000)$ which is a minimum.

2. Chain Rule

Exercise 2.1

Q1 **a)** $\dfrac{dy}{dx} = 2(x + 7)$

b) $\dfrac{dy}{dx} = 10(2x - 1)^4$

c) $\dfrac{dy}{dx} = -24(4 - x)^7$

d) $\dfrac{dy}{dx} = -14(3 - 2x)^6$

e) $\dfrac{dy}{dx} = 10x(x^2 + 3)^4$

f) $\dfrac{dy}{dx} = 20x(5x^2 + 3)$

g) $\dfrac{dy}{dx} = 18x(x^2 - 1)^2$

h) $\dfrac{dy}{dx} = 96x(4x^2 + 5)^5$

Q2 **a)** $f'(x) = 96x^2(4x^3 - 9)^7$

b) $f'(x) = -56x(6 - 7x^2)^3$

c) $f'(x) = (x^2 + 5x + 7)^5(12x + 30)$

d) $f'(x) = -3(x + 4)^{-4}$

e) $f'(x) = 6(5 - 3x)^{-3}$

f) $f'(x) = \dfrac{12}{(5 - 3x)^5}$

g) $f'(x) = 9x(3x^2 + 4)^{\frac{1}{2}}$

h) $f'(x) = \dfrac{3}{2\left(\sqrt{5 - 3x}\right)^3}$

Q3 **a)** $\dfrac{1}{4\sqrt{2}}$ **b)** $-\dfrac{4}{7\left(\sqrt[3]{7}\right)}$

Q4 **a)** $\left(\sqrt{x} + \dfrac{1}{\sqrt{x}}\right)^2$

$= \sqrt{x}\sqrt{x} + 2\sqrt{x}\dfrac{1}{\sqrt{x}} + \dfrac{1}{\sqrt{x}}\dfrac{1}{\sqrt{x}}$

$= x + \dfrac{1}{x} + 2$

$\dfrac{d}{dx}\left(x + \dfrac{1}{x} + 2\right) = 1 - \dfrac{1}{x^2}$

b) $y = \left(\sqrt{x} + \dfrac{1}{\sqrt{x}}\right)^2$,

so let $y = u^2$ where $u = \sqrt{x} + \dfrac{1}{\sqrt{x}}$

$\Rightarrow \dfrac{dy}{du} = 2u = 2\left(\sqrt{x} + \dfrac{1}{\sqrt{x}}\right)$,

$\dfrac{du}{dx} = \dfrac{1}{2}x^{-\frac{1}{2}} - \dfrac{1}{2}x^{-\frac{3}{2}} = \dfrac{1}{2\sqrt{x}} - \dfrac{1}{2\left(\sqrt{x}\right)^3}$

$\dfrac{dy}{dx} = \dfrac{dy}{du} \times \dfrac{du}{dx}$

$= 2\left(\sqrt{x} + \dfrac{1}{\sqrt{x}}\right) \times \left(\dfrac{1}{2\sqrt{x}} - \dfrac{1}{2\left(\sqrt{x}\right)^3}\right)$

$= 2\left(\dfrac{1}{2} + \dfrac{1}{2x} - \dfrac{1}{2x} - \dfrac{1}{2x^2}\right) = 1 - \dfrac{1}{x^2}$

Q5 $y = 80x - 112$ **Q6** $y = x - \dfrac{23}{4}$

Q7 $-\dfrac{7}{128}$

Q8 $f'(x) = \dfrac{14}{3\left(\sqrt[3]{3 - 2x}\right)^4}$ or $\dfrac{14}{3}(3 - 2x)^{-\frac{4}{3}}$

Q9 $5x - 6y + 8 = 0$

Q10 $y = 22 - 4x$ **Q11** $y = -6x - 5$

Q12 $y = (2x - 3)^7$, so let $y = u^7$
where $u = 2x - 3$

$\Rightarrow \dfrac{dy}{du} = 7u^6 = 7(2x - 3)^6$, $\dfrac{du}{dx} = 2$

$\dfrac{dy}{dx} = \dfrac{dy}{du} \times \dfrac{du}{dx} = 7(2x - 3)^6 \times 2$
$\qquad = 14(2x - 3)^6$

Use the chain rule again to find $\dfrac{d^2y}{dx^2}$:

$\dfrac{dy}{dx} = 14(2x - 3)^6$, so let $\dfrac{dy}{dx} = 14u^6$

where $u = 2x - 3$

$\Rightarrow \dfrac{d}{du}\left(\dfrac{dy}{dx}\right) = 84u^5 = 84(2x - 3)^5$, $\dfrac{du}{dx} = 2$

$\dfrac{d^2y}{dx^2} = \dfrac{d}{dx}\left(\dfrac{dy}{dx}\right) = \dfrac{d}{du}\left(\dfrac{dy}{dx}\right) \times \dfrac{du}{dx}$

$= 84(2x - 3)^5 \times 2 = 168(2x - 3)^5$

At a point of inflection, $\dfrac{d^2y}{dx^2} = 0$

$\Rightarrow 2x - 3 = 0 \Rightarrow x = \dfrac{3}{2}$

When $x < \dfrac{3}{2}$, $(2x - 3) < 0 \Rightarrow \dfrac{d^2y}{dx^2} < 0$

When $x > \dfrac{3}{2}$, $(2x - 3) > 0 \Rightarrow \dfrac{d^2y}{dx^2} > 0$

So the sign of $\dfrac{d^2y}{dx^2}$ changes at $x = \dfrac{3}{2}$,

so this is a point of inflection.

$x = \dfrac{3}{2} \Rightarrow y = (2 \times \dfrac{3}{2} - 3)^7 = 0$

So the coordinates of the point of

inflection are $\left(\dfrac{3}{2}, 0\right)$.

Q13 The curve is convex for $x > 8$ and
concave for $x < 8$.

*Here, you have to differentiate y using the
chain rule (let $y = u^3$, where $u = \dfrac{x}{4} - 2$)
to find $\dfrac{dy}{dx}$, then use the chain rule again to
find $\dfrac{d^2y}{dx^2}$. The curve is convex for $\dfrac{d^2y}{dx^2} > 0$
and concave for $\dfrac{d^2y}{dx^2} < 0$, so solve the
inequalities to find the ranges of x.*

Exercise 2.2

Q1 **a)** -1 **b)** 0.1 **c)** $-\dfrac{1}{7}$

d) $\dfrac{4}{3}$ **e)** $-\dfrac{1}{11}$ **f)** -2

Q2 $\dfrac{dy}{dx} = \dfrac{1}{18y^2(2y^3 - 5)^2}$

Q3 **a)** $x = \sqrt{4 + y} \Rightarrow x = u^{\frac{1}{2}}$, $u = 4 + y$

$\Rightarrow \dfrac{dx}{du} = \dfrac{1}{2}u^{-\frac{1}{2}} = \dfrac{1}{2}\dfrac{1}{\sqrt{4 + y}}$, $\dfrac{du}{dy} = 1$

$\dfrac{dx}{dy} = \dfrac{dx}{du} \times \dfrac{du}{dy} = \dfrac{1}{2}\dfrac{1}{\sqrt{4 + y}} \times 1$

$= \dfrac{1}{2\sqrt{4 + y}} = \dfrac{1}{2x}$

$\Rightarrow \dfrac{dy}{dx} = 2x$

b) $x = \sqrt{4 + y} \Rightarrow x^2 = 4 + y$

$\Rightarrow y = x^2 - 4 \Rightarrow \dfrac{dy}{dx} = 2x$

3. Differentiation of e^x, $\ln x$ and a^x

Exercise 3.1

Q1 **a)** $\dfrac{dy}{dx} = 3e^{3x}$ **b)** $\dfrac{dy}{dx} = 2e^{2x - 5}$

c) $\frac{dy}{dx} = e^{x+7}$ **d)** $\frac{dy}{dx} = 3e^{3x+9}$

e) $\frac{dy}{dx} = -2e^{7-2x}$ **f)** $\frac{dy}{dx} = 3x^2\,e^{x^3}$

Q2 **a)** $f'(x) = (3x^2 + 3)e^{x^3+3x}$
  b) $f'(x) = (3x^2 - 3)e^{x^3-3x-5}$
  c) $f'(x) = (4x + 1)e^{x(2x + 1)}$
  d) $f'(x) = (4x^3 - 2x)e^{x^4-x^2}$

Q3 **a)** $f'(x) = \frac{1}{2}(e^x + e^{-x})$
  b) $f'(x) = (2x + 7)e^{x^2+7x+12}$
  c) $f'(x) = (4x^3 + 6x)e^{x^4+3x^2} + 4e^{2x}$
  d) $f'(x) = 24e^{8x} - 10x^4e^{2x^5}$

Q4 $y = 2x + 1$

Q5 $x = 3 - \ln 2$

Q6 $y = 4e^2x - 3e^2$

Q7 $\frac{dy}{dx} = f'(x)e^{f(x)} - 1 = 2e^{2x-4} - 1$,

$\frac{d^2y}{dx^2} = 2 \times f'(x)e^{f(x)} = 4e^{2x-4}$

$4e^{2x-4} > 0$ for all values of x, so $\frac{d^2y}{dx^2}$ is always positive, which means the graph of $y = e^{2x-4} - x$ is always convex.

Q8 $y = -\frac{1}{3}x + 4$

Q9 The graph has one point of inflection, at $\left(\frac{1}{2}, \frac{3}{2}e\right)$.

Q10 If y has a stationary point, the gradient $\frac{dy}{dx}$ will be 0.
$\frac{dy}{dx} = f'(x)e^{f(x)} = (3x^2 - 3)e^{x^3-3x-5}$
So if $\frac{dy}{dx} = 0$, either $3x^2 - 3 = 0$ or $e^{x^3-3x-5} = 0$.

If $3x^2 - 3 = 0 \Rightarrow 3(x^2 - 1) = 0$
$\Rightarrow x^2 = 1 \Rightarrow x = \pm1$
and if $e^{x^3-3x-5} = 0$, there are no solutions.
So the gradient is 0 when $x = \pm1$
$\Rightarrow$ the curve has stationary points at $x = \pm1$.

Q11 $x = \frac{1}{3}\ln 2$, and this is a minimum point.

Exercise 3.2

Q1 **a)** $\frac{dy}{dx} = \frac{1}{x}$ **b)** $\frac{dy}{dx} = \frac{1}{1+x}$

  c) $\frac{dy}{dx} = \frac{5}{1+5x}$ **d)** $\frac{dy}{dx} = \frac{8}{2x-1}$

Q2 **a)** $\frac{dy}{dx} = \frac{2x}{1+x^2}$ **b)** $\frac{dy}{dx} = \frac{2}{2+x}$

  c) $\frac{dy}{dx} = \frac{9}{x}$ **d)** $\frac{dy}{dx} = \frac{3x+2}{x^2+x}$

Q3 **a)** $f'(x) = -\frac{1}{x}$ **b)** $f'(x) = \frac{1}{2x}$

  c) $f'(x) = -\frac{1}{2x}$

Q4 $f'(x) = \dfrac{2\sqrt{x-4} - 1}{2\,(x\sqrt{x-4} - x + 4)}$

Q5 **a)** $y = -x + \ln 36 - 2$
  b) $y = x + \ln 36 - 2$

Q6 **a)** $y = -\frac{3}{2}x + \ln 9 - \frac{9}{2}$
  b) $y = -3x + \ln 36$

Q7 There is one stationary point, which occurs at (1, 0).

Exercise 3.3

Q1 **a)** $\frac{dy}{dx} = 5^x \ln 5$

  b) $\frac{dy}{dx} = 7^x \ln 7$

  c) $\frac{dy}{dx} = (2 \ln 3)\,3^{2x}$

  d) $\frac{dy}{dx} = -(10^{-x} \ln 10)$

  e) $\frac{dy}{dx} = (q \ln p)p^{qx}$

Q2 **a)** Let $u = 4x$, then $y = 2^u$ and
    $\frac{dy}{dx} = \frac{d}{du}(2^u) \times \frac{d}{dx}(4x) = 4(2^{4x} \ln 2)$
  b) $y = (1024 \ln 2)\,x + 256 - 2048 \ln 2$
    or $y = (1024 \ln 2)\,x + 256(1 - 8 \ln 2)$

Q3 **a)** $p = 5$ **b)** $160 \ln 2$

Q4 **a)** Let $u = x^3$, then $y = p^u$, and so
    $\frac{dy}{dx} = \frac{d}{du}(p^u) \times \frac{d}{dx}(x^3) = 3x^2(p^{x^3} \ln p)$
  b) $p = 3$
  c) $y = (9 \ln 3)x + (3 - 9 \ln 3)$

Q5 When $x = 25$, $y = 4^5 = 1024$,
    so $a = 1024$.
    Let $u = x^{\frac{1}{2}}$ and $y = 4^u$, so
    $\frac{dy}{dx} = \frac{d}{du}(4^u)\frac{d}{dx}(x^{\frac{1}{2}}) = \frac{1}{2}x^{-\frac{1}{2}}(4^{\sqrt{x}} \ln 4)$
    The gradient of the tangent when $x = 25$ is $\frac{1}{10}(1024 \ln 4) = 102.4 \ln 4$
    Putting this into $y = mx + c$ gives:
    $1024 = 2560 \ln 4 + c$
    $\Rightarrow c = 1024 - 2560 \ln 4$.
    So the equation of the tangent is
    $y = (102.4 \ln 4)x + (1024 - 2560 \ln 4)$
    $\Rightarrow y = 142x - 2520$ to 3 s.f.

Q6 **a)** $\frac{dy}{dx} = -3(2^{-3x} \ln 2)$

  b) $b = \frac{1}{64}$ and $\frac{dy}{dx} = -\frac{3}{64} \ln 2$

  c) At $\left(2, \frac{1}{64}\right)$, the gradient of the tangent is $-\frac{3}{64} \ln 2$.
    Putting this into $y = mx + c$ gives:
    $\frac{1}{64} = -\frac{6}{64} \ln 2 + c$
    $\Rightarrow c = \frac{1}{64} + \frac{6}{64} \ln 2$.
    So the equation of the tangent is
    $y = \frac{1 + 6\ln 2}{64} - \left(\frac{3\ln 2}{64}\right)x$
    $\Rightarrow 64y = 1 + 6 \ln 2 - (3 \ln 2)x$

4. Differentiating Trig Functions

Exercise 4.1

Q1 **a)** $\frac{dy}{dx} = 3 \cos (3x)$

  b) $\frac{dy}{dx} = 2 \sin (-2x)$

  c) $\frac{dy}{dx} = -\frac{1}{2} \sin \frac{x}{2}$

  d) $\frac{dy}{dx} = \cos \left(x + \frac{\pi}{4}\right)$

  e) $\frac{dy}{dx} = 3 \sec^2 \frac{x}{2}$

  f) $\frac{dy}{dx} = 15 \sec^2 (5x)$

Q2 **a)** $f'(x) = 6 \sec^2 (2x - 1)$
  b) $f'(x) = 3(\sec^2 x + \sec^2 (3x))$
  c) $f'(x) = 2x \cos (x^2 + \frac{\pi}{3})$
  d) $f'(x) = 2 \sin x \cos x$
  e) $f'(x) = 6 \sin^2 x \cos x$
  f) $f'(x) = -4 \sin x \cos^3 x + 2 \sec^2 2x$

Q3 **a)** $f'(x) = 3 \cos x - 2 \sin x$
  b) $x = 0.983$ (3 s.f.)

Q4 $\frac{dy}{dx} = \sec x \tan x$

Q5 **a)** Let $y = f(x)$, where $f(x) = \sin x$.
    Then $\frac{dy}{dx} = \lim_{h\to 0}\left[\frac{f(x+h) - f(x)}{(x+h) - x}\right]$
    $= \lim_{h\to 0}\left[\frac{\sin(x+h) - \sin x}{(x+h) - x}\right]$
    Using the sin addition formula:
    $\frac{dy}{dx} = \lim_{h\to 0}\left[\frac{\sin x \cos h + \cos x \sin h - \sin x}{(x+h) - x}\right]$
    $= \lim_{h\to 0}\left[\frac{\sin x(\cos h - 1) + \cos x \sin h}{h}\right]$
    $= \lim_{h\to 0}\left[\frac{\sin x(\cos h - 1)}{h} + \frac{\cos x \sin h}{h}\right]$
    Using small angle approximations,
    $\sin h \approx h$ and $\cos h \approx 1 - \frac{1}{2}h^2$, so:
    $\frac{dy}{dx} = \lim_{h\to 0}\left[\frac{\sin x \times \left(-\frac{1}{2}h^2\right)}{h} + \frac{\cos x \times h}{h}\right]$
    $= \lim_{h\to 0}\left[-\frac{h \sin x}{2} + \cos x\right] = \cos x$

  b) Let $y = f(x)$, where $f(x) = \cos x$.
    Then $\frac{dy}{dx} = \lim_{h\to 0}\left[\frac{f(x+h) - f(x)}{(x+h) - x}\right]$
    $= \lim_{h\to 0}\left[\frac{\cos(x+h) - \cos x}{(x+h) - x}\right]$
    Using the cos addition formula:
    $\frac{dy}{dx} = \lim_{h\to 0}\left[\frac{\cos x \cos h - \sin x \sin h - \cos x}{(x+h) - x}\right]$
    $= \lim_{h\to 0}\left[\frac{\cos x(\cos h - 1) - \sin x \sin h}{h}\right]$
    $= \lim_{h\to 0}\left[\frac{\cos x(\cos h - 1)}{h} - \frac{\sin x \sin h}{h}\right]$
    Using small angle approximations,
    $\cos h \approx 1 - \frac{1}{2}h^2$ and $\sin h \approx h$, so:
    $\frac{dy}{dx} = \lim_{h\to 0}\left[\frac{\cos x \times \left(-\frac{1}{2}h^2\right)}{h} - \frac{\sin x \times h}{h}\right]$
    $= \lim_{h\to 0}\left[-\frac{h \cos x}{2} - \sin x\right] = -\sin x$

Q6 **a)** $y = \cos^2 x$, so let $y = u^2$ where $u = \cos x$
    $\frac{dy}{dx} = \frac{dy}{du} \times \frac{du}{dx} = (2 \cos x) \times (-\sin x)$
    $= -2 \sin x \cos x$

  b) Using the double angle formula:
    $\cos (2x) \equiv 2 \cos^2 x - 1$
    $\Rightarrow \cos^2 x = \frac{1}{2}(\cos (2x) + 1)$
    $\frac{dy}{dx} = \frac{1}{2} \times 2 \times (-\sin (2x)) = -\sin (2x)$
    From the double angle formula for sin: $-\sin (2x) \equiv -2 \sin x \cos x$

Q7 First part:
$y = 6 \cos^2 x = 6(\cos x)^2$, so let $y = 6u^2$
where $u = \cos x$
$\Rightarrow \dfrac{dy}{du} = 12u = 12 \cos x$, $\dfrac{du}{dx} = -\sin x$
$\dfrac{dy}{dx} = \dfrac{dy}{du} \times \dfrac{du}{dx} = -12 \sin x \cos x$

Second part:
$y = 2 \sin (2x)$, so let $y = 2 \sin u$
where $u = 2x$
$\Rightarrow \dfrac{dy}{du} = 2 \cos u = 2 \cos (2x)$, $\dfrac{du}{dx} = 2$
$\dfrac{dy}{dx} = \dfrac{dy}{du} \times \dfrac{du}{dx} = 4 \cos (2x)$

Putting it all together:
$\dfrac{dy}{dx} = -12 \sin x \cos x - 4 \cos (2x)$

Double angle formula:
$2 \sin x \cos x \equiv \sin (2x)$
$\Rightarrow -12 \sin x \cos x - 4 \cos (2x)$
$= -6 \sin (2x) - 4 \cos (2x)$

Q8 $\dfrac{1}{\sqrt{2}}$

Q9 $y = \dfrac{1}{2}x - \dfrac{\pi}{8}$ (or $4x - 8y - \pi = 0$)

Q10 **a)** $y = x + \dfrac{\pi}{6} - \dfrac{\sqrt{3}}{2}$

   b) $y = -x + \dfrac{\pi}{6} + \dfrac{\sqrt{3}}{2}$

Q11 **a)** $y = 2 \sin (2x) \cos x$
   $\Rightarrow y = 4 \sin x \cos^2 x$
   (from double angle formula $\sin (2x)$
   $\equiv 2 \sin x \cos x$)
   $\Rightarrow y = 4 \sin x (1 - \sin^2 x)$
   (from $\sin^2 x + \cos^2 x \equiv 1$)
   $\Rightarrow y = 4 \sin x - 4 \sin^3 x$

   b) $\dfrac{dy}{dx} = 4 \cos x - 12 \sin^2 x \cos x$

Exercise 4.2

Q1 **a)** $\dfrac{dy}{dx} = -2 \sin (2x) \cos (\cos (2x))$

   b) $\dfrac{dy}{dx} = -6 \tan (3x)$

   c) $\dfrac{dy}{dx} = \dfrac{2 \sec^2 x}{\tan x}$ (or $2 \sec x \, \text{cosec} \, x$)

   d) $\dfrac{dy}{dx} = 2 \sec^2 (2x) \, e^{\tan (2x)}$

Q2 **a)** $\dfrac{dy}{dx} = 8x \sin^3 x^2 \cos x^2$

   b) $\dfrac{dy}{dx} = 2 \, e^{\sin^2 x} \sin x \cos x$

   c) $\dfrac{dy}{dx} = 6 \tan (3x) \sec^2 (3x) + \cos x$

   d) $\dfrac{dy}{dx} = -4 \sin (2x) \, e^{2 \cos (2x)}$
   $\qquad - 4 \sin (2x) \cos (2x)$

5. Product Rule
Exercise 5.1

Q1 **a)** $y = x(x + 2) = x^2 + 2x$
   $\dfrac{dy}{dx} = 2x + 2$

   b) $u = x$, $v = x + 2 \Rightarrow \dfrac{du}{dx} = 1$, $\dfrac{dv}{dx} = 1$
   $\dfrac{dy}{dx} = u\dfrac{dv}{dx} + v\dfrac{du}{dx} = x + (x + 2) = 2x + 2$

Q2 **a)** $\dfrac{dy}{dx} = x(x + 6)^2(5x + 12)$

   b) $\dfrac{dy}{dx} = x^2(5x + 2)^3(35x + 6)$

   c) $\dfrac{dy}{dx} = x^2 e^x(x + 3)$

   d) $\dfrac{dy}{dx} = e^{4x}(4x + 1)$

   e) $\dfrac{dy}{dx} = e^{x^2}(2x^2 + 1)$

   f) $\dfrac{dy}{dx} = e^{2x}(\cos x + 2 \sin x)$

   g) $\dfrac{dy}{dx} = 4x^3 \cos x - x^4 \sin x$

   h) $\dfrac{dy}{dx} = x + 2x \ln x$

Q3 **a)** $f'(x) = \dfrac{x^3}{2(x + 3)^{\frac{1}{2}}} + 3x^2(x + 3)^{\frac{1}{2}}$

   b) $f'(x) = -\dfrac{x^2}{2(\sqrt{x - 7})^3} + \dfrac{2x}{\sqrt{x - 7}}$

   c) $f'(x) = x^3(1 + 4 \ln x)$

   d) $f'(x) = 8 + 4 \ln x^2$

   e) $f'(x) = 2x^2(3 \cos x - x \sin x)$

   f) $f'(x) = 2x(\cos (2x) - x \sin (2x))$

   g) $f'(x) = \cos^2 x - \sin^2 x = \cos 2x$

   h) $f'(x) = \sqrt{x} \sec^2 x + \dfrac{\tan x}{2\sqrt{x}}$

Q4 **a)** $\dfrac{dy}{dx} = 4x^3 + 6x^2 - 2$

   b) $\dfrac{dy}{dx} = 4x^3 + 6x^2 - 2$

   c) $y = (x + 1)^2(x^2 - 1)$
   $= (x + 1)^2(x + 1)(x - 1) = (x + 1)^3(x - 1)$

Q5 The curve is concave when $x < -2$

Q6 $13x - 12y + 46 = 0$

Q7 **a)** $5x - 108y + 47 = 0$

   b) $324x + 15y - 1630 = 0$

Q8 $\dfrac{dy}{dx} = \dfrac{5x^2 + 12x}{2\sqrt{x + 3}} \, e^{x^2\sqrt{x + 3}}$

Q9 $f'(x) = \dfrac{10x - 31}{2(2x + 1)(x - 4)}$

Q10 The stationary points are $(1, 1)$ and $\left(-\dfrac{1}{2}, -\dfrac{e^{\frac{3}{4}}}{2}\right)$.

Q11 **a)** The stationary points are $(2, 0)$, $(-4, 0)$ and $(-0.4, 268.74)$.

   b) $\dfrac{d^2y}{dx^2} = 4(x + 4)(5x^2 + 4x - 10)$
   $(2, 0)$ is a minimum point
   $(-4, 0)$ is a point of inflection
   $(-0.4, 268.74)$ is a maximum point

6. Quotient Rule
Exercise 6.1

Q1 **a)** $\dfrac{dy}{dx} = -\dfrac{8}{(x - 3)^2}$

   b) $\dfrac{dy}{dx} = \dfrac{(x - 7)^3(-x - 1)}{(5 - x)^4}$

   c) $\dfrac{dy}{dx} = \dfrac{e^x(x - 2)}{x^3}$

   d) $\dfrac{dy}{dx} = \dfrac{-3x - 3}{(x - 1)^3}$

Q2 **a)** $f'(x) = \dfrac{9x^2}{(x + 3)^4}$

   b) $f'(x) = \dfrac{3x^2 - 28x}{2(\sqrt{x - 7})^3}$

   c) $f'(x) = \dfrac{4}{e^{4x} + e^{-4x} + 2}$

d) $f'(x) = \dfrac{\sin x - x \cos x}{\sin^2 x}$

   e) $f'(x) = \dfrac{x \cos x - \sin x}{x^2}$

   f) $f'(x) = \dfrac{1 - 3 \ln x}{x^4}$

Q3 $f'(x) = 2x \cot x - x^2 \, \text{cosec}^2 \, x$

Q4 The coordinates of the stationary point are $\left(\dfrac{8}{5}, \dfrac{25}{32}\right)$.
$\dfrac{dy}{dx} = \dfrac{8 - 5x}{2x^3}$ and $\dfrac{d^2y}{dx^2} = \dfrac{5x - 12}{x^4}$
When $x = \dfrac{8}{5}$, $\dfrac{d^2y}{dx^2} = \dfrac{-4}{\left(\dfrac{8}{5}\right)^4}$
Since the denominator is positive, $\dfrac{d^2y}{dx^2}$ is negative, and so the stationary point must be a maximum.

Q5 The only point of inflection occurs at the point $\left(2, \dfrac{2}{e^2}\right)$

Q6 **a)** $\dfrac{dy}{dx} = \dfrac{\cos (2x) + 2x \sin (2x)}{\cos^2 (2x)}$

   b) $\dfrac{dy}{dx} = 0$ if $\cos (2x) + 2x \sin (2x) = 0$
   $\Rightarrow -\cos (2x) = 2x \sin (2x)$
   $\Rightarrow 2x = -\dfrac{\cos (2x)}{\sin (2x)} = -\cot (2x)$
   $\Rightarrow x = -\dfrac{1}{2} \cot (2x)$

Q7 **a)** $y = 4x + 1 - 2\pi$

   b) $y = -\dfrac{1}{4}x + 1 + \dfrac{\pi}{8}$

Q8 $4 + \dfrac{4\pi\sqrt{3}}{3}$

Q9 $u = x - \sin x$, $v = 1 + \cos x$
   $\Rightarrow \dfrac{du}{dx} = 1 - \cos x$, $\dfrac{dv}{dx} = -\sin x$
   $\dfrac{dy}{dx} = \dfrac{v\dfrac{du}{dx} - u\dfrac{dv}{dx}}{v^2}$
   $= \dfrac{[(1 + \cos x)(1 - \cos x)] - [(x - \sin x)(-\sin x)]}{(1 + \cos x)^2}$
   $= \dfrac{1 - \cos^2 x - \sin^2 x + x \sin x}{(1 + \cos x)^2}$
   $= \dfrac{1 - 1 + x \sin x}{(1 + \cos x)^2} = \dfrac{x \sin x}{(1 + \cos x)^2}$

Q10 $f'(x) = \dfrac{9x + 5}{(3x + 1)(2x + 1)}$

Q11 The stationary points are $(0, 1)$, $\left(\pi, -\dfrac{1}{7}\right)$ and $(2\pi, 1)$.

Q12 $\dfrac{dy}{dx} = \dfrac{2e^{\frac{1+x}{1-x}}}{(1 - x)^2}$
   Use the chain rule on $e^{f(x)}$, then use the quotient rule to find $f'(x)$.

Q13 The values of x where $\dfrac{2 + 3x^2}{3x - 1}$ is increasing are $x < \dfrac{1 - \sqrt{7}}{3}$ and $x > \dfrac{1 + \sqrt{7}}{3}$.

7. More Trig Differentiation
Exercise 7.1

Q1 **a)** $y = \dfrac{\cos x}{\sin x}$, so let $u = \cos x$ and $v = \sin x$
   Then $\dfrac{du}{dx} = -\sin x$ and $\dfrac{dv}{dx} = \cos x$

Using the quotient rule,

$$\frac{dy}{dx} = \frac{v\frac{du}{dx} - u\frac{dv}{dx}}{v^2}$$

$$= \frac{\sin x(-\sin x) - \cos x \cos x}{\sin^2 x}$$

$$= \frac{-(\sin^2 x + \cos^2 x)}{\sin^2 x}$$

$$= -\frac{1}{\sin^2 x} = -\csc^2 x$$

As $\frac{\cos x}{\sin x} = \cot x$, when $y = \cot x$,
$\frac{dy}{dx} = -\csc^2 x$

b) E.g. $y = \csc x = \frac{1}{\sin x}$, so let $u = 1$
and $v = \sin x$

Then $\frac{du}{dx} = 0$ and $\frac{dv}{dx} = \cos x$
Using the quotient rule,

$$\frac{dy}{dx} = \frac{v\frac{du}{dx} - u\frac{dv}{dx}}{v^2}$$

$$= \frac{(\sin x \times 0) - (1 \times \cos x)}{\sin^2 x}$$

$$= -\frac{\cos x}{\sin^2 x} = -\frac{1}{\sin x} \times \frac{\cos x}{\sin x}$$

$$= -\csc x \cot x$$

c) E.g. $y = \sec x = \frac{1}{\cos x}$, so let $u = 1$
and $v = \cos x$

Then $\frac{du}{dx} = 0$ and $\frac{dv}{dx} = -\sin x$
Using the quotient rule,

$$\frac{dy}{dx} = \frac{v\frac{du}{dx} - u\frac{dv}{dx}}{v^2}$$

$$= \frac{(\cos x \times 0) - (1 \times -\sin x)}{\cos^2 x}$$

$$= \frac{\sin x}{\cos^2 x} = \frac{1}{\cos x} \times \frac{\sin x}{\cos x}$$

$$= \sec x \tan x$$

Q2 a) $\frac{dy}{dx} = -2\csc(2x)\cot(2x)$

b) $\frac{dy}{dx} = -2\csc^2 x \cot x$

c) $\frac{dy}{dx} = -7\csc^2(7x)$

d) $\frac{dy}{dx} = -7\cot^6 x \csc^2 x$

e) $\frac{dy}{dx} = x^3(4\cot x - x\csc^2 x)$

f) $\frac{dy}{dx} = 2(x + \sec x)(1 + \sec x \tan x)$

g) $\frac{dy}{dx} = -2x\csc(x^2 + 5)\cot(x^2 + 5)$

h) $\frac{dy}{dx} = e^{3x}\sec x (\tan x + 3)$

i) $\frac{dy}{dx} = 3(2x + \cot x)^2(2 - \csc^2 x)$

Q3 a) $f'(x) = \frac{(x + 3)\sec x \tan x - \sec x}{(x + 3)^2}$

b) $f'(x) = -\frac{\sec\frac{1}{x}\tan\frac{1}{x}}{x^2}$

c) $f'(x) = \frac{\tan\sqrt{x}}{2\sqrt{x}\cos\sqrt{x}}$

Q4 a) $f'(x) = 2(\sec x + \csc x)(\sec x \tan x - \csc x \cot x)$

b) $f'(x) = \frac{x\sec^2 x - \tan x}{x^2}$

c) $f'(x) = e^x \csc x (1 - \cot x)$

d) $f'(x) = e^{3x}\sec x[\tan x + 3]$

e) $f'(x) = e^{3x}(3\cot 4x - 4\csc^2 4x)$

f) $f'(x) = -2e^{-2x}\csc 4x\,[2\cot 4x + 1]$

g) $f'(x) = \csc x\left(\frac{1}{x} - \ln x \cot x\right)$

h) $f'(x) = \frac{1}{2}\tan x\sqrt{\sec x}$

i) $f'(x) = e^{\sec x}\sec x \tan x$

Q5 a) $f'(x) = -\cot x$

b) $\ln(\csc x) = \ln\left(\frac{1}{\sin x}\right)$
$= \ln 1 - \ln(\sin x)$
$= -\ln(\sin x)$ (as $\ln 1 = 0$)
$f'(x) = -\frac{\cos x}{\sin x} = -\frac{1}{\tan x} = -\cot x$

Q6 $f'(x) = \frac{1 + \sec x \tan x}{x + \sec x}$

Q7 $\frac{dy}{dx} = \frac{x\sec\sqrt{x^2 + 5}\,\tan\sqrt{x^2 + 5}}{\sqrt{x^2 + 5}}$

8. Connected Rates of Change

Exercise 8.1

Q1 $\frac{dV}{dt} = -0.3x^2$ cm³ min⁻¹

Q2 121.5 cm³ °C⁻¹

Q3 −221.17 cm² h⁻¹ (2 d.p.)

Q4 $\frac{dV}{d\theta} = 8 \times 10^{-5}\pi r^2$ m³ °C⁻¹

Q5 −1236.53 J cm⁻¹ (2 d.p.)

Q6 $\frac{dV}{dt} = -0.05\pi r^2$ cm³ h⁻¹

Q7 a) $A = \frac{\sqrt{3}x^2}{4}$

b) $\frac{dV}{dt} = 6\sqrt{3}\,x$ mm³ per day

c) 5.20 mm³ per day (2 d.p.)

Q8 a) $\frac{dn}{dt} = 104\lambda 2^{\lambda t}\ln 2$ per day

Use the fact that n is directly proportional to D to write this as n = kD, then use the information given to find the value of k. Differentiate your expressions for n and D, then use the chain rule to find the rate of change of n with respect to time.

b) 1.15×10^4 per day (3 s.f.)

Q9 a) $\frac{dh}{dt} = -\frac{3}{10\pi r^2}$ cm s⁻¹

b) $\frac{1}{2\pi} = 0.159$ cm min⁻¹ (3 s.f.)

Q10 a) $\frac{dr}{d\theta} = \frac{k}{2\pi r^2}$ cm °C⁻¹

b) 0.155 cm °C⁻¹ (3 s.f.)

9. Differentiation with Parametric Equations

Exercise 9.1

Q1 a) $\frac{dy}{dx} = \frac{3t^2 - 1}{2t}$ b) $\frac{dy}{dx} = \frac{4t}{3t^2 + 1}$

c) $\frac{dy}{dx} = \frac{3t - 2}{4t^2}$ d) $\frac{dy}{dx} = \frac{2t - 4}{\sin t}$

e) $\frac{dy}{dx} = -\tan t$ f) $\frac{dy}{dx} = \frac{2t - 4}{e^t}$

Q2 a) $\frac{dy}{dx} = \frac{e^{2t}}{t}$ b) e^2

Q3 a) $\frac{dy}{dx} = \frac{12t^2 - 4t}{3e^{3t}}$ b) 0

Q4 a) $\frac{dy}{dx} = \frac{2\cos t - t\sin t}{3t}$ b) $-\frac{2}{3\pi}$

Q5 a) $\frac{dy}{dx} = \frac{t^3\cos t + (3t^2 - 1)\sin t}{2t\sin t + t^2\cos t}$ b) π

Q6 a) $\frac{dy}{dx} = 6t^2 - 3t^3$ b) 9

c) The stationary points occur at $t = 0$ and $t = 2$. At $t = 0$, x is not defined. At $t = 2$, the coordinates are $(\ln 2, 4)$.

Exercise 9.2

Q1 $7x - 2y - 45 = 0$

Q2 $10x - 7y - 19 = 0$

Q3 $y = \frac{2}{3}x - \pi$

Q4 $y = x + 3$

Q5 $y = 2x + \frac{\pi^2}{4}$

Q6 a) $y = 4 - 3x$ b) $(8, 0)$

Q7 a) $\frac{dy}{dx} = \frac{\theta\cos\theta + \sin\theta}{2\cos 2\theta - 2\sin\theta}$

b) When $\theta = \frac{\pi}{2}$, $\frac{dy}{dx} = -\frac{1}{4}$, $x = 0$
and $y = \frac{\pi}{2}$.
So the equation of the tangent is
$y = \frac{\pi}{2} - \frac{1}{4}x$ and the equation of the
normal is $y = 4x + \frac{\pi}{2}$.

Q8 a) $s = 1$

b) $\frac{dy}{dx} = \frac{3s^2 - s - 2s\ln s}{s^2 + 3s^2\ln s} = \frac{3s - 1 - 2\ln s}{s + 3s\ln s}$
From a), when $x = 0$, $s = 1$.
When $s = 1$: $\frac{dy}{dx} = 2$, $x = 0$ and $y = 1$.
Putting this into $y = mx + c$ gives:
$1 = 2(0) + c \Rightarrow c = 1$.
So the equation of the tangent is
$y = 2x + 1$.

Q9 a) Using the quotient rule,
$$\frac{dy}{d\theta} = \frac{-\theta^3\sin\theta - 3\theta^2\cos\theta}{\theta^6}$$
$$= \frac{-\theta\sin\theta - 3\cos\theta}{\theta^4}$$
$$\frac{dx}{d\theta} = \theta^2\cos\theta + 2\theta\sin\theta$$
Hence $\frac{dy}{dx} = \frac{-\theta\sin\theta - 3\cos\theta}{\theta^6\cos\theta + 2\theta^5\sin\theta}$
When $\theta = \pi$, $\frac{dy}{dx} = \frac{-\pi(0) - 3(-1)}{\pi^6(-1) + 2\pi^5(0)}$
$= -\frac{3}{\pi^6}$.

b) $y = \frac{\pi^6}{3}x - \frac{1}{\pi^3}$

10. Implicit Differentiation

Exercise 10.1

Q1 a) $\frac{dy}{dx} = \frac{2x}{1 + 3y^2}$

b) $\frac{dy}{dx} = \frac{1 - x}{y - 1}$

c) $\frac{dy}{dx} = (6x + \cos x)\cos^2 y$

d) $\frac{dy}{dx} = \frac{9x^2 - 1}{2y + 4}$

e) $\frac{dy}{dx} = \frac{5 - 5x^4}{2y - 6}$

f) $\frac{dy}{dx} = \frac{2x + \sin x}{\cos y - 3y^2}$

g) $\dfrac{dy}{dx} = \dfrac{4y - 3x^2y^2 + \sin x}{2x^3y - 4x}$

h) $\dfrac{dy}{dx} = \dfrac{3x^2 - e^x}{e^y + 1}$

i) $\dfrac{dy}{dx} = \dfrac{3x^2 + 4 - 3y^2 - 4xy}{6xy + 2x^2}$

Q2 a) $\dfrac{dy}{dx} = \dfrac{3x^2 + 2y}{4y^3 - 2x}$

b) $\dfrac{dy}{dx} = \dfrac{3x^2 - 2xy}{x^2 + 2y}$

c) $\dfrac{dy}{dx} = \dfrac{\cos x - y^3}{3xy^2 + 1}$

d) $\dfrac{dy}{dx} = \dfrac{y + y\sin x - \sin y}{\cos x + x\cos y - x}$

e) $\dfrac{dy}{dx} = \dfrac{y - e^x}{e^y - x}$

f) $\dfrac{dy}{dx} = \dfrac{1 + 2x^2}{3xy^2 + x}$

g) $\dfrac{dy}{dx} = \dfrac{6xy^2 - 2e^{2x}}{3e^{3y} - 6x^2y}$

h) $\dfrac{dy}{dx} = \dfrac{5x^5 - x\ln x - x - y}{x\ln x - 3xy^2}$

Q3 a) At (0, 1):
LHS: $e^0 + 2\ln 1 = 1$, RHS: $1^3 = 1$
So (0, 1) is a point on the curve.

b) At (0, 1) the gradient is 1.

Q4 a) $\dfrac{dy}{dx} = \dfrac{2y - 3x^2}{2y - 2x}$

b) Putting $x = -2$ into the equation gives: $-8 + y^2 + 4y = 0$
Complete the square to solve:
$(y + 2)^2 - 4 - 8 = 0$
$\Rightarrow y + 2 = \pm\sqrt{12} = \pm 2\sqrt{3}$
so $y = -2 \pm 2\sqrt{3}$

c) $1 - \dfrac{4}{3}\sqrt{3}$

Q5 a) $a = \dfrac{1}{2}$

b) At $(1, -1)$, $\dfrac{dy}{dx} = -\dfrac{4}{3}$ and at $\left(1, \dfrac{1}{2}\right)$, $\dfrac{dy}{dx} = \dfrac{5}{6}$.

Q6 a) $y = 2$ and $y = -2$

b) At $(1, 2)$, $\dfrac{dy}{dx} = -\dfrac{3}{2}$ and at $(1, -2)$, $\dfrac{dy}{dx} = \dfrac{1}{2}$

Exercise 10.2

Q1 a) $(-1, 2.62)$ and $(-1, 0.38)$

b) Putting $x = 0$ into the equation gives:
$3y - y^2 = 0 \Rightarrow y(3 - y) = 0$
$\Rightarrow y = 0$ and $y = 3$
Differentiating:
$2x + 2 + 3\dfrac{dy}{dx} - 2y\dfrac{dy}{dx} = 0$
$\Rightarrow \dfrac{dy}{dx} = \dfrac{2x + 2}{2y - 3}$
At $(0, 0)$, $\dfrac{dy}{dx} = \dfrac{2(0)+2}{2(0)-3} = -\dfrac{2}{3}$
The y-intercept is 0 (as it goes through (0, 0)).
So the equation of the tangent is
$y = -\dfrac{2}{3}x$ or $3y = -2x$.
At $(0, 3)$, $\dfrac{dy}{dx} = \dfrac{2(0)+2}{2(3)-3} = \dfrac{2}{3}$
The y-intercept is 3 (as it goes through (0, 3)). Putting this into
$y = mx + c$ gives the equation of the tangent as $y = \dfrac{2}{3}x + 3$.

Q2 a) There are 4 stationary points with coordinates $(0, 0)$, $(0, 1)$, $\left(-\dfrac{2}{3}, 1.13\right)$ and $\left(-\dfrac{2}{3}, -0.13\right)$.

b) Putting $x = 2$ into the equation gives:
$8 + 4 + y = y^2 \Rightarrow y^2 - y - 12 = 0$
$\Rightarrow (y - 4)(y + 3) = 0$
$\Rightarrow y = 4$ and $y = -3$
Differentiating:
$3x^2 + 2x + \dfrac{dy}{dx} = 2y\dfrac{dy}{dx}$
$\Rightarrow \dfrac{dy}{dx} = \dfrac{3x^2 + 2x}{2y - 1}$
At $(2, 4)$, $\dfrac{dy}{dx} = \dfrac{3(2^2) + 2(2)}{2(4) - 1} = \dfrac{16}{7}$
Putting this into $y = mx + c$ gives:
$4 = \dfrac{16}{7}(2) + c \Rightarrow c = -\dfrac{4}{7}$
So the equation of the tangent is
$y = \dfrac{16}{7}x - \dfrac{4}{7}$ or $16x - 7y - 4 = 0$.
At $(2, -3)$, $\dfrac{dy}{dx} = \dfrac{3(2^2) + 2(2)}{2(-3) - 1} = -\dfrac{16}{7}$
Putting this into $y = mx + c$ gives:
$-3 = -\dfrac{16}{7}(2) + c \Rightarrow c = \dfrac{11}{7}$
So the equation of the tangent is
$y = \dfrac{11}{7} - \dfrac{16}{7}x$ or $16x + 7y - 11 = 0$.

Q3 a) $x = 3$ and $x = -2$
At $(-2, 1)$, the equation of the normal is $y = -\dfrac{7}{5}x - \dfrac{9}{5}$ or $7x + 5y + 9 = 0$.
At $(3, 1)$, the equation of the normal is $y = \dfrac{12}{5}x - \dfrac{31}{5}$ or $12x - 5y - 31 = 0$.

b) $\left(\dfrac{22}{19}, -\dfrac{65}{19}\right)$

Q4 a) $a = -4$ and $b = 1$ ($a < b$).
Differentiating:
$e^x + 2y\dfrac{dy}{dx} - y - x\dfrac{dy}{dx} = -3\dfrac{dy}{dx}$
$\Rightarrow \dfrac{dy}{dx} = \dfrac{y - e^x}{2y - x + 3}$
At $(0, 1)$, $\dfrac{dy}{dx} = \dfrac{1 - e^0}{2(1) - 0 + 3} = 0$
so this is a stationary point.

b) At $(0, -4)$, the equation of the tangent is $y = x - 4$ and the equation of the normal is $y = -x - 4$.

Q5 $y = \arccos x \Rightarrow \cos y = x$
Differentiating:
$-\sin y \dfrac{dy}{dx} = 1$
$\Rightarrow \dfrac{dy}{dx} = -\dfrac{1}{\sin y} = -\dfrac{1}{\sqrt{\sin^2 y}}$
$= -\dfrac{1}{\sqrt{1 - \cos^2 y}}$
Using $\cos y = x$: $\dfrac{dy}{dx} = -\dfrac{1}{\sqrt{1 - x^2}}$

Q6 $y = \arctan x \Rightarrow \tan y = x$
Differentiating:
$\sec^2 y \dfrac{dy}{dx} = 1 \Rightarrow \dfrac{dy}{dx} = \dfrac{1}{\sec^2 y}$
Using the identity $\sec^2 y \equiv 1 + \tan^2 y$:
$\dfrac{dy}{dx} = \dfrac{1}{1 + \tan^2 y}$
Using $\tan y = x$: $\dfrac{dy}{dx} = \dfrac{1}{1 + x^2}$
as required.

Q7 a) When $x = 1$: $0 + y^2 = y + 6$
$\Rightarrow y^2 - y - 6 = 0 \Rightarrow (y - 3)(y + 2) = 0$
$\Rightarrow y = 3$ and $y = -2$.
So the curve passes through $(1, 3)$ and $(1, -2)$.

b) At $(1, 3)$, the equation of the normal is $y = 4 - x$.
At $(1, -2)$, the equation of the normal is $y = -x - 1$.
Because the gradients are the same, these lines are parallel and can never intersect.

Q8 When $y = 0$: $1 + x^2 = 0 + 4x$
$\Rightarrow x^2 - 4x + 1 = 0$
Complete the square to solve:
$(x - 2)^2 - 4 + 1 = 0 \Rightarrow x - 2 = \pm\sqrt{3}$
$\Rightarrow x = 2 \pm \sqrt{3}$
So $a = 2 + \sqrt{3}$ and $b = 2 - \sqrt{3}$.
Differentiating:
$e^y\dfrac{dy}{dx} + 2x = 3y^2\dfrac{dy}{dx} + 4$
$\Rightarrow \dfrac{dy}{dx} = \dfrac{2x - 4}{3y^2 - e^y}$
At $(2 + \sqrt{3}, 0)$,
$\dfrac{dy}{dx} = \dfrac{4 + 2\sqrt{3} - 4}{3(0) - e^0} = -2\sqrt{3}$
$0 = -2\sqrt{3}(2 + \sqrt{3}) + c \Rightarrow c = 4\sqrt{3} + 6$
So the tangent at this point is
$y = 4\sqrt{3} + 6 - 2\sqrt{3}x$.
At $(2 - \sqrt{3}, 0)$,
$\dfrac{dy}{dx} = \dfrac{4 - 2\sqrt{3} - 4}{3(0) - e^0} = 2\sqrt{3}$
$0 = 2\sqrt{3}(2 - \sqrt{3}) + c \Rightarrow c = 6 - 4\sqrt{3}$
So the tangent at this point is
$y = 2\sqrt{3}x + 6 - 4\sqrt{3}$.

Q9 Differentiating:
$\ln x\dfrac{dy}{dx} + \dfrac{y}{x} + 2x = 2y\dfrac{dy}{dx} - \dfrac{dy}{dx}$
$\dfrac{dy}{dx} = \dfrac{\dfrac{y}{x} + 2x}{2y - \ln x - 1} = \dfrac{y + 2x^2}{2xy - x\ln x - x}$
$y + 2x^2 = 0 \Rightarrow \dfrac{dy}{dx} = \dfrac{y + 2x^2}{2xy - x\ln x - x} = 0$
So if a point on the curve satisfies
$y + 2x^2 = 0$, then it's a stationary point.

Q10 Use the chain rule to find $f'(x)$:
$y = \arccos u, \; u = x^2$
$\dfrac{dy}{dx} = \dfrac{dy}{du} \times \dfrac{du}{dx} = -\dfrac{1}{\sqrt{1 - u^2}} \times 2x$
$= -\dfrac{2x}{\sqrt{1 - x^4}}$
When $x = \dfrac{1}{\sqrt{2}}$, $y = \arccos x^2$
$= \arccos \dfrac{1}{2} = \dfrac{\pi}{3}$
$\dfrac{dy}{dx} = -\dfrac{2\left(\dfrac{1}{\sqrt{2}}\right)}{\sqrt{1 - \left(\dfrac{1}{\sqrt{2}}\right)^4}} = -\dfrac{\dfrac{2}{\sqrt{2}}}{\sqrt{1 - \dfrac{1}{(\sqrt{2})^4}}}$
$= -\dfrac{\sqrt{2}}{\sqrt{1 - \dfrac{1}{4}}} = -\dfrac{\sqrt{2}}{\sqrt{\dfrac{3}{4}}} = -\dfrac{\sqrt{2}}{\dfrac{\sqrt{3}}{2}} = -\dfrac{2\sqrt{2}}{\sqrt{3}}$
Rationalising the denominator:
$= -\dfrac{2\sqrt{2} \times \sqrt{3}}{\sqrt{3} \times \sqrt{3}} = -\dfrac{2\sqrt{6}}{3}$
So the tangent has a gradient of $-\dfrac{2\sqrt{6}}{3}$ and passes through the point $\left(\dfrac{1}{\sqrt{2}}, \dfrac{\pi}{3}\right)$.

$y = mx + c \Rightarrow \dfrac{\pi}{3} = -\dfrac{2\sqrt{6}}{3} \times \dfrac{1}{\sqrt{2}} + c$
$c = \dfrac{\pi}{3} + \dfrac{2\sqrt{3}}{3} = \dfrac{\pi + 2\sqrt{3}}{3}$
So the equation of the tangent is
$y = -\dfrac{2\sqrt{6}}{3}x + \dfrac{\pi + 2\sqrt{3}}{3}$

Q11 a) $y = \frac{e^4}{6}(x - 4)$

b) $y = 6e^{-4}(4 - x)$

c) The lines intersect when
$$\frac{e^4}{6}(x - 4) = 6e^{-4}(4 - x)$$
$$\Rightarrow e^8(x - 4) = 36(4 - x)$$
$$\Rightarrow e^8 x + 36x = 4e^8 + 144$$
$$\Rightarrow x(e^8 + 36) = 4e^8 + 144$$
$$\Rightarrow x = \frac{4e^8 + 144}{e^8 + 36}$$

Q12 At $(2, -5)$, the equation of the tangent is
$y = -\frac{25}{16}x - \frac{15}{8}$ or $16y = -25x - 30$
At $(2, 3)$, the equation of the tangent is
$y = \frac{25}{16}x - \frac{1}{8}$ or $16y = 25x - 2$
The two tangents intersect when:
$-25x - 30 = 25x - 2 \Rightarrow 50x = -28$
$\Rightarrow x = -\frac{14}{25}$
And $16y = 25\left(-\frac{14}{25}\right) - 2 \Rightarrow 16y = -16$
$\Rightarrow y = -1$.
So they intersect at $\left(-\frac{14}{25}, -1\right)$.

Q13 a) When $x = \frac{\pi}{2}$, $y = \frac{\pi}{3}$
When $x = \pi$, $y = \frac{2\pi}{3}$

b) At $\left(\frac{\pi}{2}, \frac{\pi}{3}\right)$, the equation of the
tangent is $y = -\frac{1}{\sqrt{3}}x + \frac{(2 + \sqrt{3})\pi}{6}$
At $\left(\pi, \frac{2\pi}{3}\right)$, the equation of the
tangent is $y = -\frac{1}{\sqrt{3}}x + \frac{(2 + \sqrt{3})\pi}{3}$.

Q14 Differentiating:
$$\left(\frac{2}{3}y\right)\frac{dy}{dx} = 18x^2 - \left(2y + 2x\frac{dy}{dx}\right)$$
$$\left(\frac{2}{3}y + 2x\right)\frac{dy}{dx} = 18x^2 - 2y$$
$$\frac{dy}{dx} = \frac{18x^2 - 2y}{\frac{2}{3}y + 2x} = \frac{9x^2 - y}{\frac{1}{3}y + x} = \frac{27x^2 - 3y}{y + 3x}$$
When $\frac{dy}{dx} = 0$, $27x^2 - 3y = 0$
$\Rightarrow 3y = 27x^2 \Rightarrow y = 9x^2$
Substitute $y = 9x^2$ back into the original
equation:
$\frac{1}{3}(9x^2)^2 = 6x^3 - 2x(9x^2)$
$\Rightarrow 27x^4 = 6x^3 - 18x^3$
$\Rightarrow 27x^4 + 12x^3 = 0$
$\Rightarrow 3x^3(9x + 4) = 0$
So the stationary points occur when
$x = 0$ and $x = -\frac{4}{9}$.
When $x = 0$, $y = 9(0)^2 = 0$
When $x = -\frac{4}{9}$, $y = 9\left(-\frac{4}{9}\right)^2 = \frac{16}{9}$
So the stationary points are at $(0, 0)$
and $\left(-\frac{4}{9}, \frac{16}{9}\right)$.

Review Exercise —
Chapter 22

Q1 a) (i) $x < 2$ **(ii)** $x > 2$

b) (i) $(2, 6)$

(ii) $f'(2) = -6 \ne 0$, so this is not a
stationary point of inflection.

Q2 a) $\frac{dy}{dx} = \frac{3x^2 + 4x}{2\sqrt{x^3 + 2x^2}}$

b) $\frac{dy}{dx} = -\frac{3x^2 + 4x}{2(\sqrt{x^3 + 2x^2})^3}$

c) $\frac{dy}{dx} = 10xe^{5x^2}$

d) $\frac{dy}{dx} = -\frac{2x}{6 - x^2}$

Q3 a) $\frac{dy}{dx} = 6x(x^2 - 1)^2$

b) $x + 108y - 2918 = 0$

Q4 a) $\frac{dy}{dx} = \frac{e^x + 2e^{2x}}{2\sqrt{e^x + e^{2x}}}$

b) $\frac{dy}{dx} = 6e^{2x + 1} + \frac{2x}{1 - x^2} + 6x^2$

c) $\frac{dy}{dx} = 16^x \ln 16 + \frac{e^{\sqrt{x}}}{2\sqrt{x}} - \tan x$

Q5 a) (i) $\frac{dy}{dx} = \frac{1}{2x}$ **(ii)** $\frac{dy}{dx} = \frac{e^x}{2}$

b) $\frac{dy}{dx} = \cos^2 y$

Q6 a) $f'(x) = 2 \sin(x + 2) \cos(x + 2)$

b) $f'(x) = -6 \sin(3x)$

c) $f'(x) = \frac{\sec^2 x}{2\sqrt{\tan x}}$

Q7 $f'(x) = -3e^{\cos(3x)} \sin(3x)$

Q8 $f'(x) = 3x^2(\sec^2 x^3)(\sin(4x))$
         $+ 4\cos(4x)\tan x^3$

Q9 a) -6 **b)** 0.841 to 3 s.f.

Q10 $\frac{9\sqrt{2}\,e}{4}$

Q11 $\frac{dy}{dx} = \frac{x + 3(x^2 + 3)\tan(3x)}{(\sqrt{x^2 + 3})\cos(3x)}$
*Here, you have to use the quotient rule — but
you have to use the chain rule to differentiate
both u and v before you can put them in the
quotient rule formula. Finally, you have to do
a bit of rearranging to tidy up the fraction.*

Q12 a) $\frac{dy}{dx} = \frac{2}{x}\cos x - \ln x^2 \sin x$

b) $\frac{dy}{dx} = \frac{(x + 2)(2x - 1)e^{x^2 - x} - 4e^{x^2 - x}}{(x + 2)^5}$

Q13 $\left(\frac{1}{2}, \sqrt{2}\,e^{\frac{1}{2}}\right)$

Q14 $f'(x) = -\frac{2x\sin x^2}{\ln(2x)} - \frac{\cos x^2}{x(\ln(2x))^2}$

Q15 $y = 7 - 4x$

Q16 $y = \frac{2\sqrt{2}}{3}x + 3\sqrt{2} - \frac{2\sqrt{2}\,\pi}{3}$

Q17 1.51 to 2 d.p.

Q18 a) $\frac{dy}{dx} = -\frac{1}{2}\cot x\sqrt{\csc x}$

b) $\frac{dy}{dx} = -2x\csc^2(x^2 + 5)$

c) $\frac{dy}{dx} = \frac{\sec x(x\tan x - 2)}{x^3}$

d) $\frac{dy}{dx} = e^{2x}\csc(5x)(-5\cot(5x) + 2)$

Q19 $A = 2(x)(2x) + 2(x)(3x) + 2(2x)(3x)$
$= 4x^2 + 6x^2 + 12x^2 = 22x^2$ So $\frac{dA}{dx} = 44x$
$V = (x)(2x)(3x) = 6x^3$. So $\frac{dV}{dx} = 18x^2$
$$\frac{dA}{dt} = \frac{dA}{dx} \times \frac{dx}{dt} = 44x \times \frac{dx}{dt}$$
and $\frac{dx}{dt} = \frac{dx}{dV} \times \frac{dV}{dt} = \frac{1}{\left(\frac{dV}{dx}\right)} \times \frac{dV}{dt}$
$$= \frac{1}{18x^2} \times 3 = \frac{1}{6x^2}$$
So $\frac{dA}{dt} = 44x \times \frac{1}{6x^2} = \frac{22}{3x}$

Q20 a) $\frac{dV}{d\theta} = -10\,000\,\pi r^2$ km^3 K^{-1}

b) Density $\rho = \frac{m}{V} = \frac{m}{kD^3}$
So $\frac{d\rho}{dD} = -\frac{3m}{kD^4}$
From the question,
$\frac{dD}{d\theta} = -215$ km K^{-1}, so
$$\frac{d\rho}{d\theta} = \frac{d\rho}{dD} \times \frac{dD}{d\theta}$$
$$= -\frac{3m}{kD^4} \times -215$$
$$= \frac{645m}{kD^4} \text{ kg km}^{-3}\text{ K}^{-1}$$

Q21 a) $\frac{dy}{dx} = \frac{9t^2 - 4}{2t}$

b) The stationary points are $\left(\frac{4}{9}, -\frac{16}{9}\right)$
and $\left(\frac{4}{9}, \frac{16}{9}\right)$.

Q22 a) $\frac{dy}{dx} = \frac{6t^2 - 2t}{\ln t + 1}$ **b)** 4

c) E.g. you can't evaluate $\frac{dy}{dx}$ at this
point as the curve itself is not defined
when $t = 0$ as the value of x cannot
be evaluated.

Q23 a) $\frac{dy}{dx} = 3(t + 1)$

b) The stationary point is $(7, 10)$.

Q24 a) The coordinates of the turning points
are $(0, -5)$ and $(-36, 27)$ (i.e. $a = 0$,
$b = -5$, $c = -36$ and $d = 27$).

b) $t = 0$ or $t = \frac{-3 \pm 3\sqrt{5}}{2}$. When $t = 0$,
$x = 0$ and $y = 0$, so C passes through
the origin.

c) $y = \frac{15}{8}x - \frac{11}{2}$ or $8y = 15x - 44$

Q25 a) When $s = 0$, the equation of the
tangent is $y = x + 1$.
When $s = 2$, the equation of the
tangent is $y = \left(\frac{7e^2}{9}\right)x - \frac{15e^4}{9}$
or $9y = 7e^2 x - 15e^4$.

b) $x = \frac{9 + 15e^4}{7e^2 - 9}$, $y = \frac{9 + 15e^4}{7e^2 - 9} + 1$

Q26 Take the log of both sides of the
equation:
$y = a^x \Rightarrow \ln y = \ln a^x \Rightarrow \ln y = x \ln a$
(using log laws)
Now use implicit differentiation
to find $\frac{dy}{dx}$:
$\ln y = x \ln a \quad \Rightarrow \frac{d}{dx}(\ln y) = \frac{d}{dx}(x \ln a)$
$\Rightarrow \frac{d}{dy}(\ln y)\frac{dy}{dx} = \ln a$
$\Rightarrow \frac{1}{y}\frac{dy}{dx} = \ln a \Rightarrow \frac{dy}{dx} = y \ln a$
So as $y = a^x$, $\frac{dy}{dx} = a^x \ln a$

Q27 a) $\frac{\pi^3}{16}$

b) $y = \frac{\pi^3}{16}x - \frac{3\pi}{4}$ or $16y = \pi^3 x - 12\pi$

c) $\theta = \frac{\pi}{4}, \frac{3\pi}{4}, \frac{5\pi}{4}$... etc.

The solution with $0 \le \theta \le \frac{\pi}{2}$ is $\theta = \frac{\pi}{4}$.

When $\theta = \frac{\pi}{4}$, $x = \frac{8\sqrt{2}}{\pi^2}$, so the coordinates of the first point where the curve cuts the x-axis are $\left(\frac{8\sqrt{2}}{\pi^2}, 0\right)$.

Q28 a) $\frac{dy}{dx} = \frac{t-6}{3t^2 + 2t}$

b) The coordinates of the turning point are $(252, -18)$.

c) When $y = 0$, $t = 0$ or $t = 12$.
When $t = 0$, the gradient is undefined.
When $t = 12$, the equation of the tangent is $y = \frac{1}{76}x - \frac{468}{19}$.

Q29 a) $\frac{dy}{dx} = \frac{8x - 14xy}{4y + 7x^2}$

b) $\frac{dy}{dx} = \frac{12x^3 - 2y^2}{1 + 4xy}$

c) $\frac{dy}{dx} = \frac{\sin x \sin y + y}{\cos x \cos y - x}$

Q30 a) $-\frac{64}{9}$ **b)** $-\frac{1}{2}$

Q31 a) $a = 1$ **b)** -2

c) From part a), you know that $a = 1$. So if $(1, 1)$ is a turning point, the gradient here will be 0.
$\frac{dy}{dx} = \frac{2x - 2xy}{x^2 + 2y} = \frac{2-2}{1+2} = 0$,
so $(1, 1)$ is a turning point.

Q32 a) Substitute $x = 0$ and $y = 1$ into the equation: $1\cos 0 - 1 = 0\sin 0$, that is, $1 - 1 = 0$, so this is a solution.

b) $\frac{dy}{dx} = \frac{x\cos x + (1+y)\sin x}{\cos x - 2y}$
At a turning point, $\frac{dy}{dx} = 0$, so if $(0, 1)$ is a turning point then $\frac{dy}{dx} = 0$ here.
Substitute in $x = 0$ and $y = 1$:
$\frac{dy}{dx} = \frac{0\cos 0 + 2\sin 0}{\cos 0 - 2} = \frac{0}{-1} = 0$
so $(0, 1)$ is a turning point.

Q33 a) $\frac{dy}{dx} = \frac{\cos x - x\sin x + y\cos x}{3y^2 - \sin x}$

b) At the stationary points, $\frac{dy}{dx} = 0$, hence $\cos x - x\sin x + y\cos x = 0$
$y\cos x = x\sin x - \cos x$,
so $y = \frac{x\sin x}{\cos x} - \frac{\cos x}{\cos x} = x\tan x - 1$, as required.

c) When $x = \frac{\pi}{2}$, $\frac{\pi}{2}(0) + y = y^3$,
hence $y^3 - y = 0$
$\Rightarrow y(y+1)(y-1) = 0$, giving $y = 0$, $y = 1$ and $y = -1$, so the three points on the curve have coordinates $(\frac{\pi}{2}, 0)$, $(\frac{\pi}{2}, 1)$ and $(\frac{\pi}{2}, -1)$.

d) At $(\frac{\pi}{2}, 0)$, the equation of the tangent is $y = \frac{\pi}{2}x - \frac{\pi^2}{4}$.
At $(\frac{\pi}{2}, 1)$, the equation of the tangent is $y = (1 + \frac{\pi^2}{8}) - \frac{\pi}{4}x$.

At $(\frac{\pi}{2}, -1)$, the equation of the tangent is $y = (\frac{\pi^2}{8} - 1) - \frac{\pi}{4}x$.
The last two tangents both have gradient $-\frac{\pi}{4}$, so they are parallel and will never intersect.

Q34 $4y + 4y^2 = 8 \Rightarrow y^2 + y - 2 = 0$
$\Rightarrow (y-1)(y+2) = 0$
$\Rightarrow y = 1$ or $y = -2$, so $a = 1$ and $b = -2$.
$\frac{dy}{dx} = \frac{2 - xy^2}{2 + x^2 y}$
At $(2, 1)$, $\frac{dy}{dx} = 0$, so $(2, 1)$ is a stationary point and the equation of the tangent is $y = 1$. At $(2, -2)$, the equation of the tangent is $y = x - 4$. The tangents intersect where $1 = x - 4$, so $x = 5$, $y = 1$.

Q35 a) $a = 3$, $b = -2$

b) At $(1, 3)$: $\frac{dy}{dx} = \frac{4}{5}$ and the equation of the normal is $4y = 17 - 5x$.

At $(1, -2)$: $\frac{dy}{dx} = \frac{1}{5}$ and the equation of the normal is $y = 3 - 5x$.

c) $\left(-\frac{1}{3}, \frac{14}{3}\right)$

Chapter 23: Integration 2

1. Integration of $(ax + b)^n$

Exercise 1.1

Q1 a) $\int (x+10)^{10}\,dx = \frac{1}{11}(x+10)^{11} + C$

b) $\int (5x)^7\,dx = \frac{78125x^8}{8} + C$

c) $\int (5x+2)^4\,dx = \frac{1}{25}(5x+2)^5 + C$

d) $\int (3-5x)^{-2}\,dx = \frac{1}{5(3-5x)} + C$

e) $\int (3x-4)^{-\frac{4}{3}}\,dx = \frac{-1}{\sqrt[3]{3x-4}} + C$

Q2 a) $\int 8(2x-4)^4\,dx = 8\int (2x-4)^4\,dx$
$= 8 \times \left(\frac{1}{2 \times 5}(2x-4)^5 + c\right)$
$= \frac{8}{10}(2x-4)^5 + C$
$= \frac{4}{5}(2x-4)^5 + C = \frac{4(2x-4)^5}{5} + C$

b) $\frac{8}{5}$

Q3 a) $\frac{4}{49}$ **b)** $\frac{1}{8}$ **c)** $\frac{1}{6}$

Q4 $f(x) = -\frac{1}{35}(8-7x)^5 + \frac{4}{35}$

2. Integration of e^x and $\frac{1}{x}$

Exercise 2.1

Q1 a) $\int 2e^x\,dx = 2e^x + C$

b) $\int 4x + 7e^x\,dx = 2x^2 + 7e^x + C$

c) $\int e^{10x}\,dx = \frac{1}{10}e^{10x} + C$

d) $\int e^{-3x} + x\,dx = -\frac{1}{3}e^{-3x} + \frac{1}{2}x^2 + C$

e) $\int e^{\frac{7}{2}x}\,dx = \frac{2}{7}e^{\frac{7}{2}x} + C$

f) $\int e^{4x-2}\,dx = \frac{1}{4}e^{4x-2} + C$

g) $\int \frac{1}{2}e^{-\frac{3}{2}x}\,dx = -\frac{1}{3}e^{-\frac{3}{2}x} + C$

h) $\int e^{4(\frac{x}{3}+1)}\,dx = \frac{3}{4}e^{4(\frac{x}{3}+1)} + C$

Q2 $y = -2e^{-5x-1} + \frac{2}{e}$

Q3 $\int e^{8y+5}\,dy = \frac{1}{8}e^{8y+5} + C$

Q4 a) $\frac{1}{2}(e^6 - e^4)$ **b)** $e^{12} - 1$

c) $\frac{1}{2}(e^{2\pi} - 1)$ **d)** $6e - \frac{3}{e^2} - 6\sqrt{e} + \frac{3}{e}$

Exercise 2.2

Q1 a) $\int \frac{19}{x}\,dx = 19\ln|x| + C$

b) $\int \frac{1}{7x}\,dx = \frac{1}{7}\ln|x| + C$

c) $\int \frac{1}{7x+2}\,dx = \frac{1}{7}\ln|7x+2| + C$

d) $\int \frac{4}{1-3x}\,dx = -\frac{4}{3}\ln|1-3x| + C$

e) $\int \frac{-2}{3-8x}\,dx = \frac{1}{4}\ln|3-8x| + C$

Q2 $\int \frac{1}{8x} - \frac{20}{x}\,dx = -\frac{159}{8}\ln|x| + C$

Q3 a) $\int \frac{6}{x} - \frac{3}{x}\,dx = \int \frac{3}{x}\,dx$
$= 3\ln|x| + C = \ln|x^3| + C$

b) $3\ln\left(\frac{5}{4}\right)$ or $\ln\left(\frac{125}{64}\right)$

Q4 $\int_{-b}^{a} 15(5+3x)^{-1}\,dx = \int_{-b}^{a} \frac{15}{(5+3x)}\,dx$
$= \left[15 \times \frac{1}{3}\ln|5+3x|\right]_{-b}^{a} = 5[\ln|5+3x|]_{-b}^{a}$
$= 5(\ln|5+3a| - \ln|5+3b|)$
$= 5\ln\left(\left|\frac{5+3a}{5+3b}\right|\right) = 5\ln\left|\frac{5+3a}{5+3b}\right|$
$= \ln\left|\frac{5+3a}{5+3b}\right|^5$

Q5 $f(x) = -\frac{4}{9}\ln|10 - 9x| + 2$

Q6 a) $\int_{-3}^{0} \frac{-7}{16-2x}\,dx$

b) $\int_{-3}^{0} \frac{-7}{16-2x} = \left[-7 \times \frac{1}{-2}\ln|16-2x|\right]_{-3}^{0}$
$= \frac{7}{2}[\ln|16-2x|]_{-3}^{0} = \frac{7}{2}(\ln 16 - \ln 22)$
$= \frac{7}{2}\ln\frac{16}{22} = \frac{7}{2}\ln\frac{8}{11} = \ln\left[\left(\frac{8}{11}\right)^{\frac{7}{2}}\right]$

Q7 $A = \frac{e^{15}+5}{6}$

3. Integration of Trigonometric Functions

Exercise 3.1

Q1 a) $\int \frac{1}{7}\cos x\,dx = \frac{1}{7}\sin x + C$

b) $\int -3\sin x\,dx = 3\cos x + C$

c) $\int -3\cos x - 3\sin x\,dx$
$= -3\sin x + 3\cos x + C$

d) $\int \sin 5x \, dx = -\frac{1}{5}\cos 5x + C$

e) $\int \cos\left(\frac{x}{7}\right) dx = 7\sin\left(\frac{x}{7}\right) + C$

f) $\int 2\sin(-3x) \, dx = \frac{2}{3}\cos(-3x) + C$

g) $\int 5\cos\left(3x + \frac{\pi}{5}\right) dx$

$= \frac{5}{3}\sin\left(3x + \frac{\pi}{5}\right) + C$

h) $\int -4\sin\left(4x - \frac{\pi}{3}\right) dx$

$= \cos\left(4x - \frac{\pi}{3}\right) + C$

i) $\int \cos(4x + 3) + \sin(3 - 4x) \, dx$

$= \frac{1}{4}\sin(4x + 3) + \frac{1}{4}\cos(3 - 4x) + C$

Q2 $\int \frac{1}{2}\cos 3\theta - \sin\theta \, d\theta$

$= \frac{1}{6}\sin 3\theta + \cos\theta + C$

Q3 **a)** 1 **b)** 2 **c)** $\frac{1}{3}$ **d)** $\frac{6}{\pi}$

Q4 **a)** $\int_1^2 2\pi\cos\left(\frac{\pi x}{2}\right) dx = -4$

b) Since the function doesn't cross the x-axis for 1 < x < 2, the described area has to be either entirely above the x-axis or entirely below it. So, because the integral gives a negative value, this means that all of the area is below the x-axis.

Q5 $\int_{\frac{\pi}{3}}^{\frac{\pi}{2}} \sin(-x) + \cos(-x) \, dx$

$= \int_{\frac{\pi}{3}}^{\frac{\pi}{2}} -\sin x + \cos x \, dx$

$= [-(-\cos x) + \sin x]_{\frac{\pi}{3}}^{\frac{\pi}{2}} = [\cos x + \sin x]_{\frac{\pi}{3}}^{\frac{\pi}{2}}$

$= \left[\cos\left(\frac{\pi}{2}\right) + \sin\left(\frac{\pi}{2}\right)\right] - \left[\cos\left(\frac{\pi}{3}\right) + \sin\left(\frac{\pi}{3}\right)\right]$

$= [0 + 1] - \left[\frac{1}{2} + \frac{\sqrt{3}}{2}\right] = 1 - \frac{1}{2} - \frac{\sqrt{3}}{2}$

$= \frac{1}{2} - \frac{\sqrt{3}}{2} = \frac{1 - \sqrt{3}}{2}$

Q6 $\int_{-2\pi}^{\pi} 5\cos\frac{x}{6} \, dx = \left[\frac{5}{\left(\frac{1}{6}\right)}\sin\left(\frac{x}{6}\right)\right]_{-2\pi}^{\pi}$

$= 30\left[\sin\left(\frac{x}{6}\right)\right]_{-2\pi}^{\pi}$

$= 30\left(\sin\left(\frac{\pi}{6}\right) - \sin\left(-\frac{\pi}{3}\right)\right)$

$= 30\left(\frac{1}{2} - \left(-\frac{\sqrt{3}}{2}\right)\right)$

$= 30\left(\frac{1 + \sqrt{3}}{2}\right) = 15(1 + \sqrt{3})$

Exercise 3.2

Q1 **a)** $\int 2\sec^2 x + 1 \, dx = 2\tan x + x + C$

b) $\int \sec^2 9x \, dx = \frac{1}{9}\tan 9x + C$

c) $\int 20\sec^2 3y \, dy = \frac{20}{3}\tan 3y + C$

d) $\int \sec^2 \frac{x}{7} \, dx = 7\tan\left(\frac{x}{7}\right) + C$

e) $\int_0^{\frac{\pi}{3}} -\frac{1}{\cos^2\theta} \, d\theta = -\sqrt{3}$

f) $\int_0^{\frac{\pi}{4}} 3\sec^2(-3x) \, dx = -1$

Q2 $\sqrt{3}$

Q3 $\int \sec^2(x + \alpha) + \sec^2(3x + \beta) \, dx$

$= \tan(x + \alpha) + \frac{1}{3}\tan(3x + \beta) + C$

Q4 $\int_{\frac{\pi}{12}}^{\frac{\pi}{6}} 5A\sec^2\left(\frac{\pi}{3} - 2\theta\right) d\theta = \frac{5\sqrt{3}A}{6}$

Exercise 3.3

Q1 **a)** $\int \cosec^2 11x \, dx = -\frac{1}{11}\cot 11x + C$

b) $\int 5\sec 10\theta \tan 10\theta \, d\theta$

$= \frac{1}{2}\sec 10\theta + C$

c) $\int -\cosec(x + 17)\cot(x + 17) \, dx$

$= \cosec(x + 17) + C$

d) $\int -3\cosec 3x \cot 3x \, dx$

$= \cosec 3x + C$

e) $\int 13\sec\left(\frac{\pi}{4} - x\right)\tan\left(\frac{\pi}{4} - x\right) dx$

$= -13\sec\left(\frac{\pi}{4} - x\right) + C$

Q2 $\int 10\cosec^2\left(\alpha - \frac{x}{2}\right)$

$- 60\sec(\alpha - 6x)\tan(\alpha - 6x) \, dx$

$= 20\cot\left(\alpha - \frac{x}{2}\right) + 10\sec(\alpha - 6x) + C$

Q3 $\int_{\frac{\pi}{12}}^{\frac{\pi}{8}} 6\sec 2x \tan 2x + 6\cosec 2x \cot 2x \, dx$

$= 6 - 2\sqrt{3}$

Q4 Evaluate the integral to get:

$-\frac{1}{3}\left(\frac{1}{\tan\left(\frac{\pi}{2}\right)} - \frac{1}{\tan\left(\frac{\pi}{4}\right)}\right)$

If you try to evaluate $\frac{1}{\tan\left(\frac{\pi}{2}\right)}$ with your calculator you'll probably get an error. Using trigonometrical identities:

$\frac{1}{\tan\left(\frac{\pi}{2}\right)} = \frac{\cos\left(\frac{\pi}{2}\right)}{\sin\left(\frac{\pi}{2}\right)} = \frac{0}{1} = 0.$

So the integral evaluates as

$-\frac{1}{3}(0 - 1) = \frac{1}{3}.$

4. Integration of $\frac{f'(x)}{f(x)}$

Exercise 4.1

Q1 **a)** $\int \frac{4x^3}{x^4 - 1} dx = \ln|x^4 - 1| + C$

b) $\int \frac{2x - 1}{x^2 - x} dx = \ln|x^2 - x| + C$

c) $\int \frac{x^4}{3x^5 + 6} dx = \frac{1}{15}\ln|3x^5 + 6| + C$

d) $\int \frac{12x^3 + 18x^2 - 3}{x^4 + 2x^3 - x} dx$

$= 3\ln|x^4 + 2x^3 - x| + C$

Q2 **a)** $\int \frac{e^x}{e^x + 6} dx = \ln|e^x + 6| + C$

b) $\int \frac{2(e^{2x} + 3e^x)}{e^{2x} + 6e^x} dx = \ln|e^{2x} + 6e^x| + C$

c) $\int \frac{e^x}{3(e^x + 3)} dx = \frac{1}{3}\ln|e^x + 3| + C$

d) $\int \frac{18e^{3x+4}}{2e^{3x+4} + 8} dx = 3\ln|2e^{3x+4} + 8| + C$

Q3 **a)** $\int \frac{2\cos 2x}{1 + \sin 2x} dx = \ln|1 + \sin 2x| + C$

b) $\int \frac{\sin 3x}{\cos 3x - 1} dx$

$= -\frac{1}{3}\ln|\cos 3x - 1| + C$

c) $\int \frac{3\cosec x \cot x + 6x}{\cosec x - x^2 + 4} dx$

$= -3\ln|\cosec x - x^2 + 4| + C$

d) $\int \frac{\sec^2 x}{\tan x} dx = \ln|\tan x| + C$

e) $\int \frac{\sec x \tan x}{\sec x + 5} dx = \ln|\sec x + 5| + C$

f) $\int \frac{-5\cosec^2 5x}{\cot 5x} dx = \ln|\cot 5x| + C$

Q4 $\frac{d}{dx}(\sin(2x + 7)) = 2\cos(2x + 7)$

$\int \frac{4\cos(2x + 7)}{\sin(2x + 7)} dx$

$= 2\int \frac{2\cos(2x + 7)}{\sin(2x + 7)} dx$

$= 2(\ln|\sin(2x + 7)| + C)$

$= 2(\ln|\sin(2x + 7)| + \ln k)$

$= 2\ln|k\sin(2x + 7)|$

Exercise 4.2

Q1 **a)** $\int 2\tan x \, dx = -2\ln|\cos x| + C$

b) $\int \tan 2x \, dx = -\frac{1}{2}\ln|\cos 2x| + C$

c) $\int 4\cosec x \, dx$

$= -4\ln|\cosec x + \cot x| + C$

d) $\int \cot 3x \, dx = \frac{1}{3}\ln|\sin 3x| + C$

e) $\int \frac{1}{2}\sec 2x \, dx$

$= \frac{1}{4}\ln|\sec 2x + \tan 2x| + C$

f) $\int 3\cosec 6x \, dx$

$= -\frac{1}{2}\ln|\cosec 6x + \cot 6x| + C$

Q2 $\int \frac{\sec^2 x}{2\tan x} - 4\sec 2x \tan 2x$

$+ \frac{\cosec 2x \cot 2x - 1}{\cosec 2x + 2x} dx$

$= \frac{1}{2}\ln|\tan x| - 2\sec 2x$

$- \frac{1}{2}\ln|\cosec 2x + 2x| + C$

Split the integral into parts and use some standard results. The first and third integrals were put in the form $\int \frac{f'(x)}{f(x)} dx$, and the second one you can tackle by reversing the result $\frac{d}{dx}(\sec 2x) = 2\sec 2x \tan 2x$.

Q3 **a)** $f'(x) = \sec^2 x + \sec x \tan x$.

$\frac{f'(x)}{f(x)} = \frac{\sec^2 x + \sec x \tan x}{\sec x + \tan x}$

$= \sec x\left(\frac{\sec x + \tan x}{\sec x + \tan x}\right) = \sec x$

b) Using $\int \frac{f'(x)}{f(x)} dx = \ln|f(x)| + C$ with your working from part a) gives:

$\int \sec x \, dx = \int \sec x\left(\frac{\sec x + \tan x}{\sec x + \tan x}\right) dx$

$= \int \frac{\sec^2 x + \sec x \tan x}{\sec x + \tan x} dx$

$= \ln|\sec x + \tan x| + C$

Here, you have multiplied the inside of the integral by a fraction which is the same on the top and bottom (it's equal to 1, so it'll make no difference).

This trick is also used in the proof of $\int cosec\,x\,dx = -\ln|cosec\,x + cot\,x| + C$.

5. Integrating $\frac{du}{dx}f'(u)$

Exercise 5.1

Q1 **a)** $\int 2xe^{x^2}\,dx = e^{x^2} + C$

b) $\int 6x^2e^{2x^3}\,dx = e^{2x^3} + C$

c) $\int \frac{1}{2\sqrt{x}}e^{\sqrt{x}}\,dx = e^{\sqrt{x}} + C$

d) $\int x^3e^{x^4}\,dx = \frac{1}{4}e^{x^4} + C$

e) $\int (4x-1)e^{(x^2-\frac{1}{2}x)}\,dx = 2e^{(x^2-\frac{1}{2}x)} + C$

f) $\int 2x\sin(x^2+1)\,dx = -\cos(x^2+1) + C$

g) $\int x^3\cos(x^4)\,dx = \frac{1}{4}\sin(x^4) + C$

h) $\int x\sec^2(x^2)\,dx = \frac{1}{2}\tan(x^2) + C$

i) $\int e^{\cos x}\sin x\,dx = -e^{\cos x} + C$

j) $\int \cos 2x\,e^{\sin 2x}\,dx = \frac{1}{2}e^{\sin 2x} + C$

k) $\int \sec^2 x\,e^{\tan x}\,dx = e^{\tan x} + C$

l) $\int \sec x\tan x\,e^{\sec x}\,dx = e^{\sec x} + C$

Exercise 5.2

Q1 **a)** $\int 6x(x^2+5)^2\,dx = (x^2+5)^3 + C$

b) $\int (2x+7)(x^2+7x)^4\,dx = \frac{1}{5}(x^2+7x)^5 + C$

c) $\int (x^3+2x)(x^4+4x^2)^3\,dx = \frac{1}{16}(x^4+4x^2)^4 + C$

d) $\int \frac{2x}{(x^2-1)^3}\,dx = -\frac{1}{2(x^2-1)^2} + C$

e) $\int \frac{6e^{3x}}{(e^{3x}-5)^2}\,dx = -2(e^{3x}-5)^{-1} + C$

f) $\int \sin x\cos^5 x\,dx = -\frac{1}{6}\cos^6 x + C$

g) $\int 2\sec^2 x\tan^3 x\,dx = \frac{1}{2}\tan^4 x + C$

h) $\int 3e^x(e^x+4)^2\,dx = (e^x+4)^3 + C$

i) $\int 32(2e^{4x}-3x)(e^{4x}-3x^2)^7\,dx = 2(e^{4x}-3x^2)^8 + C$

j) $\int \frac{\cos x}{(2+\sin x)^4}\,dx = -\frac{1}{3(2+\sin x)^3} + C$

k) $\int 5\,cosec\,x\cot x\,cosec^4 x\,dx = -cosec^5 x + C$

l) $\int 2\,cosec^2 x\cot^3 x\,dx = -\frac{1}{2}\cot^4 x + C$

Q2 **a)** $\int 6\tan x\sec^6 x\,dx = \sec^6 x + C$

b) $\int \cot x\,cosec^3 x\,dx = -\frac{1}{3}cosec^3 x + C$

c) $\int 30\,cosec^2 x\cot^5 x\,dx = -5\cot^6 x + C$

Q3 **a)** $\int 4(\cos x\,e^{\sin x})(e^{\sin x}-5)^3\,dx = (e^{\sin x}-5)^4 + C$

b) $\int (\sin x\,e^{\cos x}-4)(e^{\cos x}+4x)^6\,dx = -\frac{1}{7}(e^{\cos x}+4x)^7 + C$

c) $\int 5\sec^2 x\,e^{\tan x}(e^{\tan x}+3)^4\,dx = (e^{\tan x}+3)^5 + C$

Q4 **a)** $\int \frac{\sin x}{\cos^5 x}\,dx = \frac{1}{4\cos^4 x} + C$

b) $\int \frac{\sec^2 x}{\tan^4 x}\,dx = -\frac{1}{3\tan^3 x} + C$

c) $\int \cot x\,cosec\,x\sqrt{cosec\,x}\,dx = -\frac{2}{3}(\sqrt{cosec\,x})^3 + C$

6. Using Trigonometric Identities in Integration

Exercise 6.1

Q1 **a)** $\int \cos^2 x\,dx = \frac{1}{4}\sin 2x + \frac{1}{2}x + C$

b) $\int 6\sin x\cos x\,dx = -\frac{3}{2}\cos 2x + C$

c) $\int \sin^2 6x\,dx = \frac{1}{2}x - \frac{1}{24}\sin 12x + C$

d) $\int \frac{2\tan 2x}{1-\tan^2 2x}\,dx = -\frac{1}{4}\ln|\cos 4x| + C$
$\left(\text{or} = \frac{1}{4}\ln|\sec 4x| + C\right)$

e) $\int 2\sin 4x\cos 4x\,dx = -\frac{1}{8}\cos 8x + C$

f) $\int 2\cos^2 4x\,dx = \frac{1}{8}\sin 8x + x + C$

g) $\int \cos x\sin x\,dx = -\frac{1}{4}\cos 2x + C$

h) $\int \sin 3x\cos 3x\,dx = -\frac{1}{12}\cos 6x + C$

i) $\int \frac{6\tan 3x}{1-\tan^2 3x}\,dx = -\frac{1}{2}\ln|\cos 6x| + C$
$\left(\text{or} = \frac{1}{2}\ln|\sec 6x| + C\right)$

j) $\int 5\sin 2x\cos 2x\,dx = -\frac{5}{8}\cos 4x + C$

k) $\int (\sin x+\cos x)^2\,dx = x - \frac{1}{2}\cos 2x + C$

l) $\int 4\sin x\cos x\cos 2x\,dx = -\frac{1}{4}\cos 4x + C$

Q2 **a)** $\int (\cos x+\sin x)(\cos x-\sin x)\,dx = \frac{1}{2}\sin 2x + C$

b) $\int \sin^2 x\cot x\,dx = -\frac{1}{4}\cos 2x + C$

Q3 **a)** $\int_0^{\frac{\pi}{4}} \sin^2 x\,dx = \frac{\pi}{8} - \frac{1}{4}$

b) $\int_0^\pi \cos^2 2x\,dx = \frac{\pi}{2}$

c) $\int_0^\pi \sin\frac{x}{2}\cos\frac{x}{2}\,dx = 1$

d) $\int_{\frac{\pi}{4}}^{\frac{\pi}{2}} \sin^2 2x\,dx = \frac{\pi}{8}$

e) $\int_0^{\frac{\pi}{4}} \cos 2x\sin 2x\,dx = \frac{1}{4}$

f) $\int_{\frac{\pi}{4}}^{\frac{\pi}{2}} \sin^2 x - \cos^2 x\,dx = \frac{1}{2}$

Exercise 6.2

Q1 **a)** $\int \cot^2 x - 4\,dx = -\cot x - 5x + C$

b) $\int \tan^2 x\,dx = \tan x - x + C$

c) $\int 3\cot^2 x\,dx = -3\cot x - 3x + C$

d) $\int \tan^2 4x\,dx = \frac{1}{4}\tan 4x - x + C$

Q2 $\int_0^{\frac{\pi}{4}} \tan^2 x + \cos^2 x - \sin^2 x\,dx = \frac{6-\pi}{4}$

Q3 **a)** $\int (\sec x+\tan x)^2\,dx$
$= 2\tan x + 2\sec x - x + C$

b) $\int (\cot x+cosec\,x)^2\,dx$
$= -2\cot x - 2\,cosec\,x - x + C$

c) $\int 4+\cot^2 3x\,dx = 3x - \frac{1}{3}\cot 3x + C$

d) $\int \cos^2 4x + \cot^2 4x\,dx$
$= \frac{1}{16}\sin 8x - \frac{1}{4}\cot 4x - \frac{1}{2}x + C$

Q4 **a)** $\int \tan^3 x + \tan^5 x\,dx = \frac{1}{4}\tan^4 x + C$

b) $\int \cot^5 x + \cot^3 x\,dx = -\frac{1}{4}\cot^4 x + C$

c) $\int \sin^3 x\,dx = -\cos x + \frac{1}{3}\cos^3 x + C$

Q5 You want to find A and B, where $\frac{A+B}{2} = 4x$, and $\frac{A-B}{2} = x$.
Solve simultaneously:
$\frac{A+B}{2} + \frac{A-B}{2} = 4x + x \implies A = 5x$.
So $B = 3x$. Then $2\sin 4x\cos x$
$\equiv 2\sin\left(\frac{5x+3x}{2}\right)\cos\left(\frac{5x-3x}{2}\right)$
$\equiv \sin 5x + \sin 3x$
So
$\int 2\sin 4x\cos x\,dx = \int \sin 5x + \sin 3x\,dx$
$= -\frac{1}{5}\cos 5x - \frac{1}{3}\cos 3x + C$

7. Finding Area using Integration

Exercise 7.1

Q1 **a)** 32
Find the points where the curve and the line intersect by solving $3x^2 + 4 = 16$, giving $x = -2$ or 2. So they intersect at $x = -2$ and $x = 2$. The area is found by subtracting the integral of $3x^2 + 4$ between -2 and 2 from the integral of 16 between -2 and 2 (which is a rectangle measuring 16 by 4).

b) 12
When $x = 2$, $y = 2^3 + 4 = 12$ so find the area under the line from $x = 0$ to $x = 2$ (a rectangle measuring 12 by 2) minus the integral of the curve between $x = 0$ and $x = 2$.

c) $\frac{15}{4}$
First solve to find the point of intersection of $y = 4$ and $y = \frac{1}{x^2}$: $4 = \frac{1}{x^2}$, giving $x = \pm\frac{1}{2}$. From the diagram, you can see that the point you want is $x = \frac{1}{2}$. So the required area is the area under the line $y = 4$ from $x = 0$ to $x = \frac{1}{2}$ (a rectangle measuring $\frac{1}{2}$ by 4) added to the area under the curve $y = \frac{1}{x^2}$ from $x = \frac{1}{2}$ to $x = 4$.

d) $\frac{32}{3}$

Solve $-1 - (x - 3)^2 = -5$, which gives $x = 1$ and $x = 5$. Be careful — this area is below the x-axis so the integral will be negative, but area must be positive. The area you want is the area above the line between 1 and 5 (a rectangle measuring 5 by 4) minus the area between the curve and the x-axis between 1 and 5.

e) $\frac{4}{3}$

Solve $x^2 = 2x$ which gives $x = O$ and $x = 2$. So the area is the area under the line between O and 2, minus the area under the curve between O and 2.

f) 8

Solve $x^3 = 4x$ which gives $x = O$ and $x = \pm 2$. The area above the x-axis is the same as the area below the x-axis (from the symmetry of the graph). For the area above the x-axis, find the area under the line from $x = O$ to $x = 2$, minus the area under the curve from $x = O$ to $x = 2$.

For parts e) and f) you could have used the formula for finding the area of a triangle rather than integrating.

Q2 **a)** $\frac{1}{6}$ **b)** $\frac{4}{27}$

Exercise 7.2
Q1 **a)** 9 **b)** $\frac{4}{3}$

Q2 $3\sqrt{2} - 3$

Q3 The area of each grey section is the integral of the upper function minus the integral of the lower function.
So the total grey area is:
$$\left(\int_0^\pi 5\sin x\, dx - \int_0^\pi 4\sin x\, dx\right)$$
$$+\left(\int_0^\pi 3\sin x\, dx - \int_0^\pi 2\sin x\, dx\right)$$
$$+\left(\int_0^\pi \sin x\, dx\right)$$
$$= 5\int_0^\pi \sin x\, dx - 4\int_0^\pi \sin x\, dx$$
$$+ 3\int_0^\pi \sin x\, dx - 2\int_0^\pi \sin x\, dx + \int_0^\pi \sin x\, dx$$
$$= (5 - 4 + 3 - 2 + 1)\int_0^\pi \sin x\, dx$$
$$= 3\int_0^\pi \sin x\, dx = 3[-\cos x]_0^\pi$$
$$= 3[(-\cos \pi) - (-\cos 0)]$$
$$= 3[(-(-1) - (-1)] = 3(1 + 1) = 6$$

Exercise 7.3
Q1 $\frac{32}{3}$

Q2 36

Q3 $\frac{2\pi}{3} + \sqrt{3}$

Q4 Solving $x^2 = ax \Rightarrow x^2 - ax = 0$
$\Rightarrow x(x - a) = 0 \Rightarrow x = 0$ or $x = a$
Draw a diagram:

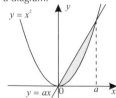

The area is given by the area under the line $y = ax$ between 0 and a, minus the area under the curve $y = x^2$ between 0 and a.
$$\int_0^a ax\, dx = \left[\frac{ax^2}{2}\right]_0^a = \left(\frac{a^3}{2}\right) - \left(\frac{a \times 0^2}{2}\right) = \frac{a^3}{2}$$
$$\int_0^a x^2\, dx = \left[\frac{x^3}{3}\right]_0^a = \left(\frac{a^3}{3}\right) - \left(\frac{0^3}{3}\right) = \frac{a^3}{3}$$
So the area is $\frac{a^3}{2} - \frac{a^3}{3} = \frac{a^3}{6}$.
The area is 36, so $\frac{a^3}{6} = 36$
$\Rightarrow a^3 = 216 \Rightarrow a = 6$.

Exercise 7.4
Q1 **a)** 88 **b)** ln 25
c) 8 **d)** $e - 1$

Q2 **a)** $\frac{45}{4}$ **b)** $e^3 - 1$
c) 1 **d)** ln 2

Q3 1

8. Parametric Integration
Exercise 8.1
Q1 **a)** $\int -12\, dt$

b) $\int \frac{3t^2 - 4}{2\sqrt{t}}\, dt$ or $\int \left(\frac{3}{2}t^{\frac{3}{2}} - 2t^{-\frac{1}{2}}\right)\, dt$

c) $\int 3t^3\, dt$

d) $\int 2\sin\theta\cos^2\theta\, d\theta$

e) $\int 5\sec^4 5\theta\, d\theta$

f) $\int 10e^{2t}t^4\, dt$

Q2 **a)** $\int (4t + 3)\, dt = 2t^2 + 3t + C$

b) $\int (30t^2 - 6t)\, dt = 10t^3 - 3t^2 + C$

c) $\int -16t\, dt = -8t^2 + C$

d) $\int (32t^3 - 136t^2 + 120t)\, dt$
$$= 8t^4 - \frac{136}{3}t^3 + 60t^2 + C$$

e) $\int (8t^2 - 2t)\, dt = \frac{8}{3}t^3 - t^2 + C$

f) $\int (15t^4 + 3t^2)\, dt = 3t^5 + t^3 + C$

Q3 $x = \cos 3\theta + 4 \Rightarrow \frac{dx}{d\theta} = -3\sin 3\theta$
$y = 2\cos 3\theta$
$$\int y\, dx = \int y\frac{dx}{d\theta}\, d\theta$$
$$= \int (2\cos 3\theta)(-3\sin 3\theta)\, d\theta$$
$$= \int -6\sin 3\theta\cos 3\theta\, d\theta$$
$$= \int -3(2\sin 3\theta\cos 3\theta)\, d\theta$$
$$= \int -3\sin 6\theta\, d\theta$$
(using the double angle formula for sin).
$$\int -3\sin 6\theta\, d\theta = \left(-\frac{3}{6}\right)(-\cos 6\theta) + C$$
$$= \frac{1}{2}\cos 6\theta + C \text{ as required.}$$

Q4 $y\frac{dx}{dt} = 3(2t - 8)$, $\int_{-2}^2 3(2t - 8)\, dt = -96$

Q5 $y\frac{dx}{dt} = \frac{5}{t} \times 6t = 30$, $\int_1^5 30\, dt = 120$

Q6 a) When $x = 8$, $t = 1$
When $x = 120$, $t = 5$

b) $\int_1^5 24t^4 + 12t^3\, dt = 16\,867.2$

9. Integration by Substitution
Exercise 9.1
Q1 **a)** $\int 12(x + 3)^5\, dx = 2(x + 3)^6 + C$

b) $\int (11 - x)^4\, dx = -\frac{1}{5}(11 - x)^5 + C$

c) $\int 24x(x^2 + 4)^3\, dx = 3(x^2 + 4)^4 + C$

d) $\int \sin^5 x\cos x\, dx = \frac{1}{6}\sin^6 x + C$

e) $\int x(x - 1)^5\, dx$
$$= \frac{1}{7}(x - 1)^7 + \frac{1}{6}(x - 1)^6 + C$$

f) $\int 5\tan^4 x\sec^2 x\, dx = \tan^5 x + C$

Q2 **a)** $\int 21(x + 2)^6\, dx = 3(x + 2)^7 + C$

b) $\int (5x + 4)^3\, dx = \frac{1}{20}(5x + 4)^4 + C$

c) $\int x(2x + 3)^3\, dx$
$$= \frac{1}{20}(2x + 3)^5 - \frac{3}{16}(2x + 3)^4 + C$$

d) $\int 24x(x^2 - 5)^7\, dx = \frac{3}{2}(x^2 - 5)^8 + C$

Q3 **a)** $\int 6x\sqrt{x + 1}\, dx$
$$= \frac{12}{5}(\sqrt{x + 1})^5 - 4(\sqrt{x + 1})^3 + C$$

b) $\int \frac{x}{\sqrt{4 - x}}\, dx$
$$= \frac{2}{3}(\sqrt{4 - x})^3 - 8(\sqrt{4 - x}) + C$$

c) $\int \frac{15(\ln x)^4}{x}\, dx = 3(\ln x)^5 + C$

Q4 **a)** $\int \frac{4x}{\sqrt{(2x - 1)}}\, dx$
$$= \frac{2}{3}(\sqrt{2x - 1})^3 + 2(\sqrt{2x - 1}) + C$$
Use the substitution $u = (\sqrt{2x - 1})$.

b) $\int \frac{1}{4 - \sqrt{x}}\, dx$
$$= -2\sqrt{x} - 8\ln|4 - \sqrt{x}| + C$$
Use the substitution $u = 4 - \sqrt{x}$.

c) $\int \frac{e^{2x}}{1 + e^x}\, dx = e^x - \ln(1 + e^x) + C$
Use the substitution $u = e^x$.

d) $\int 6x\sqrt{x^2 + 5}\, dx = 2(\sqrt{x^2 + 5})^3 + C$
Use the substitution $u = (\sqrt{x^2 + 5})$.

Q5 Let $u = f(x) \Rightarrow \frac{du}{dx} = f'(x)$
$\Rightarrow dx = \frac{1}{f'(x)}\, du$
So $\int (n + 1)f'(x)[f(x)]^n\, dx$
$$= \int (n + 1)f'(x)u^n \times \frac{1}{f'(x)}\, du$$
$$= \int (n + 1)u^n\, du = u^{n + 1} + C$$
$$= [f(x)]^{n + 1} + C, \text{ as required.}$$

Exercise 9.2
Q1 **a)** $\int_{\frac{5}{3}}^1 (3x - 2)^4\, dx = \frac{1}{15}$

b) $\int_{-2}^1 2x(x + 3)^4\, dx = \frac{687}{5}(= 137.4)$

c) $\int_0^{\frac{\pi}{6}} 8\sin^3 x\cos x\, dx = \frac{1}{8}$

d) $\int_0^3 x\sqrt{x+1}\ dx = \frac{116}{15}$

Q2 a) $\int_2^{\sqrt{5}} x(x^2-3)^4\ dx = \frac{31}{10}\ (=3.1)$

b) $\int_1^2 x(3x-4)^3\ dx = \frac{12}{5}\ (=2.4)$

c) $\int_2^{10} \frac{x}{\sqrt{x-1}}\ dx = \frac{64}{3}$

Q3 $\int_1^4 \frac{1}{3-\sqrt{x}}\ dx = -2+6\ln 2$

Q4 $\int_0^1 2e^x(1+e^x)^3\ dx = 87.6$ (1 d.p.)

Q5 $\int_1^5 \frac{x}{\sqrt{3x+1}}\ dx = \frac{100}{27}$

Exercise 9.3

Q1 $\int_0^1 \frac{1}{1+x^2}\ dx = \frac{\pi}{4}$

Q2 $\int_0^{\frac{\pi}{6}} 3\sin x \sin 2x\ dx = \frac{1}{4}$

Q3 $\int_1^{\sqrt{3}} \frac{1}{(4-x^2)^{\frac{3}{2}}}\ dx = \frac{\sqrt{3}}{6}$

Q4 $\int_{\frac{1}{2}}^1 \frac{1}{x^2\sqrt{1-x^2}}\ dx = \sqrt{3}$

Q5 $\int 2\tan^3 x\ dx = \sec^2 x - \ln(\sec^2 x) + C$

10. Integration by Parts
Exercise 10.1

Q1 a) $\int xe^x\ dx = xe^x - e^x + C$
b) $\int xe^{-x}\ dx = -xe^{-x} - e^{-x} + C$
c) $\int xe^{-\frac{x}{3}}\ dx = -3xe^{-\frac{x}{3}} - 9e^{-\frac{x}{3}} + C$
d) $\int x(e^x+1)\ dx = xe^x - e^x + \frac{1}{2}x^2 + C$

Q2 a) $\int 2x\cos x\ dx = 2x\sin x + 2\cos x + C$
b) $\int 3x\cos\frac{1}{2}x\ dx$
$= 6x\sin\frac{1}{2}x + 12\cos\frac{1}{2}x + C$

Q3 a) $\int 2\ln x\ dx = 2x\ln x - 2x + C$
b) $\int x^4\ln x\ dx = \frac{1}{5}x^5\ln x - \frac{1}{25}x^5 + C$
c) $\int \ln 4x\ dx = x\ln 4x - x + C$
d) $\int \ln x^3\ dx = x\ln x^3 - 3x + C$

Q4 a) $\int \frac{x}{e^{2x}}\ dx = -\frac{x}{2e^{2x}} - \frac{1}{4e^{2x}} + C$
b) $\int (x+1)\sqrt{x+2}\ dx$
$= \frac{2}{3}(x+1)(x+2)^{\frac{3}{2}} - \frac{4}{15}(x+2)^{\frac{5}{2}} + C$
c) $\int \ln(x+1)\ dx$
$= (x+1)\ln|x+1| - x + C$

Exercise 10.2

Q1 a) $\int_0^\pi x\sin x\ dx = \pi$
b) $\int_{-\frac{\pi}{2}}^{\frac{\pi}{2}} 2x(1-\sin x)\ dx = -4$
c) $\int_{-1}^1 20x(x+1)^3\ dx = 48$
d) $\int_0^{1.5} 30x\sqrt{2x+1}\ dx = 58$

Q2 a) $\int_0^1 12xe^{2x}\ dx = 3e^2 + 3$
b) $\int_0^{\frac{\pi}{3}} 18x\sin 3x\ dx = 2\pi$
c) $\int_1^2 \frac{1}{x^2}\ln x\ dx = \frac{1}{2} - \frac{1}{2}\ln 2$
d) $\int_0^{\frac{\pi}{12}} 6x\cos 2x\ dx$
$= \frac{\pi + 6\sqrt{3} - 12}{8}$ $\left(\text{or } \frac{\pi}{8} + \frac{3\sqrt{3}}{4} - \frac{3}{2}\right)$

Exercise 10.3

Q1 a) $\int x^2 e^x\ dx = x^2 e^x - 2xe^x + 2e^x + C$
b) $\int x^2\cos x\ dx$
$= x^2\sin x + 2x\cos x - 2\sin x + C$
c) $\int 4x^2\sin 2x\ dx$
$= -2x^2\cos 2x + 2x\sin 2x + \cos 2x + C$
d) $\int 40x^2(2x-1)^4\ dx$
$= 4x^2(2x-1)^5 - \frac{2x}{3}(2x-1)^6 +$
$\frac{1}{21}(2x-1)^7 + C$

Q2 $\int_{-1}^0 x^2(x+1)^4\ dx = \frac{1}{105}$

Q3 Area $= \frac{1}{4} - \frac{5}{4}e^{-2}$

11. Integrating Using Partial Fractions
Exercise 11.1

Q1 a) $\int \frac{3}{(x+1)(x+2)}\ dx$
$= 3\ln|x+1| - 3\ln|x+2| + C$
b) $\int \frac{24(x-1)}{9-4x^2}\ dx$
$= -\ln|3-2x| - 5\ln|3+2x| + C$
c) $\int \frac{21x-82}{(x-2)(x-3)(x-4)}\ dx$
$= \ln|x-4| + 19\ln|x-3|$
$- 20\ln|x-2| + C$

Q2 $\int_0^1 \frac{x}{(x-2)(x-3)}\ dx = \ln\frac{32}{27}$

Q3 a) $\frac{6}{2x^2-5x+2} \equiv \frac{2}{x-2} - \frac{4}{2x-1}$
b) $\int \frac{6}{2x^2-5x+2}\ dx = \ln\left[\left(\frac{x-2}{2x-1}\right)^2\right] + C$
c) $\int_3^5 \frac{6}{2x^2-5x+2}\ dx = \ln\frac{25}{9}$

Q4 $\int_1^2 \frac{3x+5}{x(x+10)}\ dx = 0.564$ (3 d.p.)

Q5 Begin by writing the function as partial fractions.
$\frac{-(t+3)}{(3t+2)(t+1)} \equiv \frac{A}{(3t+2)} + \frac{B}{(t+1)}$
$\Rightarrow -(t+3) \equiv A(t+1) + B(3t+2)$
Substituting $t = -1$ gives:
$-2 = -B \Rightarrow B = 2$
Equating coefficients of t gives
$A + 3B = -1 \Rightarrow A + 6 = -1 \Rightarrow A = -7$
So $\frac{-(t+3)}{(3t+2)(t+1)} \equiv \frac{2}{(t+1)} - \frac{7}{(3t+2)}$

The integral can be expressed:
$\int_0^{\frac{2}{3}} \frac{-(t+3)}{(3t+2)(t+1)}\ dt$
$= \int_0^{\frac{2}{3}} \frac{2}{(t+1)} - \frac{7}{(3t+2)}\ dt$
$= \left[2\ln|t+1| - \frac{7}{3}\ln|3t+2|\right]_0^{\frac{2}{3}}$
$= \left[2\ln\left|\frac{5}{3}\right| - \frac{7}{3}\ln|4|\right] - \left[2\ln|1| - \frac{7}{3}\ln|2|\right]$
$= \left[2\ln\left(\frac{5}{3}\right) - \frac{7}{3}\ln(4)\right] - \left[0 - \frac{7}{3}\ln(2)\right]$
$= 2\ln\left(\frac{5}{3}\right) - \frac{7}{3}\ln(4) + \frac{7}{3}\ln(2)$
$= 2\ln\left(\frac{5}{3}\right) - \frac{7}{3}(\ln(4) - \ln(2))$
$= 2\ln\left(\frac{5}{3}\right) - \frac{7}{3}\ln\left(\frac{4}{2}\right) = 2\ln\frac{5}{3} - \frac{7}{3}\ln 2$

Q6 $\int_9^{16} \frac{4}{\sqrt{x}(9x-4)}\ dx = \frac{2}{3}\ln\frac{55}{49}$
Use the given substitution to write the integral in terms of u (you'll need to replace the limits and the dx as well), then write as partial fractions and integrate with the new limits.

12. Differential Equations
Exercise 12.1

Q1 $\frac{dN}{dt} = kN$, for some $k > 0$.
Q2 $\frac{dx}{dt} = \frac{k}{x^2}$, for some $k > 0$.
Q3 Let the variable t represent time. Then $\frac{dA}{dt} = -k\sqrt{A}$, for some $k > 0$.
Q4 Let the variable t represent time. Then $\frac{dy}{dt} = -k(y - \lambda)$, for some $k > 0$.
Q5 Let the variable t represent time. Then $\frac{dV}{dt} = kV - 20$, for some $k > 0$.

Exercise 12.2

Q1 a) $y = 2x^4 + C$ b) $y = ke^{5x}$
c) $y = ke^{2x^3}$ d) $y = kx$
e) $y = ke^{\sin x} - 1$ f) $y = \frac{k(x-4)^2}{\sqrt{2x-5}}$

Q2 a) $A = 9t^2 + 30t + 25$
b) $y^2 + x^2 = 4$
c) $x^3 = (3t + 12)^2$
d) $V = 4e^{3t} + 1$
e) $\sin y = \frac{x}{2}$
f) $\frac{x}{x+1} = \frac{1}{2}e^{10t}$

Q3 a) $\frac{dV}{dt} = a - bV \Rightarrow \frac{1}{a-bV}\ dV = dt$
$\Rightarrow \int \frac{1}{a-bV}\ dV = \int 1\ dt$
$\Rightarrow -\frac{1}{b}\ln|a-bV| = t + C$
$\Rightarrow \ln|a-bV| = -bt - bC$
b and C are both constants, so let $-bC = \ln k$:
$\Rightarrow \ln|a-bV| = -bt + \ln k$
$\Rightarrow a - bV = ke^{-bt}$
$\Rightarrow bV = a - ke^{-bt} \Rightarrow V = \frac{a}{b} - Ae^{-bt}$
(letting $A = k \div b$)

b) $A = \frac{3a}{4b}$
c) As t gets very large, V approaches $\frac{a}{b}$.

Exercise 12.3

Q1 **a)** $\frac{dN}{dt} = kN \Rightarrow \frac{1}{N} dN = k\,dt$

$\Rightarrow \int \frac{1}{N} dN = \int k\,dt$

$\Rightarrow \ln N = kt + \ln A$

$\Rightarrow N = e^{kt + \ln A} = Ae^{kt}$

Note that you don't need to put modulus signs in ln N here, as N can't be negative — you can't have a negative number of germs in your body. The same principle will apply to a lot of real-life differential equations questions.

b) When $t = 24$, $N = 1600$

c) Some possible answers are:
- The number of germs doubles every 8 hours, so over a long time the model becomes unrealistic because the total number of germs will become very large.
- The number of germs is a discrete variable (you can't have half of a germ) but the model is a continuous function.
- The model does not account for the differences between patients or other conditions such as the presence of other germs or chemicals.

Q2 **a)** $\frac{dV}{dt} \propto V \Rightarrow \frac{dV}{dt} = -kV$,

for some $k > 0$

$\Rightarrow \frac{1}{V} dV = -k\,dt$

$\Rightarrow \int \frac{1}{V} dV = \int -k\,dt$

$\Rightarrow \ln V = -kt + \ln A \Rightarrow V = Ae^{-kt}$

$t = 0,\ V = V_0 \Rightarrow V_0 = Ae^0 = A$

$\Rightarrow V = V_0 e^{-kt}$

b) 4 years, 4 months (or 52 months)

Q3 **a)** $\frac{dx}{dt} = \frac{1}{x^2(t+1)}$, $V = x^3 \Rightarrow \frac{dV}{dx} = 3x^2$

So $\frac{dV}{dt} = \frac{dV}{dx} \times \frac{dx}{dt}$

$= \frac{3x^2}{x^2(t+1)} = \frac{3}{t+1}$

b) 1.72 seconds (3 s.f.)

Q4 **a)** $y = p - Ae^{-kt}$

b) 66 days (to the nearest day)

c)

$y = 30\,000 - 20\,000e^{0.2\ln 0.9t}$

30 000

10 000

d) No, the target will not be achieved.

e) Some possible answers are:
- The model suggests that the number of signatures eventually reaches the entire population of 30 000 (if you round to the nearest whole number). It may be more accurate to assume that there are some people who will never sign the petition, no matter how much time elapses, and allow for this in the model.

- The number of signatures is a discrete variable, and the model uses a continuous function. Adjusting the function to only allow integer values of y would fix this.

- The model does not account for people entering or leaving the town. Adjusting the function so that p varies with time may make the model more accurate.

Review Exercise — Chapter 23

Q1 **a)** $\int \frac{1}{\sqrt[3]{(2-11x)}} dx = -\frac{3}{22}(2-11x)^{\frac{2}{3}} + C$

b) Integrate the curve between the two limits:

$\int_{-\frac{123}{11}}^{-\frac{62}{11}} \frac{1}{\sqrt[3]{(2-11x)}} dx$

$= -\frac{3}{22}[(\sqrt[3]{2-11x})^2]_{-\frac{123}{11}}^{-\frac{62}{11}}$

$= -\frac{3}{22}([(\sqrt[3]{2+62})^2] - [(\sqrt[3]{2+123})^2])$

$= -\frac{3}{22}((\sqrt[3]{64})^2 - (\sqrt[3]{125})^2)$

$= -\frac{3}{22}(16-25) = \frac{27}{22}$

Q2 $y = -\frac{2}{21}(1-7x)^{\frac{3}{2}} + \frac{23}{21}$

Q3 **a)** $\int 4e^{2x} dx = 2e^{2x} + C$

b) $\int e^{3x-5} dx = \frac{1}{3}e^{3x-5} + C$

c) $\int \frac{2}{3x} dx = \frac{2}{3}\ln|x| + C$

d) $\int \frac{2}{2x+1} dx = \ln|2x+1| + C$

Q4 $P = (2x - x^2)^{-8}$

Q5 **a)** $\int \cos(x+A) dx = \sin(x+A) + C$

b) $\int \sin(A-x) dx = \cos(A-x) + C$

c) $\int \text{cosec}^2((A+B)t + A + B)\,dt$

$= -\frac{1}{A+B}\cot((A+B)t + A + B) + C$

Q6 **a)** $\int \cos 4x - \sec^2 7x\, dx$

$= \frac{1}{4}\sin 4x - \frac{1}{7}\tan 7x + C$

b) $\int 6\sec 3x \tan 3x - \text{cosec}^2\frac{x}{5} dx$

$= 2\sec 3x + 5\cot\frac{x}{5} + C$

Q7 **a)** $\int \frac{\cos x}{\sin x} dx = \ln|\sin x| + C$

b) $\int \frac{20x^4 + 12x^2 - 12}{x^5 + x^3 - 3x} dx$

$= 4\ln|x^5 + x^3 - 3x| + C$

c) $\int \frac{10e^{4x} + 5}{5e^{4x} + 10x} dx = \frac{1}{2}\ln|5e^{4x} + 10x| + C$

Q8 **a)** $\int 3x^2 e^{x^3} dx = e^{x^3} + C$

b) $\int 2x\cos(x^2)e^{\sin(x^2)} dx = e^{\sin(x^2)} + C$

c) $\int \sec 4x \tan 4x\, e^{\sec 4x} dx = \frac{1}{4}e^{\sec 4x} + C$

Q9 $\int \frac{2\tan 3x}{1-\tan^2 3x} dx = -\frac{1}{6}\ln|\cos 6x| + C$

$\left(\text{or} = \frac{1}{6}\ln|\sec 6x| + C\right)$

Q10 **a)** $\int 2\sin^2 x\, dx = x - \frac{1}{2}\sin 2x + C$

b) $\int \sin 2x \cos 2x\, dx = -\frac{1}{8}\cos 4x + C$

c) $\int \tan^2 x + 1\, dx = \tan x + C$

Q11 **a)** 16
Set the two curves equal to each other and solve for x to find the points of intersection — the curves cross at x = −1 and x = 3. Then integrate each curve between −1 and 3, and subtract the area under the bottom curve from the area under the top curve.

b) 3.75 − ln 16
Set the curve and the line equal to each other and solve for x to find the points of intersection — they cross at x = 0.5 and x = 2. Then integrate the curve between 0.5 and 2, and subtract this area from the area of the trapezium with parallel sides of 4 and 1 and height 1.5.

c) $\frac{\pi}{2}$
Find the value of x for which tan x = 1 (x = $\frac{\pi}{4}$), so integrate y = tan x between 0 and $\frac{\pi}{4}$. Find the area of the rectangle formed by the x-axis, the line y = −1 and the lines x = ±$\frac{\pi}{4}$ then subtract the first area (as the unshaded area between −$\frac{\pi}{4}$ and 0 will be the same as the first area found by the symmetry of the graph). Alternatively, you could solve this problem without integrating if you realise that, due to the symmetry of tan x, the area required is exactly the same as the rectangle described above.

Q12 **a)** $\int_2^3 y^4\, dy = \frac{211}{5}\ (= 42.2)$

b) $\int_{\frac{\pi}{6}}^{\frac{\pi}{4}} \tan y\, dy = \ln\left(\frac{\sqrt{6}}{2}\right)$

c) $\int_4^{16} \frac{1}{\sqrt{y}} dy = 4$

Q13 **a)** When $x = 4$, $t = 1$.
When $x = 12$, $t = 3$.

b) $\int_1^3 (4t-1)(2t)\, dt = 61\frac{1}{3}$

Q14 $x = 2t^3 \Rightarrow t = \sqrt[3]{\frac{x}{2}}$

When $x = 2$, $t = \sqrt[3]{\frac{2}{2}} = 1$.

When $x = 54$, $t = \sqrt[3]{\frac{54}{2}} = 3$.

$y = \frac{2}{t}$ and $\frac{dx}{dt} = 6t^2$

$\int_2^{54} y\, dx = \int_1^3 y\frac{dx}{dt} dt = \int_1^3 \left(\frac{2}{t}\right)(6t^2)\, dt$

$= \int_1^3 12t\, dt = [6t^2]_1^3 = 54 - 6 = 48$

Q15 **a)** $\int 16x(5-x^2)^5 dx = -\frac{4}{3}(5-x^2)^6 + C$

b) $\int e^x(e^x + 1)(e^x - 1)^2 dx$

$= \frac{1}{4}(e^x - 1)^4 + \frac{2}{3}(e^x - 1)^3 + C$

c) $\int_{\frac{\pi}{4}}^{\frac{\pi}{3}} \sec^4 x \tan x\, dx = 3$

d) $\int_3^{11} \frac{2x}{\sqrt{3x-8}}\, dx = \frac{880}{27}$

Q16 a) $\int_2^4 x(x^2-4)^3\, dx = 2592$

b) $\int 3\sin\theta\cos^4\theta\, d\theta = -\frac{3}{5}\cos^5\theta + C$

Q17 a) $\int_0^{\frac{\pi}{2}} \frac{1}{4}\cos x \sin 2x\, dx = \frac{1}{6}$

b) $\int_1^{\sqrt{3}} \frac{4x}{\sqrt{1+x^2}}\, dx = 8 - 4\sqrt{2}$

Q18 a) $\int 3x^2 \ln x\, dx = x^3(\ln x - \frac{1}{3}) + C$

b) $\int 4x \cos 4x\, dx$
$= x\sin 4x + \frac{1}{4}\cos 4x + C$

c) $\int_0^4 x^2 e^{\frac{x}{2}}\, dx = 16e^2 - 16$

You'll have to use integration by parts twice here.

Q19 $\int 10x^2 e^{5x}\, dx = 2x^2 e^{5x} - \frac{4}{5}xe^{5x} + \frac{4}{25}e^{5x} + C$

Q20 $\int \frac{3x+10}{(2x+3)(x-4)}\, dx$
$= -\frac{1}{2}\ln|2x+3| + 2\ln|x-4| + C$

Q21 $\int_4^9 \frac{13x-18}{(x-3)^2(2x+1)}\, dx = \frac{5}{2} + \ln\left(\frac{54}{19}\right)$

Q22 a) $\frac{dx}{dy} = kx^2$, for some $k > 0$

b) $\frac{dV}{dt} = -\frac{k}{\sqrt{V}}$, for some $k > 0$

c) $\frac{ds}{dt} = -k(s_0 - s)$, for some $k > 0$

Q23 $y^2 = 2\sin x + C$

Q24 $x = 3e^t(t-1)$

Q25 a) $\tan x = \ln|\sin\theta| + C$

b) $\tan x = \ln|\sin\theta| + 1$

c) When $\theta = \frac{\pi}{6}$, $x = 0.298$ (to 3 d.p.)

Q26 a) $\frac{dS}{dt} = kS$

b) It will take the squirrels 8 weeks to take over the forest.

Q27 a) $T = 69e^{-0.0313t} + 21$

b) (i) 64.1 °C   **(ii)** 41.2 mins

c)
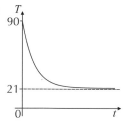

Q28 a) $\frac{dN}{dt} = kN$

b) The field will be over-run in 39 weeks.

c) $\frac{dN}{dt} = k\sqrt{N}$
The field will be over-run in 108 weeks.

---

d) Some possible answers are:
- The model could be adjusted to use a discrete-valued function, since the number of mice is a discrete variable.
- When there is only 1 mouse (i.e. $N = 1$), the population still increases, which is unrealistic. The model could be adjusted to be more accurate for low values of N.
- As t increases, N gets larger without any limit. Introducing an upper limit on t or N would show at which point the model stops being accurate.

Chapter 24: Numerical Methods

1. Location of Roots

Exercise 1.1

All the functions in this exercise are continuous over the given interval (except for the interval in Q6b), so to show there's a root all you have to do is show there's a change of sign within the interval. In the exam you might also need to write a conclusion.

Q1 a) $f(2) = -1$, $f(3) = 13$

b) $f(0.9) = 0.0738...$, $f(1.0) = -0.0907...$

c) $f(1.2) = -0.089...$, $f(1.3) = 0.459...$

d) Rearrange to get
$f(x) = 4x - 2x^3 - 15 = 0$
$f(-2.3) = 0.134$, $f(-2.2) = -2.504$

e) Rearrange to get
$f(x) = \ln(x + 3) - 5x = 0$
$f(0.23) = 0.022...$,
$f(0.24) = -0.024...$

f) Rearrange to get
$f(x) = e^{3x}\sin x - 5 = 0$
$f(0) = -5$, $f(1) = 11.9...$

Q2 $f(1.2) = 0.28$, $f(1.3) = -0.02$

Q3 $f(1.6) = 1.24...$, $f(1.7) = -0.25...$
$\Rightarrow 1.6 < \alpha < 1.7$
$f(-1) = -1$, $f(0) = 3 \Rightarrow -1 < \beta < 0$

Q4 $f(0.01) = 0.0366...$, $f(0.02) = -0.0033...$
$\Rightarrow 0.01 < \alpha < 0.02$
$f(2.4) = -0.057...$, $f(2.5) = 0.067...$
$\Rightarrow 2.4 < \beta < 2.5$

Q5 $f(2.75) = -0.45...$, $f(2.85) = 1.19...$
$\Rightarrow 2.75 < x < 2.85 \Rightarrow x = 2.8$ (1 d.p.)

Q6 a) $f(0.65) = -0.23...$, $f(0.75) = 0.16...$
$\Rightarrow 0.65 < x < 0.75$
$\Rightarrow x = 0.7$ (1 d.p.)

b) There is an asymptote in the interval $[-0.1, 0.1]$ (at $x = 0$). The function isn't continuous in this interval, so the change of sign does not mean there is a root.

Q7 $f(0.245) = 0.037...$, $f(0.255) = -0.001...$
$\Rightarrow 0.245 < x < 0.255$
$\Rightarrow x = 0.25$ (2 d.p.)

Exercise 1.2

Q1 a)
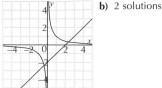
b) 2 solutions

c) $f(2.4) = -0.016...$, $f(2.5) = 0.1$
(or $f(2.4) = 0.016...$, $f(2.5) = -0.1$, if you rearranged the equation differently)

Q2 a)

b) 3 solutions

c) $f(-2) = -6$, $f(-1) = 4$

Q3 a)
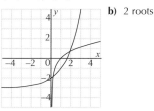
b) 2 roots

c) $f(1.8) = 0.105...$, $f(2.2) = -0.806...$,
$x = 1.9$ (1 d.p.).

Q4 a)
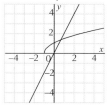

b) 1 solution

c) Rearrange to get
$f(x) = \sqrt{x+1} - 2x = 0$
$f(0.6) = 0.064...$, $f(0.7) = -0.096...$

d) $\sqrt{x+1} = 2x \Rightarrow x + 1 = 4x^2$
$\Rightarrow 4x^2 - x - 1 = 0$
$\Rightarrow x = 0.640$ (3 s.f.)

Q5 a)
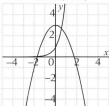

b) $e^{2x} = 3 - x^2 \Rightarrow e^{2x} + x^2 = 3$. The graphs cross twice, so 2 solutions.

c) Rearrange to get $f(x) = e^{2x} + x^2 - 3 = 0$
$f(-2) = 1.01...$, $f(-1) = -1.86...$,
$x = -1.7$ (1 d.p.)

2. Iterative Methods

Exercise 2.1

Q1 **a)** $f(1) = -3$, $f(2) = 13$

b) $x_1 = 1.414$, $x_2 = 1.179$,
$x_3 = 1.337$, $x_4 = 1.240$

Q2 **a)** $x_1 = 3.1314$, $x_2 = 3.1415$,
$x_3 = 3.1447$, $x_4 = 3.1457$,
$x_5 = 3.1460$

b) $\alpha = 3.146$ (3 d.p.)

Q3 **a)** $f(1.4) = -0.1584$, $f(1.5) = 0.5625$

b) $x_1 = 1.419$, $x_2 = 1.424$, $x_3 = 1.425$,
$x_4 = 1.425$, $x_5 = 1.425$, $x_6 = 1.425$

c) $x = 1.43$ (2 d.p.)

Q4 **a)** $f(5) = -2$, $f(6) = 4$

b) $x_1 = 5.4$, $x_2 = 5.370$, $x_3 = 5.372$,
$x_4 = 5.372$

Q5 $x = 1.56$ (2 d.p.)

Q6 **a)** $f(3) = -9.914...$, $f(4) = 14.598...$

b) $x_1 = 3.401$, $x_2 = 3.527$,
$x_3 = 3.563$, $x_4 = 3.573$

c) $f(3.5765) = -0.016...$,
$f(3.5775) = 0.0089...$
$\Rightarrow 3.5765 < x < 3.5775$
$\Rightarrow x = 3.577$ (3 d.p.)

d) $x_1 = 2.00855...$, $x_2 = 0.74525..$,
$x_3 = 0.21069...$, $x_4 = 0.12345...$,
$x_5 = 0.11313...$, $x_6 = 0.11197...$,
$x_7 = 0.11184...$, $x_8 = 0.11183...$
The formula appears to converge to
another root at $x = 0.112$ (3 d.p.)

Q7 **a)** $x_1 = -3$, $x_2 = 4$, $x_3 = -3$, $x_4 = 4$
The sequence is alternating
between -3 and 4.

b) $x_1 = 6.32455...$, $x_2 = 6.45157...$,
$x_3 = 6.50060...$, $x_4 = 6.51943...$,
$x_5 = 6.52665...$, $x_6 = 6.52941...$,
$x_7 = 6.53047...$, $x_8 = 6.53087...$
$\Rightarrow x = 6.53$ (3 s.f.)

$f(6.525) = -0.049...$,
$f(6.535) = 0.031...$
$\Rightarrow 6.525 < x < 6.535$
$\Rightarrow x = 6.53$ (3 s.f.)

Exercise 2.2

Q1 **a)** $x^4 + 7x - 3 = 0 \Rightarrow x^4 = 3 - 7x$
$\Rightarrow x = \sqrt[4]{3 - 7x}$

b) $x^4 + 7x - 3 = 0$
$\Rightarrow x^4 + 5x + 2x - 3 = 0$
$\Rightarrow 2x = 3 - 5x - x^4$
$\Rightarrow x = \dfrac{3 - 5x - x^4}{2}$

c) $x^4 + 7x - 3 = 0 \Rightarrow x^4 = 3 - 7x$
$\Rightarrow x^2 = \sqrt{3 - 7x} \Rightarrow x = \dfrac{\sqrt{3 - 7x}}{x}$

Q2 **a)** $x^3 - 2x^2 - 5 = 0 \Rightarrow x^3 = 2x^2 + 5$
$\Rightarrow x = 2 + \dfrac{5}{x^2}$

b) $x_5 = 2.7$ to 1 d.p.

c) $f(2.65) = -0.43...$, $f(2.75) = 0.67...$
$\Rightarrow 2.65 < x < 2.75$
$\Rightarrow x = 2.7$ (1 d.p.)

Q3 **a)** $x^2 + 3x - 8 = 0 \Rightarrow x^2 = 8 - 3x$
$\Rightarrow x = \dfrac{8}{x} - 3$

b) $f(-5) = 2$, $f(-4) = -4$

c) $x_1 = -4.6$, $x_2 = -4.739$, $x_3 = -4.688$,
$x_4 = -4.706$, $x_5 = -4.700$, $x_6 = -4.702$
$x = -4.70$ (2 d.p.)

Q4 **a)** $2^{x-1} = 4\sqrt{x} \Rightarrow 2^{x-1} = 2^2 x^{\frac{1}{2}}$
$\Rightarrow 2^{x-1} \times 2^{-2} = x^{\frac{1}{2}} \Rightarrow 2^{x-3} = x^{\frac{1}{2}}$
$\Rightarrow (2^{x-3})^2 = x \Rightarrow x = 2^{2x-6}$

b) $x_1 = 0.0625$, $x_2 = 0.0170$,
$x_3 = 0.0160$, $x_4 = 0.0160$

c) $f(0.01595) = 0.00038...$,
$f(0.01605) = -0.00116...$
$\Rightarrow 0.01595 < x < 0.01605$
$\Rightarrow x = 0.0160$ (4 d.p.)

Q5 **a)** $f(0.4) = -0.159...$, $f(0.5) = 0.125$

b) $\ln 2x + x^3 = 0 \Rightarrow \ln 2x = -x^3$
$\Rightarrow 2x = e^{-x^3} \Rightarrow x = \dfrac{e^{-x^3}}{2}$

c) $x = 0.455$ (3 d.p.)

Q6 **a)** $x^2 - 9x - 20 = 0 \Rightarrow x^2 = 9x + 20$
$\Rightarrow x = \sqrt{9x + 20}$
So an iterative formula is
$x_{n+1} = \sqrt{9x_n + 20}$

b) $x = 10.8$ (3 s.f.)

c) $x^2 - 9x - 20 = 0$
$\Rightarrow x^2 - 5x - 4x - 20 = 0$
$\Rightarrow 5x = x^2 - 4x - 20$
$\Rightarrow x = \dfrac{x^2 - 4x}{5} - 4$

d) $x_1 = -4.6$, $x_2 = 3.912$,
$x_3 = -4.0688...$, $x_4 = 2.5661...$,
$x_5 = -4.7358...$, $x_6 = 4.2744...$,
$x_7 = -3.7653...$, $x_8 = 1.8479...$

e) The iterations seem to be bouncing
up and down without converging to
any particular root.

3. Sketching Iterations

Exercise 3.1

Q1 **a)**

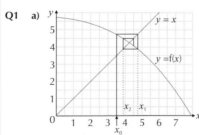

convergent cobweb diagram

b)

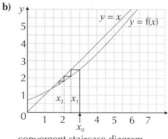

convergent staircase diagram

c)

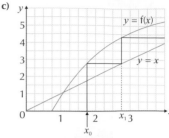

divergent staircase diagram

d)

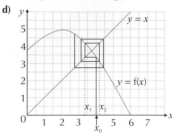

divergent cobweb diagram

4. The Newton-Raphson Method

Exercise 4.1

Q1 **a)** $x_{n+1} = x_n - \dfrac{5x_n^2 - 6}{10x_n}$

b) $x_{n+1} = x_n - \dfrac{e^{3x_n} - 4x_n^2 - 1}{3e^{3x_n} - 8x_n}$

c) $x_{n+1} = x_n - \dfrac{\sin(x_n) + x_n^3 - 1}{\cos(x_n) + 3x_n^2}$

Q2 $x = 2.3738$ (5 s.f.)

Q3 $x = -1.7720$ (5 s.f.)

Q4 $x = 2.3935$ (5 s.f.)

Q5 $x_{n+1} = x_n - \dfrac{2x_n^3 - 15x_n^2 + 109}{6x_n^2 - 30x_n}$

$x_1 = 1 - \dfrac{2(1)^3 - 15(1)^2 + 109}{6(1)^2 - 30(1)} = 1 - \dfrac{96}{-24}$
$= 1 + 4 = 5$

$x_2 = 5 - \dfrac{2(5)^3 - 15(5)^2 + 109}{6(5)^2 - 30(5)} = 5 - \dfrac{-16}{0}$

Since this involves dividing by 0,
the method fails, so $x_0 = 1$ cannot
be used to find a root.
*$f'(5) = 0$, which means that the tangent line
at x_1 is horizontal, and it won't intercept the
x-axis.*

Q6 $t = 4.03$ minutes (3 s.f.)

5. The Trapezium Rule

Exercise 5.1

Q1 **a)** 2.09 (3 s.f.) **b)** 1.74 (3 s.f.)
c) 0.441 (3 s.f.) **d)** 3.00 (3 s.f.)
e) 1.13 (3 s.f.) **f)** 23.0 (3 s.f)

Q2 0.667 (3 d.p.) **Q3** 5.947 m² (3 d.p.)

Q4 **a)**

x	0	$\dfrac{\pi}{8}$	$\dfrac{\pi}{4}$	$\dfrac{3\pi}{8}$	$\dfrac{\pi}{2}$
y	1	1.466	2.028	2.519	2.718

b) **(i)** 3.05 (2 d.p.)   **(ii)** 3.09 (2 d.p.)

c) 3.09 is the better estimate as more intervals have been used in the calculation.

Q5 **a)** **(i)** 3.44 (3 s.f.)

(ii) Lower bound = 3.146 (4 s.f.), Upper bound = 3.732 (4 s.f.)

(iii) 0.248% (3 s.f.)

b) **(i)** 0.0886 (3 s.f.)

(ii) Lower bound = 0.04163 (4 s.f.), Upper bound = 0.1355 (4 s.f.)

(iii) 2.09% (3 s.f.)

Q6 **a)** There are 6 intervals of $h = \frac{\pi}{6}$ between $-\frac{\pi}{2}$ and $\frac{\pi}{2}$.

x	$-\frac{\pi}{2}$	$-\frac{\pi}{3}$	$-\frac{\pi}{6}$	0	$\frac{\pi}{6}$	$\frac{\pi}{3}$	$\frac{\pi}{2}$
$y = \cos x$	0	0.5	$\frac{\sqrt{3}}{2}$	1	$\frac{\sqrt{3}}{2}$	0.5	0

$$\int_{-\frac{\pi}{2}}^{\frac{\pi}{2}} \cos x \, dx \approx \frac{h}{2}[y_0 + 2(y_1 + y_2 + y_3 + y_4 + y_5) + y_6]$$

$$= \frac{\left(\frac{\pi}{6}\right)}{2}[0 + 2(0.5 + \frac{\sqrt{3}}{2} + 1 + \frac{\sqrt{3}}{2} + 0.5) + 0]$$

$$= \frac{\pi}{12}[0 + 2(2 + \sqrt{3}) + 0]$$

$$= \pi\left(\frac{2(2 + \sqrt{3})}{12}\right) = \frac{\pi(2 + \sqrt{3})}{6}$$

b) It's an underestimate because, between $-\frac{\pi}{2}$ and $\frac{\pi}{2}$, the curve of the graph $y = \cos x$ is concave, so the top of each trapezium lies below the curve.

c) 2.30% (3 s.f.)

Review Exercise — Chapter 24

Q1 **a)** f(3) = –0.2794..., f(4) = 0.9893...

b) f(2.1) = 0.3025..., f(2.2) = 0.3905...

c) Rearrange to get $f(x) = x^3 - 4x^2 - 7 = 0$ f(4.3) = –1.453, f(4.5) = 3.125

Q2 There are 2 roots.

Q3 f(1.15) = –0.3291..., f(1.25) = 0.2031... $\Rightarrow 1.15 < x < 1.25 \Rightarrow x = 1.2$ (1 d.p.)

Q4 The graph touches the x-axis at x = –2 but doesn't cross it, so f(x) is never negative and there is no change of sign. *This is easy to spot if you factorise f(x): $x^2 + 4x + 4 = (x + 2)^2$. The whole function is squared, so it will never be negative.*

Q5 **a)**

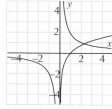

1 crossing point and therefore 1 root.

b) $f(2) = \ln 2 - \frac{2}{2} = -0.306...$, $f(3) = \ln 3 - \frac{2}{3} = 0.431...$

Q6 **a)**

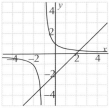

b) f(–1.4) = 0.9, f(–1.3) = –0.033..

c) $\frac{1}{x + 1} - x + 2 = 0$
$\Rightarrow 1 - x(x + 1) + 2(x + 1) = 0$
$\Rightarrow 1 - x^2 - x + 2x + 2 = 0$
$\Rightarrow -x^2 + x + 3 = 0 \Rightarrow x^2 - x - 3 = 0$

Q7 x = –0.45 (2 d.p.)

Q8 x = 2.187 (3 d.p.)

Q9 **a)** **(i)** $2x^2 - x^3 + 1 = 0 \Rightarrow 1 = x^3 - 2x^2$
$\Rightarrow x^2(x - 2) = 1 \Rightarrow x^2 = \frac{1}{x - 2}$
$\Rightarrow x = \sqrt{\frac{1}{x - 2}}$

(ii) $2x^2 - x^3 + 1 = 0 \Rightarrow x^3 = 2x^2 + 1$
$\Rightarrow x = \sqrt[3]{2x^2 + 1}$

(iii) $2x^2 - x^3 + 1 = 0 \Rightarrow 2x^2 = x^3 - 1$
$\Rightarrow x^2 = \frac{x^3 - 1}{2} \Rightarrow x = \sqrt{\frac{x^3 - 1}{2}}$

b) Using $x_{n+1} = \sqrt{\frac{1}{x_n - 2}}$ with $x_0 = 2.3$ gives:
$x_1 = 1.8257...$, $x_2 = \sqrt{\frac{1}{1.8257... - 2}}$
No real solution, so this formula does not converge to a root.

Using $x_{n+1} = \sqrt[3]{2x_n^2 + 1}$ with $x_0 = 2.3$ gives:
$x_1 = 2.2624...$, $x_2 = 2.2398...$,
$x_3 = 2.2262...$, $x_4 = 2.2180...$,
$x_5 = 2.2131...$, $x_6 = 2.2101...$
$x_7 = 2.2083...$
$\Rightarrow x = 2.21$ (2 d.p.) is a root.

Using $x_{n+1} = \sqrt{\frac{x_n^3 - 1}{2}}$ with $x_0 = 2.3$ gives:
$x_1 = 2.3629...$, $x_2 = 2.4691...$,
$x_3 = 2.6508...$, $x_4 = 2.9687...$

This sequence is diverging so does not converge to a root. The only formula that converges to a root is $x_{n+1} = \sqrt[3]{2x_n^2 + 1}$.

Q10 **a)** f(1.5) = –1.16..., f(2) = 1

b) x = 1.8 (1 d.p.)

c) $x_1 = 2.44948...$, $x_2 = 0.81876...$,
$x_3 = 2.89323...$, $x_4 = 0.40143...$,
$x_5 = 1.73724...$
The formula appears to be bouncing up and down without converging to a root.

Q11 **a)** f(1.1) = –0.06..., f(1.2) = 0.58...

b) $2x - 5 \cos x = 0 \Rightarrow 2x = 5 \cos x$
$\Rightarrow x = \frac{5}{2} \cos x$ i.e. $p = \frac{5}{2}$

c) Using the iterative formula $x_{n+1} = \frac{5}{2} \cos x_n$:
$x_1 = 1.1340$, $x_2 = 1.0576$,
$x_3 = 1.2274$, $x_4 = 0.8418$,
$x_5 = 1.6653$, $x_6 = -0.2360$,
$x_7 = 2.4307$, $x_8 = -1.8945$
The sequence at first looks like it might converge to the root in part a) but then it continues to jump up and down and diverges.

Q12 **a)** –2.180 (3 d.p.)   **b)** 1.935 (3 d.p.)

c) 1.430 (3 d.p.)   **d)** 15.708 (3 d.p.)

Q13

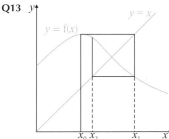

Q14

(graph showing $y = x$ and $y = f(x)$)

Q15 **a)** $(x + 2)g(x) = (x + 2)(x^3 - 4x + 1)$
$= x^4 - 4x^2 + x + 2x^3 - 8x + 2$
$= x^4 + 2x^3 - 4x^2 - 7x + 2 = f(x)$
So x = –2 is a root of f(x).
(x + 2) is a factor of f(x), so the Factor Theorem tells you that −2 is a root.

b) g(1) = –2, g(2) = 1
There is a sign change (and the function is continuous everywhere) so there is a root in this interval.

c) $x^3 - 4x + 1 = 0 \Rightarrow x^3 = 4x - 1$
$\Rightarrow x = \sqrt[3]{4x - 1}$

d) $x_1 = \sqrt[3]{4x_0 - 1} = \sqrt[3]{4(2) - 1} = 1.91293...$
$x_2 = 1.88066...$, $x_3 = 1.86842...$,
$x_4 = 1.86373...$, $x_5 = 1.86193...$,
so $\alpha = 1.86$ (3 s.f.)
Find iterations until the first three significant figures are the same from one iteration to the next.

e) $x_1 = -2 - \frac{(-2)^3 - 4(-2) + 1}{3(-2)^2 - 4} = -2.125$
$x_2 = -2.114975...$, $x_3 = -2.114907...$
so $\beta = -2.115$ (4 s.f.)
Differentiate g(x) to get $g'(x) = 3x^2 - 4$. Then you can use the Newton-Raphson formula to find β.

f) When $x_n = \frac{2\sqrt{3}}{3}$, $g'\left(\frac{2\sqrt{3}}{3}\right) = 0$
The method fails when $g'(x_n) = 0$ because it involves dividing by zero in the formula. Graphically, the tangent at x_n is horizontal, so it will never cross the x-axis.

Q16 a) 11.0 (3 s.f.)

b) $\int_1^7 \frac{5}{x}\,dx = 5\ln 7$, error = 13.1%

Q17 a)

x	...	1.3	1.4	1.5
y	...	**1.824**	1.909	**1.998**

b) 0.90 (2 d.p.)

Q18 a) 6.56 (3 s.f.) **b)** 0.936 (3 s.f.)

c) 177 (3 s.f.) **d)** 163 (3 s.f.)

Q19 4 strips: A ≈ 4586.625, error = 37.00%
6 strips: A ≈ 3906, error = 16.67%
After using the trapezium rule to
estimate the area, find the exact value
of the integral (3348) either by expanding
the brackets, or using the formula
$\int (n+1)f'(x)[f(x)]^n\,dx = [f(x)]^{n+1} + C.$
You can then use the percentage error
formula to find the error for each.

Q20 a) 5.82 (2 d.p.)

b) It is an overestimate as
the top of each trapezium
lies above the curve.

Chapter 25: Vectors 2

1. Vectors in Three Dimensions

Exercise 1.1

Q1 a) $\overrightarrow{OR} = \begin{pmatrix} 4 \\ -5 \\ 1 \end{pmatrix}$ $\overrightarrow{OS} = \begin{pmatrix} -3 \\ 0 \\ -1 \end{pmatrix}$

b) $\overrightarrow{OR} = 4\mathbf{i} - 5\mathbf{j} + \mathbf{k}$ $\overrightarrow{OS} = -3\mathbf{i} - \mathbf{k}$

Q2 $\overrightarrow{JK} = -5\mathbf{i} + 3\mathbf{j} + 3\mathbf{k}$, $\overrightarrow{KL} = 3\mathbf{i} - \mathbf{j} + 7\mathbf{k}$, $\overrightarrow{LJ}$
$= 2\mathbf{i} - 2\mathbf{j} - 10\mathbf{k}$

Q3 $\overrightarrow{GH} = \begin{pmatrix} -3 \\ 7 \\ 5 \end{pmatrix}$ $\overrightarrow{HG} = \begin{pmatrix} 3 \\ -7 \\ -5 \end{pmatrix}$

Q4 The position vector of the midpoint of
CD is at:
$\overrightarrow{OC} + \frac{1}{2}\overrightarrow{CD} = \begin{pmatrix} -1 \\ 3 \\ -5 \end{pmatrix} + \frac{1}{2}\begin{pmatrix} 4 \\ -4 \\ 6 \end{pmatrix}$

$= \begin{pmatrix} -1 \\ 3 \\ -5 \end{pmatrix} + \begin{pmatrix} 2 \\ -2 \\ 3 \end{pmatrix}$

$= \begin{pmatrix} 1 \\ 1 \\ -2 \end{pmatrix} = \overrightarrow{OM}$

So M is the midpoint of CD.

Q5 a) Point B is twice the distance of A
from the origin in each direction, so
$\overrightarrow{OB} = 2\overrightarrow{OA}$.
The position vector of B can also be
described as:
$\overrightarrow{OB} = \overrightarrow{AB} + \overrightarrow{OA}$
Substituting for $\overrightarrow{OB}$:
$2\overrightarrow{OA} = \overrightarrow{AB} + \overrightarrow{OA}$
$2\overrightarrow{OA} - \overrightarrow{OA} = \overrightarrow{AB}$
So $\overrightarrow{AB} = \overrightarrow{OA}$ — as required.

b) $\overrightarrow{OB} = 6\mathbf{i} + 2\mathbf{j} + 4\mathbf{k}$

Exercise 1.2

Q1 A vector is parallel to another if it is
multiplied by the same scalar in each
direction.
$\mathbf{a} = \left(3 \times \frac{1}{4}\right)\mathbf{i} + \left(\frac{1}{3} \times 1\right)\mathbf{j} + \left(3 \times -\frac{2}{3}\right)\mathbf{k}$
$\mathbf{a} = 3\mathbf{b}$ in the $\mathbf{i}$ and $\mathbf{k}$ directions,
but $\frac{1}{3}\mathbf{b}$ in the $\mathbf{j}$ direction,
so they are not parallel.

Q2 Model the counters as points A, B and C,
with position vectors $\overrightarrow{OA} = \mathbf{i} + 3\mathbf{k}$,
$\overrightarrow{OB} = 3\mathbf{i} + \mathbf{j} + 2\mathbf{k}$, and $\overrightarrow{OC} = 7\mathbf{i} + 3\mathbf{j}$.
$\overrightarrow{AB} = \overrightarrow{OB} - \overrightarrow{OA} = 2\mathbf{i} + \mathbf{j} - \mathbf{k}$
$\overrightarrow{BC} = \overrightarrow{OC} - \overrightarrow{OB} = 4\mathbf{i} + 2\mathbf{j} - 2\mathbf{k}$
$= 2 \times (2\mathbf{i} + \mathbf{j} - \mathbf{k}) \sim$
$= 2\overrightarrow{AB}$
$\overrightarrow{BC}$ is a scalar multiple of $\overrightarrow{AB}$, therefore
the vectors are parallel. They also share
a point (B), so they must be collinear. So
the counters must lie in a straight line.

2. Calculating with Vectors

Exercise 2.1

Q1 a) 9 **b)** 6 **c)** 21
d) $3\sqrt{11}$ **e)** $2\sqrt{14}$

Q2 a) 7 **b)** 27 **c)** 11
d) 15 **e)** $10\sqrt{3}$ **f)** $\sqrt{21}$

Q3 a) 3 **b)** 19 **c)** 13
d) 9 **e)** 23 **f)** 27

Q4 12.7 m (1 d.p.)

Q5 $|\overrightarrow{AO}| = |\overrightarrow{OA}|$
$= \sqrt{1^2 + (-4)^2 + 3^2} = \sqrt{26}$

$|\overrightarrow{BO}| = |\overrightarrow{OB}| = \sqrt{(-1)^2 + (-3)^2 + 5^2}$
$= \sqrt{35}$

$\overrightarrow{BA} = \overrightarrow{OA} - \overrightarrow{OB}$
$= (\mathbf{i} - 4\mathbf{j} + 3\mathbf{k}) - (-\mathbf{i} - 3\mathbf{j} + 5\mathbf{k})$
$= 2\mathbf{i} - \mathbf{j} - 2\mathbf{k}$
$|\overrightarrow{BA}| = \sqrt{2^2 + (-1)^2 + (-2)^2} = 3$
Triangle AOB is right-angled because:
$|\overrightarrow{AO}|^2 + |\overrightarrow{BA}|^2 = (\sqrt{26})^2 + 3^2$
$= 26 + 9$
$= 35 = (\sqrt{35})^2 = |\overrightarrow{BO}|^2$
You show it is a right-angled triangle by
showing that the lengths of the sides satisfy
Pythagoras' Theorem.

Q6 a) $\frac{4}{9}\mathbf{i} - \frac{4}{9}\mathbf{j} - \frac{7}{9}\mathbf{k}$

b) $-\frac{1}{3}\mathbf{i} + \frac{2}{3}\mathbf{j} - \frac{2}{3}\mathbf{k}$

c) $\frac{2}{\sqrt{14}}\mathbf{i} + \frac{3}{\sqrt{14}}\mathbf{j} - \frac{1}{\sqrt{14}}\mathbf{k}$

Q7 Either $q = 6$, then Q is (4, 5, 13),
or $q = -2$, then Q is (–4, 5, –3).

Exercise 2.2

Q1 a) 38.2° (1 d.p.) **b)** 36.7° (1 d.p.)
c) 106.6° (1 d.p.) **d)** 22.2° (1 d.p.)

Q2 109°

Q3 $a = \pm\sqrt{2}$
Therefore the launch speed
$|\mathbf{v}| = \sqrt{2 + (\pm\sqrt{2})^2} = 2$ ms⁻¹

Review Exercise — Chapter 25

Q1 $2\mathbf{i} - 4\mathbf{j} + 5\mathbf{k}$

Q2 $\overrightarrow{XO} = -6\mathbf{i} + \mathbf{j} = \begin{pmatrix} -6 \\ 1 \\ 0 \end{pmatrix}$,

$\overrightarrow{YO} = -4\mathbf{i} + 4\mathbf{j} - 7\mathbf{k} = \begin{pmatrix} -4 \\ 4 \\ -7 \end{pmatrix}$

Q3 a) e.g. $\mathbf{a}$ and $4\mathbf{a}$

b) e.g. $6\mathbf{i} + 8\mathbf{j} - 4\mathbf{k}$ and $9\mathbf{i} + 12\mathbf{j} - 6\mathbf{k}$

c) e.g. $\begin{pmatrix} 2 \\ 4 \\ -2 \end{pmatrix}$ and $\begin{pmatrix} 4 \\ 8 \\ -4 \end{pmatrix}$

Q4 $2\mathbf{a} + \mathbf{b} = 3\mathbf{i} - 2\mathbf{j} - 5\mathbf{k} = -\frac{1}{2}\mathbf{c}.$
They're scalar multiples, therefore they
must be parallel.

Q5 $\overrightarrow{AB} = \begin{pmatrix} -1 \\ 4 \\ 4 \end{pmatrix}$, $\overrightarrow{BC} = \begin{pmatrix} -3 \\ 12 \\ 12 \end{pmatrix} = 3\overrightarrow{AB}$.

This shows $\overrightarrow{AB}$ and $\overrightarrow{BC}$ are parallel,
and they share a point (B) so A, B and C
must be collinear.

Q6 a) $\sqrt{29}$ **b)** $\sqrt{6}$

Q7 a) $\sqrt{14}$ **b)** $\sqrt{14}$ **c)** $\sqrt{38}$

Q8 a) $\frac{1}{\sqrt{10}}\mathbf{i} - \frac{3}{\sqrt{10}}\mathbf{k}$

b) $-\frac{2}{\sqrt{33}}\mathbf{i} + \frac{2}{\sqrt{33}}\mathbf{j} + \frac{5}{\sqrt{33}}\mathbf{k}$

c) $\begin{pmatrix} -\frac{1}{\sqrt{19}} \\ -\frac{3}{\sqrt{19}} \\ \frac{3}{\sqrt{19}} \end{pmatrix}$ **d)** $\begin{pmatrix} \frac{7}{\sqrt{194}} \\ -\frac{1}{\sqrt{194}} \\ \frac{12}{\sqrt{194}} \end{pmatrix}$

Q9 $\sqrt{26}$

Q10 The coordinates of Y are (2, 5, –2).
Multiply the length of $\overrightarrow{XY}$ by its unit vector
to get $\overrightarrow{XY}$. Add $\overrightarrow{OX}$ to $\overrightarrow{XY}$ to find the
position vector of Y.

Q11 72.9°

Q12 a) R has speed $\sqrt{35}$ ms⁻¹,
S has speed $\sqrt{57}$ ms⁻¹.

b) 8 metres. **c)** 121°

d) E.g. This is a suitable model,
as there are no resistance forces
in space. This model could
be improved by including
the effects of each asteroid's
gravity on the other asteroid.

Chapter 26: Correlation and Regression

1. Regression

Exercise 1.1

Q1
a) Number of shots = explanatory variable, number of goals = response variable

b) $y = 0.204x - 1.08$

c) Positive correlation

d) -0.06

e) This estimate is unreliable because 5 shots is an extrapolation — there is no evidence that the relationship continues outside the data range. The estimate must be unreliable in this case because it is impossible to score a negative number of goals in a football match.

Exercise 1.2

Q1 $y = 76 + 2x$

Q2 a) $y = 22.4 - 4.80x$

b) $t = 51.4 - 0.480s$

Q3 $b = 1.077$ (3 d.p.)
$a = 2.067$ (3 d.p.)

2. The Product Moment Correlation Coefficient

Exercise 2.1

Q1 $r = 0.427$ to 3 s.f.
This is just closer to 0 than 1, so there appears to be a fairly weak positive correlation between the heights and weights of the teenage boys.

Q2 $r = -0.419$ to 3 s.f.
This is just closer to 0 than -1, so there appears to be a fairly weak negative correlation between p and q.

Q3 $r = -0.723$ to 3 s.f.
This is quite close to -1, and so there is a fairly strong negative correlation between the age of a patient (a) and their score on the memory test (s). The older a patient is, the lower their score on the memory test tends to be.

Exercise 2.2

Q1 a) The critical value is 0.5760. $0.5749 < 0.5760$, so there is insufficient evidence at the 2.5% level of significance to reject H_0 and to support the alternative hypothesis that there is positive correlation between the ages and weights of baby elephants.

b) The critical value is 0.5140. $0.5152 > 0.5140$, so there is evidence at the 2.5% level of significance to reject H_0 and to support the alternative hypothesis that there is positive correlation between the amount spent on food and the amount spent on petrol.

Q2 a) $r = -0.8925$ (4 d.p.)

b) $r \geq 0.7977$ or $r \leq -0.7977$

c) $r = -0.8925$ is inside the critical region so there is sufficient evidence to reject H_0 and to support the alternative hypothesis that kidney function and weight are correlated.

3. Rank Correlation

Exercise 3.1

Q1 a) The critical value is -0.7455. $-0.7504 < -0.7455$, so there is evidence at the 1% level of significance to reject H_0 (no association) and support the alternative hypothesis that there is negative association between 100 m and 1500 m times.

b) The critical value is -0.5218. $-0.5213 > -0.5218$ so there is insufficient evidence at the 1% level to reject H_0 (no association) and support the alternative hypothesis that there is negative association between the age of a pensioner and the volume they can hear from 15 m away.

Q2 a) 0.4464

b) $0.4750 > 0.4464$, so there is evidence at the 5% level of significance to reject H_0 and support the alternative hypothesis that there is positive association between the two judges' ranks.

c) The critical value is 0.6036. $0.4750 < 0.6036$, so there is insufficient evidence at the 1% level of significance to reject H_0 and support the alternative hypothesis that there is positive association between the two judges' ranks.

Review Exercise — Chapter 26

Q1 a) Explanatory variable = number of hours spent designing the cover, response variable = number of books sold in the first year.

b) $b = 1374.75 + 429.55h$ (both to 2 d.p.)

c) 3952 book sales (4 s.f.)
This is interpolation so the estimate should be reliable.

Q2 $n = 3600c - 440\ 000$

Q3 $k = 2.439$, $b = 1.248$ (both to 3 d.p.)

Q4 $r = -0.7014$ (4 d.p.)
This shows fairly strong negative correlation between x and y.

Q5 The critical value is 0.7079. $0.7126 > 0.7079$, so there is evidence at the 1% level of significance to reject H_0 and support the alternative hypothesis that there is some correlation between the age of a painting and its value.

Q6 a) $r = 0.9940$ (4 d.p.)

b) The critical value is 0.7067. $0.9940 > 0.7067$, so there is evidence at the 2.5% level of significance to reject H_0 and to support the alternative hypothesis that the length and width of leaves are positively correlated.

Q7 a) Positive association
b) No association
c) Negative association

Q8 a) $r_s \leq -0.5874$ or $r_s \geq 0.5874$

b) -0.5438 does not lie in the critical region, so there is insufficient evidence at the 5% level of significance to reject H_0 and to support the alternative hypothesis that there is some association between the judges' rankings.

c) The critical region for a 10% significance test is $r_s \leq -0.5035$ or $r_s \geq 0.5035$. $-0.5438 < -0.5035$, so it lies in the critical region, which means that there is evidence at the 10% level of significance to reject H_0 and to support the alternative hypothesis that there is some association between the judges' rankings.

Chapter 27: Probability 2

1. Conditional Probability

Exercise 1.1

Q1 a) 0.7   b) 0.1   c) 0.2

Q2 0.17

Q3 a) $\dfrac{8}{21}$ b) $\dfrac{12}{35}$

Q4 a) 0.5   b) $\dfrac{4}{11}$ c) 0.875

Q5 a) 0.445   b) 0.555

Q6 a) $\dfrac{2}{5}$ b) $\dfrac{2}{3}$

Q7 a) $\dfrac{10}{33}$ b) $\dfrac{2}{9}$ c) $\dfrac{13}{20}$

d) $\dfrac{9}{26}$ e) $\dfrac{2}{15}$

Q8 a) 0.28   b) 0.21   c) 0.11

d) $\dfrac{20}{39}$ e) 0.07

Exercise 1.2

Q1 A and B are independent.

Q2 **a)** **(i)** R and T are mutually exclusive.
 (ii) R and S are independent.

 b) **(i)** 0.25   **(ii)** $\frac{5}{9}$

Q3 **a)** 0.5712   **b)** 0.1664   **c)** 0.68
 d) 0.52   **e)** 0.68

Q4 **a)**

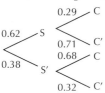

 b) 0.711 (3 s.f.)

Exercise 1.3

Q1 Let S = 'has a smartphone' and
 C = 'contract costs £25 a month or less'.
 Then the tree diagram is:

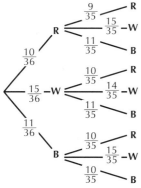

 P(S|C′) = 0.784 (3 s.f.)

Q2 Let R = red counter, W = white counter,
 B = blue counter.
 Then the tree diagram is:

 P(2nd counter blue | 1st counter not red)
 $= \frac{55}{182}$
 *You need to put the right probabilities
 from the tree diagram into the conditional
 probability formula:*
 P(2nd blue | 1st not red)
 = P(2nd blue and 1st not red) ÷ P(1st not red)
 where P(2nd blue and 1st not red)
 $= P(WB) + P(BB) = \frac{15}{36} \times \frac{11}{35} + \frac{11}{36} \times \frac{10}{35}$
 and P(1st not red) $= 1 - \frac{10}{36}$

Exercise 1.4

Q1 **a)** **(i)** $\frac{3}{5}$ **(ii)** $\frac{1}{4}$ **(iii)** $\frac{24}{55}$ **(iv)** $\frac{27}{43}$
 b) 3

Q2 **a)**

	Action	Comedy	Total
Under 20	16	10	26
20+	6	8	14
Total	22	18	40

 or in terms of the probabilities,

	Action	Comedy	Total
Under 20	0.4	0.25	0.65
20+	0.15	0.2	0.35
Total	0.55	0.45	1

 b) $\frac{5}{9}$

2. Modelling with Probability

Exercise 2.1

There are many possible answers to these questions — here are some examples:

Q1 – She has assumed that the probability of it landing on each face is equally likely — given that the shape is a cuboid, this is probably not a very good assumption.

 – She has assumed that she throws it the same way each time and that her throw gives an equal probability of each face coming up, which might not be the case.

Q2 – She has assumed that the volunteer is equally likely to choose any of the 10 cards, but some people may tend to choose cards in a particular way e.g. from the middle or from the ends more often.

 – She has assumed that the card is put back at random, and that the volunteer can't see and track the card before choosing the second one — if they could, they might intentionally try to choose the same one twice, which would affect the probability.

Q3 – He has assumed that his estimate of the probability (using the relative frequency from his data) is valid for children from any other school — there are likely to be lots of reasons why this is not the case. For example, children in urban areas may be more or less likely to walk than children in rural areas.

 – The model doesn't account for the age of the child — it might be that older children are more likely to walk while younger children get driven to school.

 – He has assumed that the probability holds on any particular day, but factors like weather will affect the probability — children would probably be more likely to walk to school on warm, sunny days than on cold, rainy days.

Review Exercise — Chapter 27

Q1 P(C|D) = 0.625, P(D|C) = 0.375

Q2 **a)** $\frac{1}{8}$ **b)** $\frac{31}{40}$ **c)** $\frac{5}{14}$ **d)** $\frac{27}{71}$

Q3 **a)** 0.26   **b)** 0.8

Q4 Let C = 'catches bus' and L = 'is late'.
 Then the tree diagram is:

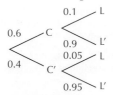

 So P(L|C′) = 0.05

Q5 E.g. Let event W = the day was on a weekend, and let event S = sold more than 150 cups of coffee.
 Then from the question, P(S|W) = $\frac{3}{10}$ and P(W′ ∩ S′) = $\frac{1}{2}$.
 The day is picked at random, so P(W) = $\frac{2}{7}$, P(W′) = $\frac{5}{7}$.
 P(W′ ∩ S) = P(W′) − P(W′ ∩ S′)
 $= \frac{5}{7} - \frac{1}{2} = \frac{3}{14}$
 P(W ∩ S) = P(W) × P(S|W)
 $= \frac{2}{7} \times \frac{3}{10} = \frac{3}{35}$
 P(S) = P(W′ ∩ S) + P(W ∩ S)
 $= \frac{3}{14} + \frac{3}{35} = \frac{3}{10}$
 So P(S) = P(S|W), so S and W are independent.
 You might have done this a different way — there are lots of possible ways to show it.

Q6

	B	C	P	Total
F	0.15	0.14	0.08	0.37
S	0.1	0.28	0.25	0.63
Total	0.25	0.42	0.33	1

 Start by filling in what you know, and what you can work out using
 $P(A|B) = \frac{P(A \cap B)}{P(B)}$, *then add in the missing numbers to get the totals right.*

Q7 **a)** E.g. He has assumed that each puzzle is equally likely to be solved first, but one of them might be easier than the others. / Most people are likely to attempt the first puzzle first, which might make it more likely to be solved first.

 b) E.g. Ariel has assumed that there is a probability of 0.5 that tomorrow is sunny and a probability of 0.5 that it is rainy, but she has not taken into account the possibility of other weather conditions or the season/recent weather.

Chapter 28: The Normal Distribution

1. The Normal Distribution

Exercise 1.1

All answers are rounded to 4 d.p.

Q1   **a)** 0.9772   **b)** 0.7257   **c)** 0.3446

Q2   **a)** 0.0512   **b)** 0.3415   **c)** 0.8897

Q3   **a)** 0.9801   **b)** 0.7854   **c)** 0.0089

Q4   **a)** 0.2525   **b)** 0.0478   **c)** 0.0912

Q5   **a)** 0.3399   **b)** 0.0801

Q6   **a)** 0.1747   **b)** 0.0970

Q7   **a)** 0.8176   **b)** 0.9381

Exercise 1.2

All answers are rounded to 4 s.f.

Q1   **a)** 0.9693   **b)** 0.8389

     c) 0.006569   **d)** 0.4443

     e) 0.5948   **f)** 0.8869

     g) 0.2676   **h)** 0.01970

     i) 0.1093   **j)** 0.7734

     k) 0.2676   **l)** 0.9608

Q2   **a)** 0.07549   **b)** 0.1962

     c) 0.4940   **d)** 0.9344

     e) 0.9031   **f)** 0.2661

     g) 0.005992   **h)** 0.2990

     i) 0.08648

Exercise 1.3

All answers are rounded to 4 d.p.

Q1   **a)** 0.2743   **b)** 0.0548

Q2   **a)** 0.8413   **b)** 0.3829

Q3   **a)** 0.8176   **b)** 0.9381

     c) 0.2108   **d)** 0.3715

Exercise 1.4

All answers in Q1 and Q3 are rounded to 3 s.f.

Q1   **a)** 13.0   **b)** 10.5   **c)** 12.5   **d)** 11.4

Q2   **a)** −2.65   **b)** 1.31   **c)** −0.49

     d) 1.90   **e)** −2.30   **f)** −0.13

Q3   **a)** 54.2   **b)** 42.8   **c)** 38.0

Exercise 1.5

Q1   **a)** 2.5758   **b)** 0.8416

     c) 0.5244   **d)** 3.0902

Q2   **a)** 26.0132   **b)** 32.84

     To solve these problems, first convert X to the standard normal variable, Z, by subtracting the mean and dividing by the standard deviation. Then use the percentage points table to find z — for part b) you need to get the probability in P(Z ≥ z) form before using the table. Finally use the value of z to find x.

Exercise 1.6

Answers are rounded to 3 s.f. where appropriate.

Q1   **a)** 14.0   **b)** 35.0   **c)** 415

     d) 11.8   **e)** 1.57   **f)** 18.0

Q2   13.3

     There's more than one way to solve this one. E.g. drawing a sketch helps you see that P(X > 20.17) = 0.025, so you can convert to Z and use the percentage points table for 0.025 to find z. Then solve the equation for μ. Or, since μ is in the middle of the data, find the average of 6.45 and 20.17.

Exercise 1.7

All answers are rounded to 3 s.f.

Q1   **a)** 4.00   **b)** 24.0   **c)** 3.91

     d) 0.0600   **e)** 0.765   **f)** 0.570

Q2   6.75

     15% of the distribution lies above 75, so P(X > 75) = 0.15. Convert this to Z and find z using the percentage points table, then solve the equation for σ in the usual way.

Exercise 1.8

For each question, convert the two probabilities to the standard normal distribution and find the z-values. Then you can form two equations in terms of μ and σ. Solve these simultaneously to find μ and σ. Answers are rounded to 1 d.p. where appropriate.

Q1   **a)** $\mu = 23$ and $\sigma = 5$

     b) $\mu = 3.7$ and $\sigma = 0.2$

     c) $\mu = 18$ and $\sigma = 2.5$

     d) $\mu = 620$ and $\sigma = 40$

     e) $\mu = 28$ and $\sigma = 4$

     f) $\mu = 57.6$ and $\sigma = 24$

Exercise 1.9

Q1   **a)** 0.0912 to 4 d.p.   **b)** 5.1078 ≈ 5

     c) 45.18 days

Q2   **a)** 79.1% to 3 s.f.   **b)** 49.2 s to 3 s.f.

Q3   **a)** 503.1 ml to 1 d.p.

     b) 0.2676 to 4 d.p.

     c) 954.3172 ≈ 954

Q4   **a)** 0.0228 to 4 d.p.

     b) 0.0548 to 4 d.p.

     c) 0.0030 to 4 d.p., assuming that the lifetimes of the batteries are independent.

     d) 400 to 3 s.f.

Q5   **a)** 5.94 cm to 3 s.f.

     b) 0.4993 to 4 d.p.

Q6   **a)** 5.01 ≈ 5 g

     b) 56.2 g to 3 s.f.

Q7 $\mu = 8.28$ cm and $\sigma = 3.37$ cm (to 3 s.f.)

     To solve this, convert P(R < 4) = 0.102 and P(R > 7) = 0.648 to the standard normal distribution. Find the z-values and form two equations in terms of μ and σ. Solve these simultaneously to find μ and σ.

2. Normal Approximation to a Binomial Distribution

Exercise 2.1

Q1   **a)** P(4.5 < Y < 5.5)

     b) P(11.5 < Y < 15.5)

     c) P(Y < 10.5)

     d) P(6.5 < Y < 8.5)

Q2   **a)** P(49.5 < Y < 50.5)

     b) P(Y < 299.5)

     c) P(Y > 98.5)

     d) P(143.5 < Y < 168.5)

Q3   **a)** P(199.5 < Y < 200.5)

     b) P(Y > 649.5)

     c) P(Y < 299.5)

     d) P(498.5 < Y < 501.5)

     e) P(249.5 < Y < 750.5)

     f) P(99.5 < Y < 899.5)

Exercise 2.2

Q1   **a)** *n* is large (600) and $p = 0.51 \approx 0.5$, so a normal approximation is suitable.

     b) *n* is large (100), but $p = 0.98$ is not close to 0.5 and $n(1 - p) = 2 < 5$, so a normal approximation is not suitable.

     c) *n* is large (100), but $p = 0.85$ is not close to 0.5. However, $np = 85 > 5$ and $n(1 - p) = 15 > 5$, so a normal approximation is suitable.

     d) *n* is not large (6), so a normal approximation is not suitable.

     e) *n* is fairly large, but $p = 0.7$ is not very close to 0.5. However, $np = 25.9 > 5$ and $n(1 - p) = 11.1 > 5$, so a normal approximation is suitable.

     f) *n* is not large (8), so a normal approximation is not suitable.

Q2   **a)** $\mu = 157.5$ and $\sigma^2 = 86.625$

     b) $\mu = 87.5$ and $\sigma^2 = 56.875$

     c) $\mu = 35.07$ and $\sigma^2 = 17.500$ (3 d.p.)

     d) $\mu = 12.5$ and $\sigma^2 = 4.6875$

Q3   **a)** 0.0126   **b)** 0.0552   **c)** 0.8297

     d) 0.7012 (all to 4 d.p.)

Exercise 2.3

Q1   **a)** 0.0277 to 4 d.p.

     b) 0.0275 to 4 d.p.

Q2   **a)** $p = 0.05$ is not close to 0.5, but $np = 50 > 5$ and $n(1 - p) = 950 > 5$, so a normal approximation is suitable.

     b) 0.0001 to 4 d.p.

3. Choosing Probability Distributions

Exercise 3.1

Q1 $\mu \approx 117$ and $\sigma \approx 13$
You might have slightly different estimates here, but that's fine as long as they're close to the given answers.

Q2 a) Most of the data values are in the middle and the number of values tails off towards the ends.
It is also fairly symmetrical.

b) $\sigma \approx 4$
You might have a slightly different estimate here, but that's fine as long as it's close to the given answer.

Q3 a) The number of successful first-serves in one game, G, can be modelled with a binomial distribution —
$G \sim B(10, 0.65)$

b) The number of successful first-serves in a match, M, can be modelled with a binomial distribution —
$M \sim B(100, 0.65)$
Alternatively, M could be approximated by a normal distribution Y — $Y \sim N(65, 22.75)$.

Q4 a) The data is continuous and the distribution is symmetrical about the mean. $6.5 - 3 \times 1.5 = 2.0$ and $6.5 + 3 \times 1.5 = 11$, so all the data is within 3 standard deviations of the mean.

b) 942 (to the nearest whole number)

Q5 a) If X is the number of people who pass their driving test first time on the day, then $X \sim B(11, 0.41)$.

b) 0.7817

4. Hypothesis Tests of the Mean of a Population

Exercise 4.1

Q1 a) There is significant evidence at the 5% level to reject H_0 in favour of the alternative hypothesis that the weight of plums from the tree has increased.

b) There is insufficient evidence at the 1% level to reject H_0.

Q2 There is significant evidence at the 1% level to reject H_0 in favour of the alternative hypothesis that Bree's mean winnings have changed.

Q3 There is significant evidence at the 5% level to reject H_0 in favour of the alternative hypothesis that the mean score this year is lower.

Q4 a) $H_0: \mu = 300$ and $H_1: \mu > 300$.

b) One-tailed test

c) There is insufficient evidence at the 1% level to reject H_0 in favour of the alternative hypothesis that the mean pigeon weight has gone up.

Q5 There is significant evidence at the 5% level to reject H_0 in favour of the alternative hypothesis that the mean waiting time for the ride is shorter than 18 minutes.

Review Exercise — Chapter 28

For Q1 to Q5, all answers are rounded to 4 d.p.

Q1 a) 0.8944   **b)** 0.0228
c) 0.0668   **d)** 0.7333

Q2 a) 0.2375   **b)** 0.2839
c) 0.3875   **d)** 0.1091

Q3 a) 0.0013   **b)** 0.9332
c) 0.3085   **d)** 0.3413

Q4 a) 0.7995   **b)** 0.9984   **c)** 0.2483
d) 0.0606   **e)** 0.0179   **f)** 0.4960
g) 0.4602   **h)** 0.7389   **i)** 0.4090
j) 0.1516   **k)** 0.5967   **l)** 0.0686

Q5 a) 0.1151   **b)** 0.6554
c) 0.4436   **d)** 0.1571

Q6 a) 64   **b)** 68   **c)** 55
d) 65   **e)** 56   **f)** 61

Q7 a) 89.0

b) $|X - 80| < b \Rightarrow 80 - b < X < 80 + b$
80 is the mean of X, and a normal distribution is symmetrical, so
$P(80 - b < X < 80 + b) = 0.8$
$\Rightarrow P(X \geq 80 + b) = 0.1$
$\Rightarrow P\left(Z \geq \dfrac{80 + b - 80}{\sqrt{15}}\right)$
$= P\left(Z \geq \dfrac{b}{\sqrt{15}}\right) = 0.1$
Using the percentage points table,
$\dfrac{b}{\sqrt{15}} = 1.2816$, so $b = 4.96$ to 3 s.f.

Q8 a) 1.36   **b)** 0.22   **c)** 1.80
d) 2.3263   **e)** −0.25
f) −2.5758   **g)** 0.68
h) 2.34   **i)** −0.25

Q9 4.08 to 3 s.f.

Q10 217

Q11 7.90 to 3 s.f.

Q12 1.08 to 3 s.f.

Q13 $\mu = 14.2$ and $\sigma = 0.519$ to 3 s.f.
To solve this, convert the probabilities to the standard normal distribution. Find the z-values and form two equations in terms of μ and σ. Then solve these simultaneously.

Q14 a) 0.5   **b)** 0.1279 to 4 d.p.
c) 0.1279 to 4 d.p.

Q15 1.757

Q16 $\mu = 131$ g and $\sigma = 9.08$ g to 3 s.f.
To solve this, convert the probabilities to the standard normal distribution. Find the z-values and form two equations in terms of μ and σ. Then solve these simultaneously.

Q17 a) $P(Y > 100.5)$
b) $P(109.5 < Y < 110.5)$
c) $P(89.5 < Y < 105.5)$
d) $P(112.5 < Y < 118.5)$

For Q18 to Q20, answers are rounded to 4 d.p.

Q18 a) 0.0484   **b)** 0.1345
c) 0.5400   **d)** 0.5095

Q19 a) 0.0803   **b)** 0.0807

c) The normal approximation is accurate to 2 d.p.

Q20 a) n is large, $np = 8 > 5$ and $n(1 - p) = 72 > 5$, so a normal approximation is suitable.

b) 0.1478   **c)** 0.0961

Q21 $\mu \approx 2.69$ and $\sigma \approx 0.11$
You might have slightly different estimates here, but that's fine as long as they're close to the given answers.

Q22 a) If X is the number of prizes won in the hour, then $X \sim B(14, 0.33)$.

b) 0.5131 (to 4 d.p.)

Q23 There is evidence to reject H_0 at the 5% significance level.

Q24 There is significant evidence at the 5% level to reject H_0 in favour of the alternative hypothesis that the mean amount of time spent studying has gone up.

There is insufficient evidence at the 1% level to reject H_0 in favour of the alternative hypothesis that the mean amount of time spent studying has gone up.

The null hypothesis can be rejected at the 5% level, but not at the 1% level.

Q25 There is sufficient evidence at the 5% level to reject H_0 in favour of H_1.

Chapter 29: Kinematics 2

1. Projectiles

Exercise 1.1

Q1 a) Horizontal component:
9.40 ms⁻¹ (3 s.f.)
Vertical component:
3.42 ms⁻¹ (3 s.f.)

b) Horizontal component:
7.61 ms⁻¹ (3 s.f.)
Vertical component:
16.3 ms⁻¹ (3 s.f.)

c) Horizontal component:
−6.32 ms⁻¹ (3 s.f.)
Vertical component:
2.50 ms⁻¹ (3 s.f.)

d) Horizontal component:
9.13 ms⁻¹ (3 s.f.)
Vertical component:
−3.27 ms⁻¹ (3 s.f.)

e) Horizontal component:
   -2.51 ms^{-1} (3 s.f.)
   Vertical component:
   -23.9 ms^{-1} (3 s.f.)

f) Horizontal component:
   -8.71 ms^{-1} (3 s.f.)
   Vertical component:
   13.4 ms^{-1} (3 s.f.)

g) Horizontal component:
   -6.68 ms^{-1} (3 s.f.)
   Vertical component:
   -3.40 ms^{-1} (3 s.f.)

h) Horizontal component:
   2.68 ms^{-1} (3 s.f.)
   Vertical component:
   -6.03 ms^{-1} (3 s.f.)

Q2 Horizontal component:
   6.55 ms^{-1} (3 s.f.)
   Vertical component:
   4.59 ms^{-1} (3 s.f.)

Q3 Horizontal component = 0 ms^{-1}
   Vertical component = 45 ms^{-1}

Q4 Horizontal component
   $= 6.1111...\cos \alpha$ ms^{-1}
   Vertical component
   $= 6.1111...\sin \alpha$ ms^{-1}

Q5 Speed: 10 ms^{-1}, Direction: $53.1°$ (3 s.f.)
   above the horizontal

Q6 Speed = 17.2 ms^{-1} (3 s.f.), Direction:
   $8.37°$ (3 s.f.) below the horizontal

Exercise 1.2

Q1 a) 1.17 s (3 s.f.)
   b) 6.74 m (3 s.f.)

Q2 a) 4.79 m (3 s.f.)
   b) 2.39 m (3 s.f.)
   c) 5.35 m (3 s.f.)

Q3 a) 1.40 s (3 s.f.)
   b) 5.77 m (3 s.f.)

Q4 a) 9.85 ms^{-1} (3 s.f.)
   b) $24.0°$ below the horizontal.

Q5 11.7 m (3 s.f.)

Q6 22.6 ms^{-1} (3 s.f.)

Q7 a) 38.6 ms^{-1} (3 s.f.)
   b) 30.0 m (3 s.f.)

Exercise 1.3

Q1 a) 2.86 s (3 s.f.)   b) 229 m (3 s.f.)
   c) E.g. The acceleration should take
   into account the increased drag from the
   water — vertical acceleration can no
   longer be assumed to be equal to g, and
   horizontal acceleration can no longer be
   assumed to be 0.

Q2 2.33 m (3 s.f.)

Q3 27.0 ms^{-1} (3 s.f.)

Exercise 1.4

Q1 1.62 s (3 s.f.)

Q2 4.35 m (3 s.f.)

Q3 a) 5.27 m (3 s.f.)
   b) Speed 18.0 ms^{-1}, direction $80.5°$
   (3 s.f.) below the horizontal

Q4 a) 1.56 s (3 s.f.)   b) 26.1 m (3 s.f.)
   c) 17.9 ms^{-1} (3 s.f.)

Q5 a) 0.958 m (3 s.f.)
   b) 6.61 ms^{-1} (3 s.f.)

Q6 a) $\theta = 60°$
   Resolve horizontally for each particle.
   When the particles collide, their
   displacements will be the same, so
   set the two equal and solve for θ.

   b) The speed of projection of A is
   8.66 ms^{-1} (3 s.f.), and the speed of
   projection of B is 17.3 ms^{-1} (3 s.f.).
   Resolve vertically for particle A, taking
   down as positive. This tells you how
   far particle A has fallen before colliding
   with B. You know the height A started
   at (45 m) so you can find the height
   at which the collision happens. Using
   this, you can calculate the height B
   has travelled upwards before colliding
   with A. Now, plug this distance into
   $s = ut + \frac{1}{2}at^2$ *to find the speed of*
   projection of each particle.

Exercise 1.5

Q1 a) Resolving vertically,
   taking up as positive:
   $s = s, u = U \sin \theta, v = 0, a = -g$
   $v^2 = u^2 + 2as$
   $0 = U^2 \sin^2 \theta - 2gs$
   $\Rightarrow s = \frac{U^2 \sin^2 \theta}{2g}$ m
   b) Resolving vertically,
   taking up as positive:
   $u = U \sin \theta, v = 0, a = -g, t = t$
   $v = u + at$
   $0 = U \sin \theta - gt$
   $\Rightarrow t = \frac{U \sin \theta}{g}$ s

Q2 Resolving vertically,
   taking up as positive:
   $s = 0, u = V\sin \alpha, a = -9.8, t = ?$
   $s = ut + \frac{1}{2}at^2$
   $0 = (V\sin \alpha) \times t - \frac{1}{2} \times 9.8t^2$
   $= t(V\sin \alpha - 4.9t)$
   $\Rightarrow t = 0$ or $\frac{V\sin \alpha}{4.9}$
   This gives the value of t when the
   particle hits the ground.
   Resolving horizontally,
   taking right as positive:
   $s = x, u = V\cos \alpha, a = 0, t = \frac{V\sin \alpha}{4.9}$
   $s = ut + \frac{1}{2}at^2$
   $x = V\cos \alpha \times \frac{V\sin \alpha}{4.9} = \frac{V^2 \cos \alpha \sin \alpha}{4.9}$
   Using the sin double angle formula
   $\frac{\sin 2A}{2} \equiv \sin A \cos A$, this gives
   $x = \frac{V^2 \sin^2 2\alpha}{2 \times 4.9} = \frac{V^2 \sin^2 2\alpha}{9.8}$
   as required.

Q3 The coordinates $(3, 1)$ give you
   the components of the projectile's
   displacement — when it passes
   through this point, its horizontal
   displacement is 3 m and its vertical
   displacement is 1 m.
   Resolving horizontally, taking right as
   positive:
   $s = 3, u = 3 \cos \alpha, a = 0, t = t$
   $s = ut + \frac{1}{2}at^2$
   $3 = (3 \cos \alpha) \times t \Rightarrow t = \frac{1}{\cos \alpha}$
   Resolving vertically, taking up as
   positive:
   $s = 1, u = 3 \sin \alpha, a = -g, t = \frac{1}{\cos \alpha}$
   $s = ut + \frac{1}{2}at^2$
   $1 = \left(3 \sin \alpha \times \frac{1}{\cos \alpha}\right)$
   $+ \left(\frac{1}{2} \times -g \times \left(\frac{1}{\cos \alpha}\right)^2\right)$
   $\Rightarrow 1 = 3 \tan \alpha - \frac{g}{2 \cos^2 \alpha}$, as required.

Q4 a) Resolving horizontally,
   taking right as positive:
   $s = x, u = u\cos \alpha, a = 0, t = t$
   $s = ut + \frac{1}{2}at^2$
   gives a horizontal position of
   $x = (u\cos \alpha)t$
   Resolving vertically,
   taking up as positive:
   $s = y, u = u\sin \alpha, a = -g, t = t$
   $s = ut + \frac{1}{2}at^2$
   gives a vertical position of
   $y = (u\sin \alpha)t - \frac{1}{2} \times gt^2$
   $= (u\sin \alpha)t - \frac{g}{2}t^2$

   b) Rearrange $x = (u\cos \alpha)t$ to make t the
   subject: $t = \frac{x}{u \cos \alpha}$.

   Now, substitute this expression for t
   into the formula for y:
   $y = \frac{x \times (u \sin \alpha)}{u \cos \alpha} - \frac{g}{2}\left(\frac{x}{u \cos \alpha}\right)^2$
   $= \frac{(u\sin \alpha)x}{u \cos \alpha} - \frac{gx^2}{2u^2 \cos^2 \alpha}$
   $= x \tan \alpha - \frac{gx^2}{2u^2 \cos^2 \alpha}$ as required.

   c) 7.98 ms^{-1} (3 s.f.)

Exercise 1.6

Q1 a) $\mathbf{v} = (12\mathbf{i} - 3.6\mathbf{j})$ ms^{-1} b) $12\mathbf{i}$ ms^{-1}
   c) $(12\mathbf{i} - 16\mathbf{j})$ ms^{-1}

Q2 a) 10.1 m (3 s.f.)
   b) 22.1 ms^{-1} (3 s.f.)
   c) $39.6°$ (3 s.f.) below the horizontal.

Q3 a) 0.719 s (3 s.f.)
   b) 7.51 m (3 s.f.)

Q4 a) $a = 40$ and $b = 16.5$
   b) $\mathbf{v} = (40\mathbf{i} - 32.5\mathbf{j})$ ms^{-1}

Q5 **a)** $\mathbf{u} = (5\mathbf{i} + 16.7\mathbf{j})$ ms^{-1}

b) $\mathbf{v} = (5\mathbf{i} - 12.7\mathbf{j})$ ms^{-1}

c) 1.02 m (3 s.f.)

d) E.g. The model could treat the ball as a three-dimensional shape with a significant diameter, instead of a particle, to better estimate the distance from the wall. The model could include other factors, such as air resistance or the spin of the ball. The model could describe the ball's motion in three dimensions rather than two, as it's unlikely to rebound perpendicular to the wall.

Q6 **a)** It is moving due north at $t = 6$ s.

b) 355° (nearest degree)

c) 1090 m (3 s.f.)

d) For example:

- The model could allow for a non-uniform acceleration due to changing resistance force.

- 3D vectors could be used to describe the variation in the submarine's depth underwater.

Q7 $p = \dfrac{\sqrt{2}}{4}$, $q = -\dfrac{7\sqrt{2}}{20}$

2. Non-Uniform Acceleration in 2 Dimensions

Exercise 2.1

Q1 **a)** **(i)** $\mathbf{v} = [(3t^2 - 3)\mathbf{i} + 2t\mathbf{j}]$ ms^{-1}

(ii) 24.7 ms^{-1} (3 s.f.), 14.0° (3 s.f.) from the positive **i**-direction.

b) **(i)** $\mathbf{a} = (6t\mathbf{i} + 2\mathbf{j})$ ms^{-2}

(ii) 24.1 ms^{-2} (3 s.f.)

Q2 $(64\mathbf{i} + \mathbf{j})$ ms^{-2}

Q3 $\mathbf{v} = \dfrac{-40}{3}\mathbf{i} + 14\mathbf{j}$ ms^{-1}

Exercise 2.2

Q1 **a)** $\mathbf{a} = 6(-\mathbf{i} + 2\mathbf{j})$ ms^{-2}

b) 1.76 s (3 s.f.)

Q2 **a)** $\mathbf{v} = [(t^2 - t + 1)\mathbf{i}$
$+ (\frac{t^3}{3} + \frac{t^2}{2} + \frac{1}{2})\mathbf{j}]$ ms^{-1}

b) 58.6 ms^{-1} (3 s.f.), 69.0° (3 s.f.) from the positive **i**-direction.

Q3 $b = -5.625$

*Integrate **v** to find the particle's displacement. Now, equate the **j** coefficients of this expression and the position vector for the point. This will give you the value of t for when the particle passes through the point. Now, equate coefficients of **i** and plug in the value of t to find b.*

Q4 **a)** $(5 - t)\mathbf{i} + (4t^2 + 2t + 6)\mathbf{j}$

b) $x = 5 - t \Rightarrow t = 5 - x$ — eqn 1
$y = 4t^2 + 2t + 6$ — eqn 1

Sub eqn 1 in eqn 2:
$y = 4(5 - x)^2 + 2(5 - x) + 6$
$= 100 - 40x + 4x^2 + 10 - 2x + 6$
$= 4x^2 - 42x + 116$

Q5 **a)** $t = 1$ s

b) $t = 3.5$ s

c) $[(t^3 + t)\mathbf{i} + (t^3 - 4t + 6)\mathbf{j}]$ m

d) $[(t^2 + 5t - 3)\mathbf{i} + (2t^2 - 7t + 13)\mathbf{j}]$ m

e) 37.1 m (3 s.f.)

Exercise 2.3

Q1 **a)** $\begin{pmatrix} e^{3t} + 3 \\ 6 + 12\sqrt{t} \end{pmatrix}$ ms^{-1}

b) $\begin{pmatrix} \frac{1}{3}e^{3t} + 3t + \frac{5}{3} \\ 6t + 8\sqrt{t^3} - 9 \end{pmatrix}$ m

Q2 **a)** $t = 2\pi$ seconds.

b) It is 1 m north of O.

Q3 **a)** When $t = \frac{1}{2}$, $\dfrac{dy}{dx} = -\dfrac{1}{24}$

Use the chain rule:

$\dfrac{dy}{dt} = \dfrac{1}{t}$ *and* $\dfrac{dx}{dt} = -\dfrac{3}{t^4}$, *so*

$\dfrac{dy}{dx} = \dfrac{dy}{dt} \div \dfrac{dx}{dt} = \dfrac{1}{t} \div \dfrac{-3}{t^4} = -\dfrac{t^3}{3}$

b) $\mathbf{r} = x\mathbf{i} + y\mathbf{j}$

$\Rightarrow \mathbf{v} = \dfrac{d\mathbf{r}}{dt} = \dfrac{dx}{dt}\mathbf{i} + \dfrac{dy}{dt}\mathbf{j}$

$= -\dfrac{3}{t^4}\mathbf{i} + \dfrac{1}{t}\mathbf{j}$

$\Rightarrow \mathbf{a} = \dfrac{d\mathbf{v}}{dt} = \dfrac{d^2x}{dt^2}\mathbf{i} + \dfrac{d^2y}{dt^2}\mathbf{j}$

$= \dfrac{12}{t^5}\mathbf{i} - \dfrac{1}{t^2}\mathbf{j}$

So when $t = \frac{1}{2}$,

$\mathbf{a} = \dfrac{12}{\left(\frac{1}{2}\right)^5}\mathbf{i} - \dfrac{1}{\left(\frac{1}{2}\right)^2}\mathbf{j}$

$= 384\mathbf{i} - 4\mathbf{j}$ (as required)

Q4 $\frac{1}{2}$ m

*Use double angle identities to change the components of **v** into expressions that are easier to integrate:*
$\cos 2t \equiv 1 - 2\sin^2 t \Rightarrow 2\sin^2 t \equiv 1 - \cos 2t$
$\sin 2t \equiv 2\sin t \cos t$
$\Rightarrow 4\sin 2t \cos 2t \equiv 2\sin 4t.$

Review Exercise — Chapter 29

Q1 Horizontal component = $u\cos\alpha$
Vertical component = $u\sin\alpha$

Q2 $\alpha = 63.0°$ (3 s.f.)

Q3 $d = 1.23$ m (3 s.f.)

Q4 **a)** 4.13 m (3 s.f.)

b) 6.94 ms^{-1} (3 s.f.)

Q5 **a)** 23.8 ms^{-1} (1 d.p.) **b)** 58 m

Q6 **a)** $(2\mathbf{i} + 3.16\mathbf{j})$ ms^{-1}

b) 2.24 s (3 s.f.)

c) 6.17 m (3 s.f.)

Q7 **a)** 1.08 s (3 s.f.) **b)** 0.551 m (3 s.f.)

c) 24.6 ms^{-1} (3 s.f.)

Q8 **a)** $(16t - 2)$ ms^{-2} **b)** $(\frac{8}{3}t^3 - t^2)$ m

Q9 **a)** 2.25 ms^{-1} **b)** -3.33 m (3 s.f.)

c) -18 m

Q10 **a)** $(4\mathbf{i} + 2t\mathbf{j})$ ms^{-2}

b) $\mathbf{r} = (2t^2\mathbf{i} + \frac{1}{3}t^3\mathbf{j})$ m

Q11 $\mathbf{v} = \dfrac{4e^{0.75t} + 47}{3}\mathbf{i} + \sin t\, \mathbf{j}$ ms^{-1}

Q12 **a)** $(2\mathbf{i} - 5\mathbf{j})$ m

b) $t = 1$ s and $t = 2$ s

c) $(5\mathbf{i} + 8\mathbf{j})$ ms^{-1}

Q13 **a)** $\mathbf{v} = [15\mathbf{i} + (12 - 10t)\mathbf{j}]$ ms^{-1}

b) $\mathbf{r} = [15t\mathbf{i} + (12t - 5t^2 + 9)\mathbf{j}]$ m

c) $(15\mathbf{i} - 18\mathbf{j})$ ms^{-1}

Q14 **a)** $\dfrac{dn}{dt} = -2$ when $n = -4$

$\Rightarrow k(-4) - 10 = -2 \Rightarrow k = -2$

$\dfrac{dn}{dt} < 0 \Rightarrow -2n - 10 < 0$

$\Rightarrow 2n + 10 > 0$

$\Rightarrow n + 5 > 0$ as required.

b) In the **i**-direction, the acceleration is a constant 0.1 ms^{-2}, so use the constant acceleration equations to find an expression for m in terms of t:

$u = 0, v = m, a = 0.1, t = ?$

$v = u + at \Rightarrow m = 0.1t$

In the **j**-direction, form the differential equation to find n in terms of t:

$\dfrac{dn}{dt} = kn - 10 = -2n - 10 = -2(n + 5)$

$\Rightarrow \int \dfrac{1}{n + 5}\, dn = \int -2\, dt$

$\ln|n + 5| = -2t + C$

When $t = 0$, $n = 0$
$\Rightarrow \ln|5| = 0 + C \Rightarrow C = \ln 5$

Rearrange to give n in terms of t:

$\ln|n + 5| = -2t + \ln 5$
$\Rightarrow |n + 5| = e^{(-2t + \ln 5)}$
From part a), $n + 5 > 0$, so you can drop the modulus.

$\Rightarrow n + 5 = e^{-2t}e^{\ln 5}$

$\Rightarrow n = 5e^{-2t} - 5 = 5(e^{-2t} - 1)$

Replace both components in $\mathbf{v} = m\mathbf{i} + n\mathbf{j}$ to give:
$\mathbf{v} = [0.1t\mathbf{i} + 5(e^{-2t} - 1)\mathbf{j}]$ ms^{-1}
as required.

Chapter 30: Dynamics

1. Resolving Forces

Exercise 1.1

Q1 **a)** $(\rightarrow) = 6.5$ N, $(\uparrow) = 0$ N

b) $(\rightarrow) = 0$ N, $(\uparrow) = 4$ N

c) $(\rightarrow) = 15.3$ N, $(\uparrow) = 12.9$ N (3 s.f.)

d) $(\rightarrow) = 7.18$ N, $(\uparrow) = 15.4$ N (3 s.f.)

e) $(\rightarrow) = -4.92$ N, $(\uparrow) = 0.868$ N (3 s.f.)

f) $(\rightarrow) = 2.60$ N (3 s.f.), $(\uparrow) = -1.5$ N

g) $(\rightarrow) = -11.3$ N (3 s.f.), $(\uparrow) = -6.5$ N

h) $(\rightarrow) = -7.78$ N, $(\uparrow) = -7.78$ N (3 s.f.)

Exercise 1.2

Q1 a) $10\mathbf{j}$ N b) $-3.2\mathbf{i}$ N

c) $\frac{21}{2}\sqrt{2}\,\mathbf{i} + \frac{21}{2}\sqrt{2}\,\mathbf{j}$ N

d) $-15.4\mathbf{i} + 7.18\mathbf{j}$ N (to 3 s.f.)

Q2 a) 15.0 (3 s.f.) b) 16.6 N (3 s.f.)

Q3 a) 44.8° (3 s.f.) b) 6.59 N (3 s.f.)

Exercise 1.3

Q1 a) 14.3 N (3 s.f.) and 21.1° (1 d.p.)

b) 9.84 N (3 s.f.) and 338.4° (1 d.p.)

c) 5.54 N (3 s.f.) and 74.3° (1 d.p.)

d) 5.21 N (3 s.f.) and 346.8° (1 d.p.)

e) 3.40 N (3 s.f.) and 50.7° (1 d.p.)

f) 7.05 N (3 s.f.) and 235.4° (1 d.p.)

Q2 a) 16 N

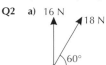

b) 32.8 N and 74.1° (to 3 s.f.)

Q3 a) 209° (3 s.f.) b) 0.135 N (3 s.f.)

Q4 34.6 N (to 3 s.f.)

Exercise 1.4

Q1 a) $X = 3.98$ N, $Y = 11.5$ N (to 3 s.f.)

b) $F = 8.17$ N (to 3 s.f.)

c) $P = 6.08$ N, $Q = 3.05$ N (to 3 s.f.)

d) $A = 7.10$ N, $B = 1.94$ N (to 3 s.f.)

Q2 $P = 8.94$ N and $\theta = 63.4°$ (to 3 s.f)

To solve this problem resolve horizontally and vertically to get two equations in terms of P and θ. Dividing the horizontal equation by the vertical equation gives the value of tan θ, which you can use to find θ. Finally use the value of θ to find P. Or you can square and add the equations to eliminate θ to find P.

Exercise 1.5

Q1 a) $T = 21.8$ N, $m = 1.70$ kg (to 3 s.f.)

b) $T = 3.38$ N, $m = 0.740$ kg (to 3 s.f.)

c) $T = 9.93$ N, $m = 0.428$ kg (to 3 s.f.)

d) $T = 4.02$ N, $m = 0.585$ kg (to 3 s.f.)

Q2 $W = 24.3$ N, $x = 27.3°$ (to 3 s.f.)

Exercise 1.6

Q1 a) $x = 53.1°$ (to 3 s.f.) b) 6 N

Q2 a) 25 N b) 3.61 kg (to 3 s.f.)

Q3 a) 0.495 kg b) 2.42 N (to 3 s.f.)

Q4 Resolve the forces parallel to the plane:
$14.7 \cos\theta = 2g\sin\theta$
$\Rightarrow \tan\theta = \dfrac{14.7}{(2\times 9.8)} = 0.75$

Exercise 1.7

Q1 a) 9.83 N b) 43.3 N (to 3 s.f.)

Q2 a) 4.41 N b) 1.82 kg (to 3 s.f.)

Q3 a) 52.7° b) 2.88 N (to 3 s.f.)

Q4

Resolving perpendicular to the plane:
$4F + 5\sin 20° = W\cos 50°$ ①

Resolving parallel to the plane:
$F + W\sin 50° = 5\cos 20°$
$F = 5\cos 20° - W\sin 50°$ ②
Substituting ② into ①,
$20\cos 20° - 4W\sin 50° + 5\sin 20° = W\cos 50°$,
$W = \dfrac{20\cos 20° + 5\sin 20°}{4\sin 50° + \cos 50°}$
$= 5.53$ N (to 3 s.f.)

2. Friction

Exercise 2.1

Q1 a) 1.25 N b) 2.4 N c) 11.25 N

d) 0 N e) 13.94 N f) 0.475 N

Q2 a) 0.25 b) 0.53 (to 2 d.p.)

c) 0.125 d) 0.46 (to 2 d.p.)

Q3 $F \leq 47.04$ N

Q4 a) $F \leq 58.8$ N, so 50 N isn't big enough to move the particle.

b) 58.8 N

Exercise 2.2

Q1 a) 4.88 N b) 4.17 N (to 3 s.f.)

Q2 a) 24.2 N (3 s.f.) b) 2.29 kg (3 s.f.)

Exercise 2.3

Q1 0.015 (2 s.f.)

Q2 Resolving perpendicular to the plane:
$R = W\cos\alpha$ ①

Resolving parallel to the plane:
$F = W\sin\alpha$ ②
$F \leq \mu R$ when the object is at rest on the plane. Substitute the values for F and R from ① and ② into $F \leq \mu R$:
$W\sin\alpha \leq \mu W\cos\alpha$
$\dfrac{W\sin\alpha}{W\cos\alpha} \leq \mu \Rightarrow \tan\alpha \leq \mu$

Q3 0.38 (2 d.p.)

Q4 Resolving parallel to the plane:
$T\cos 15° + F = 20g\sin 29°$ ①
Resolving perpendicular to the plane:
$R + T\sin 15° = 20g\cos 29°$
$R = -T\sin 15° + 20g\cos 29°$ ②
T is only just large enough to hold the sledge at rest, so the sledge is in limiting equilibrium and $F = \mu R = 0.1R$.

Substituting this and ② into ①:
$T\cos 15° + 0.1(-T\sin 15° + 20g\cos 29°) = 20g\sin 29°$
$T = \dfrac{20g\sin 29° - 2g\cos 29°}{\cos 15° - 0.1\sin 15°}$
$= \dfrac{77.880...}{0.9400...} = 82.8$ N (3 s.f.)

Q5 Resolving parallel to the wire:
$F + P\cos 45° = 0.5g\sin 10°$ ①
Resolving perpendicular to the wire:
$R + P\sin 45° = 0.5g\cos 10°$
Using $\sin 45° = \cos 45°$:
$R + P\cos 45° = 0.5g\cos 10°$ ②
Subtract ① from ②:
$R - F = 0.5g\cos 10° - 0.5g\sin 10°$
The bead is in limiting equilibrium so substitute in $F = \mu R = 0.25R$:
$R - 0.25R = 0.5g(\cos 10° - \sin 10°)$
$0.75R = 0.5g(\cos 10° - \sin 10°)$
$R = 5.30$ N (3 s.f.)

Q6 If the block is on the point of sliding up the plane:

Resolving perpendicular to the plane:
$R = 5g\cos 35° = 40.138...$ N
$F = \mu R$, so:
$F = 0.4 \times 40.138... = 16.055...$ N
Resolving parallel to the plane:
$D - F - 5g\sin 35° = 0$
$D = 16.055... + 28.105... = 44.160...$ N
If the block is on the point of sliding down the plane:

Resolving perpendicular to the plane:
$R - 5g\cos 35° - 40.138...$ N
$F = \mu R$, so
$F = 0.4 \times 40.138... = 16.055...$ N
Resolving parallel to the plane:
$D + F - 5g\sin 35° = 0$
$D = 28.105... - 16.055... = 12.049...$ N
So the range for which the block is in equilibrium is
$12.049...$ N $\leq D \leq 44.160...$ N

3. Newton's Laws of Motion

Exercise 3.1

Q1 15.625 m

Q2 a) 2.36 ms⁻² b) 13.6 m

c) 22.3 N (all to 3 s.f.)

Q3 a) 1.61 ms⁻² b) 11.2 ms⁻¹

c) 43.5 N (all to 3 s.f.)

Exercise 3.2

Q1 **a)** 2.24 ms⁻² (to 3 s.f.)

b) $a = 1$ ms⁻², so the acceleration decreases by 1.24 ms⁻² (to 3 s.f.)

Q2 **a)** $(-4\mathbf{i} - 2\mathbf{j})$ N

b) $(5.6\mathbf{i} + 0.8\mathbf{j})$ ms⁻¹

c) The new resultant force is $(0\mathbf{i} + 0\mathbf{j})$ N, so the particle will stop accelerating and will continue moving at a constant velocity.

Exercise 3.3

Q1 **a)** 8.55 m (3 s.f.) **b)** 2.81 N (3 s.f.)

Q2 **a)** 4.14 ms⁻² (3 s.f.)

b) 12.4 ms⁻¹ (3 s.f.)

Exercise 3.4

Q1 **a)**

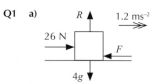

b) 39.2 N **c)** 21.2 N

d) $\mu = 0.54$ (to 2 d.p.)

Q2 **a)**

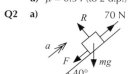

b) 5.77 kg (to 3 s.f.)

Q3 **a)**

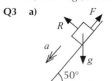

b) 0.896 s (to 3 s.f.)

Q4 1540 N (3 s.f.)

Exercise 3.5

Q1 **a)** 74.4 N **b)** 0.71 (2 d.p.)

Q2 Resolving perpendicular to the plane (↖) for A and B:
$R_A = mg \cos \theta$ and $R_B = mg \cos \theta$
So $R_A = R_B$. Since $F_A = \mu R_A$ and $F_B = \mu R_B$ the frictional forces acting on A and B are equal — call this F.
Resolving parallel to the plane (↗) for A:
$F_{net} = ma$
$20 - T - F - mg \sin \theta = ma$ ①
Resolving parallel to the plane (↗) for B:
$F_{net} = ma$
$T - F - mg \sin \theta = ma$ ②
Substituting ① into ②:
$T - F - mg \sin \theta = 20 - T - F - mg \sin \theta$
$2T = 20 \Rightarrow T = 10$ N

Exercise 3.6

Q1 **a)** 3330 N **b)** 19 100 N

c) 1.69 ms⁻² (all to 3 s.f.)

Q2 **a)** 217 N **b)** 13.5 ms⁻¹ (3 s.f.)

Q3 **a)**

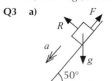

b) 0.89 (to 2 d.p.) **c)** 0.4 ms⁻¹

d) 2.83 ms⁻¹ (to 3 s.f.)

Q4 **a)** Resolving perpendicular to the 40° plane (↖) for A:
$R_A = 0.2g \cos 40°$
Using $F = \mu R$:
$F_A = 0.7 \times 0.2g \cos 40°$
$= 0.14g \cos 40°$
Resolving parallel to the 40° plane (↗) for A:
$T - F_A - 0.2g \sin 40° = 0.2a$
$T - 0.14g \cos 40°$
$\quad - 0.2g \sin 40° = 0.2a$
$\Rightarrow 5T - 0.7g \cos 40°$
$\quad - g \sin 40° = a$ ①
Resolving perpendicular to the 20° plane (↗) for B:
$R_B = 0.9g \cos 20°$
Using $F = \mu R$:
$F_B = 0.05 \times 0.9g \cos 20°$
$= 0.045g \cos 20°$
Resolving parallel to the 20° plane (↘) for B:
$F_{net} = ma$
$0.9g \sin 20° - F_B - T = 0.9a$
$0.9g \sin 20° - 0.045g \cos 20°$
$\quad - T = 0.9a$
$\Rightarrow g \sin 20° - 0.05g \cos 20°$
$\quad - (1.11...)T = a$ ②
Solving the simultaneous equations ① and ②:
$5T - 0.7g \cos 40° - g \sin 40° =$
$g \sin 20° - 0.05g \cos 20°$
$\quad - (1.11...)T$
$\Rightarrow (6.11...)T = g \sin 20°$
$\quad - 0.05g \cos 20°$
$\quad + 0.7g \cos 40° + g \sin 40°$
$\Rightarrow T = 2.363... = 2.36$ N (3 s.f.)

b) Using ① from part a):
$a = 5T - 0.7g \cos 40° - g \sin 40°$
$= (5 \times 2.363...) - 0.7g \cos 40°$
$\quad - g \sin 40° = 0.2648...$
$s = 0.35, u = 0, v = ?$
$v^2 = u^2 + 2as$
$v^2 = 2 \times 0.2648... \times 0.35 = 0.185...$
$\Rightarrow v = 0.431$ ms⁻¹ (3 s.f.)

Review Exercise — Chapter 30

Q1 **a)** $(0\mathbf{i} - 3.2\mathbf{j})$ N

b) $(-6.88\mathbf{i} + 9.83\mathbf{j})$ N (to 3 s.f.)

c) $(-3.4\mathbf{i} - 5.89\mathbf{j})$ N (to 3 s.f.)

d) $(1.53\mathbf{i} - 1.29\mathbf{j})$ N (to 3 s.f.)

Q2 **a)** 35.7° **b)** 5.49 N (to 3 s.f.)

Q3 **a)** $X = 24.4$ N, $Y = 29.8$ N (to 3 s.f.)

b) $F = 5.38$ N (to 3 s.f.)

c) $R = 40$ N, $S = 20.7$ N (to 3 s.f.)

d) $A = 7.10$ N, $B = 1.94$ N (to 3 s.f.)

Q4 $m = 14.1$ kg and $R = 107$ N (to 3 s.f.)

Q5 **a)** 0.30 **b)** 0.58 **c)** 0.32 (to 2 d.p.)

Q6 16.7° (to 3 s.f.)

Q7 0.31 (to 2 d.p.)

Q8 **a)** 1.6 N **b)** 0.051 (to 2 s.f.)

Q9 **a)** $(-5\mathbf{i} + 4\mathbf{j})$ N **b)** 16.3 m (to 3 s.f.)

Q10 **a)** 0.43 (to 2 d.p.)

b) E.g. the brick is a particle, there's no air resistance or other external forces acting, the brick's acceleration is constant, acceleration due to gravity is constant at 9.8 ms⁻².

Q11 22.9 N (to 3 s.f.)

Q12 5.12 ms⁻¹ (3 s.f.)

Q13 **a)** 2.90 ms⁻² **b)** 27.6 N

c) 20.3 N (all to 3 s.f.)

Chapter 31: Moments

1. Moments

Exercise 1.1

Q1 **a)** 7.5 Nm anticlockwise

b) 12 Nm clockwise

c) 17.5 Nm clockwise (3 s.f.)

d) 20 Nm clockwise

e) 84.6 Nm clockwise (3 s.f.)

f) 5.34 Nm anticlockwise (3 s.f.)

Exercise 1.2

Q1 18.9 Nm clockwise (3 s.f.)

Q2 **a)** 4 Nm clockwise

b) 0.5 Nm clockwise

c) 12 Nm anticlockwise

d) 37.6 Nm clockwise (3 s.f.)

e) 66.4 Nm anticlockwise (3 s.f.)

f) 48.1 Nm clockwise (3 s.f.)

Q3 73.5 Nm **Q4** $X > 24$

Q5 $0 \le d < 1.25$

Exercise 1.3

Q1 **a)** $x = 34$ N, $y = 48$ N

b) $x = 3$ N, $y = 2.4$ m

Q2 **a)** 2.4 N **b)** 1.6 N

Q3 **a)** 17.1 m (3 s.f.)
Take moments about B to get an equation in terms of the length of the rod, which you can solve.

b) $\alpha = 68.0°$ (3 s.f.)

c) $T = 88.4$ N (3 s.f.)
Resolve horizontally and vertically to get a pair of equations in terms of T and α, which you can solve simultaneously.

Exercise 1.4

Q1 **a)** 17.4 N   **b)** 0.947 m (3 s.f.)
Q2 $R_C = 43.12$ N, $R_D = 35.28$ N
Q3 **a)** $R_D = 98$ N   **b)** $M = 15$ kg
Q4 **a)** $R_C = 1.3$ N, $R_D = 2.6$ N
   b) 2.65 m (3 s.f.)
Q5 **a)** $m = 4.47$ kg (3 s.f.)
Take moments about A to get an equation in terms of m, which you can solve.
   b) $\alpha = 81.8°$ (3 s.f.)
   c) $T = 24.3$ N (3 s.f.)
Resolve horizontally and resolve vertically (or take moments about B) to get a pair of equations in terms of T and α, which you can solve simultaneously.
Q6 **a)** $T_1 = 16.6$ N, $T_2 = 5.60$ N (3 s.f.)
Resolve horizontally and vertically to get a pair of equations in terms of T_1 and T_2, which you can solve simultaneously.
   b) 0.441 m (3 s.f.)
Take moments about A to get an equation in terms of the distance from A to the rod's centre of mass, which you can solve.
Q7 4 m
Q8 **a)** $T_B = 29.4$ N, $T_C = 49$ N
   b) 0.25 m
Q9 **a)** 1.37 m
Resolve vertically and use $R_C = 4R_D$ to find $R_C = 21g$ N and $R_D = 84g$ N, then take moments about A to get an equation in terms of the distance from A to the COM, which you can then solve.
   b) 0.6175 m
Take moments about D, using the fact that $R_C = 0$.

Exercise 1.5

Q1 **a)** 70 Nm anticlockwise
   b) 53 Nm clockwise
   c) 52 Nm clockwise
   d) 39 Nm anticlockwise
   e) 33.3 Nm clockwise (3 s.f.)
   f) 60.7 Nm anticlockwise (3 s.f.)
Q2 **a)**

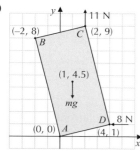

b) 3.06 kg (3 s.f.)
Use the coordinates to find the perpendicular distance from the force to the pivot — all of the forces act either horizontally or vertically so you don't need to use any angles.

2. Reaction Forces and Friction in Moments

Exercise 2.1

Q1 **a)** $T = 58.8$ N   **b)** $R = 29.4$ N
Q2 **a)** $T = 4.53$ N (3 s.f.)
   b) $|R| = 2.99$ N, $\theta = 139°$ (3 s.f.)
Q3 **a)** $T = 17.9$ N (3 s.f.)
   b) $|R| = 21.6$ N, $\theta = 38.7°$ (3 s.f.)
Q4 **a)** 4.77 m (3 s.f.)
   b) $|R| = 91.0$ N, $\theta = 186°$ (3 s.f.)
Q5 **a)** $T = 27.2$ N (3 s.f.)
   b) $|R| = 76.4$ N, $\theta = 246°$ (3 s.f.)
Q6 $T_W = 42.1$ N (3 s.f.)
   $|R| = 42.1$ N (3 s.f.), $\theta = 25°$

Exercise 2.2

Q1 **a)** $T = 172$ N (3 s.f.)
   b) $\mu = 0.36$ (2 d.p.)
Q2 **a)** $M = 0.877$ kg (3 s.f.)
   b) 1.32 m (3 s.f.)
Q3 $|D| = 0.0171$ N, $\theta = 35.0°$ (3 s.f.)
Q4 $T = 219$ N (3 s.f.), $\mu = 0.5$
Use the lengths given (AB and AC) to find the angle that T makes with the horizontal, then take moments about A to find T. You can then resolve horizontally and vertically and use $F = \mu R$ to find μ.

Exercise 2.3

Q1 **a)** 35 N   **b)** 6.72 N (3 s.f.)
   c) $\mu = 0.19$ (2 d.p.)
Q2 **a)** 10.0 N (3 s.f.) **b)** 6.24 N (3 s.f.)
   c) 3.44 N (3 s.f.)
   d) $\mu = 0.55$ (2 d.p.)
Q3 4.03 m (3 s.f.)
Q4 $D = 106$ N (3 s.f.) away from the wall.
Q5 **a)** 54.6° (3 s.f.)
   b) 0.6   **c)** 0.29 (2 d.p.)
Q6 $\mu = 1.73$ (2 d.p.)
Q7 $\mu \geq 0.84$ (2 d.p.)
Resolve forces horizontally to get F in terms of R, then use $F \leq \mu R$ and solve for μ.
Q8 $\mu \geq 0.59$ (2 d.p.)
Take moments about A to find the normal reaction at the peg, then resolve forces horizontally and vertically to find the normal reaction and the frictional force from the ground. You can then use $F \leq \mu R$.

Q9 $3.882...$ N $\leq K \leq 26.73...$ N
The upper and lower bounds for K will be when the ladder is on the point of slipping towards and away from the wall respectively, so consider these two cases separately.

Review Exercise — Chapter 31

Q1 **a)** 12 Nm anticlockwise
   b) 14.6 Nm clockwise (3 s.f.)
   c) 326 Nm clockwise (3 s.f.)
Q2 181.92 Nm   **Q3** 198 Nm (3 s.f.)
Q4 $P = 15$ N, $Q = 31$ N
Q5 $U = 6$ N, $l = 2$ m
Q6 $T_1 = 367.5$ N, $T_2 = 220.5$ N
Q7 12 m
Q8 **a)** $F = 29.3$ N   **b)** 1.25 m (3 s.f.)
Q9 **a)** $\alpha = 19.1°$ (3 s.f.)
   b) $|R| = 30$ N, $\theta = 161°$ (3 s.f.)
Q10 $0.471b$ m (3 s.f.)
Let the distance to the C.O.M. = x, then take moments about A and solve for x in terms of b.
Q11 **a)** $x = 0.889$ m (3 s.f.)
Use the lengths given (1.2 m and 0.9 m) to find α (or just find sin α = 0.6 and cos α = 0.8), then take moments about A and solve for x.
   b) $\mu \geq 0.40$ (2 d.p.)
Resolve horizontally to find the normal reaction force from the wall, and resolve vertically to find the frictional force. Then use $F \leq \mu R$ and solve for μ.
Q12 **a)**

Taking moments about the base of the ladder: $N = \dfrac{98}{\sqrt{3}}$ N
Resolving vertically: $R = 196$ N
Resolving horizontally: $F = N$
$F = \mu R \implies \dfrac{98}{\sqrt{3}} = 196\mu$
$\implies \mu = \dfrac{\sqrt{3}}{6}$, as required.
   b) 84.9 N (3 s.f.)
Q13 $\mu \geq 0.25$ (2 d.p.)
Take moments about the base of the ladder to find the normal reaction from the wall, and resolve horizontally to show that this is equal to the frictional force from the floor. Resolve vertically to find the normal reaction from the ground and then use $F \leq \mu R$.
Q14 $\mu = 0.35$ (2 d.p.)

Index